THE MATHEMATICA® BOOK

STEPHEN WOLFRAM

THE *MATHEMATICA*® BOOK

Third Edition

Library of Congress Cataloging-in-Publication Data

Wolfram, Stephen, 1959 –
    The Mathematica book / Stephen Wolfram. — 3rd ed.
        p.   cm.
    Rev. ed. of: Mathematica. 2nd ed. 1991.
    Includes index.
    ISBN 0–9650532–0–2 (alk. paper). — ISBN 0–9650532–1–0 (pbk.)
    ISBN 0–521–58889–8 (alk. paper). — ISBN 0–521–58888–X (pbk.)
    1. Mathematica (Computer file) 2. Mathematics—Data processing.
I. Wolfram, Stephen. Mathematica. II. Title.
QA76.95.W65 1996
510'.285'53—dc20
                                                                    96–7218
                                                                    CIP

A catalog record for this book is also available from the British Library.

For the latest updates and corrections to this book:
visit http://www.wolfram.com/book–updates *or send
blank email to* book–updates–responder@wolfram.com

Comments on this book will be welcomed at:
comments@wolfram.com

**In publications that refer to the *Mathematica*
system, please cite this book as:**
Stephen Wolfram, *The Mathematica Book*, 3rd ed.
(Wolfram Media/Cambridge University Press, 1996)

*Previous editions published by Addison-Wesley Publishing Company under the title
Mathematica: A System for Doing Mathematics by Computer*

Copublishers:

WOLFRAM
M E D I A

ISBN 0–9650532–0–2 Hardback
ISBN 0–9650532–1–0 Paperback

Wolfram Media, Inc.
web: http://www.wolfram–media.com; *email:* info@wolfram–media.com
phone: +1–217–398–9090; *fax:* +1–217–398–9095
mail: 100 Trade Center Drive, Champaign, IL 61820, USA

CAMBRIDGE
UNIVERSITY PRESS

ISBN 0–521–58889–8 Hardback
ISBN 0–521–58888–X Paperback

The Press Syndicate of the University of Cambridge
The Pitt Building, Trumpington Street, Cambridge CB2 1RP, UK
40 West 20th Street, New York, NY 10011–4211, USA
10 Stamford Road, Oakleigh, Melbourne 3166, Australia

*Retail and library orders worldwide should be directed to Cambridge
University Press and their distributors. Permissions and foreign rights
inquiries should be directed to Wolfram Media.*

WOLFRAM RESEARCH

Wolfram Research, Inc.
web: http://www.wolfram.com
email: info@wolfram.com
phone: 217–398–0700
fax: 217–398–0747
mail: 100 Trade Center Drive
Champaign, IL 61820
USA

Wolfram Research Europe Ltd.
web: http://www.wolfram.co.uk
email: info@wolfram.co.uk
phone: +44–(0)1993–883400
fax: +44–(0)1993–883800
mail: 10 Blenheim Office Park
Lower Road, Long Hanborough
Oxfordshire OX8 8LN
UNITED KINGDOM

Wolfram Research Asia Ltd.
web: http://www.wolfram.co.jp
email: info@wolfram.co.jp
phone: +81–(0)3–5276–0506
fax: +81–(0)3–5276–0509
mail: Izumi Building 8F
3–2–15 Misaki-cho
Chiyoda-ku, Tokyo 101
JAPAN

MATHEMATICA®

Note: All services are also available at wolfram.co.uk and wolfram.co.jp, as well as at wolfram.com.

General information:
info@wolfram.com
http://www.wolfram.com

Frequently asked technical and other questions:
http://www.wolfram.com/faq

Central index of *Mathematica*–related material:
http://www.wolfram.com/central

Current *Mathematica* version information:
info@wolfram.com
http://www.wolfram.com/versions

Orders and customer service:
orders@wolfram.com
http://www.wolfram.com/orders

User registration and password requests:
register@wolfram.com
http://www.wolfram.com/register
Institutional and other non-owner users are also encouraged to register.

Technical support and bug reports:
support@wolfram.com
http://www.wolfram.com/support
Support is available only to registered users.

Mathematica training information:
training@wolfram.com
http://www.wolfram.com/training

Information for educators:
education@wolfram.com
http://www.wolfram.com/education

Suggestions:
suggestions@wolfram.com
http://www.wolfram.com/suggestions

Comments and feedback:
comments@wolfram.com
http://www.wolfram.com/comments
Information about applications of Mathematica, large and small, is always welcome.

Mathematica Archive:
Wolfram Research maintains an archive of Mathematica-related documents. Publications and other non-proprietary material are welcome at:

The Mathematica Archive
Wolfram Research, Inc.
100 Trade Center Drive
Champaign, IL 61820, USA
email: archive@wolfram.com
web: http://www.wolfram.com/archive

Mathematica Products Catalog:
http://www.wolfram.com/catalog
To request a current catalog of all Wolfram Research products, use the web site, or send email to info@wolfram.com, or contact Wolfram Research.

Mathematica Bookstore:
http://www.wolfram.com/bookstore
To request a current list of titles, send blank email to bookstore–responder@wolfram.com.

MathSource Electronic Library:
http://www.wolfram.com/mathsource
ftp: mathsource.wolfram.com
mail server: mathsource@wolfram.com
administrator: mathsource–admin@wolfram.com

MathUser Newsletter:
http://www.wolfram.com/mathuser
To request a free subscription, use the web site, or send email to mathuser@wolfram.com, or contact Wolfram Research.

mathgroup news group:
news: comp.soft–sys.math.mathematica
http://www.wolfram.com/mathgroup

Book Credits

Editors: Jerome Walsh, George Beck and Joe Grohens • *Typesetters:* Joe Kaiping, Phil Wall and Glenn Scholebo • *Lead proofreader:* Jan Progen • *Proofreaders:* Carol Ordal, Wendy Leung, Angela Latham, Kurt Kessinger, Madhav Chari and John Garvey • *Testers:* Anna Marichev and Kevin Leuthold • *Production programmers:* Jeff Adams and Joe Kaiping • *Formula gallery developer:* Michael Trott • *Cover, part openers and graphics gallery designers:* John Bonadies and Jody Jasinski • *Book designers:* John Bonadies and André Kuzniarek • *Font designer:* André Kuzniarek • *On-line version developers:* Chris LaReau and Robby Villegas • *Project managers:* George Beck and Joe Grohens • *Manufacturing managers:* Jody Jasinski and Rachel Lively • *Business developer:* Dianne Littwin • *Additional content checkers:* Members of Wolfram Research technical support, quality assurance and R&D groups, as well as *Mathematica* beta testers.

For Mathematica software credits, see About Mathematica *in the Mathematica front end.*

About the Author

Stephen Wolfram is the creator of *Mathematica* and is widely regarded as the most important innovator in scientific and technical computing today. Born in London in 1959, he was educated at Eton, Oxford and Caltech. He published his first scientific paper at the age of fifteen, and had received his PhD in theoretical physics from Caltech by the age of twenty. Wolfram's early scientific work was mainly in high-energy physics, quantum field theory and cosmology, and included several now-classic results. Having started to use computers in 1973, Wolfram rapidly became a leader in the emerging field of scientific computing, and in 1979 he began the construction of SMP—the first modern computer algebra system—which he released commercially in 1981.

In recognition of his early work in physics and computing, Wolfram became in 1981 the youngest recipient of a MacArthur Prize Fellowship. Late in 1981, Wolfram then set out on an ambitious new direction in science: to develop a general theory of complexity in nature. Wolfram's key idea was to use computer experiments to study the behavior of simple computer programs known as cellular automata. And in 1982 he made the first in a series of startling discoveries about the origins of complexity. The publication of Wolfram's papers on cellular automata led to a major shift in scientific thinking, and laid the groundwork for a new field of science that Wolfram named "complex systems research".

Through the mid-1980s, Wolfram continued his work on complexity, discovering a number of fundamental connections between computation and nature, and inventing such concepts as computational irreducibility. Wolfram's work led to a wide range of applications—and provided the main scientific foundations for the popular movements known as complexity theory and artificial life. Wolfram himself used his ideas to develop a new randomness generation system and a new approach to computational fluid dynamics—both of which are now in widespread use.

Following his scientific work on complex systems research, Wolfram in 1986 founded the first research center and first journal in the field. Then, after a highly successful career in academia—first at Caltech, then at the Institute for Advanced Study in Princeton, and finally as Professor of Physics, Mathematics and Computer Science at the University of Illinois—Wolfram launched Wolfram Research, Inc.

Wolfram began the development of *Mathematica* in late 1986. The first version of *Mathematica* was released on June 23, 1988, and was immediately hailed as a major advance in the field of computing. In the years that followed, the popularity of *Mathematica* grew rapidly, and Wolfram Research became established as a world leader in the software industry, widely recognized for excellence in both technology and business.

Following the release of *Mathematica* Version 2 in 1991, Wolfram began to divide his time between *Mathematica* development and scientific research. Building on his work from the mid-1980s, Wolfram made a sequence of major discoveries to be described in his forthcoming book *A New Kind of Science*. In addition to solving some fundamental existing scientific problems, Wolfram's recent work points the way to a whole new approach to science and mathematics.

Wolfram has been president and CEO of Wolfram Research since its inception, and remains personally responsible for the design of the core *Mathematica* system.

Other books by Stephen Wolfram:
- *Cellular Automata and Complexity: Collected Papers* (1993)
- *A New Kind of Science* (forthcoming)
  (*For information send email to* info@new-science.com)

Author's web site:
http://www.wolfram.com/s.wolfram

Author's address:
email: s.wolfram@wolfram.com
mail: 100 Trade Center Drive
   Champaign, IL 61820, USA

For comments on this book or Mathematica send email to comments@wolfram.com

About *Mathematica*

Mathematica is the world's only fully integrated environment for technical computing. First released in 1988, it has had a profound effect on the way computers are used in many technical and other fields.

It is often said that the release of *Mathematica* marked the beginning of modern technical computing. Ever since the 1960s individual packages had existed for specific numerical, algebraic, graphical and other tasks. But the visionary concept of *Mathematica* was to create once and for all a single system that could handle all the various aspects of technical computing in a coherent and unified way. The key intellectual advance that made this possible was the invention of a new kind of symbolic computer language that could for the first time manipulate the very wide range of objects involved in technical computing using only a fairly small number of basic primitives.

When *Mathematica* 1.0 was released, the *New York Times* wrote that "the importance of the program cannot be overlooked", and *Business Week* later ranked *Mathematica* among the ten most important new products of the year. *Mathematica* was also hailed in the technical community as a major intellectual and practical revolution.

At first, *Mathematica*'s impact was felt mainly in the physical sciences, engineering and mathematics. But over the years, *Mathematica* has become important in a remarkably wide range of fields. *Mathematica* is used today throughout the sciences—physical, biological, social and other—and counts many of the world's foremost scientists among its enthusiastic supporters. It has played a crucial role in many important discoveries, and has been the basis for thousands of technical papers. In engineering, *Mathematica* has become a standard tool for both development and production, and by now many of the world's important new products rely at one stage or another in their design on *Mathematica*. In commerce, *Mathematica* has played a significant role in the growth of sophisticated financial modeling, as well as being widely used in many kinds of general planning and analysis. *Mathematica* has also emerged as an important tool in computer science and software development: its language component is widely used as a research, prototyping and interface environment.

The largest part of *Mathematica*'s user community consists of technical professionals. But *Mathematica* is also heavily used in education, and there are now many hundreds of courses—from high school to graduate school—based on it. In addition, with the availability of student versions, *Mathematica* has become an important tool for both technical and non-technical students around the world.

The diversity of *Mathematica*'s user base is striking. It spans all continents, ages from below ten up, and includes for example artists, composers, linguists and lawyers. There are also many hobbyists from all walks of life who use *Mathematica* to further their interests in science, mathematics and computing.

Ever since *Mathematica* was first released, its user base has grown steadily, and by now the total number of users is above a million. *Mathematica* has become a standard in a great many organizations, and it is used today in all of the Fortune 50 companies, all of the 15 major departments of the U.S. government, and all of the 50 largest universities in the world.

At a technical level, *Mathematica* is widely regarded as a major feat of software engineering. It is one of the largest single application programs ever developed, and it contains a vast array of novel algorithms and important technical innovations. Among these innovations is the concept of platform-independent interactive documents known as notebooks. Notebooks have already become the standard for many kinds of courseware and reports, and with the new capabilities added in *Mathematica* 3.0 they are poised to emerge as a general standard for publishing technical documents on the web and elsewhere.

The development of *Mathematica* has been carried out at Wolfram Research by a world-class team led by Stephen Wolfram. The success of *Mathematica* has fueled the continuing growth of Wolfram Research, and has allowed a large community of independent *Mathematica*-related businesses to develop. There are today nearly a hundred specialized commercial packages available for *Mathematica*, as well as several periodicals and more than two hundred books devoted to the system.

Some New Features of *Mathematica* 3.0

The first major new version of *Mathematica* in several years, 3.0 strengthens the core computational capabilities of *Mathematica*, and adds some revolutionary new features. Throughout this book, items that are new are indicated by +■ ; those that are changed are indicated by ~■ . Except as noted in Section A.13, 3.0 is fully compatible with earlier versions.

Numerical Computation

- Adaptive precision control to generate results with guaranteed precision.
- High-performance compilation of list-oriented, procedural and functional numerical operations.
- Optimized algorithms for one- and higher-dimensional interpolation.
- Optimized algorithms for solution of differential equations.
- Solution of boundary value ordinary differential equations, and initial value partial differential equations.
- High-dimensional numerical integration.
- Optimized minimization algorithms.
- LU and Jordan decomposition of matrices.
- Numerical differentiation.
- Automatic comparison and manipulation of exact numeric quantities.
- Support for exact implicitly-defined algebraic numbers.
- Support for interval arithmetic.
- Fully adjustable global numerical precision control model.
- New capabilities for extracting segments of digits in exact and inexact numbers.
- Machine-independent mechanisms for input and output of numbers without loss of precision.

Algebraic Computation

- Enhanced and optimized simplification of algebraic expressions.
- Simplification of expressions involving special functions.
- Built-in functions for transformations on trigonometric expressions.
- Greatly extended indefinite and definite symbolic integration.

- Support for principal values and assumptions on parameters in integrals.
- Greatly extended symbolic sums and products.
- Greatly extended symbolic solution of ordinary and partial differential equations.
- Optimized symbolic linear algebra.
- Enhanced handling of exact numerical quantities.
- Generation and system-wide support for algebraic numbers.
- Highly optimized Gröbner basis reduction.

Mathematical Functions

- Faster evaluation of many special functions.
- Fresnel integrals and hyperbolic sine and cosine integrals.
- Inverse error function, gamma function and beta function.
- Product log function.
- $_pF_q$ generalized hypergeometric functions and Meijer G functions.
- Additional Weierstrass, elliptic and related functions.
- Mathieu functions.
- Stieltjes constants.
- Built-in Fibonacci numbers and polynomials.

Graphics

- Full typesetting capabilities for labels and text in plots.
- Automatic conversions to EPS, TIFF, GIF and other formats.
- Kernel control of animation in notebooks.
- Absolute offset specifications in graphics primitives.
- Direct control of final graphics size, resolution, etc.
- Direct generation of text strings for graphics in various formats.

Programming and Core System

- Faster execution speed and lower memory usage for typical kernel operations.
- Dumping of function definitions for optimized loading.

- Powerful new general symbolic programming functions, including ReplaceList and Split.
- Pattern-based non-local control flow with Throw and Catch.
- Separate support for verbatim and held patterns.
- Enhanced control of basic evaluation.
- New functions and enhancements for string manipulation.
- Extensive support for manipulation of non-ASCII characters.

Input and Output

- Support for WYSIWYG fully editable two-dimensional typeset input and output.
- Extended *Mathematica* language incorporating special characters and two-dimensional notation.
- Over 700 special characters for mathematical and other notation.
- Support for traditional math textbook notation for output and heuristic input.
- Top-quality typeset output with advanced adjustable layout rules.
- Complete symbolic language for specifying two-dimensional typeset structures.
- Two-dimensional input and manipulation of arrays and matrices.
- Complete support for international character sets and Unicode.
- TEX conversion with line-breaking information.
- Optimized textual import and export of typeset structures.

Notebook Interface

- Programmable documents based on underlying symbolic representation.
- Symbolic language for specifying user interface operations.
- Customizable palettes that can execute any kernel or front end operation.
- Integrated active elements and hyperlinks in notebooks.
- Separate style environments for screen and printing.
- New style sheets for varied document types.
- Language-based control of all features of text, graphics, cells and notebooks.
- In-line typesetting and graphics embedded in text.
- Enhanced text formatting capabilities including full text justification.

- Integrated customizable notebook-based on-line help with hyperlinks and the full text of this book.
- Fully platform-independent notebook file format.
- Notebook conversion to TEX, HTML and other external formats.
- Option inspector for interactive control of all notebooks and front end properties.
- Keyboard commands for editing and notebook navigation; drag and drop.

System Interface

- Additional kernel directory and file manipulation functions.
- Support for multi-platform external program clusters.
- Optimized *MathLink* external program interface.
- Loopback links for storing expressions in external programs.
- Direct support for arrays in external programs.
- Shared libraries for *MathLink*.
- Uniform layout of system files across all platforms.
- Automatic initialization of kernel and front end functionality as well as documentation for add-ons.
- Support for multi-lingual versions and all standard keyboard character encodings.
- Direct CD-ROM executability.
- TCP-based network license server.
- OLE support under Microsoft Windows.

Standard Add-on Packages

- Manipulating and solving algebraic inequalities.
- Symmetric polynomials.
- Manipulating quaternions and elements of Galois fields.
- Complete integrals and differential invariants of nonlinear PDEs.
- Z transforms.
- Primitive roots for arbitrary algebraic extensions.
- Numerical residue and series computations.
- Data smoothing and filtering.
- Classical and robust multivariate descriptive statistics.
- Linear and nonlinear regression with diagnostics.
- Simplified arithmetic and algebra without complex numbers.
- Full on-line documentation of all packages.

The Role of This Book

The Scope of the Book

This book is intended to be a complete introduction to *Mathematica*. It describes essentially all the capabilities of *Mathematica*, and assumes no prior knowledge of the system.

In most uses of *Mathematica*, you will need to know only a small part of the system. This book is organized to make it easy for you to learn the part you need for a particular calculation. In many cases, for example, you may be able to set up your calculation simply by adapting some appropriate examples from the book.

You should understand, however, that the examples in this book are chosen primarily for their simplicity, rather than to correspond to realistic calculations in particular application areas.

There are many other publications that discuss *Mathematica* from the viewpoint of particular classes of applications. In some cases, you may find it better to read one of these publications first, and read this book only when you need a more general perspective on *Mathematica*.

Mathematica is a system built on a fairly small set of very powerful principles. This book describes those principles, but by no means spells out all of their implications. In particular, while the book describes the elements that go into *Mathematica* programs, it does not give detailed examples of complete programs. For those, you should look at other publications.

The Mathematica System Described in the Book

This book describes the standard *Mathematica* kernel, as it exists on all computers that run *Mathematica*. All supported features of the kernel in *Mathematica* Version 3.0 are covered in this book. Most of the important features of the front end are also discussed.

Mathematica is an open software system that can be customized in a wide variety of ways. It is important to realize that this book covers only the full basic *Mathematica* system. If your system is customized in some way, then it may behave differently from what is described in the book.

The most common form of customization is the addition of various *Mathematica* function definitions. These may come, for example, from loading a *Mathematica* package. Some-times the definitions may actually modify the behavior of functions described in this book. In other cases, the definitions may simply add a collection of new functions that are not described in the book. In certain applications, it may be primarily these new functions that you use, rather than the standard ones described in the book.

This book describes what to do when you interact directly with the standard *Mathematica* kernel and notebook front end. Sometimes, however, you may not be using the standard *Mathematica* system directly. Instead, *Mathematica* may be an embedded component of another system that you are using. This system may for example call on *Mathematica* only for certain computations, and may hide the details of those computations from you. Most of what is in this book will only be useful if you can give explicit input to *Mathematica*. If all of your input is substantially modified by the system you are using, then you must rely on the documentation for that system.

Additional Standard Mathematica Documentation

The following are available in printed form for all standard versions of *Mathematica*, and can be ordered from Wolfram Research:

- *Getting Started with Mathematica*: a booklet describing installation, basic operation, and troubleshooting of *Mathematica* on specific computer systems.

- *Standard Add-on Packages*: a book describing standard add-on packages available for *Mathematica*.

Extensive on-line documentation is included with most versions of *Mathematica*. All such documentation can be accessed from the Help Browser in the *Mathematica* notebook front end.

In addition, the following sources of information are available on the web (note that all of these are available at wolfram.co.uk and wolfram.co.jp as well as wolfram.com):

- http://www.wolfram.com: the main Wolfram Research web site, giving extensive information on *Mathematica* and its applications.

- http://www.wolfram.com/faq: answers to frequently asked questions about *Mathematica*.

- http://www.wolfram.com/book-updates: corrections and updates to this book.

Suggestions about Learning *Mathematica*

Getting Started

As with any other computer system, there are a few points that you need to get straight before you can even start using *Mathematica*. For example, you absolutely must know how to type your input to *Mathematica*. To find out these kinds of basic points, you should read at least the first section of Part 1 in this book.

Once you know the basics, you can begin to get a feeling for *Mathematica* by typing in some examples from this book. Always be sure that you type in exactly what appears in the book—do not change any capitalization, bracketing, etc.

After you have tried a few examples from the book, you should start experimenting for yourself. Change the examples slightly, and see what happens. You should look at each piece of output carefully, and try to understand why it came out as it did.

After you have run through some simple examples, you should be ready to take the next step: learning to go through what is needed to solve a complete problem with *Mathematica*.

Solving a Complete Problem

You will probably find it best to start by picking a specific problem to work on. Pick a problem that you understand well—preferably one whose solution you could easily reproduce by hand. Then go through each step in solving the problem, learning what you need to know about *Mathematica* to do it. Always be ready to experiment with simple cases, and understand the results you get with these, before going back to your original problem.

In going through the steps to solve your problem, you will learn about various specific features of *Mathematica*, typically from sections of Part 1. After you have done a few problems with *Mathematica*, you should get a feeling for many of the basic features of the system.

When you have built up a reasonable knowledge of the features of *Mathematica*, you should go back and learn about the overall structure of the *Mathematica* system. You can do this by systematically reading Part 2 of this book. What you will discover is that many of the features that seemed unrelated actually fit together into a coherent overall structure. Knowing this structure will make it much easier for you to understand and remember the specific features you have already learned.

The Principles of *Mathematica*

You should not try to learn the overall structure of *Mathematica* too early. Unless you have had broad experience with advanced computer languages or pure mathematics, you will probably find Part 2 difficult to understand at first. You will find the structure and principles it describes difficult to remember, and you will always be wondering why particular aspects of them might be useful. However, if you first get some practical experience with *Mathematica*, you will find the overall structure much easier to grasp. You should realize that the principles on which *Mathematica* is built are very general, and it is usually difficult to understand such general principles before you have seen specific examples.

One of the most important aspects of *Mathematica* is that it applies a fairly small number of principles as widely as possible. This means that even though you have used a particular feature only in a specific situation, the principle on which that feature is based can probably be applied in many other situations. One reason it is so important to understand the underlying principles of *Mathematica* is that by doing so you can leverage your knowledge of specific features into a more general context. As an example, you may first learn about transformation rules in the context of algebraic expressions.

But the basic principle of transformation rules applies to any symbolic expression. Thus you can also use such rules to modify the structure of, say, an expression that represents a *Mathematica* graphics object.

Changing the Way You Work

Learning to use *Mathematica* well involves changing the way you solve problems. When you move from pencil and paper to *Mathematica* the balance of what aspects of problem solving are difficult changes. With pencil and paper, you can often get by with a fairly imprecise initial formulation of your problem. Then when you actually do calculations in solving the problem, you can usually fix up the formulation as you go along. However, the calculations you do have to be fairly simple, and you cannot afford to try out many different cases.

When you use *Mathematica*, on the other hand, the initial formulation of your problem has to be quite precise. However, once you have the formulation, you can easily do many different calculations with it. This means that you can effectively carry out many mathematical experiments on your problem. By looking at the results you get, you can then refine the original formulation of your problem.

There are typically many different ways to formulate a given problem in *Mathematica*. In almost all cases, however, the most direct and simple formulations will be best. The more you can formulate your problem in *Mathematica* from the beginning, the better. Often, in fact, you will find that formulating your problem directly in *Mathematica* is better than first trying to set up a traditional mathematical formulation, say an algebraic one. The main point is that *Mathematica* allows you to express not only traditional mathematical operations, but also algorithmic and structural ones. This greater range of possibilities gives you a better chance of being able to find a direct way to represent your original problem.

Writing Programs

For most of the more sophisticated problems that you want to solve with *Mathematica*, you will have to create *Mathematica* programs. *Mathematica* supports several types of programming, and you have to choose which one to use in each case. It turns out that no single type of programming suits all cases well. As a result, it is very important that you learn several different types of programming.

If you already know a traditional programming language such as BASIC, C, Fortran or Pascal, you will probably find it easiest to learn procedural programming in *Mathematica*, using Do, For and so on. But while almost any *Mathematica* program can, in principle, be written in a procedural way, this is rarely the best approach. In a symbolic system like *Mathematica*, functional and rule-based programming typically yields programs that are more efficient, and easier to understand.

If you find yourself using procedural programming a lot, you should make an active effort to convert at least some of your programs to other types. At first, you may find functional and rule-based programs difficult to understand. But after a while, you will find that their global structure is usually much easier to grasp than procedural programs. And as your experience with *Mathematica* grows over a period of months or years, you will probably find that you write more and more of your programs in non-procedural ways.

Learning the Whole System

As you proceed in using and learning *Mathematica*, it is important to remember that *Mathematica* is a large system. Although after a while you should know all of its basic principles, you may never learn the details of all its features. As a result, even after you have had a great deal of experience with *Mathematica*, you will undoubtedly still find it useful to look through this book. When you do so, you are quite likely to notice features that you never noticed before, but that with your experience, you can now see how to use.

How to Read This Book

If at all possible, you should read this book in conjunction with using an actual *Mathematica* system. When you see examples in the book, you should try them out on your computer.

You can get a basic feeling for what *Mathematica* does by looking at "A Tour of *Mathematica*" on page 1, and the "Graphics Gallery" and "Formula Gallery" at the end of the main text in this book. You may also find it useful to try out examples from the Tour with your own copy of *Mathematica*.

Whatever your background, you should make sure to look at the first three or four sections in Part 1 before you start to use *Mathematica* on your own. These sections describe the basics that you need to know in order to use *Mathematica* at any level.

The remainder of Part 1 shows you how to do many different kinds of computations with *Mathematica*. If you are trying to do a specific calculation, you will often find it sufficient just to look at the sections of Part 1 that discuss the features of *Mathematica* you need to use. A good approach is to try and find examples in the book which are close to what you want to do.

The emphasis in Part 1 is on using the basic functions that are built into *Mathematica* to carry out various different kinds of computations.

Part 2, on the other hand, discusses the basic structure and principles that underlie all of *Mathematica*. Rather than describing a sequence of specific features, Part 2 takes a more global approach. If you want to learn how to create your own *Mathematica* functions, you should read Part 2.

Part 3 is intended for those with more sophisticated mathematical interests and knowledge. It covers the more advanced mathematical features of *Mathematica*, as well as describing some features already mentioned in Part 1 in greater mathematical detail.

Each part of the book is divided into sections and subsections. There are two special kinds of subsections, indicated by the following headings:

- **Advanced Topic**: Advanced material which can be omitted on a first reading.

- **Special Topic**: Material relevant only for certain users or certain computer systems.

The main parts in this book are intended to be pedagogical, and can meaningfully be read in a sequential fashion. The Appendix, however, is intended solely for reference purposes. Once you are familiar with *Mathematica*, you will probably find the list of functions in the Appendix the best place to look up details you need.

About the Examples in This Book

All the examples given in this book were generated by running an actual copy of *Mathematica* Version 3.0. If you have a copy of this version, you should be able to reproduce the examples on your computer as they appear in the book.

There are, however, a few points to watch:

- Until you are familiar with *Mathematica*, make sure to type the input *exactly* as it appears in the book. Do not change any of the capital letters or brackets. Later, you will learn what things you can change. When you start out, however, it is important that you do not make any changes; otherwise you may not get the same results as in the book.

- Never type the prompt `In[n]:=` that begins each input line. Type only the text that follows this prompt.

- You will see that the lines in each dialog are numbered in sequence. Most subsections in the book contain separate dialogs. To make sure you get exactly what the book says, you should start a new *Mathematica* session each time the book does.

- Some "Special Topic" subsections give examples that may be specific to particular computer systems.

- Any examples that involve random numbers will generally give different results than in the book, since the sequence of random numbers produced by *Mathematica* is different in every session.

- Some examples that use machine-precision arithmetic may come out differently on different computer systems. This is a result of differences in floating-point hardware. If you use arbitrary-precision *Mathematica* numbers, you should not see differences.

- Almost all of the examples show output as it would be generated in `StandardForm` with a notebook interface to *Mathematica*. Output with a text-based interface will look similar, but not identical.

- Almost all of the examples in this book assume that your computer or terminal uses a standard U.S. ASCII character set. If you cannot find some of the characters you need on your keyboard, or if *Mathematica* prints out different characters than you see in the book, you will need to look at your computer documentation to find the correspondence with the character set you are using. The most common problem is that the dollar sign character (SHIFT-4) may come out as your local currency character.

- If the version of *Mathematica* is more recent than the one used to produce this book, then it is possible that some results you get may be different.

- Most of the examples in "A Tour of *Mathematica*", as well as Parts 1 and 2, are chosen so as to be fairly quick to execute. Assuming you have a machine with a clock speed of over about 100 MHz (and most machines produced in 1995 or later do), then few of the examples should take more than a few seconds to execute. If they do, there is probably something wrong. Section 1.3.12 describes how to stop the calculation.

Outline Table of Contents

Table of Contents

Part 2.   Principles of *Mathematica*

Part 3.   Advanced Mathematics in *Mathematica*

A Tour of Mathematica

The purpose of this Tour is to show examples of a few of the things that Mathematica can do. The Tour is in no way intended to be complete—it is just a sampling of a few of Mathematica's capabilities. It also concentrates only on general features, and does not address how these features can be applied in particular fields. Nevertheless, by reading through the Tour you should get at least some feeling for the basic Mathematica system.

Sometimes, you may be able to take examples from this Tour and immediately adapt them for your own purposes. But more often, you will have to look at some of Part 1, or at on-line Mathematica documentation, before you embark on serious work with Mathematica. If you do try repeating examples from the Tour, it is very important that you enter them exactly as they appear here. Do not change capitalization, types of brackets, etc.

On most versions of Mathematica, you will be able to find this Tour on line as part of the Mathematica help system. Even if you do not have access to a running copy of Mathematica 3.0, you may still be able to try out the examples in this Tour by visiting *http://www.wolfram.com/tour*.

A Tour of *Mathematica*

A Tour of *Mathematica*

Mathematica as a Calculator

You can use *Mathematica* just like a calculator: you type in questions, and *Mathematica* prints back the answers.

> Note: All examples here use only ordinary keyboard input. Page 14 shows how to enter fully formatted input.

Mathematica adds the In and Out labels; you do not type them. You end each line with [SHIFT]-[RETURN].

In[1]:= **3 + 5**

Out[1]= 8

In[2]:= **57.1 ^ 100**

Out[2]= 4.60904×10^{175}

In[3]:= **Inverse[{{1, 2}, {3, 4}}]**

Out[3]= $\left\{ \{-2, 1\}, \left\{ \frac{3}{2}, -\frac{1}{2} \right\} \right\}$

Ask Mathematica what 3 + 5 is; it prints back 8.

This stands for "to the power of".

This asks Mathematica to work out the inverse of a 2 x 2 matrix.

Mathematica represents matrices as lists of lists.

Mathematica can handle formulas as well as numbers.

This asks Mathematica to integrate a simple function.

In[1]:= **Integrate[Sqrt[x] Sqrt[1 + x], x]**

Out[1]= $\sqrt{1 + x} \left(\frac{\sqrt{x}}{4} + \frac{x^{3/2}}{2} \right) - \frac{\text{ArcSinh}\left[\sqrt{x} \right]}{4}$

This asks Mathematica to solve a quadratic equation.

This stands for mathematical equality.

In[2]:= **Solve[x^2 + x == a, x]**

Out[2]= $\left\{ \left\{ x \rightarrow \frac{1}{2} \left(-1 - \sqrt{1 + 4 a} \right) \right\}, \left\{ x \rightarrow \frac{1}{2} \left(-1 + \sqrt{1 + 4 a} \right) \right\} \right\}$

The result is a list of rules for x convenient for use in other calculations.

Mathematica can also create two- and three-dimensional graphics.

This creates a 2D plot of a simple function.

In[1]:= **Plot[Sin[x] + Sin[1.6 x], {x, 0, 40}]**

In[1]:= **Plot3D[Sin[xy], {x, 0, 4}, {y, 0, 4}]**

Here is a 3D plot.

Part of the Basic Calculations palette.

▷ **Arithmetic and Numbers**
▷ **Algebra**
▷ **Lists and Matrices**
▽ **Trigonometric and Exponential Functions**

▽ Trigonometric

Sin[■]	ArcSin[■]
Cos[■]	ArcCos[■]
Tan[■]	ArcTan[■]

Manipulation of trigonometric expressions to alternate forms.

TrigExpand[■]
TrigFactor[■]
TrigReduce[■]

Mathematica comes with a collection of palettes that let you do many operations by clicking buttons rather than typing commands.

Power Computing with *Mathematica*

Even though you can use it as easily as a calculator, *Mathematica* gives you access to immense computational power.

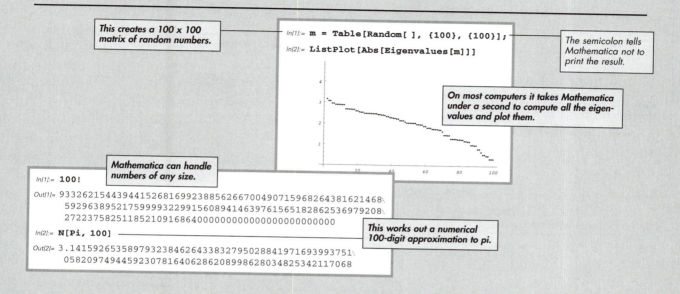

This creates a 100 x 100 matrix of random numbers.

```
In[1]:= m = Table[Random[ ], {100}, {100}];

In[2]:= ListPlot[Abs[Eigenvalues[m]]]
```

The semicolon tells *Mathematica* not to print the result.

On most computers it takes *Mathematica* under a second to compute all the eigenvalues and plot them.

Mathematica can handle numbers of any size.

```
In[1]:= 100!

Out[1]= 933262154439441526816992388562667004907159682643816214685
        592963895217599993229915608941463976156518286253697920827
        223758251185210916864000000000000000000000000
```

```
In[2]:= N[Pi, 100]

Out[2]= 3.141592653589793238462643383279502884197169399375105820974
        944592307816406286208998628034825342117068
```

This works out a numerical 100-digit approximation to pi.

Mathematica can work with formulas of any length—solving problems that would have taken years by hand.

This asks *Mathematica* to factor a polynomial.

```
In[1]:= Factor[x^99 + y^99]
```

$$Out[1]= (x + y) \ (x^2 - x y + y^2) \ (x^6 - x^3 y^3 + y^6) \ (x^{10} - x^9 y + x^8 y^2 -$$
$$x^7 y^3 + x^6 y^4 - x^5 y^5 + x^4 y^6 - x^3 y^7 + x^2 y^8 - x y^9 + y^{10})$$
$$(x^{20} + x^{19} y - x^{17} y^3 - x^{16} y^4 + x^{14} y^6 + x^{13} y^7 - x^{11} y^9 - x^{10} y^{10} -$$
$$x^9 y^{11} + x^7 y^{13} + x^6 y^{14} - x^4 y^{16} - x^3 y^{17} + x y^{19} + y^{20})$$
$$(x^{60} + x^{57} y^3 - x^{51} y^9 - x^{48} y^{12} + x^{42} y^{18} + x^{39} y^{21} - x^{33} y^{27} - x^{30} y^{30} -$$
$$x^{27} y^{33} + x^{21} y^{39} + x^{18} y^{42} - x^{12} y^{48} - x^9 y^{51} + x^3 y^{57} + y^{60})$$

Mathematica calls on sophisticated algorithms to simplify formulas.

```
In[2]:= Simplify[%]
```

$$Out[2]= x^{99} + y^{99}$$

This stands for the previous result.

Mathematica has achieved world records—for both size and speed—in many kinds of computations.

This tells *Mathematica* to show only a shortened version of the result.

```
In[1]:= PartitionsP[1840926] // Short

Out[1]//Short=
        2450302181664532415866532417964619750
        603617389925811289155524232965904373
```

Mathematica takes only a few minutes to work out how many ways 1840926 can be partitioned into sums—a frontier number theory calculation.

This indicates 1433 omitted digits.

Accessing Algorithms in *Mathematica*

Whenever you use *Mathematica* you are accessing the
world's largest collection of computational algorithms.

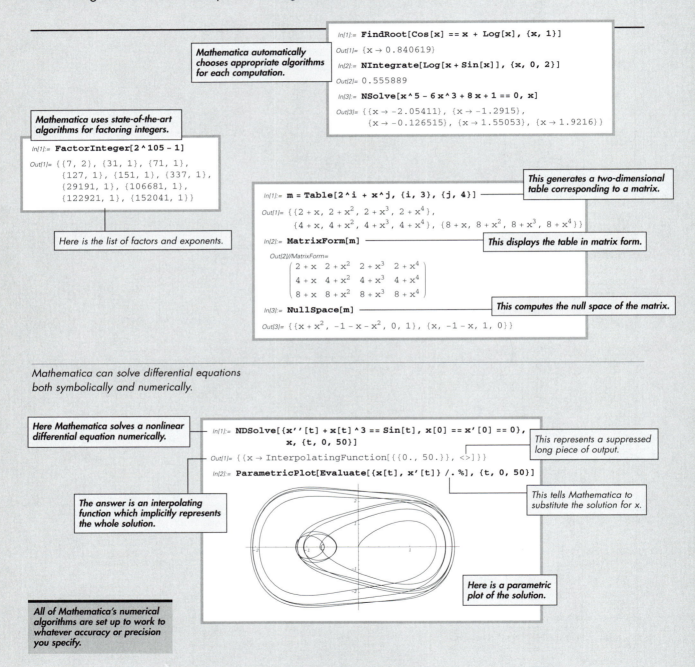

Mathematica automatically chooses appropriate algorithms for each computation.

```
In[1]:= FindRoot[Cos[x] == x + Log[x], {x, 1}]
Out[1]= {x → 0.840619}
In[2]:= NIntegrate[Log[x + Sin[x]], {x, 0, 2}]
Out[2]= 0.555889
In[3]:= NSolve[x^5 - 6 x^3 + 8 x + 1 == 0, x]
Out[3]= {{x → -2.05411}, {x → -1.2915},
         {x → -0.126515}, {x → 1.55053}, {x → 1.9216}}
```

Mathematica uses state-of-the-art algorithms for factoring integers.

```
In[1]:= FactorInteger[2^105 - 1]
Out[1]= {{7, 2}, {31, 1}, {71, 1},
         {127, 1}, {151, 1}, {337, 1},
         {29191, 1}, {106681, 1},
         {122921, 1}, {152041, 1}}
```

Here is the list of factors and exponents.

```
In[1]:= m = Table[2^i + x^j, {i, 3}, {j, 4}]
Out[1]= {{2 + x, 2 + x^2, 2 + x^3, 2 + x^4},
         {4 + x, 4 + x^2, 4 + x^3, 4 + x^4}, {8 + x, 8 + x^2, 8 + x^3, 8 + x^4}}
In[2]:= MatrixForm[m]
```

This generates a two-dimensional table corresponding to a matrix.

$$\begin{pmatrix} 2 + x & 2 + x^2 & 2 + x^3 & 2 + x^4 \\ 4 + x & 4 + x^2 & 4 + x^3 & 4 + x^4 \\ 8 + x & 8 + x^2 & 8 + x^3 & 8 + x^4 \end{pmatrix}$$

This displays the table in matrix form.

```
In[3]:= NullSpace[m]
Out[3]= {{x + x^2, -1 - x - x^2, 0, 1}, {x, -1 - x, 1, 0}}
```

This computes the null space of the matrix.

Mathematica can solve differential equations both symbolically and numerically.

Here Mathematica solves a nonlinear differential equation numerically.

```
In[1]:= NDSolve[{x''[t] + x[t]^3 == Sin[t], x[0] == x'[0] == 0},
         x, {t, 0, 50}]
Out[1]= {{x → InterpolatingFunction[{{0., 50.}}, <>]}}
In[2]:= ParametricPlot[Evaluate[{x[t], x'[t]} /. %], {t, 0, 50}]
```

This represents a suppressed long piece of output.

The answer is an interpolating function which implicitly represents the whole solution.

This tells Mathematica to substitute the solution for x.

Here is a parametric plot of the solution.

All of Mathematica's numerical algorithms are set up to work to whatever accuracy or precision you specify.

Mathematical Knowledge in *Mathematica*

Mathematica incorporates the knowledge from the world's mathematical handbooks—and uses its own revolutionary algorithms to go much further.

Mathematica knows about all the hundreds of special functions in pure and applied mathematics.

Mathematica can evaluate special functions with any parameters to any precision.

Mathematica is now able to do vastly more integrals than were ever before possible for either humans or computers.

Here is a definite integral.

Here is a symbolic sum.

The results often require special functions.

Mathematica can solve a wide range of ordinary and partial differential equations.

Mathematica's algorithms can generate a huge range of mathematical results.

This finds the billionth prime number.

This stands for $\sqrt{-1}$.

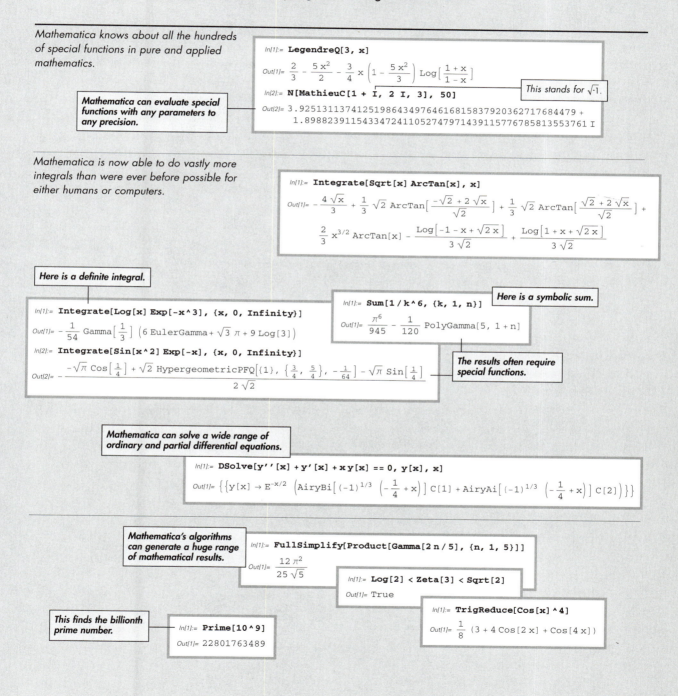

In[1]:= `LegendreQ[3, x]`

Out[1]= $\frac{2}{3} - \frac{5 x^2}{2} - \frac{3}{4} x \left(1 - \frac{5 x^2}{3}\right) \text{Log}\left[\frac{1+x}{1-x}\right]$

In[2]:= `N[MathieuC[1 + I, 2 I, 3], 50]`

Out[2]= 3.9251311374125198643497646168158379203362717684479 + 1.8988239115433472411052747971439115776785813553761 I

In[1]:= `Integrate[Sqrt[x] ArcTan[x], x]`

Out[1]= $-\frac{4\sqrt{x}}{3} + \frac{1}{3}\sqrt{2}\,\text{ArcTan}\left[\frac{-\sqrt{2}+2\sqrt{x}}{\sqrt{2}}\right] + \frac{1}{3}\sqrt{2}\,\text{ArcTan}\left[\frac{\sqrt{2}+2\sqrt{x}}{\sqrt{2}}\right] + \frac{2}{3}x^{3/2}\text{ArcTan}[x] - \frac{\text{Log}\left[-1-x+\sqrt{2x}\right]}{3\sqrt{2}} + \frac{\text{Log}\left[1+x+\sqrt{2x}\right]}{3\sqrt{2}}$

In[1]:= `Integrate[Log[x] Exp[-x^3], {x, 0, Infinity}]`

Out[1]= $-\frac{1}{54}\text{Gamma}\left[\frac{1}{3}\right]\left(6\,\text{EulerGamma}+\sqrt{3}\,\pi+9\,\text{Log}[3]\right)$

In[2]:= `Integrate[Sin[x^2] Exp[-x], {x, 0, Infinity}]`

Out[2]= $\dfrac{-\sqrt{\pi}\,\text{Cos}\left[\frac{1}{4}\right]+\sqrt{2}\,\text{HypergeometricPFQ}\left[\{1\},\left\{\frac{3}{4},\frac{5}{4}\right\},-\frac{1}{64}\right]-\sqrt{\pi}\,\text{Sin}\left[\frac{1}{4}\right]}{2\sqrt{2}}$

In[1]:= `Sum[1 / k^6, {k, 1, n}]`

Out[1]= $\frac{\pi^6}{945} - \frac{1}{120}\text{PolyGamma}[5, 1+n]$

In[1]:= `DSolve[y''[x] + y'[x] + x y[x] == 0, y[x], x]`

Out[1]= $\left\{\left\{y[x] \to E^{-x/2}\left(\text{AiryBi}\left[(-1)^{1/3}\left(-\frac{1}{4}+x\right)\right]C[1] + \text{AiryAi}\left[(-1)^{1/3}\left(-\frac{1}{4}+x\right)\right]C[2]\right)\right\}\right\}$

In[1]:= `FullSimplify[Product[Gamma[2 n / 5], {n, 1, 5}]]`

Out[1]= $\frac{12\,\pi^2}{25\sqrt{5}}$

In[1]:= `Log[2] < Zeta[3] < Sqrt[2]`

Out[1]= True

In[1]:= `TrigReduce[Cos[x]^4]`

Out[1]= $\frac{1}{8}\left(3 + 4\,\text{Cos}[2x] + \text{Cos}[4x]\right)$

In[1]:= `Prime[10^9]`

Out[1]= 22801763489

Building Up Computations

Being able to work with formulas lets you easily
integrate all the parts of a computation.

In[1]:= **Eigenvalues[{{3, 1}, {2, 6}}]**

Out[1]= $\left\{ \frac{1}{2} \left(9 - \sqrt{17} \right), \frac{1}{2} \left(9 + \sqrt{17} \right) \right\}$

Here are the eigenvalues of a matrix of numbers.

Mathematica can still compute the eigenvalues even when symbolic parameters are introduced.

In[1]:= **v = Eigenvalues[{{3, 1}, {2, b}}]**

Out[1]= $\left\{ \frac{1}{2} \left(3 + b - \sqrt{17 - 6b + b^2} \right), \frac{1}{2} \left(3 + b + \sqrt{17 - 6b + b^2} \right) \right\}$

This expression is a compact representation of the eigenvalues for any value of b.

In[2]:= **Plot[Evaluate[v], {b, -10, 10}]**

This takes the formula for the eigenvalues and immediately plots it.

This picture shows how the eigenvalues vary with b.

You can solve for the value of b at which the first eigenvalue is zero.

In[3]:= **Solve[First[v] == 0, b]**

Out[3]= $\left\{ \left\{ b \to \frac{2}{3} \right\} \right\}$

Or find the integral from 0 to c.

In[4]:= **Integrate[First[v], {b, 0, c}]**

Out[4]= $-\frac{3\sqrt{17}}{4} - 2\,\text{ArcSinh}\left[\frac{3}{2\sqrt{2}}\right] +$
$\frac{1}{4}\left(c^2 + 3\sqrt{17 - 6c + c^2} - c\left(-6 + \sqrt{17 - 6c + c^2}\right) - 8\,\text{ArcSinh}\left[\frac{-3 + c}{2\sqrt{2}}\right] \right)$

Mathematica's functions are carefully designed so that output from one can easily be used as input to others.

This finds the series expansion of the result.

In[5]:= **Series[%, {c, 0, 5}]**

Out[5]= $\frac{1}{4}\left(6 - 2\sqrt{17} \right)c + \frac{1}{4}\left(1 + \frac{3}{\sqrt{17}}\right)c^2 - \frac{2c^3}{51\sqrt{17}} - \frac{3c^4}{578\sqrt{17}} - \frac{14c^5}{24565\sqrt{17}} + O[c]^6$

In[6]:= **FindRoot[%4 == 1 + c, {c, 1}]**

Out[6]= $\{c \to -0.554408\}$

This searches numerically for a root.

This generates a table of the first 20 primes.

In[1]:= **Table[Prime[i], {i, 20}]**

Out[1]= {2, 3, 5, 7, 11, 13, 17, 19, 23, 29, 31, 37, 41, 43, 47, 53, 59, 61, 67, 71}

In[2]:= **Fit[%, {Log[x], x, x^2}, x]**

Fit produces an approximate formula.

Out[2]= $3.55559\,x + 0.0403706\,x^2 - 5.22256\,\text{Log}[x]$

In[3]:= **Sum[%, {x, 1, 20}]**

Out[3]= 641.437

This computes the sum of the first 20 primes using the approximate formula.

In[4]:= **Sum[Prime[i], {i, 1, 20}]**

Out[4]= 639

Here is the exact result.

Handling Data

Mathematica lets you import data in any format, then manipulate it using powerful and flexible functions.

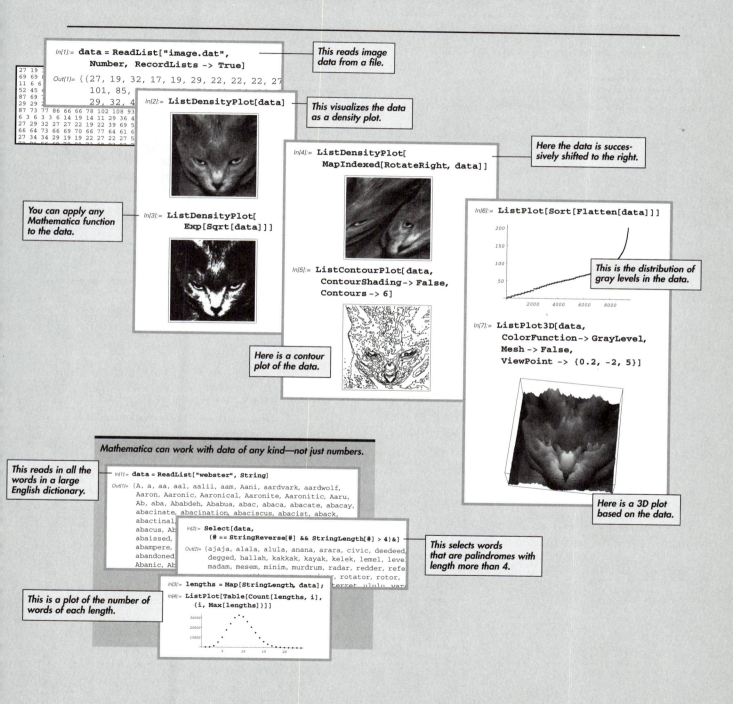

```
In[1]:= data = ReadList["image.dat",
          Number, RecordLists -> True]

Out[1]= {{27, 19, 32, 17, 19, 29, 22, 22, 22, 27
          101, 85,
          29, 32, 4
```

This reads image data from a file.

```
27 19
69 69
11 6 6
52 45
87 69
29 29
87 73 77 86 66 66 78 102 108 93
6 3 6 3 6 14 19 14 11 29 36 4
29 29 32 27 27 22 19 22 39 69 5
66 64 73 66 69 70 66 77 64 61 6
27 34 34 29 19 19 22 27 22 27 5
```

```
In[2]:= ListDensityPlot[data]
```

This visualizes the data as a density plot.

You can apply any Mathematica function to the data.

```
In[3]:= ListDensityPlot[
          Exp[Sqrt[data]]]
```

```
In[4]:= ListDensityPlot[
          MapIndexed[RotateRight, data]]
```

Here the data is successively shifted to the right.

```
In[5]:= ListContourPlot[data,
          ContourShading-> False,
          Contours -> 6]
```

Here is a contour plot of the data.

```
In[6]:= ListPlot[Sort[Flatten[data]]]
```

This is the distribution of gray levels in the data.

```
In[7]:= ListPlot3D[data,
          ColorFunction-> GrayLevel,
          Mesh -> False,
          ViewPoint -> {0.2, -2, 5}]
```

Here is a 3D plot based on the data.

Mathematica can work with data of any kind—not just numbers.

This reads in all the words in a large English dictionary.

```
In[1]:= data = ReadList["webster", String]

Out[1]= {A, a, aa, aal, aalii, aam, Aani, aardvark, aardwolf,
          Aaron, Aaronic, Aaronical, Aaronite, Aaronitic, Aaru,
          Ab, aba, Ababdeh, Ababua, abac, abaca, abacate, abacay,
          abacinate, abacination, abaciscus, abacist, aback,
          abactinal
          abacus, Ab
          abaissed,
          abampere,
          abandoned
          Abanic, Ab
```

```
In[2]:= Select[data,
          (# == StringReverse[#] && StringLength[#] > 4)&]

Out[2]= {ajaja, alala, alula, anana, arara, civic, deedeed,
          degged, hallah, kakkak, kayak, kelek, lemel, leve
          madam, mesem, minim, murdrum, radar, redder, refe
                                              , rotator, rotor,
                                    terret ululu var
```

This selects words that are palindromes with length more than 4.

```
In[3]:= lengths = Map[StringLength, data];
In[4]:= ListPlot[Table[Count[lengths, i],
          {i, Max[lengths]}]]
```

This is a plot of the number of words of each length.

Visualization with *Mathematica*

Mathematica makes it easy to create stunning visual images.

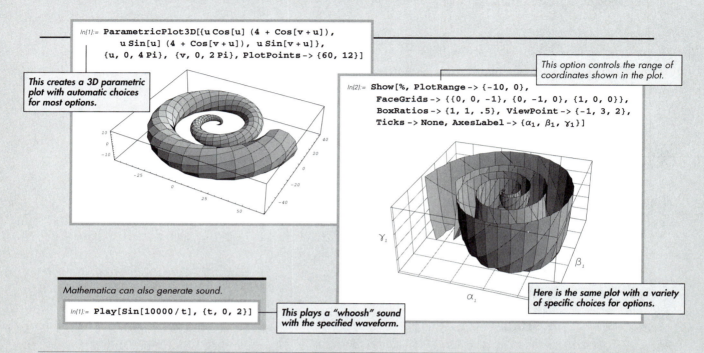

```
In[1]:= ParametricPlot3D[{u Cos[u] (4 + Cos[v + u]),
        u Sin[u] (4 + Cos[v + u]), u Sin[v + u]},
       {u, 0, 4 Pi}, {v, 0, 2 Pi}, PlotPoints -> {60, 12}]
```

This creates a 3D parametric plot with automatic choices for most options.

This option controls the range of coordinates shown in the plot.

```
In[2]:= Show[%, PlotRange -> {-10, 0},
        FaceGrids -> {{0, 0, -1}, {0, -1, 0}, {1, 0, 0}},
        BoxRatios -> {1, 1, .5}, ViewPoint -> {-1, 3, 2},
        Ticks -> None, AxesLabel -> {α₁, β₁, γ₁}]
```

Here is the same plot with a variety of specific choices for options.

Mathematica can also generate sound.

```
In[1]:= Play[Sin[10000 / t], {t, 0, 2}]
```

This plays a "whoosh" sound with the specified waveform.

Mathematica includes primitives from which you can build up 2D and 3D graphics of any complexity.

```
In[1]:= g = Flatten[Table[Point[{p / q, Denominator[p / q]}],
        {q, 100}, {p, q - 1}]]
```

$Out[1]= \{\text{Point}[\{\frac{1}{2}, 2\}], \text{Point}[\{\frac{1}{3}, 3\}],$
$\text{Point}[\{\frac{3}{}, 4\}], \text{Point}[\{\frac{1}{}, 5\}],$

Here is a list of point primitives.

```
In[2]:= Show[Graphics[g, Frame -> True]]
```

This is the corresponding 2D graphic.

```
In[1]:= g = Flatten[Table[If[Mod[Multinomial[x, y, z], 2] == 1,
        Cuboid[1.2 {x, y, -z}], {}],
       {x, 0, 15}, {y, 0, 15}, {z, 0, 15}]]
```

$Out[1]= \{\text{Cuboid}[\{0, 0, 0\}], \text{Cuboid}[\{0, 0, -1.2\}],$
$\text{Cuboid}[\{0, 0, -2.4\}], \text{Cuboid}[\{0, 0, -3$

Here is a list of cuboid primitives.

```
In[2]:= Show[Graphics3D[g]]
```

This is the corresponding 3D graphic.

```
In[1]:= Table[Plot3D[Sin[2 x] Sin[2 y] Cos[t],
    {x, 0, Pi}, {y, 0, Pi}, PlotRange -> {-1, 1},
    BoxRatios -> {1, 1, 1}], {t, 0, Pi, Pi / 6}]
```

Mathematica lets you produce animated movies as well as static graphics.

Mathematica has made possible many new kinds of scientific, technical, and artistic images.

You can create diagrams of any complexity.

You can create representations of abstract mathematical objects.

You can visualize structures of any kind.

Latitude
38 South

Nov 17
3:20 am

South   West   North

You can display data in any format.

Mathematica Notebooks

Every *Mathematica* notebook is a complete interactive document which combines text, tables, graphics, calculations and other elements.

A Section Heading

◊ *A Calculation*

$ln[1]:= \texttt{Plot}[\texttt{Sin}[\xi] + \texttt{Sin}[\sqrt{\xi}], \{\xi, 0, 100\pi\}];$

◊ *A Subsection*

◊ *Another Subsection*

◊ *Basic Features of Notebooks*

Here is some ordinary text. It can be in any **font**, face, SIZE, color, etc.

Text can contain formulas such as $\int \frac{1}{\alpha+1}\, d\alpha$. It can also contain Hyperlinks.

| Forward | Backward | Reverse |

More Advanced Layout

| $\alpha^2 - \beta$ | $(\alpha - \beta)\,(\alpha + \beta)$ | $\alpha^2 - \beta^3$ |
| $\alpha^3 - \beta^2$ | $\alpha^3 - \beta^2$ | $(\alpha - \beta)\,(\alpha^2 + \alpha\,\beta + \beta^2)$ |

Like other objects in *Mathematica*, the cells in a notebook, and in fact the whole notebook itself, are all ultimately represented as *Mathematica* expressions. With the standard notebook front end, you can use the command Show Expression to see the text of the *Mathematica* expression that corresponds to any particular cell.

Like other objects in *Mathematica*, the cells in a notebook, and in fact the whole notebook itself, are all ultimately represented as *Mathematica* expressions. With the standard notebook front end, you can use the command Show Expression to see the text of the *Mathematica* expression that corresponds to any particular cell.

Mathematica notebooks are automatically retargeted for screen or printout—optimizing fonts and layout for each medium.

A notebook targeted for presentation.

A notebook targeted for printout.

Notebooks are automatically organized in a hierarchy of cells.

You can close groups of cells so you see only their headings.

You can use hyperlinks to jump within a notebook or between notebooks.

You can set up buttons to perform any action you specify.

Each cell can be assigned a style from a style sheet.

Title
Subtitle
Subsubtitle
Section
Subsection
Subsubsection
Text

Millions of pages of technical documents now exist as Mathematica notebooks.

Zeta and Related Functions

LerchPhi[z , s , a]	Lerch's transcendent $\Phi(z, s, a)$
PolyLog[n , z]	polylogarithm function $\text{Li}_n(z)$
RiemannSiegelTheta[t]	Riemann−Siegel function $\vartheta(t)$
RiemannSiegelZ[t]	Riemann−Siegel function $Z(t)$
StieltjesGamma[n]	Stieltjes constants γ_n
Zeta[s]	Riemann zeta function $\zeta(s)$
Zeta[s , a]	generalized Riemann zeta function $\zeta(s, a)$

Zeta and related functions.

The **Riemann zeta function** Zeta[s] is defined by the relation $\zeta(s) = \sum_k \frac{1}{k^s}$ (for $s > 1$). Zeta functions with integer arguments arise in evaluating various sums and integrals. *Mathematica* gives exact results when possible for zeta functions with integer arguments.

There is an analytic continuation of $\zeta(s)$ for arbitrary complex $s \neq 1$. The zeta function for complex arguments is central to number-theoretic studies of the distribution of primes. Of particular importance are the values on the critical line $\text{Re}\, s = \frac{1}{2}$.

In studying $\zeta(\frac{1}{2} + it)$, it is often convenient to define the two analytic **Riemann-Siegel functions** RiemannSiegelZ[t] and RiemannSiegelTheta[t] according to $Z(t) = e^{i\vartheta(t)}\zeta(\frac{1}{2} + it)$ and $\vartheta(t) = \text{Im}\log\Gamma(\frac{1}{4} + it/2) - \frac{1}{2}\log\pi\, t$.

The whole of this book is available on line as Mathematica notebooks.

Mathematica provides hundreds of options that allow you to give notebooks any look you want—and to generate full publication-quality documents.

Mathematica notebooks can be built up using explicit commands as well as interactively.

This tells Mathematica to print three cells in subsection style.

This joins text strings together.

```
Do[StylePrint["Heading " <>
    ToString[i], "Subsection"],
    {i, 3}]
```

This is how Mathematica represents a cell.

```
Cell["A Subsection Heading", "Subsection",
  CellFrame -> True, CellDingbat->"\[FilledCircle]"]
```

● **A Subsection Heading**

Here is the cell.

```
In[1]:= Do[StylePrint["Heading " <>
        ToString[i], "Subsection"],
        {i, 3}]
```

■ **Heading 1**

■ **Heading 2**

■ **Heading 3**

Here are the three new cells.

Palettes and Buttons

Palettes and buttons provide a simple but fully customizable point-and-click interface to *Mathematica*.

Mathematica comes with a collection of ready-to-use standard palettes.

Part of the standard Basic Calculations palette.

| ▪ . □ |
| Cross[▪, □] |
| Outer[▪, □, □] |
| Det[▪] |
| Inverse[▪] |
| Transpose[▪] |
| Eigenvalues[▪] |
| Eigenvectors[▪] |
| LinearSolve[▪, □] |
| RowReduce[▪] |

à	á	â	ã	ä	å	æ	ç
è	ê	ë	ì	í	î	ï
ñ	ò	ó	ô	õ
ú	û	ü	ý	ÿ	þ
Á	Â	Ã	Ä	Å	Æ
É	Ê	Ë	Ì	Í	Î
Ł	Ñ	Ò	Ó	Ô	Õ
Ù	Ú	Û
f	«	»

A standard palette for European characters.

The complete Basic Calculations palette is organized as a notebook with palettes inside it.

▷ Arithmetic Operations
▷ Algebra
▷ Lists and Matrices
▽ Trigonometric and Exponential Functions

▽ Trigonometric

Sin[▪]	ArcSin[▪]
Cos[▪]	ArcCos[▪]
Tan[▪]	ArcTan[▪]

Manipulation of trigonometric expressions to alternate forms.

| TrigExpand[▪] |
| TrigFactor[▪] |

Palettes work like extensions to your keyboard.

| α | β | γ |
| δ | ε | ζ |

2 (1 + |

Clicking the ε button pastes the ε character into your notebook.

2 (1 + ε |

The ▪ indicates where the current selection should be inserted.

| √▪ | Log[▪] |
| ▪² | Exp[▪] |

Clicking the button takes the highlighted selection and wraps a square root around it.

1 + Sin[x] + Cos[x]

1 + √Sin[x] + Cos[x]

It is easy to create your own custom palettes.

Palettes can be part of a note-book or can stand alone.

Darken[▪]	Lighten[▪]
EdgeSelect[▪]	□
□	□

A button waiting to be filled.

You can create custom palettes to do any function or manipulate any expression.

| Expand[▪] |
| Factor[▪] |
| Simplify[▪] |

Clicking the button immediately factors in place the expression you have selected.

1 + a^2 + 2 a b + b^2 + (p + q) ^ 2

1 + (a + b)² + (p + q) ^ 2

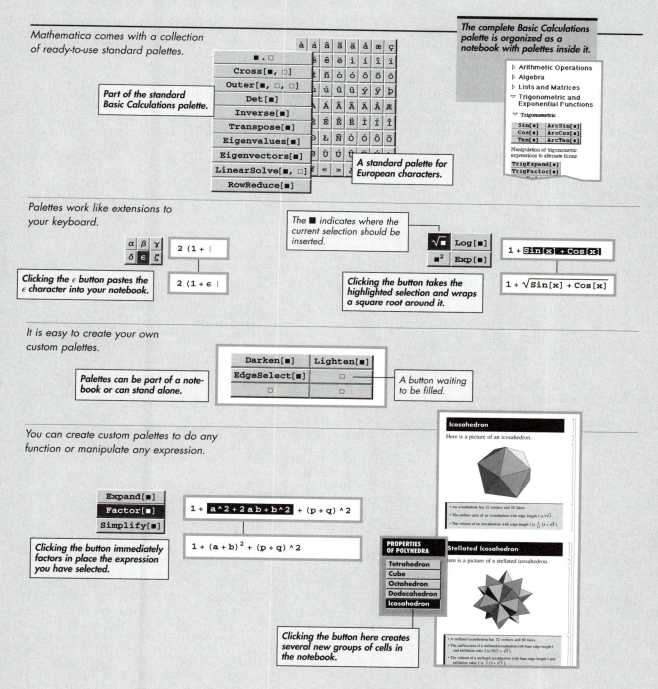

Icosahedron

Here is a picture of an icosahedron.

- An icosahedron has 12 vertices and 20 faces.
- The surface area of an icosahedron with edge length 1 is $5\sqrt{3}$.
- The volume of an icosahedron with edge length 1 is $\frac{5}{12}(3+\sqrt{5})$.

PROPERTIES OF POLYHEDRA

| Tetrahedron |
| Cube |
| Octahedron |
| Dodecahedron |
| Icosahedron |

Stellated Icosahedron

Here is a picture of a stellated icosahedron.

- A stellated icosahedron has 32 vertices and 60 faces.
- The surface area of a stellated icosahedron with base edge length 1 and stellation ratio 2 is $30(1+\sqrt{5})$.
- The volume of a stellated icosahedron with base edge length 1 and stellation ratio 2 is $\frac{5}{2}(3+\sqrt{5})$.

Clicking the button here creates several new groups of cells in the notebook.

Mathematical Notation

Mathematica notebooks fully support standard mathematical notation—for both output and input.

Mathematica combines the compactness of mathematical notation with the precision of a computer language.

Here is an integral input using only ordinary keyboard characters.

$In[1]:=$ **Integrate[Log[1 + x] / Sqrt[x], x]**

$Out[1]=$ $-4\sqrt{x} + 4\,\mathrm{ArcTan}\left[\sqrt{x}\right] + 2\sqrt{x}\,\mathrm{Log}[1 + x]$

Here is the same integral entered in two-dimensional form with special characters.

You can enter this form using a palette or directly from the keyboard.

$In[1]:=$ $\displaystyle\int \frac{\mathrm{Log}[1+\xi]}{\sqrt{\xi}}\,\mathbb{d}\xi$

`:int: Log[1 + :x:] CTRL / CTRL 2 :x: CTRL ⎵ :dd: :x:`

$Out[1]=$ $-4\sqrt{\xi} + 4\,\mathrm{ArcTan}\left[\sqrt{\xi}\right] + 2\sqrt{\xi}\,\mathrm{Log}[1 + \xi]$

This stands for the ESC key.

You can use any of the notation in this palette for input.

$$-4\sqrt{\xi} + \left(4\,\mathrm{ArcTan}\left[\sqrt{\xi}\right] + 2\,\pi\right) + 2\sqrt{\xi}\,\mathrm{Log}[1 + \xi]$$

Mathematica always lets you edit output—and use it again as input.

Mathematica can generate output in traditional textbook form.

$In[2]:=$ **TraditionalForm[%]**

$Out[2]//TraditionalForm=$
$$4\tan^{-1}\left(\sqrt{\xi}\right) + 2\sqrt{\xi}\,\log(\xi + 1) - 4\sqrt{\xi}$$

Mathematica's StandardForm is precise and unambiguous. TraditionalForm requires heuristics for interpretation.

Mathematica produces top-quality output for formulas of any size or complexity.

$In[1]:=$ $\displaystyle\sum_{\mu=0}^{\infty} \frac{\varphi^{\mu}\,\mathrm{Cos}\left[\frac{\pi\mu}{4}\right]}{\mu!^{2}\,(\mu^{2}+\kappa)\,(\mu^{2}-\lambda)}$ **// TraditionalForm**

$Out[1]//TraditionalForm=$
$$\left(-\lambda\,_1F_2\left(-i\sqrt{\kappa};1,1-i\sqrt{\kappa};e^{-\frac{i\pi}{4}}\varphi\right) - \lambda\,_1F_2\left(i\sqrt{\kappa};1,i\sqrt{\kappa}+1;e^{-\frac{i\pi}{4}}\varphi\right) - \right.$$
$$\kappa\,_1F_2\left(-\sqrt{\lambda};1,1-\sqrt{\lambda};e^{-\frac{i\pi}{4}}\varphi\right) - \kappa\,_1F_2\left(\sqrt{\lambda};1,\sqrt{\lambda}+1;e^{-\frac{i\pi}{4}}\varphi\right)\Big/$$
$$4\kappa\left(\sqrt{\kappa}-i\sqrt{\lambda}\right)\left(\sqrt{\kappa}+i\sqrt{\lambda}\right)\lambda +$$
$$\left(-\lambda\,_1F_2\left(-i\sqrt{\kappa};1,1-i\sqrt{\kappa};e^{\frac{i\pi}{4}}\varphi\right) - \lambda\,_1F_2\left(i\sqrt{\kappa};1,i\sqrt{\kappa}+1;e^{\frac{i\pi}{4}}\varphi\right) - \right.$$

Mathematica supports over 700 special characters with new fonts optimized for both screen and printer.

Script
Double-struck
Gothic
Greek

All characters have consistent full names; some also have aliases and TEX names.

Mathematica makes it easy to work with abstract notation.

$In[1]:=$ **Table$\left[\mathcal{G}\diamond\overline{\alpha_i\oplus\beta_i}\Longrightarrow\underset{i}{\overset{3-i}{\eth}}, \{i, 3\}\right]$**

$Out[1]=$ $\left\{\mathcal{G}\diamond\overline{\alpha_1\oplus\beta_1}\Longrightarrow\underset{1}{\overset{2}{\eth}},\ \mathcal{G}\diamond\overline{\alpha_2\oplus\beta_2}\Longrightarrow\underset{2}{\overset{1}{\eth}},\ \mathcal{G}\diamond\overline{\alpha_3\oplus\beta_3}\Longrightarrow\underset{3}{\overset{0}{\eth}}\right\}$

Mathematica and Your Computing Environment

Mathematica runs compatibly across all major computer systems, and lets you exchange data in many standard formats.

The standard *Mathematica* system consists of two parts:

The kernel—which actually does computations.

The front end—which handles user interaction and notebooks.

From within one notebook you can run several *Mathematica* kernels—on local or remote computers.

Macintosh

NEXTSTEP

X Windows

Microsoft Windows

Notebook files contain only plain text and are completely portable.

This is what you get when you copy the integral into an external text application such as email.

You can export graphics and formulas to other programs in EPS, GIF, etc., and then manipulate them.

Mathematica lets you import external graphics and sounds into notebooks.

Complete Mathematica notebooks can be exported in formats such as HTML, TEX and RTF.

Mathematica uses the Unicode standard to ensure portability of international character sets.

You can easily connect to external programs.

Mathematica provides system-independent functions for file manipulation.

Here is a plot of the size distribution of files in a file system.

The Unifying Idea of *Mathematica*

Mathematica is built on the powerful unifying idea that everything can be represented as a symbolic expression.

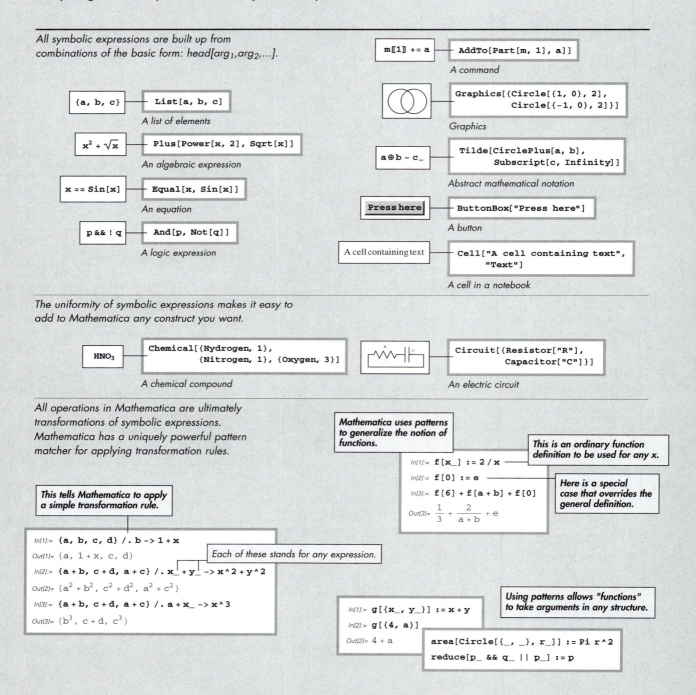

All symbolic expressions are built up from combinations of the basic form: head[arg₁,arg₂,...].

{a, b, c}	**List[a, b, c]**

A list of elements

x² + √x	**Plus[Power[x, 2], Sqrt[x]]**

An algebraic expression

x == Sin[x]	**Equal[x, Sin[x]]**

An equation

p && ! q	**And[p, Not[q]]**

A logic expression

m[[1]] += a	**AddTo[Part[m, 1], a]]**

A command

	Graphics[{Circle[{1, 0}, 2], Circle[{-1, 0}, 2]}]

Graphics

a⊕b ~ c∞	**Tilde[CirclePlus[a, b], Subscript[c, Infinity]]**

Abstract mathematical notation

Press here	**ButtonBox["Press here"]**

A button

A cell containing text	**Cell["A cell containing text", "Text"]**

A cell in a notebook

The uniformity of symbolic expressions makes it easy to add to *Mathematica* any construct you want.

HNO₃	**Chemical[{Hydrogen, 1}, {Nitrogen, 1}, {Oxygen, 3}]**

A chemical compound

	Circuit[{Resistor["R"], Capacitor["C"]}]

An electric circuit

All operations in *Mathematica* are ultimately transformations of symbolic expressions. *Mathematica* has a uniquely powerful pattern matcher for applying transformation rules.

Mathematica uses patterns to generalize the notion of functions.

This is an ordinary function definition to be used for any x.

In[1]:= **f[x_] := 2 / x**

In[2]:= **f[0] := e**

In[3]:= **f[6] + f[a + b] + f[0]**

Here is a special case that overrides the general definition.

Out[3]= $\frac{1}{3} + \frac{2}{a + b} + e$

This tells Mathematica to apply a simple transformation rule.

In[1]:= **{a, b, c, d} /. b -> 1 + x**

Out[1]= {a, 1 + x, c, d}

Each of these stands for any expression.

In[2]:= **{a + b, c + d, a + c} /. x_ + y_ -> x^2 + y^2**

Out[2]= {a² + b², c² + d², a² + c²}

In[3]:= **{a + b, c + d, a + c} /. a + x_ -> x^3**

Out[3]= {b³, c + d, c³}

In[1]:= **g[{x_, y_}] := x + y**

In[2]:= **g[{4, a}]**

Out[2]= 4 + a

Using patterns allows "functions" to take arguments in any structure.

area[Circle[{_, _}, r_]] := Pi r^2

reduce[p_ && q_ || p_] := p

Mathematica as a Programming Language

Mathematica is an unprecedentedly flexible and intuitive programming language.

Mathematica incorporates a range of programming paradigms—so you can write every program in its most natural way.

Mathematica includes advanced programming methods from modern computer science—and adds a host of new ideas of its own.

```
In[1]:= z = a;
        Do[Print[z *= z + i], {i, 3}]
        a (1 + a)
        a (1 + a) (2 + a (1 + a))
        a (1 + a) (2 + a (1 + a)) (3 + a (1 + a) (2 + a (1 + a)))
```
Procedural programming

```
In[1]:= 1 + {a, b, c} ^ 2
Out[1]= {1 + a², 1 + b², 1 + c²}
In[2]:= Table[i^j, {i, 4}, {j, i}]
Out[2]= {{1}, {2, 4}, {3, 9, 27}, {4, 16, 64, 256}}
In[3]:= Flatten[%]
Out[3]= {1, 2, 4, 3, 9, 27, 4, 16, 64, 256}
In[4]:= Partition[%, 2]
Out[4]= {{1, 2}, {4, 3}, {9, 27}, {4, 16}, {64, 256}}
```
List-based programming

Many operations are automatically threaded over lists.

This flattens out sublists.

This partitions into sublists of length 2.

```
In[1]:= NestList[f, x, 4]
Out[1]= {x, f[x], f[f[x]], f[f[f[x]]], f[f[f[f[x]]]]}
In[2]:= NestList[(1 + #) ^ 2 &, x, 3]
Out[2]= {x, (1 + x)², (1 + (1 + x)²)², (1 + (1 + (1 + x)²)²)²}
```
Functional programming

This is a pure function.

```
In[1]:= p[x_ + y_] := p[x] + p[y]
In[2]:= p[a + b + c]
Out[2]= p[a] + p[b] + p[c]
In[3]:= s[{x__, a_, y__}, a_] := {a, x, x, y, y}
In[4]:= s[{1, 2, 3, 4, 5, 6}, 4]
Out[4]= {4, 1, 2, 3, 1, 2, 3, 5, 6, 5, 6}
```
Rule-based programming

This stands for any sequence of expressions.

```
In[1]:= StringReplace["aababbaabaababababa",
        {"aa" -> "AAA", "ba" -> "V"}]
Out[1]= AAAVbVaVaVVV
```
String-based programming

```
h /: h[x_] + h[y_] := hplus[x, y]
h /: p[h[x_], x_] := hp[x]
h /: f_[h[x_]] := fh[f, x]
```
Object-oriented programming

This associates the definition with the object h.

Here are three definitions to be associated with the object h.

Mathematica gives you the flexibility to write programs in many different styles.

```
f = Factorial
f[n_] := n!
f[n_] := Gamma[n - 1]
f[n_] := n f[n - 1] ; f[1] = 1
f[n_] := Product[i, {i, n}]
f[n_] := Module[{t = 1},
  Do[t = t * i, {i, n}]; t]
f[n_] := Module[{t = 1, i},
  For[i = 1, i <= n, i++, t *= i]; t]
f[n_] := Apply[Times, Range[n]]
f[n_] := Fold[Times, 1, Range[n]]
f[n_] := If[n == 1, 1, n f[n - 1]]
f = If[#1 == 1, 1, #1 #0[#1 - 1]]&
f[n_] := Fold[#2[#1]&, 1,
  Array[Function[t, # t]&, n]]
```
A dozen definitions of the factorial function

```
In[1]:= Position[{1, 2, 3, 4, 5} / 2, _Integer]
Out[1]= {{2}, {4}}
In[2]:= MapIndexed[Power, {a, b, c, d}]
Out[2]= {{a}, {b²}, {c³}, {d⁴}}
In[3]:= FixedPointList[If[EvenQ[#], # / 2, #]&, 10 ^ 5]
Out[3]= {100000, 50000, 25000, 12500, 6250, 3125, 3125}
In[4]:= ReplaceList[{a, b, c, d, e},
                    {x__, y__} -> {{x}, {y}}]
Out[4]= {{{a}, {b, c, d, e}}, {{a, b}, {c, d, e}},
         {{a, b, c}, {d, e}}, {{a, b, c, d}, {e}}}
```
Mixed programming paradigms

Many of Mathematica's most powerful functions mix different programming paradigms.

Writing Programs in *Mathematica*

Mathematica's high-level programming constructs let you build sophisticated programs more quickly than ever before.

Single-line *Mathematica* programs can perform complex operations. This one produces a one-dimensional random walk.

```
RandomWalk[n_] := NestList[(# + (-1) ^ Random[Integer]) &, 0, n]
```

In[2]:= ListPlot[RandomWalk[200], PlotJoined -> True]

Here is a plot of a 200-step random walk.

The directness of *Mathematica* programs makes them easy to generalize. This one produces a random walk in d dimensions.

```
RandomWalk[n_, d_] := NestList[
   (# + (-1) ^ Table[Random[Integer], {d}]) &, Table[0, {d}], n]
```

In[2]:= Show[Graphics3D[
         Line[RandomWalk[1000, 3]]]]

Here is a plot of a 3D random walk.

Here is a direct program for a step in the Life cellular automaton.

```
LifeStep[a_List] :=
   MapThread[If[(#1 == 1 && #2 == 4) || #2 == 3, 1, 0] &,
      {a, Sum[RotateLeft[a, {i, j}], {i, -1, 1}, {j, -1, 1}]}, 2]
```

```
LifeStep[list_] :=
   With[{u = Split[Sort[Flatten[Outer[Plus, list, N9, 1], 1]]]},
      Union[Cases[u, {x_, _, _} -> x],
         Intersection[Cases[u, {x_, _, _, _} -> x], list]]]
N9 = Flatten[Array[List, {3, 3}, -1], 1] ;
```

Mathematica's rich structure also makes it easy to implement this alternative highly optimized algorithm.

Mathematica makes it easy to build up programs from components.

```
CenterList[n_Integer] :=
   ReplacePart[Table[0, {n}], 1, Ceiling[n / 2]]

ElementaryRule[num_Integer] :=
   IntegerDigits[num, 2, 8]

CAStep[rule_List, a_List] := rule[[
   8 - (RotateLeft[a] + 2 (a + 2 RotateRight[a]))]]

CAEvolveList[rule_List, init_List, t_Integer] :=
   NestList[CAStep[rule, #] &, init, t]

CAGraphics[history_List] :=
   Graphics[Raster[1 - Reverse[history]],
      AspectRatio -> Automatic]
```

Mathematica is a uniquely scalable language—suitable for programs of any size.

In[6]:= Show[CAGraphics[CAEvolveList[
         ElementaryRule[30],
         CenterList[101], 50]]]

Mathematica has a compiler for optimizing programs that work with lists and numbers.

```
FareySequence[q_] :=
   Apply[Union, Array[Range[# - 1] / # &, q]]

TransferMatrix[α_, ξ_, p_] :=
   {{ξ + If[1 - α ≤ Mod[p α, 1] < 1, 1, 0], -1}, {1, 0}}

TransferMatrixList[α_, ξ_] :=
   Table[TransferMatrix[α, ξ, p],
      {p, 0, Denominator[α] - 1}]

TransferMatrixProduct[α_, ξ_] :=
   Fold[Expand[Dot[##]] &,
      TransferMatrixList[α, ξ

EnergyPolynomial[α_, ξ_] :=
   Transpose[TransferMat

Spectrum[α_, ξ_] := ξ /. N
   EnergyPolynomial[α, ξ
```

In[8]:= Show[Graphics[
         SpectrumData /@
         FareySequence[20]]]

Mathematica programs can mix numerical, symbolic and graphics operations. This short program solves a sophisticated quantum model.

```
Impedance[Resistor[r_], ω_] := r

Impedance[Capacitor[c_], ω_] := 1 / (j ω c)

Impedance[Inductor[l_], ω_] := j ω l

Impedance[SeriesElement[e_], ω_] :=
   Apply[Plus, Map[Impedance[#, ω] &, e]]

Impedance[ParallelElement[e_], ω_] :=
   1 / Apply[Plus, 1 / Map[Impedance[#, ω] &, e]]
```

In[6]:= Impedance[SeriesElement[Table[ParallelElement[
         Table[SeriesElement[{Resistor[R_n]}], {n}]],
         {n, 1, 4}]], ω] // Simplify

Out[6]= $R_1 + \frac{1}{12} (6 R_2 + 4 R_3 + 3 R_4)$

Mathematica programs are often a direct translation of material in textbooks.

```
g[k_] := 1 + FixedPoint[N[1 / (1 + #)], k] &, 1]
g[k_] := FixedPoint[N[Sqrt[1 + #]], k] &, 1]
```

Mathematica programs provide unprecedentedly clear ways to express algorithms. Both of these programs approximate the Golden Ratio to k digits.

```
Ω[n_] := Apply[Plus, Map[Last, FactorInteger[n]]]
μ[n_] := MoebiusMu[n]
```

$$p[x_] := - \sum_{k=1}^{\lfloor \log[2, x] \rfloor} \mu[k] \sum_{n=2}^{\lfloor x^{1/k} \rfloor} \mu[n] \, \Omega[n] \left\lfloor \frac{x^{1/k}}{n} \right\rfloor \,/; x > 0$$

Mathematica programs allow a unique combination of mathematical and computational notation.

Building Systems with *Mathematica*

Mathematica has everything you need to create complete systems for technical and non-technical applications.

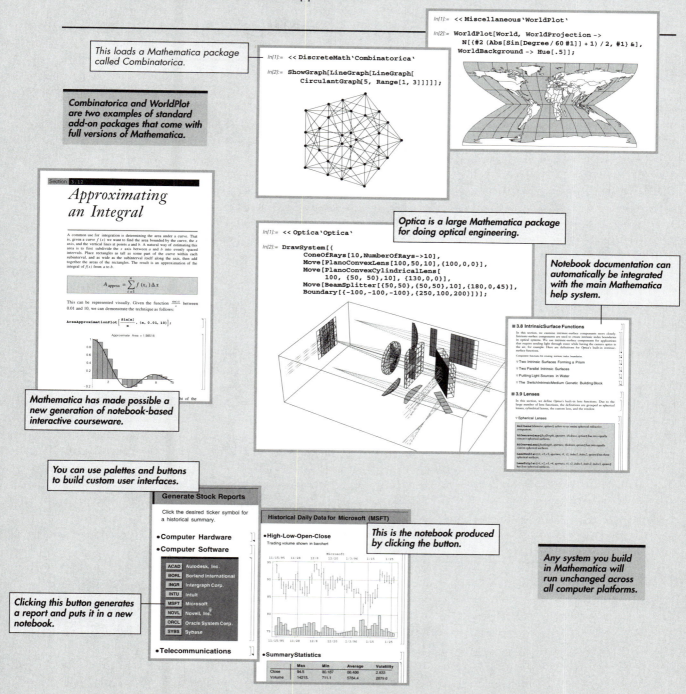

This loads a *Mathematica* package called *Combinatorica.*

Combinatorica and WorldPlot are two examples of standard add-on packages that come with full versions of Mathematica.

```
In[1]:= << Miscellaneous`WorldPlot`

In[2]:= WorldPlot[World, WorldProjection ->
          N[{#2 (Abs[Sin[Degree / 60 #1]] + 1) / 2, #1} &],
          WorldBackground -> Hue[.5]];
```

```
In[1]:= << DiscreteMath`Combinatorica`

In[2]:= ShowGraph[LineGraph[LineGraph[
            CirculantGraph[5, Range[1, 3]]]]];
```

Section 3·12

Approximating an Integral

A common use for integration is determining the area under a curve. That is, given a curve $f(x)$ we want to find the area bounded by the curve, the x axis, and the vertical lines at points a and b. A natural way of estimating this area is to first subdivide the x axis between a and b into evenly spaced intervals. Place rectangles as tall as some part of the curve within each subinterval, and as wide as the subinterval itself along the axis, then add together the areas of the rectangles. The result is an approximation of the integral of $f(x)$ from a to b.

$$A_{approx} = \sum_{i=1}^{n} f(x_i) \Delta x$$

This can be represented visually. Given the function $\frac{\sin[x]}{x}$ between 0.01 and 10, we can demonstrate the technique as follows:

```
AreaApproximationPlot[Sin[x]/x, {x, 0.01, 10}];
```

Mathematica has made possible a new generation of notebook-based interactive courseware.

Optica is a large *Mathematica* package for doing optical engineering.

```
In[1]:= << Optica`Optica`

In[2]:= DrawSystem[{
            ConeOfRays[10,NumberOfRays->10],
            Move[PlanoConvexLens[100,50,10],{100,0,0}],
            Move[PlanoConvexCylindricalLens[
                100, {50, 50},10], {130,0,0}],
            Move[BeamSplitter[{50,50},{50,50},10],{180,0,45}],
            Boundary[{-100,-100,-100},{250,100,200}]}];
```

Notebook documentation can automatically be integrated with the main *Mathematica* help system.

■ 3.8 IntrinsicSurface Functions

▽ Two Intrinsic Surfaces Forming a Prism
▽ Two Parallel Intrinsic Surfaces
▽ Putting Light Sources in Water
▽ The SwitchIntrinsicMedium Genetic Building Block

■ 3.9 Lenses

▽ Spherical Lenses

You can use palettes and buttons to build custom user interfaces.

Generate Stock Reports

Click the desired ticker symbol for a historical summary.

● Computer Hardware
● Computer Software

ACAD	Autodesk, Inc.
BORL	Borland International
INGR	Intergraph Corp.
INTU	Intuit
MSFT	Microsoft
NOVL	Novell, Inc.
ORCL	Oracle System Corp.
SYBS	Sybase

● Telecommunications

Clicking this button generates a report and puts it in a new notebook.

Historical Daily Data for Microsoft (MSFT)

● High-Low-Open-Close
Trading volume shown in barchart

This is the notebook produced by clicking the button.

● SummaryStatistics

	Max	Min	Average	Volatility
Close	94.5	80.187	88.406	2.833
Volume	14215.	711.1	5784.4	2879.6

Any system you build in Mathematica will run unchanged across all computer platforms.

Mathematica as a Software Component

Mathematica has a modular architecture that makes
it easy to use as a highly powerful software component.

■ An example of a calculation

$$In[1]:= \int \sqrt{\text{Log}[x]} \; dx$$

$$Out[1]= -\frac{1}{2} \sqrt{\pi} \; \text{Erfi}\left[\sqrt{\text{Log}[x]}\right] + x \sqrt{\text{Log}[x]}$$

**Here is the standard notebook
front end to *Mathematica*.**

```
In[1]:= Integrate[Sqrt[Log[x]],x]

               -(Sqrt[Pi] Erfi[Sqrt[Log[x]]])
Out[1] = ----------------------------------- + x Sqrt[Log[x]]
                              2
```

**You can also access the *Mathematica*
kernel directly from a raw terminal.**

**MathLink provides a general program-level interface
between *Mathematica* and external programs.**

```
/* Integrate[Sqrt[Log[x]],x] */

MLPutFunction( stdlink, "EvaluatePacket", 1);
  MLPutFunction( stdlink, "Integrate", 2);
    MLPutFunction( stdlink, "Sqrt", 1);
      MLPutFunction( stdlink, "Log", 1);
        MLPutSymbol( stdlink, "x");
      MLPutSymbol( stdlink, "x");
MLEndPacket( stdlink );
```

C code for calling *Mathematica*

You can use MathLink to access the *Mathematica*
kernel from many kinds of programs.

Microsoft Word front end to *Mathematica*

A web site that calls *Mathematica*

Microsoft Excel linked to *Mathematica*

MathLink can also be used to access other
programs from within the *Mathematica* kernel.

```
In[12]:= Map[LinkWrite[#,
             EvaluatePacket[Unevaluated[$System]]]&,
         links];
In[13]:= Map[First[LinkRead[#]], links]
Out[13]= {MicrosoftWindows95,
          Power Macintosh, IBM RISC System / 6000,
          HP - UX PA - RISC, NEXTSTEP Intel,
          DEC OSF / 1 AXP, L...
```

**You can use MathLink to communicate
between *Mathematica* kernels on different
computers across a network.**

```
In[1]:= Install["anneal"];
In[2]:= TSPTour[Table[Random[], {100}, {2}]]

Out[2]= {10, 7, 34, 30, 46, 40, 43, 38, 65, 57, 28, 23, 8...
         78, 94, 6, 92, 32, 18, 26, 98, 56, 31, 97, 37, 4...
         27, 49, 11, 84, 44, 96, 16, 76, 82, 68, 55, 36, ...
         52, 29, 95, 67, 79, 21, 59, 13, 1, 17, 73, 5, 71...
         63, 81, 48, 2, 99, 88, 89,...
         85, 9, 86, 33, 41, 58, 64,...
         60, 66, 22, 50, 69, 72, 61...
         8, 90, 35, 74, 47, 39, 14...
```

Link to a C subroutine library

```
:Begin:
:Function:      anneal
:Pattern:       TSPTour[r:{{_, _}..}]
:Arguments:     (First[Transpose[r]], Last[Transpose[r]],
                Length[r], Range[Length[r]])
:ArgumentTypes: (RealList, RealList, Integer, IntegerList)
:ReturnType:    Manual
:End:
```

**MathLink allows you to set up
templates to specify how external
programs should be called.**

```
ParametricPlot3D[
  {(2 + Cos[u/2] Sin[v] - Sin[u/2] Sin[2 v]) Cos[...
   (2 + Cos[u/2] Sin[v] - Sin[u/2] Sin[2 v]) Sin...
   Sin[u/2] Sin[v] + Cos[u/2] Sin[2 v...
  {v, 0, 2 Pi}, {u, 0, 2 Pi},
```

Link to a photorealistic renderer

The World of *Mathematica*

With over a million users worldwide, a vast array of
Mathematica products and services now exists.

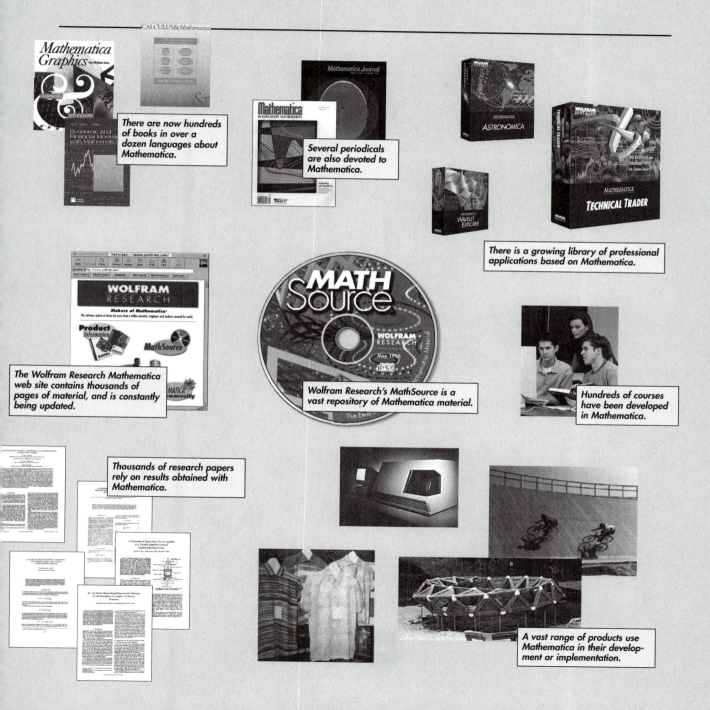

CALCULUS&*Mathematica*

There are now hundreds of books in over a dozen languages about Mathematica.

Several periodicals are also devoted to Mathematica.

There is a growing library of professional applications based on Mathematica.

The Wolfram Research Mathematica web site contains thousands of pages of material, and is constantly being updated.

Wolfram Research's MathSource is a vast repository of Mathematica material.

Hundreds of courses have been developed in Mathematica.

Thousands of research papers rely on results obtained with Mathematica.

A vast range of products use Mathematica in their development or implementation.

Part 1

This part gives a self-contained introduction to Mathematica, concentrating on using Mathematica as an interactive problem-solving system.

When you have read this part, you should have sufficient knowledge of Mathematica to tackle many kinds of practical problems.

You should realize, however, that what is discussed in this part is in many respects just the surface of Mathematica. Underlying all the various features and capabilities that are discussed, there are powerful and general principles. These principles are discussed in Part 2. To get the most out of Mathematica, you will need to understand them.

This part does not assume that you have used a computer before. In addition, most of the material in it requires no knowledge of mathematics beyond high-school level. The more advanced mathematical aspects of Mathematica are discussed in Part 3 of this book.

Part 1

A Practical Introduction to *Mathematica*

1.0 Running *Mathematica*

To find out how to install and run *Mathematica* you should read the documentation that came with your copy of *Mathematica*. The details differ from one computer system to another, and are affected by various kinds of customization that can be done on *Mathematica*. Nevertheless, this section outlines two common cases.

Note that although the details of running *Mathematica* differ from one computer system to another, the structure of *Mathematica* calculations is the same in all cases. You enter input, then *Mathematica* processes it, and returns a result.

■ 1.0.1 Notebook Interfaces

double-click the *Mathematica* icon	a typical graphical action for starting *Mathematica*
mathematica	the operating system command to start *Mathematica*
text ending with SHIFT-RETURN	input for *Mathematica* (SHIFT-ENTER on some keyboards)
choose the Quit menu item	exiting *Mathematica*

Running *Mathematica* with a notebook interface.

On most computer systems, *Mathematica* supports a "notebook" interface in which you interact with *Mathematica* by creating interactive documents.

If you use your computer via a purely graphical interface, you will typically double-click the *Mathematica* icon to start *Mathematica*. If you use your computer via a textually based operating system, you will typically type the command mathematica to start *Mathematica*.

When *Mathematica* starts up, it usually gives you a blank notebook. You enter *Mathematica* input into the notebook, then type SHIFT-RETURN to make *Mathematica* process your input. (To type SHIFT-RETURN, hold down the SHIFT key, then press RETURN.) You can use the standard editing features of your graphical interface to prepare your input, which may go on for several lines. SHIFT-RETURN tells *Mathematica* that you have finished your input.

After you send *Mathematica* input from your notebook, *Mathematica* will label your input with `In[n]:=`. It labels the corresponding output `Out[n]=`.

You type 2 + 2, then end your input with SHIFT-RETURN. *Mathematica* processes the input, then adds the input label *In[1]:=*, and gives the output.

```
2 + 2
```

```
In[1]:= 2 + 2
Out[1]= 4
```

Throughout this book, "dialogs" with *Mathematica* are shown in the following way:

With a notebook interface, you just type in 2 + 2. *Mathematica* then adds the label *In[1]:=*, and prints the result.

In[1]:= 2 + 2

Out[1]= 4

Page xv discusses some important details about reproducing the dialogs on your computer system. Section 1.3 gives more information about *Mathematica* notebooks.

You should realize that notebooks are part of the "front end" to *Mathematica*. The *Mathematica* kernel which actually performs computations may be run either on the same computer as the front end, or on another computer connected via some kind of network or line. In most cases, the kernel is not even started until you actually do a calculation with *Mathematica*.

To exit *Mathematica*, you typically choose the Quit menu item in the notebook interface.

■ 1.0.2 Text-Based Interfaces

`math`	the operating system command to start *Mathematica*
text ending with SHIFT-RETURN	input for *Mathematica* on all systems
text ending with RETURN	simpler form for input available on some systems
CONTROL-D or `Quit[ ]`	exiting *Mathematica*

Running *Mathematica* with a text-based interface.

With a text-based interface, you interact with your computer primarily by typing text on the keyboard. This kind of interface is available for *Mathematica* on almost all computer systems.

To start *Mathematica* with a text-based interface, you typically type the command `math` at an operating system prompt. On some systems, you may also be able to start *Mathematica* with a text-based interface by double-clicking on a *Mathematica* Kernel icon.

When *Mathematica* has started, it will print the prompt *In[1]:=*, signifying that it is ready for your input. You can then type your input. On any system, you can tell *Mathematica* that you have finished giving input by typing SHIFT-RETURN. On some systems, typing RETURN or ENTER alone is sufficient.

Mathematica will then process the input, and generate a result. If it prints the result out, it will label it with *Out[1]=*.

Throughout this book, dialogs with *Mathematica* are shown in the following way:

The computer prints *In[1]:=*. You just type in 2 + 2. The line that starts with *Out[1]=* is the result from *Mathematica*.

```
In[1]:= 2 + 2

Out[1]= 4
```

Page xv discusses some important details about reproducing the dialogs on your computer system. Note that you do not explicitly type the *In[n]:=* prompt; only type the text that follows this prompt.

Note also that most of the actual dialogs given in the book show output in the form you get with a notebook interface to *Mathematica*; output with a text-based interface looks similar, but lacks such features as special characters and font size changes.

Section 1.0.1 gives more details on running *Mathematica* with a text-based interface. To exit *Mathematica*, either type CONTROL-D or `Quit[ ]` at an input prompt.

1.1 Numerical Calculations

■ 1.1.1 Arithmetic

You can do arithmetic with *Mathematica* just as you would on an electronic calculator.

This is the sum of two numbers.	*In[1]:=* **2.3 + 5.63**
	Out[1]= 7.93
Here the / stands for division, and the ^ stands for power.	*In[2]:=* **2.4 / 8.9 ^ 2**
	Out[2]= 0.0302992
Spaces denote multiplication in *Mathematica*. You can use a * for multiplication if you want to.	*In[3]:=* **2 3 4**
	Out[3]= 24
You can type arithmetic expressions with parentheses.	*In[4]:=* **(3 + 4) ^ 2 - 2 (3 + 1)**
	Out[4]= 41
Spaces are not needed, though they often make your input easier to read.	*In[5]:=* **(3+4)^2-2(3+1)**
	Out[5]= 41

x^y	power
$-x$	minus
x/y	divide
$x\ y\ z$ or $x*y*z$	multiply
$x+y+z$	add

Arithmetic operations in *Mathematica*.

Arithmetic operations in *Mathematica* are grouped according to the standard mathematical conventions. As usual, 2 ^ 3 + 4, for example, means (2 ^ 3) + 4, and not 2 ^ (3 + 4). You can always control grouping by explicitly using parentheses.

This result is given in scientific notation.	*In[6]:=* **2.4 ^ 45**
	Out[6]= 1.28678×10^{17}
You can enter numbers in scientific notation like this.	*In[7]:=* **2.3 10^70**
	Out[7]= 2.3×10^{70}
Or like this.	*In[8]:=* **2.3*^70**
	Out[8]= 2.3×10^{70}

■ 1.1.2 Exact and Approximate Results

A standard electronic calculator does all your calculations to a particular accuracy, say ten decimal digits. With *Mathematica*, however, you can often get *exact* results.

Mathematica gives an *exact* result for 2^{100}, even though it has 31 decimal digits.	`In[1]:= 2 ^ 100` `Out[1]= 1267650600228229401496703205376`

You can tell *Mathematica* to give you an approximate numerical result, just as a calculator would, by ending your input with //N. The N stands for "numerical". It must be a capital letter. Section 2.1.3 will explain what the // means.

This gives an approximate numerical result.	`In[2]:= 2 ^ 100 //N` `Out[2]= 1.26765×10`^{30}
Mathematica can give results in terms of rational numbers.	`In[3]:= 1/3 + 2/7` `Out[3]= `$\frac{13}{21}$
//N always gives the approximate numerical result.	`In[4]:= 1/3 + 2/7 //N` `Out[4]= 0.619048`

---

expr //N	give an approximate numerical value for *expr*

Getting numerical approximations.

When you type in an integer like 7, *Mathematica* assumes that it is exact. If you type in a number like 4.5, with an explicit decimal point, *Mathematica* assumes that it is accurate only to a fixed number of decimal places.

This is taken to be an exact rational number, and reduced to its lowest terms.	`In[5]:= 452/62` `Out[5]= `$\frac{226}{31}$
Whenever you give a number with an explicit decimal point, *Mathematica* produces an approximate numerical result.	`In[6]:= 452.3/62` `Out[6]= 7.29516`
Here again, the presence of the decimal point makes *Mathematica* give you an approximate numerical result.	`In[7]:= 452./62` `Out[7]= 7.29032`
When any number in an arithmetic expression is given with an explicit decimal point, you get an approximate numerical result for the whole expression.	`In[8]:= 1. + 452/62` `Out[8]= 8.29032`

■ 1.1.3 Some Mathematical Functions

Mathematica includes a very large collection of mathematical functions. Section 3.2 gives the complete list. Here are a few of the common ones.

Sqrt[x]	square root ($\sqrt{x}$)
Exp[x]	exponential (e^x)
Log[x]	natural logarithm ($\log_e x$)
Log[b, x]	logarithm to base b ($\log_b x$)
Sin[x], Cos[x], Tan[x]	trigonometric functions (with arguments in radians)
ArcSin[x], ArcCos[x], ArcTan[x]	
	inverse trigonometric functions
n!	factorial (product of integers $1, 2, \ldots, n$)
Abs[x]	absolute value
Round[x]	closest integer to x
Mod[n, m]	n modulo m (remainder on division of n by m)
Random[ ]	pseudorandom number between 0 and 1
Max[x, y, ...], Min[x, y, ...]	maximum, minimum of $x, y, \ldots$
FactorInteger[n]	prime factors of n (see page 723)

Some common mathematical functions.

- The arguments of all *Mathematica* functions are enclosed in *square brackets*.
- The names of built-in *Mathematica* functions begin with *capital letters*.

Two important points about functions in *Mathematica*.

It is important to remember that all function arguments in *Mathematica* are enclosed in *square brackets*, not parentheses. Parentheses in *Mathematica* are used only to indicate the grouping of terms, and never to give function arguments.

This gives $\log_e(8.4)$. Notice the capital letter for Log, and the *square brackets* for the argument.

```
In[1]:= Log[8.4]
Out[1]= 2.12823
```

Just as with arithmetic operations, *Mathematica* tries to give exact values for mathematical functions when you give it exact input.

This gives $\sqrt{16}$ as an exact integer.

```
In[2]:= Sqrt[16]
Out[2]= 4
```

This gives an approximate numerical result for $\sqrt{2}$.

```
In[3]:= Sqrt[2] //N
Out[3]= 1.41421
```

The presence of an explicit decimal point tells *Mathematica* to give an approximate numerical result.

```
In[4]:= Sqrt[2.]
Out[4]= 1.41421
```

Since you are not asking for an approximate numerical result, *Mathematica* leaves the number here in an exact symbolic form.

```
In[5]:= Sqrt[2]
Out[5]= √2
```

Here is the exact integer result for $30 \times 29 \times \ldots \times 1$. Computing factorials like this can give you very large numbers. You should be able to calculate up to at least 2000! in a short time.

```
In[6]:= 30!
Out[6]= 265252859812191058636308480000000
```

This gives the approximate numerical value of the factorial.

```
In[7]:= 30! //N
Out[7]= 2.65253×10³²
```

Pi	$\pi \simeq 3.14159$
E	$e \simeq 2.71828$
Degree	$\pi/180$: degrees-to-radians conversion factor
I	$i = \sqrt{-1}$
Infinity	∞

Some common mathematical constants.

Notice that the names of these built-in constants all begin with capital letters.

This gives the numerical value of π^2.

```
In[8]:= Pi ^ 2 //N
Out[8]= 9.8696
```

This gives the exact result for $\sin(\pi/2)$. Notice that the arguments to trigonometric functions are always in radians.

```
In[9]:= Sin[Pi/2]
Out[9]= 1
```

This gives the numerical value of sin(20°). Multiplying by the constant **Degree** converts the argument to radians.

```
In[10]:= Sin[20 Degree] //N
Out[10]= 0.34202
```

Log[*x*] gives logarithms to base *e*.

```
In[11]:= Log[E ^ 5]
Out[11]= 5
```

You can get logarithms in any base *b* using Log[*b*, *x*]. As in standard mathematical notation, the *b* is optional.

```
In[12]:= Log[2, 256]
Out[12]= 8
```

■ 1.1.4 Arbitrary-Precision Calculations

When you use //N to get a numerical result, *Mathematica* does what a standard calculator would do: it gives you a result to a fixed number of significant figures. You can also tell *Mathematica* exactly how many significant figures to keep in a particular calculation. This allows you to get numerical results in *Mathematica* to any degree of precision.

expr//N or N[*expr*]	approximate numerical value of *expr*
N[*expr*, *n*]	numerical value of *expr* calculated with *n*-digit precision

Numerical evaluation functions.

This gives the numerical value of π to a fixed number of significant digits. Typing N[Pi] is exactly equivalent to Pi //N.

```
In[1]:= N[Pi]
Out[1]= 3.14159
```

This gives π to 40 digits.

```
In[2]:= N[Pi, 40]
Out[2]= 3.141592653589793238462643383279502884197
```

Here is $\sqrt{7}$ to 30 digits.

```
In[3]:= N[Sqrt[7], 30]
Out[3]= 2.64575131106459059050161575364
```

Doing any kind of numerical calculation can introduce small roundoff errors into your results. When you increase the numerical precision, these errors typically become correspondingly smaller. Making sure that you get the same answer when you increase numerical precision is often a good way to check your results.

The quantity $e^{\pi\sqrt{163}}$ turns out to be very close to an integer. To check that the result is not, in fact, an integer, you have to use sufficient numerical precision.

```
In[4]:= N[Exp[Pi Sqrt[163]], 40]
Out[4]= 2.625374126407687439999999999999992500725972×10^17
```

■ 1.1.5 Complex Numbers

You can enter complex numbers in *Mathematica* just by including the constant I, equal to $\sqrt{-1}$. Make sure that you type a capital I.

This gives the imaginary number result *2i*.	*In[1]:=* **Sqrt[-4]**
	Out[1]= 2 I

This gives the ratio of two complex numbers.	*In[2]:=* **(4 + 3 I) / (2 - I)**
	Out[2]= 1 + 2 I

Here is the numerical value of a complex exponential.	*In[3]:=* **Exp[2 + 9 I] //N**
	Out[3]= -6.73239 + 3.04517 I

x + I *y*	the complex number $x + i\, y$
Re[*z*]	real part
Im[*z*]	imaginary part
Conjugate[*z*]	complex conjugate z^* or $\bar{z}$
Abs[*z*]	absolute value |*z*|
Arg[*z*]	the argument ϕ in $|z|e^{i\phi}$

Complex number operations.

■ 1.1.6 Getting Used to *Mathematica*

- Arguments of functions are given in *square brackets*.
- Names of built-in functions have their first letters capitalized.
- Multiplication can be represented by a space.
- Powers are denoted by ^.
- Numbers in scientific notation are entered, for example, as 2.5*^-4 or 2.5 10^-4.

Important points to remember in *Mathematica*.

This section has given you a first glimpse of *Mathematica*. If you have used other computer systems before, you will probably have noticed some similarities and some differences. Often you will find the differences the most difficult parts to remember. It may help you, however, to understand a little about *why Mathematica* is set up the way it is, and why such differences exist.

One important feature of *Mathematica* that differs from other computer languages, and from conventional mathematical notation, is that function arguments are enclosed in square brackets, not parentheses. Parentheses in *Mathematica* are reserved specifically for indicating the grouping of terms. There is obviously a conceptual distinction between giving arguments to a function and grouping terms together; the fact that the same notation has often been used for both is largely a consequence of typography and of early computer keyboards. In *Mathematica*, the concepts are distinguished by different notation.

This distinction has several advantages. In parenthesis notation, it is not clear whether $c(1 + x)$ means $c[1 + x]$ or $c*(1 + x)$. Using square brackets for function arguments removes this ambiguity. It also allows multiplication to be indicated without an explicit * or other character. As a result, *Mathematica* can handle expressions like 2x and a x or a (1 + x), treating them just as in standard mathematical notation.

You will have seen in this section that built-in *Mathematica* functions often have quite long names. You may wonder why, for example, the pseudorandom number function is called Random, rather than, say, Rand. The answer, which pervades much of the design of *Mathematica*, is consistency. There is a general convention in *Mathematica* that all function names are spelled out as full English words, unless there is a standard mathematical abbreviation for them. The great advantage of this scheme is that it is *predictable*. Once you know what a function does, you will usually be able to guess exactly what its name is. If the names were abbreviated, you would always have to remember which shortening of the standard English words was used.

Another feature of built-in *Mathematica* names is that they all start with capital letters. In later sections, you will see how to define variables and functions of your own. The capital letter convention makes it easy to distinguish built-in objects. If *Mathematica* used i to represent $\sqrt{-1}$, then you would never be able to use i as the name of one of your variables. In addition, when you read programs written in *Mathematica*, the capitalization of built-in names makes them easier to pick out.

■ 1.1.7 Mathematical Notation in Notebooks

If you use a text-based interface to *Mathematica*, then the input you give must consist only of characters that you can type directly on your computer keyboard. But if you use a notebook interface then other kinds of input become possible.

Usually there are palettes provided which operate like extensions of your keyboard, and which have buttons that you can click to enter particular forms. You can typically access standard palettes using the Palettes submenu of the File menu.

Clicking the π button in this palette will enter a pi into your notebook.

Clicking the first button in this palette will create an empty structure for entering a power. You can use the mouse to fill in the structure.

You can also give input by using special keys on your keyboard. Pressing one of these keys does not lead to an ordinary character being entered, but instead typically causes some action to occur or some structure to be created.

[ESC] p [ESC]	the symbol π
[ESC] inf [ESC]	the symbol ∞
[CTRL] [^] or [CTRL] [6]	go to the superscript for a power
[CTRL] [/]	go to the denominator for a fraction
[CTRL] [@] or [CTRL] [2]	go into a square root
[CTRL] [␣] (CONTROL-SPACE)	return from a superscript, denominator or square root

A few ways to enter special notations on a standard English-language keyboard.

Here is a computation entered using ordinary characters on a keyboard.

In[1]:= **N[Pi^2/6]**

Out[1]= 1.64493

Here is the same computation entered using a palette or special keys.

In[2]:= **N[$\dfrac{\pi^2}{6}$]**

Out[2]= 1.64493

Here is an actual sequence of keys that can be used to enter the input.

In[3]:= **N[** [ESC] **p** [ESC] [CTRL] [^] **2** [CTRL] [␣] [CTRL] [/] **6** [CTRL] [␣] **]**

Out[3]= 1.64493

In a traditional computer language such as C or Fortran, the input you give must always consist of a string of ordinary characters that can be typed directly on a keyboard. But the *Mathematica* language also allows you to give input that contains special characters, superscripts, built-up fractions, and so on.

The language incorporates many features of traditional mathematical notation. But you should realize that the goal of the language is to provide a precise and consistent way to specify computations. And as a result, it does not follow all of the somewhat haphazard details of traditional mathematical notation.

Nevertheless, as discussed on page 192, it is always possible to get *Mathematica* to produce *output* that imitates every aspect of traditional mathematical notation. And as discussed on page 192, it is also possible for *Mathematica* to import text that uses such notation, and to some extent to translate it into its own more precise language.

1.2 Building Up Calculations

■ 1.2.1 Using Previous Results

In doing calculations, you will often need to use previous results that you have got. In *Mathematica*, % always stands for your last result.

%	the last result generated
%%	the next-to-last result
%% ... % (*k* times)	the *k*th previous result
%*n*	the result on output line Out[*n*] (to be used with care)

Ways to refer to your previous results.

Here is the first result.

```
In[1]:= 77 ^ 2
Out[1]= 5929
```

This adds 1 to the last result.

```
In[2]:= % + 1
Out[2]= 5930
```

This uses both the last result, and the result before that.

```
In[3]:= 3 % + % ^ 2 + %%
Out[3]= 35188619
```

You will have noticed that all the input and output lines in *Mathematica* are numbered. You can use these numbers to refer to previous results.

This adds the results on lines 2 and 3 above.

```
In[4]:= %2 + %3
Out[4]= 35194549
```

If you use a text-based interface to *Mathematica*, then successive input and output lines will always appear in order, as they do in the dialogs in this book. However, if you use a notebook interface to *Mathematica*, as discussed in Section 1.0.1, then successive input and output lines need not appear in order. You can for example "scroll back" and insert your next calculation wherever you want in the notebook. You should realize that % is always defined to be the last result that *Mathematica* generated. This may or may not be the result that appears immediately above your present position in the notebook. With a notebook interface, the only way to tell when a particular result was generated is to look at the Out[*n*] label that it has. Because you can insert and delete anywhere in a notebook, the textual ordering of results in a notebook need have no relation to the order in which the results were generated.

■ 1.2.2 Defining Variables

When you do long calculations, it is often convenient to give *names* to your intermediate results. Just as in standard mathematics, or in other computer languages, you can do this by introducing named *variables*.

This sets the value of the *variable* x to be 5.	`In[1]:= x = 5` `Out[1]= 5`
Whenever x appears, *Mathematica* now replaces it with the value 5.	`In[2]:= x ^ 2` `Out[2]= 25`
This assigns a new value to x.	`In[3]:= x = 7 + 4` `Out[3]= 11`
pi is set to be the numerical value of π to 40-digit accuracy.	`In[4]:= pi = N[Pi, 40]` `Out[4]= 3.141592653589793238462643383279502884197`
Here is the value you defined for pi.	`In[5]:= pi` `Out[5]= 3.141592653589793238462643383279502884197`
This gives the numerical value of π^2, to the same accuracy as pi.	`In[6]:= pi ^ 2` `Out[6]= 9.869604401089358618834490999876151135313`

$x = value$	assign a value to the variable x
$x = y = value$	assign a value to both x and y
$x =.$ or $\text{Clear}[x]$	remove any value assigned to x

Assigning values to variables.

It is very important to realize that values you assign to variables are *permanent*. Once you have assigned a value to a particular variable, the value will be kept until you explicitly remove it. The value will, of course, disappear if you start a whole new *Mathematica* session.

Forgetting about definitions you made earlier is the single most common cause of mistakes when using *Mathematica*. If you set x = 5, *Mathematica* assumes that you *always* want x to have the value 5, until or unless you explicitly tell it otherwise. To avoid mistakes, you should remove values you have defined as soon as you have finished using them.

■ Remove values you assign to variables as soon as you finish using them.

A useful principle in using *Mathematica*.

The variables you define can have almost any names. There is no limit on the length of their names. One constraint, however, is that variable names can never *start* with numbers. For example, x2 could be a variable, but 2x means 2*x.

Mathematica uses both upper- and lower-case letters. There is a convention that built-in *Mathematica* objects always have names starting with upper-case (capital) letters. To avoid confusion, you should always choose names for your own variables that start with lower-case letters.

aaaaa	a variable name containing only lower-case letters
Aaaaa	a built-in object whose name begins with a capital letter

Naming conventions.

You can type formulas involving variables in *Mathematica* almost exactly as you would in mathematics. There are a few important points to watch, however.

- x y means x times y.
- xy with no space is the variable with name xy.
- 5x means 5 times x.
- x^2y means (x^2) y, not x^(2y).

Some points to watch when using variables in *Mathematica*.

■ 1.2.3 Making Lists of Objects

In doing calculations, it is often convenient to collect together several objects, and treat them as a single entity. *Lists* give you a way to make collections of objects in *Mathematica*. As you will see later, lists are very important and general structures in *Mathematica*.

A list such as {3, 5, 1} is a collection of three objects. But in many ways, you can treat the whole list as a single object. You can, for example, do arithmetic on the whole list at once, or assign the whole list to be the value of a variable.

Here is a list of three numbers.	`In[1]:= {3, 5, 1}` `Out[1]= {3, 5, 1}`
This squares each number in the list, and adds 1 to it.	`In[2]:= {3, 5, 1}^2 + 1` `Out[2]= {10, 26, 2}`

This takes differences between corresponding elements in the two lists. The lists must be the same length.

In[3]:= **{6, 7, 8} - {3.5, 4, 2.5}**

Out[3]= {2.5, 3, 5.5}

The value of **%** is the whole list.

In[4]:= **%**

Out[4]= {2.5, 3, 5.5}

You can apply any of the mathematical functions in Section 1.1.3 to whole lists.

In[5]:= **Exp[%] // N**

Out[5]= {12.1825, 20.0855, 244.692}

Just as you can set variables to be numbers, so also you can set them to be lists.

This assigns v to be a list.

In[6]:= **v = {2, 4, 3.1}**

Out[6]= {2, 4, 3.1}

Wherever v appears, it is replaced by the list.

In[7]:= **v / (v - 1)**

Out[7]= $\left\{2, \dfrac{4}{3}, 1.47619\right\}$

■ 1.2.4 Manipulating Elements of Lists

Many of the most powerful list manipulation operations in *Mathematica* treat whole lists as single objects. Sometimes, however, you need to pick out or set individual elements in a list.

You can refer to an element of a *Mathematica* list by giving its "index". The elements are numbered in order, starting at 1.

{a, b, c}	a list
Part[*list*, *i*] or *list*[[*i*]]	the ith element of *list* (the first element is *list*[[1]])
Part[*list*, {i, j, ... }] or *list*[[{i, j, ... }]]	
	a list of the ith, jth, ... elements of *list*

Operations on list elements.

This extracts the second element of the list.

In[1]:= **{5, 8, 6, 9}[[2]]**

Out[1]= 8

This extracts a list of elements.

In[2]:= **{5, 8, 6, 9}[[{3, 1, 3, 2, 4}]]**

Out[2]= {6, 5, 6, 8, 9}

This assigns the value of v to be a list.

In[3]:= **v = {2, 4, 7}**

Out[3]= {2, 4, 7}

You can extract elements of v.   *In[4]:=* **v[[2]]**

                                          Out[4]= 4

By assigning a variable to be a list, you can use *Mathematica* lists much like "arrays" in other computer languages. Thus, for example, you can reset an element of a list by assigning a value to $v[[i]]$.

Part[v, i] or $v[[i]]$ extract the ith element of a list

Part[v, i] = *value* or $v[[i]]$ = *value*
                                reset the ith element of a list

---

Array-like operations on lists.

Here is a list.   *In[5]:=* **v = {4, -1, 8, 7}**

                                          Out[5]= {4, -1, 8, 7}

This resets the third element of the list.   *In[6]:=* **v[[3]] = 0**

                                          Out[6]= 0

Now the list assigned to v has been   *In[7]:=* **v**
modified.
                                          Out[7]= {4, -1, 0, 7}

■ 1.2.5 The Four Kinds of Bracketing in *Mathematica*

Over the course of the last few sections, we have introduced each of the four kinds of bracketing used in *Mathematica*. Each kind of bracketing has a very different meaning. It is important that you remember all of them.

(*term*)   parentheses for grouping

$f[x]$ square brackets for functions

{a, b, c}   curly braces for lists

$v[[i]]$ double brackets for indexing (Part[v, i])

The four kinds of bracketing in *Mathematica*.

When the expressions you type in are complicated, it is often a good idea to put extra space inside each set of brackets. This makes it somewhat easier for you to see matching pairs of brackets. $v[[\{a, b\}]]$ is, for example, easier to recognize than $v[[\{a, b\}]]$.

■ 1.2.6 Sequences of Operations

In doing a calculation with *Mathematica*, you usually go through a sequence of steps. If you want to, you can do each step on a separate line. Often, however, you will find it convenient to put several steps on the same line. You can do this simply by separating the pieces of input you want to give with semicolons.

$expr_1$; $expr_2$; $expr_3$	do several operations, and give the result of the last one
$expr_1$; $expr_2$;	do the operations, but print no output

Ways to do sequences of operations in *Mathematica*.

This does three operations on the same line. The result is the result from the last operation.

```
In[1]:= x = 4; y = 6; z = y + 6
Out[1]= 12
```

If you end your input with a semicolon, it is as if you are giving a sequence of operations, with an "empty" one at the end. This has the effect of making *Mathematica* perform the operations you specify, but display no output.

$expr$;	do an operation, but display no output

Inhibiting output.

Putting a semicolon at the end of the line tells *Mathematica* to show no output.

```
In[2]:= x = 67 - 5 ;
```

You can still use % to get the output that would have been shown.

```
In[3]:= %
Out[3]= 62
```

1.3 Using the *Mathematica* System

~■ 1.3.1 The Structure of *Mathematica*

Mathematica kernel	the part that actually performs computations
Mathematica front end	the part that handles interaction with the user

The basic parts of the *Mathematica* system.

Mathematica is a modular software system in which the *kernel* which actually performs computations is separate from the *front end* which handles interaction with the user.

The most common type of front end for *Mathematica* is based on interactive documents known as *notebooks*. Notebooks mix *Mathematica* input and output with text, graphics, palettes and other material. You can use notebooks either for doing ongoing computations, or as means of presenting or publishing your results.

Notebook interface	interactive documents
Text-based interface	text from the keyboard
MathLink interface	communication with other programs

Common kinds of interfaces to *Mathematica*.

The notebook front end includes many menus and graphical tools for creating and reading notebook documents and for sending and receiving material from the *Mathematica* kernel.

A notebook mixing text, graphics and *Mathematica* input and output.

■ **Examples of Integrals**

Here is an example of a very simple algebraic integral:

In[1]:= $\int \dfrac{1}{x^3-1}\,dx$

Out[1]= $-\dfrac{\text{ArcTan}\left[\frac{1+2x}{\sqrt{3}}\right]}{\sqrt{3}} + \dfrac{\text{Log}[-1+x]}{3} - \dfrac{\text{Log}[1+x+x^2]}{6}$

And here is a plot of the resulting function:

In[2]:= **Plot[%, {x, 1, 2}]**

Out[2]= -Graphics-

In some cases, you may not need the sophistication of the notebook front end, and you may want instead to interact more directly with the *Mathematica* kernel. You can do this by using a text-based interface, in which text you type on the keyboard goes straight to the kernel.

A dialog with *Mathematica* using a text-based interface.

```
In[1]:= 2^100

Out[1]= 1267650600228229401496703205376

In[2]:= Integrate[1/(x^3 - 1), x]

                 1 + 2 x
         ArcTan[-------]                                    2
                 Sqrt[3]      Log[-1 + x]   Log[1 + x + x ]
Out[2]= -(---------------) + ----------- - ---------------
             Sqrt[3]              3                6
```

An important aspect of *Mathematica* is that it can interact not only with human users but also with other programs. This is achieved primarily through *MathLink*, which is a standardized protocol for two-way communication between external programs and the *Mathematica* kernel.

A fragment of C code that communicates via *MathLink* with the *Mathematica* kernel.

```
MLPutFunction(stdlink,  "EvaluatePacket", 1);

  MLPutFunction(stdlink, "Gamma", 2);
    MLPutReal(stdlink, 2);
    MLPutInteger(stdlink, n);

MLEndPacket(stdlink);
MLCheckFunction(stdlink, "ReturnPacket", &n);

MLGetReal(stdlink, &result);
```

Among the many *MathLink*-compatible programs that are now available, some are set up to serve as complete front ends to *Mathematica*. Often such front ends provide their own special user interfaces, and treat the *Mathematica* kernel purely as an embedded computational engine. If you are using *Mathematica* in this way, then only some parts of the discussion in the remainder of this section will probably be relevant.

■ 1.3.2 Differences between Computer Systems

There are many detailed differences between different kinds of computer systems. But one of the important features of *Mathematica* is that it allows you to work and create material without being concerned about such differences.

In order to fit in as well as possible with particular computer systems, the user interface for *Mathematica* on different systems is inevitably at least slightly different. But the crucial point is that beyond superficial differences, *Mathematica* is set up to work in exactly the same way on every kind of computer system.

- The language used by the *Mathematica* kernel
- The structure of *Mathematica* notebooks
- The *MathLink* communication protocol

Elements of *Mathematica* that are exactly the same on all computer systems.

The commands that you give to the *Mathematica* kernel, for example, are absolutely identical on every computer system. This means that when you write a program using these commands, you can immediately take the program and run it on any computer that supports *Mathematica*.

The structure of *Mathematica* notebooks is also the same on all computer systems. And as a result, if you create a notebook on one computer system, you can immediately take it and use it on any other system.

- The visual appearance of windows, fonts, etc.

- Mechanisms for importing and exporting material from notebooks

- Keyboard shortcuts for menu commands

Elements that can differ from one computer system to another.

Although the underlying structure of *Mathematica* notebooks is always the same, there are often superficial differences in the way notebooks look on different computer systems, and in some of the mechanisms provided for interacting with them.

The goal in each case is to make notebooks work in a way that is as familiar as possible to people who are used to a particular type of computer system.

And in addition, by adapting the details of notebooks to each specific computer system, it becomes easier to exchange material between notebooks and other programs running on that computer system.

The same *Mathematica* notebook on three different computer systems. The underlying structure is exactly the same, but some details of the presentation are different.

One consequence of the modular nature of the *Mathematica* system is that its parts can be run on different computers. Thus, for example, it is not uncommon to run the front end for *Mathematica* on one computer, while running the kernel on a quite separate computer.

Communications between the kernel and the front end are handled by *MathLink*, using whatever networking mechanisms are available.

■ 1.3.3 Special Topic: Using a Text-Based Interface

With a text-based interface, you interact with *Mathematica* just by typing successive lines of input, and getting back successive lines of output on your screen.

At each stage, *Mathematica* prints a prompt of the form `In[n]:=` to tell you that it is ready to receive input. When you have entered your input, *Mathematica* processes it, and then displays the result with a label of the form `Out[n]=`.

Different text-based interfaces use slightly different schemes for letting *Mathematica* know when you have finished typing your input. With some interfaces you press SHIFT-RETURN, while in others RETURN alone is sufficient.

In interfaces that use SHIFT-RETURN, you can continue your input for several lines by typing RETURN at the end of each line. In interfaces where RETURN is used to signify the end of your input, *Mathematica* will automatically continue reading successive lines until it has received a complete expression. Thus, for example, if you type an opening parenthesis on one line, *Mathematica* will go on reading successive lines of input until it sees the corresponding closing parenthesis. Note that if you enter a completely blank line, *Mathematica* will throw away the lines you have typed so far, and issue a new input prompt.

`%n` or `Out[n]`	the value of the nth output
`InString[n]`	the text of the nth input
`In[n]`	the nth input, for re-evaluation

Retrieving and re-evaluating previous input and output.

With a text-based interface, each line of *Mathematica* input and output appears sequentially. Often your computer system will allow you to scroll backwards to review previous work, and to cut-and-paste previous lines of input.

But whatever kind of computer system you have, you can always use *Mathematica* to retrieve or re-evaluate previous input and output. In general, re-evaluating a particular piece of input or output may give you a different result than when you evaluated it in the first place. The reason is that in between you may have reset the values of variables that are used in that piece of input or output. If you ask for `Out[n]`, then *Mathematica* will give you the final form of your n^{th} output. On the other hand, if you ask for `In[n]`, then *Mathematica* will take the nth input you gave, and re-evaluate it using whatever current assignments you have given for variables.

■ 1.3.4 Doing Computations in Notebooks

A typical *Mathematica* notebook containing text, graphics and *Mathematica* expressions. The brackets on the right indicate the extent of each cell.

Mathematica notebooks are structured interactive documents that are organized into a sequence of *cells*. Each cell contains material of a definite type—usually text, graphics, sounds or *Mathematica* expressions. When a notebook is displayed on the screen, the extent of each cell is indicated by a bracket on the right.

The notebook front end for *Mathematica* provides many ways to enter and edit the material in a notebook. Some of these ways will be standard to whatever computer system or graphical interface you are using. Others are specific to *Mathematica*.

Shift-Return or Shift-Enter   send a cell of input to the *Mathematica* kernel

Doing a computation in a *Mathematica* notebook.

Once you have prepared the material in a cell, you can send it as input to the *Mathematica* kernel simply by pressing Shift-Return or Shift-Enter. The kernel will send back whatever output is generated, and the front end will create new cells in your notebook to display this output. Note that on systems where both Return and Enter keys are available, Enter alone is typically equivalent to Shift-Return.

Here is a cell ready to be sent as input
to the *Mathematica* kernel.

> 3^100

The output from the computation is
inserted in a new cell.

> In[1]:= 3^100
>
> Out[1]= 515377520732011331036461129765621272702107522001

Most kinds of output that you get in *Mathematica* notebooks can readily be edited, just like input.
Usually *Mathematica* will make a copy of the output when you first start editing it, so you can keep
track of the original output and its edited form.

Once you have done the editing you want, you can typically just press SHIFT-RETURN to send what
you have created as input to the *Mathematica* kernel.

Here is a typical computation in a
Mathematica notebook.

> In[1]:= Integrate[Sqrt[x + 1] / Sqrt[x - 1], x]
>
> Out[1]= $\sqrt{-1 + x} \sqrt{1 + x} + 2 \text{ArcSinh}\left[\frac{\sqrt{-1 + x}}{\sqrt{2}}\right]$

Mathematica will automatically make a
copy if you start editing the output.

> In[1]:= Integrate[Sqrt[x + 1] / Sqrt[x - 1], x]
>
> Out[1]= $\sqrt{-1 + x} \sqrt{1 + x} + 2 \text{ArcSinh}\left[\frac{\sqrt{-1 + x}}{\sqrt{2}}\right]$
>
> $\sqrt{-1 + x} \sqrt{1 + x} + D\left[2 \text{ArcSinh}\left[\frac{\sqrt{-1 + x}}{\sqrt{2}}\right], x\right]$ // Simplify

After you have edited the output, you
can send it back as further input to the
Mathematica kernel.

> In[1]:= Integrate[Sqrt[x + 1] / Sqrt[x - 1], x]
>
> Out[1]= $\sqrt{-1 + x} \sqrt{1 + x} + 2 \text{ArcSinh}\left[\frac{\sqrt{-1 + x}}{\sqrt{2}}\right]$
>
> In[2]:= $\sqrt{-1 + x} \sqrt{1 + x} + D\left[2 \text{ArcSinh}\left[\frac{\sqrt{-1 + x}}{\sqrt{2}}\right], x\right]$ // Simplify
>
> Out[2]= $\frac{x^2}{\sqrt{-1 + x} \sqrt{1 + x}}$

When you do computations in a *Mathematica* notebook, each line of input is typically labeled with
In[n]:=, while each line of output is labeled with the corresponding Out[n]=.

There is no reason, however, that successive lines of input and output should necessarily appear
one after the other in your notebook. Often, for example, you will want to go back to an earlier part
of your notebook, and re-evaluate some input you gave before.

It is important to realize that wherever a particular expression appears in your notebook, it is
the line number given in In[n]:= or Out[n]= which determines when the expression was processed

by the *Mathematica* kernel. Thus, for example, the fact that one expression may appear earlier than another in your notebook does not mean that it will have been evaluated first by the kernel. This will only be the case if it has a lower line number.

Each line of input and output is given a label when it is evaluated by the kernel. It is these labels, not the position of the expression in the notebook, that indicate the ordering of evaluation by the kernel.

```
Results:
In[2]:= s^2 + 2
Out[2]= 146
In[4]:= s^2 + 2
Out[4]= 10002
Settings for s:
In[1]:= s = 12
Out[1]= 12
In[3]:= s = 100
Out[3]= 100
```

If you make a mistake and try to enter input that the *Mathematica* kernel does not understand, then the front end will produce a beep. In general, you will get a beep whenever something goes wrong in the front end. You can find out the origin of the beep using the Why the Beep? item in the Help menu.

Animate graphics	double-click the first cell in the sequence of frames
Resize a graphic	click the graphic and move the handles that appear
Find coordinates in a graphic	move around in the graphic holding down the COMMAND or ALT key (or equivalent)
Play a sound	double-click the cell that contains it

Operations on graphics and sounds.

■ 1.3.5 Notebooks as Documents

Mathematica notebooks allow you to create documents that can be viewed interactively on screen or printed on paper.

Particularly in larger notebooks, it is common to have chapters, sections and so on, each represented by groups of cells. The extent of these groups is indicated by a bracket on the right.

The grouping of cells in a notebook is indicated by nested brackets on the right.

A group of cells can be either *open* or *closed*. When it is open, you can see all the cells in it explicitly. But when it is closed, you see only the first or *heading* cell in the group.

Large notebooks are often distributed with many closed groups of cells, so that when you first look at the notebook, you see just an outline of its contents. You can then open parts you are interested in by double-clicking the appropriate brackets.

Double-clicking the bracket that spans a group of cells closes the group, leaving only the first cell visible.

When a group is closed, the bracket for it has an arrow at the bottom. Double-clicking this arrow opens the group again.

Each cell within a notebook is assigned a particular *style* which indicates its role within the notebook. Thus, for example, material intended as input to be executed by the *Mathematica* kernel is typically in Input style, while text that is intended purely to be read is typically in Text style.

The *Mathematica* front end provides menus and keyboard shortcuts for creating cells with different styles, and for changing styles of existing cells.

This shows cells in various styles. The styles define not only the format of the cell contents, but also their placement and spacing.

■ **This cell is in Section style.**

■**This cell is in Subsection style.**

□ **This cell is in Subsubsection style.**

This cell is in Text style.

This cell is in SmallText style.

       `This cell is in Input style .`

By putting a cell in a particular style, you specify a whole collection of properties for the cell, including for example how large and in what font text should be given.

The *Mathematica* front end allows you to modify such properties, either for complete cells, or for specific material within cells.

Even within a cell of a particular style, the *Mathematica* front end allows a wide range of properties to be modified separately.

Within a text cell, there can be large fonts, **bold fonts**, and *funny fonts*.

A cell can have properties such as a frame or background.

It is worth realizing that in doing different kinds of things with *Mathematica* notebooks, you are using different parts of the *Mathematica* system. Operations such as opening and closing groups of cells, doing animations and playing sounds use only a small part of the *Mathematica* front end, and these operations are supported by a widely available program known as *MathReader* that is typically distributed on the main *Mathematica* CD-ROM.

To be able to create and edit notebooks, you need more of the *Mathematica* front end. And finally, to be able to actually do computations within a *Mathematica* notebook, you need a full *Mathematica* system, with both the front end and the kernel.

MathReader	reading *Mathematica* notebooks
Mathematica front end	creating and editing *Mathematica* notebooks
Mathematica kernel	doing computations in notebooks

Programs required for different kinds of operations with notebooks.

■ 1.3.6 Active Elements in Notebooks

One of the most powerful features of *Mathematica* notebooks is that their actions can be programmed. Thus, for example, you can set up a button in a *Mathematica* notebook which causes various operations to be performed whenever you click it.

Here is a notebook that contains a button.

Click the button to get the current date: `Date[]`

Clicking the button in this case causes the current date to be displayed.

Click the button to get the current date: `Date[]`

{1995, 9, 5, 10, 40, 53}

Later in this book, we will discuss how you can set up buttons and other similar objects in *Mathematica* notebooks. But here suffice it to say that whenever a cell is indicated as *active*, typically by the presence of a stylized "A" in its cell bracket, clicking on active elements within the cell will cause actions that have been programmed for these elements to be performed.

It is common to set up *palettes* which consist of arrays of buttons. Sometimes such palettes appear as cells within a notebook. But more often, a special kind of separate notebook window is used, which can conveniently be placed on the side of your computer screen and used in conjunction with any other notebook.

Palettes consisting of arrays of buttons are often placed in separate notebooks.

In the simplest cases, the buttons in palettes serve essentially like additional keys on your keyboard. Thus, when you press a button, the character or object shown in that button is inserted into your notebook just as if you had typed it.

Here is a palette of Greek letters with buttons that act like additional keys on your keyboard.

Often, however, a button may contain a placeholder indicated by ■. This signifies that when you press the button, whatever is currently selected in your notebook will be inserted at the position of the placeholder.

The buttons here contain placeholders
indicated by ■.

Here is a notebook with an expression
selected.

$$1 + \left(1 + \left(1 + (1 + x^2)^2\right)^2\right)^2$$

Pressing the top left button in the
palette wraps the selected expression
with a square root.

$$1 + \left(1 + \sqrt{\left(1 + (1 + x^2)^2\right)^2}\right)^2$$

Sometimes buttons that contain placeholders will be programmed simply to insert a certain expression in your notebook. But more often, they will be programmed to evaluate the result, sending it as input to the *Mathematica* kernel.

These buttons are set up to perform
algebraic operations.

Simplify[■]	FullSimplify[■]
Expand[■]	Factor[■]
Apart[■]	Together[■]

Here is a notebook with an expression
selected.

$$\frac{2 + 2\,\mathrm{Cos}[2\,x]}{4} + \frac{1}{32}\,(12 - 16\,\mathrm{Cos}[2\,x] + 4\,\mathrm{Cos}[4\,x])$$

Pressing the top left button in the
palette causes the selected expression
to be simplified.

$$\frac{2 + 2\,\mathrm{Cos}[2\,x]}{4} + \mathrm{Sin}[x]^4$$

There are some situations in which it is convenient to have several placeholders in a single button. Your current selection is typically inserted at the position of the primary placeholder, indicated by ■. Additional placeholders may however be indicated by □, and you can move to the positions of successive placeholders using Tab.

Here is a palette containing buttons
with several placeholders.

Here is an expression in a notebook.

$$\frac{\text{Sin}[x]}{1+x}$$

Pressing the top left button in the palette inserts the expression in place of the ■.

$$\int \frac{\text{Sin}[x]}{1+x} \, d\square$$

You can move to the other placeholders using TAB, and then edit them to insert whatever you want.

$$\int \frac{\text{Sin}[x]}{1+x} \, dx$$

■ 1.3.7 Special Topic: Hyperlinks and Active Text

The *Mathematica* front end provides a variety of ways to search for particular words or text in *Mathematica* notebooks. But particularly when large documents or collections of documents are involved, it is often convenient to insert *hyperlinks* which immediately take you to a specific point in a notebook.

Hyperlinks are usually indicated by words or phrases that are underlined, and are often in a different color. Clicking on a hyperlink immediately takes you to wherever the hyperlink points.

Here is some text. The text can contain a <u>link</u>, which points elsewhere.

Hyperlinks in notebooks work very much like the buttons discussed in the previous section. And once again, all aspects of hyperlinks are programmable.

Indeed, it is possible to set up active text in notebooks that performs almost any kind of action.

■ 1.3.8 Getting Help in the Notebook Front End

Getting Started	a quick start to using *Mathematica*
Help Browser	looking up specific functions
Mathematica Book	on-line notebook version of this book
Answers	searchable database of common questions and answers

Typical types of help available with the notebook front end.

Included with most versions of the *Mathematica* notebook front end are a wide range of notebooks and other material that you can access to get help while you are using *Mathematica*.

An example of the Help Browser. The basic information is taken from the Reference Guide at the end of this book, supplemented with additional examples.

■ 1.3.9 Getting Help with a Text-Based Interface

?Name	show information on *Name*
??Name	show extra information on *Name*
?Aaaa*	show information on all objects whose names begin with *Aaaa*

Ways to get information directly from the *Mathematica* kernel.

This gives information on the built-in function Log.

```
In[1]:= ?Log

Log[z] gives the natural logarithm of z (logarithm to base
        e). Log[b, z] gives the logarithm to base b.
```

You can ask for information about any object, whether it is built into *Mathematica*, has been read in from a *Mathematica* package, or has been introduced by you.

When you use ? to get information, you must make sure that the question mark appears as the first character in your input line. You need to do this so that *Mathematica* can tell when you are requesting information rather than giving ordinary input for evaluation.

You can get extra information by using ??. Attributes will be discussed in Section 2.5.3.

```
In[2]:= ??Log

Log[z] gives the natural logarithm of z (logarithm to base
        e). Log[b, z] gives the logarithm to base b.

Attributes[Log] = {Listable, NumericFunction, Protected}
```

| This gives information on all *Mathematica* objects whose names begin with Lo. When there is more than one object, *Mathematica* just lists their names. | `In[3]:= ?Lo*`

`Locked        LogGamma       LogIntegral   LowerCaseQ`
`Log           LogicalExpand LongForm` |

?Aaaa will give you information on the particular object whose name you specify. Using the "metacharacter" *, however, you can get information on collections of objects with similar names. The rule is that * is a "wild card" that can stand for any sequence of ordinary characters. So, for example, ?Lo* gets information on all objects whose names consist of the letters Lo, followed by any sequence of characters.

You can put * anywhere in the string you ask ? about. For example, ?*Expand would give you all objects whose names *end* with Expand. Similarly, ?x*0 would give you objects whose names start with x, end with 0, and have any sequence of characters in between. (You may notice that the way you use * to specify names in *Mathematica* is similar to the way you use * in Unix and other operating systems to specify file names.)

| You can ask for information on most of the special input forms that *Mathematica* uses. This asks for information about the := operator. | `In[4]:= ?:=`

`lhs := rhs assigns rhs to be the delayed value of lhs. rhs`
`   is maintained in an unevaluated form. When lhs appears,`
`   it is replaced by rhs, evaluated afresh each time.` |

■ 1.3.10 *Mathematica* Packages

One of the most important features of *Mathematica* is that it is an extensible system. There is a certain amount of mathematical and other functionality that is built into *Mathematica*. But by using the *Mathematica* language, it is always possible to add more functionality.

For many kinds of calculations, what is built into the standard version of *Mathematica* will be quite sufficient. However, if you work in a particular specialized area, you may find that you often need to use certain functions that are not built into *Mathematica*.

In such cases, you may well be able to find a *Mathematica* package that contains the functions you need. *Mathematica* packages are files written in the *Mathematica* language. They consist of collections of *Mathematica* definitions which "teach" *Mathematica* about particular application areas.

| <<*package*   read in a *Mathematica* package |

Reading in *Mathematica* packages.

If you want to use functions from a particular package, you must first read the package into *Mathematica*. The details of how to do this are discussed in Section 1.11. There are various conventions that govern the names you should use to refer to packages.

This command reads in a particular *Mathematica* package.

`In[1]:= << DiscreteMath'CombinatorialFunctions'`

The Subfactorial function is defined in the package.

`In[2]:= Subfactorial[10]`

`Out[2]= 1334961`

There are a number of subtleties associated with such issues as conflicts between names of functions in different packages. These are discussed in Section 2.6.9. One point to note, however, is that you must not refer to a function that you will read from a package before actually reading in the package. If you do this by mistake, you will have to execute the command `Remove["name"]` to get rid of the function before you read in the package which defines it. If you do not call `Remove`, *Mathematica* will use "your" version of the function, rather than the one from the package.

`Remove["name"]`   remove a function that has been introduced in error

Making sure that *Mathematica* uses correct definitions from packages.

The fact that *Mathematica* can be extended using packages means that the boundary of exactly what is "part of *Mathematica*" is quite blurred. As far as usage is concerned, there is actually no difference between functions defined in packages and functions that are fundamentally built into *Mathematica*.

In fact, a fair number of the functions described in this book are actually implemented as *Mathematica* packages. However, on most *Mathematica* systems, the necessary packages have been preloaded, so that the functions they define are always present. (On some systems with severe memory limitations, even these packages may be loaded only on request.)

To blur the boundary of what is part of *Mathematica* even further, Section 2.6.11 describes how you can tell *Mathematica* automatically to load a particular package if you ever try to use a certain function. If you never use that function, then it will not be present. But as soon as you try to use it, its definition will be read in from a *Mathematica* package.

As a practical matter, the functions that should be considered "part of *Mathematica*" are probably those that are present in all *Mathematica* systems. It is these functions that are primarily discussed in this book.

Nevertheless, most versions of *Mathematica* come with a standard set of *Mathematica* packages, which contain definitions for many more functions. Some of these functions are mentioned in this book. But to get them, you must usually read in the necessary packages explicitly.

You can use the Help Browser to get information on standard *Mathematica* add-on packages.

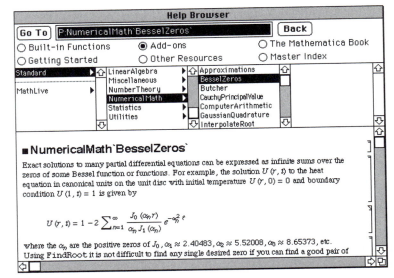

Of course, it is possible to set your *Mathematica* system up so that particular packages are pre-loaded, or are automatically loaded when needed. If you do this, then there may be many functions that appear as standard in your version of *Mathematica*, but which are not documented in this book.

One point that should be mentioned is the relationship between packages and notebooks. Both are stored as files on your computer system, and both can be read into *Mathematica*. However, a notebook is intended to be displayed, typically with a notebook interface, while a package is intended only to be used as *Mathematica* input. Many notebooks in fact contain sections that can be considered as packages, and which contain sequences of definitions intended for input to *Mathematica*.

■ 1.3.11 Warnings and Messages

Mathematica usually goes about its work silently, giving output only when it has finished doing the calculations you asked for.

However, if it looks as if *Mathematica* is doing something you definitely did not intend, *Mathematica* will usually print a message to warn you.

The square root function should have only one argument. *Mathematica* prints a message to warn you that you have given two arguments here.

```
In[1]:= Sqrt[4, 5]

Sqrt::argx:
    Sqrt called with 2 arguments; 1 argument is expected.

Out[1]= Sqrt[4, 5]
```

Each message has a name. You can switch off messages using Off.

```
In[2]:= Off[Sqrt::argx]
```

The message Sqrt::argx has now been switched off, and will no longer appear.

In[3]:= **Sqrt[4, 5]**

Out[3]= Sqrt[4, 5]

This switches Sqrt::argx back on again.

In[4]:= **On[Sqrt::argx]**

Off[*Function*::*tag*]	switch off (suppress) a message
On[*Function*::*tag*]	switch on a message

Functions for controlling message output.

■ 1.3.12 Interrupting Calculations

There will probably be times when you want to stop *Mathematica* in the middle of a calculation. Perhaps you realize that you asked *Mathematica* to do the wrong thing. Or perhaps the calculation is just taking a long time, and you want to find out what is going on.

The way that you interrupt a *Mathematica* calculation depends on what kind of interface you are using.

Command-Comma or Alt-Comma	notebook interfaces
Control-C	text-based interfaces

Typical keys to interrupt calculations in *Mathematica*.

On some computer systems, it may take *Mathematica* some time to respond to your interrupt. When *Mathematica* does respond, it will typically give you a menu of possible things to do.

continue	continue the calculation
show	show what *Mathematica* is doing
inspect	inspect the current state of your calculation
abort	abort this particular calculation
exit	exit *Mathematica* completely

Some typical options available when you interrupt a calculation in *Mathematica*.

1.4 Algebraic Calculations

■ 1.4.1 Symbolic Computation

One of the most important features of *Mathematica* is that it can do *symbolic*, as well as *numerical* calculations. This means that it can handle algebraic formulas as well as numbers.

Here is a typical numerical computation.	*In[1]:=* **3 + 62 - 1** *Out[1]=* 64
This is a symbolic computation.	*In[2]:=* **3x - x + 2** *Out[2]=* 2 + 2 x

Numerical computation	3 + 62 − 1	⟶	64
Symbolic computation	3x − x + 2	⟶	2 + 2 x

Numerical and symbolic computations.

You can type any algebraic expression into *Mathematica*.	*In[3]:=* **-1 + 2x + x^3** *Out[3]=* -1 + 2 x + x^3
Mathematica automatically carries out basic algebraic simplifications. Here it combines x^2 and $-4x^2$ to get $-3x^2$.	*In[4]:=* **x^2 + x - 4 x^2** *Out[4]=* x - 3 x^2

You can type in any algebraic expression, using the operators listed on page 29. You can use spaces to denote multiplication. Be careful not to forget the space in x y. If you type in xy with no space, *Mathematica* will interpret this as a single symbol, with the name xy, not as a product of the two symbols x and y.

Mathematica rearranges and combines terms using the standard rules of algebra.	*In[5]:=* **x y + 2 x^2 y + y^2 x^2 - 2 y x** *Out[5]=* -x y + 2 x^2 y + x^2 y^2
Here is another algebraic expression.	*In[6]:=* **(x + 2y + 1)(x - 2)^2** *Out[6]=* (-2 + x)^2 (1 + x + 2 y)
The function Expand multiplies out products and powers.	*In[7]:=* **Expand[%]** *Out[7]=* 4 - 3 x^2 + x^3 + 8 y - 8 x y + 2 x^2 y
Factor does essentially the inverse of Expand.	*In[8]:=* **Factor[%]** *Out[8]=* (-2 + x)^2 (1 + x + 2 y)

When you type in more complicated expressions, it is important that you put parentheses in the right places. Thus, for example, you have to give the expression x^{4y} in the form x^(4y). If you leave out the parentheses, you get x^4y instead. It never hurts to put in too many parentheses, but to find out exactly when you need to use parentheses, look at Section A.2.

Here is a more complicated formula, requiring several parentheses.	*In[9]:=* `Sqrt[2]/9801 (4n)! (1103 + 26390 n) / (n!^4 396^(4n))`

$$Out[9]= \frac{\sqrt{2}\ 396^{-4n}\ (1103 + 26390\,n)\ (4n)!}{9801\,n!^4}$$

When you type in an expression, *Mathematica* automatically applies its large repertoire of rules for transforming expressions. These rules include the standard rules of algebra, such as $x - x = 0$, together with much more sophisticated rules involving higher mathematical functions.

Mathematica uses standard rules of algebra to replace $(\sqrt{1+x})^4$ by $(1+x)^2$.	*In[10]:=* `Sqrt[1 + x]^4`
	Out[10]= $(1+x)^2$

Mathematica knows no rules for this expression, so it leaves the expression in the original form you gave.	*In[11]:=* `Log[1 + Cos[x]]`
	Out[11]= $\text{Log}[1 + \text{Cos}[x]]$

The notion of transformation rules is a very general one. In fact, you can think of the whole of *Mathematica* as simply a system for applying a collection of transformation rules to many different kinds of expressions.

The general principle that *Mathematica* follows is simple to state. It takes any expression you input, and gets results by applying a succession of transformation rules, stopping when it knows no more transformation rules that can be applied.

- Take any expression, and apply transformation rules until the result no longer changes.

The fundamental principle of *Mathematica*.

■ 1.4.2 Values for Symbols

When *Mathematica* transforms an expression such as x + x into 2x, it is treating the variable x in a purely symbolic or formal fashion. In such cases, x is a symbol which can stand for any expression.

Often, however, you need to replace a symbol like x with a definite "value". Sometimes this value will be a number; often it will be another expression.

To take an expression such as 1 + 2x and replace the symbol x that appears in it with a definite value, you can create a *Mathematica* transformation rule, and then apply this rule to the expression. To replace x with the value 3, you would create the transformation rule x -> 3. You must type -> as a pair of characters, with no space in between. You can think of x -> 3 as being a rule in which "x goes to 3".

To apply a transformation rule to a particular *Mathematica* expression, you type *expr /. rule*. The "replacement operator" /. is typed as a pair of characters, with no space in between.

This uses the transformation rule x->3 in the expression 1 + 2x.	$In[1]:= $ **1 + 2x /. x -> 3** $Out[1]= 7$
You can replace x with any expression. Here every occurrence of x is replaced by 2 - y.	$In[2]:= $ **1 + x + x^2 /. x -> 2 - y** $Out[2]= 3 + (2-y)^2 - y$
Here is a transformation rule. *Mathematica* treats it like any other symbolic expression.	$In[3]:= $ **x -> 3 + y** $Out[3]= x \to 3 + y$
This applies the transformation rule on the previous line to the expression x^2 - 9.	$In[4]:= $ **x^2 - 9 /. %** $Out[4]= -9 + (3+y)^2$

expr /. x -> value	replace *x* by *value* in the expression *expr*
expr /. {x -> xval, y -> yval}	perform several replacements

Replacing symbols by values in expressions.

You can apply rules together by putting the rules in a list.	$In[5]:= $ **(x + y) (x - y)^2 /. {x -> 3, y -> 1 - a}** $Out[5]= (4-a)(2+a)^2$

The replacement operator /. allows you to apply transformation rules to a particular expression. Sometimes, however, you will want to define transformation rules that should *always* be applied. For example, you might want to replace x with 3 whenever x occurs.

As discussed in Section 1.2.2, you can do this by *assigning* the value 3 to x using x = 3. Once you have made the assignment x = 3, x will always be replaced by 3, whenever it appears.

This assigns the value 3 to x.	$In[6]:= $ **x = 3** $Out[6]= 3$
Now x will automatically be replaced by 3 wherever it appears.	$In[7]:= $ **x^2 - 1** $Out[7]= 8$
This assigns the expression 1 + a to be the value of x.	$In[8]:= $ **x = 1 + a** $Out[8]= 1 + a$
Now x is replaced by 1 + a.	$In[9]:= $ **x^2 - 1** $Out[9]= -1 + (1+a)^2$

You can define the value of a symbol to be any expression, not just a number. You should realize that once you have given such a definition, the definition will continue to be used whenever the symbol appears, until you explicitly change or remove the definition. For most people, forgetting to remove values you have assigned to symbols is the single most common source of mistakes in using *Mathematica*.

x = *value*	define a value for x which will always be used
x =.	remove any value defined for x

Assigning values to symbols.

The symbol x still has the value you assigned to it above.	*In[10]:=* **x + 5 - 2x**
	Out[10]= $6 + a - 2(1 + a)$
This removes the value you assigned to x.	*In[11]:=* **x =.**
Now x has no value defined, so it can be used as a purely symbolic variable.	*In[12]:=* **x + 5 - 2x**
	Out[12]= $5 - x$

A symbol such as x can serve many different purposes in *Mathematica*, and in fact, much of the flexibility of *Mathematica* comes from being able to mix these purposes at will. However, you need to keep some of the different uses of x straight in order to avoid making mistakes. The most important distinction is between the use of x as a name for another expression, and as a symbolic variable that stands only for itself.

Traditional programming languages that do not support symbolic computation allow variables to be used only as names for objects, typically numbers, that have been assigned as values for them. In *Mathematica*, however, x can also be treated as a purely formal variable, to which various transformation rules can be applied. Of course, if you explicitly give a definition, such as x = 3, then x will always be replaced by 3, and can no longer serve as a formal variable.

You should understand that explicit definitions such as x = 3 have a global effect. On the other hand, a replacement such as *expr* /. x->3 affects only the specific expression *expr*. It is usually much easier to keep things straight if you avoid using explicit definitions except when absolutely necessary.

You can always mix replacements with assignments. With assignments, you can give names to expressions in which you want to do replacements, or to rules that you want to use to do the replacements.

This assigns a value to the symbol t.	*In[13]:=* **t = 1 + x^2**
	Out[13]= $1 + x^2$
This finds the value of t, and then replaces x by 2 in it.	*In[14]:=* **t /. x -> 2**
	Out[14]= 5
This finds the value of t for a different value of x.	*In[15]:=* **t /. x -> 5a**
	Out[15]= $1 + 25a^2$

This finds the value of t when x is
replaced by Pi, and then evaluates the
result numerically.

$In[16]:=$ **t /. x -> Pi //N**

$Out[16]=$ 10.8696

■ 1.4.3 Transforming Algebraic Expressions

There are often many different ways to write the same algebraic expression. As one example, the
expression $(1 + x)^2$ can be written as $1 + 2x + x^2$. *Mathematica* provides a large collection of functions
for converting between different forms of algebraic expressions.

Expand[*expr*]	multiply out products and powers, writing the result as a sum of terms
Factor[*expr*]	write *expr* as a product of minimal factors

Two common functions for transforming algebraic expressions.

Expand gives the "expanded form",
with products and powers multiplied
out.

$In[1]:=$ **Expand[(1 + x)^2]**

$Out[1]=$ $1 + 2x + x^2$

Factor recovers the original form.

$In[2]:=$ **Factor[%]**

$Out[2]=$ $(1 + x)^2$

It is easy to generate complicated
expressions with Expand.

$In[3]:=$ **Expand[(1 + x + 3 y)^4]**

$Out[3]=$ $1 + 4x + 6x^2 + 4x^3 + x^4 + 12y + 36xy + 36x^2y + 12x^3y +$
$\qquad 54y^2 + 108xy^2 + 54x^2y^2 + 108y^3 + 108xy^3 + 81y^4$

Factor often gives you simpler
expressions.

$In[4]:=$ **Factor[%]**

$Out[4]=$ $(1 + x + 3y)^4$

There are some cases, though, where
Factor can give you more complicated
expressions.

$In[5]:=$ **Factor[x^10 - 1]**

$Out[5]=$ $(-1 + x)(1 + x)(1 - x + x^2 - x^3 + x^4)(1 + x + x^2 + x^3 + x^4)$

In this case, Expand gives the
"simpler" form.

$In[6]:=$ **Expand[%]**

$Out[6]=$ $-1 + x^{10}$

■ 1.4.4 Simplifying Algebraic Expressions

There are many situations where you want to write a particular algebraic expression in the simplest
possible form. Although it is difficult to know exactly what one means in all cases by the "simplest
form", a worthwhile practical procedure is to look at many different forms of an expression, and pick
out the one that involves the smallest number of parts.

Simplify[*expr*]	try to find the simplest form of *expr* by applying various standard algebraic transformations
FullSimplify[*expr*]	try to find the simplest form by applying a wide range of transformations

Simplifying algebraic expressions.

Simplify writes $x^2 + 2x + 1$ in factored form.

In[1]:= **Simplify[x^2 + 2x + 1]**

Out[1]= $(1 + x)^2$

Simplify leaves $x^{10} - 1$ in expanded form, since for this expression, the factored form is larger.

In[2]:= **Simplify[x^10 - 1]**

Out[2]= $-1 + x^{10}$

You can often use Simplify to "clean up" complicated expressions that you get as the results of computations.

Here is the integral of $1/(x^4 - 1)$. Integrals are discussed in more detail in Section 1.5.3.

In[3]:= **Integrate[1/(x^4-1), x]**

Out[3]= $-\dfrac{\text{ArcTan}[x]}{2} + \dfrac{\text{Log}[-1 + x]}{4} - \dfrac{\text{Log}[1 + x]}{4}$

Differentiating the result from Integrate should give back your original expression. In this case, as is common, you get a more complicated version of the expression.

In[4]:= **D[%, x]**

Out[4]= $\dfrac{1}{4(-1 + x)} - \dfrac{1}{4(1 + x)} - \dfrac{1}{2(1 + x^2)}$

Simplify succeeds in getting back the original, more simple, form of the expression.

In[5]:= **Simplify[%]**

Out[5]= $\dfrac{1}{-1 + x^4}$

Simplify is set up to try various standard algebraic transformations on the expressions you give. Sometimes, however, it can take more sophisticated transformations to make progress in finding the simplest form of an expression.

FullSimplify tries a much wider range of transformations, involving not only algebraic functions, but also many other kinds of functions.

Simplify does nothing to this expression.

In[6]:= **Simplify[Gamma[x] Gamma[1 - x]]**

Out[6]= Gamma[1 - x] Gamma[x]

FullSimplify, however, transforms it to a simpler form.

In[7]:= **FullSimplify[Gamma[x] Gamma[1 - x]]**

Out[7]= $\pi\,\text{Csc}[\pi x]$

For fairly small expressions, FullSimplify will often succeed in making some remarkable simplifications. But for larger expressions, it often becomes unmanageably slow.

The reason for this is that to do its job, `FullSimplify` effectively has to try combining every part of an expression with every other, and for large expressions the number of cases that it has to consider can be astronomically large.

`Simplify` also has a difficult task to do, but it is set up to avoid some of the most time-consuming transformations that are tried by `FullSimplify`. For simple algebraic calculations, therefore, you may often find it convenient to apply `Simplify` quite routinely to your results.

In more complicated calculations, however, even `Simplify`, let alone `FullSimplify`, may end up needing to try a very large number of different forms, and therefore taking a long time. In such cases, you typically need to do more controlled simplification, and use your knowledge of the form you want to get to guide the process.

■ 1.4.5 Advanced Topic: Putting Expressions into Different Forms

Complicated algebraic expressions can usually be written in many different ways. *Mathematica* provides a variety of functions for converting expressions from one form to another.

In many applications, the most common of these functions are `Expand`, `Factor` and `Simplify`. However, particularly when you have rational expressions that contain quotients, you may need to use other functions.

`Expand[`*expr*`]`	multiply out products and powers
`ExpandAll[`*expr*`]`	apply Expand everywhere
`Factor[`*expr*`]`	reduce to a product of factors
`Together[`*expr*`]`	put all terms over a common denominator
`Apart[`*expr*`]`	separate into terms with simple denominators
`Cancel[`*expr*`]`	cancel common factors between numerators and denominators
`Simplify[`*expr*`]`	try a sequence of algebraic transformations and give the smallest form of *expr* found

Functions for transforming algebraic expressions.

Here is a rational expression that can be written in many different forms.

$In[1]:=$ `e = (x - 1)^2 (2 + x) / ((1 + x) (x - 3)^2)`

$$Out[1]= \frac{(-1+x)^2 (2+x)}{(-3+x)^2 (1+x)}$$

Expand expands out the numerator, but leaves the denominator in factored form.

In[2]:= **Expand[e]**

$$Out[2]= \frac{2}{(-3+x)^2\,(1+x)} - \frac{3\,x}{(-3+x)^2\,(1+x)} + \frac{x^3}{(-3+x)^2\,(1+x)}$$

ExpandAll expands out everything, including the denominator.

In[3]:= **ExpandAll[e]**

$$Out[3]= \frac{2}{9+3\,x-5\,x^2+x^3} - \frac{3\,x}{9+3\,x-5\,x^2+x^3} + \frac{x^3}{9+3\,x-5\,x^2+x^3}$$

Together collects all the terms together over a common denominator.

In[4]:= **Together[%]**

$$Out[4]= \frac{2-3\,x+x^3}{9+3\,x-5\,x^2+x^3}$$

Apart breaks the expression apart into terms with simple denominators.

In[5]:= **Apart[%]**

$$Out[5]= 1 + \frac{5}{(-3+x)^2} + \frac{19}{4\,(-3+x)} + \frac{1}{4\,(1+x)}$$

Factor factors everything, in this case reproducing the original form.

In[6]:= **Factor[%]**

$$Out[6]= \frac{(-1+x)^2\,(2+x)}{(-3+x)^2\,(1+x)}$$

According to Simplify, this is the simplest way to write the original expression.

In[7]:= **Simplify[e]**

$$Out[7]= \frac{(-1+x)^2\,(2+x)}{(-3+x)^2\,(1+x)}$$

Getting expressions into the form you want is something of an art. In most cases, it is best simply to experiment, trying different transformations until you get what you want. Often you will be able to use palettes in the front end to do this.

When you have an expression with a single variable, you can choose to write it as a sum of terms, a product, and so on. If you have an expression with several variables, there is an even wider selection of possible forms. You can, for example, choose to group terms in the expression so that one or another of the variables is "dominant".

Collect[*expr*, *x*]	group together powers of *x*
FactorTerms[*expr*, *x*]	pull out factors that do not depend on *x*

Rearranging expressions in several variables.

Here is an algebraic expression in two variables.

In[8]:= **v = Expand[(3 + 2 x)^2 (x + 2 y)^2]**

$$Out[8]= 9\,x^2 + 12\,x^3 + 4\,x^4 + 36\,x\,y + 48\,x^2\,y + 16\,x^3\,y +$$
$$36\,y^2 + 48\,x\,y^2 + 16\,x^2\,y^2$$

This groups together terms in v that involve the same power of x.

$In[9]:=$ **Collect[v, x]**

$Out[9]=$ $4x^4 + 36y^2 + x^3(12 + 16y) + x^2(9 + 48y + 16y^2) + x(36y + 48y^2)$

This groups together powers of y.

$In[10]:=$ **Collect[v, y]**

$Out[10]=$ $9x^2 + 12x^3 + 4x^4 + (36x + 48x^2 + 16x^3)y + (36 + 48x + 16x^2)y^2$

This factors out the piece that does not depend on y.

$In[11]:=$ **FactorTerms[v, y]**

$Out[11]=$ $(9 + 12x + 4x^2)(x^2 + 4xy + 4y^2)$

As we have seen, even when you restrict yourself to polynomials and rational expressions, there are many different ways to write any particular expression. If you consider more complicated expressions, involving, for example, higher mathematical functions, the variety of possible forms becomes still greater. As a result, it is totally infeasible to have a specific function built into *Mathematica* to produce each possible form. Rather, *Mathematica* allows you to construct arbitrary sets of transformation rules for converting between different forms. Many *Mathematica* packages include such rules; the details of how to construct them for yourself are given in Section 2.4.

There are nevertheless a few additional built-in *Mathematica* functions for transforming expressions.

+ TrigExpand[*expr*]	expand out trigonometric expressions into a sum of terms
+ TrigFactor[*expr*]	factor trigonometric expressions into products of terms
+ TrigReduce[*expr*]	reduce trigonometric expressions using multiple angles
+ TrigToExp[*expr*]	convert trigonometric functions to exponentials
+ ExpToTrig[*expr*]	convert exponentials to trigonometric functions
ComplexExpand[*expr*]	perform expansions assuming that all variables are real
PowerExpand[*expr*]	transform $(xy)^p$ into $x^p y^p$, etc.

Some other functions for transforming expressions.

This expands out the trigonometric expression, writing it so that all functions have argument x.

$In[12]:=$ **TrigExpand[Tan[x] Cos[2x]]**

$Out[12]=$ $Cos[x] Sin[x] - Sin[x]^2 Tan[x]$

This uses trigonometric identities to generate a factored form of the expression.

$In[13]:=$ **TrigFactor[%]**

$Out[13]=$ $(Cos[x] - Sin[x])(Cos[x] + Sin[x]) Tan[x]$

This reduces the expression by using multiple angles.

$In[14]:=$ **TrigReduce[%]**

$Out[14]=$ $Sec[x]\left(-\dfrac{Sin[x]}{2} + \dfrac{Sin[3x]}{2}\right)$

This expands the sine assuming that x
and y are both real.

$In[15]:=$ **ComplexExpand[Sin[x + I y]]**

$Out[15]=$ $\mathrm{Cosh[y]\,Sin[x] + I\,Cos[x]\,Sinh[y]}$

This does the expansion allowing x
and y to be complex.

$In[16]:=$ **ComplexExpand[Sin[x + I y], {x, y}]**

$Out[16]=$ $-\mathrm{Cosh[Im[x] + Re[y]]\,Sin[Im[y] - Re[x]]} +$
$\mathrm{I\,Cos[Im[y] - Re[x]]\,Sinh[Im[x] + Re[y]]}$

The transformations on expressions done by functions like Expand and Factor are always correct, whatever values the symbolic variables in the expressions may have. Sometimes, however, it is useful to perform transformations which are correct only if certain assumptions are made about the possible values of symbolic variables. One such transformation is performed by PowerExpand.

Mathematica does not automatically
expand out non-integer powers of
products.

$In[17]:=$ **Sqrt[x y]**

$Out[17]=$ $\sqrt{x\,y}$

PowerExpand does the expansion.

$In[18]:=$ **PowerExpand[%]**

$Out[18]=$ $\sqrt{x}\,\sqrt{y}$

The expansion is guaranteed to be
correct if x and y are both
non-negative.

$In[19]:=$ **{Sqrt[x y], Sqrt[x] Sqrt[y]} /. {x -> -1, y -> -1}**

$Out[19]=$ $\{1, -1\}$

■ 1.4.6 Picking Out Pieces of Algebraic Expressions

Coefficient[*expr*, *form*]	coefficient of *form* in *expr*
Exponent[*expr*, *form*]	maximum power of *form* in *expr*
Part[*expr*, *n*] or *expr*[[*n*]]	n^{th} term of *expr*

Functions to pick out pieces of polynomials.

Here is an algebraic expression.

$In[1]:=$ **e = Expand[(1 + 3x + 4y^2)^2]**

$Out[1]=$ $1 + 6x + 9x^2 + 8y^2 + 24xy^2 + 16y^4$

This gives the coefficient of x in e.

$In[2]:=$ **Coefficient[e, x]**

$Out[2]=$ $6 + 24y^2$

Exponent[*expr*, *y*] gives the highest
power of *y* that appears in *expr*.

$In[3]:=$ **Exponent[e, y]**

$Out[3]=$ 4

This gives the fourth term in e.

$In[4]:=$ **Part[e, 4]**

$Out[4]=$ $8y^2$

You may notice that the function Part[*expr*, *n*] used to pick out the nth term in a sum is the same as the function described in Section 1.2.4 for picking out elements in lists. This is no coincidence. In fact, as discussed in Section 2.1.5, every *Mathematica* expression can be manipulated structurally much like a list. However, as discussed in Section 2.1.5, you must be careful, because *Mathematica* often shows algebraic expressions in a form that is different from the way it treats them internally.

Coefficient works even with polynomials that are not explicitly expanded out.

```
In[5]:= Coefficient[(1 + 3x + 4y^2)^2, x]
```
$Out[5]= 6 + 24\,y^2$

Numerator[*expr*]	numerator of *expr*
Denominator[*expr*]	denominator of *expr*

Functions to pick out pieces of rational expressions.

Here is a rational expression.

```
In[6]:= r = (1 + x)/(2 (2 - y))
```
$Out[6]= \dfrac{1 + x}{2\,(2 - y)}$

Denominator picks out the denominator.

```
In[7]:= Denominator[%]
```
$Out[7]= 2\,(2 - y)$

Denominator gives 1 for expressions that are not quotients.

```
In[8]:= Denominator[1/x + 2/y]
```
$Out[8]= 1$

■ 1.4.7 Controlling the Display of Large Expressions

When you do symbolic calculations, it is quite easy to end up with extremely complicated expressions. Often, you will not even want to *see* the complete result of a computation.

If you end your input with a semicolon, *Mathematica* will do the computation you asked for, but will not display the result. You can nevertheless use % or Out[*n*] to refer to the result.

Even though you may not want to see the *whole* result from a computation, you often do need to see its basic form. You can use Short to display the *outline* of an expression, omitting some of the terms.

Ending your input with ; stops *Mathematica* from displaying the complicated result of the computation.

```
In[1]:= Expand[(x + 5 y + 10)^8] ;
```

You can still refer to the result as %. //Short displays a one-line outline of the result. The <<*n*>> stands for *n* terms that have been left out.

```
In[2]:= % //Short
```
$Out[2]//Short= 100000000 + \ll 43 \gg + 390625\,y^8$

This shows a three-line version of the expression. More parts are now visible.	$In[3]:=$ **Short[%, 3]**
	$Out[3]//Short=$ $100000000 + 80000000\,x + 28000000\,x^2 +$
	$5600000\,x^3 + \ll 37 \gg + 437500\,x^2\,y^6 +$
	$6250000\,y^7 + 625000\,x\,y^7 + 390625\,y^8$
This gives the total number of terms in the sum.	$In[4]:=$ **Length[%]**
	$Out[4]=$ 45

command ;	execute *command*, but do not print the result
expr // Short	show a one-line outline form of *expr*
Short[*expr*, *n*]	show an *n*-line outline of *expr*

Some ways to shorten your output.

■ 1.4.8 The Limits of *Mathematica*

In just one *Mathematica* command, you can easily specify a calculation that is far too complicated for any computer to do. For example, you could ask for Expand[(1+x)^(10^100)]. The result of this calculation would have $10^{100} + 1$ terms—more than the total number of particles in the universe.

You should have no trouble working out Expand[(1+x)^100] on any computer that can run *Mathematica*. But as you increase the exponent of (1+x), the results you get will eventually become too big for your computer's memory to hold. Exactly at what point this happens depends not only on the total amount of memory your computer has, but often also on such details as what other jobs happen to be running on your computer when you try to do your calculation.

If your computer does run out of memory in the middle of a calculation, most versions of *Mathematica* have no choice but to stop immediately. As a result, it is important to plan your calculations so that they never need more memory than your computer has.

Even if the result of an algebraic calculation is quite simple, the intermediate expressions that you generate in the course of the calculation can be very complicated. This means that even if the final result is small, the intermediate parts of a calculation can be too big for your computer to handle. If this happens, you can usually break your calculation into pieces, and succeed in doing each piece on its own. You should know that the internal scheme which *Mathematica* uses for memory management is such that once part of a calculation is finished, the memory used to store intermediate expressions that arose is immediately made available for new expressions.

Memory space is the most common limiting factor in *Mathematica* calculations. Time can also, however, be a limiting factor. You will usually be prepared to wait a second, or even a minute, for the result of a calculation. But you will less often be prepared to wait an hour or a day, and you will almost never be able to wait a year.

One class of calculations where time is often the limiting factor is those that effectively involve searching or testing a large number of possibilities. Integer factorization is a classic example. At some level, the problem of factoring an integer always seems to boil down to something related to testing a large number of candidate factors. As far as one knows now, the number of cases to test can increase almost as fast as the exponential of the number of digits in the integer we are trying to factor. As a result, the time needed to factor integers can increase very rapidly with the size of the integers you try to factor. In practice, you will find that `FactorInteger[`k`]` will give a result almost immediately when k has fewer than about 25 digits. But when k has 50 digits, `FactorInteger[`k`]` will often take an unmanageably long time.

In the field of computation theory, a distinction is typically drawn between algorithms which are "polynomial time", and those which are not. A polynomial time algorithm can always be executed in a time that increases only like a polynomial in the length of the input. Non-polynomial time algorithms may take times that increase exponentially with the length of their input.

The internal code of *Mathematica* typically uses polynomial time algorithms whenever it is feasible. There are some problems, however, for which no polynomial time algorithms are known. In such cases, *Mathematica* has no choice but to use non-polynomial time algorithms, which may take times that increase exponentially with the length of their input. Integer factorization is one such case. Other cases include factoring polynomials and solving equations when the number of variables involved becomes large.

Even when the time needed to do a computation does not increase exponentially, there will always come a point where the computation is too large or time-consuming to do on your particular computer system. As you work with *Mathematica*, you should develop some feeling for the limits on the kinds of calculations you can do in your particular application area.

- Doing arithmetic with numbers containing a few tens of thousands of digits.

- Expanding out a polynomial that gives a few hundred thousand terms.

- Factoring a polynomial in three variables with a few hundred terms.

- Applying a recursive rule a few hundred thousand times.

- Finding the numerical inverse of a 150×150 matrix.

- Finding the determinant of a 100×100 integer matrix.

- Finding the determinant of an 8×8 symbolic matrix.

- Finding numerical roots of a polynomial of degree 50.

- Rendering a few hundred thousand graphics primitives.

- Sorting a list of a few million elements.

- Searching a string that is a few million characters long.

- Formatting ten pages of `TraditionalForm` output.

Some operations that typically take a few seconds on a 1995 vintage workstation.

■ 1.4.9 Using Symbols to Tag Objects

There are many ways to use symbols in *Mathematica*. So far, we have concentrated on using symbols to store values and to represent mathematical variables. This section describes another way to use symbols in *Mathematica*.

The idea is to use symbols as "tags" for different types of objects.

Working with physical units gives one simple example. When you specify the length of an object, you want to give not only a number, but also the units in which the length is measured. In standard notation, you might write a length as 12 meters.

You can imitate this notation almost directly in *Mathematica*. You can for example simply use a symbol `meters` to indicate the units of our measurement.

The symbol `meters` here acts as a tag, which indicates the units used.	*In[1]:=* **12 meters** *Out[1]=* 12 meters
You can add lengths like this.	*In[2]:=* **% + 5.3 meters** *Out[2]=* 17.3 meters
This gives a speed.	*In[3]:=* **% / (25 seconds)** *Out[3]=* $\dfrac{0.692 \, \text{meters}}{\text{seconds}}$

This converts to a speed in feet per second.

In[4]:= **% /. meters -> 3.28084 feet**

$$Out[4]= \frac{2.27034\,feet}{seconds}$$

There is in fact a standard *Mathematica* package that allows you to work with units. The package defines many symbols that represent standard types of units.

Load the *Mathematica* package for handling units.

In[5]:= **<<Miscellaneous`Units`**

The package uses standardized names for units.

In[6]:= **12 Meter/Second**

$$Out[6]= \frac{12\,Meter}{Second}$$

The function Convert[*expr, units*] converts to the specified units.

In[7]:= **Convert[%, Mile/Hour]**

$$Out[7]= \frac{26.8432\,Mile}{Hour}$$

Usually you have to give prefixes for units as separate words.

In[8]:= **Convert[3 Kilo Meter / Hour, Inch / Minute]**

$$Out[8]= \frac{1968.5\,Inch}{Minute}$$

1.5 Symbolic Mathematics

■ 1.5.1 Basic Operations

Mathematica's ability to deal with symbolic expressions, as well as numbers, allows you to use it for many kinds of mathematics.

Calculus is one example. With *Mathematica*, you can differentiate an expression *symbolically*, and get a formula for the result.

This finds the derivative of x^n.

```
In[1]:= D[ x^n, x ]
Out[1]= n x^{-1+n}
```

Here is a slightly more complicated example.

```
In[2]:= D[x^2 Log[x + a], x]
```
$$Out[2]= \frac{x^2}{a+x} + 2 x \, Log[a+x]$$

$D[f, x]$	the (partial) derivative $\frac{\partial f}{\partial x}$
$Integrate[f, x]$	the indefinite integral $\int f \, dx$
$Sum[f, \{i, imin, imax\}]$	the sum $\sum_{i=imin}^{imax} f$
$Solve[lhs==rhs, x]$	solution to an equation for x
$Series[f, \{x, x_0, order\}]$	a power series expansion of f about the point $x = x_0$
$Limit[f, x->x_0]$	the limit $\lim_{x \to x_0} f$

Some symbolic mathematical operations.

Getting formulas as the results of computations is usually desirable when it is possible. There are however many circumstances where it is mathematically impossible to get an explicit formula as the result of a computation. This happens, for example, when you try to solve an equation for which there is no "closed form" solution. In such cases, you must resort to numerical methods and approximations. These are discussed in Section 1.6.

■ 1.5.2 Differentiation

Here is the derivative of x^n with respect to x.

```
In[1]:= D[ x^n, x ]
Out[1]= n x^{-1+n}
```

Mathematica knows the derivatives of
all the standard mathematical
functions.

In[2]:= D[**ArcTan[x]**, **x**]

Out[2]= $\dfrac{1}{1 + x^2}$

This differentiates three times with
respect to x.

In[3]:= D[**x^n**, {**x**, **3**}]

Out[3]= $(-2 + n)(-1 + n)\, n\, x^{-3+n}$

The function D[x^n, x] really gives a *partial* derivative, in which n is assumed not to depend on x.
Mathematica has another function, called Dt, which finds *total* derivatives, in which all variables are
assumed to be related. In mathematical notation, D[f, x] is like $\frac{\partial f}{\partial x}$, while Dt[$f$, x] is like $\frac{df}{dx}$. You can
think of Dt as standing for "derivative total".

Dt gives a *total derivative*, which
assumes that n can depend on x.
Dt[n, x] stands for $\frac{dn}{dx}$.

In[4]:= Dt[**x^n**, **x**]

Out[4]= $n\, x^{-1+n} + x^n\, \text{Dt}[n, x]\, \text{Log}[x]$

This gives the total differential $d(x^n)$.
Dt[x] is the differential dx.

In[5]:= Dt[**x^n**]

Out[5]= $n\, x^{-1+n}\, \text{Dt}[x] + x^n\, \text{Dt}[n]\, \text{Log}[x]$

D[f, x]	partial derivative $\frac{\partial}{\partial x} f$
D[f, x_1, x_2, ...]	multiple derivative $\frac{\partial}{\partial x_1} \frac{\partial}{\partial x_2} \cdots f$
D[f, {x, n}]	repeated derivative $\frac{\partial^n f}{\partial x^n}$
Dt[f]	total differential df
Dt[f, x]	total derivative $\frac{d}{dx} f$

Some differentiation functions.

As well as treating variables like x symbolically, you can also treat functions in *Mathematica* symbolically. Thus, for example, you can find formulas for derivatives of f[x], without specifying any
explicit form for the function f.

Mathematica does not know how to
differentiate f, so it gives you back a
symbolic result in terms of f'.

In[6]:= D[**f[x]**, **x**]

Out[6]= $f'[x]$

Mathematica uses the chain rule to
simplify derivatives.

In[7]:= D[**2 x f[x^2]**, **x**]

Out[7]= $2\, f[x^2] + 4 x^2\, f'[x^2]$

■ 1.5.3 Integration

Here is the integral $\int x^n \, dx$ in *Mathematica*.

$In[1]:=$ **Integrate[x^n, x]**

$Out[1]=$ $\dfrac{x^{1+n}}{1+n}$

Here is a slightly more complicated example.

$In[2]:=$ **Integrate[1/(x^4 - a^4), x]**

$Out[2]=$ $-\dfrac{\text{ArcTan}[\frac{x}{a}]}{2\,a^3} + \dfrac{\text{Log}[a-x]}{4\,a^3} - \dfrac{\text{Log}[a+x]}{4\,a^3}$

Mathematica knows how to do almost any integral that can be done in terms of standard mathematical functions. But you should realize that even though an integrand may contain only fairly simple functions, its integral may involve much more complicated functions—or may not be expressible at all in terms of standard mathematical functions.

Here is a fairly straightforward integral.

$In[3]:=$ **Integrate[Log[1 - x^2], x]**

$Out[3]=$ $-2\,x - \text{Log}[-1+x] + \text{Log}[1+x] + x\,\text{Log}[1-x^2]$

This integral can be done only in terms of a dilogarithm function.

$In[4]:=$ **Integrate[Log[1 - x^2]/x, x]**

$Out[4]=$ $-\dfrac{1}{2}\,\text{PolyLog}[2, x^2]$

This integral involves Erf.

$In[5]:=$ **Integrate[Exp[1 - x^2], x]**

$Out[5]=$ $\dfrac{1}{2}\,\text{E}\,\sqrt{\pi}\,\text{Erf}[x]$

And this one involves a Fresnel function.

$In[6]:=$ **Integrate[Sin[x^2], x]**

$Out[6]=$ $\sqrt{\dfrac{\pi}{2}}\,\text{FresnelS}\!\left[\sqrt{\dfrac{2}{\pi}}\,x\right]$

Even this integral requires a hypergeometric function.

$In[7]:=$ **Integrate[(1 - x^2)^n, x]**

$Out[7]=$ $x\,\text{Hypergeometric2F1}\!\left[\dfrac{1}{2},\,-n,\,\dfrac{3}{2},\,x^2\right]$

This integral simply cannot be done in terms of standard mathematical functions. As a result, *Mathematica* just leaves it undone.

$In[8]:=$ **Integrate[x^x, x]**

$Out[8]=$ $\displaystyle\int x^x \, dx$

Integrate[*f*, *x*]	the indefinite integral $\int f \, dx$
Integrate[*f*, *x*, *y*]	the multiple integral $\int dx \, dy \, f$
Integrate[*f*, {*x*, *xmin*, *xmax*}]	the definite integral $\int_{xmin}^{xmax} f \, dx$
Integrate[*f*, {*x*, *xmin*, *xmax*}, {*y*, *ymin*, *ymax*}]	
	the multiple integral $\int_{xmin}^{xmax} dx \int_{ymin}^{ymax} dy \, f$

Integration.

Here is the definite integral $\int_a^b \log(x) \, dx$.

```
In[9]:= Integrate[ Log[x], {x, a, b} ]
```
$$Out[9]= -a\,(-1 + Log[a]) + b\,(-1 + Log[b])$$

Here is another definite integral.

```
In[10]:= Integrate[Exp[-x^2], {x, 0, Infinity}]
```
$$Out[10]= \frac{\sqrt{\pi}}{2}$$

Mathematica cannot give you a formula for this definite integral.

```
In[11]:= Integrate[ x^x, {x, 0, 1} ]
```
$$Out[11]= \int_0^1 x^x \, dx$$

You can still get a numerical result, though.

```
In[12]:= N[ % ]
```
$$Out[12]= 0.78343$$

This evaluates the multiple integral $\int_0^1 dx \int_0^x dy \, (x^2 + y^2)$. The range of the outermost integration variable appears first.

```
In[13]:= Integrate[ x^2 + y^2, {x, 0, 1}, {y, 0, x} ]
```
$$Out[13]= \frac{1}{3}$$

■ 1.5.4 Sums and Products

This constructs the sum $\sum_{i=1}^{7} \frac{x^i}{i}$.

```
In[1]:= Sum[x^i/i, {i, 1, 7}]
```
$$Out[1]= x + \frac{x^2}{2} + \frac{x^3}{3} + \frac{x^4}{4} + \frac{x^5}{5} + \frac{x^6}{6} + \frac{x^7}{7}$$

You can leave out the lower limit if it is equal to 1.

```
In[2]:= Sum[x^i/i, {i, 7}]
```
$$Out[2]= x + \frac{x^2}{2} + \frac{x^3}{3} + \frac{x^4}{4} + \frac{x^5}{5} + \frac{x^6}{6} + \frac{x^7}{7}$$

This makes *i* increase in steps of 2, so that only odd-numbered values are included.

```
In[3]:= Sum[x^i/i, {i, 1, 5, 2}]
```
$$Out[3]= x + \frac{x^3}{3} + \frac{x^5}{5}$$

Products work just like sums.

In[4]:= **Product[x + i, {i, 1, 4}]**

Out[4]= $(1+x)(2+x)(3+x)(4+x)$

Sum[f, {i, $imin$, $imax$}]	the sum $\sum_{i=imin}^{imax} f$
Sum[f, {i, $imin$, $imax$, di}]	the sum with i increasing in steps of di
Sum[f, {i, $imin$, $imax$}, {j, $jmin$, $jmax$}]	the nested sum $\sum_{i=imin}^{imax} \sum_{j=jmin}^{jmax} f$
Product[f, {i, $imin$, $imax$}]	the product $\prod_{i=imin}^{imax} f$

Sums and products.

This sum is computed symbolically as a function of n.

In[5]:= **Sum[i^2, {i, 1, n}]**

Out[5]= $\dfrac{1}{6} n (1+n) (1+2n)$

Mathematica can also give an exact result for this infinite sum.

In[6]:= **Sum[1/i^4, {i, 1, Infinity}]**

Out[6]= $\dfrac{\pi^4}{90}$

As with integrals, simple sums can lead to complicated results.

In[7]:= **Sum[1/(i^4 + 2), {i, 1, Infinity}]**

Out[7]= $(3\,\mathrm{Cos}[2^{3/4}\pi] - 3\,\mathrm{Cosh}[2^{3/4}\pi] -$
$2\,2^{3/4}\pi\,\mathrm{Sin}[2^{3/4}\pi] - 2\,2^{3/4}\pi\,\mathrm{Sinh}[2^{3/4}\pi]) /$
$(16\,(\mathrm{Cos}[2^{3/4}\pi] - \mathrm{Cosh}[2^{3/4}\pi]))$

This sum cannot be evaluated exactly using standard mathematical functions.

In[8]:= **Sum[1/(i! + (2i)!), {i, 1, Infinity}]**

Out[8]= $\displaystyle\sum_{i=1}^{\infty} \frac{1}{i! + (2i)!}$

You can nevertheless find a numerical approximation to the result.

In[9]:= **N[%]**

Out[9]= 0.373197

Mathematica also has a notation for multiple sums and products.
Sum[f, {i, $imin$, $imax$}, {j, $jmin$, $jmax$}] represents a sum over i and j, which would be written in standard mathematical notation as $\sum_{i=imin}^{imax} \sum_{j=jmin}^{jmax} f$. Notice that in *Mathematica* notation, as in standard mathematical notation, the range of the *outermost* variable is given *first*.

This is the multiple sum $\sum_{i=1}^{3} \sum_{j=1}^{i} x^i y^j$. Notice that the outermost sum over i is given first, just as in the mathematical notation.

In[10]:= **Sum[x^i y^j, {i, 1, 3}, {j, 1, i}]**

Out[10]= $x\,y + x^2\,y + x^3\,y + x^2\,y^2 + x^3\,y^2 + x^3\,y^3$

The way the ranges of variables are specified in `Sum` and `Product` is an example of the rather general *iterator notation* that *Mathematica* uses. You will see this notation again when we discuss generating tables and lists using `Table` (Section 1.8.2), and when we describe `Do` loops (Section 1.7.3).

{imax}	iterate *imax* times, without incrementing any variables
{i, imax}	*i* goes from 1 to *imax* in steps of 1
{i, imin, imax}	*i* goes from *imin* to *imax* in steps of 1
{i, imin, imax, di}	*i* goes from *imin* to *imax* in steps of *di*
{i, imin, imax}, {j, jmin, jmax}, ...	*i* goes from *imin* to *imax*, and for each such value, *j* goes from *jmin* to *jmax*, etc.

Mathematica iterator notation.

■ 1.5.5 Equations

Section 1.2.2 discussed *assignments* such as $x = y$ which *set* x equal to y. This section discusses *equations*, which *test* equality. The equation $x == y$ tests whether x is equal to y.

This *tests* whether 2 + 2 and 4 are equal. The result is the symbol True.	`In[1]:= 2 + 2 == 4`
	`Out[1]= True`

It is very important that you do not confuse $x = y$ with $x == y$. While $x = y$ is an *imperative* statement that actually causes an assignment to be done, $x == y$ merely *tests* whether x and y are equal, and causes no explicit action. If you have used the C programming language, you will recognize that the notation for assignment and testing in *Mathematica* is the same as in C.

$x = y$	assigns x to have value y
$x == y$	tests whether x and y are equal

Assignments and tests.

This *assigns* x to have value 4.	`In[2]:= x = 4`
	`Out[2]= 4`
If you ask for x, you now get 4.	`In[3]:= x`
	`Out[3]= 4`
This *tests* whether x is equal to 4. In this case, it is.	`In[4]:= x == 4`
	`Out[4]= True`

x is equal to 4, not 6.	$In[5]:=$ **x == 6**
	$Out[5]=$ False
This removes the value assigned to x.	$In[6]:=$ **x =.**

The tests we have used so far involve only numbers, and always give a definite answer, either True or False. You can also do tests on symbolic expressions.

Mathematica cannot get a definite result for this test unless you give x a specific numerical value.	$In[7]:=$ **x == 5**
	$Out[7]=$ x == 5
If you replace x by the specific numerical value 4, the test gives False.	$In[8]:=$ **% /. x -> 4**
	$Out[8]=$ False

Even when you do tests on symbolic expressions, there are some cases where you can get definite results. An important one is when you test the equality of two expressions that are *identical*. Whatever the numerical values of the variables in these expressions may be, *Mathematica* knows that the expressions must always be equal.

The two expressions are *identical*, so the result is True, whatever the value of x may be.	$In[9]:=$ **2 x + x^2 == 2 x + x^2**
	$Out[9]=$ True
Mathematica does not try to tell whether these expressions are equal. In this case, using Expand would make them have the same form.	$In[10]:=$ **2 x + x^2 == x (2 + x)**
	$Out[10]=$ $2x + x^2 == x(2 + x)$

Expressions like x == 4 represent *equations* in *Mathematica*. There are many functions in *Mathematica* for manipulating and solving equations.

This is an *equation* in *Mathematica*. Subsection 1.5.7 will discuss how to solve it for x.	$In[11]:=$ **x^2 + 2 x - 7 == 0**
	$Out[11]=$ $-7 + 2x + x^2 == 0$
You can assign a name to the equation.	$In[12]:=$ **eqn = %**
	$Out[12]=$ $-7 + 2x + x^2 == 0$
If you ask for eqn, you now get the equation.	$In[13]:=$ **eqn**
	$Out[13]=$ $-7 + 2x + x^2 == 0$

■ 1.5.6 Relational and Logical Operators

$x \mathrel{==} y$	equal (also input as $x == y$)
$x \mathrel{!=} y$	unequal (also input as $x \neq y$)
$x > y$	greater than
$x \mathrel{>=} y$	greater than or equal to (also input as $x \geq y$)
$x < y$	less than
$x \mathrel{<=} y$	less than or equal to (also input as $x \leq y$)
$x \mathrel{==} y \mathrel{==} z$	all equal
$x \mathrel{!=} y \mathrel{!=} z$	all unequal (distinct)
$x > y > z$, etc.	strictly decreasing, etc.

Relational operators.

This tests whether 10 is less than 7. The result is `False`.

```
In[1]:= 10 < 7
Out[1]= False
```

Not all of these numbers are unequal, so this gives `False`.

```
In[2]:= 3 != 2 != 3
Out[2]= False
```

You can mix `<` and `<=`.

```
In[3]:= 3 < 5 <= 6
Out[3]= True
```

Since both of the quantities involved are numeric, *Mathematica* can determine that this is true.

```
In[4]:= Pi^E < E^Pi
Out[4]= True
```

Mathematica does not know whether this is true or false.

```
In[5]:= x > y
Out[5]= x > y
```

!*p*	not (also input as ¬*p*)
p && *q* && ...	and (also input as *p* ∧ *q* ∧ ...)
p || *q* || ...	or (also input as *p* ∨ *q* ∨ ...)
Xor[*p*, *q*, ...]	exclusive or
If[*p*, *then*, *else*]	give *then* if *p* is True, and *else* if *p* is False
LogicalExpand[*expr*]	expand out logical expressions

Logical operations.

Both tests give True, so the result is True.

```
In[6]:= 7 > 4 && 2 != 3
Out[6]= True
```

You should remember that the logical operations ==, && and || are all *double characters* in *Mathematica*. If you have used the C programming language, you will recognize this notation as being the same as in C.

Mathematica does not know whether this is true or false.

```
In[7]:= p && q
Out[7]= p && q
```

Mathematica leaves this expression unchanged.

```
In[8]:= (p || q) && !(r || s)
Out[8]= (p || q) && ! (r || s)
```

You can use LogicalExpand to expand out the terms.

```
In[9]:= LogicalExpand[ % ]
Out[9]= p && ! r && ! s || q && ! r && ! s
```

■ 1.5.7 Solving Equations

An expression like x^2 + 2 x - 7 == 0 represents an *equation* in *Mathematica*. You will often need to *solve* equations like this, to find out for what values of x they are true.

This gives the two solutions to the quadratic equation $x^2 + 2x - 7 = 0$. The solutions are given as replacements for x.

```
In[1]:= Solve[x^2 + 2x - 7 == 0, x]
Out[1]= {{x → -1 - 2√2}, {x → -1 + 2√2}}
```

Here are the numerical values of the solutions.

```
In[2]:= N[ % ]
Out[2]= {{x → -3.82843}, {x → 1.82843}}
```

You can get a list of the actual solutions for x by applying the rules generated by Solve to x using the replacement operator.

```
In[3]:= x /. %
Out[3]= {-3.82843, 1.82843}
```

You can equally well apply the rules to
any other expression involving x.

$In[4]:=$ **x^2 + 3 x /. %%**

$Out[4]=$ {3.17157, 8.82843}

Solve[*lhs* == *rhs*, *x*]	solve an equation, giving a list of rules for *x*
x /. *solution*	use the list of rules to get values for *x*
expr /. *solution*	use the list of rules to get values for an expression

Finding and using solutions to equations.

Solve always tries to give you explicit *formulas* for the solutions to equations. However, it is a basic mathematical result that, for sufficiently complicated equations, explicit algebraic formulas cannot be given. If you have an algebraic equation in one variable, and the highest power of the variable is at most four, then *Mathematica* can always give you formulas for the solutions. However, if the highest power is five or more, it may be mathematically impossible to give explicit algebraic formulas for all the solutions.

Mathematica can always solve algebraic
equations in one variable when the
highest power is less than five.

$In[5]:=$ **Solve[x^4 - 5 x^2 - 3 == 0, x]**

$Out[5]= \left\{ \left\{ x \to -\frac{1}{2} I \sqrt{2\left(-5+\sqrt{37}\right)} \right\}, \right.$

$\left\{ x \to \frac{1}{2} I \sqrt{2\left(-5+\sqrt{37}\right)} \right\}, \left\{ x \to -\sqrt{\frac{1}{2}\left(5+\sqrt{37}\right)} \right\},$

$\left. \left\{ x \to \sqrt{\frac{1}{2}\left(5+\sqrt{37}\right)} \right\} \right\}$

It can solve some equations that
involve higher powers.

$In[6]:=$ **Solve[x^6 == 1, x]**

$Out[6]= \left\{ \{x \to -1\}, \{x \to 1\}, \left\{x \to -(-1)^{1/3}\right\}, \right.$
$\left. \left\{x \to (-1)^{1/3}\right\}, \left\{x \to -(-1)^{2/3}\right\}, \left\{x \to (-1)^{2/3}\right\} \right\}$

There are some equations, however, for
which it is mathematically impossible
to find explicit formulas for the
solutions. *Mathematica* uses Root
objects to represent the solutions in this
case.

$In[7]:=$ **Solve[2 - 4 x + x^5 == 0, x]**

$Out[7]= \{\{x \to Root[2 - 4\#1 + \#1^5 \&, 1]\},$
$\{x \to Root[2 - 4\#1 + \#1^5 \&, 2]\},$
$\{x \to Root[2 - 4\#1 + \#1^5 \&, 3]\},$
$\{x \to Root[2 - 4\#1 + \#1^5 \&, 4]\},$
$\{x \to Root[2 - 4\#1 + \#1^5 \&, 5]\}\}$

Even though you cannot get explicit
formulas, you can still find the
solutions numerically.

$In[8]:=$ **N[%]**

$Out[8]= \{\{x \to -1.51851\}, \{x \to 0.508499\},$
$\{x \to 1.2436\}, \{x \to -0.116792 - 1.43845 I\},$
$\{x \to -0.116792 + 1.43845 I\}\}$

In addition to being able to solve purely algebraic equations, *Mathematica* can also solve some equations involving other functions.

After printing a warning, *Mathematica* returns one solution to this equation.

In[9]:= **Solve[Sin[x] == a, x]**

Solve::ifun:
    Inverse functions are being used by Solve, so some
        solutions may not be found.

Out[9]= {{x → ArcSin[a]}}

It is important to realize that an equation such as $\sin(x) = a$ actually has an infinite number of possible solutions, in this case differing by multiples of 2π. However, Solve by default returns just one solution, but prints a message telling you that other solutions may exist. Section 3.4.5 discusses this in more detail.

There is no explicit "closed form" solution for a transcendental equation like this.

In[10]:= **Solve[Cos[x] == x, x]**

Solve::tdep:
    The equations appear to involve transcendental
        functions of the variables in an essentially
        non-algebraic way.

Out[10]= Solve[Cos[x] == x, x]

You can find an approximate numerical solution using FindRoot, and giving a starting value for x.

In[11]:= **FindRoot[Cos[x] == x, {x, 1}]**

Out[11]= {x → 0.739085}

Solve can also handle equations involving symbolic functions. In such cases, it again prints a warning, then gives results in terms of formal inverse functions.

Mathematica returns a result in terms of the formal inverse function of f.

In[12]:= **Solve[f[x^2] == a, x]**

InverseFunction::ifun:
    Warning: Inverse functions are being used. Values may
        be lost for multivalued inverses.

Out[12]= $\left\{\left\{x \to -\sqrt{f^{(-1)}[a]}\right\}, \left\{x \to \sqrt{f^{(-1)}[a]}\right\}\right\}$

Solve[{lhs_1==rhs_1, lhs_2==rhs_2, ... }, {x, y, ... }]
    solve a set of simultaneous equations for x, y, ...

Solving sets of simultaneous equations.

You can also use *Mathematica* to solve sets of simultaneous equations. You simply give the list of equations, and specify the list of variables to solve for.

Here is a list of two simultaneous equations, to be solved for the variables x and y.

In[13]:= **Solve[{a x + y == 0, 2 x + (1-a) y == 1}, {x, y}]**

Out[13]= $\left\{\left\{x \to -\dfrac{1}{-2+a-a^2}, y \to -\dfrac{a}{2-a+a^2}\right\}\right\}$

Here are some more complicated simultaneous equations. The two solutions are given as two lists of replacements for x and y.

$In[14]:=$ **Solve[{x^2 + y^2 == 1, x + 3 y == 0}, {x, y}]**

$Out[14]= \left\{\left\{x \to -\frac{3}{\sqrt{10}}, y \to \frac{1}{\sqrt{10}}\right\}, \left\{x \to \frac{3}{\sqrt{10}}, y \to -\frac{1}{\sqrt{10}}\right\}\right\}$

This uses the solutions to evaluate the expression x + y.

$In[15]:=$ **x + y /. %**

$Out[15]= \left\{-\sqrt{\frac{2}{5}}, \sqrt{\frac{2}{5}}\right\}$

Mathematica can solve any set of simultaneous *linear* equations. It can also solve a large class of simultaneous polynomial equations. Even when it does not manage to solve the equations explicitly, *Mathematica* will still usually reduce them to a much simpler form.

When you are working with sets of equations in several variables, it is often convenient to reorganize the equations by eliminating some variables between them.

This eliminates y between the two equations, giving a single equation for x.

$In[16]:=$ **Eliminate[{a x + y == 0, 2 x + (1-a) y == 1}, y]**

$Out[16]= -1 + 2 x - a x + a^2 x == 0$

If you have several equations, there is no guarantee that there exists *any* consistent solution for a particular variable.

There is no consistent solution to these equations, so *Mathematica* returns {}, indicating that the set of solutions is empty.

$In[17]:=$ **Solve[{x==1, x==2}, x]**

$Out[17]= \{\}$

There is also no consistent solution to these equations for almost all values of a.

$In[18]:=$ **Solve[{x==1, x==a}, x]**

$Out[18]= \{\}$

The general question of whether a set of equations has any consistent solution is quite a subtle one. For example, for most values of a, the equations {x==1, x==a} are inconsistent, so there is no possible solution for x. However, if a is equal to 1, then the equations *do* have a solution. Solve is set up to give you *generic* solutions to equations. It discards any solutions that exist only when special constraints between parameters are satisfied.

If you use Reduce instead of Solve, *Mathematica* will however keep *all* the possible solutions to a set of equations, including those that require special conditions on parameters.

This shows that the equations have a solution only when a==1. The notation x==1 && a==1 represents the requirement that *both* x==1 *and* a==1 should be True.

$In[19]:=$ **Reduce[{x==1, x==a}, x]**

$Out[19]= x == 1 \&\& a == 1$

This gives the complete set of possible solutions to the equation. The answer is stated in terms of a combination of simpler equations. && indicates equations that must simultaneously be true; || indicates alternatives.

In[20]:= **Reduce[a x - b == 0, x]**

Out[20]= $b == 0 \&\& a == 0 \mid\mid a \neq 0 \&\& x == \frac{b}{a}$

This gives a more complicated combination of equations.

In[21]:= **Reduce[a x^2 - b == 0, x]**

Out[21]= $b == 0 \&\& a == 0 \mid\mid$

$a \neq 0 \&\& x == -\frac{\sqrt{b}}{\sqrt{a}} \mid\mid a \neq 0 \&\& x == \frac{\sqrt{b}}{\sqrt{a}}$

Solve[*lhs*==*rhs*, *x*]	solve an equation for *x*
Solve[{*lhs₁*==*rhs₁*, *lhs₂*==*rhs₂*, ... }, {*x, y, ...* }]	solve a set of simultaneous equations for *x, y, ...*
Eliminate[{*lhs₁*==*rhs₁*, *lhs₂*==*rhs₂*, ... }, {*x, ...* }]	eliminate *x, ...* in a set of simultaneous equations
Reduce[{*lhs₁*==*rhs₁*, *lhs₂*==*rhs₂*, ... }, {*x, y, ...* }]	give a set of simplified equations, including all possible solutions

Functions for solving and manipulating equations.

■ 1.5.8 Differential Equations

DSolve[*eqns*, *y*[*x*], *x*]	solve a differential equation for *y*[*x*], taking *x* as the independent variable
DSolve[*eqns*, *y*, *x*]	give a solution for *y* in pure function form

Solving an ordinary differential equation.

Here is the solution to the differential equation $y'(x) = ay(x) + 1$. C[1] is a coefficient which must be determined from boundary conditions.

In[1]:= **DSolve[y'[x] == a y[x] + 1, y[x], x]**

Out[1]= $\{\{y[x] \to -\frac{1}{a} + E^{ax} C[1]\}\}$

If you include an appropriate initial condition, there are no undetermined coefficients in the solution.

In[2]:= **DSolve[{y'[x] == a y[x] + 1, y[0] == 0}, y[x], x]**

Out[2]= $\{\{y[x] \to \frac{-1 + E^{ax}}{a}\}\}$

Whereas algebraic equations such as $x^2 + x = 1$ are equations for *variables*, differential equations such as $y''(x) + y'(x) = y(x)$ are equations for *functions*. In *Mathematica*, you must always give differential equations explicitly in terms of functions such as $y[x]$, and you must specify the variables such as x on which the functions depend. As a result, you must write an equation such as $y''(x) + y'(x) = y(x)$ in the form $y''[x] + y'[x] == y[x]$. You cannot write it as $y'' + y' == y$.

Mathematica can solve both linear and nonlinear ordinary differential equations, as well as lists of simultaneous equations. If you do not specify enough initial or boundary conditions, *Mathematica* will give solutions that involve an appropriate number of undetermined coefficients. Each time you use DSolve, it names the undetermined coefficients C[1], C[2], etc.

Here is a pair of simultaneous differential equations, with no initial or boundary conditions. The solution you get involves two undetermined coefficients.	$In[3]:=$ **DSolve[{x'[t] == y[t], y'[t] == x[t]},** $\qquad\qquad\qquad\qquad$ **{x[t], y[t]}, t]** $Out[3]=$ {{x[t] $\to -E^{-t}$ C[1] + E^t C[2], $\qquad\qquad$ y[t] $\to E^{-t}$ C[1] + E^t C[2]}}

When you ask DSolve to get you a solution for $y[x]$, the rules it returns specify how to replace $y[x]$ in any expression. However, these rules do not specify how to replace objects such as $y'[x]$. If you want to manipulate solutions that you get from DSolve, you will often find it better to ask for solutions for y, rather than for $y[x]$.

This gives the solution for y as a "pure function".	$In[4]:=$ **DSolve[y'[x] == x + y[x], y, x]** $Out[4]=$ {{y $\to$ ($-1 + E^{\#1}$ C[1] $- \#1 \&$)}}
You can now use the replacement operator to apply this solution to expressions involving y.	$In[5]:=$ **y''[x] + y[x] /. %** $Out[5]=$ {$-1 - x + 2 E^x$ C[1]}

Section 2.2.5 explains how the "pure function" indicated by & that appears in the result from DSolve works.

■ 1.5.9 Power Series

The mathematical operations we have discussed so far are *exact*. Given precise input, their results are exact formulas.

In many situations, however, you do not need an exact result. It may be quite sufficient, for example, to find an *approximate* formula that is valid, say, when the quantity x is small.

This gives a power series approximation to $(1 + x)^n$ for x close to 0, up to terms of order x^3.	$In[1]:=$ **Series[(1 + x)^n, {x, 0, 3}]** $Out[1]= 1 + n x + \dfrac{1}{2} (-1 + n) n x^2 +$ $\qquad \dfrac{1}{6} (-2 + n) (-1 + n) n x^3 + O[x]^4$

Mathematica knows the power series expansions for many mathematical functions.

$In[2]:=$ **Series[Exp[-a t] (1 + Sin[2 t]), {t, 0, 4}]**

$Out[2]= 1 + (2 - a) t + \left(-2a + \dfrac{a^2}{2}\right) t^2 +$

$\left(-\dfrac{4}{3} + a^2 - \dfrac{a^3}{6}\right) t^3 + \left(\dfrac{4a}{3} - \dfrac{a^3}{3} + \dfrac{a^4}{24}\right) t^4 + O[t]^5$

If you give it a function that it does not know, Series writes out the power series in terms of derivatives.

$In[3]:=$ **Series[1 + f[t], {t, 0, 3}]**

$Out[3]= 1 + f[0] + f'[0] t + \dfrac{1}{2} f''[0] t^2 + \dfrac{1}{6} f^{(3)}[0] t^3 + O[t]^4$

Power series are approximate formulas that play much the same role with respect to algebraic expressions as approximate numbers play with respect to numerical expressions. *Mathematica* allows you to perform operations on power series, in all cases maintaining the appropriate order or "degree of precision" for the resulting power series.

Here is a simple power series, accurate to order x^5.

$In[4]:=$ **Series[Exp[x], {x, 0, 5}]**

$Out[4]= 1 + x + \dfrac{x^2}{2} + \dfrac{x^3}{6} + \dfrac{x^4}{24} + \dfrac{x^5}{120} + O[x]^6$

When you do operations on a power series, the result is computed only to the appropriate order in x.

$In[5]:=$ **%^2 (1 + %)**

$Out[5]= 2 + 5x + \dfrac{13 x^2}{2} + \dfrac{35 x^3}{6} + \dfrac{97 x^4}{24} + \dfrac{55 x^5}{24} + O[x]^6$

This turns the power series back into an ordinary expression.

$In[6]:=$ **Normal[%]**

$Out[6]= 2 + 5x + \dfrac{13 x^2}{2} + \dfrac{35 x^3}{6} + \dfrac{97 x^4}{24} + \dfrac{55 x^5}{24}$

Now the square is computed *exactly*.

$In[7]:=$ **%^2**

$Out[7]= \left(2 + 5x + \dfrac{13 x^2}{2} + \dfrac{35 x^3}{6} + \dfrac{97 x^4}{24} + \dfrac{55 x^5}{24}\right)^2$

Applying Expand gives a result with eleven terms.

$In[8]:=$ **Expand[%]**

$Out[8]= 4 + 20x + 51x^2 + \dfrac{265 x^3}{3} + \dfrac{467 x^4}{4} + \dfrac{1505 x^5}{12} +$

$\dfrac{7883 x^6}{72} + \dfrac{1385 x^7}{18} + \dfrac{24809 x^8}{576} + \dfrac{5335 x^9}{288} + \dfrac{3025 x^{10}}{576}$

Series[*expr*, {*x*, x_0, *n*}]	find the power series expansion of *expr* about the point $x = x_0$ to at most n^{th} order
Normal[*series*]	truncate a power series to give an ordinary expression

Power series operations.

■ 1.5.10 Limits

Here is the expression $\sin(x)/x$.	$In[1]:=$ **t = Sin[x]/x**
	$Out[1]=$ $\dfrac{Sin[x]}{x}$

If you replace x by 0, the expression becomes 0/0, and you get an indeterminate result.

$In[2]:=$ **t /. x->0**

```
                                          1
Power::infy: Infinite expression - encountered.
                                          0
Infinity::indet:
    Indeterminate expression 0 ComplexInfinity encountered.
```

$Out[2]=$ Indeterminate

If you find the numerical value of $\sin(x)/x$ for x close to 0, however, you get a result that is close to 1.

$In[3]:=$ **t /. x->0.01**

$Out[3]=$ 0.999983

This finds the *limit* of $\sin(x)/x$ as x approaches 0. The result is indeed 1.

$In[4]:=$ **Limit[t, x->0]**

$Out[4]=$ 1

Limit[*expr*, *x*->x_0]	the limit of *expr* as *x* approaches x_0

Limits.

■ 1.5.11 Packages for Symbolic Mathematics

There are many *Mathematica* packages which implement symbolic mathematical operations. This section describes a few examples drawn from the standard set of packages distributed with *Mathematica*. As discussed in Section 1.3.10, some copies of *Mathematica* may be set up so that the functions described here are automatically loaded into *Mathematica* if they are ever needed.

Laplace Transforms

<<Calculus`LaplaceTransform`	load the Laplace transform package
LaplaceTransform[*expr*, *t*, *s*]	find the Laplace transform of *expr*
InverseLaplaceTransform[*expr*, *s*, *t*]	find the inverse Laplace transform of *expr*

Laplace transforms.

This loads the Laplace transform package. In some versions of *Mathematica,* you may not need to load this package explicitly.

In[1]:= `<<Calculus`LaplaceTransform``

This evaluates a Laplace transform.

In[2]:= `LaplaceTransform[ t^3 Exp[a t], t, s ]`

$$Out[2]= \frac{6}{(-a+s)^4}$$

Here is the inverse transform.

In[3]:= `InverseLaplaceTransform[%, s, t]`

$Out[3]= E^{a\,t}\,t^3$

Fourier Transforms

`<<Calculus`FourierTransform``	load the symbolic Fourier transform package
`FourierTransform[`*expr*`, t, s]`	find the symbolic Fourier transform of *expr*
`InverseFourierTransform[`*expr*`, s, t]`	find the inverse Fourier transform of *expr*

Fourier transforms.

This loads the symbolic Fourier transform package.

In[1]:= `<<Calculus`FourierTransform``

This evaluates a Fourier transform.

In[2]:= `FourierTransform[ t^2 Sin[t], t, w ]`

$Out[2]= -I\pi\,(\mathrm{DiracDelta}''[1-w]-\mathrm{DiracDelta}''[1+w])$

Vector Analysis

`<<Calculus'VectorAnalysis'`	load the vector analysis package
`SetCoordinates[`*system*`[`*names*`]]`	
	specify the coordinate system to be used (`Cartesian`, `Cylindrical`, `Spherical`, etc.), giving the names of the coordinates in that system
`Grad[`*f*`]`	evaluate the gradient ∇f of f in the coordinate system chosen
`Div[`*f*`]`	evaluate the divergence $\nabla \cdot f$ of the list f
`Curl[`*f*`]`	evaluate the curl $\nabla \times f$ of the list f
`Laplacian[`*f*`]`	evaluate the Laplacian $\nabla^2 f$ of f

Vector analysis.

This loads the vector analysis package. In some versions of *Mathematica*, you may not need to load the package explicitly.

```
In[1]:= <<Calculus'VectorAnalysis'
```

This specifies that a spherical coordinate system with coordinate names r, theta and phi should be used.

```
In[2]:= SetCoordinates[Spherical[r, theta, phi]]
Out[2]= Spherical[r, theta, phi]
```

This evaluates the gradient of $r^2 \sin(\theta)$ in the spherical coordinate system.

```
In[3]:= Grad[r^2 Sin[theta]]
Out[3]= {2 r Sin[theta], r Cos[theta], 0}
```

■ 1.5.12 Advanced Topic: Generic and Non-Generic Cases

This gives a result for the integral of x^n that is valid for almost all values of n.

```
In[1]:= Integrate[x^n, x]
```
$$Out[1]= \frac{x^{1+n}}{1+n}$$

For the special case of x^{-1}, however, the correct result is different.

```
In[2]:= Integrate[x^-1, x]
Out[2]= Log[x]
```

The overall goal of symbolic computation is typically to get formulas that are valid for many possible values of the variables that appear in them. It is however often not practical to try to get formulas that are valid for absolutely every possible value of each variable.

Mathematica always replaces $0/x$ by 0.	*In[3]:=* **0 / x**
	Out[3]= 0

If x is equal to 0, however, then the true result is not 0.

In[4]:= **0 / 0**

Power::infy: Infinite expression $\dfrac{1}{0}$ encountered.

Infinity::indet:
    Indeterminate expression 0 ComplexInfinity encountered.

Out[4]= Indeterminate

This construct treats both cases, but would be quite unwieldy to use.

In[5]:= **If[x != 0, 0, Indeterminate]**

Out[5]= If[x $\neq$ 0, 0, Indeterminate]

If *Mathematica* did not automatically replace $0/x$ by 0, then few symbolic computations would get very far. But you should realize that the practical necessity of making such replacements can cause misleading results to be obtained when exceptional values of parameters are used.

The basic operations of *Mathematica* are nevertheless carefully set up so that whenever possible the results obtained will be valid for almost all values of each variable.

$\sqrt{x^2}$ is not automatically replaced by x.

In[6]:= **Sqrt[x^2]**

Out[6]= $\sqrt{x^2}$

If it were, then the result here would be -2, which is incorrect.

In[7]:= **% /. x -> -2**

Out[7]= 2

This makes the assumption that x is a positive real variable, and does the replacement.

In[8]:= **PowerExpand[Sqrt[x^2]]**

Out[8]= x

+■ 1.5.13 Mathematical Notation in Notebooks

If you use the notebook front end for *Mathematica*, then you can enter some of the operations discussed in this section in special ways.

$\displaystyle\sum_{i=imin}^{imax} f$	Sum[f, {i, $imin$, $imax$}]	sum
$\displaystyle\prod_{i=imin}^{imax} f$	Product[f, {i, $imin$, $imax$}]	product
$\displaystyle\int f\,dx$	Integrate[f, x]	indefinite integral
$\displaystyle\int_{xmin}^{xmax} f\,dx$	Integrate[f, {x, $xmin$, $xmax$}]	definite integral
$\partial_x f$	D[f, x]	partial derivative
$\partial_{x,y} f$	D[f, x, y]	multivariate partial derivative

Special and ordinary ways to enter mathematical operations in notebooks.

This shows part of the standard palette for entering mathematical operations. When you press a button in the palette, the form shown in the button is inserted into your notebook, with the black square replaced by whatever you had selected in the notebook.

ESC sum ESC	summation sign $\sum$	
ESC prod ESC	product sign $\prod$	
ESC int ESC	integral sign $\int$	
ESC dd ESC	special differential $\mathbb{d}$ for use in integrals	
ESC pd ESC	partial derivative ∂	

CTRL _ or CTRL -	move to the subscript position or lower limit of an integral	
CTRL ^ or CTRL 6	move to the superscript position or upper limit of an integral	
CTRL + or CTRL =	move to the underscript position or lower limit of a sum or product	
CTRL & or CTRL 7	move to the overscript position or upper limit of a sum or product	

CTRL % or CTRL 5	switch between upper and lower positions	
CTRL ⎵ (CONTROL-SPACE)	return from upper or lower positions	

Ways to enter special notations on a standard English-language keyboard.

You can enter an integral like this. Be sure to use the special differential $\mathbb{d}$ entered as ESC dd ESC, not just an ordinary d.

$$In[1]:= \int x^n \, \mathbb{d}x$$

$$Out[1]= \frac{x^{1+n}}{1+n}$$

Here is the actual key sequence you type to get the input.

$$In[2]:= \text{ESC int ESC } x \text{ CTRL } \hat{\ } \text{ n CTRL } \textbackslash\_\ \text{ ESC dd ESC } x$$

$$Out[2]= \frac{x^{1+n}}{1+n}$$

1.6 Numerical Mathematics

■ 1.6.1 Basic Operations

Exact symbolic results are usually very desirable when they can be found. In many calculations, however, it is not possible to get symbolic results. In such cases, you must resort to numerical methods.

N[*expr*]	numerical value of an expression (see Section 1.1)
NIntegrate[*f*, {*x*, *xmin*, *xmax*}]	numerical approximation to $\int_{xmin}^{xmax} f \, dx$
NSum[*f*, {*i*, *imin*, Infinity}]	numerical approximation to $\sum_{imin}^{\infty} f$
NSolve[*lhs*==*rhs*, *x*]	numerical approximation to the solutions of a polynomial equation
FindRoot[*lhs*==*rhs*, {*x*, x_0}]	search for a numerical solution to an equation, starting with $x = x_0$
FindMinimum[*f*, {*x*, x_0}]	search for a minimum of *f*, starting with $x = x_0$

Basic numerical operations.

Mathematica maintains this expression in an exact, symbolic, form.	`In[1]:= (3 + Sqrt[2])^3` $Out[1]= \left(3 + \sqrt{2}\right)^3$
You can even use standard symbolic operations on it.	`In[2]:= Expand[ % ]` $Out[2]= 45 + 29\sqrt{2}$
N[*expr*] gives you a numerical approximation.	`In[3]:= N[ % ]` $Out[3]= 86.0122$

Functions such as Integrate always try to get exact results for computations. When they cannot get exact results, they typically return unevaluated. You can then find numerical approximations by explicitly applying N. Functions such as NIntegrate do the calculations numerically from the start, without first trying to get an exact result.

There is no exact formula for this integral, so *Mathematica* returns it unevaluated.	`In[4]:= Integrate[Sin[Sin[x]], {x, 1, 2}]` $Out[4]= \int_{1}^{2} Sin[Sin[x]] dx$
You can use N to get an approximate numerical result.	`In[5]:= N[ % ]` $Out[5]= 0.81645$

NIntegrate does the integral numerically from the start.

`In[6]:= NIntegrate[Sin[Sin[x]], {x, 1, 2}]`

`Out[6]= 0.81645`

■ 1.6.2 Numerical Sums, Products and Integrals

`NSum[`*f*`, {`*i*`,` *imin*`, Infinity}]`	numerical approximation to $\sum_{imin}^{\infty} f$
`NProduct[`*f*`, {`*i*`,` *imin*`, Infinity}]`	numerical approximation to $\prod_{imin}^{\infty} f$
`NIntegrate[`*f*`, {`*x*`,` *xmin*`,` *xmax*`}]`	numerical approximation to $\int_{xmin}^{xmax} f\,dx$
`NIntegrate[`*f*`, {`*x*`,` *xmin*`,` *xmax*`}, {`*y*`,` *ymin*`,` *ymax*`}]`	the multiple integral $\int_{xmin}^{xmax} dx \int_{ymin}^{ymax} dy\, f$

Numerical sums, products and integrals.

Here is a numerical approximation to $\sum_{i=1}^{\infty} \frac{1}{i^3}$.

`In[1]:= NSum[1/i^3, {i, 1, Infinity}]`

`Out[1]= 1.20206`

NIntegrate can handle singularities at the end points of the integration region.

`In[2]:= NIntegrate[1/Sqrt[x (1-x)], {x, 0, 1}]`

`Out[2]= 3.14159`

You can do numerical integrals over infinite regions.

`In[3]:= NIntegrate[Exp[-x^2], {x, -Infinity, Infinity}]`

`Out[3]= 1.77245`

Here is a double integral over a triangular domain. Note the order in which the variables are given.

`In[4]:= NIntegrate[ Sin[x y], {x, 0, 1}, {y, 0, x} ]`

`Out[4]= 0.119906`

■ 1.6.3 Numerical Equation Solving

`NSolve[`*lhs*`==`*rhs*`,` *x*`]`	solve a polynomial equation numerically
`NSolve[{`*lhs*$_1$`==`*rhs*$_1$`,` *lhs*$_2$`==`*rhs*$_2$`, ... }, {`*x*`,` *y*`, ... }]`	solve a system of polynomial equations numerically
`FindRoot[`*lhs*`==`*rhs*`, {`*x*`,` *x*$_0$`}]`	search for a numerical solution to an equation, starting at $x = x_0$
`FindRoot[{`*lhs*$_1$`==`*rhs*$_1$`,` *lhs*$_2$`==`*rhs*$_2$`, ... }, {`*x*`,` *x*$_0$`}, {`*y*`,` *y*$_0$`}, ... ]`	search for numerical solutions to simultaneous equations

Numerical root finding and minimization.

NSolve gives you numerical approximations to all the roots of a polynomial equation.

```
In[1]:= NSolve[ x^5 + x + 1 == 0, x ]
Out[1]= {{x → -0.754878}, {x → -0.5 - 0.866025 I},
          {x → -0.5 + 0.866025 I}, {x → 0.877439 - 0.744862 I},
          {x → 0.877439 + 0.744862 I}}
```

You can also use NSolve to solve sets of simultaneous equations numerically.

```
In[2]:= NSolve[{x + y == 2, x - 3 y + z == 3, x - y + z == 0},
                {x, y, z}]
Out[2]= {{x → 3.5, y → -1.5, z → -5.}}
```

If your equations involve only linear functions or polynomials, then you can use NSolve to get numerical approximations to all the solutions. However, when your equations involve more complicated functions, there is in general no systematic procedure for finding all solutions, even numerically. In such cases, you can use FindRoot to search for solutions. You have to give FindRoot a place to start its search.

This searches for a numerical solution, starting at $x = 1$.

```
In[3]:= FindRoot[ 3 Cos[x] == Log[x], {x, 1} ]
Out[3]= {x → 1.44726}
```

The equation has several solutions. If you start at a different x, FindRoot may return a different solution.

```
In[4]:= FindRoot[ 3 Cos[x] == Log[x], {x, 10} ]
Out[4]= {x → 13.1064}
```

You can search for solutions to sets of equations. Here the solution involves complex numbers.

```
In[5]:= FindRoot[{x==Log[y], y==Log[x]}, {x, I}, {y, 2}]
Out[5]= {x → 0.318131 + 1.33724 I, y → 0.318131 + 1.33724 I}
```

■ 1.6.4 Numerical Differential Equations

> NDSolve[*eqns*, *y*, {*x*, *xmin*, *xmax*}]
>   solve numerically for the function *y*, with the independent variable *x* in the range *xmin* to *xmax*
>
> NDSolve[*eqns*, {*y*$_1$, *y*$_2$, ... }, {*x*, *xmin*, *xmax*}]
>   solve a system of equations for the *y*$_i$

Numerical solution of ordinary differential equations.

This generates a numerical solution to the equation $y'(x) = y(x)$ with $0 < x < 2$. The result is given in terms of an InterpolatingFunction.

```
In[1]:= NDSolve[{y'[x] == y[x], y[0] == 1}, y, {x, 0, 2}]
Out[1]= {{y → InterpolatingFunction[{{0., 2.}}, <>]}}
```

Here is the value of $y(1.5)$.

```
In[2]:= y[1.5] /. %
Out[2]= {4.48171}
```

With an algebraic equation such as $x^2 + 3x + 1 = 0$, each solution for x is simply a single number. For a differential equation, however, the solution is a *function*, rather than a single number. For example, in the equation $y'(x) = y(x)$, you want to get an approximation to the function $y(x)$ as the independent variable x varies over some range.

Mathematica represents numerical approximations to functions as InterpolatingFunction objects. These objects are functions which, when applied to a particular x, return the approximate value of $y(x)$ at that point. The InterpolatingFunction effectively stores a table of values for $y(x_i)$, then interpolates this table to find an approximation to $y(x)$ at the particular x you request.

$y[x]$ /. *solution*	use the list of rules for the function y to get values for $y[x]$
InterpolatingFunction[*data*][x]	
	evaluate an interpolated function at the point x
Plot[Evaluate[$y[x]$ /. *solution*], {x, *xmin*, *xmax*}]	
	plot the solution to a differential equation

Using results from NDSolve.

This solves a system of two coupled differential equations.

```
In[3]:= NDSolve[ {y'[x] == z[x], z'[x] == -y[x], y[0] == 0,
                  z[0] == 1}, {y, z}, {x, 0, Pi} ]

Out[3]= {{y → InterpolatingFunction[{{0., 3.14159}}, <>],
          z → InterpolatingFunction[{{0., 3.14159}}, <>]}}
```

Here is the value of z[2] found from the solution.

```
In[4]:= z[2] /. %
Out[4]= {-0.416147}
```

Here is a plot of the solution for z[x] found on line 3. Plot is discussed in Section 1.9.1.

```
In[5]:= Plot[Evaluate[z[x] /. %3], {x, 0, Pi}]
```

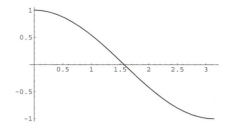

■ 1.6.5 Numerical Optimization

`ConstrainedMin[`*f*`, `*ineqs*`, {`*x*`, `*y*`, ... }]`	minimize the linear function *f* subject to the linear constraints *ineqs*
`FindMinimum[`*f*`, {`*x*`, `x_0`}]`	search for a local minimum of the arbitrary function *f*, starting at $x = x_0$
`FindMinimum[`*f*`, {`*x*`, `x_0`}, {`*y*`, `y_0`}, ... ]`	search for a local minimum in several variables

Numerical minimization functions.

The function `ConstrainedMin` allows you to solve linear programming problems in which you give a linear function *f*, then find its minimum over a domain specified by a list of linear inequalities. `ConstrainedMin` assumes that all the variables you give are constrained to be non-negative.

This gives the minimum value of $x - y - z$ in the specified domain, followed by the values of *x*, *y* and *z* at which the value is attained.

```
In[1]:= ConstrainedMin[x - y - z, {y + z < 3, x > 7},
                                            {x, y, z}]

Out[1]= {4, {x → 7, y → 3, z → 0}}
```

When the function you want to minimize is linear, you can always use `ConstrainedMin` to find its global minimum. For more complicated functions, however, there is usually no systematic way to find a global minimum. Instead, you can use `FindMinimum` to search for local minima.

This searches for a local minimum of $x \cos(x)$, starting at $x = 1$.

```
In[2]:= FindMinimum[x Cos[x], {x, 1}]

Out[2]= {-3.28837, {x → 3.42562}}
```

With a different starting point, you may reach a different local minimum.

```
In[3]:= FindMinimum[x Cos[x], {x, 10}]

Out[3]= {-9.47729, {x → 9.52933}}
```

This finds a minimum of $\sin(xy)$.

```
In[4]:= FindMinimum[Sin[x y], {x, 2}, {y, 2}]

Out[4]= {-1., {x → 2.1708, y → 2.1708}}
```

■ 1.6.6 Manipulating Numerical Data

When you have numerical data, it is often convenient to find a simple formula that approximates it. For example, you can try to "fit" a line or curve through the points in your data.

Fit[{y_1, y_2, ... }, {f_1, f_2, ... }, x]
          fit the values y_n to a linear combination of functions f_i

Fit[{{x_1, y_1}, {x_2, y_2}, ... }, {f_1, f_2, ... }, x]
          fit the points (x_n, y_n) to a linear combination of the f_i

---

Functions for fitting curves.

This generates a table of the numerical values of the exponential function. Table will be discussed in Section 1.8.2.

```
In[1]:= data = Table[ Exp[x/5.] , {x, 7}]
Out[1]= {1.2214, 1.49182, 1.82212, 2.22554,
            2.71828, 3.32012, 4.0552}
```

This finds a least-squares fit to data of the form $c_1 + c_2 x + c_3 x^2$. The elements of data are assumed to correspond to values 1, 2, ... of x.

```
In[2]:= Fit[data, {1, x, x^2}, x]
Out[2]= 1.09428 + 0.0986337 x + 0.0459482 x^2
```

This finds a fit of the form $c_1 + c_2 x + c_3 x^3 + c_4 x^5$.

```
In[3]:= Fit[data, {1, x, x^3, x^5}, x]
Out[3]= 0.96806 + 0.246829 x + 0.00428281 x^3 - 6.57948×10^-6 x^5
```

This gives a table of x, y pairs.

```
In[4]:= data = Table[ {x, Exp[Sin[x]]} , {x, 0., 1., 0.2}]
Out[4]= {{0., 1.}, {0.2, 1.21978}, {0.4, 1.47612},
            {0.6, 1.75882}, {0.8, 2.04901}, {1., 2.31978}}
```

This finds a fit to the new data, of the form $c_1 + c_2 \sin(x) + c_3 \sin(2x)$.

```
In[5]:= Fit[%, {1, Sin[x], Sin[2x]}, x]
Out[5]= 0.989559 + 2.04199 Sin[x] - 0.418176 Sin[2x]
```

One common way of picking out "signals" in numerical data is to find the *Fourier transform*, or frequency spectrum, of the data.

Fourier[*data*]	numerical Fourier transform
InverseFourier[*data*]	inverse Fourier transform

Fourier transforms.

Here is a simple square pulse.

```
In[6]:= data = {1, 1, 1, 1, -1, -1, -1, -1}
Out[6]= {1, 1, 1, 1, -1, -1, -1, -1}
```

This takes the Fourier transform of the pulse.

```
In[7]:= Fourier[data]
Out[7]= {0. + 0. I, 0.707107 + 1.70711 I,
            0. + 0. I, 0.707107 + 0.292893 I,
            0. + 0. I, 0.707107 - 0.292893 I,
            0. + 0. I, 0.707107 - 1.70711 I}
```

Note that the `Fourier` function in *Mathematica* is defined with the sign convention typically used in the physical sciences—opposite to the one often used in electrical engineering. Section 3.8.3 gives more details.

■ 1.6.7 Statistics Packages

The standard set of packages distributed with *Mathematica* includes several for doing statistical analyses of data.

`Statistics`DescriptiveStatistics``	descriptive statistics functions
`Statistics`MultivariateDescriptiveStatistics``	
	multivariate descriptive statistics functions
`Statistics`ContinuousDistributions``	properties of continuous statistical distributions
`Statistics`DiscreteDistributions``	properties of discrete statistical distributions
`Statistics`HypothesisTests``	hypothesis tests based on the normal distribution
`Statistics`ConfidenceIntervals``	confidence intervals derived from the normal distribution
`Statistics`MultinormalDistribution``	properties of distributions based on the multivariate normal distribution
`Statistics`LinearRegression``	linear regression analysis
`Statistics`NonlinearFit``	nonlinear fitting of data
`Statistics`DataSmoothing``	smoothing of data
`Statistics`DataManipulation``	utilities for data manipulation

Some standard statistical analysis packages.

```
<<Statistics`DescriptiveStatistics`
```
load the descriptive statistics package

Mean[*data*]	mean (average value)
Median[*data*]	median (central value)
Variance[*data*]	variance
StandardDeviation[*data*]	standard deviation

LocationReport[*data*], DispersionReport[*data*], ShapeReport[*data*]
give lists of quantities characterizing the statistical distribution of data

Basic descriptive statistics.

This loads the descriptive statistics package. In some versions of *Mathematica*, you may not need to load this package explicitly.

```
In[1]:= <<Statistics`DescriptiveStatistics`
```

Here is some "data".

```
In[2]:= data = {4.3, 7.2, 8.4, 5.8, 9.2, 3.9}
Out[2]= {4.3, 7.2, 8.4, 5.8, 9.2, 3.9}
```

This gives the mean of your data.

```
In[3]:= Mean[data]
Out[3]= 6.46667
```

Here is the variance.

```
In[4]:= Variance[data]
Out[4]= 4.69467
```

This gives a list of rules for various quantities that characterize the dispersion of your data.

```
In[5]:= DispersionReport[data]
Out[5]= {Variance → 4.69467,
         StandardDeviation → 2.16672, SampleRange → 5.3,
         MeanDeviation → 1.8, MedianDeviation → 2.05,
         QuartileDeviation → 2.05}
```

1.7 Functions and Programs

■ 1.7.1 Defining Functions

In this part of the book, we have seen many examples of functions that are built into *Mathematica*. In this section, we discuss how you can add your own simple functions to *Mathematica*. Part 2 will describe in much greater detail the mechanisms for adding functions to *Mathematica*.

As a first example, consider adding a function called f which squares its argument. The *Mathematica* command to define this function is f[x_] := x^2. The _ (referred to as "blank") on the left-hand side is very important; what it means will be discussed below. For now, just remember to put a _ on the left-hand side, but not on the right-hand side, of your definition.

This defines the function f. Notice the _ on the left-hand side.	$In[1]:=$ **f[x_] := x^2**
f squares its argument.	$In[2]:=$ **f[a+1]**
	$Out[2]=$ $(1+a)^2$
The argument can be a number.	$In[3]:=$ **f[4]**
	$Out[3]=$ 16
Or it can be a more complicated expression.	$In[4]:=$ **f[3x + x^2]**
	$Out[4]=$ $(3x+x^2)^2$
You can use f in a calculation.	$In[5]:=$ **Expand[f[(x+1+y)]]**
	$Out[5]=$ $1+2x+x^2+2y+2xy+y^2$
This shows the definition you made for f.	$In[6]:=$ **?f**
	Global`f
	f[x_] := x^2

f[x_] := x^2	define the function f
?f	show the definition of *f*
Clear[*f*]	clear all definitions for *f*

Defining a function in *Mathematica*.

The names like f that you use for functions in *Mathematica* are just symbols. Because of this, you should make sure to avoid using names that begin with capital letters, to prevent confusion with built-in *Mathematica* functions. You should also make sure that you have not used the names for anything else earlier in your session.

Mathematica functions can have any number of arguments.	`In[7]:= hump[x_, xmax_] := (x - xmax)^2 / xmax`
You can use the hump function just as you would any of the built-in functions.	`In[8]:= 2 + hump[x, 3.5]` $Out[8]= 2 + 0.285714 (-3.5 + x)^2$
This gives a new definition for hump, which overwrites the previous one.	`In[9]:= hump[x_, xmax_] := (x - xmax)^4`
The new definition is displayed.	`In[10]:= ?hump` `Global`hump` `hump[x_, xmax_] := (x - xmax)^4`
This clears all definitions for hump.	`In[11]:= Clear[hump]`

When you have finished with a particular function, it is always a good idea to clear definitions you have made for it. If you do not do this, then you will run into trouble if you try to use the same function for a different purpose later in your *Mathematica* session. You can clear all definitions you have made for a function or symbol *f* by using `Clear[f]`.

■ 1.7.2 Functions as Procedures

In many kinds of calculations, you may find yourself typing the same input to *Mathematica* over and over again. You can save yourself a lot of typing by defining a *function* that contains your input commands.

This constructs a product of three terms, and expands out the result.	`In[1]:= Expand[ Product[x + i, {i, 3}] ]` $Out[1]= 6 + 11 x + 6 x^2 + x^3$
This does the same thing, but with four terms.	`In[2]:= Expand[ Product[x + i, {i, 4}] ]` $Out[2]= 24 + 50 x + 35 x^2 + 10 x^3 + x^4$
This defines a function exprod which constructs a product of *n* terms, then expands it out.	`In[3]:= exprod[n_] := Expand[ Product[ x + i, {i, 1, n} ] ]`
Every time you use the function, it will execute the Product and Expand operations.	`In[4]:= exprod[5]` $Out[4]= 120 + 274 x + 225 x^2 + 85 x^3 + 15 x^4 + x^5$

The functions you define in *Mathematica* are essentially procedures that execute the commands you give. You can have several steps in your procedures, separated by semicolons.

The result you get from the whole function is simply the last expression in the procedure. Notice that you have to put parentheses around the procedure when you define it like this.	`In[5]:= cex[n_, i_] := ( t = exprod[n]; Coefficient[t, x^i] )`

This "runs" the procedure.   *In[6]:=* **cex[5, 3]**

                                              Out[6]= 85

$expr_1$; $expr_2$; ...	a sequence of expressions to evaluate
Module[{a, b, ... }, *proc*]	a procedure with local variables *a, b, ...*

Constructing procedures.

When you write procedures in *Mathematica*, it is usually a good idea to make variables you use inside the procedures *local*, so that they do not interfere with things outside the procedures. You can do this by setting up your procedures as *modules*, in which you give a list of variables to be treated as local.

The function cex defined above is not a module, so the value of t "escapes", and exists even after the function returns.

In[7]:= **t**

Out[7]= $120 + 274 x + 225 x^2 + 85 x^3 + 15 x^4 + x^5$

This function is defined as a module with local variable u.

In[8]:= **ncex[n_, i_] :=**
Module[{u}, u = exprod[n]; Coefficient[u, x^i]]

The function gives the same result as before.

In[9]:= **ncex[5, 3]**

Out[9]= 85

Now, however, the value of u does not escape from the function.

In[10]:= **u**

Out[10]= u

■ 1.7.3 Repetitive Operations

In using *Mathematica*, you sometimes need to repeat an operation many times. There are many ways to do this. Often the most natural is in fact to set up a structure such as a list with many elements, and then apply your operation to each of the elements.

Another approach is to use the *Mathematica* function Do, which works much like the iteration constructs in languages such as C and Fortran. Do uses the standard *Mathematica* iterator notation introduced for Sum and **Product** in Section 1.5.4.

Do[*expr*, {*i*, *imax*}]	evaluate *expr* with *i* running from 1 to *imax*
Do[*expr*, {*i*, *imin*, *imax*, *di*}]	evaluate *expr* with *i* running from *imin* to *imax* in steps of *di*
Print[*expr*]	print *expr*
Table[*expr*, {*i*, *imax*}]	make a list of the values of *expr* with *i* running from 1 to *imax*

Implementing repetitive operations.

This prints out the values of the first five factorials.

```
In[1]:= Do[ Print[i!], {i, 5} ]
1
2
6
24
120
```

It is often more useful to have a list of results, which you can then manipulate further.

```
In[2]:= Table[ i!, {i, 5} ]
Out[2]= {1, 2, 6, 24, 120}
```

If you do not give an iteration variable, *Mathematica* simply repeats the operation you have specified, without changing anything.

```
In[3]:= r = 1; Do[ r = 1/(1 + r), {100} ]; r
```

$$Out[3]= \frac{573147844013817084101}{927372692193078999176}$$

■ 1.7.4 Transformation Rules for Functions

Section 1.4.2 discussed how you can use transformation rules of the form $x \rightarrow value$ to replace symbols by values. The notion of transformation rules in *Mathematica* is, however, quite general. You can set up transformation rules not only for symbols, but for any *Mathematica* expression.

Applying the transformation rule x -> 3 replaces x by 3.

```
In[1]:= 1 + f[x] + f[y] /. x -> 3
Out[1]= 1 + f[3] + f[y]
```

You can also use a transformation rule for f[x]. This rule does not affect f[y].

```
In[2]:= 1 + f[x] + f[y] /. f[x] -> p
Out[2]= 1 + p + f[y]
```

f[t_] is a *pattern* that stands for f with any argument.

```
In[3]:= 1 + f[x] + f[y] /. f[t_] -> t^2
Out[3]= 1 + x² + y²
```

Probably the most powerful aspect of transformation rules in *Mathematica* is that they can involve not only literal expressions, but also *patterns*. A pattern is an expression such as f[t_] which contains a blank (underscore). The blank can stand for any expression. Thus, a transformation rule for f[t_] specifies how the function f with *any* argument should be transformed. Notice that, in contrast, a transformation rule for f[x] without a blank, specifies only how the literal expression f[x] should be transformed, and does not, for example, say anything about the transformation of f[y].

When you give a function definition such as f[t_] := t^2, all you are doing is telling *Mathematica* to automatically apply the transformation rule f[t_] -> t^2 whenever possible.

You can set up transformation rules for expressions of any form.	*In[4]:=* **f[a b] + f[c d] /. f[x_ y_] -> f[x] + f[y]**
	Out[4]= f[a] + f[b] + f[c] + f[d]
This uses a transformation rule for x^p_.	*In[5]:=* **1 + x^2 + x^4 /. x^p_ -> f[p]**
	Out[5]= 1 + f[2] + f[4]

Sections 2.3 and 2.4 will explain in detail how to set up patterns and transformation rules for any kind of expression. Suffice it to say here that in *Mathematica* all expressions have a definite symbolic structure; transformation rules allow you to transform parts of that structure.

1.8 Lists

■ 1.8.1 Collecting Objects Together

We first encountered lists in Section 1.2.3 as a way of collecting numbers together. In this section, we shall see many different ways to use lists. You will find that lists are some of the most flexible and powerful objects in *Mathematica*. You will see that lists in *Mathematica* represent generalizations of several standard concepts in mathematics and computer science.

At a basic level, what a *Mathematica* list essentially does is to provide a way for you to collect together several expressions of any kind.

Here is a list of numbers.	`In[1]:= {2, 3, 4}` `Out[1]= {2, 3, 4}`
This gives a list of symbolic expressions.	`In[2]:= x^% - 1` `Out[2]= {-1 + x^2, -1 + x^3, -1 + x^4}`
You can differentiate these expressions.	`In[3]:= D[%, x]` `Out[3]= {2x, 3x^2, 4x^3}`
And then you can find values when x is replaced with 3.	`In[4]:= % /. x -> 3` `Out[4]= {6, 27, 108}`

The mathematical functions that are built into *Mathematica* are mostly set up to be "listable" so that they act separately on each element of a list. This is, however, not true of all functions in *Mathematica*. Unless you set it up specially, a new function f that you introduce will treat lists just as single objects. Sections 2.2.4 and 2.2.10 will describe how you can use Map and Thread to apply a function like this separately to each element in a list.

■ 1.8.2 Making Tables of Values

You can use lists as tables of values. You can generate the tables, for example, by evaluating an expression for a sequence of different parameter values.

This gives a table of the values of i^2, with *i* running from 1 to 6.	`In[1]:= Table[i^2, {i, 6}]` `Out[1]= {1, 4, 9, 16, 25, 36}`
Here is a table of $\sin(n/5)$ for *n* from 0 to 4.	`In[2]:= Table[Sin[n/5], {n, 0, 4}]` `Out[2]= {0, Sin[\frac{1}{5}], Sin[\frac{2}{5}], Sin[\frac{3}{5}], Sin[\frac{4}{5}]}`
This gives the numerical values.	`In[3]:= N[%]` `Out[3]= {0, 0.198669, 0.389418, 0.564642, 0.717356}`

You can also make tables of formulas.

In[4]:= **Table[x^i + 2i, {i, 5}]**

Out[4]= $\{2 + x, 4 + x^2, 6 + x^3, 8 + x^4, 10 + x^5\}$

Table uses exactly the same iterator notation as the functions Sum and Product, which were discussed in Section 1.5.4.

In[5]:= **Product[x^i + 2i, {i, 5}]**

Out[5]= $(2 + x)(4 + x^2)(6 + x^3)(8 + x^4)(10 + x^5)$

This makes a table with values of x running from 0 to 1 in steps of 0.25.

In[6]:= **Table[Sqrt[x], {x, 0, 1, 0.25}]**

Out[6]= $\{0, 0.5, 0.707107, 0.866025, 1.\}$

You can perform other operations on the lists you get from Table.

In[7]:= **%^2 + 3**

Out[7]= $\{3, 3.25, 3.5, 3.75, 4.\}$

TableForm displays lists in a "tabular" format. Notice that both words in the name TableForm begin with capital letters.

In[8]:= **% // TableForm**

```
                          3
                          3.25
Out[8]//TableForm=        3.5
                          3.75
                          4.
```

All the examples so far have been of tables obtained by varying a single parameter. You can also make tables that involve several parameters. These multidimensional tables are specified using the standard *Mathematica* iterator notation, discussed in Section 1.5.4.

This makes a table of $x^i + y^j$ with *i* running from 1 to 3 and *j* running from 1 to 2.

In[9]:= **Table[x^i + y^j, {i, 3}, {j, 2}]**

Out[9]= $\{\{x + y, x + y^2\}, \{x^2 + y, x^2 + y^2\}, \{x^3 + y, x^3 + y^2\}\}$

The table in this example is a *list of lists*. The elements of the outer list correspond to successive values of *i*. The elements of each inner list correspond to successive values of *j*, with *i* fixed.

Sometimes you may want to generate a table by evaluating a particular expression many times, without incrementing any variables.

This creates a list containing four copies of the symbol x.

In[10]:= **Table[x, {4}]**

Out[10]= $\{x, x, x, x\}$

This gives a list of four pseudorandom numbers. Table re-evaluates Random[ ] for each element in the list, so that you get a different pseudorandom number.

In[11]:= **Table[Random[ ], {4}]**

Out[11]= $\{0.0560708, 0.6303, 0.359894, 0.871377\}$

Table[f, {imax}]	give a list of *imax* values of f
Table[f, {i, imax}]	give a list of the values of f as i runs from 1 to *imax*
Table[f, {i, imin, imax}]	give a list of values with i running from *imin* to *imax*
Table[f, {i, imin, imax, di}]	use steps of *di*
Table[f, {i, imin, imax}, {j, jmin, jmax}, ...]	generate a multidimensional table
TableForm[list]	display a list in tabular form

Functions for generating tables.

You can use the operations discussed in Section 1.2.4 to extract elements of the table.

This creates a 2×2 table, and gives it the name m.

```
In[12]:= m = Table[i - j, {i, 2}, {j, 2}]
Out[12]= {{0, -1}, {1, 0}}
```

This extracts the first sublist from the list of lists that makes up the table.

```
In[13]:= m[[1]]
Out[13]= {0, -1}
```

This extracts the second element of that sublist.

```
In[14]:= %[[2]]
Out[14]= -1
```

This does the two operations together.

```
In[15]:= m[[1,2]]
Out[15]= -1
```

This displays m in a "tabular" form.

```
In[16]:= TableForm[m]

Out[16]//TableForm=   0    -1
                      1     0
```

t[[i]] or Part[t, i]	give the ith sublist in t (also input as t[[i]])
t[[{i_1, i_2, ... }]] or Part[t, {i_1, i_2, ... }]	give a list of the i_1th, i_2th, ... parts of t
t[[i, j, ...]] or Part[t, i, j, ...]	give the part of t corresponding to t[[i]][[j]] ...

Ways to extract parts of tables.

As we mentioned in Section 1.2.4, you can think of lists in *Mathematica* as being analogous to "arrays". Lists of lists are then like two-dimensional arrays. When you lay them out in a tabular form, the two indices of each element are like its x and y coordinates.

You can use `Table` to generate arrays with any number of dimensions.

This generates a three-dimensional $2 \times 2 \times 2$ array. It is a list of lists of lists.	`In[17]:= Table[i j^2 k^3, {i, 2}, {j, 2}, {k, 2}]` `Out[17]= {{{1, 8}, {4, 32}}, {{2, 16}, {8, 64}}}`

■ 1.8.3 Vectors and Matrices

Vectors and matrices in *Mathematica* are simply represented by lists and by lists of lists, respectively.

$$\{a,\ b,\ c\} \quad \text{vector } (a, b, c)$$

$$\{\{a,\ b\},\ \{c,\ d\}\} \quad \text{matrix } \begin{pmatrix} a & b \\ c & d \end{pmatrix}$$

The representation of vectors and matrices by lists.

This is a 2×2 matrix.	`In[1]:= m = {{a, b}, {c, d}}` `Out[1]= {{a, b}, {c, d}}`
Here is the first row.	`In[2]:= m[[1]]` `Out[2]= {a, b}`
Here is the element m_{12}.	`In[3]:= m[[1,2]]` `Out[3]= b`
This is a two-component vector.	`In[4]:= v = {x, y}` `Out[4]= {x, y}`
The objects p and q are treated as scalars.	`In[5]:= p v + q` `Out[5]= {q + px, q + py}`
Vectors are added component by component.	`In[6]:= v + {xp, yp} + {xpp, ypp}` `Out[6]= {x + xp + xpp, y + yp + ypp}`
This takes the dot ("scalar") product of two vectors.	`In[7]:= {x, y} . {xp, yp}` `Out[7]= x xp + y yp`
You can also multiply a matrix by a vector.	`In[8]:= m . v` `Out[8]= {a x + b y, c x + d y}`
Or a matrix by a matrix.	`In[9]:= m . m` `Out[9]= {{a² + bc, ab + bd}, {ac + cd, bc + d²}}`

Or a vector by a matrix.

$In[10]:=$ **v . m**

$Out[10]=$ {a x + c y, b x + d y}

This combination makes a scalar.

$In[11]:=$ **v . m . v**

$Out[11]=$ x (a x + c y) + y (b x + d y)

Because of the way *Mathematica* uses lists to represent vectors and matrices, you never have to distinguish between "row" and "column" vectors.

Table[f, {i, n}]	build a length-n vector by evaluating f with $i = 1, 2, \ldots, n$
Array[a, n]	build a length-n vector of the form {a[1], a[2], ... }
Range[n]	create the list {1, 2, 3, ... , n}
Range[n_1, n_2]	create the list {n_1, n_1+1, ... , n_2}
Range[n_1, n_2, dn]	create the list {n_1, n_1+dn, ... , n_2}
list[[i]] or Part[*list*, i]	give the ith element in the vector *list*
Length[*list*]	give the number of elements in *list*
ColumnForm[*list*]	display the elements of *list* in a column
$c\ v$	multiply by a scalar
a . b	vector dot product
Cross[a, b]	vector cross product (also input as $a \times b$)

Functions for vectors.

Table[f, {i, m}, {j, n}]	build an $m \times n$ matrix by evaluating f with i ranging from 1 to m and j ranging from 1 to n
Array[a, {m, n}]	build an $m \times n$ matrix with i, j^{th} element a[i, j]
IdentityMatrix[n]	generate an $n \times n$ identity matrix
DiagonalMatrix[*list*]	generate a square matrix with the elements in *list* on the diagonal
list[[i]] or Part[*list*, i]	give the ith row in the matrix *list*
list[[i, j]] or Part[*list*, i, j]	give the i, j^{th} element in matrix *list*
Dimensions[*list*]	give the dimensions of a matrix represented by *list*
MatrixForm[*list*]	display *list* in matrix form

Functions for matrices.

This builds a 3×3 matrix s with elements $s_{ij} = i + j$.

```
In[12]:= s = Table[i+j, {i, 3}, {j, 3}]
Out[12]= {{2, 3, 4}, {3, 4, 5}, {4, 5, 6}}
```

This displays s in standard two-dimensional matrix format.

```
In[13]:= MatrixForm[s]
```
$$Out[13]//MatrixForm= \begin{pmatrix} 2 & 3 & 4 \\ 3 & 4 & 5 \\ 4 & 5 & 6 \end{pmatrix}$$

This gives a vector with symbolic elements. You can use this in deriving general formulas that are valid with any choice of vector components.

```
In[14]:= Array[a, 4]
Out[14]= {a[1], a[2], a[3], a[4]}
```

This gives a 3×2 matrix with symbolic elements. Section 2.2.6 will discuss how you can produce other kinds of elements with **Array**.

```
In[15]:= Array[p, {3, 2}]
Out[15]= {{p[1, 1], p[1, 2]}, {p[2, 1], p[2, 2]},
          {p[3, 1], p[3, 2]}}
```

Here are the dimensions of the matrix on the previous line.

```
In[16]:= Dimensions[%]
Out[16]= {3, 2}
```

This generates a 3×3 diagonal matrix.

```
In[17]:= DiagonalMatrix[{a, b, c}]
Out[17]= {{a, 0, 0}, {0, b, 0}, {0, 0, c}}
```

$c\ m$	multiply by a scalar
$a\ .\ b$	matrix product
Inverse[m]	matrix inverse
MatrixPower[m, n]	n^{th} power of a matrix
Det[m]	determinant
Transpose[m]	transpose
Eigenvalues[m]	eigenvalues
Eigenvectors[m]	eigenvectors
Eigenvalues[N[m]], Eigenvectors[N[m]]	
	numerical eigenvalues and eigenvectors

Some mathematical operations on matrices.

Here is the 2×2 matrix of symbolic variables that was defined above.

```
In[18]:= m
Out[18]= {{a, b}, {c, d}}
```

This gives its determinant.

In[19]:= **Det[m]**

Out[19]= $-bc + ad$

Here is the transpose of m.

In[20]:= **Transpose[m]**

Out[20]= {{a, c}, {b, d}}

This gives the inverse of m in symbolic form.

In[21]:= **Inverse[m]**

Out[21]= $\left\{\left\{\dfrac{d}{-bc+ad}, -\dfrac{b}{-bc+ad}\right\}, \left\{-\dfrac{c}{-bc+ad}, \dfrac{a}{-bc+ad}\right\}\right\}$

Here is a particular 3×3 rational matrix known as a "Hilbert matrix".

In[22]:= **h = Table[1/(i+j-1), {i, 3}, {j, 3}]**

Out[22]= $\left\{\left\{1, \dfrac{1}{2}, \dfrac{1}{3}\right\}, \left\{\dfrac{1}{2}, \dfrac{1}{3}, \dfrac{1}{4}\right\}, \left\{\dfrac{1}{3}, \dfrac{1}{4}, \dfrac{1}{5}\right\}\right\}$

This gives its inverse.

In[23]:= **Inverse[h]**

Out[23]= {{9, -36, 30}, {-36, 192, -180}, {30, -180, 180}}

Taking the dot product of the inverse with the original matrix gives the identity matrix.

In[24]:= **% . h**

Out[24]= {{1, 0, 0}, {0, 1, 0}, {0, 0, 1}}

Here is a 3×3 matrix.

In[25]:= **r = Table[i+j+1, {i, 3}, {j, 3}]**

Out[25]= {{3, 4, 5}, {4, 5, 6}, {5, 6, 7}}

Eigenvalues gives the eigenvalues of the matrix.

In[26]:= **Eigenvalues[r]**

Out[26]= $\left\{0, \dfrac{1}{2}\left(15 - \sqrt{249}\right), \dfrac{1}{2}\left(15 + \sqrt{249}\right)\right\}$

This gives a numerical approximation to the matrix.

In[27]:= **rn = N[r]**

Out[27]= {{3., 4., 5.}, {4., 5., 6.}, {5., 6., 7.}}

Here are numerical approximations to the eigenvalues.

In[28]:= **Eigenvalues[rn]**

Out[28]= {15.3899, -0.389867, 1.37205×10^{-15}}

Section 3.7 discusses other matrix operations that are built into *Mathematica*.

~■ 1.8.4 Getting Pieces of Lists

First[*list*]	the first element in *list*
Last[*list*]	the last element
Part[*list*, *n*] or *list*[[*n*]]	the nth element
Part[*list*, -*n*] or *list*[[-*n*]]	the nth element from the end
Part[*list*, {n_1, n_2, ... }] or *list*[[{n_1, n_2, ... }]]	the list of elements at positions n_1, n_2, ...

Picking out elements of lists.

We will use this list for the examples.

```
In[1]:= t = {a,b,c,d,e,f,g}
Out[1]= {a, b, c, d, e, f, g}
```

Here is the last element of t.

```
In[2]:= Last[t]
Out[2]= g
```

This gives the third element.

```
In[3]:= t[[3]]
Out[3]= c
```

This gives a list of the first and fourth elements.

```
In[4]:= t[[ {1, 4} ]]
Out[4]= {a, d}
```

Take[*list*, *n*]	the first *n* elements in *list*
Take[*list*, -*n*]	the last *n* elements
Take[*list*, {*m*, *n*}]	elements *m* through *n* (inclusive)
Rest[*list*]	*list* with its first element dropped
Drop[*list*, *n*]	*list* with its first *n* elements dropped
Drop[*list*, -*n*]	*list* with its last *n* elements dropped
Drop[*list*, {*m*, *n*}]	*list* with elements *m* through *n* dropped

Picking out sequences in lists.

This gives the first three elements of the list t defined above.

```
In[5]:= Take[t, 3]
Out[5]= {a, b, c}
```

This gives the last three elements.	*In[6]:=* **Take[t, -3]**
	Out[6]= {e, f, g}
This gives elements 2 through 5 inclusive.	*In[7]:=* **Take[t, {2, 5}]**
	Out[7]= {b, c, d, e}
This gives t with the first element dropped.	*In[8]:=* **Rest[t]**
	Out[8]= {b, c, d, e, f, g}
This gives t with its first three elements dropped.	*In[9]:=* **Drop[t, 3]**
	Out[9]= {d, e, f, g}
This gives t with only its third element dropped.	*In[10]:=* **Drop[t, {3, 3}]**
	Out[10]= {a, b, d, e, f, g}

Part[*list*, i, j, ...] or *list*[[i, j, ...]]
  the element *list*[[i]][[j]] ...

Part[*list*, {i_1, i_2, ... }, {j_1, j_2, ... }, ...] or *list*[[{i_1, i_2, ... }, {j_1, j_2, ... }, ...]]
  the list of elements obtained by picking out parts i_1, i_2, ...
  at the first level, etc.

Extracting parts of nested lists.

Here is a list of lists.	*In[11]:=* **t = {{a, b, c}, {d, e, f}}**
	Out[11]= {{a, b, c}, {d, e, f}}
This picks out the first sublist.	*In[12]:=* **t[[1]]**
	Out[12]= {a, b, c}
This picks out the second element in the first sublist.	*In[13]:=* **t[[1, 2]]**
	Out[13]= b
This is equivalent to t[[1, 2]], but is clumsier to write.	*In[14]:=* **t[[1]][[2]]**
	Out[14]= b
This gives a list containing two copies of the second part of t, followed by one copy of the first part.	*In[15]:=* **t[[{2, 2, 1}]]**
	Out[15]= {{d, e, f}, {d, e, f}, {a, b, c}}

For each of the parts picked out on the previous line, this gives a list of their second and third parts.

`In[16]:= t[[{2, 2, 1}, {2, 3}]]`

`Out[16]= {{e, f}, {e, f}, {b, c}}`

+ Extract[*list*, {*i*, *j*, ... }]	the element at position {*i*, *j*, ... } in *list*
+ Extract[*list*, {{*i*₁, *j*₁, ... }, {*i*₂, *j*₂, ... }, ... }]	

the list of elements at positions $\{i_1, j_1, \ldots\}$, $\{i_2, j_2, \ldots\}$, ...

Another way to extract parts of nested lists.

This extracts the element at position {2, 1} in t.

`In[17]:= Extract[t, {2, 1}]`

`Out[17]= d`

This extracts a list of three elements from t.

`In[18]:= Extract[t, {{1, 1}, {2, 2}, {2, 3}}]`

`Out[18]= {a, e, f}`

Section 2.1.5 will show how all the functions in this section can be generalized to work not only on lists, but on any *Mathematica* expressions.

The functions in this section allow you to pick out pieces that occur at particular positions in lists. Section 2.3.2 will show how you can use functions like `Select` and `Cases` to pick out elements of lists based not on their positions, but instead on their properties.

■ 1.8.5 Testing and Searching List Elements

Position[*list*, *form*]	the positions at which *form* occurs in *list*
Count[*list*, *form*]	the number of times *form* appears as an element of *list*
MemberQ[*list*, *form*]	test whether *form* is an element of *list*
FreeQ[*list*, *form*]	test whether *form* occurs nowhere in *list*

Testing and searching for elements of lists.

The previous section discussed how to extract pieces of lists based on their positions or indices. *Mathematica* also has functions that search and test for elements of lists, based on the values of those elements.

This gives a list of the positions at which a appears in the list.

`In[1]:= Position[{a, b, c, a, b}, a]`

`Out[1]= {{1}, {4}}`

Count counts the number of occurrences of a.	*In[2]:=* **Count[{a, b, c, a, b}, a]**
	Out[2]= 2
This shows that a is an element of {a, b, c}.	*In[3]:=* **MemberQ[{a, b, c}, a]**
	Out[3]= True
On the other hand, d is not.	*In[4]:=* **MemberQ[{a, b, c}, d]**
	Out[4]= False
This assigns m to be the 3×3 identity matrix.	*In[5]:=* **m = IdentityMatrix[3]**
	Out[5]= {{1, 0, 0}, {0, 1, 0}, {0, 0, 1}}
This shows that 0 does occur *somewhere* in m.	*In[6]:=* **FreeQ[m, 0]**
	Out[6]= False
This gives a list of the positions at which 0 occurs in m.	*In[7]:=* **Position[m, 0]**
	Out[7]= {{1, 2}, {1, 3}, {2, 1}, {2, 3}, {3, 1}, {3, 2}}
Extract takes the list of positions and shows that the element at each position is indeed 0.	*In[8]:=* **Extract[m, %]**
	Out[8]= {0, 0, 0, 0, 0, 0}

As discussed in Section 2.3.2, the functions Count and Position, as well as MemberQ and FreeQ, can be used not only to search for *particular* list elements, but also to search for classes of elements which match specific "patterns".

■ 1.8.6 Adding, Removing and Modifying List Elements

Prepend[*list*, *element*]	add *element* at the beginning of *list*
Append[*list*, *element*]	add *element* at the end of *list*
Insert[*list*, *element*, *i*]	insert *element* at position *i* in *list*
Insert[*list*, *element*, *−i*]	insert at position *i* counting from the end of *list*
Insert[*list*, *element*, {*i*, *j*, ... }]	insert at position *i*, *j*, ... in *list*
Delete[*list*, *i*]	delete the element at position *i* in *list*
Delete[*list*, {*i*, *j*, ... }]	delete at position *i*, *j*, ... in *list*

Functions for adding and deleting elements in lists.

This gives a list with x prepended.	*In[1]:=* **Prepend[{a, b, c}, x]**
	Out[1]= {x, a, b, c}

This adds x at the end.

In[2]:= **Append[{a, b, c}, x]**

Out[2]= {a, b, c, x}

This inserts x so that it becomes element number 2.

In[3]:= **Insert[{a, b, c}, x, 2]**

Out[3]= {a, x, b, c}

Negative numbers count from the end of the list.

In[4]:= **Insert[{a, b, c}, x, -2]**

Out[4]= {a, b, x, c}

Delete removes an element from the list.

In[5]:= **Delete[{a, b, c, d}, 3]**

Out[5]= {a, b, d}

ReplacePart[*list*, *element*, *i*]	replace the element at position *i* in *list*
ReplacePart[*list*, *element*, *-i*]	replace at position *i* counting from the end
ReplacePart[*list*, *element*, {*i*, *j*, ... }]	replace *list*[[*i*, *j*, ...]]
ReplacePart[*list*, *element*, {{*i*$_1$, *j*$_1$, ... }, {*i*$_2$, ... }, ... }]	replace all parts *list*[[*i*$_k$, *j*$_k$, ...]] with the same element
ReplacePart[*list*, *element*, {{*i*$_1$, ... }, ... }, {*n*$_1$, *n*$_2$, ... }]	replace part *list*[[*i*$_k$, ...]] with *element*[[*n*$_k$]]

Modifying parts of lists.

This replaces the third element in the list with x.

In[6]:= **ReplacePart[{a, b, c, d}, x, 3]**

Out[6]= {a, b, x, d}

This replaces the first and fourth parts of the list. Notice the need for double lists in specifying multiple parts to replace.

In[7]:= **ReplacePart[{a, b, c, d}, x, {{1}, {4}}]**

Out[7]= {x, b, c, x}

Here is a 3×3 identity matrix.

In[8]:= **IdentityMatrix[3]**

Out[8]= {{1, 0, 0}, {0, 1, 0}, {0, 0, 1}}

This replaces the $(2, 2)$ component of the matrix by x.

In[9]:= **ReplacePart[%, x, {2, 2}]**

Out[9]= {{1, 0, 0}, {0, x, 0}, {0, 0, 1}}

■ 1.8.7 Combining Lists

Join[*list*$_1$, *list*$_2$, ...]	concatenate lists together
Union[*list*$_1$, *list*$_2$, ...]	combine lists, removing repeated elements and sorting the result

Functions for combining lists.

Join concatenates any number of lists together.

In[1]:= **Join[{a, b, c}, {x, y}, {c, {d, e}, a}]**

Out[1]= {a, b, c, x, y, c, {d, e}, a}

Union combines lists, keeping only distinct elements.

In[2]:= **Union[{a, b, c}, {c, a, d}, {a, d}]**

Out[2]= {a, b, c, d}

■ 1.8.8 Advanced Topic: Lists as Sets

Mathematica usually keeps the elements of a list in exactly the order you originally entered them. If you want to treat a *Mathematica* list like a mathematical *set*, however, you may want to ignore the order of elements in the list.

Union[*list*$_1$, *list*$_2$, ...]	give a list of the distinct elements in the *list*$_i$
Intersection[*list*$_1$, *list*$_2$, ...]	give a list of the elements that are common to all the *list*$_i$
Complement[*universal*, *list*$_1$, ...]	give a list of the elements that are in *universal*, but not in any of the *list*$_i$

Set theoretical functions.

Union gives the elements that occur in *any* of the lists.

In[1]:= **Union[{c, a, b}, {d, a, c}, {a, e}]**

Out[1]= {a, b, c, d, e}

Intersection gives only elements that occur in *all* the lists.

In[2]:= **Intersection[{a, c, b}, {b, a, d, a}]**

Out[2]= {a, b}

Complement gives elements that occur in the first list, but not in any of the others.

In[3]:= **Complement[{a, b, c, d}, {a, d}]**

Out[3]= {b, c}

■ 1.8.9 Rearranging Lists

Sort[*list*]	sort the elements of *list* into a standard order
Union[*list*]	sort elements, removing any duplicates
Reverse[*list*]	reverse the order of elements in *list*
RotateLeft[*list*, *n*]	rotate the elements of *list* *n* places to the left
RotateRight[*list*, *n*]	rotate *n* places to the right
RotateLeft[*list*], RotateRight[*list*]	
	rotate by one position

Functions for rearranging lists.

This sorts the elements of a list into a standard order. In simple cases like this, the order is alphabetical or numerical.

```
In[1]:= Sort[{b, a, c, a, b}]
Out[1]= {a, a, b, b, c}
```

This sorts the elements, removing any duplicates.

```
In[2]:= Union[{b, a, c, a, b}]
Out[2]= {a, b, c}
```

This reverses the list.

```
In[3]:= Reverse[{a, b, c, d}]
Out[3]= {d, c, b, a}
```

This rotates ("shifts") the elements in the list two places to the left.

```
In[4]:= RotateLeft[{a, b, c, d, e}, 2]
Out[4]= {c, d, e, a, b}
```

You can rotate to the right by giving a negative displacement, or by using RotateRight.

```
In[5]:= RotateLeft[{a, b, c, d, e}, -2]
Out[5]= {d, e, a, b, c}
```

■ 1.8.10 Grouping Together Elements of Lists

Partition[*list*, *n*]	partition *list* into *n* element pieces
Partition[*list*, *n*, *d*]	use offset *d* for successive pieces
Split[*list*]	split *list* into pieces consisting of runs of identical elements

Functions for grouping together elements of lists.

Here is a list.

```
In[1]:= t = {a, b, c, d, e, f, g}
Out[1]= {a, b, c, d, e, f, g}
```

This groups the elements of the list in pairs, and in this case throws away the single element which is left at the end.

In[2]:= **Partition[t, 2]**

Out[2]= {{a, b}, {c, d}, {e, f}}

This groups elements in triples. There is no overlap between the triples.

In[3]:= **Partition[t, 3]**

Out[3]= {{a, b, c}, {d, e, f}}

This makes triples of elements, with each successive triple offset by just one element.

In[4]:= **Partition[t, 3, 1]**

Out[4]= {{a, b, c}, {b, c, d}, {c, d, e}, {d, e, f}, {e, f, g}}

This splits up the list into runs of identical elements.

In[5]:= **Split[{a, a, b, b, b, a, a, a, b}]**

Out[5]= {{a, a}, {b, b, b}, {a, a, a}, {b}}

■ 1.8.11 Mathematical Operations on Lists

Section 2.2.3 will discuss in detail how to do mathematical operations on lists. Here are a couple of cases that often occur in practice; Section 2.2.3 will give many generalizations.

Apply[Plus, *list*] or Plus @@ *list*

      add together all the elements in *list*

Apply[Times, *list*] or Times @@ *list*

      multiply together all the elements in *list*

Simple mathematical operations on lists.

This adds all the elements in a list.

In[1]:= **Apply[Plus, {a, b, c, d}]**

Out[1]= a + b + c + d

■ 1.8.12 Advanced Topic: Rearranging Nested Lists

You will encounter nested lists if you use matrices or generate multidimensional arrays and tables. Rearranging nested lists can be a complicated affair, and you will often have to experiment to get the right combination of commands.

Transpose[*list*]	interchange the top two levels of lists
Transpose[*list*, {*m*, *n*, ... }]	put first level at level *m*, second level at level *n*, ...
Flatten[*list*]	flatten out all levels in *list*
Flatten[*list*, *n*]	flatten out the top *n* levels in *list*
FlattenAt[*list*, *i*]	flatten out a sublist that appears at position *i*
FlattenAt[*list*, {*i*, *j*, ... }]	flatten out a sublist at position *i*, *j*, ...
FlattenAt[*list*, {{*i*₁, *j*₁, ... }, {*i*₂, ... }, ... }]	
	flatten out several sublists
RotateLeft[*list*, {*n*₁, *n*₂, ... }]	rotate successive levels by n_i places
Partition[*list*, {*n*₁, *n*₂, ... }, {*d*₁, *d*₂, ... }]	
	partition successive levels into n_i element pieces with offsets d_i

Functions for rearranging nested lists.

Here is a 3×2 array.

```
In[1]:= t = {{a, b}, {c, d}, {e, f}}
Out[1]= {{a, b}, {c, d}, {e, f}}
```

You can rearrange it to get a 2×3 array.

```
In[2]:= Transpose[t]
Out[2]= {{a, c, e}, {b, d, f}}
```

This "flattens out" sublists. You can think of it as effectively just removing the inner sets of braces.

```
In[3]:= Flatten[t]
Out[3]= {a, b, c, d, e, f}
```

Here is a $2 \times 2 \times 2$ array.

```
In[4]:= t = Table[i^2 +j^2 +k^2, {i, 2}, {j, 2}, {k, 2}]
Out[4]= {{{3, 6}, {6, 9}}, {{6, 9}, {9, 12}}}
```

This flattens out all the levels.

```
In[5]:= Flatten[t]
Out[5]= {3, 6, 6, 9, 6, 9, 9, 12}
```

This flattens only the first level of sublists.

```
In[6]:= Flatten[t, 1]
Out[6]= {{3, 6}, {6, 9}, {6, 9}, {9, 12}}
```

This flattens out only the sublist that appears at position 2.

```
In[7]:= FlattenAt[{{a, b}, {c, d}}, 2]
Out[7]= {{a, b}, c, d}
```

There are many other operations you can perform on nested lists. We will discuss some more of them when we look at Map, Apply, Scan and Level in Part 2.

■ 1.8.13 Advanced Topic: Combinatorial Operations

You can use lists to set up many kinds of combinatorial calculations. Here are a few examples.

Permutations[*list*]	give all possible orderings of *list*
Outer[List, *list*$_1$, *list*$_2$]	give lists of elements in *list*$_1$ and *list*$_2$ combined in all possible ways
Outer[List, *list*$_1$, *list*$_2$, *n*]	combine only elements on the top *n* levels
OrderedQ[*list*]	give True if the elements of *list* are in order
Signature[*list*]	give the signature of the permutation needed to put *list* into standard order

Some combinatorial operations on lists.

This gives the 3! = 6 possible permutations of three elements.

```
In[1]:= Permutations[{a,b,c}]
Out[1]= {{a, b, c}, {a, c, b}, {b, a, c}, {b, c, a},
          {c, a, b}, {c, b, a}}
```

This combines the list elements in all possible ways. This operation is analogous to a mathematical "outer product" (see Section 3.7.11).

```
In[2]:= Outer[List, {a, b}, {c, d}]
Out[2]= {{{a, c}, {a, d}}, {{b, c}, {b, d}}}
```

1.9 Graphics and Sound

■ 1.9.1 Basic Plotting

Plot[*f*, {*x*, *xmin*, *xmax*}]	plot *f* as a function of *x* from *xmin* to *xmax*
Plot[{*f*₁, *f*₂, ... }, {*x*, *xmin*, *xmax*}]	plot several functions together

Basic plotting functions.

This plots a graph of sin(*x*) as a function of *x* from 0 to 2π.

In[1]:= **Plot[Sin[x], {x, 0, 2Pi}]**

You can plot functions that have singularities. *Mathematica* will try to choose appropriate scales.

In[2]:= **Plot[Tan[x], {x, -3, 3}]**

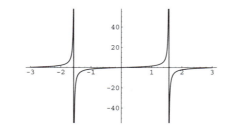

You can give a list of functions to plot.   *In[3]:=* `Plot[{Sin[x], Sin[2x], Sin[3x]}, {x, 0, 2Pi}]`

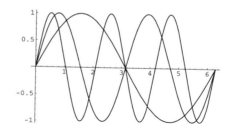

To get smooth curves, *Mathematica* has to evaluate functions you plot at a large number of points. As a result, it is important that you set things up so that each function evaluation is as quick as possible.

When you ask *Mathematica* to plot an object, say *f*, as a function of *x*, there are two possible approaches it can take. One approach is first to try and evaluate *f*, presumably getting a symbolic expression in terms of *x*, and then subsequently evaluate this expression numerically for the specific values of *x* needed in the plot. The second approach is first to work out what values of *x* are needed, and only subsequently to evaluate *f* with those values of *x*.

If you type `Plot[f, {x, xmin, xmax}]` it is the second of these approaches that is used. This has the advantage that *Mathematica* only tries to evaluate *f* for specific numerical values of *x*; it does not matter whether sensible values are defined for *f* when *x* is symbolic.

There are, however, some cases in which it is much better to have *Mathematica* evaluate *f* before it starts to make the plot. A typical case is when *f* is actually a command that generates a table of functions. You want to have *Mathematica* first produce the table, and then evaluate the functions, rather than trying to produce the table afresh for each value of *x*. You can do this by typing `Plot[Evaluate[f], {x, xmin, xmax}]`.

This makes a plot of the Bessel functions $J_n(x)$ with *n* running from 1 to 4. The `Evaluate` tells *Mathematica* *first* to make the table of functions, and only *then* to evaluate them for particular values of **x**.

In[4]:= `Plot[Evaluate[Table[BesselJ[n, x], {n, 4}]],`
`{x, 0, 10}]`

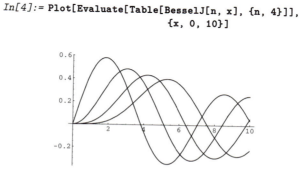

This finds the numerical solution to a differential equation, as discussed in Section 1.6.4.

In[5]:= `NDSolve[{y'[x] == Sin[y[x]], y[0] == 1}, y, {x, 0, 4}]`
Out[5]= `{{y → InterpolatingFunction[{{0., 4.}}, <>]}}`

Here is a plot of the solution. The Evaluate tells *Mathematica* to first set up an InterpolatingFunction object, then evaluate this at a sequence of x values.

In[6]:= **Plot[Evaluate[y[x] /. %], {x, 0, 4}]**

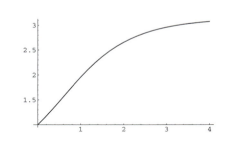

Plot[*f*, {*x*, *xmin*, *xmax*}]	*first* choose specific numerical values for *x*, then evaluate *f* for each value of *x*
Plot[Evaluate[*f*], {*x*, *xmin*, *xmax*}]	*first* evaluate *f*, then choose specific numerical values of *x*
Plot[Evaluate[Table[*f*, ...]], {*x*, *xmin*, *xmax*}]	generate a list of functions, and then plot them
Plot[Evaluate[y[*x*] /. *solution*], {*x*, *xmin*, *xmax*}]	plot a numerical solution to a differential equation obtained from NDSolve

Methods for setting up objects to plot.

■ 1.9.2 Special Topic: How Graphics Are Output

The details of how *Mathematica* outputs graphics vary between different computer systems and different *Mathematica* interfaces. The documentation that came with your copy of *Mathematica* should tell you what is relevant in your case.

With text-based *Mathematica* interfaces, each piece of graphics output typically fills your complete screen, or causes a new window to be created which is then filled with graphics. The details of how you get rid of the graphics vary from one system to another. Note that when you start *Mathematica* with a text-based interface, you may have to load a *Mathematica* package to tell *Mathematica* how you want graphics output to be done. The details of this should be described in the documentation that came with your copy of *Mathematica*.

With a notebook-based *Mathematica* interface, each piece of graphics is placed in a cell in your notebook. The *Mathematica* front end allows you to manipulate the graphics in several ways, for example by resizing them, or redisplaying them with different options.

Many *Mathematica* systems allow you to collect together sequences of graphic images and display them in quick succession to produce an animated "movie". Notebook-based interfaces typically allow you to select a sequence of cells to serve as the frames in your animation. Many text-based interfaces also provide animation capabilities; typically the function `ShowAnimation[{`g_1`,` g_2`, ... }]`, where the g_i are pieces of graphics output, generates a movie.

You should understand that when *Mathematica* produces any kind of graphics output, it does so in three stages. The first stage is to execute commands like `Plot` to produce a sequence of *Mathematica* graphics primitives. These primitives, to be discussed in Section 2.9, represent objects such as lines, points and polygons as *Mathematica* expressions. The second stage of producing graphics output is to convert these graphics primitives to a standardized device-independent representation of your graphical image. *Mathematica* generates this representation in the PostScript page description language.

The final stage of graphics output is to take the PostScript description of a graphical image, and render it on the particular device you want. In a notebook-based interface, the *Mathematica* front end performs this rendering. On other systems, the rendering is usually done by an external program which is automatically called from within *Mathematica*.

The importance of using PostScript as a graphics description language is that it can be rendered on many different kinds of devices, including both displays and printers, and it can be imported into many kinds of programs. Specific versions of *Mathematica* come with various conversion utilities to produce Encapsulated PostScript form, and other standard graphics formats.

With text-based *Mathematica* interfaces, the command `PSPrint[`*graphics*`]` is typically set up to print a piece of graphics. The command `Display["`*file*`",` *graphics*`, "EPS"]` saves the encapsulated PostScript representation of the graphics in a file.

Although most graphics from *Mathematica* are first converted to PostScript, and then rendered on particular devices, there are some cases where it is more convenient to render directly from the original *Mathematica* form. One example is on systems that manipulate images of three-dimensional objects in real time. On such systems, the function `Live[`*graphics*`]` is typically set up to produce a "live" version of a piece of *Mathematica* graphics, which can then be manipulated directly using the various tools available on the particular computer system.

■ 1.9.3 Options

When *Mathematica* plots a graph for you, it has to make many choices. It has to work out what the scales should be, where the function should be sampled, how the axes should be drawn, and so on. Most of the time, *Mathematica* will probably make pretty good choices. However, if you want to get the very best possible pictures for your particular purposes, you may have to help *Mathematica* in making some of its choices.

There is a general mechanism for specifying "options" in *Mathematica* functions. Each option has a definite name. As the last arguments to a function like `Plot`, you can include a sequence of rules of the form *name->value*, to specify the values for various options. Any option for which you do not give an explicit rule is taken to have its "default" value.

Plot[*f*, {*x*, *xmin*, *xmax*}, *option->value*]

make a plot, specifying a particular value for an option

Choosing an option for a plot.

A function like Plot has many options that you can set. Usually you will need to use at most a few of them at a time. If you want to optimize a particular plot, you will probably do best to experiment, trying a sequence of different settings for various options.

Each time you produce a plot, you can specify options for it. Section 1.9.4 will also discuss how you can change some of the options, even after you have produced the plot.

option name	default value	
AspectRatio	1/GoldenRatio	the height-to-width ratio for the plot; Automatic sets it from the absolute x and y coordinates
Axes	Automatic	whether to include axes
AxesLabel	None	labels to be put on the axes: *ylabel* specifies a label for the y axis, {*xlabel*, *ylabel*} for both axes
AxesOrigin	Automatic	the point at which axes cross
TextStyle	$TextStyle	the default style to use for text in the plot
FormatType	StandardForm	the default format type to use for text in the plot
DisplayFunction	$DisplayFunction	how to display graphics; Identity causes no display
Frame	False	whether to draw a frame around the plot
FrameLabel	None	labels to be put around the frame; give a list in clockwise order starting with the lower x axis
FrameTicks	Automatic	what tick marks to draw if there is a frame; None gives no tick marks
GridLines	None	what grid lines to include: Automatic includes a grid line for every major tick mark
PlotLabel	None	an expression to be printed as a label for the plot
PlotRange	Automatic	the range of coordinates to include in the plot: All includes all points
Ticks	Automatic	what tick marks to draw if there are axes; None gives no tick marks

Some of the options for Plot. These can also be used in Show.

Here is a plot with all options having their default values.

In[1]:= `Plot[Sin[x^2], {x, 0, 3}]`

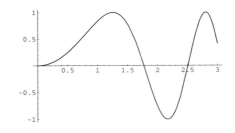

This draws axes on a frame around the plot.

In[2]:= `Plot[Sin[x^2], {x, 0, 3}, Frame->True]`

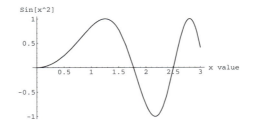

This specifies labels for the x and y axes. The expressions you give as labels are printed just as they would be if they appeared as *Mathematica* output. You can give any piece of text by putting it inside a pair of double quotes.

In[3]:= `Plot[Sin[x^2], {x, 0, 3},`
            `AxesLabel -> {"x value", "Sin[x^2]"} ]`

You can give several options at the same time, in any order.

In[4]:= `Plot[Sin[x^2], {x, 0, 3}, Frame -> True,`
`GridLines -> Automatic]`

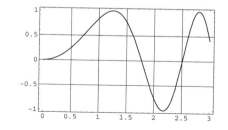

Setting the `AspectRatio` option changes the whole shape of your plot. `AspectRatio` gives the ratio of width to height. Its default value is the inverse of the Golden Ratio—supposedly the most pleasing shape for a rectangle.

In[5]:= `Plot[Sin[x^2], {x, 0, 3}, AspectRatio -> 1]`

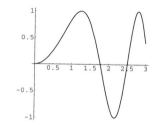

Automatic	use internal algorithms
None	do not include this
All	include everything
True	do this
False	do not do this

Some common settings for various options.

When *Mathematica* makes a plot, it tries to set the *x* and *y* scales to include only the "interesting" parts of the plot. If your function increases very rapidly, or has singularities, the parts where it gets too large will be cut off. By specifying the option `PlotRange`, you can control exactly what ranges of *x* and *y* coordinates are included in your plot.

`Automatic`	show at least a large fraction of the points, including the "interesting" region (the default setting)
`All`	show all points
{*ymin*, *ymax*}	show a specific range of *y* values
{*xrange*, *yrange*}	show the specified ranges of *x* and *y* values

Settings for the option `PlotRange`.

The setting for the option PlotRange gives explicit *y* limits for the graph. With the *y* limits specified here, the bottom of the curve is cut off.

In[6]:= `Plot[Sin[x^2], {x, 0, 3}, PlotRange -> {0, 1.2}]`

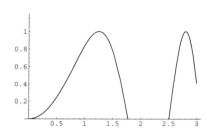

Mathematica always tries to plot functions as smooth curves. As a result, in places where your function wiggles a lot, *Mathematica* will use more points. In general, *Mathematica* tries to *adapt* its sampling of your function to the form of the function. There is, however, a limit, which you can set, to how finely *Mathematica* will ever sample a function.

The function $\sin(\frac{1}{x})$ wiggles infinitely often when $x \simeq 0$. *Mathematica* tries to sample more points in the region where the function wiggles a lot, but it can never sample the infinite number that you would need to reproduce the function exactly. As a result, there are slight glitches in the plot.

In[7]:= `Plot[Sin[1/x], {x, -1, 1}]`

option name	default value	
PlotStyle	Automatic	a list of lists of graphics primitives to use for each curve (see Section 2.9.3)
PlotPoints	25	the minimum number of points at which to sample the function
MaxBend	10.	the maximum kink angle between successive segments of a curve
PlotDivision	20.	the maximum factor by which to subdivide in sampling the function
Compiled	True	whether to compile the function being plotted

More options for Plot. These cannot be used in Show.

It is important to realize that since *Mathematica* can only sample your function at a limited number of points, it can always miss features of the function. By increasing PlotPoints, you can make *Mathematica* sample your function at a larger number of points. Of course, the larger you set PlotPoints to be, the longer it will take *Mathematica* to plot *any* function, even a smooth one.

Since Plot needs to evaluate your function many times, it is important to make each evaluation as quick as possible. As a result, *Mathematica* usually *compiles* your function into a low-level pseudocode that can be executed very efficiently. One potential problem with this, however, is that the pseudocode allows only machine-precision numerical operations. If the function you are plotting requires higher-precision operations, you may have to switch off compilation in Plot. You can do this by setting the option Compiled -> False. Note that *Mathematica* can only compile "in-line code"; it cannot for example compile functions that you have defined. As a result, you should, when possible, use Evaluate as described on page 129 to evaluate any such definitions and get a form that the *Mathematica* compiler can handle.

■ 1.9.4 Redrawing and Combining Plots

Mathematica saves information about every plot you produce, so that you can later redraw it. When you redraw plots, you can change some of the options you use.

Show[*plot*]	redraw a plot
Show[*plot*, *option->value*]	redraw with options changed
Show[*plot*₁, *plot*₂, ...]	combine several plots
Show[GraphicsArray[{{*plot*₁, *plot*₂, ... }, ... }]]	draw an array of plots
InputForm[*plot*]	show the information that is saved about a plot

Functions for manipulating plots.

Here is a simple plot. -Graphics- is usually printed on the output line to stand for the information that *Mathematica* saves about the plot.

In[1]:= **Plot[ChebyshevT[7, x], {x, -1, 1}]**

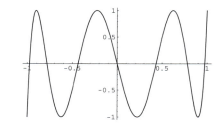

This redraws the plot from the previous line.

In[2]:= **Show[%]**

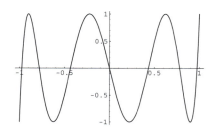

When you redraw the plot, you can change some of the options. This changes the choice of *y* scale.

In[3]:= **Show[%, PlotRange -> {-1, 2}]**

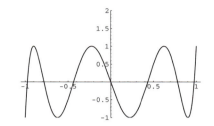

This takes the plot from the previous line, and changes another option in it.

In[4]:= **Show[%, PlotLabel -> "A Chebyshev Polynomial"]**

By using Show with a sequence of different options, you can look at the same plot in many different ways. You may want to do this, for example, if you are trying to find the best possible setting of options.

You can also use Show to combine plots. It does not matter whether the plots have the same scales: *Mathematica* will always choose new scales to include the points you want.

This sets gj0 to be a plot of $J_0(x)$ from $x = 0$ to 10.

In[5]:= **gj0 = Plot[BesselJ[0, x], {x, 0, 10}]**

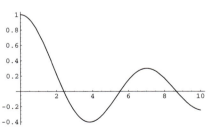

Here is a plot of $Y_1(x)$ from $x = 1$ to 10.

In[6]:= **gy1 = Plot[BesselY[1, x], {x, 1, 10}]**

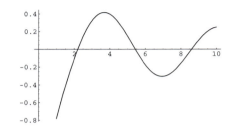

This shows the previous two plots combined into one. Notice that the scale is adjusted appropriately.

In[7]:= **gjy = Show[gj0, gy1]**

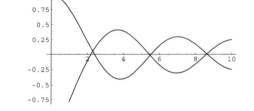

Using **Show[***plot$_1$***, ***plot$_2$***, ...]** you can combine several plots into one. **GraphicsArray** allows you to draw several plots in an array.

Show[GraphicsArray[{*plot$_1$***, ***plot$_2$***, ... }]]**
          draw several plots side by side

Show[GraphicsArray[{{*plot$_1$***}, {***plot$_2$***}, ... }]]**
          draw a column of plots

Show[GraphicsArray[{{*plot$_{11}$***, ***plot$_{12}$***, ... }, ... }]]**
          draw a rectangular array of plots

Show[GraphicsArray[*plots***, GraphicsSpacing -> {***h***, ***v***}]]**
          put the specified horizontal and vertical spacing between the
          plots

Drawing arrays of plots.

This shows the plots given above in an array.

In[8]:= **Show[GraphicsArray[{{gj0, gjy}, {gy1, gjy}}]]**

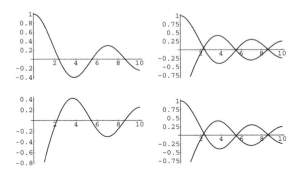

If you redisplay an array of plots using Show, any options you specify will be used for the whole array, rather than for individual plots.

In[9]:= **Show[%, Frame->True, FrameTicks->None]**

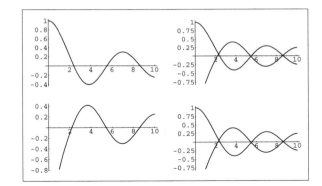

Here is a way to change options for all   *In[10]:=* **Show[% /. (Ticks -> Automatic) -> (Ticks -> None)]**
the plots in the array.

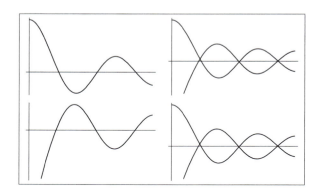

GraphicsArray by default puts a narrow border around each of the plots in the array it gives. You can change the size of this border by setting the option **GraphicsSpacing -> {h, v}**. The parameters *h* and *v* give the horizontal and vertical spacings to be used, as fractions of the width and height of the plots.

This increases the horizontal spacing,   *In[11]:=* **Show[%, GraphicsSpacing -> {0.3, 0}]**
but decreases the vertical spacing
between the plots in the array.

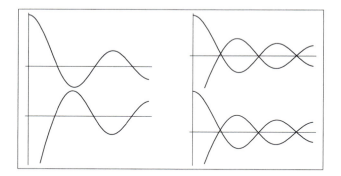

When you make a plot, *Mathematica* saves the list of points it used, together with some other information. Using what is saved, you can redraw plots in many different ways with **Show**. However, you should realize that no matter what options you specify, **Show** still has the same basic set of points to work with. So, for example, if you set the options so that *Mathematica* displays a small portion of your original plot magnified, you will probably be able to see the individual sample points that **Plot** used. Options like **PlotPoints** can only be set in the original **Plot** command itself. (*Mathematica* always plots the actual points it has; it avoids using smoothed or splined curves, which can give misleading results in mathematical graphics.)

Here is a simple plot.

In[12]:= **Plot[Cos[x], {x, -Pi, Pi}]**

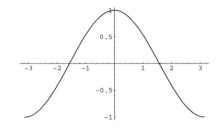

This shows a small region of the plot in a magnified form. At this resolution, you can see the individual line segments that were produced by the original **Plot** command.

In[13]:= **Show[%, PlotRange -> {{0, .3}, {.92, 1}}]**

■ 1.9.5 Advanced Topic: Manipulating Options

There are a number of functions built into *Mathematica* which, like **Plot**, have various options you can set. *Mathematica* provides some general mechanisms for handling such options.

If you do not give a specific setting for an option to a function like **Plot**, then *Mathematica* will automatically use a default value for the option. The function **Options[***function, option***]** allows you to find out the default value for a particular option. You can reset the default using **SetOptions[***function, option->value***]**. Note that if you do this, the default value you have given will stay until you explicitly change it.

Options[*function***]**	give a list of the current default settings for all options
Options[*function, option***]**	give the default setting for a particular option
SetOptions[*function, option->value, ...* **]**	reset defaults

Manipulating default settings for options.

Here is the default setting for the
PlotRange option of Plot.

In[1]:= **Options[Plot, PlotRange]**

Out[1]= {PlotRange → Automatic}

This resets the default for the
PlotRange option. The semicolon
stops *Mathematica* from printing out the
rather long list of options for Plot.

In[2]:= **SetOptions[Plot, PlotRange->All]** ;

Until you explicitly reset it, the default
for the PlotRange option will now be
All.

In[3]:= **Options[Plot, PlotRange]**

Out[3]= {PlotRange → All}

The graphics objects that you get from Plot or Show store information on the options they use.
You can get this information by applying the Options function to these graphics objects.

Options[*plot*]	show all the options used for a particular plot
Options[*plot*, *option*]	show the setting for a specific option
FullOptions[*plot*, *option*]	show the actual form used for a specific option, even if the setting for the option is Automatic or All

Getting information on options used in plots.

Here is a plot, with default settings for
all options.

In[4]:= **g = Plot[SinIntegral[x], {x, 0, 20}]**

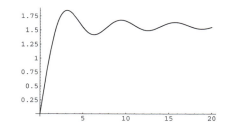

The setting used for the PlotRange
option was All.

In[5]:= **Options[g, PlotRange]**

Out[5]= {PlotRange → All}

FullOptions gives the *actual*
automatically chosen values used for
PlotRange.

In[6]:= **FullOptions[g, PlotRange]**

Out[6]= {{-0.499999, 20.5}, {-0.0462976, 1.89823}}

■ 1.9.6 Contour and Density Plots

ContourPlot[*f*, {*x*, *xmin*, *xmax*}, {*y*, *ymin*, *ymax*}]
          make a contour plot of *f* as a function of *x* and *y*
DensityPlot[*f*, {*x*, *xmin*, *xmax*}, {*y*, *ymin*, *ymax*}]
          make a density plot of *f*

Contour and density plots.

This gives a contour plot of the
function $\sin(x)\sin(y)$.

In[1]:= **ContourPlot[Sin[x] Sin[y], {x, -2, 2}, {y, -2, 2}]**

A contour plot gives you essentially a "topographic map" of a function. The contours join points on the surface that have the same height. The default is to have contours corresponding to a sequence of equally spaced *z* values. Contour plots produced by *Mathematica* are by default shaded, in such a way that regions with higher *z* values are lighter.

option name	default value	
ColorFunction	Automatic	what colors to use for shading; Hue uses a sequence of hues
Contours	10	the total number of contours, or the list of z values for contours
PlotRange	Automatic	the range of values to be included; you can specify {*zmin*, *zmax*}, All or Automatic
ContourShading	True	whether to use shading
PlotPoints	15	number of evaluation points in each direction
Compiled	True	whether to compile the function being plotted

Some options for ContourPlot. The first set can also be used in Show.

Particularly if you use a display or printer that does not handle gray levels well, you may find it better to switch off shading in contour plots.

In[2]:= **Show[%, ContourShading -> False]**

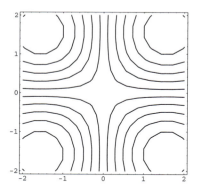

You should realize that if you do not evaluate your function on a fine enough grid, there may be inaccuracies in your contour plot. One point to notice is that whereas a curve generated by Plot may be inaccurate if your function varies too quickly in a particular region, the shape of contours can be inaccurate if your function varies too slowly. A rapidly varying function gives a regular pattern of contours, but a function that is almost flat can give irregular contours. You can typically overcome such problems by increasing the value of PlotPoints.

Density plots show the values of your function at a regular array of points. Lighter regions are higher.

In[3]:= **DensityPlot[Sin[x] Sin[y], {x, -2, 2}, {y, -2, 2}]**

You can get rid of the mesh like this. But unless you have a very large number of regions, plots usually look better when you include the mesh.

In[4]:= **Show[%, Mesh -> False]**

option name	default value	
ColorFunction	Automatic	what colors to use for shading; Hue uses a sequence of hues
Mesh	True	whether to draw a mesh
PlotPoints	15	number of evaluation points in each direction
Compiled	True	whether to compile the function being plotted

Some options for DensityPlot. The first set can also be used in Show.

■ 1.9.7 Three-Dimensional Surface Plots

Plot3D[*f*, {*x*, *xmin*, *xmax*}, {*y*, *ymin*, *ymax*}]
                                    make a three-dimensional plot of *f* as a function of the
                                    variables *x* and *y*

Basic 3D plotting function.

This makes a three-dimensional plot of   *In[1]:=* **Plot3D[Sin[x y], {x, 0, 3}, {y, 0, 3}]**
the function sin(*xy*).

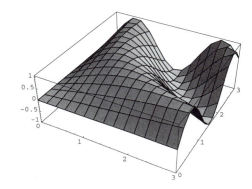

There are many options for three-dimensional plots in *Mathematica*. Some will be discussed in this section; others will be described in Section 2.9.

The first set of options for three-dimensional plots is largely analogous to those provided in the two-dimensional case.

option name	default value	
Axes	True	whether to include axes
AxesLabel	None	labels to be put on the axes: *zlabel* specifies a label for the *z* axis, {*xlabel*, *ylabel*, *zlabel*} for all axes
Boxed	True	whether to draw a three-dimensional box around the surface
ColorFunction	Automatic	what colors to use for shading; Hue uses a sequence of hues
TextStyle	$TextStyle	the default style to use for text in the plot
FormatType	StandardForm	the default format type to use for text in the plot
DisplayFunction	$DisplayFunction	how to display graphics; Identity causes no display
FaceGrids	None	how to draw grids on faces of the bounding box; All draws a grid on every face
HiddenSurface	True	whether to draw the surface as solid
Lighting	True	whether to color the surface using simulated lighting
Mesh	True	whether an *xy* mesh should be drawn on the surface
PlotRange	Automatic	the range of coordinates to include in the plot: you can specify All, {*zmin*, *zmax*} or {{*xmin*,*xmax*},{*ymin*,*ymax*},{*zmin*,*zmax*}}
Shading	True	whether the surface should be shaded or left white
ViewPoint	{1.3, -2.4, 2}	the point in space from which to look at the surface
PlotPoints	15	the number of points in each direction at which to sample the function; {n_x, n_y} specifies different numbers in the *x* and *y* directions
Compiled	True	whether to compile the function being plotted

Some options for Plot3D. The first set can also be used in Show.

This redraws the plot on the previous line, with options changed. With this setting for PlotRange, only the part of the surface in the range $-0.5 \le z \le 0.5$ is shown.

In[2]:= **Show[%, PlotRange -> {-0.5, 0.5}]**

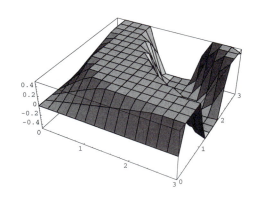

When you make the original plot, you can choose to sample more points. You will need to do this to get good pictures of functions that wiggle a lot.

In[3]:= **Plot3D[10 Sin[x + Sin[y]], {x, -10, 10}, {y, -10, 10},
                PlotPoints -> 40]**

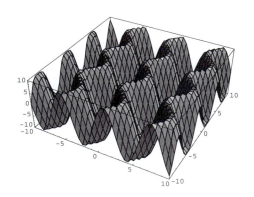

Here is the same plot, with labels for the axes, and grids added to each face.

In[4]:= **Show[%, AxesLabel -> {"Time", "Depth", "Value"},**
                         FaceGrids -> All]

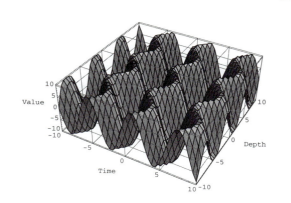

Probably the single most important issue in plotting a three-dimensional surface is specifying where you want to look at the surface from. The `ViewPoint` option for `Plot3D` and `Show` allows you to specify the point $\{x, y, z\}$ in space from which you view a surface. The details of how the coordinates for this point are defined will be discussed in Section 2.9.10. In many versions of *Mathematica*, there are ways to choose three-dimensional view points interactively, then get the coordinates to give as settings for the `ViewPoint` option.

Here is a surface, viewed from the default view point {1.3, −2.4, 2}. This view point is chosen to be "generic", so that visually confusing coincidental alignments between different parts of your object are unlikely.

In[5]:= **Plot3D[Sin[x y], {x, 0, 3}, {y, 0, 3}]**

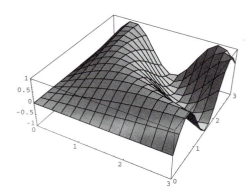

This redraws the picture, with the view point directly in front. Notice the perspective effect that makes the back of the box look much smaller than the front.

In[6]:= **Show[%, ViewPoint -> {0, -2, 0}]**

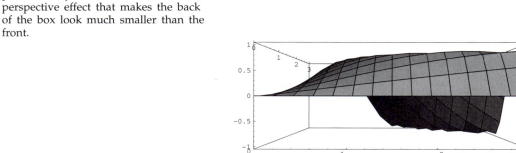

{1.3, -2.4, 2}	default view point
{0, -2, 0}	directly in front
{0, -2, 2}	in front and up
{0, -2, -2}	in front and down
{-2, -2, 0}	left-hand corner
{2, -2, 0}	right-hand corner
{0, 0, 2}	directly above

Typical choices for the ViewPoint option.

The human visual system is not particularly good at understanding complicated mathematical surfaces. As a result, you need to generate pictures that contain as many clues as possible about the form of the surface.

View points slightly above the surface usually work best. It is generally a good idea to keep the view point close enough to the surface that there is some perspective effect. Having a box explicitly drawn around the surface is helpful in recognizing the orientation of the surface.

Here is a plot with the default settings for surface rendering options.

In[7]:= `g = Plot3D[Exp[-(x^2+y^2)], {x, -2, 2}, {y, -2, 2}]`

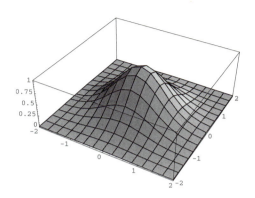

This shows the surface without the mesh drawn. It is usually much harder to see the form of the surface if the mesh is not there.

In[8]:= `Show[g, Mesh -> False]`

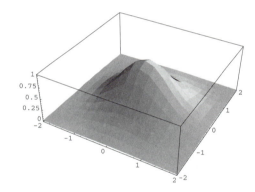

This shows the surface with no   *In[9]:=* **Show[g, Shading -> False]**
shading. Some display devices may
not be able to show shading.

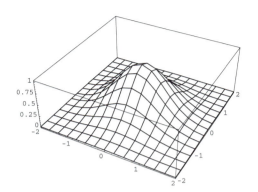

The inclusion of shading and a mesh are usually great assets in understanding the form of a surface. On some vector graphics output devices, however, you may not be able to get shading. You should also realize that when shading is included, it may take a long time to render the surface on your output device.

To add an extra element of realism to three-dimensional graphics, *Mathematica* by default colors three-dimensional surfaces using a simulated lighting model. In the default case, *Mathematica* assumes that there are three light sources shining on the object from the upper right of the picture. Section 2.9.12 describes how you can set up other light sources, and how you can specify the reflection properties of an object.

While in most cases, particularly with color output devices, simulated lighting is an asset, it can sometimes be confusing. If you set the option `Lighting -> False`, then *Mathematica* will not use simulated lighting, but will instead shade all surfaces with gray levels determined by their height.

Plot3D usually colors surfaces using a   *In[10]:=* **Plot3D[Sin[x y], {x, 0, 3}, {y, 0, 3}]**
simulated lighting model.

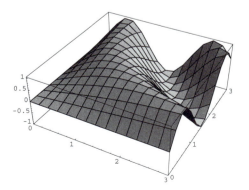

Lighting -> False switches off the
simulated lighting, and instead shades
surfaces with gray levels determined
by height.

In[11]:= **Show[%, Lighting -> False]**

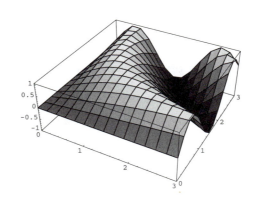

With **Lighting -> False**, *Mathematica* shades surfaces according to height. You can also tell *Mathematica* explicitly how to shade each element of a surface. This allows you effectively to use shading to display an extra coordinate at each point on your surface.

Plot3D[{*f*, GrayLevel[*s*]}, {*x*, *xmin*, *xmax*}, {*y*, *ymin*, *ymax*}]
                      plot a surface corresponding to *f*, shaded in gray according
                      to the function *s*

Plot3D[{*f*, Hue[*s*]}, {*x*, *xmin*, *xmax*}, {*y*, *ymin*, *ymax*}]
                      shade by varying color hue rather than gray level

Specifying shading functions for surfaces.

This shows a surface whose height is
determined by the function Sin[x y],
but whose shading is determined by
GrayLevel[x/3].

In[12]:= **Plot3D[{Sin[x y], GrayLevel[x/3]},**
                                {x, 0, 3}, {y, 0, 3}]

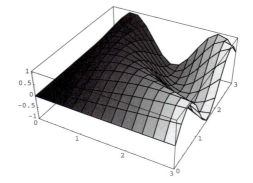

■ 1.9.8 Converting between Types of Graphics

Contour, density and surface plots are three different ways to display essentially the same information about a function. In all cases, you need the values of a function at a grid of points.

The *Mathematica* functions `ContourPlot`, `DensityPlot` and `Plot3D` all produce *Mathematica* graphics objects that include a list of the values of your function on a grid. As a result, having used any one of these functions, *Mathematica* can easily take its output and use it to produce another type of graphics.

Here is a surface plot.   `In[1]:= Plot3D[BesselJ[nu, 3x], {nu, 0, 3}, {x, 0, 3}]`

This converts the object produced by   `In[2]:= Show[ ContourGraphics[ % ] ]`
Plot3D into a contour plot.

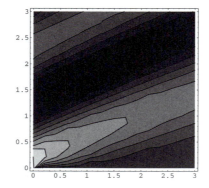

Show[ContourGraphics[*g*]]	convert to a contour plot
Show[DensityGraphics[*g*]]	convert to a density plot
Show[SurfaceGraphics[*g*]]	convert to a surface plot
Show[Graphics[*g*]]	convert to a two-dimensional image

Conversions between types of graphics.

You can use GraphicsArray to show different types of graphics together.

In[3]:= **Show[GraphicsArray[{%, %%}]]**

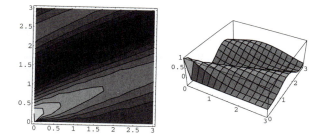

■ 1.9.9 Plotting Lists of Data

So far, we have discussed how you can use *Mathematica* to make plots of *functions*. You give *Mathematica* a function, and it builds up a curve or surface by evaluating the function at many different points.

This section describes how you can make plots from lists of data, instead of functions. (Section 1.11.3 discusses how to read data from external files and programs.) The *Mathematica* commands for plotting lists of data are direct analogs of the ones discussed above for plotting functions.

> ListPlot[{y_1, y_2, ... }]   plot y_1, y_2, ... at x values 1, 2, ...
>
> ListPlot[{{x_1, y_1}, {x_2, y_2}, ... }]
>   plot points (x_1, y_1), ...
>
> ListPlot[*list*, PlotJoined -> True]
>   join the points with lines
>
> ---
>
> ListPlot3D[{{z_{11}, z_{12}, ... }, {z_{21}, z_{22}, ... }, ... }]
>   make a three-dimensional plot of the array of heights z_{yx}
>
> ListContourPlot[*array*]   make a contour plot from an array of heights
>
> ListDensityPlot[*array*]   make a density plot

Functions for plotting lists of data.

Here is a list of values.	*In[1]:=* **t = Table[i^2, {i, 10}]** *Out[1]=* {1, 4, 9, 16, 25, 36, 49, 64, 81, 100}
This plots the values.	*In[2]:=* **ListPlot[t]**

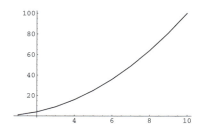

This joins the points with lines.   *In[3]:=* **ListPlot[t, PlotJoined -> True]**

This gives a list of *x, y* pairs.

In[4]:= **Table[{i^2, 4 i^2 + i^3}, {i, 10}]**

Out[4]= {{1, 5}, {4, 24}, {9, 63}, {16, 128},
{25, 225}, {36, 360}, {49, 539}, {64, 768},
{81, 1053}, {100, 1400}}

This plots the points.

In[5]:= **ListPlot[%]**

This gives a rectangular array of values. The array is quite large, so we end the input with a semicolon to stop the result from being printed out.

In[6]:= **t3 = Table[Mod[x, y], {y, 20}, {x, 30}] ;**

This makes a three-dimensional plot of the array of values.

In[7]:= **ListPlot3D[t3]**

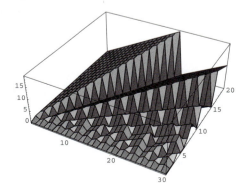

You can redraw the plot using Show, as   *In[8]:=* **Show[%, ViewPoint -> {1.5, -0.5, 0}]**
usual.

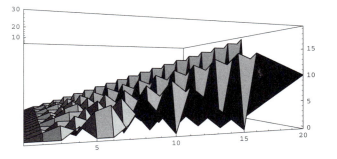

This gives a density plot of the array   *In[9]:=* **ListDensityPlot[t3]**
of values.

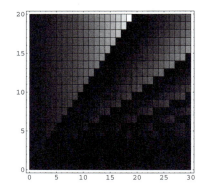

■ 1.9.10 Parametric Plots

Section 1.9.1 described how to plot curves in *Mathematica* in which you give the *y* coordinate of each point as a function of the *x* coordinate. You can also use *Mathematica* to make *parametric* plots. In a parametric plot, you give both the *x* and *y* coordinates of each point as a function of a third parameter, say *t*.

Functions for generating parametric plots.

Here is the curve made by taking the *x* coordinate of each point to be Sin[t] and the *y* coordinate to be Sin[2t].

In[1]:= **ParametricPlot[{Sin[t], Sin[2t]}, {t, 0, 2Pi}]**

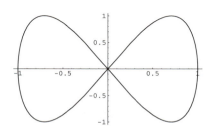

The "shape" of the curve produced depends on the ratio of height to width for the whole plot.

In[2]:= **ParametricPlot[{Sin[t], Cos[t]}, {t, 0, 2Pi}]**

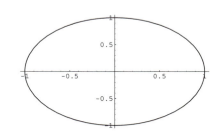

Setting the option `AspectRatio` to Automatic makes *Mathematica* preserve the "true shape" of the curve, as defined by the actual coordinate values it involves.

In[3]:= **Show[%, AspectRatio -> Automatic]**

`ParametricPlot3D[{`f_x`, `f_y`, `f_z`}, {`t`, `$tmin$`, `$tmax$`}]`
      make a parametric plot of a three-dimensional curve

`ParametricPlot3D[{`f_x`, `f_y`, `f_z`}, {`t`, `$tmin$`, `$tmax$`}, {`u`, `$umin$`, `$umax$`}]`
      make a parametric plot of a three-dimensional surface

`ParametricPlot3D[{`f_x`, `f_y`, `f_z`, `s`}, ... ]`
      shade the parts of the parametric plot according to the function s

`ParametricPlot3D[{{`f_x`, `f_y`, `f_z`}, {`g_x`, `g_y`, `g_z`}, ... }, ... ]`
      plot several objects together

Three-dimensional parametric plots.

`ParametricPlot3D[{`f_x`, `f_y`, `f_z`}, {`t`, `$tmin$`, `$tmax$`}]` is the direct analog in three dimensions of `ParametricPlot[{`f_x`, `f_y`}, {`t`, `$tmin$`, `$tmax$`}]` in two dimensions. In both cases, *Mathematica* effectively generates a sequence of points by varying the parameter *t*, then forms a curve by joining these points. With `ParametricPlot`, the curve is in two dimensions; with `ParametricPlot3D`, it is in three dimensions.

This makes a parametric plot of a helical curve. Varying t produces circular motion in the x, y plane, and linear motion in the z direction.

In[4]:= **ParametricPlot3D[{Sin[t], Cos[t], t/3}, {t, 0, 15}]**

ParametricPlot3D[$\{f_x$, f_y, $f_z\}$, $\{t$, *tmin*, *tmax*$\}$, $\{u$, *umin*, *umax*$\}$] creates a surface, rather than a curve. The surface is formed from a collection of quadrilaterals. The corners of the quadrilaterals have coordinates corresponding to the values of the f_i when t and u take on values in a regular grid.

Here the x and y coordinates for the quadrilaterals are given simply by t and u. The result is a surface plot of the kind that can be produced by Plot3D.

In[5]:= **ParametricPlot3D[{t, u, Sin[t u]},**
{t, 0, 3}, {u, 0, 3}]

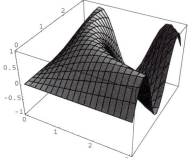

This shows the same surface as before, but with the y coordinates distorted by a quadratic transformation.

In[6]:= **ParametricPlot3D[{t, u^2, Sin[t u]},**
                             {t, 0, 3}, {u, 0, 3}]

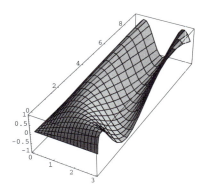

This produces a helicoid surface by taking the helical curve shown above, and at each section of the curve drawing a quadrilateral.

In[7]:= **ParametricPlot3D[{u Sin[t], u Cos[t], t/3},**
                             {t, 0, 15}, {u, -1, 1}]

In general, it is possible to construct many complicated surfaces using **ParametricPlot3D**. In each case, you can think of the surfaces as being formed by "distorting" or "rolling up" the t, u coordinate grid in a certain way.

This produces a cylinder. Varying the t parameter yields a circle in the *x, y* plane, while varying u moves the circles in the *z* direction.

```
In[8]:= ParametricPlot3D[{Sin[t], Cos[t], u},
                {t, 0, 2Pi}, {u, 0, 4}]
```

This produces a torus. Varying u yields a circle, while varying t rotates the circle around the *z* axis to form the torus.

```
In[9]:= ParametricPlot3D[
        {Cos[t] (3 + Cos[u]), Sin[t] (3 + Cos[u]), Sin[u]},
                {t, 0, 2Pi}, {u, 0, 2Pi}]
```

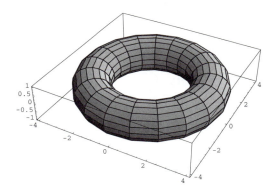

This produces a sphere.

In[10]:= `ParametricPlot3D[`
`                    {Cos[t] Cos[u], Sin[t] Cos[u], Sin[u]},`
`                    {t, 0, 2Pi}, {u, -Pi/2, Pi/2}]`

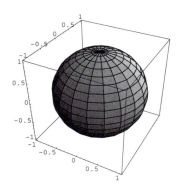

You should realize that when you draw surfaces with `ParametricPlot3D`, the exact choice of parametrization is often crucial. You should be careful, for example, to avoid parametrizations in which all or part of your surface is covered more than once. Such multiple coverings often lead to discontinuities in the mesh drawn on the surface, and may make `ParametricPlot3D` take much longer to render the surface.

■ 1.9.11 Some Special Plots

As discussed in Section 2.9, *Mathematica* includes a full graphics programming language. In this language, you can set up many different kinds of plots. A few of the common ones are included in standard *Mathematica* packages.

`<<Graphics`	load a package to set up additional graphics functions

`LogPlot[f, {x, xmin, xmax}]`	generate a log-linear plot
`LogLogPlot[f, {x, xmin, xmax}]`	generate a log-log plot
`LogListPlot[list]`	generate a log-linear plot from a list of data
`LogLogListPlot[list]`	generate a log-log plot from a list of data
`PolarPlot[r, {t, tmin, tmax}]`	generate a polar plot of the radius r as a function of angle t
`ErrorListPlot[{{x_1, y_1, dy_1}, ... }]`	generate a plot of data with error bars
`TextListPlot[{{x_1, y_1, "s_1"}, ... }]`	plot a list of data with each point given by the text string s_i
`BarChart[list]`	plot a list of data as a bar chart
`PieChart[list]`	plot a list of data as a pie chart
`PlotVectorField[{f_x, f_y}, {x, xmin, xmax}, {y, ymin, ymax}]`	plot the vector field corresponding to the vector function f
`ListPlotVectorField[list]`	plot the vector field corresponding to the two-dimensional array of vectors in *list*
`SphericalPlot3D[r, {theta, min, max}, {phi, min, max}]`	generate a three-dimensional spherical plot

Some special plotting functions defined in standard *Mathematica* packages.

This loads a standard *Mathematica* package to set up additional graphics functions.

In[1]:= `<<Graphics`

This generates a log-linear plot.

In[2]:= `LogPlot[ Exp[-x] + 4 Exp[-2x], {x, 0, 6} ]`

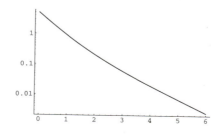

Here is a list of the first 10 primes.

In[3]:= **p = Table[Prime[n], {n, 10}]**

Out[3]= {2, 3, 5, 7, 11, 13, 17, 19, 23, 29}

This plots the primes using the integers 1, 2, 3, ... as plotting symbols.

In[4]:= **TextListPlot[p]**

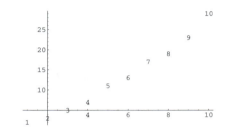

Here is a bar chart of the primes.

In[5]:= **BarChart[p]**

This gives a pie chart.

In[6]:= **PieChart[p]**

■ 1.9.12 Special Topic: Animated Graphics

On many computer systems, *Mathematica* can produce not only static images, but also animated graphics or "movies".

The basic idea in all cases is to generate a sequence of "frames" which can be displayed in rapid succession. You can use the standard *Mathematica* graphics functions described above to produce each frame. The mechanism for displaying the frames as a movie depends on the *Mathematica* interface you are using. With a notebook-based interface, you typically put the frames in a sequence of cells, then select the cells and choose a command to animate them. With text-based interfaces, there is often an external program provided for displaying animated graphics. The program can typically be accessed from inside *Mathematica* using the function **Animate**.

`<<Graphics'Animation'`	load the animation package (if necessary)
`Animate[plot, {t, tmin, tmax}]`	execute the graphics command *plot* for a sequence of values of *t*, and animate the resulting sequence of frames
`ShowAnimation[{`g_1`, `g_2`, ... }]`	produce an animation from a sequence of graphics objects

Typical ways to produce animated graphics.

When you produce a sequence of frames for a movie, it is important that different frames be consistent. Thus, for example, you should typically give an explicit setting for the **PlotRange** option, rather than using the default **Automatic** setting, in order to ensure that the scales used in different frames are the same. If you have three-dimensional graphics with different view points, you should similarly set **SphericalRegion -> True** in order to ensure that the scaling of different plots is the same.

This generates a list of graphics objects. Setting **DisplayFunction -> Identity** stops **Plot3D** from rendering the graphics it produces. Explicitly setting **PlotRange** ensures that the scale is the same in each piece of graphics.

```
In[1]:= Table[ Plot3D[ BesselJ[0, Sqrt[x^2 + y^2] + t],
              {x, -10, 10}, {y, -10, 10}, Axes -> False,
              PlotRange -> {-0.5, 1.0},
              DisplayFunction -> Identity ],
        {t, 0, 8} ] // Short

Out[1]//Short= {-SurfaceGraphics-, <<7>>, -SurfaceGraphics-}
```

On an appropriate computer system, `ShowAnimation[%]` would animate the graphics. This partitions the graphics into three rows, and shows the resulting array of images.

In[2]:= **Show[GraphicsArray[Partition[%, 3]]]**

■ 1.9.13 Sound

On most computer systems, *Mathematica* can produce not only graphics but also sound. *Mathematica* treats graphics and sound in a closely analogous way.

For example, just as you can use `Plot[f, {x, xmin, xmax}]` to plot a function, so also you can use `Play[f, {t, 0, tmax}]` to "play" a function. `Play` takes the function to define the waveform for a sound: the values of the function give the amplitude of the sound as a function of time.

Play[*f*, {*t*, 0, *tmax*}]	play a sound with amplitude *f* as a function of time *t* in seconds

Playing a function.

On a suitable computer system, this plays a pure tone with a frequency of 440 hertz for one second.

In[1]:= **Play[Sin[2Pi 440 t], {t, 0, 1}]**

Out[1]= -Sound-

Sounds produced by `Play` can have any waveform. They do not, for example, have to consist of a collection of harmonic pieces. In general, the amplitude function you give to `Play` specifies the instantaneous signal associated with the sound. This signal is typically converted to a voltage, and ultimately to a displacement. Note that *amplitude* is sometimes defined to be the *peak* signal associated with a sound; in *Mathematica*, it is always the *instantaneous* signal as a function of time.

This plays a more complex sound.

In[2]:= **Play[Sin[700 t + 25 t Sin[350 t]], {t, 0, 4}]**

Out[2]= -Sound-

Play is set up so that the time variable that appears in it is always measured in absolute seconds. When a sound is actually played, its amplitude is sampled a certain number of times every second. You can specify the sample rate by setting the option SampleRate.

Play[*f*, {*t*, 0, *tmax*}, SampleRate -> *r*]	play a sound, sampling it *r* times a second

Specifying the sample rate for a sound.

In general, the higher the sample rate, the better high-frequency components in the sound will be rendered. A sample rate of *r* typically allows frequencies up to *r*/2 hertz. The human auditory system can typically perceive sounds in the frequency range 20 to 22000 hertz (depending somewhat on age and sex). The fundamental frequencies for the 88 notes on a piano range from 27.5 to 4096 hertz.

The standard sample rate used for compact disc players is 44100. The effective sample rate in a typical telephone system is around 8000. On most computer systems, the default sample rate used by *Mathematica* is around 8000.

You can use Play[$\{f_1, f_2\}$, ...] to produce stereo sound. In general, *Mathematica* supports any number of sound channels.

ListPlay[$\{a_1, a_2, ... \}$, SampleRate -> *r*]	play a sound with a sequence of amplitude levels

Playing sampled sounds.

The function ListPlay allows you simply to give a list of values which are taken to be sound amplitudes sampled at a certain rate.

When sounds are actually rendered by *Mathematica*, only a certain range of amplitudes is allowed. The option PlayRange in Play and ListPlay specifies how the amplitudes you give should be scaled to fit in the allowed range. The settings for this option are analogous to those for the PlotRange graphics option discussed on page 136.

PlayRange -> Automatic (default)	use an internal procedure to scale amplitudes
PlayRange -> All	scale so that all amplitudes fit in the allowed range
PlayRange -> {*amin*, *amax*}	make amplitudes between *amin* and *amax* fit in the allowed range, and clip others

Specifying the scaling of sound amplitudes.

While it is often convenient to use the default setting `PlayRange -> Automatic`, you should realize that `Play` may run significantly faster if you give an explicit `PlayRange` specification, so it does not have to derive one.

Show[*sound*]	replay a sound object

Replaying a sound object.

Both `Play` and `ListPlay` return `Sound` objects which contain procedures for synthesizing sounds. You can replay a particular `Sound` object using the function `Show` that is also used for redisplaying graphics.

The internal structure of `Sound` objects is discussed in Section 2.9.18.

1.10 Input and Output in Notebooks

⁺■ 1.10.1 Entering Greek Letters

click on α	use a button in a palette
\[Alpha]	use a full name
ESC a ESC or ESC alpha ESC	use a standard alias (shown below as ⋮a⋮)
ESC \alpha ESC	use a TℇX alias
ESC &agr ESC	use an SGML alias

Ways to enter Greek letters in a notebook.

Here is a palette for entering common Greek letters.

α	β	γ	δ	ϵ	ζ	η
θ	κ	λ	μ	υ	ξ	π
ρ	σ	τ	ϕ	χ	ψ	ω
A	B	Γ	Δ	E	Z	H
ϑ	Λ	Ξ	Φ	X	Ψ	Ω

You can use Greek letters just like the ordinary letters that you type on your keyboard.

In[1]:= **Expand[(α + β)^3]**

Out[1]= $\alpha^3 + 3\alpha^2\beta + 3\alpha\beta^2 + \beta^3$

There are several ways to enter Greek letters. This input uses full names.

In[2]:= **Expand[(\[Alpha] + \[Beta])^3]**

Out[2]= $\alpha^3 + 3\alpha^2\beta + 3\alpha\beta^2 + \beta^3$

	full name	aliases		full name	aliases
α	\[Alpha]	:a:, :alpha:	Γ	\[CapitalGamma]	:G:, :Gamma:
β	\[Beta]	:b:, :beta:	Δ	\[CapitalDelta]	:D:, :Delta:
γ	\[Gamma]	:g:, :gamma:	Θ	\[CapitalTheta]	:Q:, :Th:, :Theta:
δ	\[Delta]	:d:, :delta:	Λ	\[CapitalLambda]	:L:, :Lambda:
ϵ	\[Epsilon]	:e:, :epsilon:	Π	\[CapitalPi]	:P:, :Pi:
ζ	\[Zeta]	:z:, :zeta:	Σ	\[CapitalSigma]	:S:, :Sigma:
η	\[Eta]	:h:, :et:, :eta:	Υ	\[CapitalUpsilon]	:U:, :Upsilon:
θ	\[Theta]	:q:, :th:, :theta:	Φ	\[CapitalPhi]	:F:, :Ph:, :Phi:
κ	\[Kappa]	:k:, :kappa:	X	\[CapitalChi]	:C:, :Ch:, :Chi:
λ	\[Lambda]	:l:, :lambda:	Ψ	\[CapitalPsi]	:Y:, :Ps:, :Psi:
μ	\[Mu]	:m:, :mu:	Ω	\[CapitalOmega]	:O:, :W:, :Omega:
ν	\[Nu]	:n:, :nu:			
ξ	\[Xi]	:x:, :xi:			
π	\[Pi]	:p:, :pi:			
ρ	\[Rho]	:r:, :rho:			
σ	\[Sigma]	:s:, :sigma:			
τ	\[Tau]	:t:, :tau:			
ϕ	\[Phi]	:f:, :ph:, :phi:			
φ	\[CurlyPhi]	:j:, :cph:, :cphi:			
χ	\[Chi]	:c:, :ch:, :chi:			
ψ	\[Psi]	:y:, :ps:, :psi:			
ω	\[Omega]	:o:, :w:, :omega:			

Commonly used Greek letters. In aliases : stands for the key [ESC]. TEX aliases are not listed explicitly.

Note that in *Mathematica* the letter π stands for Pi. None of the other Greek letters have special meanings.

π stands for Pi.

```
In[3]:= N[π]
Out[3]= 3.14159
```

You can use Greek letters either on their own or with other letters.

```
In[4]:= Expand[(Rαβ + Ξ)^4]
Out[4]= Rαβ^4 + 4 Rαβ^3 Ξ + 6 Rαβ^2 Ξ^2 + 4 Rαβ Ξ^3 + Ξ^4
```

The symbol $\pi\alpha$ is not related to the symbol π.

```
In[5]:= Factor[πα^4 - 1]
Out[5]= (-1 + πα) (1 + πα) (1 + πα^2)
```

⊞ 1.10.2 Entering Two-Dimensional Input

When *Mathematica* reads the text x^y, it interprets it as x raised to the power y.

$In[1]:=$ **x^y**

$Out[1]=$ x^y

In a notebook, you can also give the two-dimensional input x^y directly. *Mathematica* again interprets this as a power.

$In[2]:=$ **x^y**

$Out[2]=$ x^y

One way to enter a two-dimensional form such as x^y into a *Mathematica* notebook is to copy this form from a palette by clicking the appropriate button in the palette.

Here is a palette for entering some common two-dimensional notations.

There are also several ways to enter two-dimensional forms directly from the keyboard.

x CTRL ^ y CTRL ␣	use control keys that exist on most keyboards
x CTRL 6 y CTRL ␣	use control keys that should exist on all keyboards
\!\(x\^y\) followed by Make 2D	use only ordinary printable characters

Ways to enter a superscript directly from the keyboard. CTRL ␣ stands for CONTROL-SPACE.

You type CTRL ^ by holding down the CONTROL key, then hitting the ^ key. As soon as you do this, your cursor will jump to a superscript position. You can then type anything you want and it will appear in that position.

When you have finished, press CTRL ␣ to move back down from the superscript position. CTRL ␣ stands for CONTROL-SPACE; you type it by holding down the CONTROL key, then pressing the space bar.

This sequence of keystrokes enters x^y.

$In[3]:=$ **x** CTRL ^ **y**

$Out[3]=$ x^y

Here the whole expression y+z is in the superscript.

$In[4]:=$ **x** CTRL ^ **y + z**

$Out[4]=$ x^{y+z}

Pressing CTRL ␣ (CONTROL-SPACE) takes you down from the superscript.

$In[5]:=$ **x** CTRL ^ **y** CTRL ␣ **+ z**

$Out[5]=$ $x^y + z$

You can remember the fact that [CTRL][^] gives you a superscript by thinking of [CTRL][^] as just a more immediate form of ^. When you type x^y, *Mathematica* will leave this one-dimensional form unchanged until you explicitly process it. But if you type x [CTRL][^] y then *Mathematica* will immediately give you a superscript.

On a standard English-language keyboard, the character ^ appears as the shifted version of 6. *Mathematica* therefore accepts [CTRL][6] as an alternative to [CTRL][^]. Note that if you are using something other than a standard English-language keyboard, *Mathematica* will almost always accept [CTRL][6] but may not accept [CTRL][^].

This is an alternative input form that avoids the use of control characters.	$In[6]:= \backslash!\backslash(x \backslash^\wedge y \backslash)$ $Out[6]= x^y$
With this input form, *Mathematica* automatically understands that the + z does not go in the superscript.	$In[7]:= \backslash!\backslash(x \backslash^\wedge y + z \backslash)$ $Out[7]= x^y + z$

Using control characters minimizes the number of keystrokes that you need to type in order to enter a superscript. But particularly if you want to save your input in a file, or send it to another program, it is often more convenient to use a form that does not involve control characters. You can do this using \! sequences.

If you copy a \! sequence into *Mathematica*, it will automatically jump into two-dimensional form. But if you enter the sequence directly from the keyboard, you explicitly need to choose the Make 2D menu item in order to get the two-dimensional form.

When entered from the keyboard \(... \) sequences are shown in literal form.	$\backslash ! \backslash (x \backslash^\wedge y + z \backslash)$
Choosing the Make 2D item in the Edit menu converts these sequences into two-dimensional forms.	$x^y + z$

x [CTRL][_] y [CTRL][ ]	use control keys that exist on most keyboards
x [CTRL][-] y [CTRL][ ]	use control keys that should exist on all keyboards
$\backslash!\backslash(x\backslash\_y\backslash)$ followed by Make 2D	use only ordinary printable characters

Ways to enter a subscript directly from the keyboard.

Subscripts in *Mathematica* work very much like superscripts. However, whereas *Mathematica* automatically interprets x^y as x raised to the power y, it has no similar interpretation for x_y. Instead, it just treats x_y as a purely symbolic object.

This enters y as a subscript.

$In[8]:=$ **x** CTRL ⎡_⎤ **y**

$Out[8]=$ x$_y$

Here is another way to enter y as a subscript.

$In[9]:=$ \!\(x _ y \)

$Out[9]=$ x$_y$

x CTRL ⎡/⎤ y CTRL ⎡␣⎤	use control keys
\!\(x\/y\) followed by Make 2D	use only ordinary printable characters

Ways to enter a built-up fraction directly from the keyboard.

This enters the built-up fraction $\frac{x}{y}$.

$In[10]:=$ **x** CTRL ⎡/⎤ **y**

$Out[10]=$ $\dfrac{x}{y}$

Here the whole y + z goes into the denominator.

$In[11]:=$ **x** CTRL ⎡/⎤ **y + z**

$Out[11]=$ $\dfrac{x}{y+z}$

But pressing CONTROL-SPACE takes you out of the denominator, so the + z does not appear in the denominator.

$In[12]:=$ **x** CTRL ⎡/⎤ **y** CTRL ⎡␣⎤ **+ z**

$Out[12]=$ $\dfrac{x}{y}+z$

Mathematica automatically interprets a built-up fraction as a division.

$In[13]:=$ $\dfrac{\textbf{8888}}{\textbf{2222}}$

$Out[13]=$ 4

Here is another way to enter a built-up fraction.

$In[14]:=$ \!\(8888 \/ 2222 \)

$Out[14]=$ 4

CTRL ⎡@⎤ x CTRL ⎡␣⎤	use control keys that exist on most keyboards
CTRL ⎡2⎤ x CTRL ⎡␣⎤	use control keys that should exist on all keyboards
\!\(\@x\) followed by Make 2D	use only ordinary printable characters

Ways to enter a square root directly from the keyboard.

This enters a square root.

$In[15]:=$ CTRL ⎡@⎤ **x + y**

$Out[15]=$ $\sqrt{x+y}$

CONTROL-SPACE takes you out of the square root.

$In[16]:=$ CTRL ⎡@⎤ **x** CTRL ⎡␣⎤ **+ y**

$Out[16]=$ $\sqrt{x}+y$

Here is a form without control characters.

In[17]:= `\!\( \@ x + y \)`

Out[17]= $\sqrt{x} + y$

And here is the usual one-dimensional *Mathematica* input that gives the same output expression.

In[18]:= **Sqrt[x] + y**

Out[18]= $\sqrt{x} + y$

CTRL ^ or CTRL 6		go to the superscript position
CTRL _ or CTRL −		go to the subscript position
CTRL @ or CTRL 2		go into a square root
CTRL % or CTRL 5		go from subscript to superscript or vice versa, or to the exponent position in a root
CTRL /		go to the denominator for a fraction
CTRL ␣		return from a special position (CONTROL-SPACE)

Special input forms based on control characters. The second forms given should work on any keyboard.

This puts both a subscript and a superscript on x.

In[19]:= **x** CTRL ^ **y** CTRL % **z**

Out[19]= x_z^y

Here is another way to enter the same expression.

In[20]:= **x** CTRL _ **z** CTRL % **y**

Out[20]= x_z^y

`\!\( ... \)`	all two-dimensional input and grouping within it
x `\^` y	superscript x^y within `\!\( ... \)`
x `\_` y	subscript x_y within `\!\( ... \)`
x `\^` y `\%` z	subscript and superscript x_z^y within `\!\( ... \)`
`\@` x	square root $\sqrt{x}$ within `\!\( ... \)`
x `\/` y	built-up fraction $\frac{x}{y}$ within `\!\( ... \)`

Special input forms that generate two-dimensional input with the Make 2D menu item.

You must preface the outermost \(with \!.

$In[21]:= $ `\!\(a \/ b + \@ c \) + d`

$Out[21]= \dfrac{a}{b} + \sqrt{c} + d$

You can use \(and \) to indicate the grouping of elements in an expression without introducing explicit parentheses.

$In[22]:= $ `\!\(a \/ \( b + \@ c \) \) + d`

$Out[22]= \dfrac{a}{b + \sqrt{c}} + d$

In addition to subscripts and superscripts, *Mathematica* also supports the notion of underscripts and overscripts—elements that go directly underneath or above. Among other things, you can use underscripts and overscripts to enter the limits of sums and products.

x CTRL+$+$ y CTRL+$\_$ or x CTRL+$=$ y CTRL+$\_$	create an underscript $\underset{y}{x}$
`\!\(x\+y\)` followed by Make 2D	create an underscript $\underset{y}{x}$
x CTRL+$\&$ y CTRL+$\_$ or x CTRL+7 y CTRL+$\_$	create an overscript $\overset{y}{x}$
`\!\(x\&y\)` followed by Make 2D	create an overscript $\overset{y}{x}$

Creating underscripts and overscripts.

+■ 1.10.3 Editing and Evaluating Two-Dimensional Expressions

When you see a two-dimensional expression on the screen, you can edit it much as you would edit text. You can for example place your cursor somewhere and start typing. Or you can select a part of the expression, then remove it using the DELETE key, or insert a new version by typing it in.

In addition to ordinary text editing features, there are some keys that you can use to move around in two-dimensional expressions.

CTRL+.	select the next larger subexpression
CTRL+$\_$	move to the right of the current structure
$\rightarrow$	move to the next character
$\leftarrow$	move to the previous character

Ways to move around in two-dimensional expressions.

This shows the sequence of subexpressions selected by repeatedly typing $\boxed{\text{CTRL}}\,\boxed{.}$.

$$-\frac{\text{ArcTan}\left[\frac{1+2x}{\sqrt{3}}\right]}{\sqrt{3}}+\frac{\text{Log}[-1+x]}{3}-\frac{\text{Log}[1+x+x^2]}{6}+\frac{\text{Log}[-1+x+x^2+x^3]}{9}$$

$$-\frac{\text{ArcTan}\left[\frac{1+2x}{\sqrt{3}}\right]}{\sqrt{3}}+\frac{\text{Log}[-1+x]}{3}-\frac{\text{Log}[1+x+x^2]}{6}+\frac{\text{Log}[-1+x+x^2+x^3]}{9}$$

$$-\frac{\text{ArcTan}\left[\frac{1+2x}{\sqrt{3}}\right]}{\sqrt{3}}+\frac{\text{Log}[-1+x]}{3}-\frac{\text{Log}[1+x+x^2]}{6}+\frac{\text{Log}[-1+x+x^2+x^3]}{9}$$

$$-\frac{\text{ArcTan}\left[\frac{1+2x}{\sqrt{3}}\right]}{\sqrt{3}}+\frac{\text{Log}[-1+x]}{3}-\frac{\text{Log}[1+x+x^2]}{6}+\frac{\text{Log}[-1+x+x^2+x^3]}{9}$$

$$-\frac{\text{ArcTan}\left[\frac{1+2x}{\sqrt{3}}\right]}{\sqrt{3}}+\frac{\text{Log}[-1+x]}{3}-\frac{\text{Log}[1+x+x^2]}{6}+\frac{\text{Log}[-1+x+x^2+x^3]}{9}$$

$$-\frac{\text{ArcTan}\left[\frac{1+2x}{\sqrt{3}}\right]}{\sqrt{3}}+\frac{\text{Log}[-1+x]}{3}-\frac{\text{Log}[1+x+x^2]}{6}+\frac{\text{Log}[-1+x+x^2+x^3]}{9}$$

SHIFT-RETURN	evaluate the whole current cell
COMMAND-RETURN or ALT-RETURN	evaluate only the selected subexpression

Ways to evaluate two-dimensional expressions.

In most computations, you will want to go from one step to the next by taking the whole expression that you have generated, and then evaluating it. But if for example you are trying to manipulate a single formula to put it into a particular form, you may instead find it more convenient to perform a sequence of operations separately on different parts of the expression.

You do this by selecting each part you want to operate on, then inserting the operation you want to perform, then using COMMAND-RETURN.

Here is an expression with one part selected.

```
{Factor[x⁴ - 1], Factor[x⁵ - 1], Factor[x⁶ - 1], Factor[x⁷ - 1]}
```

Pressing COMMAND-RETURN evaluates the selected part.

```
{Factor[x⁴ - 1], (-1 + x) (1 + x + x² + x³ + x⁴), Factor[x⁶ - 1], Factor[x⁷ - 1]}
```

+■ **1.10.4 Entering Formulas**

character	short form	long form	symbol
π	⌑p⌑	\[Pi]	Pi
∞	⌑inf⌑	\[Infinity]	Infinity
$\circ$	⌑deg⌑	\[Degree]	Degree

Special forms for some common symbols. ⌑ stands for the key ESC.

This is equivalent to Sin[60 Degree].

In[1]:= **Sin[60°]**

Out[1]= $\dfrac{\sqrt{3}}{2}$

Here is the long form of the input.

In[2]:= **Sin[60 \[Degree]]**

Out[2]= $\dfrac{\sqrt{3}}{2}$

You can enter the same input like this.

In[3]:= **Sin[60 ⌑deg⌑]**

Out[3]= $\dfrac{\sqrt{3}}{2}$

Here the angle is in radians.

In[4]:= **Sin$\left[\dfrac{\pi}{3}\right]$**

Out[4]= $\dfrac{\sqrt{3}}{2}$

special characters	short form	long form	ordinary characters
$x \le y$	x ⌑<=⌑ y	x \[LessEqual] y	x <= y
$x \ge y$	x ⌑>=⌑ y	x \[GreaterEqual] y	x >= y
$x \ne y$	x ⌑!=⌑ y	x \[NotEqual] y	x != y
$x \rightarrow y$	x ⌑->⌑ y	x \[Rule] y	x -> y

Special forms for a few operators. Pages 970–975 give a complete list.

Here the replacement rule is entered
using two ordinary characters, as ->.

In[5]:= **x/(x+1) /. x -> 3 + y**

Out[5]= $\dfrac{3+y}{4+y}$

This means exactly the same.	*In[6]:=* `x/(x+1) /. x \[Rule] 3 + y`
	Out[6]= $\dfrac{3+y}{4+y}$
As does this.	*In[7]:=* `x/(x+1) /. x → 3 + y`
	Out[7]= $\dfrac{3+y}{4+y}$
Or this.	*In[8]:=* `x/(x+1) /. x :->: 3 + y`
	Out[8]= $\dfrac{3+y}{4+y}$
The special arrow form → is by default also used for output.	*In[9]:=* `Solve[x^2 == 1, x]`
	Out[9]= `{{x → -1}, {x → 1}}`

special characters	short form	long form	ordinary characters
$x \div y$	x :div: y	x `\[Divide]` y	x `/` y
$x \times y$	x :*: y	x `\[Times]` y	x `*` y
$x \times y$	x :cross: y	x `\[Cross]` y	`Cross[`x, y`]`
$x = y$	x :==: y	x `\[Equal]` y	x `==` y
$x \wedge y$	x :&&: y	x `\[And]` y	x `&&` y
$x \vee y$	x :||: y	x `\[Or]` y	x `||` y
$\neg\, x$	:!: x	`\[Not]` x	`!`x
$x \Rightarrow y$	x :=>: y	x `\[Implies]` y	`Implies[`x, y`]`
$x \cup y$	x :un: y	x `\[Union]` y	`Union[`x, y`]`
$x \cap y$	x :inter: y	x `\[Intersection]` y	`Intersection[`x, y`]`
xy	x :,: y	x `\[InvisibleComma]` y	x,y

Some operators with special forms used for input but not output.

Mathematica understands $\div$, but does not use it by default for output.	*In[10]:=* `x ÷ y`
	Out[10]= $\dfrac{x}{y}$

The forms of input discussed so far in this section use special characters, but otherwise just consist of ordinary one-dimensional lines of text. *Mathematica* notebooks, however, also make it possible to use two-dimensional forms of input.

two-dimensional	one-dimensional	
x^y	x ^ y	power
$\dfrac{x}{y}$	x / y	division
$\sqrt{x}$	Sqrt[x]	square root
$\sqrt[n]{x}$	x ^ (1/n)	nth root
$\displaystyle\sum_{i=imin}^{imax} f$	Sum[f, {i, imin, imax}]	sum
$\displaystyle\prod_{i=imin}^{imax} f$	Product[f, {i, imin, imax}]	product
$\displaystyle\int f\,dx$	Integrate[f, x]	indefinite integral
$\displaystyle\int_{xmin}^{xmax} f\,dx$	Integrate[f, {x, xmin, xmax}]	definite integral
$\partial_x f$	D[f, x]	partial derivative
$\partial_{x,y} f$	D[f, x, y]	multivariate partial derivative

Some two-dimensional forms that can be used in *Mathematica* notebooks.

You can enter two-dimensional forms using any of the mechanisms discussed on pages 175–179. Note that upper and lower limits for sums and products must be entered as overscripts and underscripts—not superscripts and subscripts.

This enters an indefinite integral. Note the use of ⦂**dd**⦂ to enter the "differential d".	*In[11]:=* ⦂**int**⦂ **f[x]** ⦂**dd**⦂ **x**
	Out[11]= $\displaystyle\int f[x]\,dx$
Here is an indefinite integral that can be explicitly evaluated.	*In[12]:=* $\displaystyle\int$ **Exp[-x²]dx**
	Out[12]= $\dfrac{1}{2}\sqrt{\pi}\,\text{Erf}[x]$

Here is the usual *Mathematica* input for this integral.	*In[13]:=* **Integrate[Exp[-x^2], x]**
	Out[13]= $\frac{1}{2} \sqrt{\pi} \text{ Erf}[x]$
This enters exactly the same integral.	*In[14]:=* **\!\(\[Integral] Exp[-x\^2] \[DifferentialD]x \)**
	Out[14]= $\frac{1}{2} \sqrt{\pi} \text{ Erf}[x]$

short form	long form	
⁞sum⁞	\[Sum]	summation sign $\sum$
⁞prod⁞	\[Product]	product sign $\prod$
⁞int⁞	\[Integral]	integral sign $\int$
⁞dd⁞	\[DifferentialD]	special d for use in integrals
⁞pd⁞	\[PartialD]	partial derivative operator ∂

Some special characters used in entering formulas. Section 3.10 gives a complete list.

You should realize that even though a summation sign can look almost identical to a capital sigma it is treated in a very different way by *Mathematica*. The point is that a sigma is just a letter; but a summation sign is an operator which tells *Mathematica* to perform a Sum operation.

Capital sigma is just a letter.	*In[15]:=* **a + \[CapitalSigma]^2**
	Out[15]= $a + \Sigma^2$
A summation sign, on the other hand, is an operator.	*In[16]:=* ESC**sum**ESC CTRL+ **n=0** CTRL% **m** CTRL␣ **1/f[n]**
	Out[16]= $\displaystyle\sum_{n=0}^{m} \frac{1}{f[n]}$
Here is another way to enter the same input.	*In[17]:=* **\!\(\[Sum] \+ \(n = 0 \) \% m 1 \/ f[n] \)**
	Out[17]= $\displaystyle\sum_{n=0}^{m} \frac{1}{f[n]}$

Much as *Mathematica* distinguishes between a summation sign and a capital sigma, it also distinguishes between an ordinary d and the special "differential d" d that is used in the standard notation for integrals. It is crucial that you use this differential d—entered as ESC**dd**ESC—when you type in an integral. If you try to use an ordinary d, *Mathematica* will just interpret this as a symbol called d—it will not understand that you are entering the second part of an integration operator.

This computes the derivative of x^n.	*In[18]:=* **∂ₓxⁿ**
	Out[18]= $n x^{-1+n}$

Here is the same derivative specified in ordinary one-dimensional form.

$In[19]:=$ **D[x^n, x]**

$Out[19]=$ $n\,x^{-1+n}$

This computes the third derivative.

$In[20]:=$ $\partial_{x,x,x}\,x^n$

$Out[20]=$ $(-2+n)\,(-1+n)\,n\,x^{-3+n}$

Here is the equivalent one-dimensional input form.

$In[21]:=$ **D[x^n, x, x, x]**

$Out[21]=$ $(-2+n)\,(-1+n)\,n\,x^{-3+n}$

■ 1.10.5 Entering Tables and Matrices

The *Mathematica* front end typically provides a Create Table/Matrix/Palette menu item which allows you to create a blank array with any specified number of rows and columns. Once you have such an array, you can then edit it to fill in whatever elements you want.

Mathematica treats an array like this as a matrix represented by a list of lists.

$In[1]:=$ $\begin{array}{ccc} a & b & c \\ 1 & 2 & 3 \end{array}$

$Out[1]=$ {{a, b, c}, {1, 2, 3}}

Putting parentheses around the array makes it look more like a matrix, but does not affect its interpretation.

$In[2]:=$ $\begin{pmatrix} a & b & c \\ 1 & 2 & 3 \end{pmatrix}$

$Out[2]=$ {{a, b, c}, {1, 2, 3}}

Using **MatrixForm** tells *Mathematica* to display the result of the Transpose as a matrix.

$In[3]:=$ **MatrixForm**$\Big[$**Transpose**$\Big[\begin{pmatrix} a & b & c \\ 1 & 2 & 3 \end{pmatrix}\Big]\Big]$

$Out[3]//MatrixForm=$ $\begin{pmatrix} a & 1 \\ b & 2 \\ c & 3 \end{pmatrix}$

CTRL ,	add a column
CTRL ↵ (CONTROL-RETURN)	add a row
TAB	go to the next □ or ■ element
CTRL ␣ (CONTROL-SPACE)	move out of the table or matrix

Entering tables and matrices.

Note that you can use CTRL , and CTRL ↵ to start building up an array, and particularly for small arrays this is often more convenient than using the Create Table/Matrix/Palette menu item.

Page 428 will describe how to adjust many aspects of the appearance of arrays you create in *Mathematica*. The Create Table/Matrix/Palette menu item typically allows you to make basic adjustments, such as drawing lines between rows or columns.

+■ 1.10.6 Subscripts, Bars and Other Modifiers

Here is a typical palette of modifiers.

Mathematica allows you to use any expression as a subscript.

$In[1]:=$ **Expand$\left[(1 + x_{1+n})^4\right]$**

$Out[1]= 1 + 4 x_{1+n} + 6 x_{1+n}^2 + 4 x_{1+n}^3 + x_{1+n}^4$

Unless you specifically tell it otherwise, *Mathematica* will interpret a superscript as a power.

$In[2]:=$ **Factor$[x_n^4 - 1]$**

$Out[2]= (-1 + x_n) (1 + x_n) (1 + x_n^2)$

CTRL $\boxed{\_}$ or CTRL $\boxed{-}$	go to the position for a subscript
CTRL $\boxed{+}$ or CTRL $\boxed{=}$	go to the position underneath
CTRL $\boxed{\wedge}$ or CTRL $\boxed{6}$	go to the position for a superscript
CTRL $\boxed{\&}$ or CTRL $\boxed{7}$	go to the position on top
CTRL $\boxed{\ }$	return from a special position (CONTROL-SPACE)

Special input forms based on control characters. The second forms given should work on any keyboard.

This enters a subscript using control keys.

$In[3]:=$ **Expand[(1 + x CTRL$\boxed{\_}$ 1+n CTRL$\boxed{\ }$)^4]**

$Out[3]= 1 + 4 x_{1+n} + 6 x_{1+n}^2 + 4 x_{1+n}^3 + x_{1+n}^4$

Just as CTRL$\boxed{\wedge}$ and CTRL$\boxed{\_}$ go to superscript and subscript positions, so also CTRL$\boxed{\&}$ and CTRL$\boxed{=}$ can be used to go to positions directly above and below. With the layout of a standard English-language keyboard CTRL$\boxed{\&}$ is directly to the right of CTRL$\boxed{\wedge}$ while CTRL$\boxed{=}$ is directly to the right of CTRL$\boxed{\_}$.

key sequence	displayed form	expression form
x CTRL $\&$ _	$\bar{x}$	OverBar[x]
x CTRL $\&$: vec :	$\vec{x}$	OverVector[x]
x CTRL $\&$ ~	$\tilde{x}$	OverTilde[x]
x CTRL $\&$ ^	$\hat{x}$	OverHat[x]
x CTRL $\&$.	$\dot{x}$	OverDot[x]
x CTRL $=$ _	$\underline{x}$	UnderBar[x]

Ways to enter some common modifiers using control keys.

Here is $\bar{x}$.

$In[4]:=$ **x** CTRL $\&$ _ CTRL $\lrcorner$

$Out[4]=$ $\overline{x}$

You can use $\bar{x}$ as a variable.

$In[5]:=$ **Solve[a^2 == %, a]**

$Out[5]=$ $\{\{a \rightarrow -\sqrt{\overline{x}}\,\}, \{a \rightarrow \sqrt{\overline{x}}\,\}\}$

key sequence	displayed form	expression form
x _ y	x_y	Subscript[x, y]
x \+ y	$\underset{y}{x}$	Underscript[x, y]
x \^ y	x^y	Superscript[x, y] (interpreted as Power[x, y])
x \& y	$\overset{y}{x}$	Overscript[x, y]
x \&_	$\bar{x}$	OverBar[x]
x \&\[RightVector]	$\vec{x}$	OverVector[x]
x \&~	$\tilde{x}$	OverTilde[x]
x \&^	$\hat{x}$	OverHat[x]
x \&.	$\dot{x}$	OverDot[x]
x \+_	$\underline{x}$	UnderBar[x]

Ways to enter modifiers without control keys. All these forms can be used only inside \!\(... \).

■ 1.10.7 Special Topic: Non-English Characters and Keyboards

If you enter text in languages other than English, you will typically need to use various additional accented and other characters. If your computer system is set up in an appropriate way, then you will often be able to enter such characters directly using standard keys on your keyboard. But however your system is set up, *Mathematica* always provides a uniform way to handle such characters.

	full name	alias			full name	alias
à	\[AGrave]	⁚a`⁚		ø	\[OSlash]	⁚o/⁚
å	\[ARing]	⁚ao⁚		ö	\[ODoubleDot]	⁚o"⁚
ä	\[ADoubleDot]	⁚a"⁚		ù	\[UGrave]	⁚u`⁚
ç	\[CCedilla]	⁚c,⁚		ü	\[UDoubleDot]	⁚u"⁚
č	\[CHacek]	⁚cv⁚		ß	\[SZ]	⁚sz⁚, ⁚ss⁚
é	\[EAcute]	⁚e'⁚		Å	\[CapitalARing]	⁚Ao⁚
è	\[EGrave]	⁚e`⁚		Ä	\[CapitalADoubleDot]	⁚A"⁚
í	\[IAcute]	⁚i'⁚		Ö	\[CapitalODoubleDot]	⁚O"⁚
ñ	\[NTilde]	⁚n~⁚		Ü	\[CapitalUDoubleDot]	⁚U"⁚
ò	\[OGrave]	⁚o`⁚				

Some common European characters.

Here is a function whose name involves an accented character.	In[1]:= **Lam\[EAcute][x, y]** Out[1]= Lamé[x, y]
This is another way to enter the same input.	In[2]:= **Lam⁚e'⁚[x, y]** Out[2]= Lamé[x, y]

You should realize that there is no uniform standard for computer keyboards around the world, and as a result it is inevitable that some details of what has been said in this chapter may not apply to your keyboard.

In particular, the identification for example of [CTRL]-[6] with [CTRL]-[^] is valid only for keyboards on which ^ appears as SHIFT-6. On other keyboards, *Mathematica* uses [CTRL]-[6] to go to a superscript position, but not necessarily [CTRL]-[^].

Regardless of how your keyboard is set up you can always use palettes or menu items to set up superscripts and other kinds of notation. And assuming you have some way to enter characters such as \, you can always give input using full names such as \[Infinity] and textual forms such as \(x\/y\).

+■ 1.10.8 Other Mathematical Notation

Mathematica supports an extremely wide range of mathematical notation, although often it does not assign a pre-defined meaning to it. Thus, for example, you can enter an expression such as x ⊕ y, but *Mathematica* will not initially make any assumption about what you mean by ⊕.

Mathematica knows that ⊕ is an operator, but it does not initially assign any specific meaning to it.	*In[1]:=* **{17 ⊕ 5, 8 ⊕ 3}** *Out[1]=* {17⊕5, 8⊕3}
This gives *Mathematica* a definition for what the ⊕ operator does.	*In[2]:=* **x_ ⊕ y_ := Mod[x + y, 2]**
Now *Mathematica* can evaluate ⊕ operations.	*In[3]:=* **{17 ⊕ 5, 8 ⊕ 3}** *Out[3]=* {0, 1}

	full name	alias			full name	alias
⊕	\[CirclePlus]	:c+:		⟶	\[LongRightArrow]	:-->:
⊗	\[CircleTimes]	:c*:		↔	\[LeftRightArrow]	:<->:
±	\[PlusMinus]	:+-:		↑	\[UpArrow]	
∧	\[Wedge]	:^:		⇌	\[Equilibrium]	:equi:
∨	\[Vee]	:v:		⊢	\[RightTee]	
≃	\[TildeEqual]	:~=:		⊃	\[Superset]	:sup:
≈	\[TildeTilde]	:~~:		⊓	\[SquareIntersection]	
~	\[Tilde]	:~:		∈	\[Element]	:elem:
∝	\[Proportional]	:prop:		∉	\[NotElement]	:!elem:
≡	\[Congruent]	:===:		∘	\[SmallCircle]	:sc:
≳	\[GreaterTilde]	:>~:		∴	\[Therefore]	
≫	\[GreaterGreater]			∣	\[VerticalSeparator]	:|:
≻	\[Succeeds]			∣	\[VerticalBar]	:_|:
▷	\[RightTriangle]			\	\[Backslash]	:\:

A few of the operators whose input is supported by *Mathematica*.

Mathematica assigns built-in meanings to ≥ and ≥, but not to ≳ or ≫.	*In[4]:=* **{3 ≥ 4, 3 ≥ 4, 3 ≳ 4, 3 ≫ 4}** *Out[4]=* {False, False, 3 ≳ 4, 3 ≫ 4}

There are some forms which look like characters on a standard keyboard, but which are interpreted in a different way by *Mathematica*. Thus, for example, \[Backslash] or :\: displays as \ but is not interpreted in the same way as a \ typed directly on the keyboard.

The \ and ∧ characters used here are different from the \ and ^ you would type directly on a keyboard.

In[5]:= **{a :\: b, a :^: b}**

Out[5]= {a \ b, a ∧ b}

Most operators work like ⊕ and go in between their operands. But some operators can go in other places. Thus, for example, :<: and :>: or \[LeftAngleBracket] and \[RightAngleBracket] are effectively operators which go around their operand.

The elements of the angle bracket operator go around their operand.

In[6]:= **\[LeftAngleBracket] 1 + x \[RightAngleBracket]**

Out[6]= ⟨1 + x⟩

	full name	alias			full name	alias
ℓ	\[ScriptL]	:scl:		Å	\[Angstrom]	:Ang:
ℰ	\[ScriptCapitalE]	:scE:		ℏ	\[HBar]	:hb:
ℛ	\[GothicCapitalR]	:goR:		£	\[Sterling]	
ℤ	\[DoubleStruckCapitalZ]	:dsZ:		∟	\[Angle]	
ℵ	\[Aleph]	:al:		•	\[Bullet]	:bu:
∅	\[EmptySet]	:es:		†	\[Dagger]	:dg:
μ	\[Micro]	:mi:		♮	\[Natural]	

Some additional letters and letter-like forms.

You can use letters and letter-like forms anywhere in symbol names.

In[7]:= **{R∅, \[Angle]ABC}**

Out[7]= {R∅, ∟ABC}

∅ is assumed to be a symbol, and so is just multiplied by a and b.

In[8]:= **a ∅ b**

Out[8]= a b ∅

⊣■ 1.10.9 Forms of Input and Output

Mathematica notebooks allow you to give input and get output in a variety of different forms. Typically the front end provides menu commands for converting cells from one form to another.

`InputForm`	a form that can be typed directly using characters on a standard keyboard
`OutputForm`	a form for output only that uses just characters on a standard keyboard
`StandardForm`	a form for input and output that makes use of special characters and positioning
`TraditionalForm`	a form primarily for output that imitates all aspects of traditional mathematical notation

Forms of input and output.

The input here works in both `InputForm` and `StandardForm`.

$In[1]:=$ **x^2 + y^2/z**

$Out[1]= x^2 + \dfrac{y^2}{z}$

Here is a version of the input appropriate for `StandardForm`.

$In[2]:= x^2 + \dfrac{y^2}{z}$

$Out[2]= x^2 + \dfrac{y^2}{z}$

`InputForm` is the most general form of input for *Mathematica*: it works whether you are using a notebook interface or a text-based interface.

With a notebook interface, output is by default produced in `StandardForm`.

$In[3]:=$ **Sqrt[x] + 1/(2 + Sqrt[y])**

$Out[3]= \sqrt{x} + \dfrac{1}{2 + \sqrt{y}}$

With a text-based interface, `OutputForm` is used instead.

$In[4]:=$ **Sqrt[x] + 1/(2 + Sqrt[y]) // OutputForm**

$Out[4]//OutputForm= Sqrt[x] + \dfrac{1}{2 + Sqrt[y]}$

With a notebook interface, the default form for both input and output is `StandardForm`.

The basic idea of `StandardForm` is to provide a precise but elegant representation of *Mathematica* expressions, making use of special characters, two-dimensional positioning, and so on.

Both input and output are given here in StandardForm.

$In[5]:= \int \frac{1}{(x^3+1)} dx$

$Out[5]= \frac{ArcTan\left[\frac{-1+2x}{\sqrt{3}}\right]}{\sqrt{3}} + \frac{1}{3} Log[1+x] - \frac{1}{6} Log[1-x+x^2]$

An important feature of StandardForm is that any output you get in this form you can also directly use as input.

$In[6]:= \frac{ArcTan\left[\frac{-1+2x}{\sqrt{3}}\right]}{\sqrt{3}} + \frac{1}{3} Log[1+x] - \frac{1}{6} Log[1-x+x^2]$

$Out[6]= \frac{ArcTan\left[\frac{-1+2x}{\sqrt{3}}\right]}{\sqrt{3}} + \frac{1}{3} Log[1+x] - \frac{1}{6} Log[1-x+x^2]$

The precise nature of StandardForm prevents it from following all of the somewhat haphazard conventions of traditional mathematical notation. *Mathematica* however also supports TraditionalForm, which uses a large collection of rules to give a rather complete rendition of traditional mathematical notation.

TraditionalForm uses lower-case names for functions, and puts their arguments in parentheses rather than square brackets.

$In[7]:= \int \frac{1}{(x^3+1)} dx // TraditionalForm$

$Out[7]//TraditionalForm= \frac{\tan^{-1}\left(\frac{2x-1}{\sqrt{3}}\right)}{\sqrt{3}} + \frac{1}{3} \log(x+1) - \frac{1}{6} \log(x^2-x+1)$

Here are a few transformations made by TraditionalForm.

$In[8]:= \{Abs[x], ArcTan[x], BesselJ[0, x], Binomial[i, j]\} // TraditionalForm$

$Out[8]//TraditionalForm= \left\{|x|, \tan^{-1}(x), J_0(x), \binom{i}{j}\right\}$

TraditionalForm is often useful for generating output that can be inserted directly into documents which use traditional mathematical notation. But you should understand that TraditionalForm is intended primarily for output: it does not have the kind of precision that is needed to provide reliable input to *Mathematica*.

Thus, for example, in TraditionalForm, Ci(x) is the representation for both Ci[x] and CosIntegral[x], so if this form appears on its own as input, *Mathematica* will have no idea which of the two interpretations is the correct one.

In StandardForm, these three expressions are all displayed in a unique and unambiguous way.

$In[9]:= \{ Ci[1+x], CosIntegral[1+x], Ci(1+x) \} // StandardForm$

$Out[9]//StandardForm= \{Ci[1+x], CosIntegral[1+x], Ci(1+x)\}$

In TraditionalForm, however, the first two are impossible to distinguish, and the third differs only in the presence of an extra space.

$In[10]:= \{ Ci[1+x], CosIntegral[1+x], Ci(1+x) \} // TraditionalForm$

$Out[10]//TraditionalForm= \{Ci(x+1), Ci(x+1), Ci(x+1)\}$

The ambiguities of TraditionalForm make it in general unsuitable for specifying input to the *Mathematica* kernel. But at least for sufficiently simple cases, *Mathematica* does include various heuristic rules for trying to interpret TraditionalForm expressions as *Mathematica* input.

Cells intended for input to the kernel are assumed by default to contain `StandardForm` expressions.

$$In[1]:= c\left(\sqrt{x} + \frac{1}{x}\right) + \Gamma(x)$$

$$Out[1]= c\left(\frac{1}{x} + \sqrt{x}\right) + x\,\Gamma$$

Here the front end was specifically told that input would be given in `TraditionalForm`. The cell bracket has a jagged line to indicate the difficulties involved.

$$In[1]:= c\left(\sqrt{x} + \frac{1}{x}\right) + \Gamma(x)$$

$$Out[1]= c\left[\frac{1}{x} + \sqrt{x}\right] + Gamma[x]$$

- The input is a copy or simple edit of previous output.
- The input has been converted from `StandardForm`, perhaps with simple edits.
- The input contains explicit hidden information giving its interpretation.
- The input contains only the simplest and most familiar notations.

Some situations in which `TraditionalForm` input can be expected to work.

Whenever *Mathematica* generates an expression in `TraditionalForm`, it automatically inserts various hidden tags so that the expression can later be interpreted unambiguously if it is given as input. And even if you edit the expression, the tags will often be left sufficiently undisturbed that unambiguous interpretation will still be possible.

This generates output in `TraditionalForm`.

In[11]:= **Exp[I Pi x] // TraditionalForm**

Out[11]//TraditionalForm= $e^{i\,\pi\,x}$

Mathematica was told to expect `TraditionalForm` input here. The input was copied from the previous output line, and thus contains hidden tags that ensure the correct interpretation.

In[12]:= $e^{i\pi x}$ **// StandardForm**

Out[12]//StandardForm= $E^{I\pi x}$

Simple editing often does not disturb the hidden tags.

In[13]:= $e^{2i\pi x}$ **// StandardForm**

Out[13]//StandardForm= $E^{2\,I\pi x}$

If you enter a `TraditionalForm` expression from scratch, or import it from outside *Mathematica*, then *Mathematica* will still do its best to guess what the expression means. When there are ambiguities, what it typically does is to assume that you are using notation in whatever way is more common in elementary mathematical applications.

In `TraditionalForm` input, this is interpreted as a derivative.	$In[14]:=$ $\dfrac{\partial\, y(x)}{\partial\, x}$ **// StandardForm** $Out[14]//StandardForm=$ y'[x]
This is interpreted as an arc tangent.	$In[15]:=$ $\tan^{-1}(x)$ **// StandardForm** $Out[15]//StandardForm=$ ArcTan[x]
This is interpreted as the square of a tangent.	$In[16]:=$ $\tan^{2}(x)$ **// StandardForm** $Out[16]//StandardForm=$ Tan[x]^{2}
There is no particularly standard traditional interpretation for this; *Mathematica* assumes that it is 1/Tan[x]^2.	$In[17]:=$ $\tan^{-2}(x)$ **// StandardForm** $Out[17]//StandardForm=$ Cot[x]^{2}

You should realize that `TraditionalForm` does not provide any kind of precise or complete way of specifying *Mathematica* expressions. Nevertheless, for some elementary purposes it may be sufficient, particularly if you use a few additional tricks.

- Use $x(y)$ for functions; $x\,(y)$ for multiplication
- Use ⦂ee⦂ for the exponential constant E
- Use ⦂ii⦂ or ⦂jj⦂ for the imaginary unit I
- Use ⦂dd⦂ for differential operators in integrals and derivatives

A few tricks for `TraditionalForm` input.

With a space f (1 + x) is interpreted as multiplication. Without a space, g(1 + x) is interpreted as a function.	$In[18]:=$ $f\,(1+x)+g(1+x)$ **// StandardForm** $Out[18]//StandardForm=$ f[1 + x] + g[1 + x]
The ordinary e is interpreted as a symbol e. The special "exponential e", entered as ⦂ee⦂, is interpreted as the exponential constant.	$In[19]:=$ $\{e^{3.7},\ e^{3.7}\}$ **// StandardForm** $Out[19]//StandardForm=$ {e$^{3.7}$, 40.4473}

∎ 1.10.10 Mixing Text and Formulas

The simplest way to mix text and formulas in a *Mathematica* notebook is to put each kind of material in a separate cell. Sometimes, however, you may want to embed a formula within a cell of text.

CTRL (or CTRL 9	begin entering a formula
CTRL) or CTRL 0	end entering a formula

Entering a formula within text.

Here is a notebook with formulas embedded in a text cell.

> This is a text cell, but it can contain formulas such as $\int \frac{1}{x^3-1} dx$ or
>
> $-\frac{\log(x^2+x+1)}{6} - \tan^{-1}\frac{\left(\frac{2x+1}{\sqrt{3}}\right)}{\sqrt{3}} + \frac{\log(x-1)}{3}$. The formulas flow with the text.

Mathematica notebooks often contain both formulas that are intended for actual evaluation by *Mathematica*, and ones that are intended just to be read in a more passive way.

You can use exactly the same mechanisms for entering formulas, whether or not they will ultimately be given as *Mathematica* input.

You should realize, however, that to make the detailed typography of typical formulas look as good as possible, *Mathematica* automatically does things such as inserting spaces around certain operators. But these kinds of adjustments can potentially be inappropriate if you use notation in very different ways from the ones *Mathematica* is expecting.

In such cases, you may have to make detailed typographical adjustments by hand, using the mechanisms discussed on page 428.

◼ 1.10.11 Displaying and Printing *Mathematica* Notebooks

Depending on the purpose for which you are using a *Mathematica* notebook, you may want to change its overall appearance. The front end allows you to specify independently the styles to be used for display on the screen and for printing. Typically you can do this by choosing appropriate items in the Format menu.

`ScreenStyleEnvironment`	styles to be used for screen display
`PrintingStyleEnvironment`	styles to be used for printed output
`Working`	standard style definitions for screen display
`Presentation`	style definitions for presentations
`Condensed`	style definitions for high display density
`Printing`	style definitions for printed output

Front end settings that define the global appearance of a notebook.

Here is a typical notebook as it appears in working form on the screen.

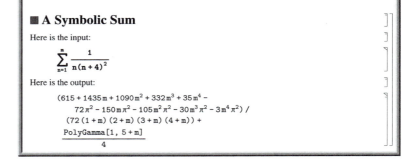

Here is the same notebook with condensed styles.

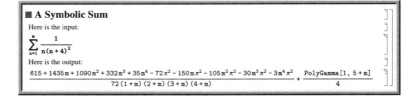

Here is a preview of how the notebook would appear when printed out.

+■ **1.10.12 Creating Your Own Palettes**

The *Mathematica* notebook front end comes with a collection of standard palettes. But it also allows you to create your own palettes.

- Set up a blank palette using Create Table/Matrix/Palette under the Input menu
- Fill in the contents
- Make the palette active using Generate Palette from Selection under the File menu

The basic steps in creating a palette.

Create Table/Matrix/Palette will create a blank palette.

You can then insert whatever you want into each button.

The menu item Generate Palette makes a separate active palette.

Clicking on a button in the palette now inserts its contents into your notebook.

$$x + y + \frac{1}{2 + \gamma^2}$$

Create Table/Matrix/Palette	set up a blank palette
Generate Palette from Selection	make a separate active palette
Generate Notebook from Palette	convert a palette back into an editable notebook
Edit Button	edit the script associated with a palette or button

Menu items for setting up palettes.

When you are creating a palette, you can use the same mechanisms to add columns and rows as you can when you are creating any other kind of table, matrix or grid. Thus CTRL[,] will add a new column of buttons, and CTRL[↵] (CONTROL-RETURN) will add a new row.

button contents	action
X	replace current selection by X
text containing $X\blacksquare Y$	replace current selection S by XSY

Contents of buttons.

In the simplest case, when you press a button in a palette what will happen is that the contents of the button will be inserted into your notebook, replacing whatever your current selection was.

Sometimes however you may not simply want to overwrite your current selection, but rather you may want to modify the selection in some way. As an example, you might want to wrap a function like `Expand` around your current selection.

You can do this by setting up a button with contents `Expand[`■`]`. The ■ can be entered as `:spl:` or `\[SelectionPlaceholder]`. In general, ■ serves as a placeholder for your current selection. When you press a button that contains ■, the ■ is first replaced by your current selection, and only then is the result inserted into your notebook.

Here is a cell in which the current selection is part of an expression.

```
1 + (1 + x)⁴ + (2 + y)³
```

Pressing a button containing `Expand[`■`]` wraps `Expand` around the current selection.

```
1 + (1 + x)⁴ + Expand[(2 + y)³]
```

Mathematica allows you to associate any action you want with a button. You can set up some common actions by using the Edit Button menu, having selected either a single button or a whole palette.

Paste	paste the contents of the button (default)
Evaluate	paste then evaluate in place what has been pasted
EvaluateCell	paste then evaluate the whole cell
CopyEvaluate	copy the current selection into a new cell, then paste and evaluate in place
CopyEvaluateCell	copy the current selection into a new cell, then paste and evaluate the whole cell

Typical actions for buttons.

With the default `Paste` setting for a button action, pressing the button modifies the contents of a cell but does no evaluation. By choosing other button actions, however, you can tell *Mathematica* to perform an evaluation every time you press the button.

With the button action `Evaluate` the result of this evaluation is made to overwrite your current selection. This is useful if you want to set up a button which modifies parts of an expression in place, say by applying `Expand[∎]` to them.

The button action `Evaluate` performs evaluation only on whatever was pasted into your current cell. The button action `EvaluateCell`, on the other hand, performs evaluation on the whole cell, generating a new cell to show the result.

Here is an expression with a part selected.

$$1 + (1+x)^4 + (2+y)^3$$

This shows the result of pressing a button containing `Expand[∎]` with an `EvaluateCell` button action.

$$1 + (1+x)^4 + \text{Expand}[(2+y)^3]$$
$$9 + (1+x)^4 + 12y + 6y^2 + y^3$$

Sometimes it is useful to be able to extract the current selection from a cell, and then operate on it in a new cell. You can do this using the button actions `CopyEvaluate` and `CopyEvaluateCell`.

Here is an expression with a part selected.

$$1 + (1+x)^4 + (2+y)^3$$

A button with a `CopyEvaluateCell` button action copies the current selection into a new cell, then pastes the contents of the button, and then performs an evaluation, putting the result into a new cell.

$$1 + (1+x)^4 + (2+y)^3$$
$$\text{In[1]:= } \text{Expand}[(2+y)^3]$$
$$\text{Out[1]= } 8 + 12y + 6y^2 + y^3$$

Create Table/Matrix/Palette	set up a blank palette
Create Button	set up a single button not in a palette
Generate Palette from Selection	make a separate window
Cell Active	activate buttons within a cell in a notebook

Ways to create active elements in the front end.

Mathematica allows you to set up a wide range of active elements in the notebook front end. In the most common case, you have a palette which consists of an array of buttons in a separate window. But you can also have arrays of buttons, or even single buttons, within the cells of an ordinary notebook.

In addition, you can make a button execute any action you want—performing computations in the *Mathematica* kernel, or changing the configuration of notebooks in the front end. Section 2.10.6 discusses how to do this.

■ 1.10.13 Setting Up Hyperlinks

| Create Hyperlink | set up the destination for a hyperlink |
| Paste | insert a hyperlink in text |

Menu items for setting up hyperlinks.

A hyperlink is a special kind of button which jumps to another part of a notebook when it is pressed. Typically hyperlinks are indicated in *Mathematica* by blue or underlined text.

To set up a hyperlink, you first go to wherever you want the destination of the hyperlink to be. Then you choose the menu item Create Hyperlink. This places on the clipboard a specification of the hyperlink.

You can then go to another part of your notebook, and paste this specification, thereby setting up a hyperlink.

+■ 1.10.14 Automatic Numbering

- Choose a cell style such as `NumberedEquation`
- Use the Create Automatic Numbering Object menu, with a counter name such as `Section`

Two ways to set up automatic numbering in a *Mathematica* notebook.

The input for each cell here is exactly the same, but the cells contain an element that displays as a progressively larger number as one goes through the notebook.

■ **1. A Section**

■ **2. A Section**

■ **3. A Section**

These cells are in `NumberedEquation` style.

$$\int \frac{x}{x+1} dx \qquad\qquad (1)$$

$$\int \frac{Sin[x]}{x+1} dx \qquad\qquad (2)$$

$$\int \frac{Log[x] + Exp[x]}{x+1} dx \qquad\qquad (3)$$

+■ 1.10.15 Exposition in *Mathematica* Notebooks

Mathematica notebooks provide the basic technology that you need to be able to create a very wide range of sophisticated interactive documents. But to get the best out of this technology you need to develop an appropriate style of exposition.

Many people at first tend to use *Mathematica* notebooks either as simple worksheets containing a sequence of input and output lines, or as on-screen versions of traditional books and other printed material. But the most effective and productive uses of *Mathematica* notebooks tend to lie at neither one of these extremes, and instead typically involve a fine-grained mixing of *Mathematica* input and output with explanatory text. In most cases the single most important factor in obtaining such fine-grained mixing is uniform use of the *Mathematica* language.

One might think that there would tend to be three kinds of material in a *Mathematica* notebook: plain text, mathematical formulas, and computer code. But one of the key ideas of *Mathematica* is to provide a single language that offers the best of both traditional mathematical formulas and computer code.

In `StandardForm`, *Mathematica* expressions have the same kind of compactness and elegance as traditional mathematical formulas. But unlike such formulas, *Mathematica* expressions are set up in a completely consistent and uniform way. As a result, if you use *Mathematica* expressions, then regardless of your subject matter, you never have to go back and reexplain your basic notation: it is always just the notation of the *Mathematica* language. In addition, if you set up your explanations in terms of *Mathematica* expressions, then a reader of your notebook can immediately take what you have given, and actually execute it as *Mathematica* input.

If one has spent many years working with traditional mathematical notation, then it takes a little time to get used to seeing mathematical facts presented as StandardForm *Mathematica* expressions. Indeed, at first one often has a tendency to try to use TraditionalForm whenever possible, perhaps with hidden tags to indicate its interpretation. But quite soon one tends to evolve to a mixture of StandardForm and TraditionalForm. And in the end it becomes clear that StandardForm alone is for most purposes the most effective form of presentation.

In traditional mathematical exposition, there are many tricks for replacing chunks of text by fragments of formulas. In StandardForm many of these same tricks can be used. But the fact that *Mathematica* expressions can represent not only mathematical objects but also procedures and algorithms increases greatly the extent to which chunks of text can be replaced by shorter and more precise material.

1.11 Files and External Operations

■ 1.11.1 Reading and Writing *Mathematica* Files

You can use files on your computer system to store definitions and results from *Mathematica*. The most general approach is to store everything as plain text that is appropriate for input to *Mathematica*. With this approach, a version of *Mathematica* running on one computer system produces files that can be read by a version running on any computer system. In addition, such files can be manipulated by other standard programs, such as text editors.

<< *name*	read in a *Mathematica* input file
expr >> *name*	output *expr* to a file as plain text
expr >>> *name*	append *expr* to a file
!! *name*	display the contents of a plain text file

Reading and writing files.

This expands $(x + y)^3$, and outputs the result to a file called tmp.	`In[1]:= Expand[ (x + y)^3 ]  >> tmp`

Here are the contents of tmp. They can be used directly as input for *Mathematica*.	`In[2]:= !!tmp`
	
	`x^3 + 3*x^2*y + 3*x*y^2 + y^3`

This reads in tmp, evaluating the *Mathematica* input it contains.	`In[3]:= <<tmp` `Out[3]=` $x^3 + 3x^2y + 3xy^2 + y^3$

If you are familiar with Unix or MS-DOS operating systems, you will recognize the *Mathematica* redirection operators >>, >>> and << as being analogous to the shell operators >, >> and <.

The redirection operators >> and >>> are convenient for storing results you get from *Mathematica*. The function Save["*name*", f, g, ...] allows you to save definitions for variables and functions.

Save["*name*", f, g, ...]	save definitions for variables or functions in a file

Saving definitions in plain text files.

Here is a definition for a function f.	`In[4]:= f[x_] := x^2 + c`

This gives c the value 17.	`In[5]:= c = 17`
	
	`Out[5]= 17`

This saves the definition of f in the file ftmp.	*In[6]:=* **Save["ftmp", f]**
Mathematica automatically saves both the actual definition of f, and the definition of c on which it depends.	*In[7]:=* **!!ftmp** f[x_] := x^2 + c c = 17
This clears the definitions of f and c.	*In[8]:=* **Clear[f, c]**
You can reinstate the definitions you saved simply by reading in the file ftmp.	*In[9]:=* **<<ftmp** *Out[9]=* 17

file.m	*Mathematica* expression file in plain text format
file.nb	*Mathematica* notebook file
file.mx	*Mathematica* definitions in DumpSave format

Typical names of *Mathematica* files.

If you use a notebook interface to *Mathematica*, then the *Mathematica* front end allows you to save complete notebooks, including not only *Mathematica* input and output, but also text, graphics and other material.

It is conventional to give *Mathematica* notebook files names that end in .nb, and most versions of *Mathematica* enforce this convention.

When you open a notebook in the *Mathematica* front end, *Mathematica* will immediately display the contents of the notebook, but it will not normally send any of these contents to the kernel for evaluation until you explicitly request this to be done.

Within a *Mathematica* notebook, however, you can use the Cell menu in the front end to identify certain cells as *initialization cells*, and if you do this, then the contents of these cells will automatically be evaluated whenever you open the notebook.

The I in the cell bracket indicates that the second cell is an initialization cell that will be evaluated whenever the notebook is opened.

> ■ **Implementation**
>
>   f[x_] := Log[x] + Log[1 - x]

It is sometimes convenient to maintain *Mathematica* material both in a notebook which contains explanatory text, and in a package which contains only raw *Mathematica* definitions. You can do this by putting the *Mathematica* definitions into opening auto-evaluate cells in the notebook. Every time you save the notebook, the front end will then allow you to save an associated .m file which contains only the raw *Mathematica* definitions.

■ 1.11.2 Advanced Topic: Finding and Manipulating Files

Although the details of how files are named and organized differ from one computer system to another, *Mathematica* provides some fairly general mechanisms for finding and handling files.

Mathematica assumes that files on your computer system are organized in a collection of *directories*. At any point, you have a *current working directory*. You can always refer to files in this directory just by giving their names.

Directory[ ]	give your current working directory
SetDirectory["*dir*"]	set your current working directory
FileNames[ ]	list the files in your current working directory
FileNames["*form*"]	list the files whose names match a certain form
<<*name*	read in a file with the specified name
<<*context*`	read in a file corresponding to the specified context
CopyFile["*file₁*", "*file₂*"]	copy *file₁* to *file₂*
DeleteFile["*file*"]	delete a file

Functions for finding and manipulating files.

This is the current working directory. The form it has differs from one computer system to another.

```
In[1]:= Directory[ ]
Out[1]= /users/sw
```

This resets the current working directory.

```
In[2]:= SetDirectory["Examples"]
Out[2]= /users/sw/Examples
```

This gives a list of all files in your current working directory whose names match the form Test*.m.

```
In[3]:= FileNames["Test*.m"]
Out[3]= {Test1.m, Test2.m, TestFinal.m}
```

Although you usually want to create files only in your current working directory, you often need to read in files from other directories. As a result, when you ask *Mathematica* to read in a file with a particular name, *Mathematica* automatically searches a list of directories (specified by the value of the search path variable $Path) to try and find a file with that name.

One issue in handling files in *Mathematica* is that the form of file and directory names varies between computer systems. This means for example that names of files which contain standard *Mathematica* packages may be quite different on different systems. Through a sequence of conventions, it is however possible to read in a standard *Mathematica* package with the same command on all systems. The way this works is that each package defines a so-called *Mathematica* context, of the form *name*`*name*`. On each system, all files are named in correspondence with the contexts they define. Then when you use the command <<*name*`*name*` *Mathematica* automatically translates the context name into the file name appropriate for your particular computer system.

FindList["*file*", "*text*"]	give a list of all lines in a file that contain the specified text
FindList[FileNames[ ], "*text*"]	
	search in all files in your current directory

Searching for text in files.

This searches all lines in the file index containing Laplace.

```
In[1]:= FindList["index", "Laplace"]

Out[1]= {Laplace transforms: Calculus`LaplaceTransform`,
            Inverse Laplace transforms:
                Calculus`LaplaceTransform`}
```

■ 1.11.3 Reading Data Files

ReadList["*file*", Number]	read numbers from a file, and return a *Mathematica* list of them
ReadList["*file*", Number, RecordLists->True]	
	read numbers from a file, making a separate list for each line in the file

Reading numerical data files.

If you have a table of numbers in a file, generated for example by an external program, you can read them into *Mathematica* using ReadList. The numbers in your file can be given in C or Fortran-like form, as 2.3E5 and so on. ReadList converts all numbers to the appropriate *Mathematica* form.

This shows the contents of the file rand.dat.

```
In[1]:= !!rand.dat

3.4      -5.7E-2      8.4E+2
4.5      -7.8E-2      1.9E+3
6.4      -0.1         4.7E+4
```

This reads the file rand.dat, and returns a list of the numbers in the file.

```
In[2]:= ReadList["rand.dat", Number]

Out[2]= {3.4, -0.057, 840., 4.5, -0.078, 1900.,
            6.4, -0.1, 47000.}
```

This reads the numbers making a separate list for each line in the file.

```
In[3]:= ReadList["rand.dat", Number, RecordLists -> True]

Out[3]= {{3.4, -0.057, 840.}, {4.5, -0.078, 1900.},
            {6.4, -0.1, 47000.}}
```

Mathematica allows you to read files in many different ways. For example, instead of reading numbers, you can read strings or "words". In addition, you can use Find to search for particular parts of files to read. These possibilities are discussed in Section 2.11.7.

■ 1.11.4 Generating C and Fortran Expressions

If you have special-purpose programs written in C or Fortran, you may want to take formulas you have generated in *Mathematica* and insert them into the source code of your programs. *Mathematica* allows you to convert mathematical expressions into C and Fortran expressions.

CForm[*expr*]	write out *expr* so it can be used in a C program
FortranForm[*expr*]	write out *expr* for Fortran

Mathematica output for programming languages.

Here is an expression, written out in standard *Mathematica* form.

$In[1]:=$ **Expand[(1 + x + y)^2]**

$Out[1]= 1 + 2x + x^2 + 2y + 2xy + y^2$

Here is the expression in Fortran form.

$In[2]:=$ **FortranForm[%]**

$Out[2]//FortranForm= 1 + 2*x + x**2 + 2*y + 2*x*y + y**2$

Here is the same expression in C form. Macros for objects like Power are defined in the C header file mdefs.h that comes with most versions of *Mathematica*.

$In[3]:=$ **CForm[%]**

$Out[3]//CForm= 1 + 2*x + Power(x,2) + 2*y + 2*x*y + Power(y,2)$

You should realize that there are many differences between *Mathematica* and C or Fortran. As a result, expressions you translate may not work exactly the same as they do in *Mathematica*. In addition, there are so many differences in programming constructs that no attempt is made to translate these automatically.

Compile[*x*, *expr*]	compile an expression into efficient internal code

A way to compile *Mathematica* expressions.

One of the common motivations for converting *Mathematica* expressions into C or Fortran is to try to make them faster to evaluate numerically. But the single most important reason that C and Fortran can potentially be more efficient than *Mathematica* is that in these languages one always specifies up front what type each variable one uses will be—integer, real number, array, and so on.

The *Mathematica* function `Compile` makes such assumptions within *Mathematica,* and generates highly efficient internal code. Usually this code runs not much if at all slower than custom C or Fortran.

■ 1.11.5 Exporting Graphics

Mathematica provides a variety of mechanisms for exporting graphics that you generate to printers and other programs.

If you use the notebook front end for *Mathematica,* then you can typically just copy and paste graphics directly using the standard mechanism available on your computer system.

`Display["`*file*`", ` *graphics*`, "`*format*`"]`	export *graphics* to a file in the specified format
`Display["!`*command*`", ` *graphics*`, "`*format*`"]`	send graphics to an external command

Ways to export *Mathematica* graphics.

The command `Display` allows you systematically to send graphics from *Mathematica* to external files and programs.

This generates a plot.
In[1]:= `Plot[Sin[x] + Sin[Sqrt[2] x], {x, 0, 10}]`

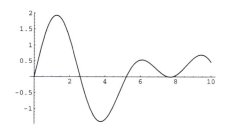

This saves the plot in a file in Encapsulated PostScript format.
In[2]:= `Display["sinplot.eps", %, "EPS"]`
Out[2]= -Graphics-

Here is a typical command for printing the plot on a Unix system.
In[3]:= `Display["!lpr", %, "EPS"]`
Out[3]= -Graphics-

"MPS"	*Mathematica* abbreviated PostScript
"EPS"	Encapsulated PostScript
"PDF"	Adobe Acrobat portable document format
"Illustrator"	Adobe Illustrator format
"PICT"	Macintosh PICT
"Metafile"	Microsoft Windows metafile
"TIFF"	TIFF
"GIF"	GIF
"PSImage"	PostScript image format
"XBitmap"	X Windows bitmap
"PCL"	Hewlett-Packard printer control language
"PBM"	portable bitmap
"MGF"	*Mathematica* system-independent raster graphics format

Typical graphics formats supported by *Mathematica*. The first group are resolution independent.

When you export a graphic outside of *Mathematica*, you usually have to specify the absolute size at which the graphic should be rendered. You can do this using the `ImageSize` option to `Display`.

`ImageSize->x` makes the width of the graphic be x printer's points; `ImageSize->72` xi thus makes the width xi inches. The default is to produce an image that is four inches wide.

+ `ImageSize`	Automatic	absolute image size in printer's points
+ `ImageRotated`	False	whether to rotate the image (landscape mode)
+ `ImageResolution`	Automatic	resolution in dpi for the image

Options for `Display`.

Within *Mathematica* graphics are manipulated in a way that is completely independent of the resolution of the computer screen or other output device on which the graphics will eventually be rendered.

Many programs and devices accept graphics in resolution-independent formats such as Encapsulated PostScript (EPS). But some require that the graphics be converted to rasters or bitmaps with a specific resolution. The `ImageResolution` option for `Display` allows you to determine what resolution in dots per inch (dpi) should be used. The lower you set this resolution, the lower the quality of the image you will get, but also the less memory the image will take to store. For screen display, typical resolutions are 72 dpi and above; for printers 300 dpi and above.

■ 1.11.6 Exporting Formulas from Notebooks

Here is a cell containing a formula.

$$-\frac{\text{ArcTan}\left[\frac{1+2x}{\sqrt{3}}\right]}{\sqrt{3}} + \frac{\text{Log}[-1+x]}{3} - \frac{\text{Log}[1+x+x^2]}{6}$$

This is what you get if you copy the formula and paste it into an external text-based program.

```
\!\(-\(ArcTan[\(1 + 2 x\)]\/\@3]\/\@3\) + Log[-1 + x]\/3
- Log[1 + x + x\^2]\/6\)
```

Pasting the text back into a notebook immediately reproduces the original formula.

$$-\frac{\text{ArcTan}\left[\frac{1+2x}{\sqrt{3}}\right]}{\sqrt{3}} + \frac{\text{Log}[-1+x]}{3} - \frac{\text{Log}[1+x+x^2]}{6}$$

Mathematica allows you to export formulas both textually and visually. You can use `Display` to tell *Mathematica* to write a visual representation of a formula into a file.

`Display["`*file*`.eps", ToBoxes[`*expr*`], "EPS"]`	
	save the visual form of *expr* to a file in EPS format
`Display["`*file*`", ToBoxes[`*expr*`], "`*format*`"]`	
	save the visual form of *expr* in the specified format

Exporting expressions in visual form.

■ 1.11.7 Generating TEX

Mathematica notebooks provide a sophisticated environment for creating technical documents. But particularly if you want to merge your work with existing material in TEX, you may find it convenient to use `TeXForm` to convert expressions in *Mathematica* into a form suitable for input to TEX.

TeXForm[*expr*]	print *expr* in TeX input form

Mathematica output for TeX.

Here is an expression, printed in standard *Mathematica* form.

$$In[1]:= \text{(x + y)^2 / Sqrt[x y]}$$

$$Out[1]= \frac{(x+y)^2}{\sqrt{xy}}$$

Here is the expression in TeX input form.

$$In[2]:= \textbf{TeXForm[\%]}$$

$$Out[2]//TeXForm= \text{\{\{\{\{\textbackslash left(x + y \textbackslash right) \}^2\}\}\textbackslash over}$$
$$\text{\{\{\textbackslash sqrt\{x\textbackslash,y\}\}\}\}}$$

+ TeXSave["*file*.tex"]	save your complete current notebook in TeX input form
+ TeXSave["*file*.tex", "*source*.nb"]	
	save a TeX version of the notebook *source*.nb

Converting complete notebooks to TeX.

In addition to being able to convert individual expressions to TeX, *Mathematica* also provides capabilities for translating complete notebooks. These capabilites can usually be accessed from the Save As Special menu in the notebook front end, where various options can be set.

+ ■ 1.11.8 Converting Notebooks to HTML

+ HTMLSave["*file*.html"]	save your complete current notebook in HTML form
+ HTMLSave["*file*.html", "*source*.nb"]	
	save an HTML version of the notebook *source*.nb

Converting notebooks to HTML.

■ 1.11.9 Splicing *Mathematica* Output into External Files

If you want to make use of *Mathematica* output in an external file such as a program or document, you will often find it useful to "splice" the output automatically into the file.

Splice["*file*.mx"]	splice *Mathematica* output into an external file named *file*.mx, putting the results in the file *file*.x
Splice["*infile*", "*outfile*"]	splice *Mathematica* output into *infile*, sending the output to *outfile*

Splicing *Mathematica* output into files.

The basic idea is to set up the definitions you need in a particular *Mathematica* session, then run Splice to use the definitions you have made to produce the appropriate output to insert into the external files.

```
#include "mdefs.h"

double f(x)
double x;
{
double y;

y = <* Integrate[Sin[x]^5, x] *> ;

return(2*y - 1) ;
}
```

A simple C program containing a *Mathematica* formula.

```
#include "mdefs.h"

double f(x)
double x;
{
double y;

y = -5*Cos(x)/8 + 5*Cos(3*x)/48 - Cos(5*x)/80 ;

return(2*y - 1) ;
}
```

The C program after processing with Splice.

■ 1.11.10 Running External Programs

Although *Mathematica* does many things well, there are some things that are inevitably better done by external programs. You can use *Mathematica* to control the external programs, or to analyze output they generate.

On almost all computer systems, it is possible to run external programs directly from within *Mathematica*. *Mathematica* communicates with the external programs through interprocess communication mechanisms such as pipes.

In the simplest cases, the only communication you need is to send and receive plain text. You can prepare input in *Mathematica*, then give it as the standard input for the external program. Or you can take the standard output of the external program, and use it as input to *Mathematica*.

In general, *Mathematica* allows you to treat streams of data exchanged with external programs just like files. In place of a file name, you give the external command to run, prefaced by an exclamation point.

<<*file*	read in a file
<<"!*command*"	run an external command, and read in the output it produces
expr >> "!*command*"	feed the textual form of *expr* to an external command
ReadList["!*command*", Number]	run an external command, and read in a list of the numbers it produces

Some ways to communicate with external programs.

This feeds the expression x^2 + y^2 as input to the external command lpr, which, on a typical Berkeley Unix system, sends output to a printer.

In[1]:= **x^2 + y^2 >> "!lpr"**

With a text-based interface, putting ! at the beginning of a line causes the remainder of the line to be executed as an external command. squares is an external program which prints numbers and their squares.

In[2]:= **!squares 4**

```
1   1
2   4
3   9
4   16
```

This runs the external command squares 4, then reads numbers from the output it produces.

In[3]:= **ReadList["!squares 4", Number, RecordLists->True]**

Out[3]= {{1, 1}, {2, 4}, {3, 9}, {4, 16}}

■ 1.11.11 *MathLink*

The previous section discussed how to exchange plain text with external programs. In many cases, however, you will find it convenient to communicate with external programs at a higher level, and to exchange more structured data with them.

On almost all computer systems, *Mathematica* supports the *MathLink* communication standard, which allows higher-level communication between *Mathematica* and external programs. In order to use *Math-Link*, an external program has to include some special source code, which is usually distributed with *Mathematica*.

MathLink allows external programs both to call *Mathematica*, and to be called by *Mathematica*. Section 2.12 discusses some of the details of *MathLink*. By using *MathLink*, you can, for example, treat *Mathematica* essentially like a subroutine embedded inside an external program. Or you can create a front end that implements your own user interface, and communicates with the *Mathematica* kernel via *MathLink*.

You can also use *MathLink* to let *Mathematica* call individual functions inside an external program. As described in Section 2.12, you can set up a *MathLink* template file to specify how particular functions in *Mathematica* should call functions inside your external program. From the *MathLink* template file, you can generate source code to include in your program. Then when you start your program, the appropriate *Mathematica* definitions are automatically made, and when you call a particular *Mathematica* function, code in your external program is executed.

`Install["command"]`	start an external program and install *Mathematica* definitions to call functions it contains
`Uninstall[link]`	terminate an external program and uninstall definitions for functions in it

Calling functions in external programs.

This starts the external program simul, and installs *Mathematica* definitions to call various functions in it.

```
In[1]:= Install["simul"]
Out[1]= LinkObject[simul, 5, 4]
```

Here is a usage message for a function that was installed in *Mathematica* to call a function in the external program.

```
In[2]:= ?srun
srun[{a, r, gamma}, x] performs a simulation  with the
   specified parameters.
```

When you call this function, it executes code in the external program.

```
In[3]:= srun[{3, 0, 7}, 5]
Out[3]= 6.781241
```

This terminates the simul program.

```
In[4]:= Uninstall["simul"]
Out[4]= simul
```

1.12 Special Topic: The Internals of *Mathematica*

∎ 1.12.1 Why You Do Not Usually Need to Know about Internals

Most of this book is concerned with explaining *what Mathematica* does, not *how* it does it. But the purpose of this chapter is to say at least a little about how *Mathematica* does what it does. Appendix A.9 gives some more details.

You should realize at the outset that while knowing about the internals of *Mathematica* may be of intellectual interest, it is usually much less important in practice than one might at first suppose.

Indeed, one of the main points of *Mathematica* is that it provides an environment where you can perform mathematical and other operations without having to think in detail about how these operations are actually carried out inside your computer.

Thus, for example, if you want to factor the polynomial $x^{15} - 1$, you can do this just by giving *Mathematica* the command `Factor[x^15 - 1]`; you do not have to know the fairly complicated details of how such a factorization is actually carried out by the internal code of *Mathematica*.

Indeed, in almost all practical uses of *Mathematica*, issues about how *Mathematica* works inside turn out to be largely irrelevant. For most purposes it suffices to view *Mathematica* simply as an abstract system which performs certain specified mathematical and other operations.

You might think that knowing how *Mathematica* works inside would be necessary in determining what answers it will give. But this is only very rarely the case. For the vast majority of the computations that *Mathematica* does are completely specified by the definitions of mathematical or other operations.

Thus, for example, 3^40 will always be 12157665459056928801, regardless of how *Mathematica* internally computes this result.

There are some situations, however, where several different answers are all equally consistent with the formal mathematical definitions. Thus, for example, in computing symbolic integrals, there are often several different expressions which all yield the same derivative. Which of these expressions is actually generated by `Integrate` can then depend on how `Integrate` works inside.

Here is the answer generated by `Integrate`.	*In[1]:=* `Integrate[1/x + 1/x^2, x]` *Out[1]=* $-\dfrac{1}{x} + \text{Log}[x]$
This is an equivalent expression that might have been generated if `Integrate` worked differently inside.	*In[2]:=* `Together[%]` *Out[2]=* $\dfrac{-1 + x\,\text{Log}[x]}{x}$

In numerical computations, a similar phenomenon occurs. Thus, for example, `FindRoot` gives you a root of a function. But if there are several roots, which root is actually returned depends on the details of how `FindRoot` works inside.

This finds a particular root of cos(*x*) + sin(*x*).

```
In[3]:= FindRoot[Cos[x] + Sin[x], {x, 10.5}]
Out[3]= {x → 14.9226}
```

With a different starting point, a different root is found. Which root is found with each starting point depends in detail on the internal algorithm used.

```
In[4]:= FindRoot[Cos[x] + Sin[x], {x, 10.8}]
Out[4]= {x → 11.781}
```

The dependence on the details of internal algorithms can be more significant if you push approximate numerical computations to the limits of their validity.

Thus, for example, if you give `NIntegrate` a pathological integrand, whether it yields a meaningful answer or not can depend on the details of the internal algorithm that it uses.

`NIntegrate` knows that this result is unreliable, and can depend on the details of the internal algorithm, so it prints warning messages.

```
In[5]:= NIntegrate[Sin[1/x], {x, 0, 1}]
NIntegrate::slwcon:
    Numerical integration converging too slowly; suspect
      one of the following: singularity, oscillatory
      integrand, or insufficient WorkingPrecision. If your
      integrand is oscillatory try using the option
      Method->Oscillatory in NIntegrate.

NIntegrate::ncvb:
    NIntegrate failed to converge to prescribed accuracy
      after 7 recursive bisections in x near x = 0.0035126
      8.
Out[5]= 0.504894
```

Traditional numerical computation systems have tended to follow the idea that all computations should yield results that at least nominally have the same precision. A consequence of this idea is that it is not sufficient just to look at a result to know whether it is accurate; you typically also have to analyze the internal algorithm by which the result was found. This fact has tended to make people believe that it is always important to know internal algorithms for numerical computations.

But with the approach that *Mathematica* takes, this is rarely the case. For *Mathematica* can usually use its arbitrary-precision numerical computation capabilities to give results where every digit that is generated follows the exact mathematical specification of the operation being performed.

Even though this is an approximate numerical computation, every digit is determined by the mathematical definition for *π*.

```
In[6]:= N[Pi, 30]
Out[6]= 3.14159265358979323846264338327 9
```

Once again, every digit here is determined by the mathematical definition for sin(*x*).

```
In[7]:= N[Sin[10^50], 20]
Out[7]= -0.78967249342931008271
```

If you use machine-precision numbers, *Mathematica* cannot give a reliable result, and the answer depends on the details of the internal algorithm used.

```
In[8]:= Sin[10.^50]
Out[8]= -0.4805
```

It is a general characteristic that whenever the results you get can be affected by the details of internal algorithms, you should not depend on these results. For if nothing else, different versions of *Mathematica* may exhibit differences in these results, either because the algorithms operate slightly differently on different computer systems, or because fundamentally different algorithms are used in versions released at different times.

This is the result for $\sin(10^{50})$ on one type of computer.

```
In[1]:= Sin[10.^50]
Out[1]= -0.4805
```

Here is the same calculation on another type of computer.

```
In[1]:= Sin[10.^50]
Out[1]= -0.0528229
```

And here is the result obtained in *Mathematica* Version 1.0.

```
In[1]:= Sin[10.^50]
Out[1]= 0.0937538
```

Particularly in more advanced applications of *Mathematica*, it may sometimes seem worthwhile to try to analyze internal algorithms in order to predict which way of doing a given computation will be the most efficient. And there are indeed occasionally major improvements that you will be able to make in specific computations as a result of such analyses.

But most often the analyses will not be worthwhile. For the internals of *Mathematica* are quite complicated, and even given a basic description of the algorithm used for a particular purpose, it is usually extremely difficult to reach a reliable conclusion about how the detailed implementation of this algorithm will actually behave in particular circumstances.

A typical problem is that *Mathematica* has many internal optimizations, and the efficiency of a computation can be greatly affected by whether the details of the computation do or do not allow a given internal optimization to be used.

■ 1.12.2 Basic Internal Architecture

numbers	sequences of binary digits
strings	sequences of character code bytes or byte pairs
symbols	pointers to the central table of symbols
general expressions	sequences of pointers to the head and elements

Internal representations used by *Mathematica*.

When you type input into *Mathematica*, a data structure is created in the memory of your computer to represent the expression you have entered.

In general, different pieces of your expression will be stored at different places in memory. Thus, for example, for a list such as {2, x, y + z} the "backbone" of the list will be stored at one place, while each of the actual elements will be stored at a different place.

The backbone of the list then consists just of three "pointers" that specify the addresses in computer memory at which the actual expressions that form the elements of the list are to be found. These expressions then in turn contain pointers to their subexpressions. The chain of pointers ends when one reaches an object such as a number or a string, which is stored directly as a pattern of bits in computer memory.

Crucial to the operation of *Mathematica* is the notion of symbols such as x. Whenever x appears in an expression, *Mathematica* represents it by a pointer. But the pointer is always to the same place in computer memory—an entry in a central table of all symbols defined in your *Mathematica* session.

This table is a repository of all information about each symbol. It contains a pointer to a string giving the symbol's name, as well as pointers to expressions which give rules for evaluating the symbol.

- Recycle memory as soon as the data in it is no longer referenced.

The basic principle of *Mathematica* memory management.

Every piece of memory used by *Mathematica* maintains a count of how many pointers currently point to it. When this count drops to zero, *Mathematica* knows that the piece of memory is no longer being referenced, and immediately makes the piece of memory available for something new.

This strategy essentially ensures that no memory is ever wasted, and that any piece of memory that *Mathematica* uses is actually storing data that you need to access in your *Mathematica* session.

- Create an expression corresponding to the input you have given.
- Process the expression using all rules known for the objects in it.
- Generate output corresponding to the resulting expression.

The basic actions of *Mathematica*.

At the heart of *Mathematica* is a conceptually simple procedure known as the *evaluator* which takes every function that appears in an expression and evaluates that function.

When the function is one of the thousand or so that are built into *Mathematica*, what the evaluator does is to execute directly internal code in the *Mathematica* system. This code is set up to perform the operations corresponding to the function, and then to build a new expression representing the result.

- **The built-in functions of *Mathematica* support universal computation.**

The basic feature that makes *Mathematica* a self-contained system.

A crucial feature of the built-in functions in *Mathematica* is that they support *universal computation*. What this means is that out of these functions you can construct programs that perform absolutely any kinds of operation that are possible for a computer.

As it turns out, small subsets of *Mathematica*'s built-in functions would be quite sufficient to support universal computation. But having the whole collection of functions makes it in practice easier to construct the programs one needs.

The underlying point, however, is that because *Mathematica* supports universal computation you never have to modify its built-in functions: all you have to do to perform a particular task is to combine these functions in an appropriate way.

Universal computation is the basis for all standard computer languages. But many of these languages rely on the idea of *compilation*. If you use C or Fortran, for example, you first write your program, then you compile it to generate machine code that can actually be executed on your computer.

Mathematica does not require you to go through the compilation step: once you have input an expression, the functions in the expression can immediately be executed.

Often *Mathematica* will preprocess expressions that you enter, arranging things so that subsequent execution will be as efficient as possible. But such preprocessing never affects the results that are generated, and can rarely be seen explicitly.

■ 1.12.3 The Algorithms of *Mathematica*

The built-in functions of *Mathematica* implement a very large number of algorithms from computer science and mathematics. Some of these algorithms are fairly old, but the vast majority had to be created or at least modified specifically for *Mathematica*. Most of the more mathematical algorithms in *Mathematica* ultimately carry out operations which at least at some time in the past were performed by hand. In almost all cases, however, the algorithms use methods very different from those common in hand calculation.

Symbolic integration provides an example. In hand calculation, symbolic integration is typically done by a large number of tricks involving changes of variables and the like.

But in *Mathematica* symbolic integration is performed by a fairly small number of very systematic procedures. For indefinite integration, the idea of these procedures is to find the most general form of the integral, then to differentiate this and try to match up undetermined coefficients.

Often this procedure produces at an intermediate stage immensely complicated algebraic expressions, and sometimes very sophisticated kinds of mathematical functions. But the great advantage of the procedure is that it is completely systematic, and its operation requires no special cleverness of the kind that only a human could be expected to provide.

In having *Mathematica* do integrals, therefore, one can be confident that it will systematically get results, but one cannot expect that the way these results are derived will have much at all to do with the way they would be derived by hand.

The same is true with most of the mathematical algorithms in *Mathematica*. One striking feature is that even for operations that are simple to describe, the systematic algorithms to perform these operations in *Mathematica* involve fairly advanced mathematical or computational ideas.

Thus, for example, factoring a polynomial in x is first done modulo a prime such as 17 by finding the null space of a matrix obtained by reducing high powers of x modulo the prime and the original polynomial. Then factorization over the integers is achieved by "lifting" modulo successive powers of the prime using a collection of intricate theorems in algebra and analysis.

The use of powerful systematic algorithms is important in making the built-in functions in *Mathematica* able to handle difficult and general cases. But for easy cases that may be fairly common in practice it is often possible to use simpler and more efficient algorithms.

As a result, built-in functions in *Mathematica* often have large numbers of extra pieces that handle various kinds of special cases. These extra pieces can contribute greatly to the complexity of the internal code, often taking what would otherwise be a five-page algorithm and making it hundreds of pages long.

Most of the algorithms in *Mathematica*, including all their special cases, were explicitly constructed by hand. But some algorithms were instead effectively created automatically by computer.

Many of the algorithms used for machine-precision numerical evaluation of mathematical functions are examples. The main parts of such algorithms are formulas which are as short as possible but which yield the best numerical approximations.

Most such formulas used in *Mathematica* were actually derived by *Mathematica* itself. Often many months of computation were required, but the result was a short formula that can be used to evaluate functions in an optimal way.

◾ 1.12.4 The Software Engineering of *Mathematica*

Mathematica is one of the more complex software systems ever constructed. Its source code is written in a combination of C and *Mathematica*, and for Version 3.0, the code for the kernel consists of about

500,000 lines of C and 80,000 lines of *Mathematica*. This corresponds to roughly 15 megabytes of data, or some 15,000 printed pages.

The C code in *Mathematica* is actually written in a custom extension of C which supports certain memory management and object-oriented features. The *Mathematica* code is optimized using `Share` and `DumpSave`.

In the *Mathematica* kernel the breakdown of different parts of the code is roughly as follows: language and system: 30%; numerical computation: 25%; algebraic computation: 25%; graphics and kernel output: 20%.

Most of this code is fairly dense and algorithmic: those parts that are in effect simple procedures or tables use minimal code since they tend to be written at a higher level—often directly in *Mathematica*.

The source code for the kernel, save a fraction of a percent, is identical for all computer systems on which *Mathematica* runs.

For the front end, however, a significant amount of specialized code is needed to support each different type of user interface environment. The front end contains about 175,000 lines of system-independent C source code, of which roughly 60,000 lines are concerned with expression formatting. Then there are between 20,000 and 50,000 lines of specific code that is customized for each user interface environment.

Mathematica uses a client-server model of computing. The front end and kernel are connected via *MathLink*—the same system as is used to communicate with other programs.

Within the C code portion of the *Mathematica* kernel, modularity and consistency are achieved by having different parts communicate primarily by exchanging complete *Mathematica* expressions.

But it should be noted that even though different parts of the system are quite independent at the level of source code, they have many algorithmic interdependencies. Thus, for example, it is common for numerical functions to make extensive use of algebraic algorithms, or for graphics code to use fairly advanced mathematical algorithms embodied in quite different *Mathematica* functions.

Since the beginning of its development in 1986, the effort spent directly on creating the source code for *Mathematica* is a substantial fraction of a thousand man-years. In addition, a comparable or somewhat larger effort has been spent on testing and verification.

The source code of *Mathematica* has changed greatly since Version 1.0 was released. The total number of lines of code in the kernel grew from 150,000 in Version 1.0 to 350,000 in Version 2.0 and nearly 600,000 in Version 3.0. In addition, at every stage existing code has been revised—so that Version 3.0 has only a few percent of its code in common with Version 1.0.

Despite these changes in internal code, however, the user-level design of *Mathematica* has remained compatible from Version 1.0 on. Much functionality has been added, but programs created for *Mathematica* Version 1.0 will almost always run absolutely unchanged under Version 3.0.

■ 1.12.5 Testing and Verification

Every version of *Mathematica* is subjected to a large amount of testing before it is released. The vast majority of this testing is done by an automated system that is written in *Mathematica*.

The automated system feeds millions of pieces of input to *Mathematica*, and checks that the output obtained from them is correct. Often there is some subtlety in doing such checking: one must account for different behavior of randomized algorithms and for such issues as differences in machine-precision arithmetic on different computers.

The test inputs used by the automated system are obtained in several ways:

■ For every *Mathematica* function, inputs are devised that exercise both common and extreme cases.

■ Inputs are devised to exercise each feature of the internal code.

■ All the examples in this book and in other books about *Mathematica* are used.

■ Standard numerical tables are optically scanned for test inputs.

■ Formulas from all standard mathematical tables are entered.

■ Exercises from textbooks are entered.

■ For pairs of functions such as `Integrate` and `D` or `Factor` and `Expand`, random expressions are generated and tested.

When tests are run, the automated testing system checks not only the results, but also side effects such as messages, as well as memory usage and speed.

There is also a special instrumented version of *Mathematica* which is set up to perform internal consistency tests. This version of *Mathematica* runs at a small fraction of the speed of the real *Mathematica*, but at every step it checks internal memory consistency, interruptibility, and so on.

The instrumented version of *Mathematica* also records which pieces of *Mathematica* source code have been accessed, allowing one to confirm that all of the various internal functions in *Mathematica* have been exercised by the tests given.

All standard *Mathematica* tests are routinely run on each version of *Mathematica*, on each different computer system. Depending on the speed of the computer system, these tests take a few days to a few weeks of computer time.

In addition, huge numbers of tests based on random inputs are run for the equivalent of many years of computer time on a sampling of different computer systems.

Even with all this testing, however, it is inevitable in a system as complex as *Mathematica* that errors will remain.

The standards of correctness for *Mathematica* are certainly much higher than for typical mathematical proofs. But just as long proofs will inevitably contain errors that go undetected for many years, so also a complex software system such as *Mathematica* will contain errors that go undetected even after millions of people have used it.

Nevertheless, particularly after all the testing that has been done on it, the probability that you will actually discover an error in *Mathematica* in the course of your work is extremely low.

Doubtless there will be times when *Mathematica* does things you do not expect. But you should realize that the probabilities are such that it is vastly more likely that there is something wrong with your input to *Mathematica* or your understanding of what is happening than with the internal code of the *Mathematica* system itself.

If you do believe that you have found a genuine error in *Mathematica*, then you should contact Wolfram Research at the addresses given in the front of this book so that the error can be corrected in future versions.

Part 2

Part 1 introduced Mathematica by showing you how to use some of its more common features. This part looks at Mathematica in a different way. Instead of discussing individual features, it concentrates on the global structure of Mathematica, and describes the framework into which all the features fit.

When you first start doing calculations with Mathematica, you will probably find it sufficient just to read the relevant parts of Part 1. However, once you have some general familiarity with the Mathematica system, you should make a point of reading this part.

This part describes the basic structure of the Mathematica language, with which you can extend Mathematica, adding your own functions, objects or other constructs. This part shows how Mathematica uses a fairly small number of very powerful symbolic programming methods to allow you to build up many different kinds of programs.

Most of this part assumes no specific prior knowledge of computer science. Nevertheless, some of it ventures into some fairly complicated issues. You can probably ignore these issues unless they specifically affect programs you are writing.

If you are an expert on computer languages, you may be able to glean some understanding of Mathematica by looking at the Reference Guide at the end of this book. Nevertheless, to get a real appreciation for the principles of Mathematica, you will have to read this part.

Part 2

Principles of *Mathematica*

2.1 Expressions

■ 2.1.1 Everything Is an Expression

Mathematica handles many different kinds of things: mathematical formulas, lists and graphics, to name a few. Although they often look very different, *Mathematica* represents all of these things in one uniform way. They are all *expressions*.

A prototypical example of a *Mathematica* expression is f[x, y]. You might use f[x, y] to represent a mathematical function $f(x, y)$. The function is named f, and it has two arguments, x and y.

You do not always have to write expressions in the form $f[x, y, ...]$. For example, x + y is also an expression. When you type in x + y, *Mathematica* converts it to the standard form Plus[x, y]. Then, when it prints it out again, it gives it as x + y.

The same is true of other "operators", such as ^ (Power) and / (Divide).

In fact, everything you type into *Mathematica* is treated as an expression.

x + y + z	Plus[x, y, z]
x y z	Times[x, y, z]
x^n	Power[x, n]
{a, b, c}	List[a, b, c]
a -> b	Rule[a, b]
a = b	Set[a, b]

Some examples of *Mathematica* expressions.

You can see the full form of any expression by using FullForm[*expr*].

Here is an expression.

```
In[1]:= x + y + z
Out[1]= x + y + z
```

This is the full form of the expression.

```
In[2]:= FullForm[%]
Out[2]//FullForm= Plus[x, y, z]
```

Here is another expression.

```
In[3]:= 1 + x^2 + (y + z)^2
Out[3]= 1 + x² + (y + z)²
```

Its full form has several nested pieces.

```
In[4]:= FullForm[%]
Out[4]//FullForm= Plus[1, Power[x, 2], Power[Plus[y, z], 2]]
```

The object *f* in an expression *f*[*x*, *y*, ...] is known as the *head* of the expression. You can extract it using `Head[`*expr*`]`. Particularly when you write programs in *Mathematica*, you will often want to test the head of an expression to find out what kind of thing the expression is.

Head gives the "function name" f.	*In[5]:=* `Head[f[x, y]]`
	Out[5]= f
Here Head gives the name of the "operator".	*In[6]:=* `Head[a + b + c]`
	Out[6]= Plus
Everything has a head.	*In[7]:=* `Head[{a, b, c}]`
	Out[7]= List
Numbers also have heads.	*In[8]:=* `Head[23432]`
	Out[8]= Integer
You can distinguish different kinds of numbers by their heads.	*In[9]:=* `Head[345.6]`
	Out[9]= Real

`Head[`*expr*`]`	give the head of an expression: the *f* in *f*[*x*, *y*]
`FullForm[`*expr*`]`	display an expression in the full form used by *Mathematica*

Functions for manipulating expressions.

■ 2.1.2 The Meaning of Expressions

The notion of expressions is a crucial unifying principle in *Mathematica*. It is the fact that every object in *Mathematica* has the same underlying structure that makes it possible for *Mathematica* to cover so many areas with a comparatively small number of basic operations.

Although all expressions have the same basic structure, there are many different ways that expressions can be used. Here are a few of the interpretations you can give to the parts of an expression.

meaning of f	meaning of x, y, ...	examples
Function	arguments or parameters	`Sin[x]`, `f[x, y]`
Command	arguments or parameters	`Expand[(x + 1)^2]`
Operator	operands	`x + y`, `a = b`
Head	elements	`{a, b, c}`
Object type	contents	`RGBColor[r, g, b]`

Some interpretations of parts of expressions.

Expressions in *Mathematica* are often used to specify operations. So, for example, typing in 2 + 3 causes 2 and 3 to be added together, while `Factor[x^6 - 1]` performs factorization.

Perhaps an even more important use of expressions in *Mathematica*, however, is to maintain a structure, which can then be acted on by other functions. An expression like {a, b, c} does not specify an operation. It merely maintains a list structure, which contains a collection of three elements. Other functions, such as `Reverse` or `Dot`, can act on this structure.

The full form of the expression {a, b, c} is `List[a, b, c]`. The head `List` performs no operations. Instead, its purpose is to serve as a "tag" to specify the "type" of the structure.

You can use expressions in *Mathematica* to create your own structures. For example, you might want to represent points in three-dimensional space, specified by three coordinates. You could give each point as `point[x, y, z]`. The "function" `point` again performs no operation. It serves merely to collect the three coordinates together, and to label the resulting object as a `point`.

You can think of expressions like `point[x, y, z]` as being "packets of data", tagged with a particular head. Even though all expressions have the same basic structure, you can distinguish different "types" of expressions by giving them different heads. You can then set up transformation rules and programs which treat different types of expressions in different ways.

■ 2.1.3 Special Ways to Input Expressions

Mathematica allows you to use special notation for many common operators. For example, although internally *Mathematica* represents a sum of two terms as `Plus[x, y]`, you can enter this expression in the much more convenient form $x + y$.

The *Mathematica* language has a definite grammar which specifies how your input should be converted to internal form. One aspect of the grammar is that it specifies how pieces of your input should be grouped. For example, if you enter an expression such as a + b ^ c, the *Mathematica* grammar specifies that this should be considered, following standard mathematical notation, as a + (b ^ c) rather than (a + b) ^ c. *Mathematica* chooses this grouping because it treats the operator ^ as having a higher *precedence* than +. In general, the arguments of operators with higher precedence are grouped before those of operators with lower precedence.

You should realize that absolutely every special input form in *Mathematica* is assigned a definite precedence. This includes not only the traditional mathematical operators, but also forms such as ->, := or the semicolons used to separate expressions in a *Mathematica* program.

The table on pages 972–977 gives all the operators of *Mathematica* in order of decreasing precedence. The precedence is arranged, where possible, to follow standard mathematical usage, and to minimize the number of parentheses that are usually needed.

You will find, for example, that relational operators such as < have lower precedence than arithmetic operators such as +. This means that you can write expressions such as x + y > 7 without using parentheses.

There are nevertheless many cases where you do have to use parentheses. For example, since ; has a lower precedence than =, you need to use parentheses to write x = (a ; b). *Mathematica* interprets the expression x = a ; b as (x = a) ; b. In general, it can never hurt to include extra parentheses, but it can cause a great deal of trouble if you leave parentheses out, and *Mathematica* interprets your input in a way you do not expect.

$f[x, y]$	standard form for $f[x, y]$
$f @ x$	prefix form for $f[x]$
$x // f$	postfix form for $f[x]$
$x \sim f \sim y$	infix form for $f[x, y]$

Four ways to write expressions in *Mathematica*.

There are several common types of operators in *Mathematica*. The + in $x + y$ is an "infix" operator. The − in $-p$ is a "prefix" operator. Even when you enter an expression such as $f[x, y, ...]$ *Mathematica* allows you to do it in ways that mimic infix, prefix and postfix forms.

This "postfix form" is exactly equivalent to f[x + y].

```
In[1]:= x + y //f
Out[1]= f[x + y]
```

You will often want to add functions like N as "afterthoughts", and give them in postfix form.

```
In[2]:= 3^(1/4) + 1  //N
Out[2]= 2.31607
```

It is sometimes easier to understand what a function is doing when you write it in infix form.

```
In[3]:= {a, b, c} ~Join~ {d, e}
Out[3]= {a, b, c, d, e}
```

You should notice that // has very low precedence. If you put *//f* at the end of any expression containing arithmetic or logical operators, the *f* is applied to the *whole expression*. So, for example, x+y //f means f[x+y], not x+f[y].

The prefix form @ has a much higher precedence. f @ x + y is equivalent to f[x] + y, not f[x + y]. You can write f[x + y] in prefix form as f @ (x + y).

■ 2.1.4 Parts of Expressions

Since lists are just a particular kind of expression, it will come as no surprise that you can refer to parts of any expression much as you refer to parts of a list.

This gets the second element in the list {a, b, c}.	*In[1]:=* **{a, b, c}[[2]]** *Out[1]=* b
You can use the same method to get the second element in the sum x + y + z.	*In[2]:=* **(x + y + z)[[2]]** *Out[2]=* y
This gives the last element in the sum.	*In[3]:=* **(x + y + z)[[-1]]** *Out[3]=* z
Part 0 is the head.	*In[4]:=* **(x + y + z)[[0]]** *Out[4]=* Plus

You can refer to parts of an expression such as *f[g[a], g[b]]* just as you refer to parts of nested lists.

This is part 1.	*In[5]:=* **f[g[a], g[b]] [[1]]** *Out[5]=* g[a]
This is part {1,1}.	*In[6]:=* **f[g[a], g[b]] [[1, 1]]** *Out[6]=* a
This extracts part {2,1} of the expression 1 + x^2.	*In[7]:=* **(1 + x^2) [[2, 1]]** *Out[7]=* x
To see what part is {2,1}, you can look at the full form of the expression.	*In[8]:=* **FullForm[1 + x^2]** *Out[8]//FullForm=* Plus[1, Power[x, 2]]

You should realize that the assignment of indices to parts of expressions is done on the basis of the internal *Mathematica* forms of the expression, as shown by FullForm. These forms do not always correspond directly with what you see printed out. This is particularly true for algebraic expressions, where *Mathematica* uses a standard internal form, but prints the expressions in special ways.

Here is the internal form of x / y.	*In[9]:=* **FullForm[x / y]** *Out[9]//FullForm=* Times[x, Power[y, -1]]

It is the internal form that is used in specifying parts.

$In[10]:=$ **(x / y)[[2]]**

$Out[10]=$ $\dfrac{1}{y}$

You can manipulate parts of expressions just as you manipulate parts of lists.

This replaces the third part of **a + b + c + d** by **x^2**. Note that the sum is automatically rearranged when the replacement is done.

$In[11]:=$ **ReplacePart[a + b + c + d, x^2, 3]**

$Out[11]=$ $a + b + d + x^2$

Here is an expression.

$In[12]:=$ **t = 1 + (3 + x)^2 / y**

$Out[12]=$ $1 + \dfrac{(3+x)^2}{y}$

This is the full form of **t**.

$In[13]:=$ **FullForm[t]**

$Out[13]//FullForm=$ Plus[1, Times[Power[Plus[3, x], 2], Power[y, -1]]]

This resets a part of the expression **t**.

$In[14]:=$ **t[[2, 1, 1]] = x**

$Out[14]=$ x

Now the form of **t** has been changed.

$In[15]:=$ **t**

$Out[15]=$ $1 + \dfrac{x^2}{y}$

Part[*expr***, ***n***]** or ***expr***[[***n***]]   the nth part of *expr*

Part[*expr***, {***n*₁, *n*₂, ... }]** or ***expr***[[{*n*₁, *n*₂, ... }]]
a combination of parts of an expression

ReplacePart[*expr***, ***elem***, ***n***]**   replace the nth part of *expr* by *elem*

Functions for manipulating parts of expressions.

Section 1.2.4 discussed how you can use lists of indices to pick out several elements of a list at a time. You can use the same procedure to pick out several parts in an expression at a time.

This picks out elements 2 and 4 in the list, and gives a list of these elements.

$In[16]:=$ **{a, b, c, d, e}[[{2, 4}]]**

$Out[16]=$ {b, d}

This picks out parts 2 and 4 of the sum, and gives a *sum* of these elements.

$In[17]:=$ **(a + b + c + d + e)[[{2, 4}]]**

$Out[17]=$ $b + d$

Any part in an expression can be viewed as being an argument of some function. When you pick out several parts by giving a list of indices, the parts are combined using the same function as in the expression.

■ 2.1.5 Manipulating Expressions like Lists

You can use most of the list operations discussed in Section 1.8 on any kind of *Mathematica* expression. By using these operations, you can manipulate the structure of expressions in many ways.

Here is an expression that corresponds to a sum of terms.	*In[1]:=* `t = 1 + x + x^2 + y^2` *Out[1]=* $1 + x + x^2 + y^2$
`Take[t, 2]` takes the first two elements from t, just as if t were a list.	*In[2]:=* `Take[t, 2]` *Out[2]=* $1 + x$
`Length` gives the number of elements in t.	*In[3]:=* `Length[t]` *Out[3]=* 4
You can use `FreeQ[`*expr*`, `*form*`]` to test whether *form* appears nowhere in *expr*.	*In[4]:=* `FreeQ[t, x]` *Out[4]=* False
This gives a list of the positions at which x appears in t.	*In[5]:=* `Position[t, x]` *Out[5]=* {{2}, {3, 1}}

You should remember that all functions which manipulate the structure of expressions act on the internal forms of these expressions. You can see these forms using `FullForm[`*expr*`]`. They may not be what you would expect from the printed versions of the expressions.

Here is a function with four arguments.	*In[6]:=* `f[a, b, c, d]` *Out[6]=* f[a, b, c, d]
You can add an argument using `Append`.	*In[7]:=* `Append[%, e]` *Out[7]=* f[a, b, c, d, e]
This reverses the arguments.	*In[8]:=* `Reverse[%]` *Out[8]=* f[e, d, c, b, a]

There are a few extra functions that can be used with expressions, as discussed in Section 2.2.10.

■ 2.1.6 Expressions as Trees

Here is an expression in full form.	*In[1]:=* `FullForm[x^3 + (1 + x)^2]` *Out[1]//FullForm=* Plus[Power[x, 3], Power[Plus[1, x], 2]]
`TreeForm` prints out expressions to show their "tree" structure.	*In[2]:=* `TreeForm[x^3 + (1 + x)^2]` *Out[2]//TreeForm=* Plus[	,	]

$$\text{Plus}\left[\begin{array}{cc} | & | \\ \text{Power[x, 3]} & \text{Power}\left[\begin{array}{cc} | & , 2 \\ \text{Plus[1, x]} & \end{array}\right] \end{array}\right]$$

You can think of any *Mathematica* expression as a tree. In the expression above, the top node in the tree consists of a Plus. From this node come two "branches", x^3 and (1 + x)^2. From the x^3 node, there are then two branches, x and 3, which can be viewed as "leaves" of the tree.

This matrix is a simple tree with just two levels.

In[3]:= **TreeForm[{{a, b}, {c, d}}]**

Out[3]//TreeForm= List$\left[\begin{matrix} | & , & | \\ \text{List[a, b]} & & \text{List[c, d]} \end{matrix}\right]$

Here is a more complicated expression.

In[4]:= **{{a b, c d^2}, {x^3 y^4}}**

Out[4]= $\{\{a\,b, c\,d^2\}, \{x^3\,y^4\}\}$

The tree for this expression has several levels. The representation of the tree here was too long to fit on a single line, so it had to be broken onto two lines.

In[5]:= **TreeForm[%]**

Out[5]//TreeForm= List$\Big[|$

                   List$\Big[|$, $|$ $\Big]$

                          Times[a, b]   Times$\Big[c, |$ $\Big]$

                                                Power[d, 2]

         $|$ $\Big]$

      List$\Big[|$ $\Big]$

            Times$\Big[|$, $|$ $\Big]$

               Power[x, 3]   Power[y, 4]

The indices that label each part of an expression have a simple interpretation in terms of trees. Descending from the top node of the tree, each index specifies which branch to take in order to reach the part you want.

■ 2.1.7 Levels in Expressions

The Part function allows you to access specific parts of *Mathematica* expressions. But particularly when your expressions have fairly uniform structure, it is often convenient to be able to refer to a whole collection of parts at the same time.

Levels provide a general way of specifying collections of parts in *Mathematica* expressions. Many *Mathematica* functions allow you to specify the levels in an expression on which they should act.

Here is a simple expression, displayed in tree form.

In[1]:= **(t = {x, {x, y}, y}) // TreeForm**

Out[1]//TreeForm= List$\Big[x, |$, y$\Big]$

                  List[x, y]

This searches for x in the expression t down to level 1. It finds only one occurrence.

In[2]:= **Position[t, x, 1]**

Out[2]= {{1}}

This searches down to level 2. Now it finds both occurrences of x.	*In[3]:=* **Position[t, x, 2]**
	Out[3]= {{1}, {2, 1}}
This searches only at level 2. It finds just one occurrence of x.	*In[4]:=* **Position[t, x, {2}]**
	Out[4]= {{2, 1}}

Position[*expr*, *form*, *n*]	give the positions at which *form* occurs in *expr* down to level *n*
Position[*expr*, *form*, {*n*}]	give the positions exactly at level *n*

Controlling Position using levels.

You can think of levels in expressions in terms of trees. The level of a particular part in an expression is simply the distance down the tree at which that part appears, with the top of the tree considered as level 0.

It is equivalent to say that the parts which appear at level *n* are those that can be specified by a sequence of exactly *n* indices.

n	levels 1 through *n*
Infinity	all levels (except 0)
{*n*}	level *n* only
{*n*₁, *n*₂}	levels n_1 through n_2
Heads -> True	include heads
Heads -> False	exclude heads

Level specifications.

Here is an expression, displayed in tree form.	*In[5]:=* **(u = f[f[g[a], a], a, h[a], f]) // TreeForm**
	Out[5]//TreeForm= f[⎮ , a, ⎮ , f]
	f[⎮ , a] h[a]
	g[a]
This searches for a at levels from 2 downwards.	*In[6]:=* **Position[u, a, {2, Infinity}]**
	Out[6]= {{1, 1, 1}, {1, 2}, {3, 1}}
This shows where f appears other than in the head of an expression.	*In[7]:=* **Position[u, f, Heads->False]**
	Out[7]= {{4}}

| This includes occurrences of f in heads of expressions. | *In[8]:=* **Position[u, f, Heads->True]**

Out[8]= {{0}, {1, 0}, {4}} |

| Level[*expr, lev*] | a list of the parts of *expr* at the levels specified by *lev* |
| Depth[*expr*] | the total number of levels in *expr* |

Testing and extracting levels.

| This gives a list of all parts of u that occur down to level 2. | *In[9]:=* **Level[u, 2]**

Out[9]= {g[a], a, f[g[a], a], a, a, h[a], f} |
| Here are the parts specifically at level 2. | *In[10]:=* **Level[u, {2}]**

Out[10]= {g[a], a, a} |

When you have got the hang of ordinary levels, you can try thinking about *negative levels*. Negative levels label parts of expressions starting at the *bottom* of the tree. Level −1 contains all the leaves of the tree: objects like symbols and numbers.

| This shows the parts of u at level −1. | *In[11]:=* **Level[u, {-1}]**

Out[11]= {a, a, a, a, f} |

You can think of expressions as having a "depth", which is equal to the maximum number of levels shown by **TreeForm**. In general, level −*n* in an expression is defined to consist of all subexpressions whose depth is *n*.

| The depth of g[a] is 2. | *In[12]:=* **Depth[g[a]]**

Out[12]= 2 |
| The parts of u at level −2 are those that have depth exactly 2. | *In[13]:=* **Level[u, {-2}]**

Out[13]= {g[a], h[a]} |

2.2 Functional Operations

■ 2.2.1 Function Names as Expressions

In an expression like $f[x]$, the "function name" f is itself an expression, and you can treat it as you would any other expression.

You can replace names of functions using transformation rules.	`In[1]:= f[x] + f[1 - x] /. f -> g` `Out[1]= g[1 - x] + g[x]`
Any assignments you have made are used on function names.	`In[2]:= p1 = p2; p1[x, y]` `Out[2]= p2[x, y]`
This defines a function which takes a function name as an argument.	`In[3]:= pf[f_, x_] := f[x] + f[1 - x]`
This gives Log as the function name to use.	`In[4]:= pf[Log, q]` `Out[4]= Log[1 - q] + Log[q]`

The ability to treat the names of functions just like other kinds of expressions is an important consequence of the symbolic nature of the *Mathematica* language. It makes possible the whole range of *functional operations* discussed in the sections that follow.

Ordinary *Mathematica* functions such as Log or Integrate typically operate on data such as numbers and algebraic expressions. *Mathematica* functions that represent functional operations, however, can operate not only on ordinary data, but also on functions themselves. Thus, for example, the functional operation InverseFunction takes a *Mathematica* function name as an argument, and represents the inverse of that function.

InverseFunction is a functional operation: it takes a *Mathematica* function as an argument, and returns another function which represents its inverse.	`In[5]:= InverseFunction[ArcSin]` `Out[5]= Sin`
The result obtained from InverseFunction is a function which you can apply to data.	`In[6]:= %[x]` `Out[6]= Sin[x]`
You can also use InverseFunction in a purely symbolic way.	`In[7]:= InverseFunction[f][x]` `Out[7]= f^{(-1)}[x]`

There are many kinds of functional operations in *Mathematica*. Some represent mathematical operations; others represent various kinds of procedures and algorithms.

Unless you are familiar with advanced symbolic languages, you will probably not recognize most of the functional operations discussed in the sections that follow. At first, the operations may seem difficult to understand. But it is worth persisting. Functional operations provide one of the most conceptually and practically efficient ways to use *Mathematica*.

■ 2.2.2 Applying Functions Repeatedly

Nest[*f*, *x*, *n*]	apply the function *f* nested *n* times to *x*
NestList[*f*, *x*, *n*]	generate the list {*x*, *f*[*x*], *f*[*f*[*x*]], ... }, where *f* is nested up to *n* deep
FixedPoint[*f*, *x*]	apply the function *f* repeatedly until the result no longer changes
FixedPointList[*f*, *x*]	generate the list {*x*, *f*[*x*], *f*[*f*[*x*]], ... }, stopping when the elements no longer change
FixedPoint[*f*, *x*, SameTest -> *comp*]	stop when the function *comp* applied to two successive results yields True

Ways to apply functions of one argument repeatedly.

Nest[*f*, *x*, *n*] takes the "name" *f* of a function, and applies the function *n* times to *x*.

```
In[1]:= Nest[f, x, 4]
Out[1]= f[f[f[f[x]]]]
```

This makes a list of each successive nesting.

```
In[2]:= NestList[f, x, 4]
Out[2]= {x, f[x], f[f[x]], f[f[f[x]]], f[f[f[f[x]]]]}
```

Here is a simple function.

```
In[3]:= recip[x_] := 1/(1 + x)
```

You can iterate the function using Nest.

```
In[4]:= Nest[recip, x, 3]
```

$$Out[4]= \cfrac{1}{1 + \cfrac{1}{1 + \cfrac{1}{1+x}}}$$

Many programs you write will involve operations that need to be iterated several times. Nest and NestList are powerful constructs for doing this.

Here is a function that takes one step in Newton's approximation to $\sqrt{3}$.

```
In[5]:= newton3[x_] := N[ 1/2 ( x + 3/x ) ]
```

Here are five successive iterates of the function, starting at *x* = 1.

```
In[6]:= NestList[newton3, 1.0, 5]
Out[6]= {1., 2., 1.75, 1.73214, 1.73205, 1.73205}
```

Using the function FixedPoint, you can automatically continue applying newton3 until the result no longer changes.

```
In[7]:= FixedPoint[newton3, 1.0]
Out[7]= 1.73205
```

Here is the sequence of results.

In[8]:= **FixedPointList[newton3, 1.0]**

Out[8]= {1., 2., 1.75, 1.73214, 1.73205, 1.73205, 1.73205}

You control when FixedPointList stops by giving a function with which to compare successive results.

In[9]:= **FixedPointList[newton3, 1.0,**
         SameTest -> (Abs[#1 - #2] < 10.^-4 &)]

Out[9]= {1., 2., 1.75, 1.73214, 1.73205}

The functional operations Nest and NestList take a function f of one argument, and apply it repeatedly. At each step, they use the result of the previous step as the new argument of f.

It is important to generalize this notion to functions of two arguments. You can again apply the function repeatedly, but now each result you get supplies only one of the new arguments you need. A convenient approach is to get the other argument at each step from the successive elements of a list.

FoldList[f, x, {a, b, ... }]	create the list {x, $f[x, a]$, $f[f[x, a], b]$, ... }
Fold[f, x, {a, b, ... }]	give the last element of the list produced by FoldList[f, x, {a, b, ... }]

Ways to repeatedly apply functions of two arguments.

Here is an example of what FoldList does.

In[10]:= **FoldList[f, x, {a, b, c}]**

Out[10]= {x, f[x, a], f[f[x, a], b], f[f[f[x, a], b], c]}

Fold gives the last element of the list produced by FoldList.

In[11]:= **Fold[f, x, {a, b, c}]**

Out[11]= f[f[f[x, a], b], c]

This gives a list of cumulative sums.

In[12]:= **FoldList[Plus, 0, {a, b, c}]**

Out[12]= {0, a, a + b, a + b + c}

Using Fold and FoldList you can write many elegant and efficient programs in *Mathematica*. In some cases, you may find it helpful to think of Fold and FoldList as producing a simple nesting of a family of functions indexed by their first argument.

This defines a function nextdigit.

In[13]:= **nextdigit[a_, b_] := 10 a + b**

Here is a rather elegant definition of a function that gives the number corresponding to a list of digits in base 10.

In[14]:= **tonumber[digits_] := Fold[nextdigit, 0, digits]**

Here is an example of tonumber in action.

In[15]:= **tonumber[{1, 3, 7, 2, 9, 1}]**

Out[15]= 137291

■ 2.2.3 Applying Functions to Lists and Other Expressions

In an expression like f[{a, b, c}] you are giving a list as the argument to a function. Often you need instead to apply a function directly to the elements of a list, rather than to the list as a whole. You can do this in *Mathematica* using Apply.

This makes each element of the list an argument of the function f.	*In[1]:=* **Apply[f, {a, b, c}]** *Out[1]=* f[a, b, c]
This gives Plus[a, b, c] which yields the sum of the elements in the list.	*In[2]:=* **Apply[Plus, {a, b, c}]** *Out[2]=* a + b + c
Here is the definition of the statistical mean, written using Apply.	*In[3]:=* **mean[list_] := Apply[Plus, list] / Length[list]**

Apply[*f*, {*a*, *b*, ... }]	apply *f* to a list, giving *f*[*a*, *b*, ...]
Apply[*f*, *expr*] or *f* @@ *expr*	apply *f* to the top level of an expression
Apply[*f*, *expr*, *lev*]	apply *f* at the specified levels in an expression

Applying functions to lists and other expressions.

What Apply does in general is to replace the head of an expression with the function you specify. Here it replaces Plus by List.	*In[4]:=* **Apply[List, a + b + c]** *Out[4]=* {a, b, c}
Here is a matrix.	*In[5]:=* **m = {{a, b, c}, {b, c, d}}** *Out[5]=* {{a, b, c}, {b, c, d}}
Using Apply without an explicit level specification replaces the top-level list with f.	*In[6]:=* **Apply[f, m]** *Out[6]=* f[{a, b, c}, {b, c, d}]
This applies f only to parts of m at level 1.	*In[7]:=* **Apply[f, m, {1}]** *Out[7]=* {f[a, b, c], f[b, c, d]}
This applies f at levels 0 through 1.	*In[8]:=* **Apply[f, m, {0, 1}]** *Out[8]=* f[f[a, b, c], f[b, c, d]]

■ 2.2.4 Applying Functions to Parts of Expressions

If you have a list of elements, it is often important to be able to apply a function separately to each of the elements. You can do this in *Mathematica* using Map.

This applies f separately to each element in a list.

In[1]:= **Map[f, {a, b, c}]**

Out[1]= {f[a], f[b], f[c]}

This defines a function which takes the first two elements from a list.

In[2]:= **take2[list_] := Take[list, 2]**

You can use Map to apply take2 to each element of a list.

In[3]:= **Map[take2, {{1, 3, 4}, {5, 6, 7}, {2, 1, 6, 6}}]**

Out[3]= {{1, 3}, {5, 6}, {2, 1}}

Map[*f*, {*a*, *b*, ... }]	apply *f* to each element in a list, giving {*f*[*a*], *f*[*b*], ... }

Applying a function to each element in a list.

What Map[*f*, *expr*] effectively does is to "wrap" the function *f* around each element of the expression *expr*. You can use Map on any expression, not just a list.

This applies f to each element in the sum.

In[4]:= **Map[f, a + b + c]**

Out[4]= f[a] + f[b] + f[c]

This applies Sqrt to each argument of g.

In[5]:= **Map[Sqrt, g[x^2, x^3]]**

Out[5]= g$\left[\sqrt{x^2}, \sqrt{x^3} \right]$

Map[*f*, *expr*] applies *f* to the first level of parts in *expr*. You can use MapAll[*f*, *expr*] to apply *f* to *all* the parts of *expr*.

This defines a 2 × 2 matrix m.

In[6]:= **m = {{a, b}, {c, d}}**

Out[6]= {{a, b}, {c, d}}

Map applies f to the first level of m, in this case the rows of the matrix.

In[7]:= **Map[f, m]**

Out[7]= {f[{a, b}], f[{c, d}]}

MapAll applies f at *all* levels in m. If you look carefully at this expression, you will see an f wrapped around every part.

In[8]:= **MapAll[f, m]**

Out[8]= f[{f[{f[a], f[b]}], f[{f[c], f[d]}]}]

In general, you can use level specifications as described on page 236 to tell Map to which parts of an expression to apply your function.

This applies f only to the parts of m at level 2.

In[9]:= **Map[f, m, {2}]**

Out[9]= {{f[a], f[b]}, {f[c], f[d]}}

Setting the option Heads->True wraps f around the head of each part, as well as its elements.

In[10]:= **Map[f, m, Heads->True]**

Out[10]= f[List][f[{a, b}], f[{c, d}]]

Map[*f, expr*] or *f* /@ *expr*	apply *f* to the first-level parts of *expr*
MapAll[*f, expr*] or *f* //@ *expr*	apply *f* to all parts of *expr*
Map[*f, expr, lev*]	apply *f* to each part of *expr* at levels specified by *lev*

Ways to apply a function to different parts of expressions.

Level specifications allow you to tell Map to which levels of parts in an expression you want a function applied. With MapAt, however, you can instead give an explicit list of parts where you want a function applied. You specify each part by giving its indices, as discussed in Section 2.1.4.

Here is a 2 × 3 matrix.

In[11]:= **mm = {{a, b, c}, {b, c, d}}**

Out[11]= {{a, b, c}, {b, c, d}}

This applies f to parts {1, 2} and {2, 3}.

In[12]:= **MapAt[f, mm, {{1, 2}, {2, 3}}]**

Out[12]= {{a, f[b], c}, {b, c, f[d]}}

This gives a list of the positions at which b occurs in mm.

In[13]:= **Position[mm, b]**

Out[13]= {{1, 2}, {2, 1}}

You can feed the list of positions you get from Position directly into MapAt.

In[14]:= **MapAt[f, mm, %]**

Out[14]= {{a, f[b], c}, {f[b], c, d}}

To avoid ambiguity, you must put each part specification in a list, even when it involves only one index.

In[15]:= **MapAt[f, {a, b, c, d}, {{2}, {3}}]**

Out[15]= {a, f[b], f[c], d}

MapAt[*f, expr,* {*part$_1$, part$_2$, ...* }]	
	apply *f* to specified parts of *expr*

Applying a function to specific parts of an expression.

Here is an expression.

In[16]:= **t = 1 + (3 + x)^2 / x**

Out[16]= $1 + \dfrac{(3 + x)^2}{x}$

This is the full form of t.

In[17]:= **FullForm[t]**

Out[17]//FullForm= Plus[1, Times[Power[x, -1], Power[Plus[3, x], 2]]]

You can use MapAt on any expression. Remember that parts are numbered on the basis of the full forms of expressions.

In[18]:= **MapAt[f, t, {{2, 1, 1}, {2, 2}}]**

Out[18]= $1 + \dfrac{f\left[(3 + x)^2\right]}{f[x]}$

`MapIndexed[f, expr]`	apply *f* to the elements of an expression, giving the part specification of each element as a second argument to *f*
`MapIndexed[f, expr, lev]`	apply *f* to parts at specified levels, giving the list of indices for each part as successive arguments to *f*

Applying a function to parts and their indices.

This applies f to each element in a list, giving the index of the element as a second argument to f.	`In[19]:= MapIndexed[f, {a, b, c}]`
	
	`Out[19]= {f[a, {1}], f[b, {2}], f[c, {3}]}`

This applies f to both levels in a matrix.	`In[20]:= MapIndexed[f, {{a, b}, {c, d}}, 2]`
	
	`Out[20]= {f[{f[a, {1, 1}], f[b, {1, 2}]}, {1}],`
	`        f[{f[c, {2, 1}], f[d, {2, 2}]}, {2}]}`

Map allows you to apply a function of one argument to parts of an expression. Sometimes, however, you may instead want to apply a function of several arguments to corresponding parts of several different expressions. You can do this using MapThread.

`MapThread[f, {expr_1, expr_2, ... }]`	apply *f* to corresponding elements in each of the *expr_i*
`MapThread[f, {expr_1, expr_2, ... }, lev]`	apply *f* to parts of the *expr_i* at the specified level

Applying a function to several expressions at once.

This applies f to corresponding pairs of list elements.	`In[21]:= MapThread[f, {{a, b, c}, {ap, bp, cp}}]`
	
	`Out[21]= {f[a, ap], f[b, bp], f[c, cp]}`

MapThread works with any number of expressions, so long as they have the same structure.	`In[22]:= MapThread[f, {{a, b}, {ap, bp}, {app, bpp}}]`
	
	`Out[22]= {f[a, ap, app], f[b, bp, bpp]}`

Functions like Map allow you to create expressions with parts modified. Sometimes you simply want to go through an expression, and apply a particular function to some parts of it, without building a new expression. A typical case is when the function you apply has certain "side effects", such as making assignments, or generating output.

`Scan[f, expr]`	evaluate *f* applied to each element of *expr* in turn
`Scan[f, expr, lev]`	evaluate *f* applied to parts of *expr* on levels specified by *lev*

Evaluating functions on parts of expressions.

Map constructs a new list in which f has been applied to each element of the list.	`In[23]:= `**`Map[f, {a, b, c}]`** `Out[23]= {f[a], f[b], f[c]}`
Scan evaluates the result of applying a function to each element, but does not construct a new expression.	`In[24]:= `**`Scan[Print, {a, b, c}]`** a b c
Scan visits the parts of an expression in a depth-first walk, with the leaves visited first.	`In[25]:= `**`Scan[Print, 1 + x^2, Infinity]`** 1 x 2 $\quad$2 x

■ 2.2.5 Pure Functions

`Function[`x`, `*body*`]`	a pure function in which x is replaced by any argument you provide
`Function[{`x_1`, `x_2`, ... }, `*body*`]`	a pure function that takes several arguments
body `&`	a pure function in which arguments are specified as `#` or `#1`, `#2`, `#3`, etc.

Pure functions.

When you use functional operations such as `Nest` and `Map`, you always have to specify a function to apply. In all the examples above, we have used the "name" of a function to specify the function. Pure functions allow you to give functions which can be applied to arguments, without having to define explicit names for the functions.

This defines a function h.	`In[1]:= `**`h[x_] := f[x] + g[x]`**
Having defined h, you can now use its name in Map.	`In[2]:= `**`Map[h, {a, b, c}]`** `Out[2]= {f[a] +g[a], f[b] +g[b], f[c] +g[c]}`
Here is a way to get the same result using a pure function.	`In[3]:= `**`Map[ f[#] + g[#] &, {a, b, c} ]`** `Out[3]= {f[a] +g[a], f[b] +g[b], f[c] +g[c]}`

There are several equivalent ways to write pure functions in *Mathematica*. The idea in all cases is to construct an object which, when supplied with appropriate arguments, computes a particular function. Thus, for example, if *fun* is a pure function, then *fun*`[a]` evaluates the function with argument *a*.

Here is a pure function which represents the operation of squaring.	`In[4]:= `**`Function[x, x^2]`** `Out[4]= Function[x, x`^{2}`]`
Supplying the argument n to the pure function yields the square of n.	`In[5]:= `**`%[n]`** `Out[5]= n`^{2}

You can use a pure function wherever you would usually give the name of a function.

You can use a pure function in Map.	*In[6]:=* **Map[Function[x, x^2], a + b + c]**
	Out[6]= $a^2 + b^2 + c^2$
Or in Nest.	*In[7]:=* **Nest[Function[q, 1/(1+q)], x, 3]**
	Out[7]= $\dfrac{1}{1 + \frac{1}{1 + \frac{1}{1+x}}}$
This sets up a pure function with two arguments and then applies the function to the arguments a and b.	*In[8]:=* **Function[{x, y}, x^2 + y^3] [a, b]**
	Out[8]= $a^2 + b^3$

If you are going to use a particular function repeatedly, then you can define the function using $f[x\_] := body$, and refer to the function by its name f. On the other hand, if you only intend to use a function once, you will probably find it better to give the function in pure function form, without ever naming it.

If you are familiar with formal logic or the LISP programming language, you will recognize *Mathematica* pure functions as being like λ expressions or anonymous functions. Pure functions are also close to the pure mathematical notion of operators.

#	the first variable in a pure function
#*n*	the nth variable in a pure function
##	the sequence of all variables in a pure function
##*n*	the sequence of variables starting with the nth one

Short forms for pure functions.

Just as the name of a function is irrelevant if you do not intend to refer to the function again, so also the names of arguments in a pure function are irrelevant. *Mathematica* allows you to avoid using explicit names for the arguments of pure functions, and instead to specify the arguments by giving "slot numbers" #*n*. In a *Mathematica* pure function, #*n* stands for the nth argument you supply. # stands for the first argument.

#^2 & is a short form for a pure function that squares its argument.	*In[9]:=* **Map[#^2 &, a + b + c]**
	Out[9]= $a^2 + b^2 + c^2$
This applies a function that takes the first two elements from each list. By using a pure function, you avoid having to define the function separately.	*In[10]:=* **Map[Take[#, 2]&, {{2, 1, 7}, {4, 1, 5}, {3, 1, 2}}]**
	Out[10]= {{2, 1}, {4, 1}, {3, 1}}

Using short forms for pure functions, you can simplify the definition of tonumber given on page 240.

In[11]:= `tonumber[digits_] := Fold[(10 #1 + #2)&, 0, digits]`

When you use short forms for pure functions, it is very important that you do not forget the ampersand. If you leave the ampersand out, *Mathematica* will not know that the expression you give is to be used as a pure function.

When you use the ampersand notation for pure functions, you must be careful about the grouping of pieces in your input. As shown on page 977 the ampersand notation has fairly low precedence, which means that you can type expressions like #1 + #2 & without parentheses. On the other hand, if you want, for example, to set an option to be a pure function, you need to use parentheses, as in *option* -> (*fun* &).

Pure functions in *Mathematica* can take any number of arguments. You can use ## to stand for all the arguments that are given, and ##*n* to stand for the *n*th and subsequent arguments.

stands for all arguments.

In[12]:= `f[##, ##]& [x, y]`

Out[12]= `f[x, y, x, y]`

##2 stands for all arguments except the first one.

In[13]:= `Apply[f[##2, #1]&, {{a, b, c}, {ap, bp}}, {1}]`

Out[13]= `{f[b, c, a], f[bp, ap]}`

■ 2.2.6 Building Lists from Functions

`Array[f, n]`	generate a length n list of the form $\{f[1], f[2], \ldots \}$
`Array[f, {n_1, n_2, \ldots }]`	generate an $n_1 \times n_2 \times \ldots$ nested list, each of whose entries consists of f applied to its indices
`NestList[f, x, n]`	generate a list of the form $\{x, f[x], f[f[x]], \ldots \}$, where f is nested up to n deep
`FoldList[f, x, {a, b, \ldots }]`	generate a list of the form $\{x, f[x, a], f[f[x, a], b], \ldots \}$
`ComposeList[{f_1, f_2, \ldots }, x]`	generate a list of the form $\{x, f_1[x], f_2[f_1[x]], \ldots \}$

Making lists from functions.

This makes a list of 5 elements, each of the form p[*i*].

In[1]:= `Array[p, 5]`

Out[1]= `{p[1], p[2], p[3], p[4], p[5]}`

Here is another way to produce the same list.

In[2]:= `Table[p[i], {i, 5}]`

Out[2]= `{p[1], p[2], p[3], p[4], p[5]}`

This produces a list whose elements are $i + i^2$.

In[3]:= `Array[ # + #^2 &, 5]`

Out[3]= `{2, 6, 12, 20, 30}`

This generates a 2 × 3 matrix whose entries are m[*i, j*].

```
In[4]:= Array[m, {2, 3}]
Out[4]= {{m[1, 1], m[1, 2], m[1, 3]},
          {m[2, 1], m[2, 2], m[2, 3]}}
```

This generates a 3 × 3 matrix whose elements are the squares of the sums of their indices.

```
In[5]:= Array[Plus[##]^2 &, {3, 3}]
Out[5]= {{4, 9, 16}, {9, 16, 25}, {16, 25, 36}}
```

NestList and **FoldList** were discussed in Section 2.2.2. Particularly by using them with pure functions, you can construct some very elegant and efficient *Mathematica* programs.

This gives a list of results obtained by successively differentiating x^n with respect to x.

```
In[6]:= NestList[ D[#, x]&, x^n, 3 ]
Out[6]= {x^n, n x^{-1+n}, (-1+n) n x^{-2+n}, (-2+n) (-1+n) n x^{-3+n}}
```

■ 2.2.7 Selecting Parts of Expressions with Functions

Section 1.2.4 showed how you can pick out elements of lists based on their *positions*. Often, however, you will need to select elements based not on *where* they are, but rather on *what* they are.

Select[*list, f*] selects elements of *list* using the function *f* as a criterion. **Select** applies *f* to each element of *list* in turn, and keeps only those for which the result is **True**.

This selects the elements of the list for which the pure function yields **True**, i.e., those numerically greater than 4.

```
In[1]:= Select[{2, 15, 1, a, 16, 17}, # > 4 &]
Out[1]= {15, 16, 17}
```

You can use **Select** to pick out pieces of any expression, not just elements of a list.

This gives a sum of terms involving x, y and z.

```
In[2]:= t = Expand[(x + y + z)^2]
Out[2]= x^2 + 2 x y + y^2 + 2 x z + 2 y z + z^2
```

You can use **Select** to pick out only those terms in the sum that do not involve the symbol x.

```
In[3]:= Select[t, FreeQ[#, x]&]
Out[3]= y^2 + 2 y z + z^2
```

Select[*expr, f*]	select the elements in *expr* for which the function *f* gives **True**
Select[*expr, f, n*]	select the first *n* elements in *expr* for which the function *f* gives **True**

Selecting pieces of expressions.

Section 2.3.5 discusses some "predicates" that are often used as criteria in **Select**.

This gives the first element which satisfies the criterion you specify.

```
In[4]:= Select[{-1, 3, 10, 12, 14}, # > 3 &, 1]
Out[4]= {10}
```

■ 2.2.8 Expressions with Heads That Are Not Symbols

In most cases, you want the head *f* of a *Mathematica* expression like *f*[*x*] to be a single symbol. There are, however, some important applications of heads that are not symbols.

This expression has f[3] as a head. You can use heads like this to represent "indexed functions".	*In[1]:=* **f[3][x, y]**
	Out[1]= f[3] [x, y]

You can use any expression as a head. Remember to put in the necessary parentheses.	*In[2]:=* **(a + b)[x]**
	Out[2]= (a + b) [x]

One case where we have already encountered the use of complicated expressions as heads is in working with pure functions in Section 2.2.5. By giving Function[*vars*, *body*] as the head of an expression, you specify a function of the arguments to be evaluated.

With the head Function[x, x^2], the value of the expression is the square of the argument.	*In[3]:=* **Function[x, x^2] [a + b]**
	Out[3]= $(a + b)^2$

There are several constructs in *Mathematica* which work much like pure functions, but which represent specific kinds of functions, typically numerical ones. In all cases, the basic mechanism involves giving a head which contains complete information about the function you want to use.

Function[*vars*, *body*][*args*]	pure function
InterpolatingFunction[*data*][*args*]	
	approximate numerical function (generated by Interpolation and NDSolve)
CompiledFunction[*data*][*args*]	compiled numerical function (generated by Compile)

Some expressions which have heads that are not symbols.

NDSolve returns a list of rules that give y as an InterpolatingFunction object.	*In[4]:=* **NDSolve[{y''[x] == y[x], y[0]==y'[0]==1}, y, {x, 0, 5}]**
	Out[4]= {{y → InterpolatingFunction[{{0., 5.}}, <>]}}

Here is the InterpolatingFunction object.	*In[5]:=* **y /. First[%]**
	Out[5]= InterpolatingFunction[{{0., 5.}}, <>]

You can use the InterpolatingFunction object as a head to get numerical approximations to values of the function y.	*In[6]:=* **% [3.8]**
	Out[6]= 44.7015

Another important use of more complicated expressions as heads is in implementing *functionals* and *functional operators* in mathematics.

As one example, consider the operation of differentiation. As will be discussed in Section 3.5.4, an expression like `f'` represents a *derivative function*, obtained from `f` by applying a functional operator to it. In *Mathematica*, `f'` is represented as `Derivative[1][f]`: the "functional operator" `Derivative[1]` is applied to `f` to give another function, represented as `f'`.

This expression has a head which represents the application of the "functional operator" `Derivative[1]` to the "function" `f`.	*In[7]:=* `f'[x] // FullForm` *Out[7]//FullForm=* `Derivative[1][f][x]`
You can replace the head `f'` with another head, such as `fp`. This effectively takes `fp` to be a "derivative function" obtained from `f`.	*In[8]:=* `% /. f' -> fp` *Out[8]=* `fp[x]`

■ 2.2.9 Advanced Topic: Working with Operators

You can think of an expression like $f[x]$ as being formed by applying an *operator f* to the expression x. You can think of an expression like $f[g[x]]$ as the result of *composing* the operators f and g, and applying the result to x.

`Composition[`f, g, ... `]`	the composition of functions f, g, ...
`InverseFunction[`f`]`	the inverse of a function f
`Identity`	the identity function

Some functional operations.

This represents the composition of the functions f, g and h.	*In[1]:=* `Composition[f, g, h]` *Out[1]=* `Composition[f, g, h]`
You can manipulate compositions of functions symbolically.	*In[2]:=* `InverseFunction[Composition[%, q]]` *Out[2]=* `Composition[q`$^{(-1)}$`, h`$^{(-1)}$`, g`$^{(-1)}$`, f`$^{(-1)}$`]`
The composition is evaluated explicitly when you supply a specific argument.	*In[3]:=* `%[x]` *Out[3]=* `q`$^{(-1)}$`[h`$^{(-1)}$`[g`$^{(-1)}$`[f`$^{(-1)}$`[x]]]]`

You can get the sum of two expressions in *Mathematica* just by typing $x + y$. Sometimes it is also worthwhile to consider performing operations like addition on *operators*.

You can think of this as containing a sum of two operators f and g.	*In[4]:=* `(f + g)[x]` *Out[4]=* `(f + g)[x]`
Using `Through`, you can convert the expression to a more explicit form.	*In[5]:=* `Through[%, Plus]` *Out[5]=* `f[x] + g[x]`

This corresponds to the mathematical operator $1 + \frac{\partial}{\partial x}$.

In[6]:= **Identity + (D[#, x]&)**

Out[6]= Identity + (∂_x #1&)

Mathematica does not automatically apply the separate pieces of the operator to an expression.

In[7]:= **% [x^2]**

Out[7]= (Identity + (∂_x #1&)) [x^2]

You can use Through to apply the operator.

In[8]:= **Through[%, Plus]**

Out[8]= 2 x + x^2

Identity[*expr*]	the identity function
Through[*p*[*f*$_1$, *f*$_2$][*x*], *q*]	give *p*[*f*$_1$[*x*], *f*$_2$[*x*]] if *p* is the same as *q*
Operate[*p*, *f*[*x*]]	give *p*[*f*][*x*]
Operate[*p*, *f*[*x*], *n*]	apply *p* at level *n* in *f*
MapAll[*p*, *expr*, Heads->True]	apply *p* to all parts of *expr*, including heads

Operations for working with operators.

This has a complicated expression as a head.

In[9]:= **t = ((1 + a)(1 + b))[x]**

Out[9]= ((1 + a) (1 + b)) [x]

Functions like Expand do not automatically go inside heads of expressions.

In[10]:= **Expand[%]**

Out[10]= ((1 + a) (1 + b)) [x]

With the Heads option set to True, MapAll goes inside heads.

In[11]:= **MapAll[Expand, t, Heads->True]**

Out[11]= (1 + a + b + a b) [x]

The replacement operator /. does go inside heads of expressions.

In[12]:= **t /. a->1**

Out[12]= (2 (1 + b)) [x]

You can use Operate to apply a function specifically to the head of an expression.

In[13]:= **Operate[p, t]**

Out[13]= p[(1 + a) (1 + b)] [x]

∎ 2.2.10 Structural Operations

Mathematica contains some powerful primitives for making structural changes to expressions. You can use these primitives both to implement mathematical properties such as associativity and distributivity, and to provide the basis for some succinct and efficient programs.

This section describes various operations that you can explicitly perform on expressions. Section 2.5.3 will describe how some of these operations can be performed automatically on all expressions with a particular head by assigning appropriate attributes to that head.

You can use the *Mathematica* function Sort[*expr*] to sort elements not only of lists, but of expressions with any head. In this way, you can implement the mathematical properties of commutativity or symmetry for arbitrary functions.

You can use Sort to put the arguments of any function into a standard order.	*In[1]:=* **Sort[f[c, a, b]]** *Out[1]=* f[a, b, c]

Sort[*expr*]	sort the elements of a list or other expression into a standard order
Sort[*expr*, *pred*]	sort using the function *pred* to determine whether pairs are in order
OrderedQ[*expr*]	give True if the elements of *expr* are in standard order, and False otherwise
Order[*expr*₁, *expr*₂]	give 1 if $expr_1$ comes before $expr_2$ in standard order, and −1 if it comes after

Sorting into order.

The second argument to Sort is a function used to determine whether pairs are in order. This sorts numbers into descending order.	*In[2]:=* **Sort[{5, 1, 8, 2}, (#2 < #1)&]** *Out[2]=* {8, 5, 2, 1}
This sorting criterion puts elements that do not depend on x before those that do.	*In[3]:=* **Sort[{x^2, y, x+y, y-2}, FreeQ[#1, x]&]** *Out[3]=* {y, −2 + y, x + y, x²}

Flatten[*expr*]	flatten out all nested functions with the same head as *expr*
Flatten[*expr*, *n*]	flatten at most *n* levels of nesting
Flatten[*expr*, *n*, *h*]	flatten functions with head *h*
FlattenAt[*expr*, *i*]	flatten only the ith element of *expr*

Flattening out expressions.

Flatten removes nested occurrences of a function.	*In[4]:=* **Flatten[f[a, f[b, c], f[f[d]]]]** *Out[4]=* f[a, b, c, d]

You can use Flatten to "splice" sequences of elements into lists or other expressions.

In[5]:= **Flatten[{a, f[b, c], f[a, b, d]}, 1, f]**

Out[5]= {a, b, c, a, b, d}

You can use Flatten to implement the mathematical property of associativity. The function Distribute allows you to implement properties such as distributivity and linearity.

Distribute[*f*[*a* + *b* + ... , ...]]	distribute *f* over sums to give *f*[*a*, ...] + *f*[*b*, ...] + ...
Distribute[*f*[*args*], *g*]	distribute *f* over any arguments which have head *g*
Distribute[*expr*, *g*, *f*]	distribute only when the head is *f*
Distribute[*expr*, *g*, *f*, *gp*, *fp*]	distribute *f* over *g*, replacing them with *fp* and *gp*, respectively

Applying distributive laws.

This "distributes" f over a + b.

In[6]:= **Distribute[f[a + b]]**

Out[6]= f[a] + f[b]

Here is a more complicated example.

In[7]:= **Distribute[f[a + b, c + d]]**

Out[7]= f[a, c] + f[a, d] + f[b, c] + f[b, d]

In general, if *f* is distributive over Plus, then an expression like *f*[*a* + *b*] can be "expanded" to give *f*[*a*] + *f*[*b*]. The function Expand does this kind of expansion for standard algebraic operators such as Times. Distribute allows you to perform the same kind of expansion for arbitrary operators.

Expand uses the distributivity of Times over Plus to perform algebraic expansions.

In[8]:= **Expand[(a + b) (c + d)]**

Out[8]= a c + b c + a d + b d

This applies distributivity over lists, rather than sums. The result contains all possible pairs of arguments.

In[9]:= **Distribute[f[{a, b}, {c, d}], List]**

Out[9]= {f[a, c], f[a, d], f[b, c], f[b, d]}

This distributes over lists, but does so only if the head of the whole expression is f.

In[10]:= **Distribute[f[{a, b}, {c, d}], List, f]**

Out[10]= {f[a, c], f[a, d], f[b, c], f[b, d]}

This distributes over lists, making sure that the head of the whole expression is f. In the result, it uses gp in place of List, and fp in place of f.

In[11]:= **Distribute[f[{a, b}, {c, d}], List, f, gp, fp]**

Out[11]= gp[fp[a, c], fp[a, d], fp[b, c], fp[b, d]]

Related to Distribute is the function Thread. What Thread effectively does is to apply a function in parallel to all the elements of a list or other expression.

Thread[f[$\{a_1, a_2\}$, $\{b_1, b_2\}$]]	thread f over lists to give $\{f[a_1, b_1], f[a_2, b_2]\}$
Thread[f[$args$], g]	thread f over objects with head g in $args$

Functions for threading expressions.

Here is a function whose arguments are lists.	*In[12]:=* **f[{a1, a2}, {b1, b2}]**
	Out[12]= f[{a1, a2}, {b1, b2}]
Thread applies the function "in parallel" to each element of the lists.	*In[13]:=* **Thread[%]**
	Out[13]= {f[a1, b1], f[a2, b2]}
Arguments that are not lists get repeated.	*In[14]:=* **Thread[f[{a1, a2}, {b1, b2}, c, d]]**
	Out[14]= {f[a1, b1, c, d], f[a2, b2, c, d]}

As mentioned in Section 1.8.1, and discussed in more detail in Section 2.5.3, many built-in *Mathematica* functions have the property of being "listable", so that they are automatically threaded over any lists that appear as arguments.

Built-in mathematical functions such as Log are listable, so that they are automatically threaded over lists.	*In[15]:=* **Log[{a, b, c}]**
	Out[15]= {Log[a], Log[b], Log[c]}
Log is, however, not automatically threaded over equations.	*In[16]:=* **Log[x == y]**
	Out[16]= Log[x == y]
You can use Thread to get functions applied to both sides of an equation.	*In[17]:=* **Thread[%, Equal]**
	Out[17]= Log[x] == Log[y]

Outer[f, $list_1$, $list_2$]	generalized outer product
Inner[f, $list_1$, $list_2$, g]	generalized inner product

Generalized outer and inner products.

Outer[f, $list_1$, $list_2$, ...] takes all possible combinations of elements from the $list_i$, and combines them with f. Outer can be viewed as a generalization of a Cartesian product for tensors, as discussed in Section 3.7.11.

Outer forms all possible combinations of elements, and applies f to them.	*In[18]:=* **Outer[f, {a, b}, {1, 2, 3}]**
	Out[18]= {{f[a, 1], f[a, 2], f[a, 3]},
	{f[b, 1], f[b, 2], f[b, 3]}}
Here Outer produces a lower-triangular Boolean matrix.	*In[19]:=* **Outer[Greater, {1, 2, 3}, {1, 2, 3}]**
	Out[19]= {{False, False, False}, {True, False, False},
	{True, True, False}}

You can use Outer on any sequence of
expressions with the same head.

`In[20]:= Outer[ g, f[a, b], f[c, d] ]`

`Out[20]= f[f[g[a, c], g[a, d]], f[g[b, c], g[b, d]]]`

Outer, like Distribute, constructs all possible combinations of elements. On the other hand, Inner, like Thread, constructs only combinations of elements that have corresponding positions in the expressions it acts on.

Here is a structure built by Inner.

`In[21]:= Inner[f, {a, b}, {c, d}, g]`

`Out[21]= g[f[a, c], f[b, d]]`

Inner is a generalization of Dot.

`In[22]:= Inner[Times, {a, b}, {c, d}, Plus]`

`Out[22]= a c + b d`

■ 2.2.11 Sequences

The function Flatten allows you to
explicitly flatten out all sublists.

`In[1]:= Flatten[{a, {b, c}, {d, e}}]`

`Out[1]= {a, b, c, d, e}`

FlattenAt lets you specify at what
positions you want sublists flattened.

`In[2]:= FlattenAt[{a, {b, c}, {d, e}}, 2]`

`Out[2]= {a, b, c, {d, e}}`

Sequence objects automatically get
spliced in, and do not require any
explicit flattening.

`In[3]:= {a, Sequence[b, c], Sequence[d, e]}`

`Out[3]= {a, b, c, d, e}`

Sequence[e_1, e_2, ...]	a sequence of arguments that will automatically be spliced into any function

Representing sequences of arguments in functions.

Sequence works in any function.

`In[4]:= f[Sequence[a, b], c]`

`Out[4]= f[a, b, c]`

This includes functions with special
input forms.

`In[5]:= a == Sequence[b, c]`

`Out[5]= a == b == c`

Here is a common way that Sequence
is used.

`In[6]:= {a, b, f[x, y], g[w], f[z, y]} /. f->Sequence`

`Out[6]= {a, b, x, y, g[w], z, y}`

2.3 Patterns

■ 2.3.1 Introduction

Patterns are used throughout *Mathematica* to represent classes of expressions. A simple example of a pattern is the expression f[x_]. This pattern represents the class of expressions with the form f[*anything*].

The main power of patterns comes from the fact that many operations in *Mathematica* can be done not only with single expressions, but also with patterns that represent whole classes of expressions.

You can use patterns in transformation rules to specify how classes of expressions should be transformed.	*In[1]:=* **f[a] + f[b] /. f[x_] -> x^2** *Out[1]=* $a^2 + b^2$
You can use patterns to find the positions of all expressions in a particular class.	*In[2]:=* **Position[{f[a], g[b], f[c]}, f[x_]]** *Out[2]=* {{1}, {3}}

The basic object that appears in almost all *Mathematica* patterns is _ (traditionally called "blank" by *Mathematica* programmers). The fundamental rule is simply that _ *stands for any expression*. On most keyboards the _ underscore character appears as the shifted version of the - dash character.

Thus, for example, the pattern f[_] stands for any expression of the form f[*anything*]. The pattern f[x_] also stands for any expression of the form f[*anything*], but gives the name x to the expression *anything*, allowing you to refer to it on the right-hand side of a transformation rule.

You can put blanks anywhere in an expression. What you get is a pattern which matches all expressions that can be made by "filling in the blanks" in any way.

f[n_]	f with any argument, named n
f[n_, m_]	f with two arguments, named n and m
x^n_	x to any power, with the power named n
x_^n_	any expression to any power
a_ + b_	a sum of two expressions
{a1_, a2_}	a list of two expressions
f[n_, n_]	f with two *identical* arguments

Some examples of patterns.

You can construct patterns for expressions with any structure.	*In[3]:=* **f[{a, b}] + f[c] /. f[{x_, y_}] -> p[x + y]** *Out[3]=* f[c] + p[a + b]

One of the most common uses of patterns is for "destructuring" function arguments. If you make a definition for f[list_], then you need to use functions like Part explicitly in order to pick out elements of the list. But if you know for example that the list will always have two elements, then it is usually much more convenient instead to give a definition instead for f[{x_, y_}]. Then you can refer to the elements of the list directly as x and y. In addition, *Mathematica* will not use the definition you have given unless the argument of f really is of the required form of a list of two expressions.

Here is one way to define a function which takes a list of two elements, and evaluates the first element raised to the power of the second element.

```
In[4]:= g[list_] := Part[list, 1] ^ Part[list, 2]
```

Here is a much more elegant way to make the definition, using a pattern.

```
In[5]:= h[{x_, y_}] := x ^ y
```

A crucial point to understand is that *Mathematica* patterns represent classes of expressions with a given *structure*. One pattern will match a particular expression if the structure of the pattern is the same as the structure of the expression, in the sense that by filling in blanks in the pattern you can get the expression. Even though two expressions may be *mathematically equal*, they cannot be represented by the same *Mathematica* pattern unless they have the same structure.

Thus, for example, the pattern (1 + x_)^2 can stand for expressions like (1 + a)^2 or (1 + b^3)^2 that have the same *structure*. However, it cannot stand for the expression 1 + 2 a + a^2. Although this expression is *mathematically equal* to (1 + a)^2, it does not have the same *structure* as the pattern (1 + x_)^2.

The fact that patterns in *Mathematica* specify the *structure* of expressions is crucial in making it possible to set up transformation rules which change the *structure* of expressions, while leaving them mathematically equal.

It is worth realizing that in general it would be quite impossible for *Mathematica* to match patterns by mathematical, rather than structural, equivalence. In the case of expressions like (1 + a)^2 and 1 + 2 a + a^2, you can determine equivalence just by using functions like Expand and Factor. But, as discussed on page 307 there is no general way to find out whether an arbitrary pair of mathematical expressions are equal.

As another example, the pattern x^_ will match the expression x^2. It will not, however, match the expression 1, even though this could be considered as x^0. Section 2.3.9 will discuss how to construct a pattern for which this particular case will match. But you should understand that in all cases pattern matching in *Mathematica* is fundamentally structural.

The x^n_ matches only x^2 and x^3. 1 and x can mathematically be written as x^n, but do not have the same structure.

```
In[6]:= {1, x, x^2, x^3} /. x^n_ -> r[n]
Out[6]= {1, x, r[2], r[3]}
```

Another point to realize is that the structure *Mathematica* uses in pattern matching is the full form of expressions printed by FullForm. Thus, for example, an object such as 1/x, whose full form is Power[x, -1] will be matched by the pattern x_^n_, but not by the pattern x_/y_, whose full form is

`Times[x_, Power[y_, -1]]`. Again, Section 2.3.9 will discuss how you can construct patterns which can match all these cases.

The expressions in the list contain explicit powers of b, so the transformation rule can be applied.	*In[7]:=* `{a/b, 1/b^2, 2/b^2} /. b^n_ -> d[n]`
	Out[7]= `{a d[-1], d[-2], 2 d[-2]}`

Here is the full form of the list.	*In[8]:=* `FullForm[{a/b, 1/b^2, 2/b^2}]`
	Out[8]//FullForm= `List[Times[a, Power[b, -1]], Power[b, -2],`
	`Times[2, Power[b, -2]]]`

Although *Mathematica* does not use mathematical equivalences such as $x^1 = x$ when matching patterns, it does use certain structural equivalences. Thus, for example, *Mathematica* takes account of properties such as commutativity and associativity in pattern matching.

To apply this transformation rule, *Mathematica* makes use of the commutativity and associativity of addition.	*In[9]:=* `f[a + b] + f[a + c] + f[b + d] /.`
	`f[a + x_] + f[c + y_] -> p[x, y]`
	Out[9]= `f[b + d] + p[b, a]`

The discussion so far has considered only pattern objects such as x_ which can stand for any single expression. In later subsections, we discuss the constructs that *Mathematica* uses to extend and restrict the classes of expressions represented by patterns.

■ 2.3.2 Finding Expressions That Match a Pattern

`Cases[`*list*`, `*form*`]`	give the elements of *list* that match *form*
`Count[`*list*`, `*form*`]`	give the number of elements in *list* that match *form*
`Position[`*list*`, `*form*`, {1}]`	give the positions of elements in *list* that match *form*
`Select[`*list*`, `*test*`]`	give the elements of *list* on which *test* gives True

Picking out elements that match a pattern.

This gives the elements of the list which match the pattern x^_.	*In[1]:=* `Cases[ {3, 4, x, x^2, x^3}, x^_ ]`
	Out[1]= $\{x^2, x^3\}$

Here is the total number of elements which match the pattern.	*In[2]:=* `Count[ {3, 4, x, x^2, x^3}, x^_ ]`
	Out[2]= 2

You can apply functions like `Cases` not only to lists, but to expressions of any kind. In addition, you can specify the level of parts at which you want to look.

Cases[*expr*, *lhs*->*rhs*]	find elements of *expr* that match *lhs*, and give a list of the results of applying the transformation rule to them
Cases[*expr*, *lhs*->*rhs*, *lev*]	test parts of *expr* at levels specified by *lev*
Count[*expr*, *form*, *lev*]	give the total number of parts that match *form* at levels specified by *lev*
Position[*expr*, *form*, *lev*]	give the positions of parts that match *form* at levels specified by *lev*

Searching for parts of expressions that match a pattern.

This returns a list of the exponents n.

```
In[3]:= Cases[ {3, 4, x, x^2, x^3}, x^n_ -> n]
Out[3]= {2, 3}
```

The pattern _Integer matches any integer. This gives a list of integers appearing at any level.

```
In[4]:= Cases[ {3, 4, x, x^2, x^3}, _Integer, Infinity]
Out[4]= {3, 4, 2, 3}
```

Cases[*expr*, *form*, *lev*, *n*]	find only the first *n* parts that match *form*
Position[*expr*, *form*, *lev*, *n*]	give the positions of the first *n* parts that match *form*

Limiting the number of parts to search for.

This gives the positions of the first two powers of x appearing at any level.

```
In[5]:= Position[ {4, 4 + x^a, x^b, 6 + x^5}, x^_, Infinity, 2]
Out[5]= {{2, 2}, {3}}
```

The positions are specified in exactly the form used by functions such as Extract and ReplacePart discussed in Section 1.8.

```
In[6]:= ReplacePart[ {4, 4 + x^a, x^b, 6 + x^5}, zzz, % ]
Out[6]= {4, 4 + zzz, zzz, 6 + x^5}
```

DeleteCases[*expr*, *form*]	delete elements of *expr* that match *form*
DeleteCases[*expr*, *form*, *lev*]	delete parts of *expr* that match *form* at levels specified by *lev*

Deleting parts of expressions that match a pattern.

This deletes the elements which match x^n_.

```
In[7]:= DeleteCases[ {3, 4, x, x^2, x^3}, x^n_ ]
Out[7]= {3, 4, x}
```

This deletes all integers appearing at any level.

```
In[8]:= DeleteCases[ {3, 4, x, 2+x, 3+x}, _Integer, Infinity ]
Out[8]= {x, x, x}
```

+	ReplaceList[*expr*, *lhs* -> *rhs*]	find all ways that *expr* can match *lhs*

Finding arrangements of an expression that match a pattern.

This finds all ways that the sum can be written in two parts.

```
In[9]:= ReplaceList[a + b + c, x_ + y_ -> g[x, y]]
Out[9]= {g[a, b+c], g[b, a+c], g[c, a+b], g[a+b, c],
         g[a+c, b], g[b+c, a]}
```

This finds all pairs of identical elements. The pattern `___` stands for any sequence of elements.

```
In[10]:= ReplaceList[{a, b, b, b, c, c, a},
                     {___, x_, x_, ___} -> x]
Out[10]= {b, b, c}
```

■ 2.3.3 Naming Pieces of Patterns

Particularly when you use transformation rules, you often need to name pieces of patterns. An object like x_ stands for any expression, but gives the expression the name *x*. You can then, for example, use this name on the right-hand side of a transformation rule.

An important point is that when you use x_, *Mathematica* requires that all occurrences of blanks with the same name *x* in a particular expression must stand for the same expression.

Thus f[x_, x_] can only stand for expressions in which the two arguments of f are exactly the same. f[_, _], on the other hand, can stand for any expression of the form f[*x*, *y*], where *x* and *y* need not be the same.

The transformation rule applies only to cases where the two arguments of f are identical.

```
In[1]:= {f[a, a], f[a, b]} /. f[x_, x_] -> p[x]
Out[1]= {p[a], f[a, b]}
```

Mathematica allows you to give names not just to single blanks, but to any piece of a pattern. The object *x*:*pattern* in general represents a pattern which is assigned the name *x*. In transformation rules, you can use this mechanism to name exactly those pieces of a pattern that you need to refer to on the right-hand side of the rule.

_	any expression
*x*_	any expression, to be named *x*
x:*pattern*	an expression to be named *x*, matching *pattern*

Patterns with names.

This gives a name to the complete form `_^_` so you can refer to it as a whole on the right-hand side of the transformation rule.	*In[2]:=* **f[a^b] /. f[x:_^_] -> p[x]** *Out[2]=* p[a^b]
Here the exponent is named n, while the whole object is x.	*In[3]:=* **f[a^b] /. f[x:_^n_] -> p[x, n]** *Out[3]=* p[a^b, b]

When you give the same name to two pieces of a pattern, you constrain the pattern to match only those expressions in which the corresponding pieces are identical.

Here the pattern matches both cases.	*In[4]:=* **{f[h[4], h[4]], f[h[4], h[5]]} /. f[h[_], h[_]] -> q** *Out[4]=* {q, q}
Now both arguments of f are constrained to be the same, and only the first case matches.	*In[5]:=* **{f[h[4], h[4]], f[h[4], h[5]]} /. f[x:h[_], x_] -> r[x]** *Out[5]=* {r[h[4]], f[h[4], h[5]]}

■ 2.3.4 Specifying Types of Expression in Patterns

You can tell a lot about what "type" of expression something is by looking at its head. Thus, for example, an integer has head `Integer`, while a list has head `List`.

In a pattern, *_h* and *x_h* represent expressions that are constrained to have head *h*. Thus, for example, `_Integer` represents any integer, while `_List` represents any list.

x_h	an expression with head *h*
x_Integer	an integer
x_Real	an approximate real number
x_Complex	a complex number
x_List	a list
x_Symbol	a symbol

Patterns for objects with specified heads.

This replaces just those elements that are integers.	*In[1]:=* **{a, 4, 5, b} /. x_Integer -> p[x]** *Out[1]=* {a, p[4], p[5], b}

You can think of making an assignment for `f[x_Integer]` as like defining a function f that must take an argument of "type" `Integer`.

This defines a value for the function gamma when its argument is an integer.	*In[2]:=* **gamma[n_Integer] := (n - 1)!**

The definition applies only when the argument of gamma is an integer.	*In[3]:=* **gamma[4] + gamma[x]** *Out[3]=* 6 + gamma[x]
The object 4. has head Real, so the definition does not apply.	*In[4]:=* **gamma[4.]** *Out[4]=* gamma[4.]
This defines values for expressions with integer exponents.	*In[5]:=* **d[x_^n_Integer] := n x^(n-1)**
The definition is used only when the exponent is an integer.	*In[6]:=* **d[x^4] + d[(a+b)^3] + d[x^(1/2)]** *Out[6]=* $3(a+b)^2 + 4x^3 + d\left[\sqrt{x}\right]$

■ 2.3.5 Putting Constraints on Patterns

Mathematica provides a general mechanism for specifying constraints on patterns. All you need do is to put /; *condition* at the end of a pattern to signify that it applies only when the specified condition is True. You can read the operator /; as "slash-semi", "whenever" or "provided that".

pattern /; *condition*	a pattern that matches only when a condition is satisfied
lhs :> *rhs* /; *condition*	a rule that applies only when a condition is satisfied
lhs := *rhs* /; *condition*	a definition that applies only when a condition is satisfied

Putting conditions on patterns and transformation rules.

This gives a definition for fac that applies only when its argument n is positive.	*In[1]:=* **fac[n_ /; n > 0] := n!**
The definition for fac is used only when the argument is positive.	*In[2]:=* **fac[6] + fac[-4]** *Out[2]=* 720 + fac[-4]
This gives the negative elements in the list.	*In[3]:=* **Cases[{3, -4, 5, -2}, x_ /; x < 0]** *Out[3]=* {-4, -2}

You can use /; on whole definitions and transformation rules, as well as on individual patterns. In general, you can put /; *condition* at the end of any := definition or :> rule to tell *Mathematica* that the definition or rule applies only when the specified condition holds. Note that /; conditions should not usually be put at the end of = definitions or -> rules, since they will then be evaluated immediately, as discussed in Section 2.4.8.

Here is another way to give a definition which applies only when its argument n is positive.	*In[4]:=* **fac2[n_] := n! /; n > 0**

Once again, the factorial functions evaluate only when their arguments are positive.

```
In[5]:= fac2[6] + fac2[-4]
Out[5]= 720 + fac2[-4]
```

You can use the /; operator to implement arbitrary mathematical constraints on the applicability of rules. In typical cases, you give patterns which *structurally* match a wide range of expressions, but then use *mathematical* constraints to reduce the range of expressions to a much smaller set.

This rule applies only to expressions that have the structure v[x_, 1 - x_].

```
In[6]:= v[x_, 1 - x_] := p[x]
```

This expression has the appropriate structure, so the rule applies.

```
In[7]:= v[a^2, 1 - a^2]
Out[7]= p[a²]
```

This expression, while mathematically of the correct form, does not have the appropriate structure, so the rule does not apply.

```
In[8]:= v[4, -3]
Out[8]= v[4, -3]
```

This rule applies to any expression of the form w[x_, y_], with the added restriction that y == 1 - x.

```
In[9]:= w[x_, y_] := p[x] /; y == 1 - x
```

The new rule does apply to this expression.

```
In[10]:= w[4, -3]
Out[10]= p[4]
```

In setting up patterns and transformation rules, there is often a choice of where to put /; conditions. For example, you can put a /; condition on the right-hand side of a rule in the form *lhs* :> *rhs* /; *condition*, or you can put it on the left-hand side in the form *lhs* /; *condition* -> *rhs*. You may also be able to insert the condition inside the expression *lhs*. The only constraint is that all the names of patterns that you use in a particular condition must appear in the pattern to which the condition is attached. If this is not the case, then some of the names needed to evaluate the condition may not yet have been "bound" in the pattern-matching process. If this happens, then *Mathematica* uses the global values for the corresponding variables, rather than the values determined by pattern matching.

Thus, for example, the condition in f[x_, y_] /; (x + y < 2) will use values for x and y that are found by matching f[x_, y_], but the condition in f[x_ /; x + y < 2, y_] will use the global value for y, rather than the one found by matching the pattern.

As long as you make sure that the appropriate names are defined, it is usually most efficient to put /; conditions on the smallest possible parts of patterns. The reason for this is that *Mathematica* matches pieces of patterns sequentially, and the sooner it finds a /; condition which fails, the sooner it can reject a match.

Putting the /; condition around the x_ is slightly more efficient than putting it around the whole pattern.

```
In[11]:= Cases[{z[1, 1], z[-1, 1], z[-2, 2]}, z[x_ /; x < 0, y_]]
Out[11]= {z[-1, 1], z[-2, 2]}
```

You need to put parentheses around the /; piece in a case like this.

```
In[12]:= {1 + a, 2 + a, -3 + a} /. (x_ /; x < 0) + a -> p[x]
Out[12]= {1 + a, 2 + a, p[-3]}
```

It is common to use /; to set up patterns and transformation rules that apply only to expressions with certain properties. There is a collection of functions built into *Mathematica* for testing the properties of expressions. It is a convention that functions of this kind have names that end with the letter Q, indicating that they "ask a question".

IntegerQ[*expr*]	integer
EvenQ[*expr*]	even number
OddQ[*expr*]	odd number
PrimeQ[*expr*]	prime number
NumberQ[*expr*]	explicit number of any kind
NumericQ[*expr*]	numeric quantity
PolynomialQ[*expr*, {x_1, x_2, ... }]	
	polynomial in x_1, x_2, ...
VectorQ[*expr*]	a list representing a vector
MatrixQ[*expr*]	a list of lists representing a matrix
VectorQ[*expr*, NumberQ], MatrixQ[*expr*, NumberQ]	
	vectors and matrices where all elements are numbers
VectorQ[*expr*, *test*], MatrixQ[*expr*, *test*]	
	vectors and matrices for which the function *test* yields True when applied to any element

Some functions for testing mathematical properties of expressions.

The rule applies to all elements of the list that are numbers.

```
In[13]:= {2.3, 4, 7/8, a, b} /. (x_ /; NumberQ[x]) -> x^2
```
$$Out[13]= \left\{5.29, 16, \frac{49}{64}, a, b\right\}$$

This definition applies only to vectors of integers.

```
In[14]:= mi[list_] := list^2 /; VectorQ[list, IntegerQ]
```

The definition is now used only in the first case.

```
In[15]:= {mi[{2, 3}], mi[{2.1, 2.2}], mi[{a, b}]}
Out[15]= {{4, 9}, mi[{2.1, 2.2}], mi[{a, b}]}
```

An important feature of all the *Mathematica* property-testing functions whose names end in Q is that they always return False if they cannot determine whether the expression you give has a particular property.

4561 is an integer, so this returns True.	*In[16]:=* `IntegerQ[4561]` *Out[16]=* True
This returns False, since x is not known to be an integer.	*In[17]:=* `IntegerQ[x]` *Out[17]=* False

In some cases, you can explicitly specify the results that property-testing functions should give. Thus, with a definition such as x /: IntegerQ[x] = True, as discussed in Section 2.4.10, *Mathematica* will assume that x is an integer. This means that if you explicitly ask for IntegerQ[x], you will now get True, rather than False. However, *Mathematica* does not automatically propagate assertions, so it cannot determine for example that IntegerQ[x^2] is True. You must load an appropriate *Mathematica* package to make this possible.

SameQ[x, y] or x === y	x and y are identical
UnsameQ[x, y] or x =!= y	x and y are not identical
OrderedQ[{a, b, ... }]	a, b, ... are in standard order
MemberQ[*expr*, *form*]	*form* matches an element of *expr*
FreeQ[*expr*, *form*]	*form* matches nothing in *expr*
MatchQ[*expr*, *form*]	*expr* matches the pattern *form*
ValueQ[*expr*]	a value has been defined for *expr*
AtomQ[*expr*]	*expr* has no subexpressions

Some functions for testing structural properties of expressions.

With ==, the equation remains in symbolic form; === yields False unless the expressions are manifestly equal.	*In[18]:=* `{x == y, x === y}` *Out[18]=* {x == y, False}
The expression n is not a *member* of the list {x, x^n}.	*In[19]:=* `MemberQ[{x, x^n}, n]` *Out[19]=* False
However, {x, x^n} is not completely free of n.	*In[20]:=* `FreeQ[{x, x^n}, n]` *Out[20]=* False
You can use FreeQ to define a "linearity" rule for h.	*In[21]:=* `h[a_ b_, x_] := a h[b, x] /; FreeQ[a, x]`
Terms free of x are pulled out of each h.	*In[22]:=* `h[a b x, x] + h[2 (1+x) x^2, x]` *Out[22]=* $a b h[x, x] + 2 h[x^2 (1 + x), x]$

pattern **?** *test*	a pattern which matches an expression only if *test* yields **True** when applied to the expression

Another way to constrain patterns.

The construction *pattern* **/;** *condition* allows you to evaluate a condition involving pattern names to determine whether there is a match. The construction *pattern* **?** *test* instead applies a function *test* to the whole expression matched by *pattern* to determine whether there is a match. Using **?** instead of **/;** sometimes leads to more succinct definitions.

With this definition matches for `x_` are tested with the function `NumberQ`.	*In[23]:=* **p[x_?NumberQ] := x^2**
The definition applies only when p has a numerical argument.	*In[24]:=* **p[4.5] + p[3/2] + p[u]**
	Out[24]= 22.5 + p[u]
Here is a more complicated definition. Do not forget the parentheses around the pure function.	*In[25]:=* **q[{x_Integer, y_Integer} ?** **(Function[v, v.v > 4])] := qp[x + y]**
The definition applies only in certain cases.	*In[26]:=* **{q[{3, 4}], q[{1, 1}], q[{-5, -7}]}**
	Out[26]= {qp[7], q[{1, 1}], qp[-12]}

■ 2.3.6 Patterns Involving Alternatives

patt$_1$ **|** *patt*$_2$ **|** ...	a pattern that can have one of several forms

Specifying patterns that involve alternatives.

This defines h to give p when its argument is either a or b.	*In[1]:=* **h[a	b] := p**
The first two cases give p.	*In[2]:=* **{h[a], h[b], h[c], h[d]}**
	Out[2]= {p, p, h[c], h[d]}
You can also use alternatives in transformation rules.	*In[3]:=* **{a, b, c, d} /. (a | b) -> p**
	Out[3]= {p, p, c, d}
Here is another example, in which one of the alternatives is itself a pattern.	*In[4]:=* **{1, x, x^2, x^3, y^2} /. (x | x^_) -> q**
	Out[4]= {1, q, q, q, y^2}

When you use alternatives in patterns, you should make sure that the same set of names appear in each alternative. When a pattern like `(a[x_] | b[x_])` matches an expression, there will always be a definite expression that corresponds to the object x. On the other hand, if you try to match a pattern like `(a[x_] | b[y_])`, then there will be a definite expression corresponding either to x, or to y, but not to both. As a result, you cannot use x and y to refer to definite expressions, for example on the right-hand side of a transformation rule.

Here f is used to name the head, which can be either a or b.	*In[5]:=* **{a[2], b[3], c[4], a[5]} /. (f:(a|b))[x_] -> r[f, x]**
	Out[5]= {r[a, 2], r[b, 3], c[4], r[a, 5]}

■ 2.3.7 Flat and Orderless Functions

Although *Mathematica* matches patterns in a purely structural fashion, its notion of structural equivalence is quite sophisticated. In particular, it takes account of properties such as commutativity and associativity in functions like Plus and Times.

This means, for example, that *Mathematica* considers the expressions $x + y$ and $y + x$ equivalent for the purposes of pattern matching. As a result, a pattern like g[x_ + y_, x_] can match not only g[a + b, a], but also g[a + b, b].

This expression has exactly the same form as the pattern.	*In[1]:=* **g[a + b, a] /. g[x_ + y_, x_] -> p[x, y]**
	Out[1]= p[a, b]
In this case, the expression has to be put in the form g[b + a, b] in order to have the same structure as the pattern.	*In[2]:=* **g[a + b, b] /. g[x_ + y_, x_] -> p[x, y]**
	Out[2]= p[b, a]

Whenever *Mathematica* encounters an *orderless* or *commutative* function such as Plus or Times in a pattern, it effectively tests all the possible orders of arguments to try and find a match. Sometimes, there may be several orderings that lead to matches. In such cases, *Mathematica* just uses the first ordering it finds. For example, h[x_ + y_, x_ + z_] could match h[a + b, a + b] with x→a, y→b, z→b or with x→b, y→a, z→a. *Mathematica* tries the case x→a, y→b, z→b first, and so uses this match.

This can match either with x → a or with x → b. *Mathematica* tries x → a first, and so uses this match.	*In[3]:=* **h[a + b, a + b] /. h[x_ + y_, x_ + z_] -> p[x, y, z]**
	Out[3]= p[a, b, b]
ReplaceList shows both possible matches.	*In[4]:=* **ReplaceList[h[a + b, a + b],** **h[x_ + y_, x_ + z_] -> p[x, y, z]]**
	Out[4]= {p[a, b, b], p[b, a, a]}

As discussed in Section 2.5.3, *Mathematica* allows you to assign certain attributes to functions, which specify how those functions should be treated in evaluation and pattern matching. Functions can for example be assigned the attribute Orderless, which specifies that they should be treated as commutative or symmetric, and allows their arguments to be rearranged in trying to match patterns.

Orderless	commutative function: $f[b, c, a]$, etc., are equivalent to $f[a, b, c]$
Flat	associative function: $f[f[a], b]$, etc., are equivalent to $f[a, b]$
OneIdentity	$f[f[a]]$, etc., are equivalent to a
Attributes[f]	give the attributes assigned to f
SetAttributes[f, *attr*]	add *attr* to the attributes of f
ClearAttributes[f, *attr*]	remove *attr* from the attributes of f

Some attributes that can be assigned to functions.

Plus has attributes Orderless and
Flat, as well as others.

```
In[5]:= Attributes[Plus]
Out[5]= {Flat, Listable, NumericFunction, OneIdentity,
            Orderless, Protected}
```

This defines q to be an orderless or
commutative function.

```
In[6]:= SetAttributes[q, Orderless]
```

The arguments of q are automatically
sorted into order.

```
In[7]:= q[b, a, c]
Out[7]= q[a, b, c]
```

Mathematica rearranges the arguments
of q functions to find a match.

```
In[8]:= f[q[a, b], q[b, c]] /.
            f[q[x_, y_], q[x_, z_]] -> p[x, y, z]
Out[8]= p[b, a, c]
```

In addition to being orderless, functions like Plus and Times also have the property of being *flat* or *associative*. This means that you can effectively "parenthesize" their arguments in any way, so that, for example, x + (y + z) is equivalent to x + y + z, and so on.

Mathematica takes account of flatness in matching patterns. As a result, a pattern like g[x_ + y_] can match g[a + b + c], with x → a and y → (b + c).

The argument of g is written as
a + (b + c) so as to match the pattern.

```
In[9]:= g[a + b + c] /. g[x_ + y_] -> p[x, y]
Out[9]= p[a, b+c]
```

If there are no other constraints,
Mathematica will match x_ to the first
element of the sum.

```
In[10]:= g[a + b + c + d] /. g[x_ + y_] -> p[x, y]
Out[10]= p[a, b+c+d]
```

This shows all the possible matches.

```
In[11]:= ReplaceList[g[a + b + c], g[x_ + y_] -> p[x, y]]
Out[11]= {p[a, b+c], p[b, a+c], p[c, a+b], p[a+b, c],
            p[a+c, b], p[b+c, a]}
```

Here x_ is forced to match b + d.   *In[12]:=* **g[a + b + c + d, b + d] /. g[x_ + y_, x_] -> p[x, y]**

Out[12]= p[b + d, a + c]

Mathematica can usually apply a transformation rule to a function only if the pattern in the rule covers all the arguments in the function. However, if you have a flat function, it is sometimes possible to apply transformation rules even though not all the arguments are covered.

This rule applies even though it does not cover all the terms in the sum.   *In[13]:=* **a + b + c /. a + c -> p**

Out[13]= b + p

This combines two of the terms in the sum.   *In[14]:=* **u[a] + u[b] + v[c] + v[d] /. u[x_] + u[y_] -> u[x + y]**

Out[14]= u[a + b] + v[c] + v[d]

Functions like Plus and Times are both flat and orderless. There are, however, some functions, such as Dot, which are flat, but not orderless.

Both x_ and y_ can match any sequence of terms in the dot product.   *In[15]:=* **a . b . c . d . a . b /. x_ . y_ . x_ -> p[x, y]**

Out[15]= p[a . b, c . d]

This assigns the attribute Flat to the function r.   *In[16]:=* **SetAttributes[r, Flat]**

Mathematica writes the expression in the form r[r[a, b], r[a, b]] to match the pattern.   *In[17]:=* **r[a, b, a, b] /. r[x_, x_] -> rp[x]**

Out[17]= rp[r[a, b]]

Mathematica writes this expression in the form r[a, r[r[b], r[b]], c] to match the pattern.   *In[18]:=* **r[a, b, b, c] /. r[x_, x_] -> rp[x]**

Out[18]= r[a, rp[r[b]], c]

In an ordinary function that is not flat, a pattern such as x_ matches an individual argument of the function. But in a function $f[a, b, c, \dots]$ that is flat, x_ can match objects such as $f[b, c]$ which effectively correspond to a sequence of arguments. However, in the case where x_ matches a single argument in a flat function, the question comes up as to whether the object it matches is really just the argument *a* itself, or $f[a]$. *Mathematica* chooses the first of these cases if the function carries the attribute OneIdentity, and chooses the second case otherwise.

This adds the attribute OneIdentity to the function r.   *In[19]:=* **SetAttributes[r, OneIdentity]**

Now x_ matches individual arguments, without r wrapped around them.   *In[20]:=* **r[a, b, b, c] /. r[x_, x_] -> rp[x]**

Out[20]= r[a, rp[b], c]

The functions Plus, Times and Dot all have the attribute OneIdentity, reflecting the fact that Plus[x] is equivalent to x, and so on. However, in representing mathematical objects, it is often convenient to deal with flat functions that do not have the attribute OneIdentity.

■ 2.3.8 Functions with Variable Numbers of Arguments

Unless *f* is a flat function, a pattern like *f*[*x*_, *y*_] stands only for instances of the function with exactly two arguments. Sometimes you need to set up patterns that can allow any number of arguments.

You can do this using *multiple blanks*. While a single blank such as x_ stands for a single *Mathematica* expression, a double blank such as x__ stands for a sequence of one or more expressions.

Here x__ stands for the sequence of expressions (a, b, c).	`In[1]:= f[a, b, c] /. f[x__] -> p[x, x, x]` `Out[1]= p[a, b, c, a, b, c, a, b, c]`
Here is a more complicated definition, which picks out pairs of duplicated elements in h.	`In[2]:= h[a___, x_, b___, x_, c___] := hh[x] h[a, b, c]`
The definition is applied twice, picking out the two paired elements.	`In[3]:= h[2, 3, 2, 4, 5, 3]` `Out[3]= h[4, 5] hh[2] hh[3]`

"Double blanks" __ stand for sequences of one or more expressions. "Triple blanks" ___ stand for sequences of zero or more expressions. You should be very careful whenever you use triple blank patterns. It is easy to make a mistake that can lead to an infinite loop. For example, if you define p[x_, y___] := p[x] q[y], then typing in p[a] will lead to an infinite loop, with y repeatedly matching a sequence with zero elements. Unless you are sure you want to include the case of zero elements, you should always use double blanks rather than triple blanks.

_	any single expression
*x*_	any single expression, to be named *x*
__	any sequence of one or more expressions
*x*__	sequence named *x*
*x*__*h*	sequence of expressions, all of whose heads are *h*
___	any sequence of zero or more expressions
*x*___	sequence of zero or more expressions named *x*
*x*___*h*	sequence of zero or more expressions, all of whose heads are *h*

More kinds of pattern objects.

Notice that with flat functions such as `Plus` and `Times`, *Mathematica* automatically handles variable numbers of arguments, so you do not explicitly need to use double or triple blanks, as discussed in Section 2.3.7.

When you use multiple blanks, there are often several matches that are possible for a particular expression. In general, *Mathematica* tries first those matches that assign the shortest sequences of arguments to the first multiple blanks that appear in the pattern.

This gives a list of all the matches that *Mathematica* tries.	`In[4]:= ReplaceList[f[a, b, c, d], f[x__, y__] -> g[{x}, {y}]]`
	`Out[4]= {g[{a}, {b, c, d}], g[{a, b}, {c, d}],`
	`        g[{a, b, c}, {d}]}`

Many kinds of enumeration can be done by using `ReplaceList` with various kinds of patterns.	`In[5]:= ReplaceList[f[a, b, c, d], f[___, x__] -> g[x]]` `Out[5]= {g[a, b, c, d], g[b, c, d], g[c, d], g[d]}`

This effectively enumerates all sublists with at least one element.	`In[6]:= ReplaceList[f[a, b, c, d], f[___, x__, ___] -> g[x]]`
	`Out[6]= {g[a], g[a, b], g[b], g[a, b, c], g[b, c], g[c],`
	`        g[a, b, c, d], g[b, c, d], g[c, d], g[d]}`

■ 2.3.9 Optional and Default Arguments

Sometimes you may want to set up functions where certain arguments, if omitted, are given "default values". The pattern $x\_:v$ stands for an object that can be omitted, and if so, will be replaced by the default value v.

This defines a function j with a required argument x, and optional arguments y and z, with default values 1 and 2, respectively.	`In[1]:= j[x_, y_:1, z_:2] := jp[x, y, z]`
The default value of z is used here.	`In[2]:= j[a, b]` `Out[2]= jp[a, b, 2]`
Now the default values of both y and z are used.	`In[3]:= j[a]` `Out[3]= jp[a, 1, 2]`

$x\_:v$	an expression which, if omitted, is taken to have default value v
$x\_h:v$	an expression with head h and default value v
$x\_.$	an expression with a built-in default value

Pattern objects with default values.

Some common *Mathematica* functions have built-in default values for their arguments. In such cases, you need not explicitly give the default value in $x\_:v$, but instead you can use the more convenient notation $x\_.$ in which a built-in default value is assumed.

x_ + y_.	default for y is 0
x_ y_.	default for y is 1
x_^y_.	default for y is 1

Some patterns with optional pieces.

Here a matches the pattern x_ + y_.
with y taken to have the default
value 0.

In[4]:= {f[a], f[a + b]} /. f[x_ + y_.] -> p[x, y]

Out[4]= {p[a, 0], p[b, a]}

Because Plus is a flat function, a pattern such as x_ + y_ can match a sum with any number of terms. This pattern cannot, however, match a single term such as a. However, the pattern x_ + y_. contains an optional piece, and can match either an explicit sum of terms in which both x_ and y_ appear, or a single term x_, with y taken to be 0.

Using constructs such as *x_.*, you can easily construct single patterns that match expressions with several different structures. This is particularly useful when you want to match several mathematically equal forms that do not have the same structure.

The pattern matches g[a^2], but not
g[a + b].

In[5]:= {g[a^2], g[a + b]} /. g[x_^n_] -> p[x, n]

Out[5]= {p[a, 2], g[a + b]}

By giving a pattern in which the
exponent is optional, you can match
both cases.

In[6]:= {g[a^2], g[a + b]} /. g[x_^n_.] -> p[x, n]

Out[6]= {p[a, 2], p[a + b, 1]}

The pattern a_. + b_. x_ matches any
linear function of x_.

In[7]:= lin[a_. + b_. x_, x_] := p[a, b]

In this case, b → 1.

In[8]:= lin[1 + x, x]

Out[8]= p[1, 1]

Here b → 1 and a → 0.

In[9]:= lin[y, y]

Out[9]= p[0, 1]

Standard *Mathematica* functions such as Plus and Times have built-in default values for their arguments. You can also set up defaults for your own functions, as described in Section A.5.1.

■ 2.3.10 Setting Up Functions with Optional Arguments

When you define a complicated function, you will often want to let some of the arguments of the function be "optional". If you do not give those arguments explicitly, you want them to take on certain "default" values.

Built-in *Mathematica* functions use two basic methods for dealing with optional arguments. You can choose between the same two methods when you define your own functions in *Mathematica*.

The first method is to have the meaning of each argument determined by its position, and then to allow one to drop arguments, replacing them by default values. Almost all built-in *Mathematica* functions that use this method drop arguments from the end. For example, the built-in function Flatten[*list*, *n*] allows you to drop the second argument, which is taken to have a default value of Infinity.

You can implement this kind of "positional" argument using _: patterns.

f[*x_*, *k_*:*kdef*] := *value*	a typical definition for a function whose second argument is optional, with default value *kdef*

Defining a function with positional arguments.

This defines a function with an optional second argument. When the second argument is omitted, it is taken to have the default value Infinity.

In[1]:= **f[list_, n_:Infinity] := f0[list, n]**

Here is a function with two optional arguments.

In[2]:= **fx[list_, n1_:1, n2_:2] := fx0[list, n1, n2]**

Mathematica assumes that arguments are dropped from the end. As a result m here gives the value of n1, while n2 has its default value of 2.

In[3]:= **fx[k, m]**

Out[3]= fx0[k, m, 2]

The second method that built-in *Mathematica* functions use for dealing with optional arguments is to give explicit names to the optional arguments, and then to allow their values to be given using transformation rules. This method is particularly convenient for functions like Plot which have a very large number of optional parameters, only a few of which usually need to be set in any particular instance.

The typical arrangement is that values for "named" optional arguments can be specified by including the appropriate transformation rules at the end of the arguments to a particular function. Thus, for example, the rule PlotJoined->True, which specifies the setting for the named optional argument PlotJoined, could appear as ListPlot[*list*, PlotJoined->True].

When you set up named optional arguments for a function *f*, it is conventional to store the default values of these arguments as a list of transformation rules assigned to Options[*f*].

$f[x\_, opts\_\_\_] := value$	a typical definition for a function with zero or more named optional arguments
name /. {*opts*} /. Options[*f*]	replacements used to get the value of a named optional argument in the body of the function

Named arguments.

This sets up default values for two named optional arguments opt1 and opt2 in the function fn.	*In[4]:=* **Options[fn] = { opt1 -> 1, opt2 -> 2 }** *Out[4]=* {opt1 → 1, opt2 → 2}
This gives the default value for opt1.	*In[5]:=* **opt1 /. Options[fn]** *Out[5]=* 1
The rule opt1->3 is applied first, so the default rule for opt1 in Options[fn] is not used.	*In[6]:=* **opt1 /. opt1->3 /. Options[fn]** *Out[6]=* 3
Here is the definition for a function fn which allows zero or more named optional arguments to be specified.	*In[7]:=* **fn[x_, opts___] := k[x, opt2/.{opts}/.Options[fn]]**
With no optional arguments specified, the default rule for opt2 is used.	*In[8]:=* **fn[4]** *Out[8]=* k[4, 2]
If you explicitly give a rule for opt2, it will be used before the default rules stored in Options[fn] are tried.	*In[9]:=* **fn[4, opt2->7]** *Out[9]=* k[4, 7]

■ 2.3.11 Repeated Patterns

expr..	a pattern or other expression repeated one or more times
expr...	a pattern or other expression repeated zero or more times

Repeated patterns.

Multiple blanks such as $x\_\_$ allow you to give patterns in which sequences of arbitrary expressions can occur. The *Mathematica pattern repetition operators* .. and ... allow you to construct patterns in which particular forms can be repeated any number of times. Thus, for example, f[a..] represents any expression of the form f[a], f[a, a], f[a, a, a] and so on.

The pattern f[a..] allows the argument a to be repeated any number of times.	*In[1]:=* **Cases[{ f[a], f[a, b, a], f[a, a, a] }, f[a..]]** *Out[1]=* {f[a], f[a, a, a]}

This pattern allows any number of a arguments, followed by any number of b arguments.	*In[2]:=* `Cases[{ f[a], f[a, a, b], f[a, b, a], f[a, b, b] },` `                                    f[a.., b..]]` *Out[2]=* {f[a, a, b], f[a, b, b]}
Here each argument can be either a or b.	*In[3]:=* `Cases[{ f[a], f[a, b, a], f[a, c, a] }, f[(a | b)..]]` *Out[3]=* {f[a], f[a, b, a]}

You can use `..` and `...` to represent repetitions of any pattern. If the pattern contains named parts, then each instance of these parts must be identical.

This defines a function whose argument must consist of a list of pairs.	*In[4]:=* `v[x:{{_, _}..}] := Transpose[x]`
The definition applies in this case.	*In[5]:=* `v[{{a1, b1}, {a2, b2}, {a3, b3}}]` *Out[5]=* {{a1, a2, a3}, {b1, b2, b3}}
With this definition, the second elements of all the pairs must be the same.	*In[6]:=* `vn[x:{{_, n_}..}] := Transpose[x]`
The definition applies in this case.	*In[7]:=* `vn[{{a, 2}, {b, 2}, {c, 2}}]` *Out[7]=* {{a, b, c}, {2, 2, 2}}

■ 2.3.12 Verbatim Patterns

`Verbatim[`*expr*`]`	an expression that must be matched verbatim

Verbatim patterns.

Here the x_ in the rule matches any expression.	*In[1]:=* `{f[2], f[a], f[x_], f[y_]} /. f[x_] -> x^2` *Out[1]=* {4, a², x_², y_²}
The `Verbatim` tells *Mathematica* that only the exact expression x_ should be matched.	*In[2]:=* `{f[2], f[a], f[x_], f[y_]} /. f[Verbatim[x_]] -> x^2` *Out[2]=* {f[2], f[a], x², f[y_]}

■ 2.3.13 Patterns for Some Common Types of Expression

Using the objects described above, you can set up patterns for many kinds of expressions. In all cases, you must remember that the patterns must represent the structure of the expressions in *Mathematica* internal form, as shown by `FullForm`.

Especially for some common kinds of expressions, the standard output format used by *Mathematica* is not particularly close to the full internal form. But it is the internal form that you must use in setting up patterns.

*n*_Integer	an integer *n*
*x*_Real	an approximate real number *x*
*z*_Complex	a complex number *z*
Complex[*x*_, *y*_]	a complex number $x + iy$
Complex[*x*_Integer, *y*_Integer]	a complex number where both real and imaginary parts are integers
(*r*_Rational | *r*_Integer)	rational number or integer *r*
Rational[*n*_, *d*_]	a rational number $\frac{n}{d}$
(*x*_ /; NumberQ[*x*] && Im[*x*]==0)	a real number of any kind
(*x*_ /; NumberQ[*x*])	a number of any kind

Some typical patterns for numbers.

Here are the full forms of some numbers.

```
In[1]:= {2, 2.5, 2.5 + I, 2/7} // FullForm
Out[1]//FullForm= List[2, 2.5, Complex[2.5, 1], Rational[2, 7]]
```

The rule picks out each piece of the complex numbers.

```
In[2]:= {2.5 - I, 3 + I} /. Complex[x_, y_] -> p[x, y]
Out[2]= {p[2.5, -1], p[3, 1]}
```

The fact that these expressions have different full forms means that you cannot use *x*_ + I *y*_ to match a complex number.

```
In[3]:= {2.5 - I, x + I y} // FullForm
Out[3]//FullForm= List[Complex[2.5, -1],
                       Plus[x, Times[Complex[0, 1], y]]]
```

The pattern here matches both ordinary integers, and complex numbers where both the real and imaginary parts are integers.

```
In[4]:= Cases[ {2.5 - I, 2, 3 + I, 2 - 0.5 I, 2 + 2 I},
               _Integer | Complex[_Integer, _Integer] ]
Out[4]= {2, 3 + I, 2 + 2 I}
```

As discussed in Section 1.4.1, *Mathematica* puts all algebraic expressions into a standard form, in which they are written essentially as a sum of products of powers. In addition, ratios are converted into products of powers, with denominator terms having negative exponents, and differences are converted into sums with negated terms. To construct patterns for algebraic expressions, you must use this standard form. This form often differs from the way *Mathematica* prints out the algebraic expressions. But in all cases, you can find the full internal form using FullForm[*expr*].

Here is a typical algebraic expression.

```
In[5]:= -1/z^2 - z/y + 2 (x z)^2 y
```

$$Out[5]= -\frac{1}{z^2} - \frac{z}{y} + 2x^2 y z^2$$

This is the full internal form of the expression.

In[6]:= **FullForm[%]**

Out[6]//FullForm= Plus[Times[-1, Power[z, -2]],
                    Times[-1, Power[y, -1], z],
                    Times[2, Power[x, 2], y, Power[z, 2]]]

This is what you get by applying a transformation rule to all powers in the expression.

In[7]:= **% /. x_^n_ -> e[x, n]**

Out[7]= $-z\,e[y, -1] - e[z, -2] + 2\,y\,e[x, 2]\,e[z, 2]$

$x\_ + y\_$	a sum of two or more terms
$x\_ + y\_.$	a single term or a sum of terms
$n\_Integer\ x\_$	an expression with an explicit integer multiplier
$a\_. + b\_.\ x\_$	a linear expression $a + bx$
$x\_ \wedge n\_$	x^n with $n \neq 0, 1$
$x\_ \wedge n\_.$	x^n with $n \neq 0$
$a\_. + b\_.\ x\_ + c\_.\ x\_\wedge 2$	a quadratic expression with non-zero linear term

Some typical patterns for algebraic expressions.

This pattern picks out linear functions of x.

In[8]:= **{1, a, x, 2 x, 1 + 2 x} /. a_. + b_. x -> p[a, b]**

Out[8]= {1, a, p[0, 1], p[0, 2], p[1, 2]}

x_List or $x:\{\_\_\_\}$	a list
x_List /; VectorQ[x]	a vector containing no sublists
x_List /; VectorQ[x, NumberQ]	a vector of numbers
$x:\{\_\_\_List\}$ or $x:\{\{\_\_\_\}...\}$	a list of lists
x_List /; MatrixQ[x]	a matrix containing no sublists
x_List /; MatrixQ[x, NumberQ]	a matrix of numbers
$x:\{\{\_,\ \_\}...\}$	a list of pairs

Some typical patterns for lists.

This defines a function whose argument must be a list containing lists with either one or two elements.

In[9]:= **h[x:{ ({_} | {_, _})... }] := q**

The definition applies in the second and third cases.

In[10]:= **{h[{a, b}], h[{{a}, {b}}], h[{{a}, {b, c}}]}**

Out[10]= {h[{a, b}], q, q}

■ 2.3.14 An Example: Defining Your Own Integration Function

Now that we have introduced the basic features of patterns in *Mathematica*, we can use them to give a more or less complete example. We will show how you could define your own simple integration function in *Mathematica*.

From a mathematical point of view, the integration function is defined by a sequence of mathematical relations. By setting up transformation rules for patterns, you can implement these mathematical relations quite directly in *Mathematica*.

mathematical form	Mathematica definition
$\int (y+z)\,dx = \int y\,dx + \int z\,dx$	`integrate[y_ + z_, x_] := integrate[y, x] + integrate[z, x]`
$\int c\,y\,dx = c \int y\,dx$ (c independent of x)	`integrate[c_ y_, x_] := c integrate[y, x] /; FreeQ[c, x]`
$\int c\,dx = c\,x$	`integrate[c_, x_] := c x /; FreeQ[c, x]`
$\int x^n\,dx = \frac{x^{(n+1)}}{n+1}$, $n \neq -1$	`integrate[x_^n_., x_] := x^(n+1)/(n+1) /; FreeQ[n, x] && n != -1`
$\int \frac{1}{ax+b}\,dx = \frac{\log(ax+b)}{a}$	`integrate[1/(a_. x_ + b_.), x_] := Log[a x + b]/a /; FreeQ[{a,b}, x]`
$\int e^{ax+b}\,dx = \frac{1}{a}\,e^{ax+b}$	`integrate[Exp[a_. x_ + b_.], x_] := Exp[a x + b]/a /; FreeQ[{a,b}, x]`

Definitions for an integration function.

This implements the linearity relation for integrals:
$\int (y+z)\,dx = \int y\,dx + \int z\,dx$.

```
In[1]:= integrate[y_ + z_, x_] :=
            integrate[y, x] + integrate[z, x]
```

The associativity of Plus makes the linearity relation work with any number of terms in the sum.

```
In[2]:= integrate[a x + b x^2 + 3, x]
Out[2]= integrate[3, x] + integrate[a x, x] +
            integrate[b x^2, x]
```

This makes integrate pull out factors that are independent of the integration variable x.

```
In[3]:= integrate[c_ y_, x_] := c integrate[y, x] /; FreeQ[c, x]
```

Mathematica tests each term in each product to see whether it satisfies the FreeQ condition, and so can be pulled out.

```
In[4]:= integrate[a x + b x^2 + 3, x]
Out[4]= integrate[3, x] + a integrate[x, x] +
            b integrate[x^2, x]
```

This gives the integral $\int c\,dx = cx$ of a constant.

```
In[5]:= integrate[c_, x_] := c x /; FreeQ[c, x]
```

Now the constant term in the sum can be integrated.

```
In[6]:= integrate[a x + b x^2 + 3, x]
Out[6]= 3 x + a integrate[x, x] + b integrate[x², x]
```

This gives the standard formula for the integral of x^n. By using the pattern x_^n_., rather than x_^n_, we include the case of $x^1 = x$.

```
In[7]:= integrate[x_^n_., x_] :=
                    x^(n+1)/(n+1) /; FreeQ[n, x] && n != -1
```

Now this integral can be done completely.

```
In[8]:= integrate[a x + b x^2 + 3, x]
```
$$Out[8]= 3 x + \frac{a x^2}{2} + \frac{b x^3}{3}$$

Of course, the built-in integration function Integrate (with a capital I) could have done the integral anyway.

```
In[9]:= Integrate[a x + b x^2 + 3, x]
```
$$Out[9]= 3 x + \frac{a x^2}{2} + \frac{b x^3}{3}$$

Here is the rule for integrating the reciprocal of a linear function. The pattern a_. x_ + b_. stands for any linear function of x.

```
In[10]:= integrate[1/(a_. x_ + b_.), x_] :=
                    Log[a x + b]/a /; FreeQ[{a,b}, x]
```

Here both a and b take on their default values.

```
In[11]:= integrate[1/x, x]
Out[11]= Log[x]
```

Here is a more complicated case. The symbol a now matches 2 p.

```
In[12]:= integrate[1/(2 p x - 1), x]
```
$$Out[12]= \frac{Log[-1 + 2 p x]}{2 p}$$

You can go on and add many more rules for integration. Here is a rule for integrating exponentials.

```
In[13]:= integrate[Exp[a_. x_ + b_.], x_] :=
                    Exp[a x + b]/a /; FreeQ[{a,b}, x]
```

2.4 Transformation Rules and Definitions

~■ 2.4.1 Applying Transformation Rules

expr /. *lhs* -> *rhs*	apply a transformation rule to *expr*
expr /. {*lhs₁* -> *rhs₁*, *lhs₂* -> *rhs₂*, ... }	try a sequence of rules on each part of *expr*

Applying transformation rules.

The replacement operator /.
(pronounced "slash-dot") applies rules
to expressions.

```
In[1]:= x + y /. x -> 3
Out[1]= 3 + y
```

You can give a list of rules to apply.
Each rule will be tried once on each
part of the expression.

```
In[2]:= x + y /. {x -> a, y -> b}
Out[2]= a + b
```

expr /. {*rules₁*, *rules₂*, ... }	give a list of the results from applying each of the *rulesᵢ* to *expr*

Applying lists of transformation rules.

If you give a list of lists of rules, you
get a list of results.

```
In[3]:= x + y /. {{x -> 1, y -> 2}, {x -> 4, y -> 2}}
Out[3]= {3, 6}
```

Functions such as Solve and NSolve
return lists whose elements are lists of
rules, each representing a solution.

```
In[4]:= Solve[x^3 - 5x^2 +2x + 8 == 0, x]
Out[4]= {{x → -1}, {x → 2}, {x → 4}}
```

When you apply these rules, you get a
list of results, one corresponding to
each solution.

```
In[5]:= x^2 + 6 /. %
Out[5]= {7, 10, 22}
```

When you use *expr* /. *rules*, each rule is tried in turn on each part of *expr*. As soon as a rule applies,
the appropriate transformation is made, and the resulting part is returned.

The rule for x^3 is tried first; if it does
not apply, the rule for x^n_ is used.

```
In[6]:= {x^2, x^3, x^4} /. {x^3 -> u, x^n_ -> p[n]}
Out[6]= {p[2], u, p[4]}
```

A result is returned as soon as the rule
has been applied, so the inner instance
of h is not replaced.

```
In[7]:= h[x + h[y]] /. h[u_] -> u^2
Out[7]= (x + h[y])²
```

The replacement *expr* /. *rules* tries each rule just once on each part of *expr*.

Since each rule is tried just once, this serves to swap x and y.

In[8]:= **{x^2, y^3} /. {x -> y, y -> x}**

Out[8]= {y², x³}

You can use this notation to apply one set of rules, followed by another.

In[9]:= **x^2 /. x -> (1 + y) /. y -> b**

Out[9]= (1 + b)²

Sometimes you may need to go on applying rules over and over again, until the expression you are working on no longer changes. You can do this using the repeated replacement operation *expr* //. *rules* (or ReplaceRepeated[*expr*, *rules*]).

expr /. *rules*	try rules once on each part of *expr*
expr //. *rules*	try rules repeatedly until the result no longer changes

Single and repeated rule application.

With the single replacement operator /. each rule is tried only once on each part of the expression.

In[10]:= **x^2 + y^6 /. {x -> 2 + a, a -> 3}**

Out[10]= (2 + a)² + y⁶

With the repeated replacement operator //. the rules are tried repeatedly until the expression no longer changes.

In[11]:= **x^2 + y^6 //. {x -> 2 + a, a -> 3}**

Out[11]= 25 + y⁶

Here the rule is applied only once.

In[12]:= **log[a b c d] /. log[x_ y_] -> log[x] + log[y]**

Out[12]= log[a] + log[b c d]

With the repeated replacement operator, the rule is applied repeatedly, until the result no longer changes.

In[13]:= **log[a b c d] //. log[x_ y_] -> log[x] + log[y]**

Out[13]= log[a] + log[b] + log[c] + log[d]

When you use //. (pronounced "slash-slash-dot"), *Mathematica* repeatedly passes through your expression, trying each of the rules given. It goes on doing this until it gets the same result on two successive passes.

If you give a set of rules that is circular, then //. can keep on getting different results forever. In practice, the maximum number of passes that //. makes on a particular expression is determined by the setting for the option MaxIterations. If you want to keep going for as long as possible, you can use ReplaceRepeated[*expr*, *rules*, MaxIterations -> Infinity]. You can always stop by explicitly interrupting *Mathematica*.

By setting the option MaxIterations, you can explicitly tell ReplaceRepeated how many times to try the rules you give.

In[14]:= **ReplaceRepeated[x, x -> x + 1, MaxIterations -> 1000]**

ReplaceRepeated::rrlim:
    Exiting after x scanned 1000 times.

Out[14]= 1000 + x

The replacement operators /. and //. share the feature that they try each rule on every subpart of your expression. On the other hand, Replace[*expr*, *rules*] tries the rules only on the whole of *expr*, and not on any of its subparts.

You can use Replace, together with functions like Map and MapAt, to control exactly which parts of an expression a replacement is applied to. Remember that you can use the function ReplacePart[*expr*, *new*, *pos*] to replace part of an expression with a specific object.

The operator /. applies rules to all subparts of an expression.	*In[15]:=* **x^2 /. x -> a** *Out[15]=* a^2
Replace applies rules only to the whole expression.	*In[16]:=* **Replace[x^2, x^2 -> b]** *Out[16]=* b
No replacement is done here.	*In[17]:=* **Replace[x^2, x -> a]** *Out[17]=* x^2

expr /. *rules*	apply rules to all subparts of *expr*
Replace[*expr*, *rules*]	apply rules to the whole of *expr* only

Applying rules to whole expressions.

Replace returns the result from using the first rule that applies.	*In[18]:=* **Replace[f[u], {f[x_] -> x^2, f[x_] -> x^3}]** *Out[18]=* u^2
ReplaceList gives a list of the results from every rule that applies.	*In[19]:=* **ReplaceList[f[u], {f[x_] -> x^2, f[x_] -> x^3}]** *Out[19]=* $\{u^2, u^3\}$
If a single rule can be applied in several ways, ReplaceList gives a list of all the results.	*In[20]:=* **ReplaceList[a + b + c, x_ + y_ -> g[x, y]]** *Out[20]=* {g[a, b+c], g[b, a+c], g[c, a+b], g[a+b, c], g[a+c, b], g[b+c, a]}
This gives a list of ways of breaking the original list in two.	*In[21]:=* **ReplaceList[{a, b, c, d}, {x__, y__} -> g[{x}, {y}]]** *Out[21]=* {g[{a}, {b, c, d}], g[{a, b}, {c, d}], g[{a, b, c}, {d}]}
This finds all sublists that are flanked by the same element.	*In[22]:=* **ReplaceList[{a, b, c, a, d, b, d}, {___, x_, y__, x_, ___} -> g[x, {y}]]** *Out[22]=* {g[a, {b, c}], g[b, {c, a, d}], g[d, {b}]}

Replace[*expr*, *rules*]	apply *rules* in one way only
ReplaceList[*expr*, *rules*]	apply *rules* in all possible ways

Applying rules in one way or all possible ways.

■ 2.4.2 Manipulating Sets of Transformation Rules

You can manipulate lists of transformation rules in *Mathematica* just like other symbolic expressions. It is common to assign a name to a rule or set of rules.

This assigns the "name" sinexp to the trigonometric expansion rule.	$In[1]:=$ **sinexp = Sin[2 x_] -> 2 Sin[x] Cos[x]** $Out[1]=$ $Sin[2 x\_] \rightarrow 2 Cos[x] Sin[x]$
You can now request the rule "by name".	$In[2]:=$ **Sin[2 (1 + x)^2] /. sinexp** $Out[2]=$ $2 Cos[(1+x)^2] Sin[(1+x)^2]$

You can use lists of rules to represent mathematical and other relations. Typically you will find it convenient to give names to the lists, so that you can easily specify the list you want in a particular case.

In most situations, it is only one rule from any given list that actually applies to a particular expression. Nevertheless, the /. operator tests each of the rules in the list in turn. If the list is very long, this process can take a long time.

Mathematica allows you to preprocess lists of rules so that /. can operate more quickly on them. You can take any list of rules and apply the function Dispatch to them. The result is a representation of the original list of rules, but including dispatch tables which allow /. to "dispatch" to potentially applicable rules immediately, rather than testing all the rules in turn.

Here is a list of rules for the first five factorials.	$In[3]:=$ **facs = Table[f[i] -> i!, {i, 5}]** $Out[3]=$ $\{f[1] \rightarrow 1, f[2] \rightarrow 2, f[3] \rightarrow 6, f[4] \rightarrow 24, f[5] \rightarrow 120\}$
This sets up dispatch tables that make the rules faster to use.	$In[4]:=$ **dfacs = Dispatch[facs]** $Out[4]=$ $Dispatch[\{f[1] \rightarrow 1, f[2] \rightarrow 2,$ $f[3] \rightarrow 6, f[4] \rightarrow 24, f[5] \rightarrow 120\},$ $-DispatchTables-]$
You can apply the rules using the /. operator.	$In[5]:=$ **f[4] /. dfacs** $Out[5]=$ 24

Dispatch[*rules*]	create a representation of a list of rules that includes dispatch tables
expr /. *drules*	apply rules that include dispatch tables

Creating and using dispatch tables.

For long lists of rules, you will find that setting up dispatch tables makes replacement operations much faster. This is particularly true when your rules are for individual symbols or other expressions that do not involve pattern objects. Once you have built dispatch tables in such cases, you will find that the /. operator takes a time that is more or less independent of the number of rules you have. Without dispatch tables, however, /. will take a time directly proportional to the total number of rules.

■ 2.4.3 Making Definitions

The replacement operator /. allows you to apply transformation rules to a specific expression. Often, however, you want to have transformation rules automatically applied whenever possible.

You can do this by assigning explicit values to *Mathematica* expressions and patterns. Each assignment specifies a transformation rule to be applied whenever an expression of the appropriate form occurs.

expr /. *lhs* -> *rhs*	apply a transformation rule to a specific expression
lhs = *rhs*	assign a value which defines a transformation rule to be used whenever possible

Manual and automatic application of transformation rules.

This applies a transformation rule for x to a specific expression.	*In[1]:=* **(1 + x)^6 /. x -> 3 - a**
	Out[1]= $(4-a)^6$
By assigning a value to x, you tell *Mathematica* to apply a transformation rule for x whenever possible.	*In[2]:=* **x = 3 - a**
	Out[2]= $3-a$
Now x is transformed automatically.	*In[3]:=* **(1 + x)^7**
	Out[3]= $(4-a)^7$

You should realize that except inside constructs like Module and Block, all assignments you make in a *Mathematica* session are *permanent*. They continue to be used for the duration of the session, unless you explicitly clear or overwrite them.

The fact that assignments are permanent means that they must be made with care. Probably the single most common mistake in using *Mathematica* is to make an assignment for a variable like x at one point in your session, and then later to use x having forgotten about the assignment you made.

There are several ways to avoid this kind of mistake. First, you should avoid using assignments whenever possible, and instead use more controlled constructs such as the /. replacement operator. Second, you should explicitly use the deassignment operator =. or the function Clear to remove values you have assigned when you have finished with them.

Another important way to avoid mistakes is to think particularly carefully before assigning values to variables with common or simple names. You will often want to use a variable such as x as a symbolic parameter. But if you make an assignment such as x = 3, then x will be replaced by 3 whenever it occurs, and you can no longer use x as a symbolic parameter.

In general, you should be sure not to assign permanent values to any variables that you might want to use for more than one purpose. If at one point in your session you wanted the variable c to stand for the speed of light, you might assign it a value such as 3.*10^8. But then you cannot use c later in your session to stand, say, for an undetermined coefficient. One way to avoid this kind of problem is to make assignments only for variables with more explicit names, such as `SpeedOfLight`.

x =.	remove the value assigned to the object *x*
`Clear[`*x*, *y*, ... `]`	clear all the values of *x*, *y*, ...

Removing assignments.

This does not give what you might expect, because x still has the value you assigned it above.	*In[4]:=* `Factor[ x^2 - 1 ]`
	Out[4]= $(-4 + a)(-2 + a)$
This removes any value assigned to x.	*In[5]:=* `Clear[x]`
Now this gives the result you expect.	*In[6]:=* `Factor[ x^2 - 1 ]`
	Out[6]= $(-1 + x)(1 + x)$

■ 2.4.4 Special Forms of Assignment

Particularly when you write procedural programs in *Mathematica*, you will often need to modify the value of a particular variable repeatedly. You can always do this by constructing the new value and explicitly performing an assignment such as *x* = *value*. *Mathematica*, however, provides special notations for incrementing the values of variables, and for some other common cases.

i++	increment the value of *i* by 1
i--	decrement *i*
++*i*	pre-increment *i*
--*i*	pre-decrement *i*
i += *di*	add *di* to the value of *i*
i -= *di*	subtract *di* from *i*
x *= *c*	multiply *x* by *c*
x /= *c*	divide *x* by *c*

Modifying values of variables.

This assigns the value 7x to the variable t.	*In[1]:=* `t = 7x`
	Out[1]= $7x$

| This increments the value of t by 18x. | $In[2]:=$ **t += 18x** |
| | $Out[2]=$ 25 x |

| The value of t has been modified. | $In[3]:=$ **t** |
| | $Out[3]=$ 25 x |

| This sets t to 8, multiplies its value by 7, then gives the final value of t. | $In[4]:=$ **t = 8; t *= 7; t** |
| | $Out[4]=$ 56 |

The value of i++ is the value of i *before* the increment is done.	$In[5]:=$ **i=5; Print[i++]; Print[i]**
	5
	6

The value of ++i is the value of i *after* the increment.	$In[6]:=$ **i=5; Print[++i]; Print[i]**
	6
	6

$x = y = value$	assign the same value to both x and y
$\{x, y\} = \{value_1, value_2\}$	assign different values to x and y
$\{x, y\} = \{y, x\}$	interchange the values of x and y

Assigning values to several variables at a time.

| This assigns the value 5 to x and 8 to y. | $In[7]:=$ **{x, y} = {5, 8}** |
| | $Out[7]=$ {5, 8} |

| This interchanges the values of x and y. | $In[8]:=$ **{x, y} = {y, x}** |
| | $Out[8]=$ {8, 5} |

| Now x has value 8. | $In[9]:=$ **x** |
| | $Out[9]=$ 8 |

| And y has value 5. | $In[10]:=$ **y** |
| | $Out[10]=$ 5 |

| You can use assignments to lists to permute values of variables in any way. | $In[11]:=$ **{a, b, c} = {1, 2, 3}; {b, a, c} = {a, c, b}; {a, b, c}** |
| | $Out[11]=$ {3, 1, 2} |

When you write programs in *Mathematica*, you will sometimes find it convenient to take a list, and successively add elements to it. You can do this using the functions PrependTo and AppendTo.

PrependTo[v, *elem*]	prepend *elem* to the value of v
AppendTo[v, *elem*]	append *elem*
v = {v, *elem*}	make a nested list containing *elem*

Assignments for modifying lists.

This assigns the value of v to be the list {5, 7, 9}.	*In[12]:=* **v = {5, 7, 9}**
	Out[12]= {5, 7, 9}
This appends the element 11 to the value of v.	*In[13]:=* **AppendTo[v, 11]**
	Out[13]= {5, 7, 9, 11}
Now the value of v has been modified.	*In[14]:=* **v**
	Out[14]= {5, 7, 9, 11}

Although AppendTo[v, *elem*] is always equivalent to v = Append[v, *elem*], it is often a convenient notation. However, you should realize that because of the way *Mathematica* stores lists, it is usually less efficient to add a sequence of elements to a particular list than to create a nested structure that consists, for example, of lists of length 2 at each level. When you have built up such a structure, you can always reduce it to a single list using Flatten.

This sets up a nested list structure for w.	*In[15]:=* **w = {1}; Do[w = {w, k^2}, {k, 1, 4}]; w**
	Out[15]= {{{{{1}, 1}, 4}, 9}, 16}
You can use Flatten to unravel the structure.	*In[16]:=* **Flatten[w]**
	Out[16]= {1, 1, 4, 9, 16}

■ 2.4.5 Making Definitions for Indexed Objects

In many kinds of calculations, you need to set up "arrays" which contain sequences of expressions, each specified by a certain index. One way to implement arrays in *Mathematica* is by using lists. You can define a list, say a = {x, y, z, ... }, then access its elements using a[[i]], or modify them using a[[i]] = *value*. This approach has a drawback, however, in that it requires you to fill in all the elements when you first create the list.

Often, it is more convenient to set up arrays in which you can fill in only those elements that you need at a particular time. You can do this by making definitions for expressions such as a[i].

This defines a value for a[1].	*In[1]:=* **a[1] = 9**
	Out[1]= 9
This defines a value for a[2].	*In[2]:=* **a[2] = 7**
	Out[2]= 7

This shows all the values you have defined for expressions associated with a so far.	*In[3]:=* **?a**
	Global`a
	a[1] = 9
	a[2] = 7
You can define a value for a[5], even though you have not yet given values to a[3] and a[4].	*In[4]:=* **a[5] = 0**
	Out[4]= 0
This generates a list of the values of the a[i].	*In[5]:=* **Table[a[i], {i, 5}]**
	Out[5]= {9, 7, a[3], a[4], 0}

You can think of the expression a[i] as being like an "indexed" or "subscripted" variable.

a[i] = *value*	add or overwrite a value
a[i]	access a value
a[i] =.	remove a value
?a	show all defined values
Clear[a]	clear all defined values
Table[a[i], {i, 1, n}] or Array[a, n]	convert to an explicit List

Manipulating indexed variables.

When you have an expression of the form $a[i]$, there is no requirement that the "index" i be a number. In fact, *Mathematica* allows the index to be any expression whatsoever. By using indices that are symbols, you can for example build up simple databases in *Mathematica*.

This defines the "object" area with "index" square to have value 1.	*In[6]:=* **area[square] = 1**
	Out[6]= 1
This adds another result to the area "database".	*In[7]:=* **area[triangle] = 1/2**
	Out[7]= $\frac{1}{2}$
Here are the entries in the area database so far.	*In[8]:=* **?area**
	Global`area
	area[square] = 1
	area[triangle] = 1/2
You can use these definitions wherever you want. You have not yet assigned a value for area[pentagon].	*In[9]:=* **4 area[square] + area[pentagon]**
	Out[9]= 4 + area[pentagon]

■ 2.4.6 Making Definitions for Functions

Section 1.7.1 discussed how you can define functions in *Mathematica*. In a typical case, you would type in f[x_] = x^2 to define a function f. (Actually, the definitions in Section 1.7.1 used the := operator, rather than the = one. Section 2.4.8 will explain exactly when to use each of the := and = operators.)

The definition f[x_] = x^2 specifies that whenever *Mathematica* encounters an expression which matches the pattern f[x_], it should replace the expression by x^2. Since the pattern f[x_] matches all expressions of the form f[*anything*], the definition applies to functions f with any "argument".

Function definitions like f[x_] = x^2 can be compared with definitions like f[a] = b for indexed variables discussed in the previous subsection. The definition f[a] = b specifies that whenever the *particular* expression f[a] occurs, it is to be replaced by b. But the definition says nothing about expressions such as f[y], where f appears with another "index".

To define a "function", you need to specify values for expressions of the form f[*x*], where the argument *x* can be anything. You can do this by giving a definition for the pattern f[x_], where the pattern object x_ stands for any expression.

f[*x*] = *value*	definition for a *specific expression x*
f[x_] = *value*	definition for *any expression*, referred to as *x*

The difference between defining an indexed variable and a function.

Making definitions for f[2] or f[a] can be thought of as being like giving values to various elements of an "array" named f. Making a definition for f[x_] is like giving a value for a set of "array elements" with arbitrary "indices". In fact, you can actually think of any function as being like an array with an arbitrarily variable index.

In mathematical terms, you can think of f as a *mapping*. When you define values for, say, f[1] and f[2], you specify the image of this mapping for various discrete points in its domain. Defining a value for f[x_] specifies the image of f on a continuum of points.

This defines a transformation rule for the *specific expression* f[x].

In[1]:= **f[x] = u**

Out[1]= u

When the specific expression f[x] appears, it is replaced by u. Other expressions of the form f[*argument*] are, however, not modified.

In[2]:= **f[x] + f[y]**

Out[2]= u + f[y]

This defines a value for f with *any expression* as an "argument".

In[3]:= **f[x_] = x^2**

Out[3]= x^2

|---|---|

The old definition for the *specific expression* f[x] is still used, but the new general definition for f[x_] is now used to find a value for f[y].

In[4]:= **f[x] + f[y]**

Out[4]= $u + y^2$

This removes all definitions for f.

In[5]:= **Clear[f]**

Mathematica allows you to define transformation rules for any expression or pattern. You can mix definitions for specific expressions such as f[1] or f[a] with definitions for patterns such as f[x_].

Many kinds of mathematical functions can be set up by mixing specific and general definitions in *Mathematica*. As an example, consider the factorial function. This particular function is in fact built into *Mathematica* (it is written $n!$). But you can use *Mathematica* definitions to set up the function for yourself.

The standard mathematical definition for the factorial function can be entered almost directly into *Mathematica*, in the form: f[n_] := n f[n-1]; f[1] = 1. This definition specifies that for any n, f[n] should be replaced by n f[n-1], except that when n is 1, f[1] should simply be replaced by 1.

Here is the value of the factorial function with argument 1.

In[6]:= **f[1] = 1**

Out[6]= 1

Here is the general recursion relation for the factorial function.

In[7]:= **f[n_] := n f[n-1]**

Now you can use these definitions to find values for the factorial function.

In[8]:= **f[10]**

Out[8]= 3628800

The results are the same as you get from the built-in version of factorial.

In[9]:= **10!**

Out[9]= 3628800

■ 2.4.7 The Ordering of Definitions

When you make a sequence of definitions in *Mathematica*, some may be more general than others. *Mathematica* follows the principle of trying to put more general definitions after more specific ones. This means that special cases of rules are typically tried before more general cases.

This behavior is crucial to the factorial function example given in the previous section. Regardless of the order in which you entered them, *Mathematica* will always put the rule for the special case f[1] ahead of the rule for the general case f[n_]. This means that when *Mathematica* looks for the value of an expression of the form f[n], it tries the special case f[1] first, and only if this does not apply, it tries the general case f[n_]. As a result, when you ask for f[5], *Mathematica* will keep on using the general rule until the "end condition" rule for f[1] applies.

■ *Mathematica* tries to put specific definitions before more general definitions.

Treatment of definitions in *Mathematica*.

If *Mathematica* did not follow the principle of putting special rules before more general ones, then the special rules would always be "shadowed" by more general ones. In the factorial example, if the rule for f[n_] was ahead of the rule for f[1], then even when *Mathematica* tried to evaluate f[1], it would use the general f[n_] rule, and it would never find the special f[1] rule.

Here is a general definition for f[n_].	*In[1]:=* **f[n_] := n f[n-1]**
Here is a definition for the special case f[1].	*In[2]:=* **f[1] = 1**
	Out[2]= 1
Mathematica puts the special case before the general one.	*In[3]:=* **?f**
	Global`f
	f[1] = 1
	f[n_] := n*f[n - 1]

In the factorial function example used above, it is clear which rule is more general. Often, however, there is no definite ordering in generality of the rules you give. In such cases, *Mathematica* simply tries the rules in the order you give them.

These rules have no definite ordering in generality.	*In[4]:=* **log[x_ y_] := log[x] + log[y] ; log[x_^n_] := n log[x]**
Mathematica stores the rules in the order you gave them.	*In[5]:=* **?log**
	Global`log
	log[(x_)*(y_)] := log[x] + log[y]
	log[(x_)^(n_)] := n*log[x]
This rule is a special case of the rule for log[x_ y_].	*In[6]:=* **log[2 x_] := log[x] + log2**
Mathematica puts the special rule before the more general one.	*In[7]:=* **?log**
	Global`log
	log[2*(x_)] := log[x] + log2
	log[(x_)*(y_)] := log[x] + log[y]
	log[(x_)^(n_)] := n*log[x]

Although in many practical cases, *Mathematica* can recognize when one rule is more general than another, you should realize that this is not always possible. For example, if two rules both contain complicated /; conditions, it may not be possible to work out which is more general, and, in fact, there may not be a definite ordering. Whenever the appropriate ordering is not clear, *Mathematica* stores rules in the order you give them.

■ 2.4.8 Immediate and Delayed Definitions

You may have noticed that there are two different ways to make assignments in *Mathematica*: *lhs* = *rhs* and *lhs* := *rhs*. The basic difference between these forms is *when* the expression *rhs* is evaluated. *lhs* = *rhs* is an *immediate assignment*, in which *rhs* is evaluated at the time when the assignment is made. *lhs* := *rhs*, on the other hand, is a *delayed assignment*, in which *rhs* is not evaluated when the assignment is made, but is instead evaluated each time the value of *lhs* is requested.

lhs = *rhs* (immediate assignment)	*rhs* is evaluated when the assignment is made
lhs := *rhs* (delayed assignment)	*rhs* is evaluated each time the value of *lhs* is requested

The two types of assignments in *Mathematica*.

This uses the := operator to define the function ex.	`In[1]:= ex[x_] := Expand[(1 + x)^2]`
Because := was used, the definition is maintained in an unevaluated form.	`In[2]:= ?ex` `Global`ex`  `ex[x_] := Expand[(1 + x)^2]`
When you make an assignment with the = operator, the right-hand side is evaluated immediately.	`In[3]:= iex[x_] = Expand[(1 + x)^2]` $Out[3]= 1 + 2x + x^2$
The definition now stored is the result of the Expand command.	`In[4]:= ?iex` `Global`iex`  `iex[x_] = 1 + 2*x + x^2`
When you execute ex, the Expand is performed.	`In[5]:= ex[y + 2]` $Out[5]= 9 + 6y + y^2$
iex simply substitutes its argument into the already expanded form, giving a different answer.	`In[6]:= iex[y + 2]` $Out[6]= 1 + 2(2 + y) + (2 + y)^2$

As you can see from the example above, both = and := can be useful in defining functions, but they have different meanings, and you must be careful about which one to use in a particular case.

One rule of thumb is the following. If you think of an assignment as giving the final "value" of an expression, use the = operator. If instead you think of the assignment as specifying a "command" for finding the value, use the := operator. If in doubt, it is usually better to use the := operator than the = one.

lhs = *rhs*	*rhs* is intended to be the "final value" of *lhs* (e.g., `f[x_] = 1 - x^2`)
lhs := *rhs*	*rhs* gives a "command" or "program" to be executed whenever you ask for the value of *lhs* (e.g., `f[x_] := Expand[1 - x^2]`)

Interpretations of assignments with the = and := operators.

Although := is probably used more often than = in defining functions, there is one important case in which you must use = to define a function. If you do a calculation, and get an answer in terms of a symbolic parameter x, you often want to go on and find results for various specific values of x. One way to do this is to use the /. operator to apply appropriate rules for x in each case. It is usually more convenient however, to use = to define a function whose argument is x.

Here is an expression involving x.	*In[7]:=* `D[Log[Sin[x]]^2, x]`
	Out[7]= $2 \mathrm{Cot}[x] \mathrm{Log}[\mathrm{Sin}[x]]$
This defines a function whose argument is the value to be taken for x.	*In[8]:=* `dlog[x_] = %`
	Out[8]= $2 \mathrm{Cot}[x] \mathrm{Log}[\mathrm{Sin}[x]]$
Here is the result when x is taken to be 1 + a.	*In[9]:=* `dlog[1 + a]`
	Out[9]= $2 \mathrm{Cot}[1+a] \mathrm{Log}[\mathrm{Sin}[1+a]]$

An important point to notice in the example above is that there is nothing special about the name x that appears in the x_ pattern. It is just a symbol, indistinguishable from an x that appears in any other expression.

f[x_] = *expr*	define a function which gives the value *expr* for any particular value of x

Defining functions for evaluating expressions.

You can use = and := not only to define functions, but also to assign values to variables. If you type x = *value*, then *value* is immediately evaluated, and the result is assigned to x. On the other hand, if you type x := *value*, then *value* is not immediately evaluated. Instead, it is maintained in an unevaluated form, and is evaluated afresh each time x is used.

This evaluates Random[ ] to find a pseudorandom number, then assigns this number to r1.	*In[10]:=* `r1 = Random[ ]`
	Out[10]= 0.0560708
Here Random[ ] is maintained in an unevaluated form, to be evaluated afresh each time r2 is used.	*In[11]:=* `r2 := Random[ ]`

Here are values for r1 and r2.

In[12]:= **{r1, r2}**

Out[12]= {0.0560708, 0.6303}

The value of r1 never changes. Every time r2 is used, however, a new pseudorandom number is generated.

In[13]:= **{r1, r2}**

Out[13]= {0.0560708, 0.359894}

The distinction between immediate and delayed assignments is particularly important when you set up chains of assignments.

This defines a to be 1.

In[14]:= **a = 1**

Out[14]= 1

Here a + 2 is evaluated to give 3, and the result is assigned to be the value of ri.

In[15]:= **ri = a + 2**

Out[15]= 3

Here a + 2 is maintained in an unevaluated form, to be evaluated every time the value of rd is requested.

In[16]:= **rd := a + 2**

In this case, ri and rd give the same values.

In[17]:= **{ri, rd}**

Out[17]= {3, 3}

Now the value of a is changed.

In[18]:= **a = 2**

Out[18]= 2

Now rd uses the new value for a, while ri keeps its original value.

In[19]:= **{ri, rd}**

Out[19]= {3, 4}

You can use delayed assignments such as *t := rhs* to set up variables whose values you can find in a variety of different "environments". Every time you ask for *t*, the expression *rhs* is evaluated using the current values of the objects on which it depends.

The right-hand side of the delayed assignment is maintained in an unevaluated form.

In[20]:= **t := {a, Factor[x^a - 1]}**

This sets a to 4, then finds the value of t.

In[21]:= **a = 4; t**

Out[21]= {4, $(-1 + x) (1 + x) (1 + x^2)$}

Here a is 6.

In[22]:= **a = 6; t**

Out[22]= {6, $(-1 + x) (1 + x) (1 - x + x^2) (1 + x + x^2)$}

In the example above, the symbol a acts as a "global variable", whose value affects the value of t. When you have a large number of parameters, many of which change only occasionally, you may find this kind of setup convenient. However, you should realize that implicit or hidden dependence of one variable on others can often become quite confusing. When possible, you should make all dependencies explicit, by defining functions which take all necessary parameters as arguments.

lhs -> rhs	*rhs* is evaluated when the rule is given
lhs :> rhs	*rhs* is evaluated when the rule is used

Two types of transformation rules in *Mathematica*.

Just as you can make immediate and delayed assignments in *Mathematica*, so you can also set up immediate and delayed transformation rules.

The right-hand side of this rule is evaluated when you give the rule.	`In[23]:= f[x_] -> Expand[(1 + x)^2]` `Out[23]= f[x_] → 1 + 2 x + x`^{2}
A rule like this is probably not particularly useful.	`In[24]:= f[x_] -> Expand[x]` `Out[24]= f[x_] → x`
Here the right-hand side of the rule is maintained in an unevaluated form, to be evaluated every time the rule is used.	`In[25]:= f[x_] :> Expand[x]` `Out[25]= f[x_] :→ Expand[x]`
Applying the rule causes the expansion to be done.	`In[26]:= f[(1 + p)^2] /. f[x_] :> Expand[x]` `Out[26]= 1 + 2 p + p`^{2}

In analogy with assignments, you should typically use -> when you want to replace an expression with a definite value, and you should use :> when you want to give a command for finding the value.

■ 2.4.9 Functions That Remember Values They Have Found

When you make a function definition using :=, the value of the function is recomputed every time you ask for it. In some kinds of calculations, you may end up asking for the same function value many times. You can save time in these cases by having *Mathematica* remember all the function values it finds. Here is an "idiom" for defining a function that does this.

$f[x\_] := f[x] = rhs$	define a function which remembers values that it finds

Defining a function that remembers values it finds.

This defines a function f which stores all values that it finds.	`In[1]:= f[x_] := f[x] = f[x - 1] + f[x - 2]`
Here are the end conditions for the recursive function f.	`In[2]:= f[0] = f[1] = 1` `Out[2]= 1`

Here is the original definition of f.

```
In[3]:= ?f
Global'f
f[0] = 1
f[1] = 1
f[x_] := f[x] = f[x - 1] + f[x - 2]
```

This computes f[5]. The computation involves finding the sequence of values f[5], f[4], ... f[2].

```
In[4]:= f[5]
Out[4]= 8
```

All the values of f found so far are explicitly stored.

```
In[5]:= ?f
Global'f
f[0] = 1
f[1] = 1
f[2] = 2
f[3] = 3
f[4] = 5
f[5] = 8
f[x_] := f[x] = f[x - 1] + f[x - 2]
```

If you ask for f[5] again, *Mathematica* can just look up the value immediately; it does not have to recompute it.

```
In[6]:= f[5]
Out[6]= 8
```

You can see how a definition like `f[x_] := f[x] = f[x-1] + f[x-2]` works. The function `f[x_]` is defined to be the "program" `f[x] = f[x-1] + f[x-2]`. When you ask for a value of the function `f`, the "program" is executed. The program first calculates the value of `f[x-1] + f[x-2]`, then saves the result as `f[x]`.

It is often a good idea to use functions that remember values when you implement mathematical *recursion relations* in *Mathematica*. In a typical case, a recursion relation gives the value of a function f with an integer argument x in terms of values of the same function with arguments $x - 1$, $x - 2$, etc. The Fibonacci function definition $f(x) = f(x - 1) + f(x - 2)$ used above is an example of this kind of recursion relation. The point is that if you calculate say $f(10)$ by just applying the recursion relation over and over again, you end up having to recalculate quantities like $f(5)$ many times. In a case like this, it is therefore better just to *remember* the value of $f(5)$, and look it up when you need it, rather than having to recalculate it.

There is of course a trade-off involved in remembering values. It is faster to find a particular value, but it takes more memory space to store all of them. You should usually define functions to remember values only if the total number of different values that will be produced is comparatively small, or the expense of recomputing them is very great.

■ 2.4.10 Associating Definitions with Different Symbols

When you make a definition in the form *f*[*args*] = *rhs* or *f*[*args*] := *rhs*, *Mathematica* associates your definition with the object *f*. This means, for example, that such definitions are displayed when you type ?*f*. In general, definitions for expressions in which the symbol *f* appears as the head are termed *downvalues* of *f*.

Mathematica however also supports *upvalues*, which allow definitions to be associated with symbols that do not appear directly as their head.

Consider for example a definition like Exp[g[x_]] := *rhs*. One possibility is that this definition could be associated with the symbol Exp, and considered as a downvalue of Exp. This is however probably not the best thing either from the point of view of organization or efficiency.

Better is to consider Exp[g[x_]] := *rhs* to be associated with g, and to correspond to an upvalue of g.

f[*args*] := *rhs*	define a downvalue for *f*
f[*g*[*args*], ...] ^:= *rhs*	define an upvalue for *g*

Associating definitions with different symbols.

This is taken to define a downvalue for f.	*In[1]:=* **f[g[x_]] := fg[x]**
You can see the definition when you ask about f.	*In[2]:=* **?f**
	Global`f
	f[g[x_]] := fg[x]
This defines an upvalue for g.	*In[3]:=* **g/: Exp[g[x_]] := expg[x]**
The definition is associated with g.	*In[4]:=* **?g**
	Global`g
	Exp[g[x_]] ^:= expg[x]
It is not associated with Exp.	*In[5]:=* **?Exp**
	Exp[z] is the exponential function.
The definition is used to evaluate this expression.	*In[6]:=* **Exp[g[5]]**
	Out[6]= expg[5]

In simple cases, you will get the same answers to calculations whether you give a definition for *f*[*g*[*x*]] as a downvalue for *f* or an upvalue for *g*. However, one of the two choices is usually much more natural and efficient than the other.

A good rule of thumb is that a definition for *f*[*g*[*x*]] should be given as an upvalue for *g* in cases where the function *f* is more common than *g*. Thus, for example, in the case of Exp[*g*[*x*]], Exp is a built-in *Mathematica* function, while *g* is presumably a function you have added. In such a case, you will typically think of definitions for Exp[*g*[*x*]] as giving relations satisfied by *g*. As a result, it is more natural to treat the definitions as upvalues for *g* than as downvalues for Exp.

This gives the definition as an upvalue for g.	*In[7]:=* **g/: g[x_] + g[y_] := gplus[x, y]**

Here are the definitions for g so far.	*In[8]:=* **?g**
	Global'g
	Exp[g[x_]] ^:= expg[x]
	g[x_] + g[y_] ^:= gplus[x, y]

The definition for a sum of g's is used whenever possible.	*In[9]:=* **g[5] + g[7]**
	Out[9]= gplus[5, 7]

Since the full form of the pattern g[x_] + g[y_] is Plus[g[x_], g[y_]], a definition for this pattern could be given as a downvalue for Plus. It is almost always better, however, to give the definition as an upvalue for g.

In general, whenever *Mathematica* encounters a particular function, it tries all the definitions you have given for that function. If you had made the definition for g[x_] + g[y_] a downvalue for Plus, then *Mathematica* would have tried this definition whenever Plus occurs. The definition would thus be tested every time *Mathematica* added expressions together, making this very common operation slower in all cases.

However, by giving a definition for g[x_] + g[y_] as an upvalue for g, you associate the definition with g. In this case, *Mathematica* only tries the definition when it finds a g inside a function such as Plus. Since g presumably occurs much less frequently than Plus, this is a much more efficient procedure.

---

f[*g*] ^= *value*   or   *f*[*g*[*args*]] ^= *value*
              make assignments to be associated with *g*, rather than *f*

f[*g*] ^:= *value*   or   *f*[*g*[*args*]] ^:= *value*
              make delayed assignments associated with *g*

f[*arg*$_1$, *arg*$_2$, ...] ^= *value*   make assignments associated with the heads of *all* the *arg*$_i$

Shorter ways to define upvalues.

A typical use of upvalues is in setting up a "database" of properties of a particular object. With upvalues, you can associate each definition you make with the object that it concerns, rather than with the property you are specifying.

This defines an upvalue for square which gives its area.	*In[10]:=* **area[square] ^= 1**
	Out[10]= 1

This adds a definition for the perimeter.

In[11]:= **perimeter[square] ^= 4**

Out[11]= 4

Both definitions are now associated with the object square.

In[12]:= **?square**

Global`square

area[square] ^= 1

perimeter[square] ^= 4

In general, you can associate definitions for an expression with any symbol that occurs at a sufficiently high level in the expression. With an expression of the form $f[args]$, you can define an upvalue for a symbol g so long as either g itself, or an object with head g, occurs in $args$. If g occurs at a lower level in an expression, however, you cannot associate definitions with it.

g occurs as the head of an argument, so you can associate a definition with it.

In[13]:= **g/: h[w[x_], g[y_]] := hwg[x, y]**

Here g appears too deep in the left-hand side for you to associate a definition with it.

In[14]:= **g/: h[w[g[x_]], y_] := hw[x, y]**

TagSetDelayed::tagpos:
    Tag g in h[w[g[x_]], y_]
        is too deep for an assigned rule to be found.

Out[14]= $Failed

$f[\ ...\ ] := rhs$	downvalue for f
$f/: f[g[\ ...\ ]][\ ...\ ] := rhs$	downvalue for f
$g/: f[\ ...\ ,\ g,\ ...\ ] := rhs$	upvalue for g
$g/: f[\ ...\ ,\ g[\ ...\ ],\ ...\ ] := rhs$	upvalue for g

Possible positions for symbols in definitions.

As discussed in Section 2.1.2, you can use *Mathematica* symbols as "tags", to indicate the "type" of an expression. For example, complex numbers in *Mathematica* are represented internally in the form Complex[x, y], where the symbol Complex serves as a tag to indicate that the object is a complex number.

Upvalues provide a convenient mechanism for specifying how operations act on objects that are tagged to have a certain type. For example, you might want to introduce a class of abstract mathematical objects of type quat. You can represent each object of this type by a *Mathematica* expression of the form quat[*data*].

In a typical case, you might want quat objects to have special properties with respect to arithmetic operations such as addition and multiplication. You can set up such properties by defining upvalues for quat with respect to Plus and Times.

This defines an upvalue for quat with respect to Plus.	*In[15]:=* **quat[x_] + quat[y_] ^:= quat[x + y]**

The upvalue you have defined is used to simplify this expression.	*In[16]:=* **quat[a] + quat[b] + quat[c]** *Out[16]=* quat[a + b + c]

When you define an upvalue for quat with respect to an operation like Plus, what you are effectively doing is to extend the domain of the Plus operation to include quat objects. You are telling *Mathematica* to use special rules for addition in the case where the things to be added together are quat objects.

In defining addition for quat objects, you could always have a special addition operation, say quatPlus, to which you assign an appropriate downvalue. It is usually much more convenient, however, to use the standard *Mathematica* Plus operation to represent addition, but then to "overload" this operation by specifying special behavior when quat objects are encountered.

You can think of upvalues as a way to implement certain aspects of object-oriented programming. A symbol like quat represents a particular type of object. Then the various upvalues for quat specify "methods" that define how quat objects should behave under certain operations, or on receipt of certain "messages".

■ 2.4.11 Defining Numerical Values

If you make a definition such as f[x_] := *value*, *Mathematica* will use the value you give for any f function it encounters. In some cases, however, you may want to define a value that is to be used specifically when you ask for numerical values.

expr = *value*	define a value to be used whenever possible
N[*expr*] = *value*	define a value to be used for numerical approximation

Defining ordinary and numerical values.

This defines a numerical value for the function f.	*In[1]:=* **N[f[x_]] := Sum[x^-i/i^2, {i, 20}]**

Defining the numerical value does not tell *Mathematica* anything about the ordinary value of f.	*In[2]:=* **f[2] + f[5]** *Out[2]=* f[2] + f[5]

If you ask for a numerical approximation, however, *Mathematica* uses the numerical values you have defined.	*In[3]:=* **N[%]** *Out[3]=* 0.793244

You can define numerical values for both functions and symbols. The numerical values are used by all numerical *Mathematica* functions, including NIntegrate, FindRoot and so on.

N[*expr*] = *value*	define a numerical value to be used when default numerical precision is requested
N[*expr*, *n*] = *value*	define a numerical value to be used when *n*-digit precision is requested

Defining numerical values that depend on numerical precision.

This defines a numerical value for the symbol const, using 4n + 5 terms in the product for n-digit precision.

In[4]:= **N[const, n_] := Product[1 - 2^-i, {i, 2, 4n + 5}]**

Here is the value of const, computed to 30-digit precision using the value you specified.

In[5]:= **N[const, 30]**

Out[5]= 0.577576190173204842557799443858

Mathematica treats numerical values essentially like upvalues. When you define a numerical value for *f*, *Mathematica* effectively enters your definition as an upvalue for f with respect to the numerical evaluation operation N.

■ 2.4.12 Modifying Built-in Functions

Mathematica allows you to define transformation rules for any expression. You can define such rules not only for functions that you add to *Mathematica*, but also for intrinsic functions that are already built into *Mathematica*. As a result, you can enhance, or modify, the features of built-in *Mathematica* functions.

This capability is powerful, but potentially dangerous. *Mathematica* will always follow the rules you give it. This means that if the rules you give are incorrect, then *Mathematica* will give you incorrect answers.

To avoid the possibility of changing built-in functions by mistake, *Mathematica* "protects" all built-in functions from redefinition. If you want to give a definition for a built-in function, you have to remove the protection first. After you give the definition, you should usually restore the protection, to prevent future mistakes.

Unprotect[*f*]	remove protection
Protect[*f*]	add protection

Protection for functions.

Built-in functions are usually "protected", so you cannot redefine them.

```
In[1]:= Log[7] = 2
Set::write: Tag Log in Log[7] is Protected.
Out[1]= 2
```

This removes protection for Log.

```
In[2]:= Unprotect[Log]
Out[2]= {Log}
```

Now you can give your own definitions for Log. This particular definition is not mathematically correct, but *Mathematica* will still allow you to give it.

```
In[3]:= Log[7] = 2
Out[3]= 2
```

Mathematica will use your definitions whenever it can, whether they are mathematically correct or not.

```
In[4]:= Log[7] + Log[3]
Out[4]= 2 + Log[3]
```

This removes the incorrect definition for Log.

```
In[5]:= Log[7] =.
```

This restores the protection for Log.

```
In[6]:= Protect[Log]
Out[6]= {Log}
```

Definitions you give can override built-in features of *Mathematica*. In general, *Mathematica* tries to use your definitions before it uses built-in definitions.

The rules that are built into *Mathematica* are intended to be appropriate for the broadest range of calculations. In specific cases, however, you may not like what the built-in rules do. In such cases, you can give your own rules to override the ones that are built in.

There is a built-in rule for simplifying Exp[Log[*expr*]].

```
In[7]:= Exp[Log[y]]
Out[7]= y
```

You can give your own rule for Exp[Log[*expr*]], overriding the built-in rule.

```
In[8]:= (
           Unprotect[Exp] ;
           Exp[Log[expr_]] := explog[expr] ;
           Protect[Exp] ;
        )
```

Now your rule is used, rather than the built-in one.

```
In[9]:= Exp[Log[y]]
Out[9]= explog[y]
```

■ 2.4.13 Advanced Topic: Manipulating Value Lists

DownValues[*f*]	give the list of downvalues of *f*
UpValues[*f*]	give the list of upvalues of *f*
DownValues[*f*] = *rules*	set the downvalues of *f*
UpValues[*f*] = *rules*	set the upvalues of *f*

Finding and setting values of symbols.

Mathematica effectively stores all definitions you give as lists of transformation rules. When a particular symbol is encountered, the lists of rules associated with it are tried.

Under most circumstances, you do not need direct access to the actual transformation rules associated with definitions you have given. Instead, you can simply use *lhs* = *rhs* and *lhs* =. to add and remove rules. In some cases, however, you may find it useful to have direct access to the actual rules.

Here is a definition for f.

$In[1]:=$ **f[x_] := x^2**

This gives the explicit rule corresponding to the definition you made for f.

$In[2]:=$ **DownValues[f]**

$Out[2]=$ {HoldPattern[f[x_]] :> x^2}

Notice that the rules returned by DownValues and UpValues are set up so that neither their left- nor right-hand sides get evaluated. The left-hand sides are wrapped in HoldPattern, and the rules are delayed, so that the right-hand sides are not immediately evaluated.

As discussed in Section 2.4.6, *Mathematica* tries to order definitions so that more specific ones appear before more general ones. In general, however, there is no unique way to make this ordering, and you may want to choose a different ordering from the one that *Mathematica* chooses by default. You can do this by reordering the list of rules obtained from DownValues or UpValues.

Here are some definitions for the object g.

$In[3]:=$ **g[x_ + y_] := gp[x, y] ; g[x_ y_] := gm[x, y]**

This shows the default ordering used for the definitions.

$In[4]:=$ **DownValues[g]**

$Out[4]=$ {HoldPattern[g[x_ + y_]] :> gp[x, y],
           HoldPattern[g[x_ y_]] :> gm[x, y]}

This reverses the order of the definitions for g.

$In[5]:=$ **DownValues[g] = Reverse[DownValues[g]]**

$Out[5]=$ {HoldPattern[g[x_ y_]] :> gm[x, y],
           HoldPattern[g[x_ + y_]] :> gp[x, y]}

2.5 Evaluation of Expressions

■ 2.5.1 Principles of Evaluation

The fundamental operation that *Mathematica* performs is *evaluation*. Whenever you enter an expression, *Mathematica* evaluates the expression, then returns the result.

Evaluation in *Mathematica* works by applying a sequence of definitions. The definitions can either be ones you explicitly entered, or ones that are built into *Mathematica*.

Thus, for example, *Mathematica* evaluates the expression 6 + 7 using a built-in procedure for adding integers. Similarly, *Mathematica* evaluates the algebraic expression x − 3x + 1 using a built-in simplification procedure. If you had made the definition x = 5, then *Mathematica* would use this definition to reduce x − 3x + 1 to −9.

The two most central concepts in *Mathematica* are probably *expressions* and *evaluation*. Section 2.1 discussed how all the different kinds of objects that *Mathematica* handles are represented in a uniform way using expressions. This section describes how all the operations that *Mathematica* can perform can also be viewed in a uniform way as examples of evaluation.

Computation	$5 + 6$	$\longrightarrow$ 11
Simplification	$x - 3x + 1$	$\longrightarrow$ $1 - 2x$
Execution	$x = 5$	$\longrightarrow$ 5

Some interpretations of evaluation.

Mathematica is an *infinite evaluation* system. When you enter an expression, *Mathematica* will keep on using definitions it knows until it gets a result to which no definitions apply.

This defines x1 in terms of x2, and then defines x2.	`In[1]:= x1 = x2 + 2 ; x2 = 7` `Out[1]= 7`
If you ask for x1, *Mathematica* uses all the definitions it knows to give you a result.	`In[2]:= x1` `Out[2]= 9`
Here is a recursive definition in which the factorial function is defined in terms of itself.	`In[3]:= fac[1] = 1 ; fac[n_] := n fac[n-1]`
If you ask for fac[10], *Mathematica* will keep on applying the definitions you have given until the result it gets no longer changes.	`In[4]:= fac[10]` `Out[4]= 3628800`

When *Mathematica* has used all the definitions it knows, it gives whatever expression it has obtained as the result. Sometimes the result may be an object such as a number. But usually the result is an expression in which some objects are represented in a symbolic form.

Mathematica uses its built-in definitions for simplifying sums, but knows no definitions for `f[3]`, so leaves this in symbolic form.	$In[5]:=$ **f[3] + 4f[3] + 1** $Out[5]=$ $1 + 5 f[3]$

Mathematica follows the principle of applying definitions until the result it gets no longer changes. This means that if you take the final result that *Mathematica* gives, and enter it as *Mathematica* input, you will get back the same result again. (There are some subtle cases discussed in Section 2.5.12 in which this does not occur.)

If you type in a result from *Mathematica*, you get back the same expression again.	$In[6]:=$ **1 + 5 f[3]** $Out[6]=$ $1 + 5 f[3]$

At any given time, *Mathematica* can only use those definitions that it knows at that time. If you add more definitions later, however, *Mathematica* will be able to use these. The results you get from *Mathematica* may change in this case.

Here is a new definition for the function f.	$In[7]:=$ **f[x_] = x^2** $Out[7]=$ x^2

With the new definition, the results you get can change.	$In[8]:=$ **1 + 5 f[3]** $Out[8]=$ 46

The simplest examples of evaluation involve using definitions such as `f[x_] = x^2` which transform one expression directly into another. But evaluation is also the process used to execute programs written in *Mathematica*. Thus, for example, if you have a procedure consisting of a sequence of *Mathematica* expressions, some perhaps representing conditionals and loops, the execution of this procedure corresponds to the evaluation of these expressions. Sometimes the evaluation process may involve evaluating a particular expression several times, as in a loop.

The expression `Print[zzzz]` is evaluated three times during the evaluation of the Do expression.	$In[9]:=$ **Do[Print[zzzz], {3}]** zzzz zzzz zzzz

■ 2.5.2 Reducing Expressions to Their Standard Form

The built-in functions in *Mathematica* operate in a wide variety of ways. But many of the mathematical functions share an important approach: they are set up so as to reduce classes of mathematical expressions to standard forms.

The built-in definitions for the Plus function, for example, are set up to write any sum of terms in a standard unparenthesized form. The associativity of addition means that expressions like (a + b) + c, a + (b + c) and a + b + c are all equivalent. But for many purposes it is convenient for all these forms to be reduced to the single standard form a + b + c. The built-in definitions for Plus are set up to do this.

Through the built-in definitions for Plus, this expression is reduced to a standard unparenthesized form.	*In[1]:=* **(a + b) + c** *Out[1]=* a + b + c

Whenever *Mathematica* knows that a function is associative, it tries to remove parentheses (or nested invocations of the function) to get the function into a standard "flattened" form.

A function like addition is not only associative, but also commutative, which means that expressions like a + c + b and a + b + c with terms in different orders are equal. Once again, *Mathematica* tries to put all such expressions into a "standard" form. The standard form it chooses is the one in which all the terms are in a definite order, corresponding roughly to alphabetical order.

Mathematica sorts the terms in this sum into a standard order.	*In[2]:=* **c + a + b** *Out[2]=* a + b + c

flat (associative)	$f[f[a, b], c]$ is equivalent to $f[a, b, c]$, etc.
orderless (commutative)	$f[b, a]$ is equivalent to $f[a, b]$, etc.

Two important properties that *Mathematica* uses in reducing certain functions to standard form.

There are several reasons to try to put expressions into standard forms. The most important is that if two expressions are really in standard form, it is obvious whether or not they are equal.

When the two sums are put into standard order, they are immediately seen to be equal, so that two f's cancel, leaving the result 0.	*In[3]:=* **f[a + c + b] - f[c + a + b]** *Out[3]=* 0

You could imagine finding out whether a + c + b was equal to c + a + b by testing all possible orderings of each sum. It is clear that simply reducing both sums to standard form is a much more efficient procedure.

One might think that *Mathematica* should somehow automatically reduce *all* mathematical expressions to a single standard canonical form. With all but the simplest kinds of expressions, however, it is quite easy to see that you do not want the *same* standard form for all purposes.

For polynomials, for example, there are two obvious standard forms, which are good for different purposes. The first standard form for a polynomial is a simple sum of terms, as would be generated in *Mathematica* by applying the function Expand. This standard form is most appropriate if you need to add and subtract polynomials.

There is, however, another possible standard form that you can use for polynomials. By applying Factor, you can write any polynomial as a product of irreducible factors. This canonical form is useful if you want to do operations like division.

Expanded and factored forms are in a sense both equally good standard forms for polynomials. Which one you decide to use simply depends on what you want to use it for. As a result, *Mathematica* does not automatically put polynomials into one of these two forms. Instead, it gives you functions like `Expand` and `Factor` that allow you explicitly to put polynomials in whatever form you want.

Here is a list of two polynomials that are mathematically equal.	*In[4]:=* `t = {x^2 - 1, (x + 1)(x - 1)}`
	Out[4]= $\{-1 + x^2, (-1 + x)(1 + x)\}$
You can write both of them in expanded form just by applying `Expand`. In this form, the equality of the polynomials is obvious.	*In[5]:=* **`Expand[t]`**
	Out[5]= $\{-1 + x^2, -1 + x^2\}$
You can also see that the polynomials are equal by writing them both in factored form.	*In[6]:=* **`Factor[t]`**
	Out[6]= $\{(-1 + x)(1 + x), (-1 + x)(1 + x)\}$

Although it is clear that you do not always want expressions reduced to the *same* standard form, you may wonder whether it is at least *possible* to reduce all expressions to *some* standard form.

There is a basic result in the mathematical theory of computation which shows that this is, in fact, not always possible. You cannot guarantee that any finite sequence of transformations will take any two arbitrarily chosen expressions to a standard form.

In a sense, this is not particularly surprising. If you could in fact reduce all mathematical expressions to a standard form, then it would be quite easy to tell whether any two expressions were equal. The fact that so many of the difficult problems of mathematics can be stated as questions about the equality of expressions suggests that this can in fact be difficult.

■ 2.5.3 Attributes

Definitions such as `f[x_] = x^2` specify *values* for functions. Sometimes, however, you need to specify general properties of functions, without necessarily giving explicit values.

Mathematica provides a selection of *attributes* that you can use to specify various properties of functions. For example, you can use the attribute `Flat` to specify that a particular function is "flat", so that nested invocations are automatically flattened, and it behaves as if it were associative.

This assigns the attribute `Flat` to the function `f`.	*In[1]:=* **`SetAttributes[f, Flat]`**
Now `f` behaves as a flat, or associative, function, so that nested invocations are automatically flattened.	*In[2]:=* **`f[f[a, b], c]`**
	Out[2]= `f[a, b, c]`

Attributes like `Flat` can affect not only evaluation, but also operations such as pattern matching. If you give definitions or transformation rules for a function, you must be sure to have specified the attributes of the function first.

Here is a definition for the flat function f.

`In[3]:= f[x_, x_] := f[x]`

Because f is flat, the definition is automatically applied to every subsequence of arguments.

`In[4]:= f[a, a, a, b, b, b, c, c]`

`Out[4]= f[a, b, c]`

Attributes[*f*]	give the attributes of *f*
Attributes[*f*] = {*attr*₁, *attr*₂, ... }	set the attributes of *f*
Attributes[*f*] = {}	set *f* to have no attributes
SetAttributes[*f*, *attr*]	add *attr* to the attributes of *f*
ClearAttributes[*f*, *attr*]	remove *attr* from the attributes of *f*

Manipulating attributes of symbols.

This shows the attributes assigned to f.

`In[5]:= Attributes[f]`

`Out[5]= {Flat}`

This removes the attributes assigned to f.

`In[6]:= Attributes[f] = { }`

`Out[6]= {}`

Orderless	orderless, commutative function (arguments are sorted into standard order)
Flat	flat, associative function (arguments are "flattened out")
OneIdentity	$f[f[a]]$, etc. are equivalent to a for pattern matching
Listable	f is automatically "threaded" over lists that appear as arguments (e.g., $f[\{a,b\}]$ becomes $\{f[a], f[b]\}$)
Constant	all derivatives of f are zero
NumericFunction	f is assumed to have a numerical value when its arguments are numeric quantities
Protected	values of f cannot be changed
Locked	attributes of f cannot be changed
ReadProtected	values of f cannot be read
HoldFirst	the first argument of f is not evaluated
HoldRest	all but the first argument of f is not evaluated
HoldAll	none of the arguments of f are evaluated
HoldAllComplete	the arguments of f are treated as completely inert
NHoldFirst	the first argument of f is not affected by N
NHoldRest	all but the first argument of f is not affected by N
NHoldAll	none of the arguments of f are affected by N
SequenceHold	Sequence objects appearing in the arguments of f are not flattened out
Temporary	f is a local variable, removed when no longer used
Stub	Needs is automatically called if f is ever explicitly input

The complete list of attributes for symbols in *Mathematica*.

Here are the attributes for the built-in function Plus.

```
In[7]:= Attributes[Plus]
Out[7]= {Flat, Listable, NumericFunction, OneIdentity,
          Orderless, Protected}
```

An important attribute assigned to built-in mathematical functions in *Mathematica* is the attribute Listable. This attribute specifies that a function should automatically be distributed or "threaded" over lists that appear as its arguments. This means that the function effectively gets applied separately to each element in any lists that appear as its arguments.

The built-in Log function is Listable.	*In[8]:=* **Log[{5, 8, 11}]**
	Out[8]= {Log[5], Log[8], Log[11]}
This defines the function p to be listable.	*In[9]:=* **SetAttributes[p, Listable]**
Now p is automatically threaded over lists that appear as its arguments.	*In[10]:=* **p[{a, b, c}, d]**
	Out[10]= {p[a, d], p[b, d], p[c, d]}

Many of the attributes you can assign to functions in *Mathematica* directly affect the evaluation of those functions. Some attributes, however, affect only other aspects of the treatment of functions. For example, the attribute OneIdentity affects only pattern matching, as discussed in Section 2.3.7. Similarly, the attribute Constant is only relevant in differentiation, and operations that rely on differentiation.

The Protected attribute affects assignments. *Mathematica* does not allow you to make any definition associated with a symbol that carries this attribute. The functions Protect and Unprotect discussed in Section 2.4.12 can be used as alternatives to SetAttributes and ClearAttributes to set and clear this attribute. As discussed in Section 2.4.12 most built-in *Mathematica* objects are initially protected so that you do not make definitions for them by mistake.

Here is a definition for the function g.	*In[11]:=* **g[x_] = x + 1**
	Out[11]= 1 + x
This sets the Protected attribute for g.	*In[12]:=* **Protect[g]**
	Out[12]= {g}
Now you cannot modify the definition of g.	*In[13]:=* **g[x_] = x**
	Set::write: Tag g in g[x_] is Protected.
	Out[13]= x

You can usually see the definitions you have made for a particular symbol by typing ?*f*, or by using a variety of built-in *Mathematica* functions. However, if you set the attribute ReadProtected, *Mathematica* will not allow you to look at the definition of a particular symbol. It will nevertheless continue to use the definitions in performing evaluation.

Although you cannot modify it, you can still look at the definition of g.	*In[14]:=* **?g**
	Global'g
	Attributes[g] = {Protected}
	g[x_] = 1 + x
This sets the ReadProtected attribute for g.	*In[15]:=* **SetAttributes[g, ReadProtected]**
Now you can no longer read the definition of g.	*In[16]:=* **?g**
	Global'g
	Attributes[g] = {Protected, ReadProtected}

Functions like `SetAttributes` and `ClearAttributes` usually allow you to modify the attributes of a symbol in any way. However, if you once set the `Locked` attribute on a symbol, then *Mathematica* will not allow you to modify the attributes of that symbol for the remainder of your *Mathematica* session. Using the `Locked` attribute in addition to `Protected` or `ReadProtected`, you can arrange for it to be impossible for users to modify or read definitions.

`Clear[`*f*`]`	remove values for *f*, but not attributes
`ClearAll[`*f*`]`	remove both values and attributes of *f*

Clearing values and attributes.

This clears values and attributes of p which was given attribute `Listable` above.	`In[17]:=` **`ClearAll[p]`**

Now p is no longer listable.	`In[18]:=` **`p[{a, b, c}, d]`**
	`Out[18]=` p[{a, b, c}, d]

By defining attributes for a function you specify properties that *Mathematica* should assume whenever that function appears. Often, however, you want to assume the properties only in a particular instance. In such cases, you will be better off not to use attributes, but instead to call a particular function to implement the transformation associated with the attributes.

By explicitly calling `Thread`, you can implement the transformation that would be done automatically if p were listable.	`In[19]:=` **`Thread[p[{a, b, c}, d]]`**
	`Out[19]=` {p[a, d], p[b, d], p[c, d]}

`Orderless`	`Sort[`*f*`[`*args*`]]`
`Flat`	`Flatten[`*f*`[`*args*`]]`
`Listable`	`Thread[`*f*`[`*args*`]]`
`Constant`	`Dt[`*expr*`, Constants->`*f*`]`

Functions that perform transformations associated with some attributes.

Attributes in *Mathematica* can only be permanently defined for single symbols. However, *Mathematica* also allows you to set up pure functions which behave as if they carry attributes.

> `Function[`*vars*`,` *body*`, {`*attr*₁`, ... }]`
>   a pure function with attributes *attr*₁, ...

Pure functions with attributes.

This pure function applies p to the whole list.	*In[20]:=* `Function[{x}, p[x]] [{a, b, c}]`
	Out[20]= `p[{a, b, c}]`
By adding the attribute `Listable`, the function gets distributed over the elements of the list before applying p.	*In[21]:=* `Function[{x}, p[x], {Listable}] [{a, b, c}]`
	Out[21]= `{p[a], p[b], p[c]}`

■ 2.5.4 The Standard Evaluation Procedure

This section describes the standard procedure used by *Mathematica* to evaluate expressions. This procedure is the one followed for most kinds of expressions. There are however some kinds of expressions, such as those used to represent *Mathematica* programs and control structures, which are evaluated in a non-standard way. The treatment of such expressions is discussed in the sections that follow this one.

In the standard evaluation procedure, *Mathematica* first evaluates the head of an expression, and then evaluates each element of the expressions. These elements are in general themselves expressions, to which the same evaluation procedure is recursively applied.

The three `Print` functions are evaluated in turn, each printing its argument, then returning the value `Null`.	*In[1]:=* `{Print[1], Print[2], Print[3]}`
	1
	2
	3
	Out[1]= `{Null, Null, Null}`
This assigns the symbol ps to be `Plus`.	*In[2]:=* `ps = Plus`
	Out[2]= `Plus`
The head ps is evaluated first, so this expression behaves just like a sum of terms.	*In[3]:=* `ps[ps[a, b], c]`
	Out[3]= `a + b + c`

As soon as *Mathematica* has evaluated the head of an expression, it sees whether the head is a symbol that has attributes. If the symbol has the attributes `Orderless`, `Flat` or `Listable`, then immediately after evaluating the elements of the expression *Mathematica* performs the transformations associated with these attributes.

The next step in the standard evaluation procedure is to use definitions that *Mathematica* knows for the expression it is evaluating. *Mathematica* first tries to use definitions that you have made, and if there are none that apply, it tries built-in definitions.

If *Mathematica* finds a definition that applies, it performs the corresponding transformation on the expression. The result is another expression, which must then in turn be evaluated according to the standard evaluation procedure.

- Evaluate the head of the expression.

- Evaluate each element in turn.

- Apply transformations associated with the attributes `Orderless`, `Listable` and `Flat`.

- Apply any definitions that you have given.

- Apply any built-in definitions.

- Evaluate the result.

The standard evaluation procedure.

As discussed in Section 2.5.1, *Mathematica* follows the principle that each expression is evaluated until no further definitions apply. This means that *Mathematica* must continue re-evaluating results until it gets an expression which remains unchanged through the evaluation procedure.

Here is an example that shows how the standard evaluation procedure works on a simple expression. We assume that a = 7.

`2 a x + a^2 + 1`	here is the original expression
`Plus[Times[2, a, x], Power[a, 2], 1]`	
	this is the internal form
`Times[2, a, x]`	this is evaluated first
`Times[2, 7, x]`	a is evaluated to give 7
`Times[14, x]`	built-in definitions for `Times` give this result
`Power[a, 2]`	this is evaluated next
`Power[7, 2]`	here is the result after evaluating a
`49`	built-in definitions for `Power` give this result
`Plus[Times[14, x], 49, 1]`	here is the result after the arguments of Plus have been evaluated
`Plus[50, Times[14, x]]`	built-in definitions for `Plus` give this result
`50 + 14 x`	the result is printed like this

A simple example of evaluation in *Mathematica*.

Mathematica provides various ways to "trace" the evaluation process, as discussed in Section 2.5.10. The function `Trace[`*expr*`]` gives a nested list showing each subexpression generated during evaluation. (Note that the standard evaluation traverses the expression tree in a depth-first way, so that the smallest subparts of the expression appear first in the results of `Trace`.)

First set a to 7.	`In[4]:= a = 7`
	`Out[4]= 7`
This gives a nested list of all the subexpressions generated during the evaluation of the expression.	`In[5]:= Trace[2 a x + a^2 + 1]`
	`Out[5]= {{{a, 7}, 27x, 14x}, {{a, 7}, 7`^{2}`, 49},`
	`14x + 49 + 1, 50 + 14x}`

The order in which *Mathematica* applies different kinds of definitions is important. The fact that *Mathematica* applies definitions you have given before it applies built-in definitions means that you can give definitions which override the built-in ones, as discussed in Section 2.4.12.

This expression is evaluated using the built-in definition for `ArcSin`.	`In[6]:= ArcSin[1]`
	`Out[6]= `$\dfrac{\pi}{2}$
You can give your own definitions for `ArcSin`. You need to remove the protection attribute first.	`In[7]:= Unprotect[ArcSin]; ArcSin[1] = 5Pi/2;`
Your definition is used before the one that is built in.	`In[8]:= ArcSin[1]`
	`Out[8]= `$\dfrac{5\pi}{2}$

As discussed in Section 2.4.10, you can associate definitions with symbols either as upvalues or downvalues. *Mathematica* always tries upvalue definitions before downvalue ones.

If you have an expression like $f[g[x]]$, there are in general two sets of definitions that could apply: downvalues associated with f, and upvalues associated with g. *Mathematica* tries the definitions associated with g before those associated with f.

This ordering follows the general strategy of trying specific definitions before more general ones. By applying upvalues associated with arguments before applying downvalues associated with a function, *Mathematica* allows you to make definitions for special arguments which override the general definitions for the function with any arguments.

This defines a rule for f[g[x_]], to be associated with f.	`In[9]:= f/: f[g[x_]] := frule[x]`
This defines a rule for f[g[x_]], to be associated with g.	`In[10]:= g/: f[g[x_]] := grule[x]`
The rule associated with g is tried before the rule associated with f.	`In[11]:= f[g[2]]`
	`Out[11]= grule[2]`

If you remove rules associated with g, the rule associated with f is used.

In[12]:= **Clear[g] ; f[g[1]]**

Out[12]= frule[1]

■ Definitions associated with *g* are applied before definitions associated with *f* in the expression *f[g[x]]*.

The order in which definitions are applied.

Most functions such as **Plus** that are built into *Mathematica* have downvalues. There are, however, some objects in *Mathematica* which have built-in upvalues. For example, **SeriesData** objects, which represent power series, have built-in upvalues with respect to various mathematical operations.

For an expression like *f[g[x]]*, the complete sequence of definitions that are tried in the standard evaluation procedure is:

■ Definitions you have given associated with *g*;

■ Built-in definitions associated with *g*;

■ Definitions you have given associated with *f*;

■ Built-in definitions associated with *f*.

The fact that upvalues are used before downvalues is important in many situations. In a typical case, you might want to define an operation such as composition. If you give upvalues for various objects with respect to composition, these upvalues will be used whenever such objects appear. However, you can also give a general procedure for composition, to be used if no special objects are present. You can give this procedure as a downvalue for composition. Since downvalues are tried after upvalues, the general procedure will be used only if no objects with upvalues are present.

Here is a definition associated with q for composition of "q objects".

In[13]:= **q/: comp[q[x_], q[y_]] := qcomp[x, y]**

Here is a general rule for composition, associated with comp.

In[14]:= **comp[f_[x_], f_[y_]] := gencomp[f, x, y]**

If you compose two q objects, the rule associated with q is used.

In[15]:= **comp[q[1], q[2]]**

Out[15]= qcomp[1, 2]

If you compose r objects, the general rule associated with comp is used.

In[16]:= **comp[r[1], r[2]]**

Out[16]= gencomp[r, 1, 2]

In general, there can be several objects that have upvalues in a particular expression. *Mathematica* first looks at the head of the expression, and tries any upvalues associated with it. Then it successively looks at each element of the expression, trying any upvalues that exist. *Mathematica* performs this procedure first for upvalues that you have explicitly defined, and then for upvalues that are built in.

The procedure means that in a sequence of elements, upvalues associated with earlier elements take precedence over those associated with later elements.

This defines an upvalue for p with respect to c.	*In[17]:=* **p/: c[1___, p[x_], r___] := cp[x, {1, r}]**
This defines an upvalue for q.	*In[18]:=* **q/: c[1___, q[x_], r___] := cq[x, {1, r}]**
Which upvalue is used depends on which occurs first in the sequence of arguments to c.	*In[19]:=* **{c[p[1], q[2]], c[q[1], p[2]]}** *Out[19]=* {cp[1, {q[2]}], cq[1, {p[2]}]}

◾ 2.5.5 Non-Standard Evaluation

While most built-in *Mathematica* functions follow the standard evaluation procedure, some important ones do not. For example, most of the *Mathematica* functions associated with the construction and execution of programs use non-standard evaluation procedures. In typical cases, the functions either never evaluate some of their arguments, or do so in a special way under their own control.

$x = y$	do not evaluate the left-hand side
If[p, a, b]	evaluate a if p is True, and b if it is False
Do[*expr*, {n}]	evaluate *expr* n times
Plot[f, {x, ... }]	evaluate f with a sequence of numerical values for x
Function[{x}, *body*]	do not evaluate until the function is applied

Some functions that use non-standard evaluation procedures.

When you give a definition such as a = 1, *Mathematica* does not evaluate the a that appears on the left-hand side. You can see that there would be trouble if the a was evaluated. The reason is that if you had previously set a = 7, then evaluating a in the definition a = 1 would put the definition into the nonsensical form 7 = 1.

In the standard evaluation procedure, each argument of a function is evaluated in turn. This is prevented by setting the attributes HoldFirst, HoldRest and HoldAll. These attributes make *Mathematica* "hold" particular arguments in an unevaluated form.

HoldFirst	do not evaluate the first argument
HoldRest	evaluate only the first argument
HoldAll	evaluate none of the arguments

Attributes for holding function arguments in unevaluated form.

With the standard evaluation procedure, all arguments to a function are evaluated.	*In[1]:=* **f[1 + 1, 2 + 4]**
	Out[1]= f[2, 6]
This assigns the attribute HoldFirst to h.	*In[2]:=* **SetAttributes[h, HoldFirst]**
The first argument to h is now held in an unevaluated form.	*In[3]:=* **h[1 + 1, 2 + 4]**
	Out[3]= h[1 + 1, 6]
When you use the first argument to h like this, it will get evaluated.	*In[4]:=* **h[1 + 1, 2 + 4] /. h[x_, y_] -> x^y**
	Out[4]= 64
Built-in functions like Set carry attributes such as HoldFirst.	*In[5]:=* **Attributes[Set]**
	Out[5]= {HoldFirst, Protected, SequenceHold}

Even though a function may have attributes which specify that it should hold certain arguments unevaluated, you can always explicitly tell *Mathematica* to evaluate those arguments by giving the arguments in the form Evaluate[*arg*].

| Evaluate effectively overrides the HoldFirst attribute, and causes the first argument to be evaluated. | *In[6]:=* **h[Evaluate[1 + 1], 2 + 4]** |
| | *Out[6]=* h[2, 6] |

| *f*[Evaluate[*arg*]] | evaluate *arg* immediately, even though attributes of *f* may specify that it should be held |

Forcing the evaluation of function arguments.

By holding its arguments, a function can control when those arguments are evaluated. By using Evaluate, you can force the arguments to be evaluated immediately, rather than being evaluated under the control of the function. This capability is useful in a number of circumstances.

One example discussed on page 129 occurs when plotting graphs of expressions. The *Mathematica* Plot function holds unevaluated the expression you are going to plot, then evaluates it at a sequence of numerical positions. In some cases, you may instead want to evaluate the expression immediately, and have Plot work with the evaluated form. For example, if you want to plot a list of functions generated by Table, then you will want the Table operation done immediately, rather than being done every time a point is to be plotted.

Evaluate causes the list of functions to be constructed immediately, rather than being constructed at each value of x chosen by Plot.

```
In[7]:= Plot[
         Evaluate[Table[Sin[n x], {n, 1, 3}]],
                  {x, 0, 2Pi} ]
```

There are a number of built-in *Mathematica* functions which, like Plot, are set up to hold some of their arguments. You can always override this behavior using Evaluate.

The *Mathematica* Set function holds its first argument, so the symbol a is not evaluated in this case.

```
In[8]:= a = b
Out[8]= b
```

You can make Set evaluate its first argument using Evaluate. In this case, the result is the object which is the *value* of a, namely b is set to 6.

```
In[9]:= Evaluate[a] = 6
Out[9]= 6
```

b has now been set to 6.

```
In[10]:= b
Out[10]= 6
```

In most cases, you want all expressions you give to *Mathematica* to be evaluated. Sometimes, however, you may want to prevent the evaluation of certain expressions. For example, if you want to manipulate pieces of a *Mathematica* program symbolically, then you must prevent those pieces from being evaluated while you are manipulating them.

You can use the functions Hold and HoldForm to keep expressions unevaluated. These functions work simply by carrying the attribute HoldAll, which prevents their arguments from being evaluated. The functions provide "wrappers" inside which expressions remain unevaluated.

The difference between Hold[*expr*] and HoldForm[*expr*] is that in standard *Mathematica* output format, Hold is printed explicitly, while HoldForm is not. If you look at the full internal *Mathematica* form, you can however see both functions.

Hold maintains expressions in an unevaluated form.

```
In[11]:= Hold[1 + 1]
Out[11]= Hold[1 + 1]
```

HoldForm also keeps expressions unevaluated, but is invisible in standard *Mathematica* output format.

In[12]:= **HoldForm[1 + 1]**

Out[12]= 1 + 1

HoldForm is still present internally.

In[13]:= **FullForm[%]**

Out[13]//FullForm= HoldForm[Plus[1, 1]]

The function ReleaseHold removes Hold and HoldForm, so the expressions they contain get evaluated.

In[14]:= **ReleaseHold[%]**

Out[14]= 2

Hold[*expr*]	keep *expr* unevaluated
+ HoldComplete[*expr*]	keep *expr* unevaluated and prevent upvalues associated with *expr* from being used
HoldForm[*expr*]	keep *expr* unevaluated, and print without HoldForm
ReleaseHold[*expr*]	remove Hold and HoldForm in *expr*
+ Extract[*expr*, *index*, Hold]	get a part of *expr*, wrapping it with Hold to prevent evaluation
+ ReplacePart[*expr*, Hold[*value*], *index*, 1]	replace part of *expr*, extracting *value* without evaluating it

Functions for handling unevaluated expressions.

Parts of expressions are usually evaluated as soon as you extract them.

In[15]:= **Extract[Hold[1 + 1, 2 + 3], 2]**

Out[15]= 5

This extracts a part and immediately wraps it with Hold, so it does not get evaluated.

In[16]:= **Extract[Hold[1 + 1, 2 + 3], 2, Hold]**

Out[16]= Hold[2 + 3]

The last argument of 1 tells ReplacePart to extract the first part of Hold[7 + 8] before inserting it.

In[17]:= **ReplacePart[Hold[1 + 1, 2 + 3], Hold[7 + 8], 2, 1]**

Out[17]= Hold[1 + 1, 7 + 8]

f[... , Unevaluated[*expr*], ...]	give *expr* unevaluated as an argument to *f*

Temporary prevention of argument evaluation.

1 + 1 evaluates to 2, and Length[2] gives 0.

In[18]:= **Length[1 + 1]**

Out[18]= 0

This gives the unevaluated form 1 + 1   *In[19]:=* **Length[Unevaluated[1 + 1]]**
as the argument of Length.   *Out[19]=* 2

Unevaluated[*expr***]** effectively works by temporarily giving a function an attribute like **HoldFirst**, and then supplying *expr* as an argument to the function.

+	**SequenceHold**	do not flatten out **Sequence** objects that appear as arguments
+	**HoldAllComplete**	treat all arguments as completely inert

Attributes for preventing other aspects of evaluation.

By setting the attribute **HoldAll**, you can prevent *Mathematica* from evaluating the arguments of a function. But even with this attribute set, *Mathematica* will still do some transformations on the arguments. By setting **SequenceHold** you can prevent it from flattening out **Sequence** objects that appear in the arguments. And by setting **HoldAllComplete** you can also inhibit the stripping of **Unevaluated**, and prevent *Mathematica* from using any upvalues it finds associated with the arguments.

■ 2.5.6 Evaluation in Patterns, Rules and Definitions

There are a number of important interactions in *Mathematica* between evaluation and pattern matching. The first observation is that pattern matching is usually done on expressions that have already been at least partly evaluated. As a result, it is usually appropriate that the patterns to which these expressions are matched should themselves be evaluated.

The fact that the pattern is evaluated   *In[1]:=* **f[k^2] /. f[x_^(1 + 1)] -> p[x]**
means that it matches the expression   *Out[1]=* p[k]
given.

The right-hand side of the /; condition   *In[2]:=* **f[{a, b}] /. f[list_ /; Length[list] > 1] -> list^2**
is not evaluated until it is used during   *Out[2]=* {a², b²}
pattern matching.

There are some cases, however, where you may want to keep all or part of a pattern unevaluated. You can do this by wrapping the parts you do not want to evaluate with **HoldPattern**. In general, whenever **HoldPattern[***patt***]** appears within a pattern, this form is taken to be equivalent to *patt* for the purpose of pattern matching, but the expression *patt* is maintained unevaluated.

+	**HoldPattern[***patt***]**	equivalent to *patt* for pattern matching, with *patt* kept unevaluated

Preventing evaluation in patterns.

One application for `HoldPattern` is in specifying patterns which can apply to unevaluated expressions, or expressions held in an unevaluated form.

HoldPattern keeps the 1 + 1 from being evaluated, and allows it to match the 1 + 1 on the left-hand side of the `/.` operator.

In[3]:= **Hold[u[1 + 1]] /. HoldPattern[1 + 1] -> x**

Out[3]= Hold[u[x]]

Notice that while functions like `Hold` prevent evaluation of expressions, they do not affect the manipulation of parts of those expressions with `/.` and other operators.

This defines values for r whenever its argument is not an atomic object.

In[4]:= **r[x_] := x^2 /; !AtomQ[x]**

According to the definition, expressions like r[3] are left unchanged.

In[5]:= **r[3]**

Out[5]= r[3]

However, the pattern r[x_] is transformed according to the definition for r.

In[6]:= **r[x_]**

Out[6]= x_^{2}

You need to wrap HoldPattern around r[x_] to prevent it from being evaluated.

In[7]:= **{r[3], r[5]} /. HoldPattern[r[x_]] -> x**

Out[7]= {3, 5}

As illustrated above, the left-hand sides of transformation rules such as *lhs -> rhs* are usually evaluated immediately, since the rules are usually applied to expressions which have already been evaluated. The right-hand side of *lhs -> rhs* is also evaluated immediately. With the delayed rule *lhs :> rhs*, however, the expression *rhs* is not evaluated.

The right-hand side is evaluated immediately in -> but not :> rules.

In[8]:= **{{x -> 1 + 1}, {x :> 1 + 1}}**

Out[8]= {{x → 2}, {x :→ 1 + 1}}

Here are the results of applying the rules. The right-hand side of the :> rule gets inserted inside the Hold without evaluation.

In[9]:= **{x^2, Hold[x]} /. %**

Out[9]= {{4, Hold[2]}, {4, Hold[1 + 1]}}

| *lhs -> rhs* | evaluate both *lhs* and *rhs* |
| *lhs :> rhs* | evaluate *lhs* but not *rhs* |

Evaluation in transformation rules.

While the left-hand sides of transformation rules are usually evaluated, the left-hand sides of definitions are usually not. The reason for the difference is as follows. Transformation rules are typically applied using `/.` to expressions that have already been evaluated. Definitions, however, are used during the evaluation of expressions, and are applied to expressions that have not yet been completely evaluated. To work on such expressions, the left-hand sides of definitions must be maintained in a form that is at least partially unevaluated.

Definitions for symbols are the simplest case. As discussed in the previous section, a symbol on the left-hand side of a definition such as $x = value$ is not evaluated. If x had previously been assigned a value y, then if the left-hand side of $x = value$ were evaluated, it would turn into the quite unrelated definition $y = value$.

Here is a definition. The symbol on the left-hand side is not evaluated.	*In[10]:=* **k = w[3]**
	Out[10]= w[3]
This redefines the symbol.	*In[11]:=* **k = w[4]**
	Out[11]= w[4]
If you evaluate the left-hand side, then you define not the symbol k, but the *value* w[4] of the symbol k.	*In[12]:=* **Evaluate[k] = w[5]**
	Out[12]= w[5]
Now w[4] has value w[5].	*In[13]:=* **w[4]**
	Out[13]= w[5]

Although individual symbols that appear on the left-hand sides of definitions are not evaluated, more complicated expressions are partially evaluated. In an expression such as $f[args]$ on the left-hand side of a definition, the *args* are evaluated.

The 1 + 1 is evaluated, so that a value is defined for g[2].	*In[14]:=* **g[1 + 1] = 5**
	Out[14]= 5
This shows the value defined for g.	*In[15]:=* **?g**
	Global`g
	g[2] = 5

You can see why the arguments of a function that appears on the left-hand side of a definition must be evaluated by considering how the definition is used during the evaluation of an expression. As discussed in Section 2.5.1, when *Mathematica* evaluates a function, it first evaluates each of the arguments, then tries to find definitions for the function. As a result, by the time *Mathematica* applies any definition you have given for a function, the arguments of the function must already have been evaluated. An exception to this occurs when the function in question has attributes which specify that it should hold some of its arguments unevaluated.

symbol = *value*	*symbol* is not evaluated; *value* is evaluated
symbol := *value*	neither *symbol* nor *value* is evaluated
f[*args*] = *value*	*args* are evaluated; left-hand side as a whole is not
f[HoldPattern[*arg*]] = *value*	*f*[*arg*] is assigned, without evaluating *arg*
Evaluate[*lhs*] = *value*	left-hand side is evaluated completely

Evaluation in definitions.

While in most cases it is appropriate for the arguments of a function that appears on the left-hand side of a definition to be evaluated, there are some situations in which you do not want this to happen. In such cases, you can wrap HoldPattern around the parts that you do not want to be evaluated.

■ 2.5.7 Evaluation in Iteration Functions

The built-in *Mathematica* iteration functions such as Table and Sum, as well as Plot and Plot3D, evaluate their arguments in a slightly special way.

When evaluating an expression like Table[f, {i, *imax*}], the first step, as discussed on page 369, is to make the value of i local. Next, the limit *imax* in the iterator specification is evaluated. The expression f is maintained in an unevaluated form, but is repeatedly evaluated as a succession of values are assigned to i. When this is finished, the global value of i is restored.

The function Random[ ] is evaluated four separate times here, so four different pseudorandom numbers are generated.	*In[1]:=* **Table[Random[ ], {4}]** *Out[1]=* {0.0560708, 0.6303, 0.359894, 0.871377}
This evaluates Random[ ] before feeding it to Table. The result is a list of four identical numbers.	*In[2]:=* **Table[Evaluate[Random[ ]], {4}]** *Out[2]=* {0.858645, 0.858645, 0.858645, 0.858645}

In most cases, it is convenient for the function f in an expression like Table[f, {i, *imax*}] to be maintained in an unevaluated form until specific values have been assigned to i. This is true in particular if a complete symbolic form for f valid for any i cannot be found.

This defines fac to give the factorial when it has an integer argument, and to give NaN (standing for "Not a Number") otherwise.	*In[3]:=* **fac[n_Integer] := n! ; fac[x_] := NaN**
In this form, fac[i] is not evaluated until an explicit integer value has been assigned to i.	*In[4]:=* **Table[fac[i], {i, 5}]** *Out[4]=* {1, 2, 6, 24, 120}

Using Evaluate forces `fac[i]` to be evaluated with `i` left as a symbolic object.

In[5]:= **Table[Evaluate[fac[i]], {i, 5}]**

Out[5]= {NaN, NaN, NaN, NaN, NaN}

In cases where a complete symbolic form for *f* with arbitrary *i* in expressions such as `Table[f, {i, imax}]` *can* be found, it is often more efficient to compute this form first, and then feed it to `Table`. You can do this using `Table[Evaluate[f], {i, imax}]`.

The Sum in this case is evaluated separately for each value of `i`.

In[6]:= **Table[Sum[i^k, {k, 4}], {i, 8}]**

Out[6]= {4, 30, 120, 340, 780, 1554, 2800, 4680}

It is however possible to get a symbolic formula for the sum, valid for any value of `i`.

In[7]:= **Sum[i^k, {k, 4}]**

Out[7]= $i + i^2 + i^3 + i^4$

By inserting Evaluate, you tell *Mathematica* first to evaluate the sum symbolically, then to iterate over `i`.

In[8]:= **Table[Evaluate[Sum[i^k, {k, 4}]], {i, 8}]**

Out[8]= {4, 30, 120, 340, 780, 1554, 2800, 4680}

`Table[`*f*`, {`*i*`, `*imax*`}]`	keep *f* unevaluated until specific values are assigned to *i*
`Table[Evaluate[`*f*`], {`*i*`, `*imax*`}]`	evaluate *f* first with *i* left symbolic

Evaluation in iteration functions.

As discussed on page 129, it is convenient to use `Evaluate` when you plot a graph of a function or a list of functions. This causes the symbolic form of the function or list to be found first, before the iteration begins.

■ 2.5.8 Conditionals

Mathematica provides various ways to set up *conditionals*, which specify that particular expressions should be evaluated only if certain conditions hold.

lhs := *rhs* /; *test*	use the definition only if *test* evaluates to True
If[*test*, *then*, *else*]	evaluate *then* if *test* is True, and *else* if it is False
Which[*test*₁, *value*₁, *test*₂, ...]	evaluate the *test*ᵢ in turn, giving the value associated with the first one that is True
Switch[*expr*, *form*₁, *value*₁, *form*₂, ...]	
	compare *expr* with each of the *form*ᵢ, giving the value associated with the first form it matches
Switch[*expr*, *form*₁, *value*₁, *form*₂, ... , _, *def*]	
	use *def* as a default value

Conditional constructs.

The test gives False, so the *"else"* expression y is returned.

```
In[1]:= If[7 > 8, x, y]
Out[1]= y
```

Only the *"else"* expression is evaluated in this case.

```
In[2]:= If[7 > 8, Print[x], Print[y]]
y
```

When you write programs in *Mathematica*, you will often have a choice between making a single definition whose right-hand side involves several branches controlled by If functions, or making several definitions, each controlled by an appropriate /; condition. By using several definitions, you can often produce programs that are both clearer, and easier to modify.

This defines a step function, with value 1 for x > 0, and −1 otherwise.

```
In[3]:= f[x_] := If[x > 0, 1, -1]
```

This defines the positive part of the step function using a /; condition.

```
In[4]:= g[x_] := 1 /; x > 0
```

Here is the negative part of the step function.

```
In[5]:= g[x_] := -1 /; x <= 0
```

This shows the complete definition using /; conditions.

```
In[6]:= ?g
Global`g
g[x_] := 1 /; x > 0
g[x_] := -1 /; x <= 0
```

The function If provides a way to choose between two alternatives. Often, however, there will be more than two alternatives. One way to handle this is to use a nested set of If functions. Usually, however, it is instead better to use functions like Which and Switch.

This defines a function with three regions. Using True as the third test makes this the default case.

```
In[7]:= h[x_] := Which[x < 0, x^2, x > 5, x^3, True, 0]
```

This uses the first case in the Which.	*In[8]:=* **h[-5]**
	Out[8]= 25
This uses the third case.	*In[9]:=* **h[2]**
	Out[9]= 0
This defines a function that depends on the values of its argument modulo 3.	*In[10]:=* **r[x_] := Switch[Mod[x, 3], 0, a, 1, b, 2, c]**
Mod[7, 3] is 1, so this uses the second case in the Switch.	*In[11]:=* **r[7]**
	Out[11]= b
17 matches neither 0 nor 1, but does match _.	*In[12]:=* **Switch[17, 0, a, 1, b, _, q]**
	Out[12]= q

An important point about symbolic systems such as *Mathematica* is that the conditions you give may yield neither True nor False. Thus, for example, the condition x == y does not yield True or False unless x and y have specific values, such as numerical ones.

In this case, the test gives neither True nor False, so both branches in the If remain unevaluated.	*In[13]:=* **If[x == y, a, b]**
	Out[13]= If[x == y, a, b]
You can add a special fourth argument to If, which is used if the test does not yield True or False.	*In[14]:=* **If[x == y, a, b, c]**
	Out[14]= c

If[*test, then, else, unknown*]	a form of If which includes the expression to use if *test* is neither True nor False
TrueQ[*expr*]	give True if *expr* is True, and False otherwise
lhs === *rhs* or SameQ[*lhs, rhs*]	give True if *lhs* and *rhs* are identical, and False otherwise
lhs =!= *rhs* or UnsameQ[*lhs, rhs*]	give True if *lhs* and *rhs* are not identical, and False otherwise
MatchQ[*expr, form*]	give True if the pattern *form* matches *expr*, and give False otherwise

Functions for dealing with symbolic conditions.

Mathematica leaves this as a symbolic equation.	*In[15]:=* **x == y**
	Out[15]= x == y
Unless *expr* is manifestly True, TrueQ[*expr*] effectively assumes that *expr* is False.	*In[16]:=* **TrueQ[x == y]**
	Out[16]= False

Unlike ==, === tests whether two expressions are manifestly identical. In this case, they are not.

```
In[17]:= x === y
Out[17]= False
```

The main difference between *lhs* === *rhs* and *lhs* == *rhs* is that === always returns True or False, whereas == can leave its input in symbolic form, representing a symbolic equation, as discussed in Section 1.5.5. You should typically use === when you want to test the *structure* of an expression, and == if you want to test mathematical equality. The *Mathematica* pattern matcher effectively uses === to determine when one literal expression matches another.

You can use === to test the structure of expressions.

```
In[18]:= Head[a + b + c] === Times
Out[18]= False
```

The == operator gives a less useful result.

```
In[19]:= Head[a + b + c] == Times
Out[19]= Plus == Times
```

In setting up conditionals, you will often need to use combinations of tests, such as $test_1$ && $test_2$ && ... . An important point is that the result from this combination of tests will be False if *any* of the $test_i$ yield False. *Mathematica* always evaluates the $test_i$ in turn, stopping if any of the $test_i$ yield False.

$expr_1$ && $expr_2$ && $expr_3$	evaluate until one of the $expr_i$ is found to be False
$expr_1$ || $expr_2$ || $expr_3$	evaluate until one of the $expr_i$ is found to be True

Evaluation of logical expressions.

This function involves a combination of two tests.

```
In[20]:= t[x_] := (x != 0 && 1/x < 3)
```

Here both tests are evaluated.

```
In[21]:= t[2]
Out[21]= True
```

Here the first test yields False, so the second test is not tried. The second test would involve 1/0, and would generate an error.

```
In[22]:= t[0]
Out[22]= False
```

The way that *Mathematica* evaluates logical expressions allows you to combine sequences of tests where later tests may make sense only if the earlier ones are satisfied. The behavior, which is analogous to that found in languages such as C, is convenient in constructing many kinds of *Mathematica* programs.

◾ 2.5.9 Loops and Control Structures

The execution of a *Mathematica* program involves the evaluation of a sequence of *Mathematica* expressions. In simple programs, the expressions to be evaluated may be separated by semicolons, and evaluated one after another. Often, however, you need to evaluate expressions several times, in some kind of "loop".

Do[*expr*, {*i*, *imax*}]	evaluate *expr* repetitively, with *i* varying from 1 to *imax* in steps of 1
Do[*expr*, {*i*, *imin*, *imax*, *di*}]	evaluate *expr* with *i* varying from *imin* to *imax* in steps of *di*
Do[*expr*, {*n*}]	evaluate *expr* n times

Simple looping constructs.

This evaluates `Print[i^2]`, with i running from 1 to 4.

```
In[1]:= Do[Print[i^2], {i, 4}]

1
4
9
16
```

This executes an assignment for t in a loop with k running from 2 to 6 in steps of 2.

```
In[2]:= t = x; Do[t = 1/(1 + k t), {k, 2, 6, 2}]; t
```

$$Out[2]= \cfrac{1}{1+\cfrac{6}{1+\cfrac{4}{1+2x}}}$$

The way iteration is specified in Do is exactly the same as in functions like `Table` and `Sum`. Just as in those functions, you can set up several nested loops by giving a sequence of iteration specifications to Do.

This loops over values of i from 1 to 4, and for each value of i, loops over j from 1 to i-1.

```
In[3]:= Do[Print[{i,j}], {i, 4}, {j, i-1}]

{2, 1}
{3, 1}
{3, 2}
{4, 1}
{4, 2}
{4, 3}
```

Sometimes you may want to repeat a particular operation a certain number of times, without changing the value of an iteration variable. You can specify this kind of repetition in Do just as you can in `Table` and other iteration functions.

This repeats the assignment t = 1/(1+t) three times.

```
In[4]:= t = x; Do[t = 1/(1+t), {3}]; t
```

$$Out[4]= \cfrac{1}{1+\cfrac{1}{1+\cfrac{1}{1+x}}}$$

You can put a procedure inside Do.

```
In[5]:= t = 67; Do[Print[t]; t = Floor[t/2], {3}]

67
33
16
```

Nest[*f*, *expr*, *n*]	apply *f* to *expr* *n* times
FixedPoint[*f*, *expr*]	start with *expr*, and apply *f* repeatedly until the result no longer changes
FixedPoint[*f*, *expr*, SameTest -> *comp*]	stop when the function *comp* applied to two successive results yields True

Applying functions repetitively.

Do allows you to repeat operations by evaluating a particular expression many times with different values for iteration variables. Often, however, you can make more elegant and efficient programs using the functional programming constructs discussed in Section 2.2.2. Nest[*f*, *x*, *n*], for example, allows you to apply a function repeatedly to an expression.

This nests f three times.

In[6]:= **Nest[f, x, 3]**

Out[6]= f[f[f[x]]]

By nesting a pure function, you can get the same result as in the example with Do above.

In[7]:= **Nest[Function[t, 1/(1+t)], x, 3]**

$$Out[7]= \frac{1}{1 + \frac{1}{1 + \frac{1}{1+x}}}$$

Nest allows you to apply a function a specified number of times. Sometimes, however, you may simply want to go on applying a function until the results you get no longer change. You can do this using FixedPoint[*f*, *x*].

FixedPoint goes on applying a function until the result no longer changes.

In[8]:= **FixedPoint[Function[t, Print[t]; Floor[t/2]], 67]**

67
33
16
8
4
2
1
0

Out[8]= 0

You can use FixedPoint to imitate the evaluation process in *Mathematica*, or the operation of functions such as *expr* //. *rules*. In general, FixedPoint goes on until two successive results it gets are the same. By default, FixedPoint uses SameQ to test whether results are the same. You can specify an alternative function to use by setting the SameTest option.

	Catch[*expr*]	evaluate *expr* until Throw[*value*] is encountered, then return *value*
+	Catch[*expr*, *form*]	evaluate *expr* until Throw[*value*, *tag*] is encountered, where *form* matches *tag*
+	Catch[*expr*, *form*, *f*]	return *f*[*value*, *tag*] instead of *value*

Non-local control of evaluation.

When the Throw is encountered, evaluation stops, and the current value of i is returned as the value of the enclosing Catch.

```
In[9]:= Catch[Do[Print[i]; If[i > 3, Throw[i]], {i, 10}]]
1
2
3
4

Out[9]= 4
```

Throw and Catch provide a flexible way to control the process of evaluation in *Mathematica*. The basic idea is that whenever a Throw is encountered, the evaluation that is then being done is stopped, and *Mathematica* immediately returns to the nearest appropriate enclosing Catch.

Scan applies the function Print to each successive element in the list, and in the end just returns Null.

```
In[10]:= Scan[Print, {7, 6, 5, 4}]
7
6
5
4
```

The evaluation of Scan stops as soon as Throw is encountered, and the enclosing Catch returns as its value the argument of Throw.

```
In[11]:= Catch[Scan[(Print[#];
                If[# < 6, Throw[#]])&, {7, 6, 5, 4}]]
7
6
5

Out[11]= 5
```

The same result is obtained with Map, even though Map would have returned a list if its evaluation had not been stopped by encountering a Throw.

```
In[12]:= Catch[Map[(Print[#];
                If[# < 6, Throw[#]])&, {7, 6, 5, 4}]]
7
6
5

Out[12]= 5
```

You can use Throw and Catch to divert the operation of functional programming constructs, allowing for example the evaluation of such constructs to continue only until some condition has been met. Note that if you stop evaluation using Throw, then the structure of the result you get may be quite different from what you would have got if you had allowed the evaluation to complete.

Here is a list generated by repeated application of a function.

```
In[13]:= NestList[1/(# + 1)&, -2.5, 6]

Out[13]= {-2.5, -0.666667, 3., 0.25, 0.8,
          0.555555, 0.642857}
```

Since there is no `Throw` encountered, the result here is just as before.

In[14]:= **Catch[NestList[1/(# + 1)&, -2.5, 6]]**

Out[14]= {-2.5, -0.666667, 3., 0.25, 0.8,
                0.555555, 0.642857}

Now the evaluation of the `NestList` is diverted, and the single number given as the argument of `Throw` is returned.

In[15]:= **Catch[NestList**
                [If[# > 1, Throw[#], 1/(# + 1)]&, -2.5, 6]]

Out[15]= 3.

`Throw` and `Catch` operate in a completely global way: it does not matter how or where a `Throw` is generated—it will always stop evaluation and return to the enclosing `Catch`.

The `Throw` stops the evaluation of `f`, and causes the `Catch` to return just `a`, with no trace of `f` left.

In[16]:= **Catch[f[Throw[a]]]**

Out[16]= a

This defines a function which generates a `Throw` when its argument is larger than 10.

In[17]:= **g[x_] := If[x > 10, Throw[overflow], x!]**

No `Throw` is generated here.

In[18]:= **Catch[g[4]]**

Out[18]= 24

But here the `Throw` generated inside the evaluation of g returns to the enclosing `Catch`.

In[19]:= **Catch[g[40]]**

Out[19]= overflow

In small programs, it is often adequate to use Throw[*value*] and Catch[*expr*] in their simplest form. But particularly if you write larger programs that contain many separate pieces, it is usually much better to use Throw[*value*, *tag*] and Catch[*expr*, *form*]. By keeping the expressions *tag* and *form* local to a particular piece of your program, you can then ensure that your Throw and Catch will also operate only within that piece.

Here the `Throw` is caught by the inner `Catch`.

In[20]:= **Catch[f [Catch[Throw[x, a], a]], b]**

Out[20]= f[x]

But here it is caught only by the outer `Catch`.

In[21]:= **Catch[f [Catch[Throw[x, b], a]], b]**

Out[21]= x

You can use patterns in specifying the tags which a particular `Catch` should catch.

In[22]:= **Catch[Throw[x, a], a | b]**

Out[22]= x

This keeps the tag a completely local.

In[23]:= **Module[{a}, Catch[Throw[x, a], a]]**

Out[23]= x

You should realize that there is no need for the tag that appears in Throw to be a constant; in general it can be any expression.

Here the inner `Catch` catches all throws with tags less than 4, and continues the `Do`. But as soon as the tag reaches 4, the outer `Catch` is needed.

```
In[24]:= Catch[ Do[ Catch[ Throw[i^2, i], n_ /; n < 4],
                                         {i, 10} ], _]

Out[24]= 16
```

When you use `Catch[`*expr, form*`]` with `Throw[`*value, tag*`]`, the value returned by `Catch` is simply the expression *value* given in the `Throw`. If you use `Catch[`*expr, form, f*`]`, however, then the value returned by `Catch` is instead *f*`[`*value, tag*`]`.

Here f is applied to the value and tag in the Throw.

```
In[25]:= Catch[ Throw[ x, a ], a, f ]

Out[25]= f[x, a]
```

If there is no `Throw`, f is never used.

```
In[26]:= Catch[ x, a, f ]

Out[26]= x
```

`While[`*test, body*`]`	evaluate *body* repetitively, so long as *test* is `True`
`For[`*start, test, incr, body*`]`	evaluate *start*, then repetitively evaluate *body* and *incr*, until *test* fails

General loop constructs.

Functions like `Do`, `Nest` and `FixedPoint` provide structured ways to make loops in *Mathematica* programs, while `Throw` and `Catch` provide opportunities for modifying this structure. Sometimes, however, you may want to create loops that even from the outset have less structure. And in such cases, you may find it convenient to use the functions `While` and `For`, which perform operations repeatedly, stopping when a specified condition fails to be true.

The `While` loop continues until the condition fails.

```
In[27]:= n = 17; While[(n = Floor[n/2]) != 0, Print[n]]
8
4
2
1
```

The functions `While` and `For` in *Mathematica* are similar to the control structures `while` and `for` in languages such as C. Notice, however, that there are a number of important differences. For example, the roles of comma and semicolon are reversed in *Mathematica* `For` loops relative to C language ones.

This is a very common form for a For loop. `i++` increments the value of i.

```
In[28]:= For[i=1, i < 4, i++, Print[i]]
1
2
3
```

Here is a more complicated For loop. Notice that the loop terminates as soon as the test `i^2 < 10` fails.

```
In[29]:= For[i=1; t=x, i^2 < 10, i++, t = t^2 + i;
                             Print[t]]
```

$$1 + x^2$$
$$2 + (1 + x^2)^2$$
$$3 + (2 + (1 + x^2)^2)^2$$

In *Mathematica*, both `While` and `For` always evaluate the loop test before evaluating the body of the loop. As soon as the loop test fails to be `True`, `While` and `For` terminate. The body of the loop is thus only evaluated in situations where the loop test is `True`.

The loop test fails immediately, so the body of the loop is never evaluated.	*In[30]:=* `While[False, Print[x]]`

In a `While` or `For` loop, or in general in any *Mathematica* procedure, the *Mathematica* expressions you give are evaluated in a definite sequence. You can think of this sequence as defining the "flow of control" in the execution of a *Mathematica* program.

In most cases, you should try to keep the flow of control in your *Mathematica* programs as simple as possible. The more the flow of control depends for example on specific values generated during the execution of the program, the more difficult you will typically find it to understand the structure and operation of the program.

Functional programming constructs typically involve very simple flow of control. `While` and `For` loops are always more complicated, since they are set up to make the flow of control depend on the values of the expressions given as tests. Nevertheless, even in such loops, the flow of control does not usually depend on the values of expressions given in the body of the loop.

In some cases, however, you may need to construct *Mathematica* programs in which the flow of control is affected by values generated during the execution of a procedure or of the body of a loop. One way to do this, which fits in with functional programming ideas, is to use `Throw` and `Catch`. But *Mathematica* also provides various functions for modifying the flow of control which work like in languages such as C.

`Break[ ]`	exit the nearest enclosing loop
`Continue[ ]`	go to the next step in the current loop
`Return[`*expr*`]`	return the value *expr*, exiting all procedures and loops in a function
`Goto[`*name*`]`	go to the element `Label[`*name*`]` in the current procedure
`Throw[`*value*`]`	return *value* as the value of the nearest enclosing `Catch` (non-local return)

Control flow functions.

The `Break[ ]` causes the loop to terminate as soon as `t` exceeds 19.	*In[31]:=* `t = 1; Do[t *= k; Print[t];`
	`        If[t > 19, Break[]], {k, 10}]`
	
	`1`
	`2`
	`6`
	`24`

When k < 3, the `Continue[ ]` causes the loop to be continued, without executing t += 2.

```
In[32]:= t = 1; Do[t *= k; Print[t];
             If[k < 3, Continue[]]; t += 2, {k, 10}]
1
2
6
32
170
1032
7238
57920
521298
5213000
```

`Return[`*expr*`]` allows you to exit a particular function, returning a value. You can think of `Throw` as a kind of non-local return which allows you to exit a whole sequence of nested functions. Such behavior can be convenient for handling certain error conditions.

Here is an example of the use of `Return`. This particular procedure could equally well have been written without using `Return`.

```
In[33]:= f[x_] :=
             (If[x > 5, Return[big]]; t = x^3; Return[t - 7])
```

When the argument is greater than 5, the first `Return` in the procedure is used.

```
In[34]:= f[10]
Out[34]= big
```

This function "throws" error if its argument is negative.

```
In[35]:= h[x_] := If[x < 0, Throw[error], Sqrt[x]]
```

No `Throw` is generated here.

```
In[36]:= Catch[ h[6] + 2 ]
Out[36]= 2 + √6
```

But in this case a `Throw` is generated, and the whole `Catch` returns the value error.

```
In[37]:= Catch[ h[-6] + 2 ]
Out[37]= error
```

Functions like `Continue[ ]` and `Break[ ]` allow you to "transfer control" to the beginning or end of a loop in a *Mathematica* program. Sometimes you may instead need to transfer control to a particular element in a *Mathematica* procedure. If you give a `Label` as an element in a procedure, you can use `Goto` to transfer control to this element.

This goes on looping until q exceeds 6.

```
In[38]:= (q = 2; Label[begin]; Print[q]; q += 3;
             If[q < 6, Goto[begin]])
2
5
```

Note that you can use `Goto` in a particular *Mathematica* procedure only when the `Label` it specifies occurs as an element of the same *Mathematica* procedure. In general, use of `Goto` reduces the degree of structure that can readily be perceived in a program, and therefore makes the operation of the program more difficult to understand.

■ 2.5.10 Tracing Evaluation

The standard way in which *Mathematica* works is to take any expression you give as input, evaluate the expression completely, and then return the result. When you are trying to understand what *Mathematica* is doing, however, it is often worthwhile to look not just at the final result of evaluation, but also at intermediate steps in the evaluation process.

Trace[*expr*]	generate a list of all expressions used in the evaluation of *expr*
Trace[*expr*, *form*]	include only expressions which match the pattern *form*

Tracing the evaluation of expressions.

The expression 1 + 1 is evaluated immediately to 2.

In[1]:= **Trace[1 + 1]**

Out[1]= {1 + 1, 2}

The 2^3 is evaluated before the addition is done.

In[2]:= **Trace[2^3 + 4]**

Out[2]= {{2^3, 8}, 8 + 4, 12}

The evaluation of each subexpression is shown in a separate sublist.

In[3]:= **Trace[2^3 + 4^2 + 1]**

Out[3]= {{2^3, 8}, {4^2, 16}, 8 + 16 + 1, 25}

Trace[*expr*] gives a list which includes *all* the intermediate expressions involved in the evaluation of *expr*. Except in rather simple cases, however, the number of intermediate expressions generated in this way is typically very large, and the list returned by Trace is difficult to understand.

Trace[*expr*, *form*] allows you to "filter" the expressions that Trace records, keeping only those which match the pattern *form*.

Here is a recursive definition of a factorial function.

In[4]:= **fac[n_] := n fac[n-1]; fac[1] = 1**

Out[4]= 1

This gives *all* the intermediate expressions generated in the evaluation of fac[3]. The result is quite complicated.

In[5]:= **Trace[fac[3]]**

Out[5]= {fac[3], 3 fac[3 − 1], {{3 − 1, 2}, fac[2], 2 fac[2 − 1], {{2 − 1, 1}, fac[1], 1}, 2 1, 2}, 3 2, 6}

This shows only intermediate expressions of the form fac[n_].

In[6]:= **Trace[fac[3], fac[n_]]**

Out[6]= {fac[3], {fac[2], {fac[1]}}}

You can specify any pattern in Trace.

In[7]:= **Trace[fac[10], fac[n_/;n > 5]]**

Out[7]= {fac[10], {fac[9], {fac[8], {fac[7], {fac[6]}}}}}

Trace[*expr*, *form*] effectively works by intercepting every expression that is about to be evaluated during the evaluation of *expr*, and picking out those that match the pattern *form*.

If you want to trace "calls" to a function like `fac`, you can do so simply by telling `Trace` to pick out expressions of the form `fac[n_]`. You can also use patterns like `f[n_, 2]` to pick out calls with particular argument structure.

A typical *Mathematica* program, however, consists not only of "function calls" like `fac[n]`, but also of other elements, such as assignments to variables, control structures, and so on. All of these elements are represented as expressions. As a result, you can use patterns in `Trace` to pick out any kind of *Mathematica* program element. Thus, for example, you can use a pattern like `k = _` to pick out all assignments to the symbol `k`.

This shows the sequence of assignments made for k.	*In[8]:=* `Trace[(k=2; For[i=1, i<4, i++, k = i/k]; k), k=_]`
	Out[8]= $\left\{ \{k = 2\}, \left\{ \left\{k = \frac{1}{2}\right\}, \{k = 4\}, \left\{k = \frac{3}{4}\right\} \right\} \right\}$

`Trace[`*expr*`, `*form*`]` can pick out expressions that occur at any time in the evaluation of *expr*. The expressions need not, for example, appear directly in the form of *expr* that you give. They may instead occur, say, during the evaluation of functions that are called as part of the evaluation of *expr*.

Here is a function definition.	*In[9]:=* `h[n_] := (k=n/2; Do[k = i/k, {i, n}]; k)`
You can look for expressions generated during the evaluation of h.	*In[10]:=* `Trace[h[3], k=_]`
	Out[10]= $\left\{ \left\{k = \frac{3}{2}\right\}, \left\{ \left\{k = \frac{2}{3}\right\}, \{k = 3\}, \{k = 1\} \right\} \right\}$

`Trace` allows you to monitor intermediate steps in the evaluation not only of functions that you define, but also of some functions that are built into *Mathematica*. You should realize, however, that the specific sequence of intermediate steps followed by built-in *Mathematica* functions depends in detail on their implementation and optimization in a particular version of *Mathematica*.

`Trace[`*expr*`, `*f*`[___]]`	show all calls to the function *f*
`Trace[`*expr*`, `*i*` = _]`	show assignments to *i*
`Trace[`*expr*`, _ = _]`	show all assignments
`Trace[`*expr*`, Message[___]]`	show messages generated

Some ways to use Trace.

The function `Trace` returns a list that represents the "history" of a *Mathematica* computation. The expressions in the list are given in the order that they were generated during the computation. In most cases, the list returned by `Trace` has a nested structure, which represents the "structure" of the computation.

The basic idea is that each sublist in the list returned by `Trace` represents the "evaluation chain" for a particular *Mathematica* expression. The elements of this chain correspond to different forms of the same expression. Usually, however, the evaluation of one expression requires the evaluation of a number of other expressions, often subexpressions. Each subsidiary evaluation is represented by a sublist in the structure returned by `Trace`.

Here is a sequence of assignments.	*In[11]:=* **a[1] = a[2]; a[2] = a[3]; a[3] = a[4]**
	Out[11]= a[4]

This yields an evaluation chain reflecting the sequence of transformations for a[*i*] used.	*In[12]:=* **Trace[a[1]]**
	Out[12]= {a[1], a[2], a[3], a[4]}

The successive forms generated in the simplification of y + x + y show up as successive elements in its evaluation chain.	*In[13]:=* **Trace[y + x + y]**
	Out[13]= {y + x + y, x + y + y, x + 2y}

Each argument of the function f has a separate evaluation chain, given in a sublist.	*In[14]:=* **Trace[f[1 + 1, 2 + 3, 4 + 5]]**
	Out[14]= {{1 + 1, 2}, {2 + 3, 5}, {4 + 5, 9}, f[2, 5, 9]}

The evaluation chain for each subexpression is given in a separate sublist.	*In[15]:=* **Trace[x x + y y]**
	Out[15]= {{x x, x^2}, {y y, y^2}, $x^2 + y^2$}

Tracing the evaluation of a nested expression yields a nested list.	*In[16]:=* **Trace[f[f[f[1 + 1]]]]**
	Out[16]= {{{{1 + 1, 2}, f[2]}, f[f[2]]}, f[f[f[2]]]}

There are two basic ways that subsidiary evaluations can be required during the evaluation of a *Mathematica* expression. The first way is that the expression may contain subexpressions, each of which has to be evaluated. The second way is that there may be rules for the evaluation of the expression that involve other expressions which themselves must be evaluated. Both kinds of subsidiary evaluations are represented by sublists in the structure returned by `Trace`.

The subsidiary evaluations here come from evaluation of the arguments of f and g.	*In[17]:=* **Trace[f[g[1 + 1], 2 + 3]]**
	Out[17]= {{{1 + 1, 2}, g[2]}, {2 + 3, 5}, f[g[2], 5]}

Here is a function with a condition attached.	*In[18]:=* **fe[n_] := n + 1 /; EvenQ[n]**

The evaluation of fe[6] involves a subsidiary evaluation associated with the condition.	*In[19]:=* **Trace[fe[6]]**
	Out[19]= {fe[6], {{EvenQ[6], True}, RuleCondition[
	$ConditionHold[$ConditionHold[6 + 1]], True],
	$ConditionHold[$ConditionHold[6 + 1]]},
	6 + 1, 7}

You often get nested lists when you trace the evaluation of functions that are defined "recursively" in terms of other instances of themselves. The reason is typically that each new instance of the function appears as a subexpression in the expressions obtained by evaluating previous instances of the function.

Thus, for example, with the definition `fac[n_] := n fac[n-1]`, the evaluation of `fac[6]` yields the expression `6 fac[5]`, which contains `fac[5]` as a subexpression.

The successive instances of `fac` generated appear in successively nested sublists.

In[20]:= **Trace[fac[6], fac[_]]**

Out[20]= {fac[6], {fac[5],
                        {fac[4], {fac[3], {fac[2], {fac[1]}}}}}}

With this definition, fp[*n*-1] is obtained directly as the value of fp[*n*].

In[21]:= **fp[n_] := fp[n - 1] /; n > 1**

fp[*n*] never appears in a subexpression, so no sublists are generated.

In[22]:= **Trace[fp[6], fp[_]]**

Out[22]= {fp[6], fp[6 - 1], fp[5], fp[5 - 1], fp[4], fp[4 - 1],
                fp[3], fp[3 - 1], fp[2], fp[2 - 1], fp[1]}

Here is the recursive definition of the Fibonacci numbers.

In[23]:= **fib[n_] := fib[n - 1] + fib[n - 2]**

Here are the end conditions for the recursion.

In[24]:= **fib[0] = fib[1] = 1**

Out[24]= 1

This shows all the steps in the recursive evaluation of fib[5].

In[25]:= **Trace[fib[5], fib[_]]**

Out[25]= {fib[5], {fib[4], {fib[3],
                    {fib[2], {fib[1]}, {fib[0]}}, {fib[1]}},
                    {fib[2], {fib[1]}, {fib[0]}}},
                    {fib[3], {fib[2], {fib[1]}, {fib[0]}}, {fib[1]}}}

Each step in the evaluation of any *Mathematica* expression can be thought of as the result of applying a particular transformation rule. As discussed in Section 2.4.10, all the rules that *Mathematica* knows are associated with specific symbols or "tags". You can use `Trace[`*expr*`, `*f*`]` to see all the steps in the evaluation of *expr* that are performed using transformation rules associated with the symbol *f*. In this case, `Trace` gives not only the expressions to which each rule is applied, but also the results of applying the rules.

In general, `Trace[`*expr*`, `*form*`]` picks out all the steps in the evaluation of *expr* where *form* matches *either* the expression about to be evaluated, *or* the tag associated with the rule used.

`Trace[`*expr*`, `*f*`]`	show all evaluations which use transformation rules associated with the symbol *f*
`Trace[`*expr*`, `*f* | *g*`]`	show all evaluations associated with either *f* or *g*

Tracing evaluations associated with particular tags.

This shows only intermediate expressions that match fac[_].

In[26]:= **Trace[fac[3], fac[_]]**

Out[26]= {fac[3], {fac[2], {fac[1]}}}

This shows all evaluations that use transformation rules associated with the symbol `fac`.	*In[27]:=* `Trace[fac[3], fac]` *Out[27]=* {fac[3], 3 fac[3 - 1], {fac[2], 2 fac[2 - 1], {fac[1], 1}}}
Here is a rule for the `log` function.	*In[28]:=* `log[x_ y_] := log[x] + log[y]`
This traces the evaluation of `log[a b c d]`, showing all transformations associated with `log`.	*In[29]:=* `Trace[log[a b c d], log]` *Out[29]=* {log[a b c d], log[a] + log[b c d], {log[b c d], log[b] + log[c d], {log[c d], log[c] + log[d]}}}

`Trace[`*expr*`,` *form*`, TraceOn ->` *oform*`]`
         switch on tracing only within forms matching *oform*

`Trace[`*expr*`,` *form*`, TraceOff ->` *oform*`]`
         switch off tracing within any form matching *oform*

Switching off tracing inside certain forms.

`Trace[`*expr*`,` *form*`]` allows you to trace expressions matching *form* generated at any point in the evaluation of *expr*. Sometimes, you may want to trace only expressions generated during certain parts of the evaluation of *expr*.

By setting the option `TraceOn ->` *oform*, you can specify that tracing should be done only during the evaluation of forms which match *oform*. Similarly, by setting `TraceOff ->` *oform*, you can specify that tracing should be switched off during the evaluation of forms which match *oform*.

This shows all steps in the evaluation.	*In[30]:=* `Trace[log[fac[2] x]]`
	Out[30]= {{{fac[2], 2 fac[2 - 1],
	                {{2 - 1, 1}, fac[1], 1}, 21, 2}, 2 x},
	              log[2 x], log[2] + log[x]}

This shows only those steps that occur during the evaluation of `fac`.	*In[31]:=* `Trace[log[fac[2] x], TraceOn -> fac]` *Out[31]=* {{{fac[2], 2 fac[2 - 1], {{2 - 1, 1}, fac[1], 1}, 21, 2}}}
This shows only those steps that do not occur during the evaluation of `fac`.	*In[32]:=* `Trace[log[fac[2] x], TraceOff -> fac]` *Out[32]=* {{{fac[2], 2}, 2 x}, log[2 x], log[2] + log[x]}

`Trace[`*expr*`,` *lhs* `->` *rhs*`]`   find all expressions matching *lhs* that arise during the evaluation of *expr*, and replace them with *rhs*

Applying rules to expressions encountered during evaluation.

This tells Trace to return only the arguments of fib used in the evaluation of fib[5].

```
In[33]:= Trace[fib[5], fib[n_] -> n]
Out[33]= {5, {4, {3, {2, {1}, {0}}, {1}}, {2, {1}, {0}}},
          {3, {2, {1}, {0}}, {1}}}
```

A powerful aspect of the *Mathematica* Trace function is that the object it returns is basically a standard *Mathematica* expression which you can manipulate using other *Mathematica* functions. One important point to realize, however, is that Trace wraps all expressions that appear in the list it produces with HoldForm to prevent them from being evaluated. The HoldForm is not displayed in standard *Mathematica* output format, but it is still present in the internal structure of the expression.

This shows the expressions generated at intermediate stages in the evaluation process.

```
In[34]:= Trace[1 + 3^2]
Out[34]= {{3^2, 9}, 1 + 9, 10}
```

The expressions are wrapped with HoldForm to prevent them from evaluating.

```
In[35]:= Trace[1 + 3^2] // InputForm
Out[35]//InputForm= {{HoldForm[3^2], HoldForm[9]}, HoldForm[1 + 9],
          HoldForm[10]}
```

In standard *Mathematica* output format, it is sometimes difficult to tell which lists are associated with the structure returned by Trace, and which are expressions being evaluated.

```
In[36]:= Trace[{1 + 1, 2 + 3}]
Out[36]= {{1 + 1, 2}, {2 + 3, 5}, {2, 5}}
```

Looking at the input form resolves any ambiguities.

```
In[37]:= InputForm[%]
Out[37]//InputForm= {{HoldForm[1 + 1], HoldForm[2]},
          {HoldForm[2 + 3], HoldForm[5]}, HoldForm[{2, 5}]}
```

When you use a transformation rule in Trace, the result is evaluated before being wrapped with HoldForm.

```
In[38]:= Trace[fac[4], fac[n_] -> n + 1]
Out[38]= {5, {4, {3, {2}}}}
```

For sophisticated computations, the list structures returned by Trace can be quite complicated. When you use Trace[*expr*, *form*], Trace will include as elements in the lists only those expressions which match the pattern *form*. But whatever pattern you give, the nesting structure of the lists remains the same.

This shows all occurrences of fib[_] in the evaluation of fib[3].

```
In[39]:= Trace[fib[3], fib[_]]
Out[39]= {fib[3], {fib[2], {fib[1]}, {fib[0]}}, {fib[1]}}
```

This shows only occurrences of fib[1], but the nesting of the lists is the same as for fib[_].

```
In[40]:= Trace[fib[3], fib[1]]
Out[40]= {{{fib[1]}}, {fib[1]}}
```

You can set the option TraceDepth -> *n* to tell Trace to include only lists nested at most *n* levels deep. In this way, you can often pick out the "big steps" in a computation, without seeing the details. Note that by setting TraceDepth or TraceOff you can avoid looking at many of the steps in a computation, and thereby significantly speed up the operation of Trace for that computation.

This shows only steps that appear in
lists nested at most two levels deep.

In[41]:= **Trace[fib[3], fib[_], TraceDepth->2]**

Out[41]= {fib[3], {fib[2]}, {fib[1]}}

Trace[*expr*, *form*, TraceDepth -> *n*]
                       trace the evaluation of *expr*, ignoring steps that lead to lists
                       nested more than *n* levels deep

Restricting the depth of tracing.

When you use Trace[*expr*, *form*], you get a list of all the expressions which match *form* produced during the evaluation of *expr*. Sometimes it is useful to see not only these expressions, but also the results that were obtained by evaluating them. You can do this by setting the option TraceForward -> True in Trace.

This shows not only expressions which
match fac[_], but also the results of
evaluating those expressions.

In[42]:= **Trace[fac[4], fac[_], TraceForward->True]**

Out[42]= {fac[4], {fac[3], {fac[2], {fac[1], 1}, 2}, 6}, 24}

Expressions picked out using Trace[*expr*, *form*] typically lie in the middle of an evaluation chain. By setting TraceForward -> True, you tell Trace to include also the expression obtained at the end of the evaluation chain. If you set TraceForward -> All, Trace will include *all* the expressions that occur after the expression matching *form* on the evaluation chain.

With TraceForward->All, all elements
on the evaluation chain after the one
that matches fac[_] are included.

In[43]:= **Trace[fac[4], fac[_], TraceForward->All]**

Out[43]= {fac[4], 4 fac[4 - 1], {fac[3], 3 fac[3 - 1],
            {fac[2], 2 fac[2 - 1], {fac[1], 1}, 21, 2}, 32, 6},
       46, 24}

By setting the option TraceForward, you can effectively see what happens to a particular form of expression during an evaluation. Sometimes, however, you want to find out not what happens to a particular expression, but instead how that expression was generated. You can do this by setting the option TraceBackward. What TraceBackward does is to show you what *preceded* a particular form of expression on an evaluation chain.

This shows that the number 120 came
from the evaluation of fac[5] during
the evaluation of fac[10].

In[44]:= **Trace[fac[10], 120, TraceBackward->True]**

Out[44]= {{{{{{fac[5], 120}}}}}}

Here is the whole evaluation chain
associated with the generation of the
number 120.

In[45]:= **Trace[fac[10], 120, TraceBackward->All]**

Out[45]= {{{{{{fac[5], 5 fac[5 - 1], 5 24, 120}}}}}}

TraceForward and TraceBackward allow you to look forward and backward in a particular evaluation chain. Sometimes, you may also want to look at the evaluation chains within which the particular evaluation chain occurs. You can do this using TraceAbove. If you set the option TraceAbove -> True, then Trace will include the initial and final expressions in all the relevant evaluation chains. With TraceAbove -> All, Trace includes all the expressions in all these evaluation chains.

This includes the initial and final expressions in all evaluation chains which contain the chain that contains 120.

In[46]:= **Trace[fac[7], 120, TraceAbove->True]**

Out[46]= {fac[7], {fac[6], {fac[5], 120}, 720}, 5040}

This shows all the ways that fib[2] is generated during the evaluation of fib[5].

In[47]:= **Trace[fib[5], fib[2], TraceAbove->True]**

Out[47]= {fib[5], {fib[4],
       {fib[3], {fib[2], 2}, 3}, {fib[2], 2}, 5},
      {fib[3], {fib[2], 2}, 3}, 8}

Trace[*expr*, *form*, *opts*]	trace the evaluation of *expr* using the specified options
TraceForward -> True	include the final expression in the evaluation chain containing *form*
TraceForward -> All	include all expressions following *form* in the evaluation chain
TraceBackward -> True	include the first expression in the evaluation chain containing *form*
TraceBackward -> All	include all expressions preceding *form* in the evaluation chain
TraceAbove -> True	include the first and last expressions in all evaluation chains which contain the chain containing *form*
TraceAbove -> All	include all expressions in all evaluation chains which contain the chain containing *form*

Option settings for including extra steps in trace lists.

The basic way that Trace[*expr*, ...] works is to intercept each expression encountered during the evaluation of *expr*, and then to use various criteria to determine whether this expression should be recorded. Normally, however, Trace intercepts expressions only *after* function arguments have been evaluated. By setting TraceOriginal -> True, you can get Trace also to look at expressions *before* function arguments have been evaluated.

This includes expressions which match fac[_] both before and after argument evaluation.

In[48]:= **Trace[fac[3], fac[_], TraceOriginal -> True]**

Out[48]= {fac[3], {fac[3 - 1], fac[2], {fac[2 - 1], fac[1]}}}

The list structure produced by Trace normally includes only expressions that constitute steps in non-trivial evaluation chains. Thus, for example, individual symbols that evaluate to themselves are not normally included. Nevertheless, if you set TraceOriginal -> True, then Trace looks at absolutely every expression involved in the evaluation process, including those that have trivial evaluation chains.

In this case, Trace includes absolutely all expressions, even those with trivial evaluation chains.

In[49]:= **Trace[fac[1], TraceOriginal -> True]**

Out[49]= {fac[1], {fac}, {1}, fac[1], 1}

option name	default value	
TraceForward	False	whether to show expressions following *form* in the evaluation chain
TraceBackward	False	whether to show expressions preceding *form* in the evaluation chain
TraceAbove	False	whether to show evaluation chains leading to the evaluation chain containing *form*
TraceOriginal	False	whether to look at expressions before their heads and arguments are evaluated

Additional options for Trace.

When you use Trace to study the execution of a program, there is an issue about how local variables in the program should be treated. As discussed in Section 2.6.3, *Mathematica* scoping constructs such as Module create symbols with new names to represent local variables. Thus, even if you called a variable x in the original code for your program, the variable may effectively be renamed x$*nnn* when the program is executed.

Trace[*expr*, *form*] is set up so that by default a symbol *x* that appears in *form* will match all symbols with names of the form *x*$*nnn* that arise in the execution of *expr*. As a result, you can for example use Trace[*expr*, x = _] to trace assignment to all variables, local and global, that were named *x* in your original program.

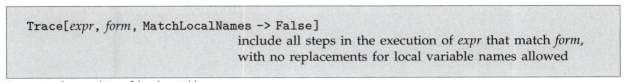

Trace[*expr*, *form*, MatchLocalNames -> False]
                      include all steps in the execution of *expr* that match *form*, with no replacements for local variable names allowed

Preventing the matching of local variables.

In some cases, you may want to trace only the global variable *x*, and not any local variables that were originally named *x*. You can do this by setting the option MatchLocalNames -> False.

This traces assignments to all variables with names of the form x$*nnn*.

In[50]:= `Trace[Module[{x}, x = 5], x = _]`

Out[50]= `{{x$1 = 5}}`

This traces assignments only to the specific global variable *x*.

In[51]:= `Trace[Module[{x}, x = 5], x = _,`
`                    MatchLocalNames -> False]`

Out[51]= `{}`

The function `Trace` performs a complete computation, then returns a structure which represents the history of the computation. Particularly in very long computations, it is however sometimes useful to see traces of the computation as it proceeds. The function `TracePrint` works essentially like `Trace`, except that it prints expressions when it encounters them, rather than saving up all of the expressions to create a list structure.

This prints expressions encountered in the evaluation of `fib[3]`.

In[52]:= `TracePrint[fib[3], fib[_]]`

```
fib[3]

 fib[3 - 1]

 fib[2]

  fib[2 - 1]

  fib[1]

  fib[2 - 2]

  fib[0]

 fib[3 - 2]

 fib[1]
```

Out[52]= `3`

The sequence of expressions printed by `TracePrint` corresponds to the sequence of expressions given in the list structure returned by `Trace`. Indentation in the output from `TracePrint` corresponds to nesting in the list structure from `Trace`. You can use the `Trace` options `TraceOn`, `TraceOff` and `TraceForward` in `TracePrint`. However, since `TracePrint` produces output as it goes, it cannot support the option `TraceBackward`. In addition, `TracePrint` is set up so that `TraceOriginal` is effectively always set to `True`.

Trace[*expr*, ...]	trace the evaluation of *expr*, returning a list structure containing the expressions encountered
TracePrint[*expr*, ...]	trace the evaluation of *expr*, printing the expressions encountered
TraceDialog[*expr*, ...]	trace the evaluation of *expr*, initiating a dialog when each specified expression is encountered
TraceScan[*f*, *expr*, ...]	trace the evaluation of *expr*, applying *f* to HoldForm of each expression encountered

Functions for tracing evaluation.

This enters a dialog when fac[5] is encountered during the evaluation of fac[10].

```
In[53]:= TraceDialog[fac[10], fac[5]]
TraceDialog::dgbgn: Entering Dialog; use Return[] to exit.
Out[54]= fac[5]
```

Inside the dialog you can for example find out where you are by looking at the "stack".

```
In[55]:= Stack[ ]
Out[55]= {TraceDialog, Times, Times, Times,
            Times, Times, fac}
```

This returns from the dialog, and gives the final result from the evaluation of fac[10].

```
In[56]:= Return[ ]
TraceDialog::dgend: Exiting Dialog.
Out[53]= 3628800
```

The function TraceDialog effectively allows you to stop in the middle of a computation, and interact with the *Mathematica* environment that exists at that time. You can for example find values of intermediate variables in the computation, and even reset those values. There are however a number of subtleties, mostly associated with pattern and module variables.

What TraceDialog does is to call the function Dialog on a sequence of expressions. The Dialog function is discussed in detail in Section 2.13.2. When you call Dialog, you are effectively starting a subsidiary *Mathematica* session with its own sequence of input and output lines.

In general, you may need to apply arbitrary functions to the expressions you get while tracing an evaluation. TraceScan[*f*, *expr*, ...] applies *f* to each expression that arises. The expression is wrapped with HoldForm to prevent it from evaluating.

In TraceScan[*f*, *expr*, ...], the function *f* is applied to expressions before they are evaluated. TraceScan[*f*, *expr*, *patt*, *fp*] applies *f* before evaluation, and *fp* after evaluation.

■ 2.5.11 Advanced Topic: The Evaluation Stack

Throughout any computation, *Mathematica* maintains an *evaluation stack* containing the expressions it is currently evaluating. You can use the function `Stack` to look at the stack. This means, for example, that if you interrupt *Mathematica* in the middle of a computation, you can use `Stack` to find out what *Mathematica* is doing.

The expression that *Mathematica* most recently started to evaluate always appears as the last element of the evaluation stack. The previous elements of the stack are the other expressions whose evaluation is currently in progress.

Thus at the point when x is being evaluated, the stack associated with the evaluation of an expression like $f[g[x]]$ will have the form $\{f[g[x]], g[x], x\}$.

`Stack[_]` gives the expressions that are being evaluated at the time when it is called, in this case including the `Print` function.	`In[1]:= f[g[ Print[Stack[_]] ]] ;`
	`{f[g[Print[Stack[_]]]]; , f[g[Print[Stack[_]]]],`
	` g[Print[Stack[_]]], Print[Stack[_]]}`

`Stack[ ]` gives the tags associated with the evaluations that are being done when it is called.	`In[2]:= f[g[ Print[Stack[ ]] ]] ;` `{CompoundExpression, f, g, Print}`

In general, you can think of the evaluation stack as showing what functions called what other functions to get to the point *Mathematica* is at in your computation. The sequence of expressions corresponds to the first elements in the successively nested lists returned by `Trace` with the option `TraceAbove` set to `True`.

`Stack[ ]`	give a list of the tags associated with evaluations that are currently being done
`Stack[_]`	give a list of all expressions currently being evaluated
`Stack[form]`	include only expressions which match *form*

Looking at the evaluation stack.

It is rather rare to call `Stack` directly in your main *Mathematica* session. More often, you will want to call `Stack` in the middle of a computation. Typically, you can do this from within a dialog, or subsidiary session, as discussed in Section 2.13.2.

Here is the standard recursive definition of the factorial function.	`In[3]:= fac[1] = 1; fac[n_] := n fac[n-1]`

This evaluates fac[10], starting a dialog when it encounters fac[4].	`In[4]:= TraceDialog[fac[10], fac[4]]`
	`TraceDialog::dgbgn: Entering Dialog; use Return[] to exit.`
	
	`Out[5]= fac[4]`

This shows what objects were being evaluated when the dialog was started.	*In[6]:=* **Stack[ ]** *Out[6]=* {TraceDialog, Times, Times, Times, Times, Times, fac}
This ends the dialog.	*In[7]:=* **Return[ ]** TraceDialog::dgend: Exiting Dialog. *Out[4]=* 3628800

In the simplest cases, the *Mathematica* evaluation stack is set up to record *all* expressions currently being evaluated. Under some circumstances, however, this may be inconvenient. For example, executing Print[Stack[ ]] will always show a stack with Print as the last function.

The function StackInhibit allows you to avoid this kind of problem. StackInhibit[*expr*] evaluates *expr* without modifying the stack.

StackInhibit prevents Print from being included on the stack.	*In[5]:=* **f[g[StackInhibit[Print[Stack[ ]]]]] ;** {CompoundExpression, f, g}

Functions like TraceDialog automatically call StackInhibit each time they start a dialog. This means that Stack does not show functions that are called within the dialog, only those outside.

StackInhibit[*expr*]	evaluate *expr* without modifying the stack
StackBegin[*expr*]	evaluate *expr* with a fresh stack
StackComplete[*expr*]	evaluate *expr* with intermediate expressions in evaluation chains included on the stack

Controlling the evaluation stack.

By using StackInhibit and StackBegin, you can control which parts of the evaluation process are recorded on the stack. StackBegin[*expr*] evaluates *expr*, starting a fresh stack. This means that during the evaluation of *expr*, the stack does not include anything outside the StackBegin. Functions like TraceDialog[*expr*, ...] call StackBegin before they begin evaluating *expr*, so that the stack shows how *expr* is evaluated, but not how TraceDialog was called.

StackBegin[*expr*] uses a fresh stack in the evaluation of *expr*.	*In[6]:=* **f[StackBegin[g[h[StackInhibit[Print[Stack[ ]]]]]]]** {g, h} *Out[6]=* f[g[h[Null]]]

Stack normally shows you only those expressions that are currently being evaluated. As a result, it includes only the latest form of each expression. Sometimes, however, you may find it useful also to see earlier forms of the expressions. You can do this using StackComplete.

What StackComplete[*expr*] effectively does is to keep on the stack the complete evaluation chain for each expression that is currently being evaluated. In this case, the stack corresponds to the sequence of expressions obtained from `Trace` with the option `TraceBackward -> All` as well as `TraceAbove -> True`.

■ 2.5.12 Advanced Topic: Controlling Infinite Evaluation

The general principle that *Mathematica* follows in evaluating expressions is to go on applying transformation rules until the expressions no longer change. This means, for example, that if you make an assignment like x = x + 1, *Mathematica* should go into an infinite loop. In fact, *Mathematica* stops after a definite number of steps, determined by the value of the global variable `$RecursionLimit`. You can always stop *Mathematica* earlier by explicitly interrupting it.

This assignment could cause an infinite loop. *Mathematica* stops after a number of steps determined by `$RecursionLimit`.

```
In[1]:= x = x + 1
```
$RecursionLimit::reclim: Recursion depth of 256 exceeded.
```
Out[1]= 255 + Hold[1 + x]
```

When *Mathematica* stops without finishing evaluation, it returns a held result. You can continue the evaluation by explicitly calling `ReleaseHold`.

```
In[2]:= ReleaseHold[%]
```
$RecursionLimit::reclim: Recursion depth of 256 exceeded.
```
Out[2]= 510 + Hold[1 + x]
```

`$RecursionLimit`	maximum depth of the evaluation stack
`$IterationLimit`	maximum length of an evaluation chain

Global variables that limit infinite evaluation.

Here is a circular definition, whose evaluation is stopped by `$IterationLimit`.

```
In[3]:= {a, b} = {b, a}
```
$IterationLimit::itlim: Iteration limit of 4096 exceeded.

$IterationLimit::itlim: Iteration limit of 4096 exceeded.
```
Out[3]= {Hold[b], Hold[a]}
```

The variables `$RecursionLimit` and `$IterationLimit` control the two basic ways that an evaluation can become infinite in *Mathematica*. `$RecursionLimit` limits the maximum depth of the evaluation stack, or equivalently, the maximum nesting depth that would occur in the list structure produced by `Trace`. `$IterationLimit` limits the maximum length of any particular evaluation chain, or the maximum length of any single list in the structure produced by `Trace`.

Functions such as `FixedPoint`, `Do` and `ReplaceRepeated` (the `//.` operator) use the global value of `$IterationLimit` as the default setting for their own `IterationLimit` option, which determines the maximum number of iterations they will allow.

`$RecursionLimit` and `$IterationLimit` are by default set to values that are appropriate for most computations, and most computer systems. You can, however, reset these variables to any integer (above a lower limit), or to `Infinity`. Note that on most computer systems, you should never set `$RecursionLimit = Infinity`, as discussed on page 687.

This resets `$RecursionLimit` and `$IterationLimit` to 20.	`In[4]:= `**`$RecursionLimit = $IterationLimit = 20`** `Out[4]= 20`

Now infinite definitions like this are stopped after just 20 steps.	`In[5]:= `**`t = {t}`**
	
	`$RecursionLimit::reclim: Recursion depth of 20 exceeded.`
	
	`Out[5]= {{{{{{{{{{{{{{{{{{Hold[{t}]}}}}}}}}}}}}}}}}}}}`

Without an end condition, this recursive definition leads to infinite computations.	`In[6]:= `**`fn[n_] := {fn[n-1], n}`**

A fairly large structure is built up before the computation is stopped.	`In[7]:= `**`fn[10]`**
	
	`$RecursionLimit::reclim: Recursion depth of 20 exceeded.`
	
	`Out[7]= {{{{{{{{{{{{{{{{{{{Hold[fn[-8 - 1]], -8}, -7},`
	`                      -6}, -5}, -4}, -3}, -2},`
	`               -1}, 0}, 1},`
	`            2},`
	`           3},`
	`          4},`
	`         5},`
	`        6},`
	`       7},`
	`      8},`
	`     9},`
	`    10}`

Here is another recursive definition.	`In[8]:= `**`fm[n_] := fm[n - 1]`**

In this case, no complicated structure is built up, and the computation is stopped by `$IterationLimit`.	`In[9]:= `**`fm[0]`**
	
	`$IterationLimit::itlim: Iteration limit of 20 exceeded.`
	
	`Out[9]= Hold[fm[-19 - 1]]`

It is important to realize that infinite loops can take up not only time but also computer memory. Computations limited by `$IterationLimit` do not normally build up large intermediate structures. But those limited by `$RecursionLimit` often do. In many cases, the size of the structures produced is a linear function of the value of `$RecursionLimit`. But in some cases, the size can grow exponentially, or worse, with `$RecursionLimit`.

An assignment like `x = x + 1` is obviously circular. When you set up more complicated recursive definitions, however, it can be much more difficult to be sure that the recursion terminates, and that you will not end up in an infinite loop. The main thing to check is that the right-hand sides of your transformation rules will always be different from the left-hand sides. This ensures that evaluation will always "make progress", and *Mathematica* will not simply end up applying the same transformation rule to the same expression over and over again.

Some of the trickiest cases occur when you have rules that depend on complicated /; conditions (see Section 2.3.5). One particularly awkward case is when the condition involves a "global variable". *Mathematica* may think that the evaluation is finished because the expression did not change. However, a side effect of some other operation could change the value of the global variable, and so should lead to a new result in the evaluation. The best way to avoid this kind of difficulty is not to use global variables in /; conditions. If all else fails, you can type Update[*s*] to tell *Mathematica* to update all expressions involving *s*. Update[ ] tells *Mathematica* to update absolutely all expressions.

■ 2.5.13 Advanced Topic: Interrupts and Aborts

Section 1.3.12 described how you can interrupt a *Mathematica* computation by pressing appropriate keys on your keyboard.

In some cases, you may want to simulate such interrupts from within a *Mathematica* program. In general, executing Interrupt[ ] has the same effect as pressing interrupt keys. On a typical system, a menu of options is displayed, as discussed in Section 1.3.12.

Interrupt[ ]	interrupt a computation
Abort[ ]	abort a computation
CheckAbort[*expr*, *failexpr*]	evaluate *expr* and return the result, or *failexpr* if an abort occurs
AbortProtect[*expr*]	evaluate *expr*, masking the effect of aborts until the evaluation is complete

Interrupts and aborts.

The function Abort[ ] has the same effect as interrupting a computation, and selecting the abort option in the interrupt menu.

You can use Abort[ ] to implement an "emergency stop" in a program. In almost all cases, however, you should try to use functions like Return and Throw, which lead to more controlled behavior.

Abort terminates the computation, so only the first Print is executed.

In[1]:= **Print[a]; Abort[ ]; Print[b]**

a

Out[1]= $Aborted

If you abort at any point during the evaluation of a *Mathematica* expression, *Mathematica* normally abandons the evaluation of the whole expression, and returns the value $Aborted.

You can, however, "catch" aborts using the function CheckAbort. If an abort occurs during the evaluation of *expr* in CheckAbort[*expr*, *failexpr*], then CheckAbort returns *failexpr*, but the abort propagates no further. Functions like Dialog use CheckAbort in this way to contain the effect of aborts.

CheckAbort catches the abort, prints c and returns the value aborted.	*In[2]:=* **CheckAbort[Print[a]; Abort[ ]; Print[b], Print[c]; aborted]** a c *Out[2]=* aborted
The effect of the Abort is contained by CheckAbort, so b is printed.	*In[3]:=* **CheckAbort[Print[a]; Abort[ ], Print[c]; aborted]; Print[b]** a c b

When you construct sophisticated programs in *Mathematica*, you may sometimes want to guarantee that a particular section of code in a program cannot be aborted, either interactively or by calling Abort. The function AbortProtect allows you to evaluate an expression, saving up any aborts until after the evaluation of the expression is complete.

The Abort is saved up until AbortProtect is finished.	*In[4]:=* **AbortProtect[Abort[ ]; Print[a]]; Print[b]** a *Out[4]=* $Aborted
The CheckAbort sees the abort, but does not propagate it further.	*In[5]:=* **AbortProtect[Abort[ ]; CheckAbort[Print[a], x]]; Print[b]** b

Even inside AbortProtect, CheckAbort will see any aborts that occur, and will return the appropriate *failexpr*. Unless this *failexpr* itself contains Abort[ ], the aborts will be "absorbed" by the CheckAbort.

■ 2.5.14 Compiling *Mathematica* Expressions

If you make a definition like f[x_] := x Sin[x], *Mathematica* will store the expression x Sin[x] in a form that can be evaluated for any x. Then when you give a particular value for x, *Mathematica* substitutes this value into x Sin[x], and evaluates the result. The internal code that *Mathematica* uses to perform this evaluation is set up to work equally well whether the value you give for x is a number, a list, an algebraic object, or any other kind of expression.

Having to take account of all these possibilities inevitably makes the evaluation process slower. However, if *Mathematica* could *assume* that x will be a machine number, then it could avoid many steps, and potentially evaluate an expression like x Sin[x] much more quickly.

Using Compile, you can construct *compiled functions* in *Mathematica*, which evaluate *Mathematica* expressions assuming that all the parameters which appear are numbers (or logical variables). Compile[{x_1, x_2, ... }, *expr*] takes an expression *expr* and returns a "compiled function" which evaluates this expression when given arguments x_1, x_2, ...

In general, `Compile` creates a `CompiledFunction` object which contains a sequence of simple instructions for evaluating the compiled function. The instructions are chosen to be close to those found in the machine code of a typical computer, and can thus be executed quickly.

`Compile[{`x_1`, `x_2`, ... }, `*expr*`]`	create a compiled function which evaluates *expr* for numerical values of the x_i

Creating compiled functions.

This defines `f` to be a pure function which evaluates `x Sin[x]` for any `x`.

```
In[1]:= f = Function[{x}, x Sin[x]]
Out[1]= Function[{x}, xSin[x]]
```

This creates a compiled function for evaluating `x Sin[x]`.

```
In[2]:= fc = Compile[{x}, x Sin[x]]
Out[2]= CompiledFunction[{x}, xSin[x], -CompiledCode-]
```

`f` and `fc` yield the same results, but `fc` runs faster when the argument you give is a number.

```
In[3]:= {f[2.5], fc[2.5]}
Out[3]= {1.49618, 1.49618}
```

`Compile` is useful in situations where you have to evaluate a particular numerical or logical expression many times. By taking the time to call `Compile`, you can get a compiled function which can be executed more quickly than an ordinary *Mathematica* function.

For simple expressions such as `x Sin[x]`, there is usually little difference between the execution speed for ordinary and compiled functions. However, as the size of the expressions involved increases, the advantage of compilation also increases. For large expressions, compilation can speed up execution by a factor as large as 20.

Compilation makes the biggest difference for expressions containing a large number of simple, say arithmetic, functions. For more complicated functions, such as `BesselK` or `Eigenvalues`, most of the computation time is spent executing internal *Mathematica* algorithms, on which compilation has no effect.

This creates a compiled function for finding values of the tenth Legendre polynomial. The `Evaluate` tells *Mathematica* to construct the polynomial explicitly before doing compilation.

```
In[4]:= pc = Compile[{x}, Evaluate[LegendreP[10, x]]]
```

$$Out[4]= \text{CompiledFunction}\Big[\{x\}, -\frac{63}{256} + \frac{3465\,x^2}{256} -$$
$$\frac{15015\,x^4}{128} + \frac{45045\,x^6}{128} - \frac{109395\,x^8}{256} + \frac{46189\,x^{10}}{256},$$
$$-\text{CompiledCode-}\Big]$$

This finds the value of the tenth Legendre polynomial with argument `0.4`.

```
In[5]:= pc[0.4]
Out[5]= 0.0968391
```

This uses built-in numerical code.

```
In[6]:= LegendreP[10, 0.4]
Out[6]= 0.0968391
```

Even though you can use compilation to speed up numerical functions that you write, you should still try to use built-in *Mathematica* functions whenever possible. Built-in functions will usually run faster than any compiled *Mathematica* programs you can create. In addition, they typically use more extensive algorithms, with more complete control over numerical precision and so on.

You should realize that built-in *Mathematica* functions quite often themselves use `Compile`. Thus, for example, `NIntegrate` by default automatically uses `Compile` on the expression you tell it to integrate. Similarly, functions like `Plot` and `Plot3D` use `Compile` on the expressions you ask them to plot. Built-in functions that use `Compile` typically have the option `Compiled`. Setting `Compiled -> False` tells the functions not to use `Compile`.

`Compile[{{`x_1`, `t_1`}, {`x_2`, `t_2`}, ... }, `*expr*`]`
  compile *expr* assuming that x_i is of type t_i

+ `Compile[{{`x_1`, `t_1`, `n_1`}, {`x_2`, `t_2`, `n_2`}, ... }, `*expr*`]`
  compile *expr* assuming that x_i is a rank n_i array of objects each of type t_i

---

`Compile[`*vars*`, `*expr*`, {{`p_1`, `pt_1`}, ... }]`
  compile *expr*, assuming that subexpressions which match p_i are of type pt_i

---

`_Integer`	machine-size integer
`_Real`	machine-precision approximate real number
`_Complex`	machine-precision approximate complex number
`True	False`	logical variable

Specifying types for compilation.

`Compile` works by making assumptions about the types of objects that occur in evaluating the expression you give. The default assumption is that all variables in the expression are approximate real numbers.

`Compile` nevertheless also allows integers, complex numbers and logical variables (`True` or `False`), as well as arrays of numbers. You can specify the type of a particular variable by giving a pattern which matches only values that have that type. Thus, for example, you can use the pattern `_Integer` to specify the integer type. Similarly, you can use `True | False` to specify a logical variable that must be either `True` or `False`.

This compiles the expression 5 i + j with the assumption that i and j are integers.

```
In[7]:= Compile[{{i, _Integer}, {j, _Integer}}, 5 i + j]
Out[7]= CompiledFunction[{i, j}, 5 i + j, -CompiledCode-]
```

This yields an integer result.	*In[8]:=* **%[8, 7]**
	Out[8]= 47
This compiles an expression that performs an operation on a matrix of integers.	*In[9]:=* **Compile[{{m, _Integer, 2}}, Apply[Plus, Flatten[m]]]**
	Out[9]= CompiledFunction[{m}, Plus@@Flatten[m], -CompiledCode-]
The list operations are now carried out in a compiled way, and the result is an integer.	*In[10]:=* **%[{{1, 2, 3}, {7, 8, 9}}]**
	Out[10]= 30

The types that Compile handles correspond essentially to the types that computers typically handle at a machine-code level. Thus, for example, Compile can handle approximate real numbers that have machine precision, but it cannot handle arbitrary-precision numbers. In addition, if you specify that a particular variable is an integer, Compile generates code only for the case when the integer is of "machine size", typically between $\pm 2^{31}$.

When the expression you ask to compile involves only standard arithmetic and logical operations, Compile can deduce the types of objects generated at every step simply from the types of the input variables. However, if you call other functions, Compile will typically not know what type of value they return. If you do not specify otherwise, Compile assumes that any other function yields an approximate real number value. You can, however, also give an explicit list of patterns, specifying what type to assume for an expression that matches a particular pattern.

This defines a function which yields an integer result when given an integer argument.	*In[11]:=* **com[i_] := Binomial[2i, i]**
This compiles x^com[i] using the assumption that com[_] is always an integer.	*In[12]:=* **Compile[{x, {i, _Integer}}, x^com[i], {{com[_], _Integer}}]**
	Out[12]= CompiledFunction[{x, i}, $x^{com[i]}$, -CompiledCode-]
This evaluates the compiled function.	*In[13]:=* **%[5.6, 1]**
	Out[13]= 31.36

The idea of Compile is to create a function which is optimized for certain types of arguments. Compile is nevertheless set up so that the functions it creates work with whatever types of arguments they are given. When the optimization cannot be used, a standard *Mathematica* expression is evaluated to find the value of the function.

Here is a compiled function for taking the square root of a variable.	*In[14]:=* **sq = Compile[{x}, Sqrt[x]]**
	Out[14]= CompiledFunction$[\{x\}, \sqrt{x}$, -CompiledCode-]
If you give a real number argument, optimized code is used.	*In[15]:=* **sq[4.5]**
	Out[15]= 2.12132

The compiled code cannot be used, so *Mathematica* prints a warning, then just evaluates the original symbolic expression.

In[16]:= **sq[1 + u]**

CompiledFunction::cfr:
    Cannot use compiled code; Argument 1 + u at position 1
      should be a machine-size real number.

Out[16]= $\sqrt{1+u}$

The compiled code generated by `Compile` must make assumptions not only about the types of arguments you will supply, but also about the types of all objects that arise during the execution of the code. Sometimes these types depend on the actual *values* of the arguments you specify. Thus, for example, `Sqrt[x]` yields a real number result for real x if x is not negative, but yields a complex number if x is negative.

`Compile` always makes a definite assumption about the type returned by a particular function. If this assumption turns out to be invalid in a particular case when the code generated by `Compile` is executed, then *Mathematica* simply abandons the compiled code in this case, and evaluates an ordinary *Mathematica* expression to get the result.

The compiled code does not expect a complex number, so *Mathematica* has to revert to explicitly evaluating the original symbolic expression.

In[17]:= **sq[-4.5]**

CompiledFunction::cfn:
    Numerical error encountered at instruction 3;
      proceeding with uncompiled evaluation.

Out[17]= 0. + 2.12132 I

An important feature of `Compile` is that it can handle not only mathematical expressions, but also various simple *Mathematica* programs. Thus, for example, `Compile` can handle conditionals and control flow structures.

In all cases, `Compile[`*vars*`, `*expr*`]` holds its arguments unevaluated. This means that you can explicitly give a "program" as the expression to compile.

This creates a compiled version of a *Mathematica* program which implements Newton's approximation to square roots.

In[18]:= **newt = Compile[{x, {n, _Integer}},**
        Module[{t}, t = x; Do[t = (t + x/t)/2, {n}]; t]
        ]

Out[18]= CompiledFunction$\left[\{x, n\}, \text{Module}\left[\{t\}, t = x; \right.\right.$

$$\text{Do}\left[t = \frac{1}{2}\left(t + \frac{x}{t}\right), \{n\}\right];$$

$$\left.\left. t\right], \text{-CompiledCode-}\right]$$

This executes the compiled code.

In[19]:= **newt[2.4, 6]**

Out[19]= 1.54919

■ 2.5.15 Advanced Topic: Manipulating Compiled Code

If you use compiled code created by `Compile` only within *Mathematica* itself, then you should never need to know the details of its internal form. Nevertheless, the compiled code can be represented by an ordinary *Mathematica* expression, and it is sometimes useful to manipulate it.

For example, you can take compiled code generated by `Compile`, and feed it to external programs or devices. You can also create `CompiledFunction` objects yourself, then execute them in *Mathematica*.

In all of these cases, you need to know the internal form of `CompiledFunction` objects. The first element of a `CompiledFunction` object is always a list of patterns which specifies the types of arguments accepted by the object. The fourth element of a `CompiledFunction` object is a *Mathematica* pure function that is used if the compiled code instruction stream fails for any reason to give a result.

`CompiledFunction[{`arg_1`, `arg_2`, ... }, {`n_i`, `n_r`, `n_c`, `n_l`}, `$instr$`, `$func$`]`
    compiled code taking arguments of type arg_i and executing
    the instruction stream $instr$ using n_k registers of type k

The structure of a compiled code object.

This shows the explicit form of the compiled code generated by `Compile`.

```
In[1]:= Compile[{x}, x^2] // InputForm

Out[1]//InputForm=
             CompiledFunction[{_Real}, {0, 0, 3, 0, 0},
          {{1, 2}, {4, 1, 0}, {20, 0, 1}, {38, 1, 1, 2}, {9, 2}},
          Function[{x}, x^2]]
```

The instruction stream in a `CompiledFunction` object consists of a list of instructions for a simple idealized computer. The computer is assumed to have numbered "registers", on which operations can be performed. There are four basic types of registers: integer, real, complex and logical. For each of these basic types it is then possible to have either a single scalar register or an array of registers of any rank. A list of the total number of registers of each type required to evaluate a particular `CompiledFunction` object is given as the second element of the object.

The actual instructions in the compiled code object are given as lists. The first element is an integer "opcode" which specifies what operation should be performed. Subsequent elements are either the numbers of registers of particular types, or literal constants. Typically the last element of the list is the number of a "destination register", into which the result of the operation should be put.

2.6 Modularity and the Naming of Things

■ 2.6.1 Modules and Local Variables

Mathematica normally assumes that all your variables are *global*. This means that every time you use a name like x, *Mathematica* normally assumes that you are referring to the *same* object.

Particularly when you write programs, however, you may not want all your variables to be global. You may, for example, want to use the name x to refer to two quite different variables in two different programs. In this case, you need the x in each program to be treated as a *local* variable.

You can set up local variables in *Mathematica* using *modules*. Within each module, you can give a list of variables which are to be treated as local to the module.

Module[{x, y, ... }, *body*]	a module with local variables *x, y, ...*

Creating modules in *Mathematica*.

This defines the global variable t to have value 17.	`In[1]:= t = 17` `Out[1]= 17`
The t inside the module is local, so it can be treated independently of the global t.	`In[2]:= Module[{t}, t=8; Print[t]]` 8
The global t still has value 17.	`In[3]:= t` `Out[3]= 17`

The most common way that modules are used is to set up temporary or intermediate variables inside functions you define. It is important to make sure that such variables are kept local. If they are not, then you will run into trouble whenever their names happen to coincide with the names of other variables.

The intermediate variable t is specified to be local to the module.	`In[4]:= f[v_] := Module[{t}, t = (1 + v)^2; t = Expand[t] ]`
This runs the function f.	`In[5]:= f[a + b]` $Out[5]= 1 + 2a + a^2 + 2b + 2ab + b^2$
The global t still has value 17.	`In[6]:= t` `Out[6]= 17`

You can treat local variables in modules just like other symbols. Thus, for example, you can use them as names for local functions, you can assign attributes to them, and so on.

This sets up a module which defines a local function f.	`In[7]:= gfac10[k_] :=` `        Module[{f, n}, f[1] = 1; f[n_] := k + n f[n-1]; f[10]]`
In this case, the local function f is just an ordinary factorial.	`In[8]:= gfac10[0]` `Out[8]= 3628800`
In this case, f is set up as a generalized factorial.	`In[9]:= gfac10[2]` `Out[9]= 8841802`

When you set up a local variable in a module, *Mathematica* initially assigns no value to the variable. This means that you can use the variable in a purely symbolic way, even if there was a global value defined for the variable outside the module.

This uses the global value of t defined above, and so yields a number.	`In[10]:= Expand[(1 + t)^3]` `Out[10]= 5832`
Here Length simply receives a number as its argument.	`In[11]:= Length[Expand[(1 + t)^3]]` `Out[11]= 0`
The local variable t has no value, so it acts as a symbol, and Expand produces the anticipated algebraic result.	`In[12]:= Module[{t}, Length[Expand[(1 + t)^3]]]` `Out[12]= 4`

`Module[{`$x = x_0$`, `$y = y_0$`, ... }, `*body*`]`

   a module with initial values for local variables

Assigning initial values to local variables.

This specifies t to be a local variable, with initial value u.	`In[13]:= g[u_] := Module[{ t = u }, t += t/(1 + u)]`
This uses the definition of g.	`In[14]:= g[a]` `Out[14]= `$a + \dfrac{a}{1+a}$

You can define initial values for any of the local variables in a module. The initial values are always evaluated before the module is executed. As a result, even if a variable x is defined as local to the module, the global x will be used if it appears in an expression for an initial value.

The initial value of u is taken to be the global value of t.	`In[15]:= Module[{t = 6, u = t}, u^2]` `Out[15]= 289`

---

lhs `:= Module[`*vars*`, `*rhs* `/; ` *cond*`]`   share local variables between *rhs* and *cond*

Using local variables in definitions with conditions.

When you set up /; conditions for definitions, you often need to introduce temporary variables. In many cases, you may want to share these temporary variables with the body of the right-hand side of the definition. *Mathematica* allows you to enclose the whole right-hand side of your definition in a module, including the condition.

This defines a function with a condition attached.	`In[16]:= h[x_] := Module[{t}, t^2 - 1 /; (t = x - 4) > 1]`

Mathematica shares the value of the local variable t between the condition and the body of the right-hand side.	`In[17]:= h[10]` `Out[17]= 35`

■ 2.6.2 Local Constants

`With[{x = x_0, y = y_0, ... }, body]`
        define local constants $x, y, ...$

Defining local constants.

`Module` allows you to set up local *variables*, to which you can assign any sequence of values. Often, however, all you really need are local *constants*, to which you assign a value only once. The *Mathematica* `With` construct allows you to set up such local constants.

This defines a global value for t.	`In[1]:= t = 17` `Out[1]= 17`

This defines a function using t as a local constant.	`In[2]:= w[x_] := With[{t = x + 1}, t + t^3]`

This uses the definition of w.	`In[3]:= w[a]` `Out[3]= 1 + a + (1 + a)^3`

t still has its global value.	`In[4]:= t` `Out[4]= 17`

Just as in `Module`, the initial values you define in `With` are evaluated before the `With` is executed.

The expression t + 1 which gives the value of the local constant t is evaluated using the global t.	`In[5]:= With[{t = t + 1}, t^2]` `Out[5]= 324`

The way `With[{x = x_0, ... }, body]` works is to take *body*, and replace every occurrence of x, etc. in it by x_0, etc. You can think of `With` as a generalization of the `/.` operator, suitable for application to *Mathematica* code instead of other expressions.

This replaces x with a.	`In[6]:= With[{x = a}, x = 5]` `Out[6]= 5`

After the replacement, the body of the With is a = 5, so a gets the global value 5.	*In[7]:=* **a** *Out[7]=* 5
This clears the value of a.	*In[8]:=* **Clear[a]**

In some respects, With is like a special case of Module, in which each local variable is assigned a value exactly once.

One of the main reasons for using With rather than Module is that it typically makes the *Mathematica* programs you write easier to understand. In a module, if you see a local variable x at a particular point, you potentially have to trace through all of the code in the module to work out the value of x at that point. In a With construct, however, you can always find out the value of a local constant simply by looking at the initial list of values, without having to trace through specific code.

If you have several With constructs, it is always the innermost one for a particular variable that is in effect. You can mix Module and With. The general rule is that the innermost one for a particular variable is the one that is in effect.

With nested With constructs, the innermost one is always the one in effect.	*In[9]:=* **With[{t = 8}, With[{t = 9}, t^2]]** *Out[9]=* 81
You can mix Module and With constructs.	*In[10]:=* **Module[{t = 8}, With[{t = 9}, t^2]]** *Out[10]=* 81
Local variables in inner constructs do not mask ones outside unless the names conflict.	*In[11]:=* **With[{t = a}, With[{u = b}, t + u]]** *Out[11]=* a + b

Except for the question of when x and *body* are evaluated, With[$\{x = x_0\}$, *body*] works essentially like *body* /. $x \rightarrow x_0$. However, With behaves in a special way when the expression *body* itself contains With or Module constructs. The main issue is to prevent the local constants in the various With constructs from conflicting with each other, or with global objects. The details of how this is done are discussed in Section 2.6.3.

The y in the inner With is renamed to prevent it from conflicting with the global y.	*In[12]:=* **With[{x = 2 + y}, Hold[With[{y = 4}, x + y]]]** *Out[12]=* Hold[With[{y\$ = 4}, (2 + y) + y\$]]

■ 2.6.3 How Modules Work

The way modules work in *Mathematica* is basically very simple. Every time any module is used, a new symbol is created to represent each of its local variables. The new symbol is given a unique name which cannot conflict with any other names. The name is formed by taking the name you specify for the local variable, followed by \$, with a unique "serial number" appended.

The serial number is found from the value of the global variable \$ModuleNumber. This variable counts the total number of times any Module of any form has been used.

■ **Module** generates symbols with names of the form *x$nnn* to represent each local variable.

The basic principle of modules in *Mathematica*.

This shows the symbol generated for t within the module.	*In[1]:=* **Module[{t}, Print[t]]**
	t$1
The symbols are different every time any module is used.	*In[2]:=* **Module[{t, u}, Print[t]; Print[u]]**
	t$2
	u$2

For most purposes, you will never have to deal directly with the actual symbols generated inside modules. However, if for example you start up a dialog while a module is being executed, then you will see these symbols. The same is true whenever you use functions like **Trace** to watch the evaluation of modules.

You see the symbols that are generated inside modules when you use **Trace**.	*In[3]:=* **Trace[Module[{t}, t = 3]]**
	Out[3]= {Module[{t}, t = 3], {t$3 = 3, 3}, 3}
This starts a dialog inside a module.	*In[4]:=* **Module[{t}, t = 6; Dialog[ ]]**
Inside the dialog, you see the symbols generated for local variables such as t.	*In[5]:=* **Stack[_]**
	Out[5]= {Module[{t}, t = 6;
	Dialog[]], t$4 = 6;
	Dialog[], Dialog[]}
You can work with these symbols as you would with any other symbols.	*In[6]:=* **t$4 + 1**
	Out[6]= 7
This returns from the dialog.	*In[7]:=* **Return[t$4 ^ 2]**
	Out[4]= 36

Under some circumstances, it is convenient explicitly to return symbols that are generated inside modules.

You can explicitly return symbols that are generated inside modules.	*In[5]:=* **Module[{t}, t]**
	Out[5]= t$6
You can treat these symbols as you would any others.	*In[6]:=* **%^2 + 1**
	Out[6]= 1 + t$6^2

Unique[*x*]	generate a new symbol with a unique name of the form *x$nnn*
Unique[{*x*, *y*, ... }]	generate a list of new symbols

Generating new symbols with unique names.

The function `Unique` allows you to generate new symbols in the same way as `Module` does. Each time you call `Unique`, `$ModuleNumber` is incremented, so that the names of new symbols are guaranteed to be unique.

This generates a unique new symbol whose name starts with x.	`In[7]:= Unique[x]` `Out[7]= x$7`
Each time you call `Unique` you get a symbol with a larger serial number.	`In[8]:= {Unique[x], Unique[x], Unique[x]}` `Out[8]= {x$8, x$9, x$10}`
If you call `Unique` with a list of names, you get the same serial number for each of the symbols.	`In[9]:= Unique[{x, xa, xb}]` `Out[9]= {x$11, xa$11, xb$11}`

You can use the standard *Mathematica* `?name` mechanism to get information on symbols that were generated inside modules or by the function `Unique`.

Executing this module generates the symbol q$*nnn*.	`In[10]:= Module[{q}, q^2 + 1]` `Out[10]= 1 + q$12`^{2}
You can see the generated symbol here.	`In[11]:= ?q*` q q$12

Symbols generated by `Module` and `Unique` behave in exactly the same way as other symbols for the purposes of evaluation. However, these symbols carry the attribute `Temporary`, which specifies that they should be removed completely from the system when they are no longer used. Thus most symbols that are generated inside modules are removed when the execution of those modules is finished. The symbols survive only if they are explicitly returned.

This shows a new q variable generated inside a module.	`In[12]:= Module[{q}, Print[q]]` q$13
The new variable is removed when the execution of the module is finished, so it does not show up here.	`In[13]:= ?q*` q q$12

You should realize that the use of names such as *x$nnn* for generated symbols is purely a convention. You can in principle give any symbol a name of this form. But if you do, the symbol may collide with one that is produced by `Module` or `Unique`.

An important point to note is that symbols generated by `Module` and `Unique` are in general unique only within a particular *Mathematica* session. The variable `$ModuleNumber` which determines the serial numbers for these symbols is always reset at the beginning of each session.

This means in particular that if you save expressions containing generated symbols in a file, and then read them into another session, there is no guarantee that conflicts will not occur.

One way to avoid such conflicts is explicitly to set `$ModuleNumber` differently at the beginning of each session. In particular, if you set `$ModuleNumber = 10^10 $SessionID`, you should avoid any conflicts. The global variable `$SessionID` should give a unique number which characterizes a particular *Mathematica* session on a particular computer. The value of this variable is determined from such quantities as the absolute date and time, the ID of your computer, and, if appropriate, the ID of the particular *Mathematica* process.

`$ModuleNumber`	the serial number for symbols generated by `Module` and `Unique`
`$SessionID`	a number that should be different for every *Mathematica* session

Variables to be used in determining serial numbers for generated symbols.

Having generated appropriate symbols to represent the local variables you have specified, `Module[`*vars*`, `*body*`]` then has to evaluate *body* using these symbols. The first step is to take the actual expression *body* as it appears inside the module, and effectively to use `With` to replace all occurrences of each local variable name with the appropriate generated symbol. After this is done, `Module` actually performs the evaluation of the resulting expression.

An important point to note is that `Module[`*vars*`, `*body*`]` inserts generated symbols only into the actual expression *body*. It does not, for example, insert such symbols into code that is called from *body*, but does not explicitly appear in *body*.

Section 2.6.6 will discuss how you can use `Block` to set up "local values" which work in a different way.

Since x does not appear explicitly in the body of the module, the local value is not used.	`In[14]:= tmp = x^2 + 1; Module[{x = 4}, tmp]` $Out[14]= 1 + x^2$

Most of the time, you will probably set up modules by giving explicit *Mathematica* input of the form `Module[`*vars*`, `*body*`]`. Since the function `Module` has the attribute `HoldAll`, the form of *body* will usually be kept unevaluated until the module is executed.

It is, however, possible to build modules dynamically in *Mathematica*. The generation of new symbols, and their insertion into *body* are always done only when a module is actually executed, not when the module is first given as *Mathematica* input.

This evaluates the body of the module immediately, making x appear explicitly.	`In[15]:= tmp = x^2 + 1; Module[{x = 4}, Evaluate[tmp]]` $Out[15]= 17$

■ 2.6.4 Advanced Topic: Variables in Pure Functions and Rules

`Module` and `With` allow you to give a specific list of symbols whose names you want to treat as local. In some situations, however, you want to automatically treat certain symbol names as local.

For example, if you use a pure function such as `Function[{x}, x + a]`, you want x to be treated as a "formal parameter", whose specific name is local. The same is true of the x that appears in a rule like `f[x_] -> x^2`, or a definition like `f[x_] := x^2`.

Mathematica uses a uniform scheme to make sure that the names of formal parameters which appear in constructs like pure functions and rules are kept local, and are never confused with global names. The basic idea is to replace formal parameters when necessary by symbols with names of the form $x\$$. By convention, $x\$$ is never used as a global name.

Here is a nested pure function.	`In[1]:= Function[{x}, Function[{y}, x + y]]`
	`Out[1]= Function[{x}, Function[{y}, x + y]]`
Mathematica renames the formal parameter y in the inner function to avoid conflict with the global object y.	`In[2]:= %[2y]`
	`Out[2]= Function[{y$}, 2 y + y$]`
The resulting pure function behaves as it should.	`In[3]:= %[a]`
	`Out[3]= a + 2 y`

In general, *Mathematica* renames the formal parameters in an object like `Function[`*vars*, *body*`]` whenever *body* is modified in any way by the action of another pure function.

The formal parameter y is renamed because the body of the inner pure function was changed.	`In[4]:= Function[{x}, Function[{y}, x + y]] [a]`
	`Out[4]= Function[{y$}, a + y$]`
Since the body of the inner function does not change, the formal parameter is not renamed.	`In[5]:= Function[{x}, x + Function[{y}, y^2]] [a]`
	`Out[5]= a + Function[{y}, y²]`

Mathematica renames formal parameters in pure functions more liberally than is strictly necessary. In principle, renaming could be avoided if the names of the formal parameters in a particular function do not actually conflict with parts of expressions substituted into the body of the pure function. For uniformity, however, *Mathematica* still renames formal parameters even in such cases.

In this case, the formal parameter x in the inner function shields the body of the function, so no renaming is needed.	`In[6]:= Function[{x}, Function[{x}, x + y]] [a]`
	`Out[6]= Function[{x}, x + y]`
Here are three nested functions.	`In[7]:= Function[{x}, Function[{y}, Function[{z}, x + y + z]]]`
	`Out[7]= Function[{x}, Function[{y},`
	`              Function[{z}, x + y + z]]]`
Both inner functions are renamed in this case.	`In[8]:= %[a]`
	`Out[8]= Function[{y$}, Function[{z$}, a + y$ + z$]]`

As mentioned on page 246, pure functions in *Mathematica* are like λ expressions in formal logic. The renaming of formal parameters allows *Mathematica* pure functions to reproduce all the semantics of standard λ expressions faithfully.

Function[{x, ... }, *body*]	local parameters
lhs -> *rhs* and *lhs* :> *rhs*	local pattern names
lhs = *rhs* and *lhs* := *rhs*	local pattern names
With[{$x = x_0$, ... }, *body*]	local constants
Module[{x, ... }, *body*]	local variables

Scoping constructs in *Mathematica*.

Mathematica has several "scoping constructs" in which certain names are treated as local. When you mix these constructs in any way, *Mathematica* does appropriate renamings to avoid conflicts.

Mathematica renames the formal parameter of the pure function to avoid a conflict.

```
In[9]:= With[{x = a}, Function[{a}, a + x]]
Out[9]= Function[{a$}, a$ + a]
```

Here the local constant in the inner With is renamed to avoid a conflict.

```
In[10]:= With[{x = y}, Hold[With[{y = 4}, x + y]]]
Out[10]= Hold[With[{y$ = 4}, y + y$]]
```

There is no conflict between names in this case, so no renaming is done.

```
In[11]:= With[{x = y}, Hold[With[{z = x + 2}, z + 2]]]
Out[11]= Hold[With[{z = y + 2}, z + 2]]
```

The local variable y in the module is renamed to avoid a conflict.

```
In[12]:= With[{x = y}, Hold[Module[{y}, x + y]]]
Out[12]= Hold[Module[{y$}, y + y$]]
```

If you execute the module, however, the local variable is renamed again to make its name unique.

```
In[13]:= ReleaseHold[%]
Out[13]= y + y$1
```

Mathematica treats transformation rules as scoping constructs, in which the names you give to patterns are local. You can set up named patterns either using $x\_$, $x\_\_$ and so on, or using x:*patt*.

The x in the h goes with the x_, and is considered local to the rule.

```
In[14]:= With[{x = 5}, g[x_, x] -> h[x]]
Out[14]= g[x_, 5] -> h[x]
```

In a rule like f[x_] -> x + y, the x which appears on the right-hand side goes with the name of the x_ pattern. As a result, this x is treated as a variable local to the rule, and cannot be modified by other scoping constructs.

The y, on the other hand, is not local to the rule, and *can* be modified by other scoping constructs. When this happens, *Mathematica* renames the patterns in the rule to prevent the possibility of a conflict.

Mathematica renames the x in the rule to prevent a conflict.

In[15]:= `With[{w = x}, f[x_] -> w + x]`

Out[15]= `f[x$_] → x + x$`

When you use `With` on a scoping construct, *Mathematica* automatically performs appropriate renamings. In some cases, however, you may want to make substitutions inside scoping constructs, without any renaming. You can do this using the `/.` operator.

When you substitute for y using `With`, the x in the pure function is renamed to prevent a conflict.

In[16]:= `With[{y = x + a}, Function[{x}, x + y]]`

Out[16]= `Function[{x$}, x$ + (a + x)]`

If you use `/.` rather than `With`, no such renaming is done.

In[17]:= `Function[{x}, x + y] /. y -> a + x`

Out[17]= `Function[{x}, x + (a + x)]`

When you apply a rule such as $f[x\_] \to rhs$, or use a definition such as $f[x\_] := rhs$, *Mathematica* implicitly has to substitute for x everywhere in the expression *rhs*. It effectively does this using the `/.` operator. As a result, such substitution does not respect scoping constructs. However, when the insides of a scoping construct are modified by the substitution, the other variables in the scoping construct are renamed.

This defines a function for creating pure functions.

In[18]:= `mkfun[var_, body_] := Function[{var}, body]`

The x and x^2 are explicitly inserted into the pure function, effectively by using the `/.` operator.

In[19]:= `mkfun[x, x^2]`

Out[19]= `Function[{x}, x²]`

This defines a function that creates a pair of nested pure functions.

In[20]:= `mkfun2[var_, body_] := Function[{x},`
`                                   Function[{var}, body + x]]`

The x in the outer pure function is renamed in this case.

In[21]:= `mkfun2[x, x^2]`

Out[21]= `Function[{x$}, Function[{x}, x² + x$]]`

■ 2.6.5 Dummy Variables in Mathematics

When you set up mathematical formulas, you often have to introduce various kinds of local objects or "dummy variables". You can treat such dummy variables using modules and other *Mathematica* scoping constructs.

Integration variables are a common example of dummy variables in mathematics. When you write down a formal integral, conventional notation requires you to introduce an integration variable with a definite name. This variable is essentially "local" to the integral, and its name, while arbitrary, must not conflict with any other names in your mathematical expression.

Here is a function for evaluating an integral.

In[1]:= `p[n_] := Integrate[f[s] s^n, {s, 0, 1}]`

When lexical scoping is used, variables are treated as local to a particular section of the *code* in a program. In dynamic scoping, the values of variables are local to a part of the *execution history* of the program.

In compiled languages like C, there is a very clear distinction between "code" and "execution history". The symbolic nature of *Mathematica* makes this distinction slightly less clear, since "code" can in principle be built up dynamically during the execution of a program.

What `Module[`*vars, body*`]` does is to treat the form of the expression *body* at the time when the module is executed as the "code" of a *Mathematica* program. Then when any of the *vars* explicitly appears in this "code", they are considered to be local.

`Block[`*vars, body*`]` does not look at the *form* of the expression *body*. Instead, throughout the evaluation of *body*, the block uses local values for the *vars*.

This defines m in terms of i.	*In[1]:=* **m = i^2**
	Out[1]= i^2
The local value for i in the block is used throughout the evaluation of i + m.	*In[2]:=* **Block[{i = a}, i + m]**
	Out[2]= $a + a^2$
Here only the i that appears explicitly in i + m is treated as a local variable.	*In[3]:=* **Module[{i = a}, i + m]**
	Out[3]= $a + i^2$

■ 2.6.8 Contexts

It is always a good idea to give variables and functions names that are as explicit as possible. Sometimes, however, such names may get inconveniently long.

In *Mathematica*, you can use the notion of "contexts" to organize the names of symbols. Contexts are particularly important in *Mathematica* packages which introduce symbols whose names must not conflict with those of any other symbols. If you write *Mathematica* packages, or make sophisticated use of packages that others have written, then you will need to know about contexts.

The basic idea is that the *full name* of any symbol is broken into two parts: a *context* and a *short name*. The full name is written as *context*`short, where the ` is the backquote or grave accent character (ASCII decimal code 96), called a "context mark" in *Mathematica*.

Here is a symbol with short name x, and context aaaa.	*In[1]:=* **aaaa`x**
	Out[1]= aaaa`x
You can use this symbol just like any other symbol.	*In[2]:=* **%^2 - %**
	Out[2]= $-aaaa`x + aaaa`x^2$
You can for example define a value for the symbol.	*In[3]:=* **aaaa`x = 78**
	Out[3]= 78

| *Mathematica* treats a`x and b`x as completely different symbols. | *In[4]:=* **a`x == b`x** |
| | *Out[4]=* a`x == b`x |

It is typical to have all the symbols that relate a particular topic in a particular context. Thus, for example, symbols that represent physical units might have a context `PhysicalUnits``. Such symbols might have full names like `PhysicalUnits`Joule` or `PhysicalUnits`Mole`.

Although you can always refer to a symbol by its full name, it is often convenient to use a shorter name.

At any given point in a *Mathematica* session, there is always a *current context* `$Context`. You can refer to symbols that are in this context simply by giving their short names.

| The default context for *Mathematica* sessions is Global`. | *In[5]:=* **$Context** |
| | *Out[5]=* Global` |

| Short names are sufficient for symbols that are in the current context. | *In[6]:=* **{x, Global`x}** |
| | *Out[6]=* {x, x} |

Contexts in *Mathematica* work somewhat like file directories in many operating systems. You can always specify a particular file by giving its complete name, including its directory. But at any given point, there is usually a current working directory, analogous to the current *Mathematica* context. Files that are in this directory can then be specified just by giving their short names.

Like directories in many operating systems, contexts in *Mathematica* can be hierarchical. Thus, for example, the full name of a symbol can involve a sequence of context names, as in $c_1`c_2`c_3`name$.

context`name  or  $c_1`c_2`$ ... `name	a symbol in an explicitly specified context
`name	a symbol in the current context
`context`name or `$c_1`c_2`$ ... `name	a symbol in a specific context relative to the current context
name	a symbol in the current context, or found on the context search path

Specifying symbols in various contexts.

| Here is a symbol in the context a`b`. | *In[7]:=* **a`b`x** |
| | *Out[7]=* a`b`x |

When you start a *Mathematica* session, the default current context is `Global``. Symbols that you introduce will usually be in this context. However, built-in symbols such as `Pi` are in the context `System``.

In order to let you easily access not only symbols in the context Global`, but also in contexts such as System`, *Mathematica* supports the notion of a *context search path*. At any point in a *Mathematica* session, there is both a current context $Context, and also a current context search path $ContextPath. The idea of the search path is to allow you to type in the short name of a symbol, then have *Mathematica* search in a sequence of contexts to find a symbol with that short name.

The context search path for symbols in *Mathematica* is analogous to the "search path" for program files provided in operating systems such as Unix and MS-DOS.

The default context path includes the contexts for system-defined symbols.	*In[8]:=* **$ContextPath** *Out[8]=* {Global`, System`}
When you type in Pi, *Mathematica* interprets it as the symbol with full name System`Pi.	*In[9]:=* **Context[Pi]** *Out[9]=* System`

Context[*s*]	the context of a symbol
$Context	the current context in a *Mathematica* session
$ContextPath	the current context search path
Contexts[ ]	a list of all contexts

Finding contexts and context search paths.

When you use contexts in *Mathematica*, there is no reason that two symbols which are in different contexts cannot have the same short name. Thus, for example, you can have symbols with the short name Mole both in the context PhysicalUnits` and in the context BiologicalOrganisms`.

There is, however, then the question of which symbol you actually get when you type in only the short name Mole. The answer to this question is determined by which of the contexts comes first in the sequence of contexts listed in the context search path.

This introduces two symbols, both with short name Mole.	*In[10]:=* **{PhysicalUnits`Mole, BiologicalOrganisms`Mole}** *Out[10]=* {PhysicalUnits`Mole, BiologicalOrganisms`Mole}
This adds two additional contexts to $ContextPath.	*In[11]:=* **$ContextPath =** **Join[$ContextPath,** **{"PhysicalUnits`", "BiologicalOrganisms`"}]** *Out[11]=* {Global`, System`, PhysicalUnits`,         BiologicalOrganisms`}
Now if you type in Mole, you get the symbol in the context PhysicalUnits`.	*In[12]:=* **Context[Mole]** *Out[12]=* PhysicalUnits`

In general, when you type in a short name for a symbol, *Mathematica* assumes that you want the symbol with that name whose context appears earliest in the context search path. As a result, symbols with the same short name whose contexts appear later in the context search path are effectively "shadowed". To refer to these symbols, you need to use their full names.

Mathematica always warns you when you introduce new symbols that "shadow" existing symbols with your current choice for $ContextPath.

This introduces a symbol with short name Mole in the context Global`. *Mathematica* warns you that the new symbol shadows existing symbols with short name Mole.	*In[13]:=* **Global`Mole**  Mole::shdw:     Symbol Mole appears in multiple contexts       {Global`, Ph<<11>>`, BiologicalOrganisms`}; definitions in context Global` may shadow or be shadowed by other definitions. *Out[13]=* Mole
Now when you type in Mole, you get the symbol in context Global`.	*In[14]:=* **Context[Mole]** *Out[14]=* Global`

If you once introduce a symbol which shadows existing symbols, it will continue to do so until you either rearrange $ContextPath, or explicitly remove the symbol. You should realize that it is not sufficient to clear the *value* of the symbol; you need to actually remove the symbol completely from *Mathematica*. You can do this using the function Remove[*s*].

Clear[*s*]	clear the values of a symbol
Remove[*s*]	remove a symbol completely from the system

Clearing and removing symbols in *Mathematica*.

This removes the symbol Global`Mole.	*In[15]:=* **Remove[Mole]**
Now if you type in Mole, you get the symbol PhysicalUnits`Mole.	*In[16]:=* **Context[Mole]** *Out[16]=* PhysicalUnits`

When *Mathematica* prints out the name of a symbol, it has to choose whether to give the full name, or just the short name. What it does is to give whatever version of the name you would have to type in to get the particular symbol, given your current settings for $Context and $ContextPath.

The short name is printed for the first symbol, so this would give that symbol if you typed it in.	*In[17]:=* **{PhysicalUnits`Mole, BiologicalOrganisms`Mole}** *Out[17]=* {Mole, BiologicalOrganisms`Mole}

If you type in a short name for which there is no symbol either in the current context, or in any context on the context search path, then *Mathematica* has to *create* a new symbol with this name. It always puts new symbols of this kind in the current context, as specified by $Context.

This introduces the new symbol with short name tree.	*In[18]:=* **tree** *Out[18]=* tree

Mathematica puts `tree` in the current context Global`.

```
In[19]:= Context[tree]
Out[19]= Global`
```

■ 2.6.9 Contexts and Packages

A typical package written in *Mathematica* introduces several new symbols intended for use outside the package. These symbols may correspond for example to new functions or new objects defined in the package.

There is a general convention that all new symbols introduced in a particular package are put into a context whose name is related to the name of the package. When you read in the package, it adds this context at the beginning of your context search path `$ContextPath`.

This reads in a package for doing Laplace transforms.

```
In[1]:= <<Calculus`LaplaceTransform`
```

The package prepends its context and related ones to `$ContextPath`.

```
In[2]:= $ContextPath
Out[2]= {Calculus`LaplaceTransform`,
           Calculus`Common`TransformCommon`,
           Calculus`DiracDelta`, Global`, System`}
```

The symbol `LaplaceTransform` is in the context set up by the package.

```
In[3]:= Context[LaplaceTransform]
Out[3]= Calculus`LaplaceTransform`
```

You can refer to the symbol using its short name.

```
In[4]:= LaplaceTransform[t^3, t, s]
```
$$Out[4]= \frac{6}{s^4}$$

The full names of symbols defined in packages are often quite long. In most cases, however, you will only need to use their short names. The reason for this is that after you have read in a package, its context is added to `$ContextPath`, so the context is automatically searched whenever you type in a short name.

There is a complication, however, when two symbols with the same short name appear in two different packages. In such a case, *Mathematica* will warn you when you read in the second package. It will tell you which symbols will be "shadowed" by the new symbols that are being introduced.

The symbol `LaplaceTransform` in the context `Calculus`LaplaceTransform`` is shadowed by the symbol with the same short name in the new package.

```
In[5]:= <<NewLaplace`

LaplaceTransform::shdw:
   Symbol LaplaceTransform appears in multiple contexts
   {NewLaplace`, Calculus`LaplaceTransform`}; definitions
     in context NewLaplace`
   may shadow or be shadowed by other definitions.
```

You can access the shadowed symbol by giving its full name.

```
In[6]:= Calculus`LaplaceTransform`LaplaceTransform[t^3, t, s]
```
$$Out[6]= \frac{6}{s^4}$$

Conflicts can occur not only between symbols in different packages, but also between symbols in packages and symbols that you introduce directly in your *Mathematica* session. If you define a symbol in your current context, then this symbol will shadow any other symbol with the same short name in packages that you read in. The reason for this is that *Mathematica* always searches for symbols in the current context before looking in contexts on the context search path.

This defines a function in the current context.	*In[7]:=* `Div[f_] = 1/f`
	Out[7]= $\dfrac{1}{f}$
Any other functions with short name Div will be shadowed by the one in your current context.	*In[8]:=* `<<Calculus`VectorAnalysis``
	`Div::shdw: Symbol Div appears in multiple contexts` `{Calculus`VectorAnalysis`, Global`}; definitions in`   `context Calculus`VectorAnalysis`` `may shadow or be shadowed by other definitions.`
This sets up the coordinate system for vector analysis.	*In[9]:=* `SetCoordinates[Cartesian[x, y, z]]`
	Out[9]= `Cartesian[x, y, z]`
This removes Div completely from the current context.	*In[10]:=* `Clear[Div]; Remove[Div]`
Now the Div from the package is used.	*In[11]:=* `Div[{x, y^2, x}]`
	Out[11]= `1 + 2 y`

If you get into the situation where unwanted symbols are shadowing the symbols you want, the best thing to do is usually to get rid of the unwanted symbols using `Remove[s]`. An alternative that is sometimes appropriate is to rearrange the entries in `$ContextPath` and to reset the value of `$Context` so as to make the contexts that contain the symbols you want be the ones that are searched first.

`$Packages`	a list of the contexts corresponding to all packages loaded into your *Mathematica* session

Getting a list of packages.

■ 2.6.10 Setting Up *Mathematica* Packages

In a typical *Mathematica* package, there are generally two kinds of new symbols that are introduced. The first kind are ones that you want to "export" for use outside the package. The second kind are ones that you want to use only internally within the package. You can distinguish these two kinds of symbols by putting them in different contexts.

The usual convention is to put symbols intended for export in a context with a name *Package`* that corresponds to the name of the package. Whenever the package is read in, it adds this context to the context search path, so that the symbols in this context can be referred to by their short names.

Symbols that are not intended for export, but are instead intended only for internal use within the package, are conventionally put into a context with the name *Package*`Private`. This context is *not* added to the context search path. As a result, the symbols in this context cannot be accessed except by giving their full names.

Package`	symbols for export
Package`Private`	symbols for internal use only
System`	built-in *Mathematica* symbols
Needed$_1$`, *Needed$_2$*`, ...	other contexts needed in the package

Contexts conventionally used in *Mathematica* packages.

There is a standard sequence of *Mathematica* commands that is typically used to set up the contexts in a package. These commands set the values of $Context and $ContextPath so that the new symbols which are introduced are created in the appropriate contexts.

BeginPackage["*Package*`"]	set *Package*` to be the current context, and put only System` on the context search path
f::usage = "*text*", ...	introduce the objects intended for export (and no others)
Begin["`Private`"]	set the current context to *Package*`Private`
f[*args*] = *value*, ...	give the main body of definitions in the package
End[ ]	revert to the previous context (here *Package*`)
EndPackage[ ]	end the package, prepending the *Package*` to the context search path

The standard sequence of context control commands in a package.

```
BeginPackage["Collatz'"]

Collatz::usage =
      "Collatz[n] gives a list of the iterates in the 3n+1 problem,
      starting from n. The conjecture is that this sequence always
      terminates."

Begin["'Private'"]

Collatz[1] := {1}

Collatz[n_Integer]  := Prepend[Collatz[3 n + 1], n] /; OddQ[n] && n > 0

Collatz[n_Integer] := Prepend[Collatz[n/2], n] /; EvenQ[n] && n > 0

End[ ]

EndPackage[ ]
```

The sample package `Collatz.m`.

The convention of defining **usage** messages at the beginning of a package is essentially a trick for creating symbols you want to export in the appropriate context. The point is that in defining these messages, the only symbols you mention are exactly the ones you want to export. These symbols are then created in the context *Package'*, which is then current.

In the actual definitions of the functions in a package, there are typically many new symbols, introduced as parameters, temporary variables, and so on. The convention is to put all these symbols in the context *Package'*`Private'`, which is not put on the context search path when the package is read in.

This reads in the sample package given above.	*In[1]:=* **<<Collatz.m**
The EndPackage command in the package adds the context associated with the package to the context search path.	*In[2]:=* **$ContextPath** *Out[2]=* {Collatz', Global', System'}
The Collatz function was created in the context Collatz'.	*In[3]:=* **Context[Collatz]** *Out[3]=* Collatz'
The parameter n is put in the private context Collatz'Private'.	*In[4]:=* **?Collatz'Private'*** Collatz'Private'n

In the `Collatz` package, the functions that are defined depend only on built-in *Mathematica* functions. Often, however, the functions defined in one package may depend on functions defined in another package.

Two things are needed to make this work. First, the other package must be read in, so that the functions needed are defined. And second, the context search path must include the context that these functions are in.

You can explicitly tell *Mathematica* to read in a package at any point using the command <<*context*`. (Section 2.11.5 discusses the tricky issue of translation from system-independent context names to system-dependent file names.) Often, however, you want to set it up so that a particular package is read in only if it is needed. The command `Needs["`*context*`"]` tells *Mathematica* to read in a package if the context associated with that package is not already in the list `$Packages`.

`Get["`*context*`"]` or <<*context*`	read in the package corresponding to the specified context
`Needs["`*context*`"]`	read in the package if the specified context is not already in `$Packages`
`BeginPackage["`*Package*`", {"`*Needed₁*`", ... }]`	begin a package, specifying that certain contexts in addition to `System`` are needed

Functions for specifying interdependence of packages.

If you use `BeginPackage["`*Package*`"]` with a single argument, *Mathematica* puts on the context search path only the *Package*` context and the contexts for built-in *Mathematica* symbols. If the definitions you give in your package involve functions from other packages, you must make sure that the contexts for these packages are also included in your context search path. You can do this by giving a list of the additional contexts as a second argument to `BeginPackage`. `BeginPackage` automatically calls `Needs` on these contexts, reading in the corresponding packages if necessary, and then making sure that the contexts are on the context search path.

`Begin["`*context*`"]`	switch to a new current context
`End[ ]`	revert to the previous context

Context manipulation functions.

Executing a function like `Begin` which manipulates contexts changes the way that *Mathematica* interprets names you type in. However, you should realize that the change is effective only in subsequent expressions that you type in. The point is that *Mathematica* always reads in a complete input expression, and interprets the names in it, before it executes any part of the expression. As a result, by the time `Begin` is executed in a particular expression, the names in the expression have already been interpreted, and it is too late for `Begin` to have an effect.

The fact that context manipulation functions do not have an effect until the *next* complete expression is read in means that you must be sure to give those functions as separate expressions, typically on separate lines, when you write *Mathematica* packages.

The name x is interpreted before this expression is executed, so the Begin has no effect.

```
In[5]:= Begin["a'"]; Print[Context[x]]; End[ ]

Global'

Out[5]= a'
```

Context manipulation functions are used primarily as part of packages intended to be read into *Mathematica*. Sometimes, however, you may find it convenient to use such functions interactively.

This can happen, for example, if you go into a dialog, say using TraceDialog, while executing a function defined in a package. The parameters and temporary variables in the function are typically in a private context associated with the package. Since this context is not on your context search path, *Mathematica* will print out the full names of the symbols, and will require you to type in these full names in order to refer to the symbols. You can however use Begin["*Package*'Private'"] to make the private context of the package your current context. This will make *Mathematica* print out short names for the symbols, and allow you to refer to the symbols by their short names.

■ 2.6.11 Automatic Loading of Packages

Previous sections have discussed explicit loading of *Mathematica* packages using <<*package* and Needs[*package*]. Sometimes, however, you may want to set *Mathematica* up so that it automatically loads a particular package when the package is needed.

You can use DeclarePackage to give the names of symbols which are defined in a particular package. Then, when one of these symbols is actually used, *Mathematica* will automatically load the package where the symbol is defined.

DeclarePackage["*context*'", {"*name*₁", "*name*₂", ... }]
  declare that a package should automatically be loaded if a symbol with any of the names *name*ᵢ is used

Arranging for automatic loading of packages.

This specifies that the symbols Div, Grad and Curl are defined in Calculus'VectorAnalysis'.

```
In[1]:= DeclarePackage["Calculus'VectorAnalysis'",
                        {"Div", "Grad", "Curl"}]

Out[1]= Calculus'VectorAnalysis'
```

When you first use Grad, *Mathematica* automatically loads the package that defines it.

```
In[2]:= Grad[x^2 + y^2, Cartesian[x, y, z]]
Out[2]= {2x, 2y, 0}
```

When you set up a large collection of *Mathematica* packages, it is often a good idea to create an additional "names file" which contains a sequence of DeclarePackage commands, specifying packages to load when particular names are used. Within a particular *Mathematica* session, you then need to load explicitly only the names file. When you have done this, all the other packages will automatically be loaded if and when they are needed.

DeclarePackage works by immediately creating symbols with the names you specify, but giving each of these symbols the special attribute Stub. Whenever *Mathematica* finds a symbol with the Stub attribute, it automatically loads the package corresponding to the context of the symbol, in an attempt to find the definition of the symbol.

■ 2.6.12 Manipulating Symbols and Contexts by Name

+	Symbol["*name*"] construct a symbol with a given name
+	SymbolName[*symb*] find the name of a symbol

Converting between symbols and their names.

Here is the symbol x.	*In[1]:=* **x // InputForm**
	Out[1]//InputForm= x
Its name is a string.	*In[2]:=* **SymbolName[x] // InputForm**
	Out[2]//InputForm= "x"
This gives the symbol x again.	*In[3]:=* **Symbol["x"] // InputForm**
	Out[3]//InputForm= x

Once you have made an assignment such as x = 2, then whenever x is evaluated, it is replaced by 2. Sometimes, however, you may want to continue to refer to x itself, without immediately getting the value of x.

You can do this by referring to x by name. The name of the symbol x is the string "x", and even though x itself may be replaced by a value, the string "x" will always stay the same.

The names of the symbols x and xp are the strings "x" and "xp".	*In[4]:=* **t = {SymbolName[x], SymbolName[xp]} // InputForm**
	Out[4]//InputForm= {"x", "xp"}
This assigns a value to x.	*In[5]:=* **x = 2**
	Out[5]= 2
Whenever you enter x it is now replaced by 2.	*In[6]:=* **{x, xp} // InputForm**
	Out[6]//InputForm= {2, xp}
The name "x" is not affected, however.	*In[7]:=* **t // InputForm**
	Out[7]//InputForm= InputForm[{"x", "xp"}]

NameQ["*form*"]	test whether any symbol has a name which matches *form*
Names["*form*"]	give a list of all symbol names which match *form*
Contexts["*form*`"]	give a list of all context names which match *form*

Referring to symbols and contexts by name.

x and xp are symbols that have been created in this *Mathematica* session; xpp is not.

```
In[8]:= {NameQ["x"], NameQ["xp"], NameQ["xpp"]}
Out[8]= {True, True, False}
```

You can specify the form of symbol names using *string patterns* of the kind discussed on page 390. "x*" stands, for example, for all names that start with x.

This gives a list of all symbol names in this *Mathematica* session that begin with x.

```
In[9]:= Names["x*"] // InputForm
Out[9]//InputForm= {"x", "xmax", "xmin", "xp", "x$"}
```

These names correspond to built-in functions in *Mathematica*.

```
In[10]:= Names["Qu*"] // InputForm
Out[10]//InputForm= {"Quartics", "QuasiMonteCarlo", "QuasiNewton",
                     "Quit", "Quotient"}
```

This asks for names "close" to WeierstrssP.

```
In[11]:= Names["WeierstrssP", SpellingCorrection->True]
Out[11]= {WeierstrassP}
```

Clear["*form*"]	clear the values of all symbols whose names match *form*
Clear["*context*`*"]	clear the values of all symbols in the specified context
Remove["*form*"]	remove completely all symbols whose names match *form*
Remove["*context*`*"]	remove completely all symbols in the specified context

Getting rid of symbols by name.

This clears the values of all symbols whose names start with x.

```
In[12]:= Clear["x*"]
```

The name "x" is still known, however.

```
In[13]:= Names["x*"]
Out[13]= {x, xmax, xmin, xp, x$}
```

But the value of x has been cleared.

```
In[14]:= {x, xp}
Out[14]= {x, xp}
```

This removes completely all symbols whose names start with x.

```
In[15]:= Remove["x*"]
```

Now not even the name "x" is known.   *In[16]:=* **Names["x*"]**

Out[16]= {}

Remove["Global`*"]	remove completely all symbols in the **Global`** context

Removing all symbols you have introduced.

If you do not set up any additional contexts, then all the symbols that you introduce in a *Mathematica* session will be placed in the **Global`** context. You can remove these symbols completely using **Remove["Global`*"]**. Built-in *Mathematica* objects are in the **System`** context, and are thus unaffected by this.

■ 2.6.13 Advanced Topic: Intercepting the Creation of New Symbols

Mathematica creates a new symbol when you first enter a particular name. Sometimes it is useful to "intercept" the process of creating a new symbol. *Mathematica* provides several ways to do this.

On[General::newsym]	print a message whenever a new symbol is created
Off[General::newsym]	switch off the message printed when new symbols are created

Printing a message when new symbols are created.

This tells *Mathematica* to print a message whenever a new symbol is created.

In[1]:= **On[General::newsym]**

Mathematica now prints a message about each new symbol that it creates.

In[2]:= **sin[k]**

General::newsym: Symbol sin is new.

General::newsym: Symbol k is new.

Out[2]= sin[k]

This switches off the message.

In[3]:= **Off[General::newsym]**

Generating a message when *Mathematica* creates a new symbol is often a good way to catch typing mistakes. *Mathematica* itself cannot tell the difference between an intentionally new name, and a misspelling of a name it already knows. But by reporting all new names it encounters, *Mathematica* allows you to see whether any of them are mistakes.

| $NewSymbol | a function to be applied to the name and context of new symbols which are created |

Performing operations when new symbols are created.

When *Mathematica* creates a new symbol, you may want it not just to print a message, but instead to perform some other action. Any function you specify as the value of the global variable $NewSymbol will automatically be applied to strings giving the name and context of each new symbol that *Mathematica* creates.

This defines a function to be applied to each new symbol which is created.

```
In[4]:= $NewSymbol = Print["Name: ", #1, "  Context: ", #2]&

Out[4]= Print[Name: , #1,  Context: , #2]&
```

The function is applied once to v and once to w.

```
In[5]:= v + w

Name: v  Context: Global`
Name: w  Context: Global`

Out[5]= v + w
```

2.7 Strings and Characters

■ 2.7.1 Properties of Strings

Much of what *Mathematica* does revolves around manipulating structured expressions. But you can also use *Mathematica* as a system for handling unstructured strings of text.

"text"	a string containing arbitrary text

Text strings.

When you input a string of text to *Mathematica* you must always enclose it in quotes. However, when *Mathematica* outputs the string it usually does not explicitly show the quotes.

You can see the quotes by asking for the input form of the string. In addition, in a *Mathematica* notebook, quotes will typically appear automatically as soon as you start to edit a string.

When *Mathematica* outputs a string, it usually does not explicitly show the quotes.

```
In[1]:= "This is a string."
Out[1]= This is a string.
```

You can see the quotes, however, by asking for the input form of the string.

```
In[2]:= InputForm[%]
Out[2]//InputForm= "This is a string."
```

The fact that *Mathematica* does not usually show explicit quotes around strings makes it possible for you to use strings to specify quite directly the textual output you want.

The strings are printed out here without explicit quotes.

```
In[3]:= Print["The value is ", 567, "."]
The value is 567.
```

You should understand, however, that even though the string "x" often appears as x in output, it is still a quite different object from the symbol x.

The string "x" is not the same as the symbol x.

```
In[4]:= "x" === x
Out[4]= False
```

You can test whether any particular expression is a string by looking at its head. The head of any string is always String.

All strings have head String.

```
In[5]:= Head["x"]
Out[5]= String
```

The pattern _String matches any string.

```
In[6]:= Cases[{"ab", x, "a", y}, _String]
Out[6]= {ab, a}
```

You can use strings just like other expressions as elements of patterns and transformations. Note, however, that you cannot assign values directly to strings.

This gives a definition for an expression that involves a string.	*In[7]:=* **z["gold"] = 79** *Out[7]=* 79
This replaces each occurrence of the string "aa" by the symbol x.	*In[8]:=* **{"aaa", "aa", "bb", "aa"} /. "aa" -> x** *Out[8]=* {aaa, x, bb, x}

■ 2.7.2 Operations on Strings

Mathematica provides a variety of functions for manipulating strings. Most of these functions are based on viewing strings as a sequence of characters, and many of the functions are analogous to ones for manipulating lists.

s_1 <> s_2 <> ... or StringJoin[{s_1, s_2, ... }]	
	join several strings together
StringLength[s]	give the number of characters in a string
StringReverse[s]	reverse the characters in a string

Operations on complete strings.

You can join together any number of strings using <>.	*In[1]:=* **"aaaaaaa" <> "bbb" <> "cccccccccc"** *Out[1]=* aaaaaaabbbcccccccccc
StringLength gives the number of characters in a string.	*In[2]:=* **StringLength[%]** *Out[2]=* 20
StringReverse reverses the characters in a string.	*In[3]:=* **StringReverse["A string."]** *Out[3]=* .gnirts A

StringTake[s, n]	make a string by taking the first n characters from s
StringTake[s, {n}]	take the nth character from s
StringTake[s, {n_1, n_2}]	take characters n_1 through n_2
StringDrop[s, n]	make a string by dropping the first n characters in s
StringDrop[s, {n_1, n_2}]	drop characters n_1 through n_2

Taking and dropping substrings.

   StringTake and **StringDrop** are the analogs for strings of **Take** and **Drop** for lists. Like **Take** and **Drop**, they use standard *Mathematica* sequence specifications, so that, for example, negative numbers count character positions from the end of a string. Note that the first character of a string is taken to have position 1.

Here is a sample string.	*In[4]:=* **alpha = "ABCDEFGHIJKLMNOPQRSTUVWXYZ"**
	Out[4]= ABCDEFGHIJKLMNOPQRSTUVWXYZ
This takes the first five characters from alpha.	*In[5]:=* **StringTake[alpha, 5]**
	Out[5]= ABCDE
Here is the fifth character in alpha.	*In[6]:=* **StringTake[alpha, {5}]**
	Out[6]= E
This drops the characters 10 through 2, counting from the end of the string.	*In[7]:=* **StringDrop[alpha, {-10, -2}]**
	Out[7]= ABCDEFGHIJKLMNOPZ

StringInsert[s, snew, n]	insert the string *snew* at position *n* in *s*
StringInsert[s, snew, {n₁, n₂, ... }]	
	insert several copies of *snew* into *s*

Inserting into a string.

   StringInsert[s, snew, n] is set up to produce a string whose n^{th} character is the first character of *snew*.

This produces a new string whose fourth character is the first character of the string "XX".	*In[8]:=* **StringInsert["abcdefgh", "XX", 4]**
	Out[8]= abcXXdefgh
Negative positions are counted from the end of the string.	*In[9]:=* **StringInsert["abcdefgh", "XXX", -1]**
	Out[9]= abcdefghXXX
Each copy of "XXX" is inserted at the specified position in the original string.	*In[10]:=* **StringInsert["abcdefgh", "XXX", {2, 4, -1}]**
	Out[10]= aXXXbcXXXdefghXXX

+	`StringReplacePart[s, snew, {m, n}]`
	replace the characters at positions *m* through *n* in *s* by the string *snew*
+	`StringReplacePart[s, snew, {{m₁, n₁}, {m₂, n₂}, ... }]`
	replace several substrings in *s* by *snew*
+	`StringReplacePart[s, {snew₁, snew₂, ... }, {{m₁, n₁}, {m₂, n₂}, ... }]`
	replace substrings in *s* by the corresponding *snewᵢ*

Replacing parts of a string.

This replaces characters 2 through 6 by the string `"XXX"`.

```
In[11]:= StringReplacePart["abcdefgh", "XXX", {2, 6}]

Out[11]= aXXXgh
```

This replaces two runs of characters by the string `"XXX"`.

```
In[12]:= StringReplacePart["abcdefgh", "XXX", {{2, 3}, {5, -1}}]

Out[12]= aXXXdXXX
```

Now the two runs of characters are replaced by different strings.

```
In[13]:= StringReplacePart["abcdefgh", {"XXX", "YYYY"},
                               {{2, 3}, {5, -1}}]

Out[13]= aXXXdYYYY
```

`StringPosition[s, sub]`	give a list of the starting and ending positions at which *sub* appears as a substring of *s*
`StringPosition[s, sub, k]`	include only the first *k* occurrences of *sub* in *s*
`StringPosition[s, {sub₁, sub₂, ... }]`	include occurrences of any of the *subᵢ*

Finding positions of substrings.

You can use `StringPosition` to find where a particular substring appears within a given string. `StringPosition` returns a list, each of whose elements corresponds to an occurrence of the substring. The elements consist of lists giving the starting and ending character positions for the substring. These lists are in the form used as sequence specifications in `StringTake`, `StringDrop` and `StringReplacePart`.

This gives a list of the positions of the substring `"abc"`.

```
In[14]:= StringPosition["abcdabcdaabcabcd", "abc"]

Out[14]= {{1, 3}, {5, 7}, {10, 12}, {13, 15}}
```

This gives only the first occurrence of `"abc"`.

```
In[15]:= StringPosition["abcdabcdaabcabcd", "abc", 1]

Out[15]= {{1, 3}}
```

This shows where both "abc" and "cd" appear. Overlaps between these strings are taken into account.

In[16]:= **StringPosition["abcdabcdaabcabcd", {"abc", "cd"}]**

Out[16]= {{1, 3}, {3, 4}, {5, 7}, {7, 8}, {10, 12},
          {13, 15}, {15, 16}}

StringReplace[*s*, {*s*$_1$ -> *sp*$_1$, *s*$_2$ -> *sp*$_2$, ... }]
      replace the *s*$_i$ by the corresponding *sp*$_i$ whenever they
      appear as substrings of *s*

Replacing substrings according to rules.

StringReplace allows you to perform replacements for substrings within a string. **StringReplace** sequentially goes through a string, testing substrings that start at each successive character position. To each substring, it tries in turn each of the transformation rules you have specified. If any of the rules apply, it replaces the substring, then continues to go through the string, starting at the character position after the end of the substring.

This replaces all occurrences of the character a by the string XX.

In[17]:= **StringReplace["abcdabcdaabcabcd", "a" -> "XX"]**

Out[17]= XXbcdXXbcdXXXXbcXXbcd

This replaces abc by Y, and d by XXX.

In[18]:= **StringReplace["abcdabcdaabcabcd",
                          {"abc" -> "Y", "d" -> "XXX"}]**

Out[18]= YXXXYXXXaYYXXX

The first occurrence of cde is not replaced because it overlaps with abc.

In[19]:= **StringReplace["abcde abacde",
                          {"abc" -> "X", "cde" -> "Y"}]**

Out[19]= Xde abaY

StringPosition[*s*, *sub*, IgnoreCase -> True]
      find where *sub* occurs in *s*, treating lower- and upper-case
      letters as equivalent

StringReplace[*s*, {*s*$_1$ -> *sp*$_1$, ... }, IgnoreCase -> True]
      replace *s*$_i$ by *sp*$_i$ in *s*, treating lower- and upper-case letters
      as equivalent

Case-independent operations.

This replaces all occurrences of "the", independent of case.

In[20]:= **StringReplace["The cat in the hat.", "the" -> "a",
                                        IgnoreCase -> True]**

Out[20]= a cat in a hat.

| Sort[{s_1, s_2, s_3, ... }] | sort a list of strings |

Sorting strings.

Sort sorts strings into standard dictionary order.

```
In[21]:= Sort[{"cat", "fish", "catfish", "Cat"}]
Out[21]= {cat, Cat, catfish, fish}
```

■ 2.7.3 String Patterns

You can use the standard *Mathematica* equality test s_1 == s_2 to test whether two strings are identical. Sometimes, however, you may want to find out whether a particular string matches a certain *string pattern*.

Mathematica allows you to define *string patterns* which consist of ordinary strings in which certain characters are interpreted as special "metacharacters". You can then use the function StringMatchQ to find out whether a particular string matches a string pattern you have defined. You should realize however that string patterns have nothing to do with the ordinary *Mathematica* patterns for expressions that were discussed in Section 2.3.

| "*string*$_1$" == "*string*$_2$" | test whether two strings are identical |
| StringMatchQ["*string*", "*pattern*"] | test whether a string matches a particular string pattern |

Matching strings.

The character * can be used in a string pattern as a metacharacter to stand for any sequence of alphanumeric characters. Thus, for example, the string pattern "a*b" would match any string which begins with an a, ends with a b, and has any number of alphanumeric characters in between. Similarly, "a*b*" would match any string that starts with a, and has any number of other characters, including at least one b.

The string matches the string pattern you have given.

```
In[1]:= StringMatchQ["aaaaabbbbcccbbb", "a*b*"]
Out[1]= True
```

The way * is used in *Mathematica* string patterns is analogous to the way it is used for file-name patterns in many operating systems. *Mathematica* however provides some other string pattern metacharacters that are tailored to matching different classes of *Mathematica* symbol names.

*	zero or more characters
@	one or more characters which are not upper-case letters
* etc.	literal * etc.

Metacharacters used in string patterns.

In *Mathematica* there is a general convention that only built-in names should contain upper-case characters. Assuming that you follow this convention, you can use @ as a metacharacter to set up string patterns which match names you have defined, but avoid matching built-in names.

```
StringMatchQ["string", "pattern", SpellingCorrection -> True]
                test whether pattern matches string, allowing a small fraction
                of characters to differ
StringMatchQ["string", "pattern", IgnoreCase -> True]
                test whether pattern matches string, treating lower- and
                upper-case letters as equivalent
```

Options for matching strings.

These strings do not match.

```
In[2]:= StringMatchQ["platypus", "paltypus"]
Out[2]= False
```

Allowing for spelling correction, these strings are considered to match.

```
In[3]:= StringMatchQ["platypus", "paltypus",
                      SpellingCorrection -> True]
Out[3]= True
```

These strings match when lower- and upper-case letters are treated as equivalent.

```
In[4]:= StringMatchQ["AAaaBBbb", "a*b*", IgnoreCase -> True]
Out[4]= True
```

■ 2.7.4 Characters in Strings

```
Characters["string"]            convert a string to a list of characters
StringJoin[{"c1", "c2", ... }]  convert a list of characters to a string
```

Converting between strings and lists of characters.

This gives a list of the characters in the string.

```
In[1]:= Characters["A string."]
Out[1]= {A,  , s, t, r, i, n, g, .}
```

You can apply standard list
manipulation operations to this list.

```
In[2]:= RotateLeft[%, 3]
Out[2]= {t, r, i, n, g, ., A,  , s}
```

StringJoin converts the list of
characters back to a single string.

```
In[3]:= StringJoin[%]
Out[3]= tring.A s
```

DigitQ[*string*]	test whether all characters in a string are digits
LetterQ[*string*]	test whether all characters in a string are letters
UpperCaseQ[*string*]	test whether all characters in a string are upper-case letters
LowerCaseQ[*string*]	test whether all characters in a string are lower-case letters

Testing characters in a string.

All characters in the string given are
letters.

```
In[4]:= LetterQ["Mixed"]
Out[4]= True
```

Not all the letters are upper case, so
the result is False.

```
In[5]:= UpperCaseQ["Mixed"]
Out[5]= False
```

ToUpperCase[*string*]	generate a string in which all letters are upper case
ToLowerCase[*string*]	generate a string in which all letters are lower case

Converting between upper and lower case.

This converts all letters to upper case.

```
In[6]:= ToUpperCase["Mixed Form"]
Out[6]= MIXED FORM
```

+ CharacterRange["c_1", "c_2"]	generate a list of all characters from c_1 and c_2

Generating ranges of characters.

This generates a list of lower-case
letters in alphabetical order.

```
In[7]:= CharacterRange["a", "h"]
Out[7]= {a, b, c, d, e, f, g, h}
```

Here is a list of upper-case letters.

```
In[8]:= CharacterRange["T", "Z"]
Out[8]= {T, U, V, W, X, Y, Z}
```

Here are some digits.

```
In[9]:= CharacterRange["0", "7"]
Out[9]= {0, 1, 2, 3, 4, 5, 6, 7}
```

`CharacterRange` will usually give meaningful results for any range of characters that have a natural ordering. The way `CharacterRange` works is by using the character codes that *Mathematica* internally assigns to every character.

This shows the ordering defined by the internal character codes used by *Mathematica*.	`In[10]:= CharacterRange["T", "f"]` `Out[10]= {T, U, V, W, X, Y, Z, [, \", ], ^, _, `, a, b, c, d, e, f}`

+■ 2.7.5 Special Characters

In addition to the ordinary characters that appear on a standard keyboard, you can include in *Mathematica* strings any of the special characters that are supported by *Mathematica*.

Here is a string containing special characters.	`In[1]:= "α⊕β⊕…"` `Out[1]= α⊕β⊕…`
You can manipulate this string just as you would any other.	`In[2]:= StringReplace[%, "⊕" -> " ⊙⊙ "]` `Out[2]= α ⊙⊙ β ⊙⊙ …`
Here is the list of the characters in the string.	`In[3]:= Characters[%]` `Out[3]= {α, , ⊙, ⊙, , β, , ⊙, ⊙, , …}`

In a *Mathematica* notebook, a special character such as α can always be displayed directly. But if you use a text-based interface, then typically the only characters that can readily be displayed are the ones that appear on your keyboard.

As a result, what *Mathematica* does in such situations is to try to approximate special characters by similar-looking sequences of ordinary characters. And when this is not practical, *Mathematica* just gives the full name of the special character.

In a *Mathematica* notebook using `StandardForm`, special characters can be displayed directly.	`In[4]:= "Lamé ⟶ αβ+"` `Out[4]= Lamé ⟶ αβ+`
In `OutputForm`, however, the special characters are approximated when possible by sequences of ordinary ones.	`In[5]:= % // OutputForm` `Out[5]//OutputForm= Lame' —> \[Alpha]\[Beta]+`

Mathematica always uses full names for special characters in `InputForm`. This means that when special characters are written out to files or external programs, they are by default represented purely as sequences of ordinary characters.

This uniform representation is crucial in allowing special characters in *Mathematica* to be used in a way that does not depend on the details of particular computer systems.

In `InputForm` the full names of all special characters are always written out explicitly.	`In[6]:= "Lamé ⟶ αβ+" // InputForm` `Out[6]//InputForm= "Lam\[EAcute] \[LongRightArrow] \[Alpha]\[Beta]+"`

+	*a*	a literal character
	\[*Name*]	a character specified using its full name
	\"	a " to be included in a string
	\\	a \ to be included in a string

Ways to enter characters in a string.

You have to use \ to "escape" any " or \ characters in strings that you enter.

```
In[7]:= "Strings can contain \"quotes\" and \\ characters."
Out[7]= Strings can contain "quotes" and \ characters.
```

\\ produces a literal \ rather than forming part of the specification of α.

```
In[8]:= "\\[Alpha] is \[Alpha]."
Out[8]= \[Alpha] is α.
```

This breaks the string into a list of individual characters.

```
In[9]:= Characters[%]
Out[9]= {\, [, A, l, p, h, a, ], , i, s, , α, .}
```

This creates a list of the characters in the full name of α.

```
In[10]:= Characters[ ToString[InputForm["α"]] ]
Out[10]= {", \, [, A, l, p, h, a, ], "}
```

And this produces a string consisting of an actual α from its full name.

```
In[11]:= ToExpression[ "\"\\[" <> "Alpha" <> "]\""]
Out[11]= α
```

■ 2.7.6 Advanced Topic: Newlines and Tabs in Strings

	\n	a newline (line feed) to be included in a string
	\t	a tab to be included in a string

Explicit representations of newlines and tabs in strings.

This prints on two lines.

```
In[1]:= "First line.\nSecond line."
Out[1]= First line.
        Second line.
```

In InputForm there is an explicit \n to represent the newline.

```
In[2]:= InputForm[%]
Out[2]//InputForm= "First line.\nSecond line."
```

When you enter a long string in *Mathematica*, it is often convenient to break your input across several lines. *Mathematica* will by default ignore such breaks, so that if you subsequently output the string, it can then be broken in whatever way is appropriate.

Mathematica ignores the line break and any tabs that follow it.	*In[3]:=* **"A string on** **two lines."** *Out[3]=* A string on two lines.
There is no newline in the string.	*In[4]:=* **InputForm[%]** *Out[4]//InputForm=* "A string on two lines."

"*text*"	line breaks in *text* are ignored
"\<*text*\>"	line breaks in *text* are stored explicitly as \n

Input forms for strings.

Now *Mathematica* keeps the newline.	*In[5]:=* **"\<A string on**
	            two lines.\>"
	
	Out[5]= A string on
	            two lines.

In InputForm, the newline is shown as an explicit \n.	*In[6]:=* **InputForm[%]** *Out[6]//InputForm=* "A string on\ntwo lines."

You should realize that even though it is possible to achieve some formatting of *Mathematica* output by creating strings which contain raw tabs and newlines, this is rarely a good idea. Typically a much better approach is to use the higher-level *Mathematica* formatting primitives to be discussed in the next two sections. These primitives will always yield consistent output, independent of such issues as the positions of tab settings on a particular device.

In strings with newlines, text is always aligned on the left.	*In[7]:=* **{"Here is\na string\non several lines.",**
	            "Here is\nanother"}
	
	Out[7]= {Here is
	            a string
	            on several lines., Here is
	            another}

The ColumnForm formatting primitive gives more control. Here text is aligned on the right.	*In[8]:=* **ColumnForm[{"First line", "Second", "Third"}, Right]**
	Out[8]= First line
	                Second
	                  Third

And here the text is centered.	*In[9]:=* **ColumnForm[{"First line", "Second", "Third"}, Center]**
	Out[9]= First line
	              Second
	               Third

Within *Mathematica* you can use formatting primitives to avoid raw tabs and newlines. But if you intend to send your output in textual form to external programs, then these programs will often expect to get raw tabs and newlines.

Note that you must either use `WriteString` or give your output in `OutputForm` in order for the raw tabs and newlines to show up. In `InputForm`, they will just be given as \t and \n.

This outputs a string to a file.	`In[10]:= "First line.\nSecond line." >> test`

Here are the contents of the file. By default, >> generates output in `InputForm`.	`In[11]:= !!test`
	
	`"First line.\nSecond line."`

This explicitly tells *Mathematica* to use `OutputForm` for the output.	`In[12]:= OutputForm["First line.\nSecond line."] >> test`

Now there is a raw newline in the file.	`In[13]:= !!test`
	
	`First line.`
	`Second line.`

■ 2.7.7 Advanced Topic: Character Codes

`ToCharacterCode["string"]`	give a list of the character codes for the characters in a string
`FromCharacterCode[n]`	construct a character from its character code
`FromCharacterCode[{n_1, n_2, ... }]`	construct a string of characters from a list of character codes

Converting to and from character codes.

Mathematica assigns every character that can appear in a string a unique *character code*. This code is used internally as a way to represent the character.

This gives the character codes for the characters in the string.	`In[1]:= ToCharacterCode["ABCD abcd"]` `Out[1]= {65, 66, 67, 68, 32, 97, 98, 99, 100}`
`FromCharacterCode` reconstructs the original string.	`In[2]:= FromCharacterCode[%]` `Out[2]= ABCD abcd`
Special characters also have character codes.	`In[3]:= ToCharacterCode["α⊕Γ⊎∅"]` `Out[3]= {945, 8853, 915, 8854, 8709}`

+ `CharacterRange["c_1", "c_2"]`	generate a list of characters with successive character codes

Generating sequences of characters.

This gives part of the English alphabet.

In[4]:= **CharacterRange["a", "k"]**

Out[4]= {a, b, c, d, e, f, g, h, i, j, k}

Here is the Greek alphabet.

In[5]:= **CharacterRange["α", "ω"]**

Out[5]= {α, β, γ, δ, ε, ζ, η, θ, ι, κ, λ, μ, ν, ξ, o, π, ρ,
ς, σ, τ, υ, φ, χ, ψ, ω}

Mathematica assigns names such as \[Alpha] to a large number of special characters. This means that you can always refer to such characters just by giving their names, without ever having to know their character codes.

This generates a string of special characters from their character codes.

In[6]:= **FromCharacterCode[{8706, 8709, 8711, 8712}]**

Out[6]= ∂∅∇∈

You can always refer to these characters by their names, without knowing their character codes.

In[7]:= **InputForm[%]**

Out[7]//InputForm= "\[PartialD]\[EmptySet]\[Del]\[Element]"

Mathematica has names for all the common characters that are used in mathematical notation and in standard European languages. But for a language such as Japanese, there are more than 3,000 additional characters, and *Mathematica* does not assign an explicit name to each of them. Instead, it refers to such characters by standardized character codes.

Here is a string containing Japanese characters.

In[8]:= **"数学"**

Out[8]= 数学

In InputForm, these characters are referred to by standardized character codes. The character codes are given in hexadecimal.

In[9]:= **InputForm[%]**

Out[9]//InputForm= "\:a0fd\:a079"

The notebook front end for *Mathematica* is typically set up so that when you enter a character in a particular font, *Mathematica* will automatically work out the character code for that character.

Sometimes, however, you may find it convenient to be able to enter characters directly using character codes.

\0	null byte (code 0)
\nnn	a character with octal code nnn
\.nn	a character with hexadecimal code nn
\:nnnn	a character with hexadecimal code nnnn

Ways to enter characters directly in terms of character codes.

For characters with character codes below 256, you can use *nnn* or \.*nn*. For characters with character codes above 256, you must use \:*nnnn*. Note that in all cases you must give a fixed number of octal or hexadecimal digits, padding with leading 0s if necessary.

This gives character codes in hexadecimal for a few characters.	*In[10]:=* **BaseForm[ToCharacterCode["Aàαℵ"], 16]**
	Out[10]//BaseForm= {41_{16}, $e0_{16}$, $3b1_{16}$, 2135_{16}}
This enters the characters using their character codes. Note the leading 0 inserted in the character code for α.	*In[11]:=* **"\.41\.e0\:03b1\:2135"**
	Out[11]= Aàαℵ

In assigning codes to characters, *Mathematica* follows three compatible standards: ASCII, ISO Latin-1, and Unicode. ASCII covers the characters on a normal American English keyboard. ISO Latin-1 covers characters in many European languages. Unicode is a more general standard which defines character codes for several tens of thousands of characters used in languages and notations around the world.

0 – 127 (\000 – \177)	ASCII characters
1 – 31 (\001 – \037)	ASCII control characters
32 – 126 (\040 – \176)	printable ASCII characters
97 – 122 (\141 – \172)	lower-case English letters
129 – 255 (\201 – \377)	ISO Latin-1 characters
192 – 255 (\240 – \377)	letters in European languages
0 – 59391 (\:0000 – \:e7ff)	Unicode standard public characters
913 – 1009 (\:0391 – \:03f1)	Greek letters
12288 – 35839 (\:3000 – \:8bff)	Chinese, Japanese and Korean characters
8450 – 8504 (\:2102 – \:2138)	modified letters used in mathematical notation
8592 – 8677 (\:2190 – \:21e5)	arrows
8704 – 8945 (\:2200 – \:22f1)	mathematical symbols and operators
64256 – 64300 (\:fb00 – \:fb2c)	Unicode private characters defined specially by *Mathematica*

A few ranges of character codes used by *Mathematica*.

2.8 Textual Input and Output

■ 2.8.1 Forms of Input and Output

Here is one way to enter a particular expression.

In[1]:= **x^2 + Sqrt[y]**

Out[1]= $x^2 + \sqrt{y}$

Here is another way to enter the same expression.

In[2]:= **Plus[Power[x, 2], Sqrt[y]]**

Out[2]= $x^2 + \sqrt{y}$

With a notebook front end, you can also enter the expression directly in this way.

In[3]:= $x^2 + \sqrt{y}$

Out[3]= $x^2 + \sqrt{y}$

Mathematica allows you to output expressions in many different ways.

In *Mathematica* notebooks, expressions are by default output in StandardForm.

In[4]:= **x^2 + Sqrt[y]**

Out[4]= $x^2 + \sqrt{y}$

OutputForm uses only ordinary keyboard characters and is the default for text-based interfaces to *Mathematica*.

In[5]:= **OutputForm[x^2 + Sqrt[y]]**

Out[5]//OutputForm= x^2 + Sqrt[y]

InputForm yields a form that can be typed directly on a keyboard.

In[6]:= **InputForm[x^2 + Sqrt[y]]**

Out[6]//InputForm= x^2 + Sqrt[y]

FullForm shows the internal form of an expression in explicit functional notation.

In[7]:= **FullForm[x^2 + Sqrt[y]]**

Out[7]//FullForm= Plus[Power[x, 2], Power[y, Rational[1, 2]]]

FullForm[*expr*]	the internal form of an expression
InputForm[*expr*]	a form suitable for direct keyboard input
OutputForm[*expr*]	a two-dimensional form using only keyboard characters
StandardForm[*expr*]	the default form used in *Mathematica* notebooks

Some output forms for expressions.

Output forms provide textual representations of *Mathematica* expressions. In some cases these textual representations are also suitable for input to *Mathematica*. But in other cases they are intended just to be looked at, or to be exported to other programs, rather than to be used as input to *Mathematica*.

TraditionalForm uses a large collection of ad hoc rules to produce an approximation to traditional mathematical notation.

$In[8]:=$ **TraditionalForm[x^2 + Sqrt[y] + Gamma[z] EllipticK[z]]**

$Out[8]//TraditionalForm= x^2 + K(z)\,\Gamma(z) + \sqrt{y}$

TeXForm yields output suitable for export to TeX.

$In[9]:=$ **TeXForm[x^2 + Sqrt[y]]**

$Out[9]//TeXForm=$ {x^2} + {\sqrt{y}}

CForm yields output that can be included in a C program. Macros for objects like Power are included in the header file mdefs.h.

$In[10]:=$ **CForm[x^2 + Sqrt[y]]**

$Out[10]//CForm=$ Power(x,2) + Sqrt(y)

FortranForm yields output suitable for export to Fortran.

$In[11]:=$ **FortranForm[x^2 + Sqrt[y]]**

$Out[11]//FortranForm=$ x**2 + Sqrt(y)

+	TraditionalForm[*expr*]	traditional mathematical notation
	TeXForm[*expr*]	output suitable for export to TeX
	CForm[*expr*]	output suitable for export to C
	FortranForm[*expr*]	output suitable for export to Fortran

Output forms not normally used for *Mathematica* input.

Section 2.8.17 will discuss how you can create your own output forms. You should realize however that in communicating with external programs it is often better to use *MathLink* to send expressions directly than to generate a textual representation for these expressions.

- Exchange textual representations of expressions.
- Exchange expressions directly via *MathLink*.

Two ways to communicate between *Mathematica* and other programs.

■ 2.8.2 How Input and Output Work

Input	convert from a textual form to an expression
Processing	do computations on the expression
Output	convert the resulting expression to textual form

Steps in the operation of *Mathematica*.

When you type something like x^2 what *Mathematica* at first sees is just the string of characters x, ^, 2. But with the usual way that *Mathematica* is set up, it immediately knows to convert this string of characters into the expression Power[x, 2].

Then, after whatever processing is possible has been done, *Mathematica* takes the expression Power[x, 2] and converts it into some kind of textual representation for output.

Mathematica reads the string of characters x, ^, 2 and converts it to the expression Power[x, 2].	*In[1]:=* **x ^ 2** *Out[1]=* x^2
This shows the expression in Fortran form.	*In[2]:=* **FortranForm[%]** *Out[2]//FortranForm=* x**2
FortranForm is just a "wrapper": the value of Out[2] is still the expression Power[x, 2].	*In[3]:=* **%** *Out[3]=* x^2

It is important to understand that in a typical *Mathematica* session In[*n*] and Out[*n*] record only the underlying expressions that are processed, not the textual representations that happen to be used for their input or output.

If you explicitly request a particular kind of output, say by using TraditionalForm[*expr*], then what you get will be labeled with Out[*n*]//TraditionalForm. This indicates that what you are seeing is *expr*//TraditionalForm, even though the value of Out[*n*] itself is just *expr*.

Mathematica also allows you to specify globally that you want output to be displayed in a particular form. And if you do this, then the form will no longer be indicated explicitly in the label for each line. But it is still the case that In[*n*] and Out[*n*] will record only underlying expressions, not the textual representations used for their input and output.

This sets t to be an expression with FortranForm explicitly wrapped around it.	*In[4]:=* **t = FortranForm[x^2 + y^2]** *Out[4]//FortranForm=* x**2 + y**2
The result on the previous line is just the expression.	*In[5]:=* **%** *Out[5]=* $x^2 + y^2$
But t contains the FortranForm wrapper, and so is displayed in FortranForm.	*In[6]:=* **t** *Out[6]//FortranForm=* x**2 + y**2
Wherever t appears, it is formatted in FortranForm.	*In[7]:=* **{t^2, 1/t}** *Out[7]=* $\left\{ \text{x**2 + y**2}^2, \dfrac{1}{\text{x**2 + y**2}} \right\}$

▪ 2.8.3 The Representation of Textual Forms

Like everything else in *Mathematica* the textual forms of expressions can themselves be represented as expressions. Textual forms that consist of one-dimensional sequences of characters can be represented directly as ordinary *Mathematica* strings. Textual forms that involve subscripts, superscripts and other two-dimensional constructs, however, can be represented by nested collections of two-dimensional boxes.

One-dimensional strings	`InputForm`, `FullForm`, etc.
Two-dimensional boxes	`StandardForm`, `TraditionalForm`, etc.

Typical representations of textual forms.

This generates the string corresponding to the textual representation of the expression in `InputForm`.	`In[1]:= ToString[x^2 + y^3, InputForm]` `Out[1]= x^2 + y^3`
`FullForm` shows the string explicitly.	`In[2]:= FullForm[%]` `Out[2]//FullForm= "x^2 + y^3"`
Here are the individual characters in the string.	`In[3]:= Characters[%]` `Out[3]= {x, ^, 2,  , +,  , y, ^, 3}`

Here is the box structure corresponding to the expression in `StandardForm`.	`In[4]:= ToBoxes[x^2 + y^3, StandardForm]`
	`Out[4]= RowBox[`
	`        {SuperscriptBox[x, 2], +, SuperscriptBox[y, 3]}]`

Here is the `InputForm` of the box structure. In this form the structure is effectively represented by an ordinary string.	`In[5]:= ToBoxes[x^2 + y^3, StandardForm] // InputForm` `Out[5]//InputForm= \(x\^2 + y\^3\)`

If you use the notebook front end for *Mathematica*, then you can see the expression that corresponds to the textual form of each cell by using the Show Expression menu item.

Here is a cell containing an expression in `StandardForm`.

$$\frac{1}{2(1+x^2)} + \text{Log}[x] - \frac{\text{Log}[1+x^2]}{2}$$

Here is the underlying representation of that expression in terms of boxes, displayed using the Show Expression menu item.

```
Cell[BoxData[
  RowBox[{
    FractionBox["1",
      RowBox[{"2", " ",
        RowBox[{"(",
          RowBox[{"1", "+",
            SuperscriptBox["x", "2"]}], ")"}]}]], "+",
    RowBox[{"Log", "[", "x", "]"}], "-",
    FractionBox[
      RowBox[{"Log", "[",
        RowBox[{"1", "+",
          SuperscriptBox["x", "2"]}], "]"}], "2"]}]], "Output"]
```

ToString[*expr*, *form*]	create a string representing the specified textual form of *expr*
ToBoxes[*expr*, *form*]	create a box structure representing the specified textual form of *expr*

Creating strings and boxes from expressions.

■ 2.8.4 The Interpretation of Textual Forms

ToExpression[*input*]	create an expression by interpreting strings or boxes

Converting from strings or boxes to expressions.

This takes a string and interprets it as an expression.

In[1]:= **ToExpression["2 + 3 + x/y"]**

$Out[1]= 5 + \dfrac{x}{y}$

Here is the box structure corresponding to the textual form of an expression in StandardForm.

In[2]:= **ToBoxes[2 + x^2, StandardForm]**

Out[2]= RowBox[{2, +, SuperscriptBox[x, 2]}]

ToExpression interprets this box structure and yields the original expression again.

In[3]:= **ToExpression[%]**

$Out[3]= 2 + x^2$

In any *Mathematica* session, *Mathematica* is always effectively using ToExpression to interpret the textual form of your input as an actual expression to evaluate.

If you use the notebook front end for *Mathematica*, then the interpretation only takes place when the contents of a cell are sent to the kernel, say for evaluation. This means that within a notebook there is no need for the textual forms you set up to correspond to meaningful *Mathematica* expressions; this is only necessary if you want to send these forms to the kernel.

FullForm	explicit functional notation
InputForm	one-dimensional notation
StandardForm	two-dimensional notation

The hierarchy of forms for standard *Mathematica* input.

Here is an expression entered in FullForm.	*In[4]:=* **Plus[1, Power[x, 2]]** *Out[4]=* $1 + x^2$
Here is the same expression entered in InputForm.	*In[5]:=* **1 + x^2** *Out[5]=* $1 + x^2$
And here is the expression entered in StandardForm.	*In[6]:=* **1 + x²** *Out[6]=* $1 + x^2$

Built into *Mathematica* is a collection of standard rules for use by ToExpression in converting textual forms to expressions.

These rules define the *grammar* of *Mathematica*. They state, for example, that *x* + *y* should be interpreted as Plus[*x*, *y*], and that x^y should be interpreted as Power[*x*, *y*]. If the input you give is in FullForm, then the rules for interpretation are very straightforward: every expression consists just of a head followed by a sequence of elements enclosed in brackets. The rules for InputForm are slightly more sophisticated: they allow operators such as +, =, and ->, and understand the meaning of expressions where these operators appear between operands. StandardForm involves still more sophisticated rules, which allow operators and operands to be arranged not just in a one-dimensional sequence, but in a full two-dimensional structure.

Mathematica is set up so that FullForm, InputForm and StandardForm form a strict hierarchy: anything you can enter in FullForm will also work in InputForm, and anything you can enter in InputForm will also work in StandardForm.

If you use a notebook front end for *Mathematica*, then you will typically want to use all the features of StandardForm. If you use a text-based interface, however, then you will typically be able to use only features of InputForm.

x^2	ordinary InputForm
\!\(x\^2\)	one-dimensional representation of StandardForm

Two versions of InputForm.

When you use StandardForm in a *Mathematica* notebook, you can enter directly two-dimensional forms such as x². But InputForm allows only one-dimensional forms. Nevertheless, even though the actual text you give in `InputForm` must be one-dimensional, it is still possible to make it represent a two-dimensional form. Thus, for example, `\!\(x\^2\)` represents the two-dimensional form x^2, and is interpreted by *Mathematica* as `Power[x, 2]`.

Here is ordinary one-dimensional input.	$In[7]:=$ **x^2 + 1/y**
	$Out[7]=$ $x^2 + \dfrac{1}{y}$
Here is input that represents a two-dimensional form.	$In[8]:=$ **\!\(x\^2 + 1\/y \)**
	$Out[8]=$ $x^2 + \dfrac{1}{y}$
Even though the input is given differently, the expressions obtained on the last two lines are exactly the same.	$In[9]:=$ **% == %%**
	$Out[9]=$ True

If you copy a two-dimensional form out of *Mathematica*, it is normally given in `\!\( ... \)` form. When you paste this one-dimensional form back into a *Mathematica* notebook, it will automatically "snap" into two-dimensional form. If you simply type a `\!\( ... \)` form into a notebook, you can get it to snap into two-dimensional form using the Make 2D menu item.

`ToExpression[`*input*, *form*`]`	attempt to create an expression assuming that *input* is given in the specified textual form

Importing from other textual forms.

`StandardForm` and its subsets `FullForm` and `InputForm` provide precise ways to represent any *Mathematica* expression in textual form. And given such a textual form, it is always possible to convert it unambiguously to the expression it represents.

`TraditionalForm` is an example of a textual form intended primarily for output. It is possible to take any *Mathematica* expression and display it in `TraditionalForm`. But `TraditionalForm` does not have the precision of `StandardForm`, and as a result there is in general no unambiguous way to go back from a `TraditionalForm` representation and get the expression it represents.

Nevertheless, `ToExpression[`*input*, `TraditionalForm]` takes text in `TraditionalForm` and attempts to interpret it as an expression.

This takes a string and interprets it as `TraditionalForm` input.	$In[10]:=$ **ToExpression["f(6)", TraditionalForm]**
	$Out[10]=$ f[6]
In `StandardForm` the same string would mean a product of terms.	$In[11]:=$ **ToExpression["f(6)", StandardForm]**
	$Out[11]=$ 6 f

When `TraditionalForm` output is generated as the result of a computation, the actual collection of boxes that represent the output typically contains special `InterpretationBox` and `TagBox` objects which specify how an expression can be reconstructed from the `TraditionalForm` output.

The same is true of `TraditionalForm` that is obtained by explicit conversion from `StandardForm`. But if you edit `TraditionalForm` extensively, or enter it from scratch, then *Mathematica* will have to try to interpret it without the benefit of any additional embedded information.

■ 2.8.5 Short and Shallow Output

When you generate a very large output expression in *Mathematica*, you often do not want to see the whole expression at once. Rather, you would first like to get an idea of the general structure of the expression, and then, perhaps, go in and look at particular parts in more detail.

The functions `Short` and `Shallow` allow you to see "outlines" of large *Mathematica* expressions.

`Short[`*expr*`]`	show a one-line outline of *expr*
`Short[`*expr, n*`]`	show an *n*-line outline of *expr*
`Shallow[`*expr*`]`	show the "top parts" of *expr*
`Shallow[`*expr, {depth, length}*`]`	show the parts of *expr* to the specified depth and length

Showing outlines of expressions.

This generates a long expression. If the whole expression were printed out here, it would go on for 23 lines.

$In[1]:=$ `t = Expand[(1 + x + y)^12]` ;

This gives a one-line "outline" of t. The <<87>> indicates that 87 terms are omitted.

$In[2]:=$ `Short[t]`

$Out[2]//Short=$ $1 + 12\,x + \ll 87 \gg + 12\,x\,y^{11} + y^{12}$

When *Mathematica* generates output, it first effectively writes the output in one long row. Then it looks at the width of text you have asked for, and it chops the row of output into a sequence of separate "lines". Each of the "lines" may of course contain superscripts and built-up fractions, and so may take up more than one actual line on your output device. When you specify a particular number of lines in `Short`, *Mathematica* takes this to be the number of "logical lines" that you want, not the number of actual physical lines on your particular output device.

Here is a four-line version of t. More terms are shown in this case.

$In[3]:=$ `Short[t, 4]`

$Out[3]//Short=$ $1 + 12\,x + 66\,x^2 + 220\,x^3 + 495\,x^4 +$
$792\,x^5 + 924\,x^6 + 792\,x^7 + 495\,x^8 + \ll 73 \gg +$
$660\,x\,y^9 + 660\,x^2\,y^9 + 220\,x^3\,y^9 + 66\,y^{10} + 132\,x\,y^{10} +$
$66\,x^2\,y^{10} + 12\,y^{11} + 12\,x\,y^{11} + y^{12}$

You can use Short with other output forms, such as InputForm.

In[4]:= **Short[InputForm[t]]**

Out[4]//Short= $1 + 12*x + \ll 88 \gg + y\string^12$

Short works by removing a sequence of parts from an expression until the output form of the result fits on the number of lines you specify. Sometimes, however, you may find it better to specify not how many final output lines you want, but which parts of the expression to drop. Shallow[*expr*, {*depth*, *length*}] includes only *length* arguments to any function, and drops all subexpressions that are below the specified depth.

Shallow shows a different outline of t.

In[5]:= **Shallow[t]**

Out[5]//Shallow= $1 + 12\,x + 66\,\text{Power}[\ll 2 \gg] + 220\,\text{Power}[\ll 2 \gg] +$
$495\,\text{Power}[\ll 2 \gg] + 792\,\text{Power}[\ll 2 \gg] +$
$924\,\text{Power}[\ll 2 \gg] + 792\,\text{Power}[\ll 2 \gg] +$
$495\,\text{Power}[\ll 2 \gg] + 220\,\text{Power}[\ll 2 \gg] + \ll 81 \gg$

This includes only 10 arguments to each function, but allows any depth.

In[6]:= **Shallow[t, {Infinity, 10}]**

Out[6]//Shallow= $1 + 12\,x + 66\,x^2 + 220\,x^3 + 495\,x^4 + 792\,x^5 +$
$924\,x^6 + 792\,x^7 + 495\,x^8 + 220\,x^9 + \ll 81 \gg$

Shallow is particularly useful when you want to drop parts in a uniform way throughout a highly nested expression, such as a large list structure returned by Trace.

Here is the recursive definition of the Fibonacci function.

In[7]:= **fib[n_] := fib[n-1] + fib[n-2] ; fib[0] = fib[1] = 1**

Out[7]= 1

This generates a large list structure.

In[8]:= **tr = Trace[fib[8]] ;**

You can use Shallow to see an outline of the structure.

In[9]:= **Shallow[tr]**

Out[9]//Shallow= $\{\text{fib}[\ll 1 \gg],$
$\text{Plus}[\ll 2 \gg], \{\{\ll 2 \gg\}, \ll 1 \gg, \ll 1 \gg,$
$\{\ll 7 \gg\}, \{\ll 7 \gg\}, \ll 1 \gg, \ll 1 \gg\}, \{\{\ll 2 \gg\},$
$\ll 1 \gg, \ll 1 \gg, \{\ll 7 \gg\}, \{\ll 7 \gg\}, \ll 1 \gg, \ll 1 \gg\},$
$\text{Plus}[\ll 2 \gg], 34\}$

Short gives you a less uniform outline, which can be more difficult to understand.

In[10]:= **Short[tr, 4]**

Out[10]//Short= $\{\text{fib}[8], \text{fib}[8-1] + \text{fib}[8-2],$
$\{\{8-1, 7\}, \text{fib}[7], \text{fib}[7-1] + \text{fib}[7-2], \ll 2 \gg,$
$13+8, 21\} \ll 1 \gg \{\{8-2, 6\}, \text{fib}[6], \ll 4 \gg, 13\},$
$21+13, 34\}$

■ 2.8.6 String-Oriented Output Formats

"text"	a string containing arbitrary text

Text strings.

The quotes are not included in standard *Mathematica* output form.	*In[1]:=* **"This is a string."**
	Out[1]= This is a string.
In input form, the quotes are included.	*In[2]:=* **InputForm[%]**
	Out[2]//InputForm= "This is a string."

You can put any kind of text into a *Mathematica* string. This includes non-English characters, as well as newlines and other control information. Section 2.7 discusses in more detail how strings work.

StringForm["*cccc*``*cccc*", x_1, x_2, ...]

output a string in which successive `` are replaced by successive x_i

StringForm["*cccc*`*i*`*cccc*", x_1, x_2, ...]

output a string in which each `*i*` is replaced by the corresponding x_i

Using format strings.

In many situations, you may want to generate output using a string as a "template", but "splicing" in various *Mathematica* expressions. You can do this using StringForm.

This generates output with each successive `` replaced by an expression.	*In[3]:=* **StringForm["x = ``, y = ``", 3, (1 + u)^2]**
	Out[3]= x = 3, y = $(1+u)^2$
You can use numbers to pick out expressions in any order.	*In[4]:=* **StringForm["{`1`, `2`, `1`}", a, b]**
	Out[4]= {a, b, a}

The string in StringForm acts somewhat like a "format directive" in the formatted output statements of languages such as C and Fortran. You can determine how the expressions in StringForm will be formatted by wrapping them with standard output format functions.

You can specify how the expressions in StringForm are formatted using standard output format functions.	*In[5]:=* **StringForm["The `` of `` is ``.", TeXForm, a/b, TeXForm[a/b]]**
	Out[5]= The TeXForm of $\dfrac{a}{b}$ is $\left\{\text{a}\backslash\text{over b}\right\}$.

You should realize that StringForm is only an output format. It does not evaluate in any way. You can use the function ToString to create an ordinary string from a StringForm object.

StringForm generates formatted output in standard *Mathematica* output form.	*In[6]:=* **StringForm["Q: `` -> ``", a, b]**
	Out[6]= Q: a -> b
In input form, you can see the actual StringForm object.	*In[7]:=* **InputForm[%]**
	Out[7]//InputForm= StringForm["Q: `` -> ``", a, b]

This creates an ordinary string from the `StringForm` object.

In[8]:= `InputForm[ToString[%]]`

Out[8]//InputForm= `"Q: a -> b"`

`StringForm` allows you to specify a "template string", then fill in various expressions. Sometimes all you want to do is to concatenate together the output forms for a sequence of expressions. You can do this using `SequenceForm`.

`SequenceForm[`*expr₁*`, `*expr₂*`, ... ]`	give the output forms of the *expr_i* concatenated together

Output of sequences of expressions.

`SequenceForm` prints as a sequence of expressions concatenated together.

In[9]:= `SequenceForm["[x = ", 56, "]"]`

Out[9]= `[x = 56]`

`ColumnForm[{`*expr₁*`, `*expr₂*`, ... }]`	a left-aligned column of objects
`ColumnForm[`*list*`, `*h*`, `*v*`]`	a column with horizontal alignment *h* (`Left`, `Center` or `Right`), and vertical alignment *v* (`Below`, `Center` or `Above`)

Output of columns of expressions.

This arranges the two expressions in a column.

In[10]:= `ColumnForm[{a + b, x^2}]`

Out[10]= a + b

x^2

`HoldForm[`*expr*`]`	give the output form of *expr*, with *expr* maintained unevaluated

Output of unevaluated expressions.

Using text strings and functions like `StringForm`, you can generate pieces of output that do not necessarily correspond to valid *Mathematica* expressions. Sometimes, however, you want to generate output that corresponds to a valid *Mathematica* expression, but only so long as the expression is not evaluated. The function `HoldForm` maintains its argument unevaluated, but allows it to be formatted in the standard *Mathematica* output form.

`HoldForm` maintains 1 + 1 unevaluated.

In[11]:= `HoldForm[1 + 1]`

Out[11]= 1 + 1

The `HoldForm` prevents the actual assignment from being done.

In[12]:= `HoldForm[x = 3]`

Out[12]= x = 3

If it was not for the HoldForm, the power would be evaluated.

In[13]:= **HoldForm[34^78]**

Out[13]= 34^{78}

■ 2.8.7 Output Formats for Numbers

ScientificForm[*expr*]	print all numbers in scientific notation
EngineeringForm[*expr*]	print all numbers in engineering notation (exponents divisible by 3)
AccountingForm[*expr*]	print all numbers in standard accounting format

Output formats for numbers.

These numbers are given in the default output format. Large numbers are given in scientific notation.

In[1]:= **{6.7^-4, 6.7^6, 6.7^8}**

Out[1]= $\{0.00049625, 90458.4, 4.06068 \times 10^{6}\}$

This gives all numbers in scientific notation.

In[2]:= **ScientificForm[%]**

Out[2]//ScientificForm= $\{4.9625 \times 10^{-4}, 9.04584 \times 10^{4}, 4.06068 \times 10^{6}\}$

This gives the numbers in engineering notation, with exponents arranged to be multiples of three.

In[3]:= **EngineeringForm[%]**

Out[3]//EngineeringForm= $\{496.25 \times 10^{-6}, 90.4584 \times 10^{3}, 4.06068 \times 10^{6}\}$

In accounting form, negative numbers are given in parentheses, and scientific notation is never used.

In[4]:= **AccountingForm[{5.6, -6.7, 10.^7}]**

Out[4]//AccountingForm= {5.6, (6.7), 10000000.}

NumberForm[*expr*, *tot*]	print at most *tot* digits of all approximate real numbers in *expr*
ScientificForm[*expr*, *tot*]	use scientific notation with at most *tot* digits
EngineeringForm[*expr*, *tot*]	use engineering notation with at most *tot* digits

Controlling the printed precision of real numbers.

Here is π^9 to 30 decimal places.

In[5]:= **N[Pi^9, 30]**

Out[5]= 29809.0993334462116665094024O124

This prints just 10 digits of π^9.

In[6]:= **NumberForm[%, 10]**

Out[6]//NumberForm= 29809.09933

This displays an array of algebraic expressions as a matrix.

In[4]:= **MatrixForm[Table[x^i - y^j, {i, 3}, {j, 3}]]**

$$Out[4]//MatrixForm= \begin{pmatrix} x - y & x - y^2 & x - y^3 \\ x^2 - y & x^2 - y^2 & x^2 - y^3 \\ x^3 - y & x^3 - y^2 & x^3 - y^3 \end{pmatrix}$$

PaddedForm[TableForm[*list*], *tot*]	print a table with all numbers padded to have room for *tot* digits
PaddedForm[TableForm[*list*], {*tot*, *frac*}]	
	put *frac* digits to the right of the decimal point in all approximate real numbers

Printing tables of numbers.

Here is a list of numbers.

In[5]:= **fac = {10!, 15!, 20!}**

Out[5]= {3628800, 1307674368000, 2432902008176640000}

TableForm displays the list in a column.

In[6]:= **TableForm[fac]**

Out[6]//TableForm=
```
        3628800
1307674368000
2432902008176640000
```

This aligns the numbers by padding each one to leave room for up to 20 digits.

In[7]:= **PaddedForm[TableForm[fac], 20]**

Out[7]//PaddedForm=
```
            3628800
      1307674368000
2432902008176640000
```

In this particular case, you could also align the numbers using the TableAlignments option.

In[8]:= **TableForm[fac, TableAlignments -> {Right}]**

Out[8]//TableForm=
```
            3628800
      1307674368000
2432902008176640000
```

This lines up the numbers, padding each one to have room for 8 digits, with 5 digits to the right of the decimal point.

In[9]:= **PaddedForm[TableForm[{6.7, 6.888, 6.99999}], {8, 5}]**

Out[9]//PaddedForm=
```
6.70000
6.88800
6.99999
```

You can use TableForm and MatrixForm to format lists that are nested to any depth, corresponding to arrays with any number of dimensions.

Here is the format for a 2×2 array of elements a[*i*, *j*].

In[10]:= **TableForm[Array[a, {2, 2}]]**

Out[10]//TableForm=
```
a[1, 1]    a[1, 2]
a[2, 1]    a[2, 2]
```

Here is a $2 \times 2 \times 2$ array.

In[11]:= **TableForm[{ Array[a, {2, 2}], Array[b, {2, 2}] }]**

Out[11]//TableForm=
```
                 a[1, 1]      a[2, 1]
                 a[1, 2]      a[2, 2]
                 b[1, 1]      b[2, 1]
                 b[1, 2]      b[2, 2]
```

And here is a $2 \times 2 \times 2 \times 2$ array.

In[12]:= **TableForm[{ {Array[a, {2, 2}], Array[b, {2, 2}]},**
              {Array[c, {2, 2}], Array[d, {2, 2}]} }]

Out[12]//TableForm=
```
              a[1, 1]  a[1, 2]      b[1, 1]  b[1, 2]
              a[2, 1]  a[2, 2]      b[2, 1]  b[2, 2]
              c[1, 1]  c[1, 2]      d[1, 1]  d[1, 2]
              c[2, 1]  c[2, 2]      d[2, 1]  d[2, 2]
```

In general, when you print an *n*-dimensional table, successive dimensions are alternately given as columns and rows. By setting the option `TableDirections -> {`*dir*$_1$, *dir*$_2$, ... `}`, where the *dir*$_i$ are `Column` or `Row`, you can specify explicitly which way each dimension should be given. By default, the option is effectively set to `{Column, Row, Column, Row, ... }`.

The option `TableDirections` allows you to specify explicitly how each dimension in a multidimensional table should be given.

In[13]:= **TableForm[{ Array[a, {2, 2}], Array[b, {2, 2}] },**
              TableDirections -> {Row, Row, Column}]

Out[13]//TableForm=
```
              a[1, 1]      a[2, 1]  b[1, 1]      b[2, 1]
              a[1, 2]      a[2, 2]  b[1, 2]      b[2, 2]
```

Whenever you make a table from a nested list such as {*list*$_1$, *list*$_2$, ... }, there is a question of whether it should be the *list*$_i$ or their elements which appear as the basic entries in the table. The default behavior is slightly different for `MatrixForm` and `TableForm`.

`MatrixForm` handles only arrays that are "rectangular". Thus, for example, to consider an array as two-dimensional, all the rows must have the same length. If they do not, `MatrixForm` treats the array as one-dimensional, with elements that are lists.

`MatrixForm` treats this as a one-dimensional array, since the rows are of differing lengths.

In[14]:= **MatrixForm[{{a, a, a}, {b, b}}]**

Out[14]//MatrixForm= $\begin{pmatrix} \{a, a, a\} \\ \{b, b\} \end{pmatrix}$

While `MatrixForm` can handle only "rectangular arrays", `TableForm` can handle arbitrary "ragged" arrays. It leaves blanks wherever there are no elements supplied.

`TableForm` can handle "ragged" arrays.

In[15]:= **TableForm[{{a, a, a}, {b, b}}]**

Out[15]//TableForm=
```
              a        a        a
              b        b
```

You can include objects that behave as "subtables".

In[16]:= **TableForm[{{a, {{p, q}, {r, s}}, a, a},**
              {{x, y}, b, b}}]

Out[16]//TableForm=
```
              a        p  q     a        a
                       r  s
              x        b        b
              y
```

You can control the number of levels in a nested list to which both `TableForm` and `MatrixForm` go by setting the option `TableDepth`.

This tells `TableForm` only to go down to depth 2. As a result {x, y} is treated as a single table entry.

$In[17]:=$ `TableForm[{{a, {x, y}}, {c, d}}, TableDepth -> 2]`

$Out[17]//TableForm=$
```
a    {x, y}
c    d
```

option name	default value	
TableDepth	Infinity	maximum number of levels to include in the table
TableDirections	{Column, Row, Column, ... }	whether to arrange dimensions as rows or columns
TableAlignments	{Left, Bottom, Left, ... }	how to align the entries in each dimension
TableSpacing	{1, 3, 0, 1, 0, ... }	how many spaces to put between entries in each dimension
TableHeadings	{None, None, ... }	how to label the entries in each dimension

Options for `TableForm`.

With the option `TableAlignments`, you can specify how each entry in the table should be aligned with its row or column. For columns, you can specify `Left`, `Center` or `Right`. For rows, you can specify `Bottom`, `Center` or `Top`. If you set `TableAlignments -> Center`, all entries will be centered both horizontally and vertically. `TableAlignments -> Automatic` uses the default choice of alignments.

Entries in columns are by default aligned on the left.

$In[18]:=$ `TableForm[{a, bbbb, cccccccc}]`

$Out[18]//TableForm=$
```
a
bbbb
cccccccc
```

This centers all entries.

$In[19]:=$ `TableForm[{a, bbbb, cccccccc},`
`            TableAlignments -> Center]`

$Out[19]//TableForm=$
```
   a
  bbbb
cccccccc
```

You can use the option `TableSpacing` to specify how much horizontal space there should be between successive columns, or how much vertical space there should be between successive rows. A setting of 0 specifies that successive objects should abut.

This leaves 6 spaces between the entries in each row, and no space between successive rows.

In[20]:= **TableForm[{{a, b}, {ccc, d}}, TableSpacing -> {0, 6}]**

Out[20]//TableForm= a   b
                     ccc   d

None	no labels in any dimension
Automatic	successive integer labels in each dimension
{{*lab*$_{11}$, *lab*$_{12}$, ... }, ... }	explicit labels

Settings for the option TableHeadings.

This puts integer labels in a $2 \times 2 \times 2$ array.

In[21]:= **TableForm[Array[a, {2, 2, 2}],**
                     TableHeadings -> Automatic]

Out[21]//TableForm=   1   2

                    1   a[1, 1, 1]   a[1, 2, 1]
                1 2   a[1, 1, 2]   a[1, 2, 2]

                    1   a[2, 1, 1]   a[2, 2, 1]
                2 2   a[2, 1, 2]   a[2, 2, 2]

This gives a table in which the rows are labeled by integers, and the columns by a list of strings.

In[22]:= **TableForm[{{a, b, c}, {ap, bp, cp}},**
                     TableHeadings ->
                       {Automatic, {"first", "middle", "last"}}]

                         first   middle   last
Out[22]//TableForm= 1   a   b   c
                    2   ap   bp   cp

This labels the rows but not the columns. TableForm automatically inserts a blank row to go with the third label.

In[23]:= **TableForm[{{2, 3, 4}, {5, 6, 1}},**
                     TableHeadings ->
                       {{"row a", "row b", "row c"}, None}]

                    row a   2   3   4
Out[23]//TableForm= row b   5   6   1
                    row c

+■ 2.8.9 Styles and Fonts in Output

StyleForm[*expr, options*]	print with the specified style options
StyleForm[*expr, "style"*]	print with the specified cell style

Specifying output styles.

The second x^2 is here shown in boldface.

In[1]:= **{x^2, StyleForm[x^2, FontWeight->"Bold"]}**

Out[1]= {x^2, $\mathbf{x^2}$}

This shows the word `text` in font sizes from 10 to 20 points.

$In[2]:=$ `Table[StyleForm["text", FontSize->s], {s, 10, 20}]`

$Out[2]=$ {text, text, text, text, text, text,

text, text, text, text, text}

This shows the text in the Tekton font.

$In[3]:=$ `StyleForm["some text", FontFamily->"Tekton"]`

$Out[3]//StyleForm=$ sometex

option	typical setting(s)	
FontSize	12	size of characters in printer's points
FontWeight	"Plain" or "Bold"	weight of characters
FontSlant	"Plain" or "Italic"	slant of characters
FontFamily	"Courier", "Times", "Helvetica"	font family
FontColor	GrayLevel[0]	color of characters
Background	GrayLevel[1]	background color for characters

A few options that can be used in StyleForm.

If you use the notebook front end for *Mathematica*, then each piece of output that is generated will by default be in the style of the cell in which the output appears. By using `StyleForm[`*expr*`, "`*style*`"]`, however, you can tell *Mathematica* to output a particular expression in a different style.

Here is an expression output in the style normally used for section headings.

$In[4]:=$ `StyleForm[x^2 + y^2, "Section"]`

$Out[4]//StyleForm=$ $\mathbf{x^2 + y^2}$

Page 547 describes in more detail how cell styles work. By using `StyleForm[`*expr*`, "`*style*`"`, *options*`]` you can generate output that is in a particular style, but with certain options modified.

◼ 2.8.10 Representing Textual Forms by Boxes

All textual forms in *Mathematica* are ultimately represented in terms of nested collections of *boxes*. Typically the elements of these boxes correspond to objects that are to be placed at definite relative positions in two dimensions.

Here are the boxes corresponding to the expression a + b.

$In[1]:=$ `ToBoxes[a + b]`

$Out[1]=$ `RowBox[{a, +, b}]`

`DisplayForm` shows how these boxes would be displayed.

$In[2]:=$ `DisplayForm[%]`

$Out[2]//DisplayForm=$ a + b

DisplayForm[*boxes*]	show *boxes* as they would be displayed

Showing the displayed form of boxes.

This displays three strings in a row.

In[3]:= **RowBox[{"a", "+", "b"}] // DisplayForm**

Out[3]//DisplayForm= a + b

This displays one string as a subscript of another.

In[4]:= **SubscriptBox["a", "i"] // DisplayForm**

Out[4]//DisplayForm= a_i

This puts two subscript boxes in a row.

In[5]:= **RowBox[{SubscriptBox["a", "1"], SubscriptBox["b", "2"]}] //**
　　　　　DisplayForm

Out[5]//DisplayForm= $a_1 b_2$

"*text*"	literal text
RowBox[{*a*, *b*, ... }]	a row of boxes or strings *a b* ...
GridBox[{{*a₁*, *b₁*, ... }, {*a₂*, *b₂*, ... }, ... }]	a grid of boxes $\begin{matrix} a_1 & b_1 & \dots \\ a_2 & b_2 & \dots \\ \vdots & \vdots \end{matrix}$
SubscriptBox[*a*, *b*]	subscript a_b
SuperscriptBox[*a*, *b*]	superscript a^b
SubsuperscriptBox[*a*, *b*, *c*]	subscript and superscript a_b^c
UnderscriptBox[*a*, *b*]	underscript $\underset{b}{a}$
OverscriptBox[*a*, *b*]	overscript $\overset{b}{a}$
UnderoverscriptBox[*a*, *b*, *c*]	underscript and overscript $\underset{b}{\overset{c}{a}}$
FractionBox[*a*, *b*]	fraction $\frac{a}{b}$
SqrtBox[*a*]	square root $\sqrt{a}$
RadicalBox[*a*, *b*]	b^{th} root $\sqrt[b]{a}$

Some basic box types.

This nests a fraction inside a radical.

In[6]:= **RadicalBox[FractionBox[x, y], n] // DisplayForm**

Out[6]//DisplayForm= $\sqrt[n]{\dfrac{x}{y}}$

This puts a superscript on a subscripted object.

In[7]:= **SuperscriptBox[SubscriptBox[a, b], c] // DisplayForm**

Out[7]//DisplayForm= $a_b{}^c$

This puts both a subscript and a superscript on the same object.

In[8]:= **SubsuperscriptBox[a, b, c] // DisplayForm**

Out[8]//DisplayForm= a_b^c

FrameBox[*box*]	render *box* with a frame drawn around it
GridBox[*list*, RowLines->True]	put lines between rows in a GridBox
GridBox[*list*, ColumnLines->True]	put lines between columns in a GridBox
GridBox[*list*, RowLines->{True, False}]	put a line below the first row, but not subsequent ones

Inserting frames and grid lines.

This shows a fraction with a frame drawn around it.

In[9]:= **FrameBox[FractionBox["x", "y"]] // DisplayForm**

Out[9]//DisplayForm= $\boxed{\dfrac{x}{y}}$

This puts lines between rows and columns of an array.

In[10]:= **GridBox[Table[i+j, {i, 3}, {j, 3}], RowLines->True, ColumnLines->True] // DisplayForm**

Out[10]//DisplayForm=

2	3	4
3	4	5
4	5	6

And this also puts a frame around the outside.

In[11]:= **FrameBox[%] // DisplayForm**

Out[11]//DisplayForm=

2	3	4
3	4	5
4	5	6

StyleBox[*boxes*, *options*]	render *boxes* with the specified option settings
StyleBox[*boxes*, "*style*"]	render *boxes* in the specified style

Modifying the appearance of boxes.

StyleBox takes the same options as StyleForm. The difference is that StyleForm acts as a "wrapper" for any expression, while StyleBox represents underlying box structure.

This shows the string "name" in italics.

In[12]:= **StyleBox["name", FontSlant->"Italic"] // DisplayForm**

Out[12]//DisplayForm= name

This shows "name" in the style used for section headings in your current notebook.	*In[13]:=* **StyleBox["name", "Section"] // DisplayForm** *Out[13]//DisplayForm=* **name**
This uses section heading style, but with characters shown in gray.	*In[14]:=* **StyleBox["name", "Section", FontColor->GrayLevel[0.5]] //** **DisplayForm** *Out[14]//DisplayForm=* name

If you use a notebook front end for *Mathematica*, then you will be able to change the style and appearance of what you see on the screen directly by using menu items. Internally, however, these changes will still be recorded by the insertion of appropriate StyleBox objects.

FormBox[*boxes*, *form*]	interpret *boxes* using rules associated with the specified form
InterpretationBox[*boxes*, *expr*]	interpret *boxes* as representing the expression *expr*
TagBox[*boxes*, *tag*]	use *tag* to guide the interpretation of *boxes*
ErrorBox[*boxes*]	indicate an error and do not attempt further interpretation of *boxes*

Controlling the interpretation of boxes.

This prints as x with a superscript.	*In[15]:=* **SuperscriptBox["x", "2"] // DisplayForm** *Out[15]//DisplayForm=* x^2
It is normally interpreted as a power.	*In[16]:=* **ToExpression[%] // InputForm** *Out[16]//InputForm=* x^2
This again prints as x with a superscript.	*In[17]:=* **InterpretationBox[SuperscriptBox["x", "2"],** **vec[x, 2]] // DisplayForm** *Out[17]//DisplayForm=* x^2
But now it is interpreted as vec[x, 2], following the specification given in the InterpretationBox.	*In[18]:=* **ToExpression[%] // InputForm** *Out[18]//InputForm=* vec[x, 2]

If you edit the boxes given in an InterpretationBox, then there is no guarantee that the interpretation specified by the interpretation box will still be correct. As a result, *Mathematica* provides various options that allow you to control the selection and editing of InterpretationBox objects.

option	default value	
Editable	False	whether to allow the contents to be edited
Selectable	True	whether to allow the contents to be selected
Deletable	True	whether to allow the box to be deleted
DeletionWarning	False	whether to issue a warning if the box is deleted
BoxAutoDelete	False	whether to strip the box if its contents are modified
StripWrapperBoxes	False	whether to remove StyleBox etc. from within *boxes* in TagBox[*boxes*, ...]

Options for InterpretationBox and related boxes.

TagBox objects are used to store information that will not be displayed but which can nevertheless be used by the rules that interpret boxes. Typically the *tag* in TagBox[*boxes*, *tag*] is a symbol which gives the head of the expression corresponding to *boxes*. If you edit only the arguments of this expression then there is a good chance that the interpretation specified by the TagBox will still be appropriate. As a result, Editable->True is the default setting for a TagBox.

The rules that *Mathematica* uses for interpreting boxes are in general set up to ignore details of formatting, such as those defined by StyleBox objects. Thus, unless StripWrapperBoxes->False, a red x, for example, will normally not be distinguished from an ordinary black x.

A red x is usually treated as identical to an ordinary one.

```
In[19]:= ToExpression[
             StyleBox[x, FontColor->RGBColor[1,0,0]]] == x

Out[19]= True
```

ButtonBox[*boxes*]	display like *boxes* but perform an action whenever *boxes* are clicked on

Setting up active elements.

In a *Mathematica* notebook it is possible to set up elements which perform an action whenever you click on them. These elements are represented internally by ButtonBox objects. When you create an expression containing a ButtonBox, you will be able to edit the contents of the ButtonBox directly so long as the Active option is False for the cell containing the expression. As soon as you set Active->True, the ButtonBox will perform its action whenever you click on it.

Section 2.10.6 discusses how to set up actions for ButtonBox objects.

+■ 2.8.11 Adjusting Details of Formatting

Mathematica provides a large number of options for adjusting the details of how expressions are formatted. In most cases, the default settings for these options will be quite adequate. But sometimes special features in the expressions you are dealing with may require you to change the options.

option	default value	
ColumnAlignments	Center	how to align columns
RowAlignments	Baseline	how to align rows
ColumnSpacings	1	spacings between columns in ems
RowSpacings	0.5	spacings between rows in x-heights
ColumnsEqual	False	whether to make all columns equal width
RowsEqual	False	whether to make all rows equal total height
ColumnWidths	Automatic	the actual width of each column in ems
RowMinHeight	1	the minimum total height in units of font size assigned to each row
GridBaseline	Axis	with what part of the whole grid the baselines of boxes around it should be aligned
ColumnLines	False	whether to draw lines between columns
RowLines	False	whether to draw lines between rows
GridDefaultElement	"□"	what to insert when a new element is interactively created

Options to GridBox.

This sets up an array of numbers.

Here is how the array is displayed with the default settings for all GridBox options.

```
In[1]:= t = Table[{i, (2i)!, (3i)!}, {i, 4}] ;

In[2]:= GridBox[t] // DisplayForm
```

$$
Out[2]//DisplayForm=
\begin{array}{lll}
1 & 2 & 6 \\
2 & 24 & 720 \\
3 & 720 & 362880 \\
4 & 40320 & 479001600
\end{array}
$$

This right justifies all the columns.

```
In[3]:= GridBox[t, ColumnAlignments->Right] // DisplayForm
```

```
            1      2         6
            2     24       720
Out[3]//DisplayForm= 3    720    362880
            4  40320  479001600
```

This left justifies the first two columns and right justifies the last one.

```
In[4]:= GridBox[t,
        ColumnAlignments->{Left, Left, Right}] // DisplayForm
```

```
            1  2           6
            2  24        720
Out[4]//DisplayForm= 3  720     362880
            4  40320  479001600
```

This sets the gutters between columns.

```
In[5]:= GridBox[t, ColumnSpacings->{5, 10}] // DisplayForm
```

```
            1        2              6
            2       24            720
Out[5]//DisplayForm= 3      720         362880
            4      40320       479001600
```

This forces all columns to be the same width.

```
In[6]:= GridBox[t, ColumnsEqual->True] // DisplayForm
```

```
            1      2        6
            2     24      720
Out[6]//DisplayForm= 3    720    362880
            4  40320  479001600
```

Usually a GridBox leaves room for any character in the current font to appear in each row. But with RowMinHeight->0 it packs rows in more tightly.

```
In[7]:= {GridBox[{{x, x}, {x, x}}],
        GridBox[{{x, x}, {x, x}}, RowMinHeight->0]} // DisplayForm
```

$$Out[7]//DisplayForm= \left\{ \begin{matrix} x & x \\ x & x \end{matrix} , \begin{matrix} x & x \\ x & x \end{matrix} \right\}$$

Center	centered (default)
Left	left justified (aligned on left edge)
Right	right justified (aligned on right edge)
"."	aligned at decimal points
"c"	aligned at the first occurrence of the specified character
{pos_1, pos_2, ... }	separate specifications for each column in the grid

Settings for the ColumnAlignments option.

In formatting complicated tables, it is often important to be able to control in detail the alignment of table entries. By setting `ColumnAlignments->"c"` you tell *Mathematica* to arrange the elements in each column so that the first occurrence of the character `"c"` in each entry is aligned.

Choosing `ColumnAlignments->"."` will therefore align numbers according to the positions of their decimal points. *Mathematica* also provides a special `\[AlignmentMarker]` character, which can be entered as ⦂am⦂. This character does not display explicitly, but can be inserted in entries in a table to mark which point in these entries should be lined up.

`Center`	centered
`Top`	tops aligned
`Bottom`	bottoms aligned
`Baseline`	baselines aligned (default)
`Axis`	axes aligned
$\{pos_1, pos_2, \dots\}$	separate specifications for each row in the grid

Settings for the `RowAlignments` option.

This is the default alignment of elements in a row of a GridBox.

```
In[8]:= GridBox[{{SuperscriptBox[x, 2], FractionBox[y, z]}}] //
            DisplayForm
```

$Out[8]//DisplayForm= x^2 \ \frac{y}{z}$

Here is what happens if the bottom of each element is aligned.

```
In[9]:= GridBox[{{SuperscriptBox[x, 2], FractionBox[y, z]}},
            RowAlignments->Bottom] // DisplayForm
```

$Out[9]//DisplayForm= {}_{x^2} \ \frac{y}{z}$

In a piece of ordinary text, successive characters are normally positioned so that their baselines are aligned. For many characters, such as m and x, the baseline coincides with the bottom of the character. But in general the baseline is the bottom of the main part of the character, and for example, in most fonts g and y have "descenders" that extend below the baseline.

This shows the alignment of characters with the default setting `RowAlignments->Baseline`.

```
In[10]:= GridBox[{{"x", "m", "g", "y"}}] // DisplayForm
```

$Out[10]//DisplayForm= $ x m g y

This is what happens if instead the bottom of each character is aligned.

```
In[11]:= GridBox[{{"x", "m", "g", "y"}}, RowAlignments->Bottom] //
            DisplayForm
```

$Out[11]//DisplayForm= $ x m g y

Like characters in ordinary text, *Mathematica* will normally position sequences of boxes so that their baselines are aligned. For many kinds of boxes the baseline is simply taken to be the baseline of the main element of the box. Thus, for example, the baseline of a `SuperScript` box x^y is taken to be the baseline of x.

The sizes of most characters are determined solely by what font they are in, as specified for example by the `FontSize` option in `StyleBox`. But there are some special expandable characters whose size can change even within a particular font. Examples are parentheses, which by default are taken to expand so as to span any expression they contain.

Parentheses by default expand to span whatever expressions they contain.

```
In[23]:= {RowBox[{"(", "X", ")"}],
            RowBox[{"(", FractionBox["X", "Y"], ")"}]} // DisplayForm
```

$$Out[23]//DisplayForm= \left\{ (X), \left(\frac{X}{Y} \right) \right\}$$

option	default value	
SpanMinSize	Automatic	minimum size of expandable characters in units of font size
SpanMaxSize	Automatic	maximum size of expandable characters in units of font size
SpanSymmetric	True	whether vertically expandable characters should be symmetric about the axis of the box they are in
SpanLineThickness	Automatic	thickness in printer's points of fraction lines etc.

`StyleBox` options for controlling expandable characters.

Parentheses within a single `RowBox` by default grow to span whatever other objects appear in the `RowBox`.

```
In[24]:= RowBox[{"(", "(", GridBox[{{X},{Y},{Z}}]}] // DisplayForm
```

$$Out[24]//DisplayForm= \left(\left(\begin{array}{c} X \\ Y \\ Z \end{array} \right. \right.$$

Some expandable characters, however, grow by default only to a limited extent.

```
In[25]:= RowBox[{"{", "[", "(",
                GridBox[{{X},{Y},{Z}}]}] // DisplayForm
```

$$Out[25]//DisplayForm= \left\{ \left[\left(\begin{array}{c} X \\ Y \\ Z \end{array} \right. \right. \right.$$

This specifies that all characters inside the `StyleBox` should be allowed to grow as large as they need.

```
In[26]:= StyleBox[%, SpanMaxSize->Infinity] // DisplayForm
```

$$Out[26]//DisplayForm= \left\{ \left[\left(\begin{array}{c} X \\ Y \\ Z \end{array} \right. \right. \right.$$

By default, expandable characters grow symmetrically.

In[27]:= **RowBox[{"(", GridBox[{{X},{Y}},**
GridBaseline->Bottom], ")"}] // DisplayForm

$$Out[27]//DisplayForm= \begin{pmatrix} X \\ Y \end{pmatrix}$$

Setting SpanSymmetric->False allows expandable characters to grow asymmetrically.

In[28]:= **{X, StyleBox[%, SpanSymmetric->False]} // DisplayForm**

$$Out[28]//DisplayForm= \left\{ X, \begin{pmatrix} X \\ Y \end{pmatrix} \right\}$$

The notebook front end typically provides a Spanning Characters menu which allows you to change the spanning characteristics of all characters within your current selection.

parentheses, arrows, bracketing bars	grow without bound
brackets, braces, slash	grow to limited size

Default characteristics of expandable characters.

The top bracket by default grows to span the OverscriptBox.

In[29]:= **OverscriptBox["xxxxxx", "\[OverBracket]"] // DisplayForm**

$$Out[29]//DisplayForm= \overline{xxxxxx}$$

The right arrow by default grows horizontally to span the column it is in.

In[30]:= **GridBox[{{"a", "xxxxxxx", "b"},**
{"a", "\[RightArrow]", "b"}}] // DisplayForm

$$Out[30]//DisplayForm= \begin{matrix} a & xxxxxxx & b \\ a & \longrightarrow & b \end{matrix}$$

The up arrow similarly grows vertically to span the row it is in.

In[31]:= **GridBox[{{FractionBox[X, Y],**
"\[UpArrow]"}}] // DisplayForm

$$Out[31]//DisplayForm= \frac{X}{Y} \ \uparrow$$

option	default value	
ScriptSizeMultipliers	0.71	how much smaller to make each level of subscripts, etc.
ScriptMinSize	4	the minimum point size to use for subscripts, etc.
ScriptBaselineShifts	{Automatic, Automatic}	the distance in x-heights to shift subscripts and superscripts

StyleBox options for controlling the size and positioning of subscripts, etc.

This sets up a collection of nested SuperscriptBox objects.

```
In[32]:= b = ToBoxes[X^X^X^X^X]
```

$Out[32]=$ SuperscriptBox[X, SuperscriptBox[X, SuperscriptBox[X, SuperscriptBox[X, X]]]]

By default, successive superscripts get progressively smaller.

```
In[33]:= b // DisplayForm
```

$Out[33]//DisplayForm=$ $X^{X^{X^{X^{X}}}}$

This tells *Mathematica* to make all levels of superscripts the same size.

```
In[34]:= StyleBox[b, ScriptSizeMultipliers->1] // DisplayForm
```

$Out[34]//DisplayForm=$ $X^{X^{X^{X^{X}}}}$

Here successive levels of superscripts are smaller, but only down to 5-point size.

```
In[35]:= StyleBox[b, ScriptMinSize->5] // DisplayForm
```

$Out[35]//DisplayForm=$ $X^{X^{X^{X^{X}}}}$

Mathematica will usually optimize the position of subscripts and superscripts in a way that depends on their environment. If you want to line up several different subscripts or superscripts you therefore typically have to use the option ScriptBaselineShifts to specify an explicit distance to shift each one.

The second subscript is by default shifted down slightly more than the first.

```
In[36]:= RowBox[{SubscriptBox["x", "0"], "+",
              SubsuperscriptBox["x", "0", "2"]}] // DisplayForm
```

$Out[36]//DisplayForm=$ $x_0 + x_0^2$

This tells *Mathematica* to apply exactly the same shift to both subscripts.

```
In[37]:= StyleBox[%, ScriptBaselineShifts->{1, Automatic}] //
                                              DisplayForm
```

$Out[37]//DisplayForm=$ $x_0 + x_0^2$

option	default value	
LimitsPositioning	Automatic	whether to change positioning in the way conventional for limits

An option to UnderoverscriptBox and related boxes.

The limits of a sum are usually displayed as underscripts and overscripts.

```
In[38]:= Sum[f[i], {i, 0, n}]
```

$$Out[38]= \sum_{i=0}^{n} f[i]$$

When the sum is shown smaller, however, it is conventional for the limits to be displayed as subscripts and superscripts.

```
In[39]:= 1/%
```

$$Out[39]= \frac{1}{\sum_{i=0}^{n} f[i]}$$

Here low and high still display directly above and below XX.	$In[40]:=$ **UnderoverscriptBox["XX", "low", "high", LimitsPositioning->True] // DisplayForm**

$$Out[40]//DisplayForm= \overset{\text{high}}{\underset{\text{low}}{XX}}$$

But now low and high are moved to subscript and superscript positions.	$In[41]:=$ **FractionBox["a", %] // DisplayForm**

$$Out[41]//DisplayForm= \frac{a}{XX^{\text{high}}_{\text{low}}}$$

LimitsPositioning->Automatic will act as if LimitsPositioning->True when the first argument of the box is an object such as \[Sum] or \[Product]. You can specify the list of such characters by setting the option LimitsPositioningTokens.

option	default value	
MultilineFunction	Automatic	what to do when a box breaks across several lines

Line breaking options for boxes.

When you are dealing with long expressions it is inevitable that they will continue beyond the length of a single line. Many kinds of boxes change their display characteristics when they break across several lines.

This displays as a built-up fraction on a single line.	$In[42]:=$ **Expand[(1 + x)^5]/Expand[(1 + y)^5]**

$$Out[42]= \frac{1 + 5x + 10x^2 + 10x^3 + 5x^4 + x^5}{1 + 5y + 10y^2 + 10y^3 + 5y^4 + y^5}$$

This breaks across several lines.	$In[43]:=$ **Expand[(1 + x)^10]/Expand[(1 + y)^5]**

$$Out[43]= (1 + 10x + 45x^2 + 120x^3 + $$
$$210x^4 + 252x^5 + 210x^6 + 120x^7 + 45x^8 + 10x^9 + x^{10}) /$$
$$(1 + 5y + 10y^2 + 10y^3 + 5y^4 + y^5)$$

You can use the option MultilineFunction to specify how a particular box should be displayed if it breaks across several lines. The setting MultilineFunction->None prevents the box from breaking at all.

You can to some extent control where expressions break across lines by inserting \[NoBreak] and \[NonBreakingSpace] characters. *Mathematica* will try to avoid ever breaking an expression at the position of such characters.

You can force *Mathematica* to break a line by explicitly inserting a \[NewLine] character, obtained in the standard notebook front end simply by typing RETURN. With default settings for options, *Mathematica* will automatically indent the next line after you type a RETURN. However, the level of indenting used will be fixed as soon as the line is started, and will not change when you edit around it. By inserting an \[IndentingNewLine] character, you can tell *Mathematica* always to maintain the correct level of indenting based on the actual environment in which a line occurs.

full name	alias	
\[NoBreak]	⁞nb⁞	inhibit a line break
\[NonBreakingSpace]	⁞nbs⁞	insert a space, inhibiting a line break on either side of it
\[NewLine]	[RET]	insert a line break, setting the indenting level at the time the new line is started
\[IndentingNewLine]	⁞nl⁞	insert a line break, always maintaining the correct indenting level

Characters for controlling line breaking.

When *Mathematica* breaks an expression across several lines, it indents intermediate lines by an amount proportional to the nesting level in the expression at which the break occurred.

The line breaks here occur only at level 1.

```
In[44]:= Range[30]
Out[44]= {1, 2, 3, 4, 5, 6,
            7, 8, 9, 10, 11, 12, 13, 14, 15, 16, 17, 18,
            19, 20, 21, 22, 23, 24, 25, 26, 27, 28, 29, 30}
```

But here the break is at a much deeper level.

```
In[45]:= Nest[List, x+y, 30]
Out[45]= {{{{{{{{{{{{{{{{{{{{{{{{{{{{{{x +
                  y}}}}}}}}}}}}}}}}}}}}}}}}}}}}}}
```

▪ 2.8.12 String Representation of Boxes

Mathematica provides a compact way of representing boxes in terms of strings. This is particularly convenient when you want to import or export specifications of boxes as ordinary text.

This generates an InputForm string that represents the SuperscriptBox.

```
In[1]:= ToString[SuperscriptBox["x", "2"], InputForm]
Out[1]= \(x\^2\)
```

This creates the SuperscriptBox.

```
In[2]:= \( x \^ 2 \)
Out[2]= SuperscriptBox[x, 2]
```

ToExpression interprets the SuperscriptBox as a power.

```
In[3]:= ToExpression[%] // FullForm
Out[3]//FullForm= Power[x, 2]
```

It is important to distinguish between forms that represent just raw boxes, and forms that represent the *meaning* of the boxes.

This corresponds to a raw
SuperscriptBox.

In[4]:= \(x \^ 2 \)

Out[4]= SuperscriptBox[x, 2]

This corresponds to the power that the
SuperscriptBox represents.

In[5]:= \!\(x \^ 2 \)

Out[5]= x^2

The expression generated here is a
power.

In[6]:= **FullForm[\!\(x \^ 2 \)]**

Out[6]//FullForm= Power[x, 2]

\(*input*\)	raw boxes
\!\(*input*\)	the meaning of the boxes

Distinguishing raw boxes from the expressions they represent.

If you copy the contents of a `StandardForm` cell into another program, such as a text editor, *Mathematica* will automatically generate a \!\(... \) form. This is done so that if you subsequently paste the form back into *Mathematica*, the original contents of the `StandardForm` cell will automatically be re-created. Without the \!, only the raw boxes corresponding to these contents would be obtained.

With default settings for options, \!\(... \) forms pasted into *Mathematica* notebooks are automatically displayed in two-dimensional form. \!\(... \) forms entered directly from the keyboard can be displayed in two-dimensional form using the Make 2D item in the Edit menu.

"\(*input*\)"	a raw character string
"\!\(*input*\)"	a string containing boxes

Embedding two-dimensional box structures in strings.

Mathematica will usually treat a \(... \) form that appears within a string just like any other sequence of characters. But by inserting a \! you can tell *Mathematica* instead to treat this form like the boxes it represents. In this way you can therefore embed box structures within ordinary character strings.

Mathematica treats this as an ordinary
character string.

In[7]:= "\(x \^ 2 \)"

Out[7]= \(x \^ 2 \)

The \! tells *Mathematica* that this string
contains boxes.

In[8]:= "\!\(x \^ 2 \)"

Out[8]= x^2

You can mix boxes with ordinary text.

In[9]:= **"box 1: \!\(x\^2\); box 2: \!\(y\^3\)"**

Out[9]= box 1: x^2; box 2: y^3

\\(box_1, box_2, ... \\)	RowBox[box_1, box_2, ...]
box_1 \\^ box_2	SuperscriptBox[box_1, box_2]
box_1 _ box_2	SubscriptBox[box_1, box_2]
box_1 _ box_2 \\% box_3	SubsuperscriptBox[box_1, box_2, box_3]
box_1 \\& box_2	OverscriptBox[box_1, box_2]
box_1 \\+ box_2	UnderscriptBox[box_1, box_2]
box_1 \\+ box_2 \\% box_3	UnderoverscriptBox[box_1, box_2, box_3]
box_1 \\/ box_2	FractionBox[box_1, box_2]
\\@ box	SqrtBox[box]
\\@ box_1 \\% box_2	RadicalBox[box_1, box_2]
form \\` *box*	FormBox[*box*, *form*]
* *input*	construct boxes from *input*

Input forms for boxes.

Mathematica requires that any input forms you give for boxes be enclosed within \\(and \\). But within these outermost \\(and \\) you can use additional \\(and \\) to specify grouping.

Here ordinary parentheses are used to indicate grouping.

```
In[10]:= \( x \/ (y + z) \) // DisplayForm
```
$$Out[10]//DisplayForm= \frac{x}{(y+z)}$$

Without the parentheses, the grouping would be different.

```
In[11]:= \( x \/ y + z \) // DisplayForm
```
$$Out[11]//DisplayForm= \frac{x}{y} + z$$

\\(and \\) specify grouping, but are not displayed as explicit parentheses.

```
In[12]:= \( x \/ \(y + z\) \) // DisplayForm
```
$$Out[12]//DisplayForm= \frac{x}{y+z}$$

The inner \\(and \\) lead to the construction of a RowBox.

```
In[13]:= \( x \/ \(y + z\) \)
Out[13]= FractionBox[x, RowBox[{y, +, z}]]
```

When you type aa+bb as input to *Mathematica*, the first thing that happens is that aa, + and bb are recognized as being separate "tokens". The same separation into tokens is done when boxes are constructed from input enclosed in \\(... \\). However, inside the boxes each token is given as a string, rather than in its raw form.

The RowBox has aa, + and bb broken into separate strings.

```
In[14]:= \( aa+bb \) // FullForm
Out[14]//FullForm= RowBox[List["aa", "+", "bb"]]
```

The spaces around the + are by default discarded.

In[15]:= \(**aa + bb** \) // **FullForm**

Out[15]//FullForm= RowBox[List["aa", "+", "bb"]]

Backslash-space inserts a literal space.

In[16]:= \(**aa \ + \ bb** \) // **FullForm**

Out[16]//FullForm= RowBox[List["aa", " ", "+", " ", "bb"]]

Here two nested RowBox objects are formed.

In[17]:= \(**aa+bb/cc** \) // **FullForm**

Out[17]//FullForm= RowBox[
              List["aa", "+", RowBox[List["bb", "/", "cc"]]]]

The same box structure is formed even when the string given does not correspond to a complete *Mathematica* expression.

In[18]:= \(**aa+bb/** \) // **FullForm**

Out[18]//FullForm= RowBox[List["aa", "+", RowBox[List["bb", "/"]]]]

Within \(... \) sequences, you can set up certain kinds of boxes by using backslash notations such as \^ and \@. But for other kinds of boxes, you need to give ordinary *Mathematica* input, prefaced by *.

This constructs a GridBox.

In[19]:= \(***GridBox[{{"a", "b"}, {"c", "d"}}]** \) // **DisplayForm**

Out[19]//DisplayForm= $\begin{matrix} a & b \\ c & d \end{matrix}$

This constructs a StyleBox.

In[20]:= \(***StyleBox["text", FontWeight->Bold]** \) // **DisplayForm**

Out[20]//DisplayForm= **text**

* in effect acts like an escape: it allows you to enter ordinary *Mathematica* syntax even within a \(... \) sequence. Note that the input you give after a * can itself in turn contain \(... \) sequences.

You can alternate nested * and \(... \). Explicit quotes are needed outside of \(... \).

In[21]:= \(**x + *GridBox[{{"a", "b"}, {\(c \^ 2\), \(d \/**
        *GridBox[{{"x","y"},{"x","y"}}] \)}}] \) // **DisplayForm**

Out[21]//DisplayForm= $x + c^2 \begin{matrix} a & b \\ \frac{d}{\begin{smallmatrix} x & y \\ x & y \end{smallmatrix}} \end{matrix}$

In the notebook front end, you can typically use CTRL-* or CTRL-8 to get a dialog box in which you can enter raw boxes—just as you do after *.

\!\(*input*\)	interpret input in the current form
\!\(*form* \` *input*\)	interpret input using the specified form

Controlling the way input is interpreted.

In a StandardForm cell, this will be interpreted in StandardForm, yielding a product.

In[22]:= \!\(**c(1+x)** \)

Out[22]= c (1 + x)

The backslash backquote sequence tells *Mathematica* to interpret this in `TraditionalForm`.	*In[23]:=* `\!\(TraditionalForm\` c(1+x) \)`
	Out[23]= c[1 + x]

When you copy the contents of a cell from a notebook into a program such as a text editor, no explicit backslash backquote sequence is usually included. But if you expect to paste what you get back into a cell of a different type from the one it came from, then you will typically need to include a backslash backquote sequence in order to ensure that everything is interpreted correctly.

■ 2.8.13 Converting between Strings, Boxes and Expressions

`ToString[`*expr*, *form*`]`	create a string representing the specified textual form of *expr*
`ToBoxes[`*expr*, *form*`]`	create boxes representing the specified textual form of *expr*
`ToExpression[`*input*, *form*`]`	create an expression by interpreting a string or boxes as input in the specified textual form
`ToString[`*expr*`]`	create a string using `OutputForm`
`ToBoxes[`*expr*`]`	create boxes using `StandardForm`
`ToExpression[`*input*`]`	create an expression using `StandardForm`

Converting between strings, boxes and expressions.

Here is a simple expression.	*In[1]:=* `x^2 + y^2`
	Out[1]= $x^2 + y^2$
This gives the `InputForm` of the expression as a string.	*In[2]:=* `ToString[x^2 + y^2, InputForm]`
	Out[2]= x^2 + y^2
In `FullForm` explicit quotes are shown around the string.	*In[3]:=* `FullForm[%]`
	Out[3]//FullForm= "x^2 + y^2"
This gives a string representation for the `StandardForm` boxes that correspond to the expression.	*In[4]:=* `ToString[x^2 + y^2, StandardForm] // FullForm`
	Out[4]//FullForm= "\!\(x\^2 + y\^2\)"
`ToBoxes` yields the boxes themselves.	*In[5]:=* `ToBoxes[x^2 + y^2, StandardForm]`
	Out[5]= RowBox[
	{SuperscriptBox[x, 2], +, SuperscriptBox[y, 2]}]

In generating data for files and external programs, it is sometimes necessary to produce two-dimensional forms which use only ordinary keyboard characters. You can do this using `OutputForm`.

This produces a string which gives a two-dimensional rendering of the expression, using only ordinary keyboard characters.	`In[6]:= ToString[x^2 + y^2, OutputForm]`
	
	`Out[6]=  2    2`
	`         x  + y`

The string consists of two lines, separated by an explicit \n newline.	`In[7]:= FullForm[%]`
	
	`Out[7]//FullForm= " 2    2\nx  + y"`

The string looks right only in a monospaced font.	`In[8]:= StyleBox[%, FontFamily->"Times"] // DisplayForm`
	
	`Out[8]//DisplayForm= 2 2`
	`                   x + y`

If you operate only with one-dimensional structures, you can effectively use `ToString` to do string manipulation with formatting functions.

This generates a string corresponding to the `OutputForm` of `StringForm`.	`In[9]:= ToString[StringForm["``^10 = ``", 4, 4^10]] // InputForm`  `Out[9]//InputForm= "4^10 = 1048576"`

InputForm	strings corresponding to keyboard input
StandardForm	strings or boxes corresponding to standard two-dimensional input (default)
TraditionalForm	strings or boxes mimicking traditional mathematical notation

Some forms handled by `ToExpression`.

This creates an expression from an `InputForm` string.	`In[10]:= ToExpression["x^2 + y^2"]`
	
	`Out[10]= x^2 + y^2`

This creates the same expression from `StandardForm` boxes.	`In[11]:= ToExpression[RowBox[{SuperscriptBox["x", "2"], "+",`
	`                SuperscriptBox["y", "2"]}]]`
	
	`Out[11]= x^2 + y^2`

Here the boxes are represented in `InputForm`.	`In[12]:= ToExpression[\(x\^2 + y\^2\)]`
	
	`Out[12]= x^2 + y^2`

This returns raw boxes.	`In[13]:= ToExpression["\(x\^2 + y\^2\)"]`
	
	`Out[13]= RowBox[`
	`          {SuperscriptBox[x, 2], +, SuperscriptBox[y, 2]}]`

This interprets the boxes.	`In[14]:= ToExpression["\!\(x\^2 + y\^2\)"]`
	
	`Out[14]= x^2 + y^2`

In `TraditionalForm` these are interpreted as functions.	`In[15]:= ToExpression["c(1 + x) + log(x)", TraditionalForm]`
	
	`Out[15]= c[1 + x] + Log[x]`

ToExpression[*input*, *form*, *h*]	create an expression, then wrap it with head *h*

Creating expressions wrapped with special heads.

This creates an expression, then immediately evaluates it.	*In[16]:=* **ToExpression["1 + 1"]**
	Out[16]= 2
This creates an expression using StandardForm rules, then wraps it in Hold.	*In[17]:=* **ToExpression["1 + 1", StandardForm, Hold]**
	Out[17]= Hold[1 + 1]
You can get rid of the Hold using ReleaseHold.	*In[18]:=* **ReleaseHold[%]**
	Out[18]= 2

SyntaxQ["*string*"]	determine whether a string represents syntactically correct *Mathematica* input
SyntaxLength["*string*"]	find out how long a sequence of characters starting at the beginning of a string is syntactically correct

Testing correctness of strings as input.

ToExpression will attempt to interpret any string as *Mathematica* input. But if you give it a string that does not correspond to syntactically correct input, then it will print a message, and return $Failed.

This is not syntactically correct input, so ToExpression does not convert it to an expression.	*In[19]:=* **ToExpression["1 +/+ 2"]**
	ToExpression::sntx: Syntax error in or before "1 +/+ 2". ^
	Out[19]= $Failed
ToExpression requires that the string correspond to a *complete Mathematica* expression.	*In[20]:=* **ToExpression["1 + 2 + "]**
	ToExpression::sntxi: Incomplete expression; more input is needed.
	Out[20]= $Failed

You can use the function SyntaxQ to test whether a particular string corresponds to syntactically correct *Mathematica* input. If SyntaxQ returns False, you can find out where the error occurred using SyntaxLength. SyntaxLength returns the number of characters which were successfully processed before a syntax error was detected.

SyntaxQ shows that this string does not correspond to syntactically correct *Mathematica* input.	*In[21]:=* **SyntaxQ["1 +/+ 2"]**
	Out[21]= False

SyntaxLength reveals that an error was detected after the third character in the string.

```
In[22]:= SyntaxLength["1 +/+ 2"]
Out[22]= 3
```

Here SyntaxLength returns a value greater than the length of the string, indicating that the input was correct so far as it went, but needs to be continued.

```
In[23]:= SyntaxLength["1 + 2 + "]
Out[23]= 10
```

■ 2.8.14 The Syntax of the *Mathematica* Language

Mathematica uses various syntactic rules to interpret input that you give, and to convert strings and boxes into expressions. The version of these rules that is used for StandardForm and InputForm in effect defines the basic *Mathematica* language. The rules used for other forms, such as TraditionalForm, follow the same overall principles, but differ in many details.

a, xyz, $\alpha\beta\gamma$	symbols
"some text", "$\alpha + \beta$"	strings
123.456, 3*^45	numbers
+, ->, ≠	operators
(* comment *)	input to be ignored

Types of tokens in the *Mathematica* language.

When you give text as input to *Mathematica*, the first thing that *Mathematica* does is to break the text into a sequence of *tokens*, with each token representing a separate syntactic unit.

Thus, for example, if you give the input xx+yy-zzzz, *Mathematica* will break this into the sequence of tokens xx, +, yy, - and zzzz. Here xx, yy and zzzz are tokens that correspond to symbols, while + and - are operators.

Operators are ultimately what determine the structure of the expression formed from a particular piece of input. The *Mathematica* language involves several general classes of operators, distinguished by the different positions in which they appear with respect to their operands.

$$
\begin{array}{ll}
x \oplus y & \texttt{CirclePlus}[x, y] \\
x \approx y & \texttt{TildeTilde}[x, y] \\
x \notin y & \texttt{NotElement}[x, y] \\
x \leftrightarrow y & \texttt{LeftRightArrow}[x, y] \\
\nabla\, x & \texttt{Del}[x] \\
\square\, x & \texttt{Square}[x] \\
\langle x, y, \dots \rangle & \texttt{AngleBracket}[x, y, \dots]
\end{array}
$$

A few *Mathematica* operators corresponding to functions without predefined values.

Mathematica follows the general convention that the function associated with a particular operator should have the same name as the special character that represents that operator.

\[Congruent] is displayed as ≡.

```
In[5]:= x \[Congruent] y
Out[5]= x ≡ y
```

It corresponds to the function Congruent.

```
In[6]:= FullForm[%]
Out[6]//FullForm= Congruent[x, y]
```

$$
\begin{array}{ll}
x\ \texttt{\textbackslash[}\textit{name}\texttt{]}\ y & \textit{name}[x, y] \\
\texttt{\textbackslash[}\textit{name}\texttt{]}\ x & \textit{name}[x] \\
\texttt{\textbackslash[Left}\textit{name}\texttt{]}\ x, y, \dots \texttt{\textbackslash[Right}\textit{name}\texttt{]} & \textit{name}[x, y, \dots]
\end{array}
$$

The conventional correspondence in *Mathematica* between operator names and function names.

You should realize that even though the functions `CirclePlus` and `CircleTimes` do not have built-in evaluation rules, the operators ⊕ and ⊗ do have built-in precedences. Pages 972–977 list all the operators recognized by *Mathematica,* in order of their precedence.

The operators ⊗ and ⊕ have definite precedences—with ⊗ higher than ⊕.

```
In[7]:= x ⊗ y ⊕ z // FullForm
Out[7]//FullForm= Mod[Plus[z, CircleTimes[x, y]], 2]
```

x_y	`Subscript[`x`, `y`]`		$\overset{y}{x}$	`Overscript[`x`, `y`]`
x_+	`SubPlus[`x`]`		$\underset{y}{x}$	`Underscript[`x`, `y`]`
x_-	`SubMinus[`x`]`		$\overline{x}$	`OverBar[`x`]`
x_*	`SubStar[`x`]`		$\vec{x}$	`OverVector[`x`]`
x^+	`SuperPlus[`x`]`		$\tilde{x}$	`OverTilde[`x`]`
x^-	`SuperMinus[`x`]`		$\hat{x}$	`OverHat[`x`]`
x^*	`SuperStar[`x`]`		$\dot{x}$	`OverDot[`x`]`
$x^\dagger$	`SuperDagger[`x`]`		$\underline{x}$	`UnderBar[`x`]`

Some two-dimensional forms without built-in meanings.

Subscripts have no built-in meaning in *Mathematica*.	*In[8]:=* **x₂ + y₂ // InputForm** *Out[8]//InputForm=* Subscript[x, 2] + Subscript[y, 2]
Most superscripts are however interpreted as powers by default.	*In[9]:=* **x² + y² // InputForm** *Out[9]//InputForm=* x^2 + y^2
A few special superscripts are not interpreted as powers.	*In[10]:=* **x† + y⁺ // InputForm** *Out[10]//InputForm=* SuperDagger[x] + SuperPlus[y]
Bar and hat are interpreted as OverBar and OverHat.	*In[11]:=* **x̄ + ŷ // InputForm** *Out[11]//InputForm=* OverBar[x] + OverHat[y]

■ 2.8.16 Defining Output Formats

Just as *Mathematica* allows you to define how expressions should be evaluated, so also it allows you to define how expressions should be formatted for output. The basic idea is that whenever *Mathematica* is given an expression to format for output, it first calls Format[*expr*] to find out whether any special rules for formatting the expression have been defined. By assigning a value to Format[*expr*] you can therefore tell *Mathematica* that you want a particular kind of expression to be output in a special way.

This tells *Mathematica* to format bin objects in a special way.	*In[1]:=* **Format[bin[x_, y_]] := MatrixForm[{{x}, {y}}]**
Now bin objects are output to look like binomial coefficients.	*In[2]:=* **bin[i + j, k]** *Out[2]=* $\begin{pmatrix} i+j \\ k \end{pmatrix}$
Internally, however, bin objects are still exactly the same.	*In[3]:=* **FullForm[%]** *Out[3]//FullForm=* bin[Plus[i, j], k]

Format[$expr_1$] := $expr_2$	define $expr_1$ to be formatted like $expr_2$
Format[$expr_1$, $form$] := $expr_2$	give a definition only for a particular output form

Defining your own rules for formatting.

By making definitions for Format, you can tell *Mathematica* to format a particular expression so as to look like another expression. You can also tell *Mathematica* to run a program to determine how a particular expression should be formatted.

This specifies that *Mathematica* should run a simple program to determine how xrep objects should be formatted.

In[4]:= **Format[xrep[n_]] := StringJoin[Table["x", {n}]]**

The strings are created when each xrep is formatted.

In[5]:= **xrep[1] + xrep[4] + xrep[9]**

Out[5]= x + xxxx + xxxxxxxxx

Internally however the expression still contains xrep objects.

In[6]:= **% /. xrep[n_] -> x^n**

Out[6]= x + x^4 + x^9

Prefix[$f[x]$, h]	prefix form $h\ x$
Postfix[$f[x]$, h]	postfix form $x\ h$
Infix[$f[x, y, ...\ ]$, h]	infix form $x\ h\ y\ h\ ...$
Prefix[$f[x]$]	standard prefix form f @ x
Postfix[$f[x]$]	standard postfix form x // #f
Infix[$f[x, y, ...\ ]$]	standard infix form $x \sim f \sim y \sim f \sim ...$
PrecedenceForm[$expr$, n]	an object to be parenthesized with a precedence level n

Output forms for operators.

This prints with f represented by the "prefix operator" <>.

In[7]:= **Prefix[f[x], "<>"]**

Out[7]= <>x

Here is output with the "infix operator" <>.

In[8]:= **s = Infix[{a, b, c}, "<>"]**

Out[8]= a<>b<>c

By default, the "infix operator" <> is assumed to have "higher precedence" than ^, so no parentheses are inserted.

In[9]:= **s^2**

Out[9]= a<>b<>c^2

When you have an output form involving operators, the question arises of whether the arguments of some of them should be parenthesized. As discussed in Section 2.1.3, this depends on the "precedence" of the operators. When you set up output forms involving operators, you can use `PrecedenceForm` to specify the precedence to assign to each operator. *Mathematica* uses integers from 1 to 1000 to represent "precedence levels". The higher the precedence level for an operator, the less it needs to be parenthesized.

Here `<>` is treated as an operator with precedence 100. This precedence turns out to be low enough that parentheses are inserted.	*In[10]:=* `PrecedenceForm[s, 100]^2` *Out[10]=* $(a<>b<>c)^2$

When you make an assignment for `Format[`*expr*`]`, you are defining the output format for *expr* in all standard types of *Mathematica* output. By making definitions for `Format[`*expr*, *form*`]`, you can specify formats to be used in specific output forms.

This specifies the TeXForm for the symbol x.	*In[11]:=* `Format[x, TeXForm] := "{\\bf x}"`

The output format for x that you specified is now used whenever the TEX form is needed.	*In[12]:=* `TeXForm[1 + x^2]` *Out[12]//TeXForm=* `1 + {{{\bf x}}^2}`

■ 2.8.17 Advanced Topic: Low-Level Input and Output Rules

`MakeBoxes[`*expr*, *form*`]`	construct boxes to represent *expr* in the specified form
`MakeExpression[`*boxes*, *form*`]`	construct an expression corresponding to *boxes*

Low-level functions for converting between expressions and boxes.

MakeBoxes generates boxes without evaluating its input.	*In[1]:=* `MakeBoxes[2 + 2, StandardForm]` *Out[1]=* `RowBox[{2, +, 2}]`

MakeExpression interprets boxes but uses HoldComplete to prevent the resulting expression from being evaluated.	*In[2]:=* `MakeExpression[%, StandardForm]` *Out[2]=* `HoldComplete[2 + 2]`

Built into *Mathematica* are a large number of rules for generating output and interpreting input. Particularly in `StandardForm`, these rules are carefully set up to be consistent, and to allow input and output to be used interchangeably.

It is fairly rare that you will need to modify these rules. The main reason is that *Mathematica* already has built-in rules for the input and output of many operators to which it does not itself assign specific meanings.

Thus, if you want to add, for example, a generalization form of addition, you can usually just use an operator like ⊕ for which *Mathematica* already has built-in input and output rules.

This outputs using the ⊕ operator.

In[3]:= `CirclePlus[u, v, w]`

Out[3]= u ⊕ v ⊕ w

Mathematica understands ⊕ on input.

In[4]:= `u ⊕ v ⊕ w // FullForm`

Out[4]//FullForm= CirclePlus[u, v, w]

In dealing with output, you can make definitions for Format[*expr*] to change the way that a particular expression will be formatted. You should realize, however, that as soon as you do this, there is no guarantee that the output form of your expression will be interpreted correctly if it is given as *Mathematica* input.

If you want to, *Mathematica* allows you to redefine the basic rules that it uses for the input and output of all expressions. You can do this by making definitions for MakeBoxes and MakeExpression. You should realize, however, that unless you make such definitions with great care, you are likely to end up with inconsistent results.

This defines how gplus objects should be output in StandardForm.

In[5]:= `gplus /: MakeBoxes[gplus[x_, y_, n_], StandardForm] :=`
`    RowBox[ {MakeBoxes[x, StandardForm],`
`        SubscriptBox["\[CirclePlus]", MakeBoxes[n, StandardForm]],`
`        MakeBoxes[y, StandardForm]} ]`

gplus is now output using a subscripted ⊕.

In[6]:= `gplus[a, b, m+n]`

Out[6]= a ⊕ₘ₊ₙ b

Mathematica cannot however interpret this as input.

In[7]:= `a ⊕ₘ₊ₙ b`

Syntax::sntxi:
    Incomplete expression; more input is needed.

This tells *Mathematica* to interpret a subscripted ⊕ as a specific piece of FullForm input.

In[7]:= `MakeExpression[RowBox[{x_, SubscriptBox[`
`            "\[CirclePlus]", n_], y_}], StandardForm] :=`
`    MakeExpression[RowBox[`
`        {"gplus", "[", x, ",", y, ",", n, "]"}], StandardForm]`

Now the subscripted ⊕ is interpreted as a gplus.

In[8]:= `a ⊕ₘ₊ₙ b // FullForm`

Out[8]//FullForm= gplus[a, b, Plus[m, n]]

When you give definitions for MakeBoxes, you can think of this as essentially a lower-level version of giving definitions for Format. An important difference is that MakeBoxes does not evaluate its argument, so you can define rules for formatting expressions without being concerned about how these expressions would evaluate.

In addition, while Format is automatically called again on any results obtained by applying it, the same is not true of MakeBoxes. This means that in giving definitions for MakeBoxes you explicitly have to call MakeBoxes again on any subexpressions that still need to be formatted.

- ■ Break input into tokens.

- ■ Strip spacing characters.

- ■ Construct boxes using built-in operator precedences.

- ■ Strip StyleBox and other boxes not intended for interpretation.

- ■ Apply rules defined for MakeExpression.

Operations done on *Mathematica* input.

■ 2.8.18 Generating Unstructured Output

The functions described so far in this section determine *how* expressions should be formatted when they are printed, but they do not actually cause anything to be printed.

In the most common way of using *Mathematica* you never in fact explicitly have to issue a command to generate output. Usually, *Mathematica* automatically prints out the final result that it gets from processing input you gave. Sometimes, however, you may want to get *Mathematica* to print out expressions at intermediate stages in its operation. You can do this using the function Print.

Print[$expr_1$, $expr_2$, ...]	print the $expr_i$, with no spaces in between, but with a newline (line feed) at the end

Printing expressions.

Print prints its arguments, with no spaces in between, but with a newline (line feed) at the end.

```
In[1]:= Print[a, b]; Print[c]
ab
c
```

This prints a table of the first five integers and their squares.

```
In[2]:= Do[Print[i, " ", i^2], {i, 5}]
1  1
2  4
3  9
4  16
5  25
```

Print simply takes the arguments you give, and prints them out one after the other, with no spaces in between. In many cases, you will need to print output in a more complicated format. You can do this by giving an output form as an argument to Print.

This prints the matrix in the form of a table.

```
In[3]:= Print[TableForm[{{1, 2}, {3, 4}}]]
1   2

3   4
```

Here the output format is specified using `StringForm`.	*In[4]:=* **Print[StringForm["x = ``, y = ``", a^2, b^2]]**
	x = a², y = b²

The output generated by `Print` is usually given in the standard *Mathematica* output format. You can however explicitly specify that some other output format should be used.

This prints output in *Mathematica* input form.	*In[5]:=* **Print[InputForm[a^2 + b^2]]**
	a^2 + b^2

You should realize that `Print` is only one of several mechanisms available in *Mathematica* for generating output. Another is the function `Message` described in Section 2.8.21, used for generating named messages. There are also a variety of lower-level functions described in Section 2.11.3 which allow you to produce output in various formats both as part of an interactive session, and for files and external programs.

+■ 2.8.19 Generating Styled Output in Notebooks

+ `StylePrint[`*expr*`, "`*style*`"]`	create a new cell containing *expr* in the specified style
+ `StylePrint[`*expr*`]`	use the default style for the notebook

Generating styled output in notebooks.

This generates a cell in section heading style.	*In[1]:=* **StylePrint["The heading", "Section"];**

■ **The heading**

This generates a cell in input style.	*In[2]:=* **StylePrint[x^2 + y^2, "Input"]**

■ **The heading**
  x² + y²

Mathematica provides many capabilities for manipulating the contents of notebooks, as discussed in Section 2.10. `StylePrint` handles the simple case when all you want to do is to add a cell of a particular style.

■ 2.8.20 Requesting Input

Mathematica usually works by taking whatever input you give, and then processing it. Sometimes, however, you may want to have a program you write explicitly request more input. You can do this using `Input` and `InputString`.

`Input[ ]`	read an expression as input
`InputString[ ]`	read a string as input
`Input["`*prompt*`"]`	issue a prompt, then read an expression
`InputString["`*prompt*`"]`	issue a prompt then read a string

Interactive input.

Exactly how `Input` and `InputString` work depends on the computer system and *Mathematica* interface you are using. With a text-based interface, they typically just wait for standard input, terminated with a newline. With a notebook interface, however, they typically get the front end to put up a "dialog box", in which the user can enter input.

In general, `Input` is intended for reading complete *Mathematica* expressions. `InputString`, on the other hand, is for reading arbitrary strings.

■ 2.8.21 Messages

Mathematica has a general mechanism for handling messages generated during computations. Many built-in *Mathematica* functions use this mechanism to produce error and warning messages. You can also use the mechanism for messages associated with functions you write.

The basic idea is that every message has a definite name, of the form *symbol::tag*. You can use this name to refer to the message. (The object *symbol::tag* has head `MessageName`.)

`Off[`*s::tag*`]`	switch off a message, so it is not printed
`On[`*s::tag*`]`	switch on a message

Controlling the printing of messages.

As discussed in Section 1.3.11, you can use `On` and `Off` to control the printing of particular messages. Most messages associated with built-in functions are switched on by default. You can use `Off` to switch them off if you do not want to see them.

This prints a warning message.	*In[1]:=* **Log[a, b, c]**
	Log::argt: Log called with 3 arguments; 1 or 2 arguments are expected.
	Out[1]= Log[a, b, c]
You can switch off the message like this.	*In[2]:=* **Off[Log::argt]**
Now no warning message is produced.	*In[3]:=* **Log[a, b, c]**
	Out[3]= Log[a, b, c]

Although most messages associated with built-in functions are switched on by default, there are some which are switched off by default, and which you will see only if you explicitly switch them on. An example is the message General::newsym, discussed in Section 2.6.13, which tells you every time a new symbol is created.

s::tag	give the text of a message
s::tag = string	set the text of a message
Messages[*s*]	show all messages associated with *s*

Manipulating messages.

The text of a message with the name *s::tag* is stored simply as the value of *s::tag*, associated with the symbol *s*. You can therefore see the text of a message simply by asking for *s::tag*. You can set the text by assigning a value to *s::tag*.

If you give LinearSolve a singular matrix, it prints a warning message.	*In[4]:=* **LinearSolve[{{1, 1}, {2, 2}}, {3, 5}]**
	LinearSolve::nosol: Linear equation encountered which has no solution.
	Out[4]= LinearSolve[{{1, 1}, {2, 2}}, {3, 5}]
Here is the text of the message.	*In[5]:=* **LinearSolve::nosol**
	Out[5]= Linear equation encountered which has no solution.
This redefines the message.	*In[6]:=* **LinearSolve::nosol = "Matrix encountered is not invertible."**
	Out[6]= Matrix encountered is not invertible.
Now the new form will be used.	*In[7]:=* **LinearSolve[{{1, 1}, {2, 2}}, {3, 5}]**
	LinearSolve::nosol: Matrix encountered is not invertible.
	Out[7]= LinearSolve[{{1, 1}, {2, 2}}, {3, 5}]

Messages are always stored as strings suitable for use with StringForm. When the message is printed, the appropriate expressions are "spliced" into it. The expressions are wrapped with HoldForm to prevent evaluation. In addition, any function that is assigned as the value of the global variable

`$MessagePrePrint` is applied to the resulting expressions before they are given to `StringForm`. The default for `$MessagePrePrint` is `Short`.

Most messages are associated directly with the functions that generate them. There are, however, some "general" messages, which can be produced by a variety of functions.

If you give the wrong number of arguments to a function *F*, *Mathematica* will warn you by printing a message such as *F*`::argx`. If *Mathematica* cannot find a message named *F*`::argx`, it will use the text of the "general" message `General::argx` instead. You can use `Off[`*F*`::argx]` to switch off the argument count message specifically for the function *F*. You can also use `Off[General::argx]` to switch off all messages that use the text of the general message.

Mathematica prints a message if you give the wrong number of arguments to a built-in function.	*In[8]:=* **Sqrt[a, b]** Sqrt::argx: Sqrt called with 2 arguments; 1 argument is expected. *Out[8]=* Sqrt[a, b]
This argument count message is a general one, used by many different functions.	*In[9]:=* **General::argx** *Out[9]=* `1` called with `2` arguments; 1 argument is expected.

If something goes very wrong with a calculation you are doing, it is common to find that the same warning message is generated over and over again. This is usually more confusing than useful. As a result, *Mathematica* keeps track of all messages that are produced during a particular calculation, and stops printing a particular message if it comes up more than three times. Whenever this happens, *Mathematica* prints the message `General::stop` to let you know. If you really want to see all the messages that *Mathematica* tries to print, you can do this by switching off `General::stop`.

`$MessageList`	a list of the messages produced during a particular computation
`MessageList[`*n*`]`	a list of the messages produced during the processing of the *n*th input line in a *Mathematica* session

Finding out what messages were produced during a computation.

In every computation you do, *Mathematica* maintains a list `$MessageList` of all the messages that are produced. In a standard *Mathematica* session, this list is cleared after each line of output is generated. However, during a computation, you can access the list. In addition, when the *n*th output line in a session is generated, the value of `$MessageList` is assigned to `MessageList[`*n*`]`.

This returns $MessageList, which gives a list of the messages produced.

In[10]:= **Sqrt[a, b, c]; Exp[a, b]; $MessageList**

Sqrt::argx:
   Sqrt called with 3 arguments; 1 argument is expected.

Exp::argx: Exp called with 2
      arguments; 1 argument is expected.

Out[10]= {Sqrt::argx, Exp::argx}

The message names are wrapped in HoldForm to stop them from evaluating.

In[11]:= **InputForm[%]**

Out[11]//InputForm= {HoldForm[Sqrt::argx], HoldForm[Exp::argx]}

In writing programs, it is often important to be able to check automatically whether any messages were generated during a particular calculation. If messages were generated, say as a consequence of producing indeterminate numerical results, then the result of the calculation may be meaningless.

Check[*expr*, *failexpr*]	if no messages are generated during the evaluation of *expr*, then return *expr*, otherwise return *failexpr*
Check[*expr*, *failexpr*, $s_1::t_1$, $s_2::t_2$, ...]	check only for the messages $s_i::t_i$

Checking for warning messages.

Evaluating 1^0 produces no messages, so the result of the evaluation is returned.

In[12]:= **Check[1^0, err]**

Out[12]= 1

Evaluating 0^0 produces a message, so the second argument of Check is returned.

In[13]:= **Check[0^0, err]**

Power::indet: Indeterminate expression 0^0 encountered.

Out[13]= err

Check[*expr*, *failexpr*] tests for all messages that are actually printed out. It does not test for messages whose output has been suppressed using Off.

In some cases you may want to test only for a specific set of messages, say ones associated with numerical overflow. You can do this by explicitly telling Check the names of the messages you want to look for.

The message generated by Sin[1, 2] is ignored by Check, since it is not the one specified.

In[14]:= **Check[Sin[1, 2], err, General::ind]**

Sin::argx: Sin called with 2
      arguments; 1 argument is expected.

Out[14]= Sin[1, 2]

| Message[*s::tag*] | print a message |
| Message[*s::tag, expr*₁, ...] | print a message, with the *expr*ᵢ spliced into its string form |

Generating messages.

By using the function `Message`, you can mimic all aspects of the way in which built-in *Mathematica* functions generate messages. You can for example switch on and off messages using `On` and `Off`, and `Message` will automatically look for `General::`*tag* if it does not find the specific message *s::tag*.

This defines the text of a message associated with f.

```
In[15]:= f::overflow = "Factorial argument `1` too large."
Out[15]= Factorial argument `1` too large.
```

Here is the function f.

```
In[16]:= f[x_] :=
            If[x > 10,
               (Message[f::overflow, x]; Infinity), x!]
```

When the argument of f is greater than 10, the message is generated.

```
In[17]:= f[20]

f::overflow: Factorial argument 20 too large.

Out[17]= ∞
```

This switches off the message.

```
In[18]:= Off[f::overflow]
```

Now the message is no longer generated.

```
In[19]:= f[20]
Out[19]= ∞
```

When you call `Message`, it first tries to find a message with the explicit name you have specified. If this fails, it tries to find a message with the appropriate tag associated with the symbol `General`. If this too fails, then *Mathematica* takes any function you have defined as the value of the global variable `$NewMessage`, and applies this function to the symbol and tag of the message you have requested.

By setting up the value of `$NewMessage` appropriately, you can, for example, get *Mathematica* to read in the text of a message from a file when that message is first needed.

■ 2.8.22 International Messages

The standard set of messages for built-in *Mathematica* functions are written in American English. In some versions of *Mathematica*, messages are also available in other languages. In addition, if you set up messages yourself, you can give ones in other languages.

Languages in *Mathematica* are conventionally specified by strings. The languages are given in English, in order to avoid the possibility of needing special characters. Thus, for example, the French language is specified in *Mathematica* as "French".

Graphics[*list*]	general two-dimensional graphics
DensityGraphics[*list*]	density plot
ContourGraphics[*list*]	contour plot
SurfaceGraphics[*list*]	three-dimensional surface
Graphics3D[*list*]	general three-dimensional graphics
GraphicsArray[*list*]	array of other graphics objects

Graphics objects in *Mathematica*.

The functions like Plot and ListPlot discussed in Section 1.9 all work by building up *Mathematica* graphics objects, and then displaying them.

Graphics	Plot, ListPlot, ParametricPlot
DensityGraphics	DensityPlot, ListDensityPlot
ContourGraphics	ContourPlot, ListContourPlot
SurfaceGraphics	Plot3D, ListPlot3D
Graphics3D	ParametricPlot3D

Generating graphics objects by plotting functions and data.

You can create other kinds of graphical images in *Mathematica* by building up your own graphics objects. Since graphics objects in *Mathematica* are just symbolic expressions, you can use all the standard *Mathematica* functions to manipulate them.

Once you have created a graphics object, you must then display it. The function Show allows you to display any *Mathematica* graphics object.

Show[g]	display a graphics object
Show[g_1, g_2, ...]	display several graphics objects combined
Show[GraphicsArray[{{g_{11}, g_{12}, ... }, ... }]]	
	display an array of graphics objects

Displaying graphics objects.

This uses Table to generate a polygon graphics primitive.

```
In[3]:= poly = Polygon[
            Table[N[{Cos[n Pi/5], Sin[n Pi/5]}], {n, 0, 5}] ]
Out[3]= Polygon[{{1., 0}, {0.809017, 0.587785},
            {0.309017, 0.951056}, {-0.309017, 0.951056},
            {-0.809017, 0.587785}, {-1., 0}}]
```

This creates a two-dimensional graphics object that contains the polygon graphics primitive. In standard output format, the graphics object is given simply as -Graphics-.

```
In[4]:= Graphics[ poly ]
Out[4]= -Graphics-
```

InputForm shows the complete graphics object.

```
In[5]:= InputForm[%]
Out[5]//InputForm=
        Graphics[Polygon[{{1., 0},
            {0.8090169943749474, 0.5877852522924732},
            {0.3090169943749474, 0.9510565162951536},
            {-0.3090169943749474, 0.9510565162951536},
            {-0.8090169943749474, 0.5877852522924732}, {-1., 0}}]]
```

This displays the graphics object you have created.

```
In[6]:= Show[%]
```

| Graphics directives | Examples: RGBColor, Thickness, SurfaceColor |
| Graphics options | Examples: PlotRange, Ticks, AspectRatio, ViewPoint |

Local and global ways to modify graphics.

Given a particular list of graphics primitives, *Mathematica* provides two basic mechanisms for modifying the final form of graphics you get. First, you can insert into the list of graphics primitives certain *graphics directives*, such as RGBColor, which modify the subsequent graphical elements in the list. In this way, you can specify how a particular set of graphical elements should be rendered.

This takes the list of graphics primitives created above, and adds the graphics directive GrayLevel[0.3].

```
In[7]:= Graphics[ {GrayLevel[0.3], poly} ]
Out[7]= -Graphics-
```

This shows the line as a two-dimensional graphics object.

In[2]:= **sawgraph = Show[Graphics[sawline]]**

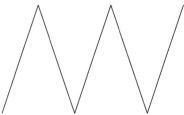

This redisplays the line, with axes added.

In[3]:= **Show[%, Axes -> True]**

You can combine graphics objects that you have created explicitly from graphics primitives with ones that are produced by functions like **Plot**.

This produces an ordinary *Mathematica* plot.

In[4]:= **Plot[Sin[Pi x], {x, 0, 6}]**

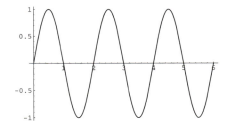

This combines the plot with the sawtooth picture made above.

In[5]:= **Show[%, sawgraph]**

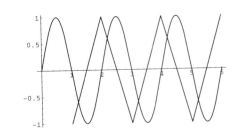

You can combine different graphical elements simply by giving them in a list. In two-dimensional graphics, *Mathematica* will render the elements in exactly the order you give them. Later elements are therefore effectively drawn on top of earlier ones.

Here is a list of two Rectangle graphics elements.

In[6]:= **{Rectangle[{1, -1}, {2, -0.6}],**
Rectangle[{4, .3}, {5, .8}]}

Out[6]= {Rectangle[{1, -1}, {2, -0.6}],
Rectangle[{4, 0.3}, {5, 0.8}]}

This draws the rectangles on top of the line that was defined above.

In[7]:= **Show[Graphics[{sawline, %}]]**

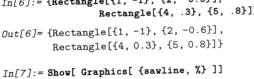

The Polygon graphics primitive takes a list of x, y coordinates, corresponding to the corners of a polygon. *Mathematica* joins the last corner with the first one, and then fills the resulting area.

Here are the coordinates of the corners of a regular pentagon.

In[8]:= **pentagon = Table[{Sin[2 Pi n/5], Cos[2 Pi n/5]}, {n, 5}]**

$$Out[8]= \left\{\left\{\frac{1}{2}\sqrt{\frac{1}{2}(5+\sqrt{5})}, \frac{1}{4}(-1+\sqrt{5})\right\},\right.$$
$$\left\{\frac{1}{2}\sqrt{\frac{1}{2}(5-\sqrt{5})}, \frac{1}{4}(-1-\sqrt{5})\right\},$$
$$\left\{-\frac{1}{2}\sqrt{\frac{1}{2}(5-\sqrt{5})}, \frac{1}{4}(-1-\sqrt{5})\right\},$$
$$\left.\left\{-\frac{1}{2}\sqrt{\frac{1}{2}(5+\sqrt{5})}, \frac{1}{4}(-1+\sqrt{5})\right\}, \{0, 1\}\right\}$$

This displays the pentagon. With the default choice of aspect ratio, the pentagon looks somewhat squashed.

In[9]:= `Show[ Graphics[ Polygon[pentagon] ] ]`

This chooses the aspect ratio so that the shape of the pentagon is preserved.

In[10]:= `Show[%, AspectRatio -> Automatic]`

Mathematica can handle polygons which fold over themselves.

In[11]:= `Show[Graphics[`
`        Polygon[ {{-1, -1}, {1, 1}, {1, -1}, {-1, 1}} ] ]]`

Circle[{*x*, *y*}, *r*]	a circle with radius *r* centered at the point {*x*, *y*}
Circle[{*x*, *y*}, {*r_x*, *r_y*}]	an ellipse with semi-axes r_x and r_y
Circle[{*x*, *y*}, *r*, {*theta_1*, *theta_2*}]	
	a circular arc
Circle[{*x*, *y*}, {*r_x*, *r_y*}, {*theta_1*, *theta_2*}]	
	an elliptical arc
Disk[{*x*, *y*}, *r*], etc.	filled disks

Circles and disks.

This shows two circles with radius 2. Setting the option AspectRatio -> Automatic makes the circles come out with their natural aspect ratio.

```
In[12]:= Show[ Graphics[
             {Circle[{0, 0}, 2], Circle[{1, 1}, 2]} ],
                        AspectRatio -> Automatic ]
```

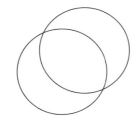

This shows a sequence of disks with progressively larger semi-axes in the *x* direction, and progressively smaller ones in the *y* direction.

```
In[13]:= Show[ Graphics[
             Table[Disk[{3n, 0}, {n/4, 2-n/4}], {n, 4}] ],
                        AspectRatio -> Automatic ]
```

Mathematica allows you to generate arcs of circles, and segments of ellipses. In both cases, the objects are specified by starting and finishing angles. The angles are measured counterclockwise in radians with zero corresponding to the positive *x* direction.

This draws a 140° wedge centered at the origin.

```
In[14]:= Show[ Graphics[ Disk[{0, 0}, 1, {0, 140 Degree}] ],
              AspectRatio -> Automatic ]
```

`Raster[{{`a_{11}`, `a_{12}`, ... }, {`a_{21}`, ... }, ... }]`
array of gray levels between 0 and 1

`Raster[`*array*`, {{`*xmin, ymin*`}, {`*xmax, ymax*`}}, {`*zmin, zmax*`}]`
array of gray levels between *zmin* and *zmax* drawn in the rectangle defined by {*xmin, ymin*} and {*xmax, ymax*}

`RasterArray[{{`g_{11}`, `g_{12}`, ... }, {`g_{21}`, ... }, ... }]`
rectangular array of cells colored according to the graphics directives g_{ij}

Raster-based graphics elements.

Here is a 4 × 4 array of values between 0 and 1.

```
In[15]:= modtab = Table[Mod[i, j]/3, {i, 4}, {j, 4}] // N
Out[15]= {{0, 0.333333, 0.333333, 0.333333},
          {0, 0, 0.666667, 0.666667}, {0, 0.333333, 0, 1.},
          {0, 0, 0.333333, 0}}
```

This uses the array of values as gray levels in a raster.

In[16]:= **Show[Graphics[Raster[%]]]**

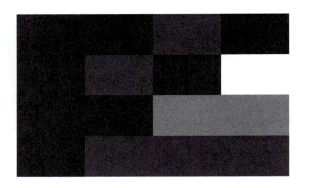

This shows two overlapping copies of the raster.

In[17]:= **Show[Graphics[{Raster[modtab, {{0, 0}, {2, 2}}],**
                Raster[modtab, {{1.5, 1.5}, {3, 2}}]}]]

In the default case, Raster always generates an array of gray cells. As described on page 497, you can use the option ColorFunction to apply a "coloring function" to all the cells.

You can also use the graphics primitive RasterArray. While Raster takes an array of *values*, RasterArray takes an array of *Mathematica graphics directives*. The directives associated with each cell are taken to determine the color of that cell. Typically the directives are chosen from the set GrayLevel, RGBColor or Hue. By using RGBColor and Hue directives, you can create color rasters using RasterArray.

This gives a dot-dashed line.   *In[10]:=* **Show[Graphics[{Dashing[{0.01, 0.05, 0.05, 0.05}],**
                                                         Line[{{-1, -1}, {1, 1}}]}]]

One way to use *Mathematica* graphics directives is to insert them directly into the lists of graphics primitives used by graphics objects. Sometimes, however, you want the graphics directives to be applied more globally, and for example to determine the overall "style" with which a particular type of graphical element should be rendered. There are typically graphics options which can be set to specify such styles in terms of lists of graphics directives.

PlotStyle -> *style*	specify a style to be used for all curves in Plot
PlotStyle -> {{*style₁*}, {*style₂*}, ... }	specify styles to be used (cyclically) for a sequence of curves in Plot
MeshStyle -> *style*	specify a style to be used for a mesh in density and surface graphics
BoxStyle -> *style*	specify a style to be used for the bounding box in three-dimensional graphics

Some graphics options for specifying styles.

This generates a plot in which the   *In[11]:=* **Plot[BesselJ[2, x], {x, 0, 10},**
curve is given in a style specified by   **PlotStyle -> {{Thickness[0.02], GrayLevel[0.5]}}]**
graphics directives.

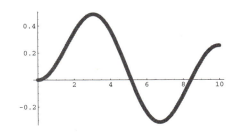

`GrayLevel[0.5]`	gray
`RGBColor[1, 0, 0]`, etc.	red, etc.
`Thickness[0.05]`	thick
`Dashing[{0.05, 0.05}]`	dashed
`Dashing[{0.01, 0.05, 0.05, 0.05}]`	dot-dashed

Some typical styles.

The various "style options" allow you to specify how particular graphical elements in a plot should be rendered. *Mathematica* also provides options that affect the rendering of the whole plot.

`Background -> ` *color*	specify the background color for a plot
`DefaultColor -> ` *color*	specify the default color for a plot
`Prolog -> g`	give graphics to render before a plot is started
`Epilog -> g`	give graphics to render after a plot is finished

Graphics options that affect whole plots.

This draws the whole plot on a gray background.

```
In[12]:= Plot[Sin[Sin[x]], {x, 0, 10},
             Background -> GrayLevel[0.6]]
```

This makes the default color white.   *In[13]:=* **Show[%, DefaultColor -> GrayLevel[1]]**

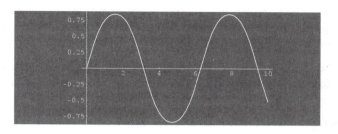

■ 2.9.4 Coordinate Systems for Two-Dimensional Graphics

When you set up a graphics object in *Mathematica*, you give coordinates for the various graphical elements that appear. When *Mathematica* renders the graphics object, it has to translate the original coordinates you gave into "display coordinates" which specify where each element should be placed in the final display area.

Sometimes, you may find it convenient to specify the display coordinates for a graphical element directly. You can do this by using "scaled coordinates" Scaled[{*sx*, *sy*}] rather than {*x*, *y*}. The scaled coordinates are defined to run from 0 to 1 in *x* and *y*, with the origin taken to be at the lower-left corner of the display area.

{*x*, *y*}	original coordinates
Scaled[{*sx*, *sy*}]	scaled coordinates

Coordinate systems for two-dimensional graphics.

The rectangle is drawn at a fixed position relative to the display area, independent of the original coordinates used for the plot.

In[1]:= **Plot[Tan[x], {x, 0, 2Pi},**
        Prolog ->
            Rectangle[Scaled[{0.7, 0.7}], Scaled[{1, 1}]]]

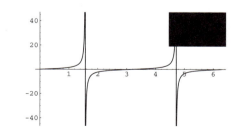

When you use $\{x, y\}$ or `Scaled[{sx, sy}]`, you are specifying position either completely in original coordinates, or completely in scaled coordinates. Sometimes, however, you may need to use a combination of these coordinate systems. For example, if you want to draw a line at a particular point whose length is a definite fraction of the width of the plot, you will have to use original coordinates to specify the basic position of the line, and scaled coordinates to specify its length.

You can use `Scaled[{dsx, dsy}, {x, y}]` to specify a position using a mixture of original and scaled coordinates. In this case, $\{x, y\}$ gives a position in original coordinates, and $\{dsx, dsy\}$ gives the offset from the position in scaled coordinates.

Note that you can use `Scaled` with either one or two arguments to specify radii in `Disk` and `Circle` graphics elements.

`Scaled[{sdx, sdy}, {x, y}]`	scaled offset from original coordinates
`Offset[{adx, ady}, {x, y}]`	absolute offset from original coordinates
`Offset[{adx, ady}, Scaled[{sx, sy}]]`	absolute offset from scaled coordinates

Positions specified as offsets.

Each line drawn here has an absolute length of 6 printer's points.

```
In[2]:= Show[Graphics[Table[
            Line[{{x, x^2}, Offset[{0, 6}, {x, x^2}]}],
            {x, 10}], Frame->True]]
```

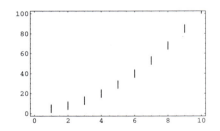

You can also use `Offset` inside `Circle` with just one argument to create a circle with a certain absolute radius.

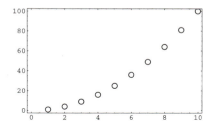

In most kinds of graphics, you typically want the relative positions of different objects to adjust automatically when you change the coordinates or the overall size of your plot. But sometimes you may instead want the offset from one object to another to be constrained to remain fixed. This can be the case, for example, when you are making a collection of plots in which you want certain features to remain consistent, even though the different plots have different forms.

`Offset[{adx, ady}, position]` allows you to specify the position of an object by giving an absolute offset from a position that is specified in original or scaled coordinates. The units for the offset are printer's points, equal to $\frac{1}{72}$ of an inch.

When you give text in a plot, the size of the font that is used is also specified in printer's points. A 10-point font, for example, therefore has letters whose basic height is 10 printer's points. You can use `Offset` to move text around in a plot, and to create plotting symbols or icons which match the size of text.

`PlotRange -> {{xmin, xmax}, {ymin, ymax}}`	the range of original coordinates to include in the plot
`PlotRegion -> {{sxmin, sxmax}, {symin, symax}}`	the region of the display specified in scaled coordinates which the plot fills

Options which determine translation from original to display coordinates.

When *Mathematica* renders a graphics object, one of the first things it has to do is to work out what range of original x and y coordinates it should actually display. Any graphical elements that are outside this range will be "clipped", and not shown.

The option `PlotRange` specifies the range of original coordinates to include. As discussed on page 135, the default setting is `PlotRange -> Automatic`, which makes *Mathematica* try to choose a range which includes all "interesting" parts of a plot, while dropping "outliers". By setting

`PlotRange -> All`, you can tell *Mathematica* to include everything. You can also give explicit ranges of coordinates to include.

This sets up a polygonal object whose corners have coordinates between roughly ±1.

```
In[4]:= obj = Polygon[
            Table[{Sin[n Pi/10], Cos[n Pi/10]} + 0.05 (-1)^n,
                                               {n, 20}]] ;
```

In this case, the polygonal object fills almost the whole display area.

```
In[5]:= Show[Graphics[obj]]
```

With the default `PlotRange -> Automatic`, the outlying point is not included, but does affect the range of coordinates chosen.

```
In[6]:= Show[ Graphics[{obj, Point[{20, 20}]}] ]
```

With `PlotRange -> All`, the outlying point is included, and the coordinate system is correspondingly modified.

```
In[7]:= Show[%, PlotRange -> All]
```

The option `PlotRange` allows you to specify a rectangular region in the original coordinate system, and to drop any graphical elements that lie outside this region. In order to render the remaining elements, however, *Mathematica* then has to determine how to position this rectangular region with respect to the final display area.

The option `PlotRegion` allows you to specify where the corners of the rectangular region lie within the final display area. The positions of the corners are specified in scaled coordinates, which are defined to run from 0 to 1 across the display area. The default is `PlotRegion -> {{0, 1}, {0, 1}}`, which specifies that the rectangular region should fill the whole display area.

By specifying `PlotRegion`, you can effectively add "margins" around your plot.

```
In[8]:= Plot[ArcTan[x], {x, 0, 10},
            PlotRegion -> {{0.2, 0.8}, {0.3, 0.7}}]
```

`AspectRatio -> r`	make the ratio of height to width for the display area equal to *r*
`AspectRatio -> Automatic`	determine the shape of the display area from the original coordinate system

Specifying the shape of the display area.

What we have discussed so far is how *Mathematica* translates the original coordinates you specify into positions in the final display area. What remains to discuss, however, is what the final display area is like.

On most computer systems, there is a certain fixed region of screen or paper into which the *Mathematica* display area must fit. How it fits into this region is determined by its "shape" or aspect ratio. In general, the option `AspectRatio` specifies the ratio of height to width for the final display area.

It is important to note that the setting of `AspectRatio` does not affect the meaning of the scaled or display coordinates. These coordinates always run from 0 to 1 across the display area. What `AspectRatio` does is to change the shape of this display area.

This generates a graphic object corresponding to a hexagon.

```
In[9]:= hex = Graphics[Polygon[
            Table[{Sin[n Pi/3], Cos[n Pi/3]}, {n, 6}] ]] ;
```

This renders the hexagon in a display area whose height is three times its width.

In[10]:= **Show[hex, AspectRatio -> 3]**

For two-dimensional graphics, `AspectRatio` is set by default to the fixed value of `1/GoldenRatio`. Sometimes, however, you may want to determine the aspect ratio for a plot from the original coordinate system used in the plot. Typically what you want is for one unit in the *x* direction in the original coordinate system to correspond to the same distance in the final display as one unit in the *y* direction. In this way, objects that you define in the original coordinate system are displayed with their "natural shape". You can make this happen by setting the option `AspectRatio -> Automatic`.

With `AspectRatio -> Automatic`, the aspect ratio of the final display area is determined from the original coordinate system, and the hexagon is shown with its "natural shape".

In[11]:= **Show[hex, AspectRatio -> Automatic]**

Using scaled coordinates, you can specify the sizes of graphical elements as fractions of the size of the display area. You cannot, however, tell *Mathematica* the actual physical size at which a particular graphical element should be rendered. Of course, this size ultimately depends on the details of your graphics output device, and cannot be determined for certain within *Mathematica*. Nevertheless, graphics directives such as `AbsoluteThickness` discussed on page 481 do allow you to indicate "absolute sizes" to use for particular graphical elements. The sizes you request in this way will be respected by most, but not all, output devices. (For example, if you optically project an image, it is neither possible nor desirable to maintain the same absolute size for a graphical element within it.)

■ 2.9.5 Labeling Two-Dimensional Graphics

Axes -> True	give a pair of axes
GridLines -> Automatic	draw grid lines on the plot
Frame -> True	put axes on a frame around the plot
PlotLabel -> "*text*"	give an overall label for the plot

Ways to label two-dimensional plots.

Here is a plot, using the default Axes -> True.

In[1]:= **bp = Plot[BesselJ[2, x], {x, 0, 10}]**

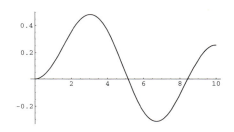

Setting Frame -> True generates a frame with axes, and removes tick marks from the ordinary axes.

In[2]:= **Show[bp, Frame -> True]**

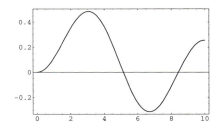

This includes grid lines, which are shown in light blue on color displays.

In[3]:= **Show[%, GridLines -> Automatic]**

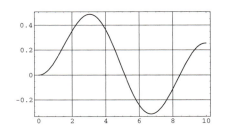

`Axes -> False`	draw no axes
`Axes -> True`	draw both x and y axes
`Axes -> {False, True}`	draw a y axis but no x axis
`AxesOrigin -> Automatic`	choose the crossing point for the axes automatically
`AxesOrigin -> {x, y}`	specify the crossing point
`AxesStyle -> `*style*	specify the style for axes
`AxesStyle -> {{`*xstyle*`}, {`*ystyle*`}}`	specify individual styles for axes
`AxesLabel -> None`	give no axis labels
`AxesLabel -> `*ylabel*	put a label on the y axes
`AxesLabel -> {`*xlabel*`, `*ylabel*`}`	put labels on both x and y axes

Options for axes.

This makes the axes cross at the point {5, 0}, and puts a label on each axis.

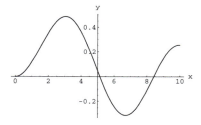

`Ticks -> None`	draw no tick marks
`Ticks -> Automatic`	place tick marks automatically
`Ticks -> {`*xticks*`, `*yticks*`}`	tick mark specifications for each axis

Settings for the `Ticks` option.

With the default setting `Ticks -> Automatic`, *Mathematica* creates a certain number of major and minor tick marks, and places them on axes at positions which yield the minimum number of decimal digits in the tick labels. In some cases, however, you may want to specify the positions and properties of tick marks explicitly. You will need to do this, for example, if you want to have tick marks at multiples of π, or if you want to put a nonlinear scale on an axis.

None	draw no tick marks
Automatic	place tick marks automatically
$\{x_1, x_2, \ldots\}$	draw tick marks at the specified positions
$\{\{x_1, label_1\}, \{x_2, label_2\}, \ldots\}$	draw tick marks with the specified labels
$\{\{x_1, label_1, len_1\}, \ldots\}$	draw tick marks with the specified scaled lengths
$\{\{x_1, label_1, \{plen_1, mlen_1\}\}, \ldots\}$	draw tick marks with the specified lengths in the positive and negative directions
$\{\{x_1, label_1, len_1, style_1\}, \ldots\}$	draw tick marks with the specified styles
func	a function to be applied to *xmin, xmax* to get the tick mark option

Tick mark options for each axis.

This gives tick marks at specified positions on the x axis, and chooses the tick marks automatically on the y axis.

In[5]:= **Show[bp, Ticks -> {{0, Pi, 2Pi, 3Pi}, Automatic}]**

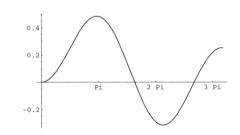

This adds tick marks with no labels at multiples of $\pi/2$.

In[6]:= **Show[bp,**
**   Ticks -> {{0, {Pi/2, ""}, Pi, {3Pi/2, ""},**
**   2Pi, {5Pi/2, ""}, 3Pi}, Automatic}]**

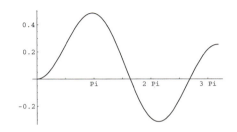

Particularly when you want to create complicated tick mark specifications, it is often convenient to define a "tick mark function" which creates the appropriate tick mark specification given the minimum and maximum values on a particular axis.

This defines a function which gives a list of tick mark positions with a spacing of 1.

In[7]:= `units[xmin_, xmax_] :=`
`Range[Floor[xmin], Floor[xmax], 1]`

This uses the `units` function to specify tick marks for the *x* axis.

In[8]:= `Show[bp, Ticks -> {units, Automatic}]`

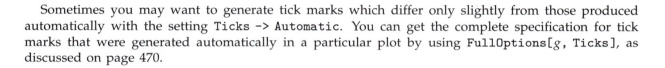

Sometimes you may want to generate tick marks which differ only slightly from those produced automatically with the setting `Ticks -> Automatic`. You can get the complete specification for tick marks that were generated automatically in a particular plot by using `FullOptions[g, Ticks]`, as discussed on page 470.

`Frame -> False`	draw no frame
`Frame -> True`	draw a frame around the plot
`FrameStyle -> `*style*	specify a style for the frame
`FrameStyle -> {{`*xmstyle*`}, {`*ymstyle*`}, ... }`	specify styles for each edge of the frame
`FrameLabel -> None`	give no frame labels
`FrameLabel -> {`*xmlabel, ymlabel*`, ... }`	put labels on edges of the frame
`RotateLabel -> False`	do not rotate text in labels
`FrameTicks -> None`	draw no tick marks on frame edges
`FrameTicks -> Automatic`	position tick marks automatically
`FrameTicks -> {{`*xmticks, ymticks*`, ... }}`	specify tick marks for frame edges

Options for frame axes.

The `Axes` option allows you to draw a single pair of axes in a plot. Sometimes, however, you may instead want to show the scales for a plot on a frame, typically drawn around the whole plot. The option `Frame` allows you effectively to draw four axes, corresponding to the four edges of the frame around a plot. These four axes are ordered clockwise, starting from the one at the bottom.

This draws frame axes, and labels each of them.

```
In[9]:= Show[bp, Frame -> True,
           FrameLabel -> {"label 1", "label 2",
                          "label 3", "label 4"}]
```

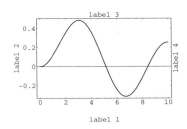

GridLines -> None	draw no grid lines
GridLines -> Automatic	position grid lines automatically
GridLines -> {*xgrid*, *ygrid*}	specify grid lines in analogy with tick marks

Options for grid lines.

Grid lines in *Mathematica* work very much like tick marks. As with tick marks, you can specify explicit positions for grid lines. There is no label or length to specify for grid lines. However, you can specify a style.

This generates *x* but not *y* grid lines.

```
In[10]:= Show[bp, GridLines -> {Automatic, None}]
```

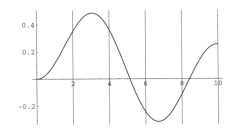

■ 2.9.6 Making Plots within Plots

Section 1.9.4 described how you can make regular arrays of plots using `GraphicsArray`. Using the `Rectangle` graphics primitive, however, you can combine and superimpose plots in any way.

Rectangle[{*xmin*, *ymin*}, {*xmax*, *ymax*}, *graphics*]
                 render a graphics object within the specified rectangle

---

Creating a subplot.

Here is a three-dimensional plot.

In[1]:= `p3 = Plot3D[Sin[x] Exp[y], {x, -5, 5}, {y, -2, 2}]`

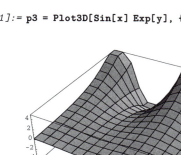

This creates a two-dimensional graphics object which contains two copies of the three-dimensional plot.

In[2]:= `Show[Graphics[ {Rectangle[{0, 0}, {1, 1}, p3],`
                      `Rectangle[{0.8, 0.8}, {1.2, 1.4}, p3]} ]]`

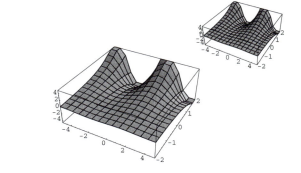

Mathematica can render any graphics object within a `Rectangle`. In all cases, what it puts in the rectangle is a scaled down version of what would be obtained if you displayed the graphics object on its own. Notice that in general the display area for the graphics object will be sized so as to touch at least one pair of edges of the rectangle.

■ 2.9.7 Density and Contour Plots

`DensityGraphics[`*array*`]`	density plot
`ContourGraphics[`*array*`]`	contour plot

Graphics objects that represent density and contour plots.

The functions `DensityPlot` and `ContourPlot` discussed in Section 1.9.6 work by creating `ContourGraphics` and `DensityGraphics` objects containing arrays of values.

Most of the options for density and contour plots are the same as those for ordinary two-dimensional plots. There are, however, a few additional options.

option name	default value	
`ColorFunction`	`Automatic`	how to assign colors to each cell
`Mesh`	`True`	whether to draw a mesh
`MeshStyle`	`Automatic`	a style for the mesh

Additional options for density plots.

In a density plot, the color of each cell represents its value. By default, each cell is assigned a gray level, running from black to white as the value of the cell increases. In general, however, you can specify other "color maps" for the relation between the value of a cell and its color. The option `ColorFunction` allows you to specify a function which is applied to each cell value to find the color of the cell. The cell values are scaled so as to run between 0 and 1 in a particular density plot. The function you give as the setting for `ColorFunction` may return any *Mathematica* color directive, such as `GrayLevel`, `Hue` or `RGBColor`. A common setting to use is `ColorFunction -> Hue`.

Here is a density plot with the default ColorFunction.

In[1]:= **DensityPlot[Sin[x y], {x, -1, 1}, {y, -1, 1}]**

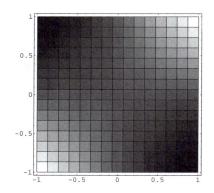

This gives a density plot with a different "color map".

In[2]:= **Show[%, ColorFunction -> (GrayLevel[#^3]&)]**

option name	default value	
Contours	10	what contours to use
ContourLines	True	whether to draw contour lines
ContourStyle	Automatic	style to use for contour lines
ContourShading	True	whether to shade regions in the plot
ColorFunction	Automatic	how to assign colors to contour levels

Options for contour plots.

In constructing a contour plot, the first issue is what contours to use. With the default setting Contours -> 10, *Mathematica* uses a sequence of 10 contour levels equally spaced between the minimum and maximum values defined by the PlotRange option.

Contours -> n	use a sequence of n equally spaced contours
Contours -> $\{z_1, z_2, \dots\}$	use contours with values $z_1, z_2, \dots$

Specifying contours.

This creates a contour plot with two contours.

In[3]:= ContourPlot[Sin[x y], {x, -1, 1}, {y, -1, 1},
          Contours -> {-.5, .5}]

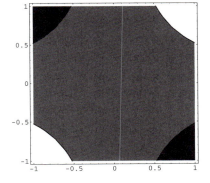

There are some slight subtleties associated with labeling density and contour plots. Both the Axes and Frame options from ordinary two-dimensional graphics can be used. But setting AxesOrigin -> Automatic keeps the axes outside the plot in both cases.

■ 2.9.8 Three-Dimensional Graphics Primitives

One of the most powerful aspects of graphics in *Mathematica* is the availability of three-dimensional as well as two-dimensional graphics primitives. By combining three-dimensional graphics primitives, you can represent and render three-dimensional objects in *Mathematica*.

Point[{x, y, z}]   point with coordinates x, y, z

Line[{{x_1, y_1, z_1}, {x_2, y_2, z_2}, ... }]
line through the points {x_1, y_1, z_1}, {x_2, y_2, z_2}, ...

Polygon[{{x_1, y_1, z_1}, {x_2, y_2, z_2}, ... }]
filled polygon with the specified list of corners

Cuboid[{*xmin*, *ymin*, *zmin*}, {*xmax*, *ymax*, *zmax*}]
cuboid

Text[*expr*, {x, y, z}]   text at position {x, y, z} (see Section 2.9.16)

Three-dimensional graphics elements.

Every time you evaluate rcoord, it generates a random coordinate in three dimensions.

```
In[1]:= rcoord := {Random[ ], Random[ ], Random[ ]}
```

This generates a list of 20 random points in three-dimensional space.

```
In[2]:= pts = Table[Point[rcoord], {20}] ;
```

Here is a plot of the points.

```
In[3]:= Show[ Graphics3D[ pts ] ]
```

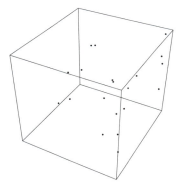

This gives a plot showing a line
through 10 random points in three
dimensions.

In[4]:= **Show[Graphics3D[Line[Table[rcoord, {10}]]]]**

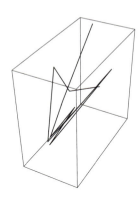

If you give a list of graphics elements in two dimensions, *Mathematica* simply draws each element
in turn, with later elements obscuring earlier ones. In three dimensions, however, *Mathematica* collects
together all the graphics elements you specify, then displays them as three-dimensional objects, with
the ones in front in three-dimensional space obscuring those behind.

Every time you evaluate rantri, it
generates a random triangle in
three-dimensional space.

In[5]:= **rantri := Polygon[Table[rcoord, {3}]]**

This draws a single random triangle.

In[6]:= **Show[Graphics3D[rantri]]**

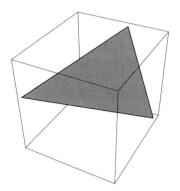

This draws a collection of 5 random triangles. The triangles in front obscure those behind.

In[7]:= **Show[Graphics3D[Table[rantri, {5}]]]**

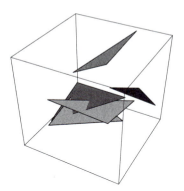

By creating an appropriate list of polygons, you can build up any three-dimensional object in *Mathematica*. Thus, for example, all the surfaces produced by `ParametricPlot3D` are represented simply as lists of polygons.

The package `Graphics`Polyhedra`` contains examples of lists of polygons which correspond to polyhedra in three dimensions.

This loads a package which defines various polyhedra.

In[8]:= **<<Graphics`Polyhedra`**

Here is the list of polygons corresponding to a tetrahedron centered at the origin.

In[9]:= **Tetrahedron[ ]**

Out[9]= {Polygon[{{0, 0, 1.73205}, {0, 1.63299, -0.57735},
            {-1.41421, -0.816497, -0.57735}}],
        Polygon[{{0, 0, 1.73205},
            {-1.41421, -0.816497, -0.57735},
            {1.41421, -0.816497, -0.57735}}],
        Polygon[{{0, 0, 1.73205},
            {1.41421, -0.816497, -0.57735},
            {0, 1.63299, -0.57735}}],
        Polygon[{{0, 1.63299, -0.57735},
            {1.41421, -0.816497, -0.57735},
            {-1.41421, -0.816497, -0.57735}}]}

This displays the tetrahedron as a three-dimensional object.

In[10]:= **Show[Graphics3D[%]]**

Dodecahedron[ ] is another three-dimensional object defined in the polyhedra package.

In[11]:= **Show[Graphics3D[Dodecahedron[ ]]]**

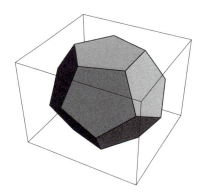

This shows four intersecting dodecahedra.

In[12]:= **Show[Graphics3D[**
Table[Dodecahedron[0.8 {k, k, k}], {k, 0, 3}]]]

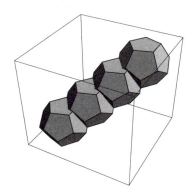

Mathematica allows polygons in three dimensions to have any number of vertices. However, these vertices should lie in a plane, and should form a convex figure. If they do not, then *Mathematica* will break the polygon into triangles, which are planar by definition, before rendering it.

Cuboid[{*x*, *y*, *z*}]	a unit cube with opposite corners having coordinates {*x*, *y*, *z*} and {*x*+1, *y*+1, *z*+1}
Cuboid[{*xmin*, *ymin*, *zmin*}, {*xmax*, *ymax*, *zmax*}]	a cuboid (rectangular parallelepiped) with opposite corners having the specified coordinates

Cuboid graphics elements.

This draws 20 random unit cubes in three-dimensional space.

In[13]:= **Show[Graphics3D[Table[Cuboid[10 rcoord], {20}]]]**

■ 2.9.9 Three-Dimensional Graphics Directives

In three dimensions, just as in two dimensions, you can give various graphics directives to specify how the different elements in a graphics object should be rendered.

All the graphics directives for two dimensions also work in three dimensions. There are however some additional directives in three dimensions.

Just as in two dimensions, you can use the directives `PointSize`, `Thickness` and `Dashing` to tell *Mathematica* how to render `Point` and `Line` elements. Note that in three dimensions, the lengths that appear in these directives are measured as fractions of the total width of the display area for your plot.

This generates a list of 20 random points in three dimensions.

In[1]:= **pts = Table[Point[Table[Random[ ], {3}]], {20}];**

This displays the points, with each one being a circle whose diameter is 5% of the display area width.

`In[2]:= Show[Graphics3D[ { PointSize[0.05], pts } ]]`

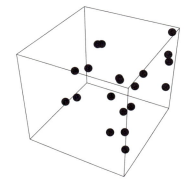

As in two dimensions, you can use `AbsolutePointSize`, `AbsoluteThickness` and `AbsoluteDashing` if you want to measure length in absolute units.

This generates a line through 10 random points in three dimensions.

`In[3]:= line = Line[Table[Random[ ], {10}, {3}]] ;`

This shows the line dashed, with a thickness of 2 printer's points.

`In[4]:= Show[Graphics3D[ { AbsoluteThickness[2],`
`                          AbsoluteDashing[{5, 5}], line } ]]`

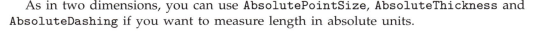

For `Point` and `Line` objects, the color specification directives also work the same in three dimensions as in two dimensions. For `Polygon` objects, however, they can work differently.

In two dimensions, polygons are always assumed to have an intrinsic color, specified directly by graphics directives such as `RGBColor`. In three dimensions, however, *Mathematica* also provides the option of generating colors for polygons using a more physical approach based on simulated illumination. With the default option setting `Lighting -> True` for `Graphics3D` objects, *Mathematica* ignores explicit colors specified for polygons, and instead determines all polygon colors using the simulated illumination model. Even in this case, however, explicit colors are used for points and lines.

Lighting -> False	intrinsic colors
Lighting -> True	colors based on simulated illumination (default)

The two schemes for coloring polygons in three dimensions.

This loads a package which defines various polyhedra.

`In[5]:= <<Graphics`Polyhedra``

This draws an icosahedron, using the same gray level for all faces.

`In[6]:= Show[Graphics3D[{GrayLevel[0.7], Icosahedron[ ]}],`
`                         Lighting -> False]`

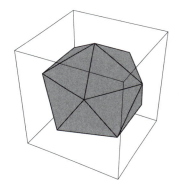

With the default setting Lighting -> True, the colors of polygons are determined by the simulated illumination model, and explicit color specifications are ignored.

`In[7]:= Show[%, Lighting -> True]`

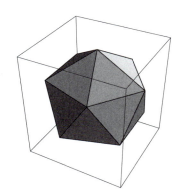

Explicit color directives are, however, always followed for points and lines.

In[8]:= **Show[{%, Graphics3D[{GrayLevel[0.5], Thickness[0.05], Line[{{0, 0, -2}, {0, 0, 2}}]}]}]**

EdgeForm[ ]	draw no lines at the edges of polygons
EdgeForm[*g*]	use the graphics directives *g* to determine how to draw lines at the edges of polygons

Giving graphics directives for all the edges of polygons.

When you render a three-dimensional graphics object in *Mathematica*, there are two kinds of lines that can appear. The first kind are lines from explicit Line primitives that you included in the graphics object. The second kind are lines that were generated as the edges of polygons.

You can tell *Mathematica* how to render all lines of the second kind by giving a list of graphics directives inside EdgeForm.

This renders a dodecahedron with its edges shown as thick gray lines.

In[9]:= **Show[Graphics3D[{EdgeForm[{GrayLevel[0.5], Thickness[0.02]}], Dodecahedron[ ]}]]**

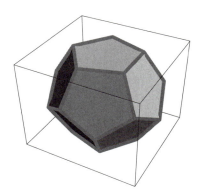

FaceForm[*gfront*, *gback*]	use *gfront* graphics directives for the front face of each polygon, and *gback* for the back

Rendering the fronts and backs of polygons differently.

An important aspect of polygons in three dimensions is that they have both front and back faces. *Mathematica* uses the following convention to define the "front face" of a polygon: if you look at a polygon from the front, then the corners of the polygon will appear counterclockwise, when taken in the order that you specified them.

This defines a dodecahedron with one face removed.

In[10]:= **d = Drop[Dodecahedron[ ], {6}] ;**

You can now see inside the dodecahedron.

In[11]:= **Show[Graphics3D[d]]**

This makes the front (outside) face of each polygon light gray, and the back (inside) face dark gray.

In[12]:= **Show[Graphics3D[**
{FaceForm[GrayLevel[0.8], GrayLevel[0.3]], d}],
Lighting -> False]

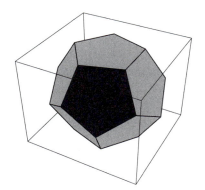

■ 2.9.10 Coordinate Systems for Three-Dimensional Graphics

Whenever *Mathematica* draws a three-dimensional object, it always effectively puts a cuboidal box around the object. With the default option setting `Boxed -> True`, *Mathematica* in fact draws the edges of this box explicitly. But in general, *Mathematica* automatically "clips" any parts of your object that extend outside of the cuboidal box.

The option `PlotRange` specifies the range of *x*, *y* and *z* coordinates that *Mathematica* should include in the box. As in two dimensions the default setting is `PlotRange -> Automatic`, which makes *Mathematica* use an internal algorithm to try and include the "interesting parts" of a plot, but drop outlying parts. With `PlotRange -> All`, *Mathematica* will include all parts.

This loads a package defining various polyhedra.	`In[1]:= <<Graphics`Polyhedra``
This creates a stellated icosahedron.	`In[2]:= stel = Stellate[Icosahedron[ ]] ;`
Here is the stellated icosahedron, drawn in a box.	`In[3]:= Show[Graphics3D[stel], Axes -> True]`

With this setting for `PlotRange`, many parts of the stellated icosahedron lie outside the box, and are clipped.

`In[4]:= Show[%, PlotRange -> {-1, 1}]`

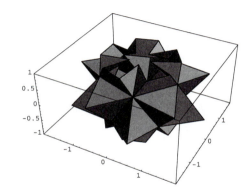

Much as in two dimensions, you can use either "original" or "scaled" coordinates to specify the positions of elements in three-dimensional objects. Scaled coordinates, specified as `Scaled[{sx, sy, sz}]` are taken to run from 0 to 1 in each dimension. The coordinates are set up to define a right-handed coordinate system on the box.

$\{x, y, z\}$	original coordinates
`Scaled[{sx, sy, sz}]`	scaled coordinates, running from 0 to 1 in each dimension

Coordinate systems for three-dimensional objects.

This puts a cuboid in one corner of the box.

```
In[5]:= Show[Graphics3D[{stel,
            Cuboid[Scaled[{0, 0, 0}],
               Scaled[{0.2, 0.2, 0.2}]]}]]
```

Once you have specified where various graphical elements go inside a three-dimensional box, you must then tell *Mathematica* how to draw the box. The first step is to specify what shape the box should be. This is analogous to specifying the aspect ratio of a two-dimensional plot. In three dimensions, you can use the option `BoxRatios` to specify the ratio of side lengths for the box. For `Graphics3D` objects, the default is `BoxRatios -> Automatic`, specifying that the shape of the box should be determined from the ranges of actual coordinates for its contents.

`BoxRatios -> {xr, yr, zr}`	specify the ratio of side lengths for the box
`BoxRatios -> Automatic`	determine the ratio of side lengths from the range of actual coordinates (default for `Graphics3D`)
`BoxRatios -> {1, 1, 0.4}`	specify a fixed shape of box (default for `SurfaceGraphics`)

Specifying the shape of the bounding box for three-dimensional objects.

This displays the stellated icosahedron in a tall box.

In[6]:= **Show[Graphics3D[stel], BoxRatios -> {1, 1, 5}]**

To produce an image of a three-dimensional object, you have to tell *Mathematica* from what view point you want to look at the object. You can do this using the option **ViewPoint**.

Some common settings for this option were given on page 152. In general, however, you can tell *Mathematica* to use any view point, so long as it lies outside the box.

View points are specified in the form **ViewPoint -> {*sx*, *sy*, *sz*}**. The values *si* are given in a special coordinate system, in which the center of the box is {0, 0, 0}. The special coordinates are scaled so that the longest side of the box corresponds to one unit. The lengths of the other sides of the box in this coordinate system are determined by the setting for the **BoxRatios** option. For a cubical box, therefore, each of the special coordinates runs from $-1/2$ to $1/2$ across the box. Note that the view point must always lie outside the box.

This generates a picture using the default view point {1.3, -2.4, 2}.

In[7]:= **surf = Plot3D[(2 + Sin[x]) Cos[2 y],**
            {x, -2, 2}, {y, -3, 3},
                AxesLabel -> {"x", "y", "z"}]

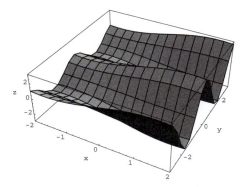

This is what you get with a view point close to one of the corners of the box.

In[8]:= **Show[surf, ViewPoint -> {1.2, 1.2, 1.2}]**

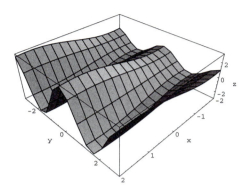

As you move away from the box, the perspective effect gets smaller.

In[9]:= **Show[surf, ViewPoint -> {5, 5, 5}]**

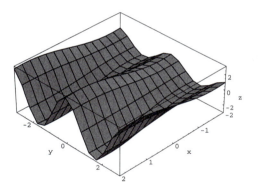

option name	default value	
ViewPoint	{1.3, -2.4, 2}	the point in a special scaled coordinate system from which to view the object
ViewCenter	Automatic	the point in the scaled coordinate system which appears at the center of the final image
ViewVertical	{0, 0, 1}	the direction in the scaled coordinate system which appears as vertical in the final image

Specifying the position and orientation of three-dimensional objects.

In making a picture of a three-dimensional object you have to specify more than just *where* you want to look at the object from. You also have to specify how you want to "frame" the object in your final image. You can do this using the additional options `ViewCenter` and `ViewVertical`.

`ViewCenter` allows you to tell *Mathematica* what point in the object should appear at the center of your final image. The point is specified by giving its scaled coordinates, running from 0 to 1 in each direction across the box. With the setting `ViewCenter -> {1/2, 1/2, 1/2}`, the center of the box will therefore appear at the center of your final image. With many choices of view point, however, the box will not appear symmetrical, so this setting for `ViewCenter` will not center the whole box in the final image area. You can do this by setting `ViewCenter -> Automatic`.

`ViewVertical` specifies which way up the object should appear in your final image. The setting for `ViewVertical` gives the direction in scaled coordinates which ends up vertical in the final image. With the default setting `ViewVertical -> {0, 0, 1}`, the z direction in your original coordinate system always ends up vertical in the final image.

With this setting for `ViewCenter`, a corner of the box appears in the center of your image.

In[10]:= **Show[surf, ViewCenter -> {1, 1, 1}]**

This setting for `ViewVertical` makes the x axis of the box appear vertical in your image.

In[11]:= **Show[surf, ViewVertical -> {1, 0, 0}]**

When you set the options `ViewPoint`, `ViewCenter` and `ViewVertical`, you can think about it as specifying how you would look at a physical object. `ViewPoint` specifies where your head is relative to the object. `ViewCenter` specifies where you are looking (the center of your gaze). And `ViewVertical` specifies which way up your head is.

In terms of coordinate systems, settings for `ViewPoint`, `ViewCenter` and `ViewVertical` specify how coordinates in the three-dimensional box should be transformed into coordinates for your image in the final display area.

For some purposes, it is useful to think of the coordinates in the final display area as three dimensional. The x and y axes run horizontally and vertically, respectively, while the z axis points into the page. Positions specified in this "display coordinate system" remain fixed when you change `ViewPoint` and so on. The positions of light sources discussed in the next section are defined in this display coordinate system.

Box coordinate system	measured relative to the box around your object
Display coordinate system	measured relative to your final display area

Coordinate systems for three-dimensional graphics.

Once you have obtained a two-dimensional image of a three-dimensional object, there are still some issues about how this image should be rendered. The issues however are identical to those that occur for two-dimensional graphics. Thus, for example, you can modify the final shape of your image by changing the `AspectRatio` option. And you specify what region of your whole display area your image should take up by setting the `PlotRegion` option.

This modifies the aspect ratio of the final image.

`In[12]:= Show[surf, Axes -> False, AspectRatio -> 0.3]`

Mathematica usually scales the images of three-dimensional objects to be as large as possible, given the display area you specify. Although in most cases this scaling is what you want, it does have the consequence that the size at which a particular three-dimensional object is drawn may vary with the orientation of the object. You can set the option `SphericalRegion -> True` to avoid such variation. With this option setting, *Mathematica* effectively puts a sphere around the three-dimensional bounding box, and scales the final image so that the whole of this sphere fits inside the display area you specify. The sphere has its center at the center of the bounding box, and is drawn so that the bounding box just fits inside it.

This draws a rather elongated version of the plot.

`In[13]:= Show[surf, BoxRatios -> {1, 5, 1}]`

With `SphericalRegion -> True`, the final image is scaled so that a sphere placed around the bounding box would fit in the display area.

`In[14]:= Show[%, SphericalRegion -> True]`

By setting `SphericalRegion -> True`, you can make the scaling of an object consistent for all orientations of the object. This is useful if you create animated sequences which show a particular object in several different orientations.

SphericalRegion -> False	scale three-dimensional images to be as large as possible
SphericalRegion -> True	scale images so that a sphere drawn around the three-dimensional bounding box would fit in the final display area

Changing the magnification of three-dimensional images.

■ 2.9.11 Plotting Three-Dimensional Surfaces

By giving an appropriate list of graphics primitives, you can represent essentially any three-dimensional object in *Mathematica* with Graphics3D. You can represent three-dimensional surfaces with Graphics3D by giving explicit lists of polygons with adjacent edges.

If you need to represent arbitrary surfaces which can fold over and perhaps intersect themselves, there is no choice but to use explicit lists of polygons with Graphics3D, as ParametricPlot3D does.

However, there are many cases in which you get simpler surfaces. For example, Plot3D and ListPlot3D yield surfaces which never fold over, and have a definite height at every x, y point. You can represent simple surfaces like these in *Mathematica* without giving an explicit list of polygons. Instead, all you need do is to give an array which specifies the z height at every point in an x, y grid. The graphics object SurfaceGraphics[*array*] represents a surface constructed in this way.

Graphics3D[*primitives*]	arbitrary three-dimensional objects, including folded surfaces
SurfaceGraphics[*array*]	simple three-dimensional surfaces

Three-dimensional graphics objects.

Here is a 4 × 4 array of values.

```
In[1]:= moda = Table[Mod[i, j], {i, 4}, {j, 4}]
Out[1]= {{0, 1, 1, 1}, {0, 0, 2, 2}, {0, 1, 0, 3},
         {0, 0, 1, 0}}
```

This uses the array to give the height of each point on the surface.

In[2]:= **Show[SurfaceGraphics[moda]]**

Both `Plot3D` and `ListPlot3D` work by creating `SurfaceGraphics` objects.

Graphics3D[*surface*]   convert SurfaceGraphics to Graphics3D

Converting between representations of surfaces.

If you apply `Graphics3D` to a `SurfaceGraphics` object, *Mathematica* will generate a `Graphics3D` object containing an explicit list of polygons representing the surface in the `SurfaceGraphics` object. Whenever you ask *Mathematica* to combine two `SurfaceGraphics` objects together, it automatically converts them both to `Graphics3D` objects.

Here is a surface represented by a `SurfaceGraphics` object.

In[3]:= **Plot3D[(1 - Sin[x]) (2 - Cos[2 y]),**
                   {x, -2, 2}, {y, -2, 2}]

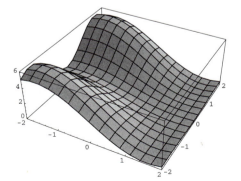

Here is another surface.

In[4]:= **Plot3D[(2 + Sin[x]) (1 + Cos[2 y]),
        {x, -2, 2}, {y, -2, 2}]**

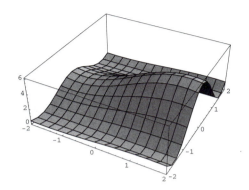

Mathematica shows the two surfaces together by converting each of them to a `Graphics3D` object containing an explicit list of polygons.

In[5]:= **Show[%, %%]**

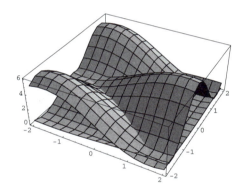

option name	default value	
Mesh	True	whether to draw a mesh on the surface
MeshStyle	Automatic	graphics directives specifying how to render the mesh
MeshRange	Automatic	the original range of coordinates corresponding to the mesh

Mesh options in `SurfaceGraphics`.

When you create a surface using `SurfaceGraphics`, the default is to draw a rectangular mesh on the surface. As discussed on page 153, including this mesh typically makes it easier for one to see the shape of the surface. You can nevertheless get rid of the mesh by setting the option `Mesh -> False`. You can also set the option `MeshStyle` to a list of graphics directives which specify thickness, color or other properties of the mesh lines.

A `SurfaceGraphics` object contains an array of values which specify the height of a surface at points in an *x*, *y* grid. By setting the option `MeshRange`, you can give the range of original *x* and *y* coordinates that correspond to the points in this grid. When you use
`Plot3D[f, {x, xmin, xmax}, {y, ymin, ymax}]` to generate a `SurfaceGraphics` object, the setting `MeshRange -> {{xmin, xmax}, {ymin, ymax}}` is automatically generated. The setting for `MeshRange` is used in labeling the *x* and *y* axes in surface plots, and in working out polygon coordinates if you convert a `SurfaceGraphics` object to an explicit list of polygons in a `Graphics3D` object.

None	leave out clipped parts of the surface, so that you can see through
Automatic	show the clipped part of the surface with the same shading as an actual surface in the same position would have (default setting)
GrayLevel[*i*], RGBColor[*r*, *g*, *b*], etc.	show the clipped part of the surface with a particular gray level, color, etc.
{*bottom*, *top*}	give different specifications for parts that are clipped at the bottom and top

Settings for the `ClipFill` option.

The option `PlotRange` works for `SurfaceGraphics` as it does for other *Mathematica* graphics objects. Any parts of a surface that lie outside the range of coordinates defined by `PlotRange` will be "clipped". The option `ClipFill` allows you to specify what should happen to the parts of a surface that are clipped.

Here is a three-dimensional plot in which the top and bottom of the surface are clipped. With the default setting for ClipFill, the clipped parts are shown as they would be if they were part of the actual surface.

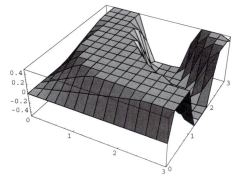

With ClipFill->None, parts of the surface which are clipped are left out, so that you can "see through" the surface there. *Mathematica* always leaves out parts of the surface that correspond to places where the value of the function you are plotting is not a real number.

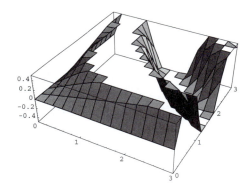

This makes the bottom clipped face white (gray level 1), and the top one black.

In[8]:= **Show[%, ClipFill -> {GrayLevel[1], GrayLevel[0]}]**

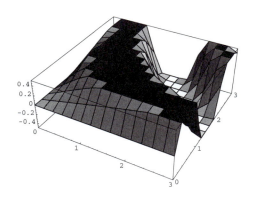

Whenever *Mathematica* draws a surface, it has to know not only the height, but also the color of the surface at each point. With the default setting `Lighting -> True`, *Mathematica* colors the surface using a simulated lighted model. However, with `Lighting -> False`, *Mathematica* uses a "color function" to determine how to color the surface.

The default color function takes the height of the surface, normalized to run from 0 to 1, and colors each part of the surface with a gray level corresponding to this height. There are two ways to change the default.

First, if you set the option `ColorFunction -> c`, then *Mathematica* will apply the function c to each height value to determine the color to use at that point. With `ColorFunction -> Hue`, *Mathematica* will for example color the surface with a range of hues.

`Plot3D[`*f*`, ... , ColorFunction -> `*c*`]`	apply c to the normalized values of f to determine the color of each point on a surface
`ListPlot3D[`*array*`, ColorFunction -> `*c*`]`	apply c to the elements of *array* to determine color
`SurfaceGraphics[`*array*`, ColorFunction -> `*c*`]`	apply c to the elements of *array* to determine color

Specifying functions for coloring surfaces.

With `Lighting -> False`, the default is to color surfaces with gray scales determined by height.

```
In[9]:= exp = Plot3D[Exp[-Sqrt[x^2 + y^2]],
            {x, -2, 2}, {y, -2, 2}, Lighting -> False,
                    PlotPoints -> 25]
```

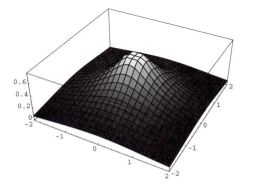

This defines a function which maps alternating ranges of values into black and white.

```
In[10]:= stripes[f_] :=
            If[Mod[f, 1] > 0.5, GrayLevel[1], GrayLevel[0]]
```

This shows the surface colored with black and white stripes.

In[11]:= **Show[exp, ColorFunction -> (stripes[5 #]&)]**

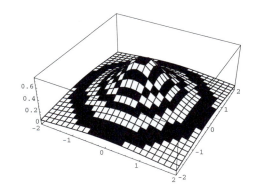

The second way to change the default coloring of surfaces is to supply an explicit second array along with the array of heights. ColorFunction is then applied to the elements of this second array, rather than the array of heights, to find the color directives to use. In the second array, you can effectively specify the value of another coordinate for each point on the surface. This coordinate will be plotted using color, rather than position.

You can generate an array of color values automatically using Plot3D[{*f*, *s*}, ...]. If you give the array explicitly in ListPlot3D or SurfaceGraphics, you should realize that with an $n \times n$ array of heights, you need an $(n-1) \times (n-1)$ array to specify colors. The reason is that the heights are specified for *points* on a grid, whereas the colors are specified for *squares* on the grid.

When you supply a second function or array to Plot3D, ListPlot3D, and so on, the default setting for the ColorFunction option is Automatic. This means that the function or array should contain explicit *Mathematica* color directives, such as GrayLevel or RGBColor. However, if you give another setting, such as ColorFunction -> Hue, then the function or array can yield pure numbers or other data which are converted to color directives when the function specified by ColorFunction is applied.

Plot3D[{*f*, *s*}, {*x*, *xmin*, *xmax*}, {*y*, *ymin*, *ymax*}]	
	plot a surface whose height is determined by *f* and whose color is determined by *s*
ListPlot3D[*height*, *color*]	generate a colored surface plot from an array of heights and colors
SurfaceGraphics[*height*, *color*]	a graphics object representing a surface with a specified array of heights and colors

Specifying arrays of colors for surfaces.

This plots a surface with gray level determined by the *y* coordinate.

```
In[12]:= Plot3D[{Sin[x] Sin[y]^2, GrayLevel[y/3]},
                 {x, 0, 3}, {y, 0, 3}]
```

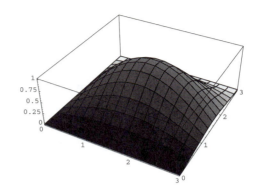

This puts a random gray level in each grid square. Notice that the array of grid squares is 9×9, whereas the array of grid points is 10×10.

```
In[13]:= ListPlot3D[ Table[i/j, {i, 10}, {j, 10}],
            Table[GrayLevel[Random[ ]], {i, 9}, {j, 9}] ]
```

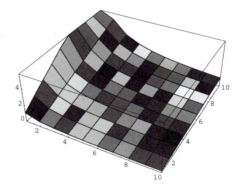

■ 2.9.12 Lighting and Surface Properties

With the default option setting Lighting -> True, *Mathematica* uses a simulated lighting model to determine how to color polygons in three-dimensional graphics.

Mathematica allows you to specify two components to the illumination of an object. The first is "ambient lighting", which produces uniform shading all over the object. The second is light from a collection of point sources, each with a particular position and color. *Mathematica* adds together the light from all of these sources in determining the total illumination of a particular polygon.

> AmbientLight -> *color*   diffuse isotropic lighting
>
> LightSources -> {{pos_1, col_1}, {pos_2, col_2}, ... }
>   point light sources with specified positions and colors

Options for simulated illumination.

The default lighting used by *Mathematica* involves three point light sources, and no ambient component. The light sources are colored respectively red, green and blue, and are placed at 45° angles on the right-hand side of the object.

Here is a surface, shaded using simulated lighting using the default set of lights.

In[1]:= **Plot3D[Sin[x + Sin[y]], {x, -3, 3}, {y, -3, 3},**
                        Lighting -> True]

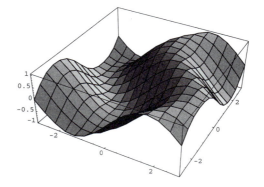

This shows the result of adding ambient light, and removing all point light sources.

In[2]:= **Show[%, AmbientLight -> GrayLevel[0.5],**
                        LightSources -> {}]

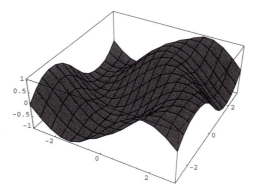

This adds a single point light source at the left-hand side of the image.

In[3]:= **Show[%,**
         LightSources -> {{{-1, 0, 0.5}, GrayLevel[0.5]}}]

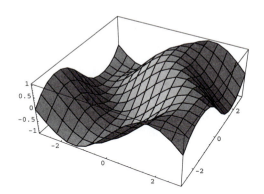

The positions of light sources in *Mathematica* are specified in the *display* coordinate system. The *x* and *y* coordinates are in the plane of the final display, and the *z* coordinate goes into the plane. Using this coordinate system ensures that the light sources remain fixed with respect to the viewer, even when the relative positions of the viewer and object change.

The end of the Graphics Gallery later in this book shows some examples of results obtained with various different arrangements of light sources.

Even though the view point is changed, the light source is kept fixed on the left-hand side of the image.

In[4]:= **Show[%, ViewPoint -> {2, 2, 6}]**

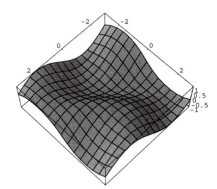

The perceived color of a polygon depends not only on the light which falls on the polygon, but also on how the polygon reflects that light. You can use the graphics directive **SurfaceColor** to specify the way that polygons reflect light.

If you do not explicitly use `SurfaceColor` directives, *Mathematica* effectively assumes that all polygons have matte white surfaces. Thus the polygons reflect light of any color incident on them, and do so equally in all directions. This is an appropriate model for materials such as uncoated white paper.

Using `SurfaceColor`, however, you can specify more complicated models. The basic idea is to distinguish two kinds of reflection: *diffuse* and *specular*.

In diffuse reflection, light incident on a surface is scattered equally in all directions. When this kind of reflection occurs, a surface has a "dull" or "matte" appearance. Diffuse reflectors obey Lambert's Law of light reflection, which states that the intensity of reflected light is $\cos(\alpha)$ times the intensity of the incident light, where α is the angle between the incident light direction and the surface normal vector. Note that when $\alpha > 90°$, there is no reflected light.

In specular reflection, a surface reflects light in a mirror-like way. As a result, the surface has a "shiny" or "gloss" appearance. With a perfect mirror, light incident at a particular angle is reflected at exactly the same angle. Most materials, however, scatter light to some extent, and so lead to reflected light that is distributed over a range of angles. *Mathematica* allows you to specify how broad the distribution is by giving a *specular exponent*, defined according to the Phong lighting model. With specular exponent n, the intensity of light at an angle θ away from the mirror reflection direction is assumed to vary like $\cos(\theta)^n$. As $n \to \infty$, therefore, the surface behaves like a perfect mirror. As n decreases, however, the surface becomes less "shiny", and for $n = 0$, the surface is a completely diffuse reflector. Typical values of n for actual materials range from about 1 to several hundred.

Most actual materials show a mixture of diffuse and specular reflection. In addition, they typically behave as if they have a certain intrinsic color. When the incident light is white, the reflected light has the color of the material. When the incident light is not white, each color component in the reflected light is a product of the corresponding component in the incident light and in the intrinsic color of the material.

In *Mathematica*, you can specify reflection properties by giving an intrinsic color associated with diffuse reflection, and another one associated with specular reflection. To get no reflection of a particular kind, you must give the corresponding intrinsic color as black, or `GrayLevel[0]`. For materials that are effectively "white", you can specify intrinsic colors of the form `GrayLevel[a]`, where a is the reflectance or albedo of the surface.

The end of the Graphics Gallery shows examples of results obtained with various choices of reflection parameters.

`SurfaceColor[GrayLevel[a]]`	matte surface with albedo a
`SurfaceColor[RGBColor[r, g, b]]`	matte surface with intrinsic color
`SurfaceColor[diff, spec]`	surface with diffuse intrinsic color *diff* and specular intrinsic color *spec*
`SurfaceColor[diff, spec, n]`	surface with specular exponent n

Specifying surface properties of lighted polygons.

This loads a package containing various graphics objects.

In[5]:= **<<Graphics`Shapes`**

Sphere creates a graphics object which represents a sphere.

In[6]:= **s = Sphere[ ] ;**

This shows the sphere with the default matte white surface.

In[7]:= **Show[Graphics3D[s]]**

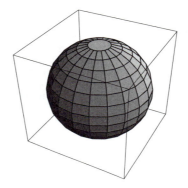

This makes the sphere have low diffuse reflectance, but high specular reflectance. As a result, the sphere has a "specular highlight" near the light sources, and is quite dark elsewhere.

In[8]:= **Show[Graphics3D[{**
SurfaceColor[GrayLevel[0.2],
GrayLevel[0.8], 5], s}]]

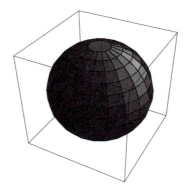

When you set up light sources and surface colors, it is important to make sure that the total intensity of light reflected from a particular polygon is never larger than 1. You will get strange effects if the intensity is larger than 1.

■ 2.9.13 Labeling Three-Dimensional Graphics

Mathematica provides various options for labeling three-dimensional graphics. Some of these options are directly analogous to those for two-dimensional graphics, discussed in Section 2.9.5. Others are different.

Boxed -> True	draw a cuboidal bounding box around the graphics (default)
Axes -> True	draw x, y and z axes on the edges of the box (default for SurfaceGraphics)
Axes -> {False, False, True}	draw the z axis only
FaceGrids -> All	draw grid lines on the faces of the box
PlotLabel -> *text*	give an overall label for the plot

Some options for labeling three-dimensional graphics.

This loads a package containing various polyhedra.

In[1]:= **<<Graphics`Polyhedra`**

The default for Graphics3D is to include a box, but no other forms of labeling.

In[2]:= **Show[Graphics3D[Dodecahedron[ ]]]**

Setting `Axes -> True` adds *x*, *y* and *z* axes.

`In[3]:= Show[%, Axes -> True]`

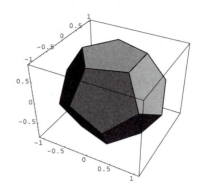

This adds grid lines to each face of the box.

`In[4]:= Show[%, FaceGrids -> All]`

`BoxStyle -> ` *style*	specify the style for the box
`AxesStyle -> ` *style*	specify the style for axes
`AxesStyle -> {{`*xstyle*`}, {`*ystyle*`}, {`*zstyle*`}}`	specify separate styles for each axis

Style options.

This makes the box dashed, and draws axes which are thicker than normal.

```
In[5]:= Show[Graphics3D[Dodecahedron[ ]],
            BoxStyle -> Dashing[{0.02, 0.02}],
            Axes -> True, AxesStyle -> Thickness[0.01]]
```

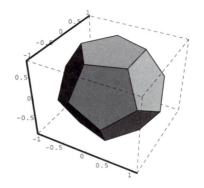

By setting the option Axes -> True, you tell *Mathematica* to draw axes on the edges of the three-dimensional box. However, for each axis, there are in principle four possible edges on which it can be drawn. The option AxesEdge allows you to specify on which edge to draw each of the axes.

AxesEdge -> Automatic	use an internal algorithm to choose where to draw all axes
AxesEdge -> {*xspec*, *yspec*, *zspec*}	give separate specifications for each of the x, y and z axes
None	do not draw this axis
Automatic	decide automatically where to draw this axis
{*dir_i*, *dir_j*}	specify on which of the four possible edges to draw this axis

Specifying where to draw three-dimensional axes.

This draws the x on the edge with larger y and z coordinates, draws no y axis, and chooses automatically where to draw the z axis.

In[6]:= **Show[Graphics3D[Dodecahedron[ ]], Axes -> True,**
                    AxesEdge -> {{1, 1}, None, Automatic}]

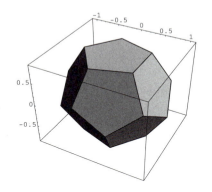

When you draw the x axis on a three-dimensional box, there are four possible edges on which the axis can be drawn. These edges are distinguished by having larger or smaller y and z coordinates. When you use the specification $\{dir_y, dir_z\}$ for where to draw the x axis, you can set the dir_i to be +1 or −1 to represent larger or smaller values for the y and z coordinates.

AxesLabel -> None	give no axis labels
AxesLabel -> *zlabel*	put a label on the z axis
AxesLabel -> {*xlabel*, *ylabel*, *zlabel*}	
	put labels on all three axes

Axis labels in three-dimensional graphics.

You can use AxesLabel to label edges of the box, without necessarily drawing scales on them.

In[7]:= **Show[Graphics3D[Dodecahedron[ ]], Axes -> True,**
                    AxesLabel -> {"x", "y", "z"}, Ticks -> None]

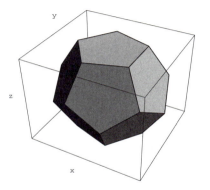

`Ticks -> None`	draw no tick marks
`Ticks -> Automatic`	place tick marks automatically
`Ticks -> {`*xticks*`, `*yticks*`, `*zticks*`}`	tick mark specifications for each axis

Settings for the `Ticks` option.

You can give the same kind of tick mark specifications in three dimensions as were described for two-dimensional graphics in Section 2.9.5.

`FaceGrids -> None`	draw no grid lines on faces
`FaceGrids -> All`	draw grid lines on all faces
`FaceGrids -> {`*face*$_1$`, `*face*$_2$`, ... }`	draw grid lines on the faces specified by the *face*$_i$
`FaceGrids -> {{`*face*$_1$`, {`*xgrid*$_1$`, `*ygrid*$_1$`}}, ... }`	use *xgrid*$_i$, *ygrid*$_i$ to determine where and how to draw grid lines on each face

Drawing grid lines in three dimensions.

Mathematica allows you to draw grid lines on the faces of the box that surrounds a three-dimensional object. If you set `FaceGrids -> All`, grid lines are drawn in gray on every face. By setting `FaceGrids -> {`*face*$_1$`, `*face*$_2$`, ... }` you can tell *Mathematica* to draw grid lines only on specific faces. Each face is specified by a list {*dir*$_x$, *dir*$_y$, *dir*$_z$}, where two of the *dir*$_i$ must be 0, and the third one is +1 or −1. For each face, you can also explicitly tell *Mathematica* where and how to draw the grid lines, using the same kind of specifications as you give for the `GridLines` option in two-dimensional graphics.

This draws grid lines only on the top and bottom faces of the box.

`In[8]:= Show[Graphics3D[Dodecahedron[ ]],`
`            FaceGrids -> {{0, 0, 1}, {0, 0, -1}}]`

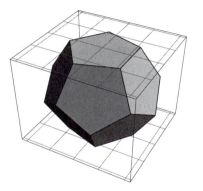

■ 2.9.14 Advanced Topic: Low-Level Graphics Rendering

All *Mathematica* graphics functions such as `Show` and `Plot` have an option `DisplayFunction`, which specifies how the *Mathematica* graphics objects they produce should actually be displayed. The way this works is that the setting you give for `DisplayFunction` is automatically applied to each graphics object that is produced.

`DisplayFunction -> $DisplayFunction`	
	default setting
`DisplayFunction -> Identity`	generate no display
`DisplayFunction -> f`	apply *f* to graphics objects to produce display

Settings for the `DisplayFunction` option.

Within the *Mathematica* kernel, graphics are always represented by graphics objects involving graphics primitives. When you actually render graphics, however, they must be converted to a lower-level form which can be processed by a *Mathematica* front end, such as a notebook interface, or by other external programs.

The standard low-level form that *Mathematica* uses for graphics is *PostScript*. The *Mathematica* function `Display` takes any *Mathematica* graphics object, and converts it into a block of PostScript code. It can then send this code to a file, an external program, or in general any output stream.

`Display["file", graphics]`	store the PostScript for a piece of *Mathematica* graphics in a file
`Display["!program", graphics]`	send the PostScript to an external program
`Display[stream, graphics]`	send the PostScript to an arbitrary stream
`DisplayString[graphics]`	generate a string of PostScript

Converting *Mathematica* graphics to PostScript.

The default value of the global variable `$DisplayFunction` is `Function[ Display[$Display, #] ]`. With this default, graphics objects produced by functions like `Show` and `Plot` are automatically converted to PostScript, and sent to whatever stream is specified by the value of the global variable `$Display`. The variable `$Display` is typically set during the initialization of a particular *Mathematica* session.

> PostScript["*string*$_1$", "*string*$_2$", ...]
>
> > a two-dimensional graphics primitive giving PostScript code to include verbatim

Inserting verbatim PostScript code.

With the standard two-dimensional graphics primitives in *Mathematica* you can produce most of the effects that can be obtained with PostScript. Sometimes, however, you may find it necessary to give PostScript code directly. You can do this using the special two-dimensional graphics primitive PostScript.

The strings you specify in the PostScript primitive will be inserted verbatim into the final Post-Script code generated by Display. You should use the PostScript primitive with care. For example, it is crucial that the code you give restores the PostScript stack to exactly its original state when it is finished. In addition, to specify positions of objects, you will have to understand the coordinate scaling that *Mathematica* does in its PostScript output. Finally, any PostScript primitives that you insert can only work if they are supported in the final PostScript interpreter that you use to display your graphics.

The PostScript primitive gives raw PostScript code which draws a Bézier curve.

```
In[1]:= Show[Graphics[ {
            PostScript[".008 setlinewidth"],
            PostScript[".1 .1 moveto"],
            PostScript["1.1 .6 -.1 .6 .9 .1 curveto stroke"] },
                Frame -> True]]
```

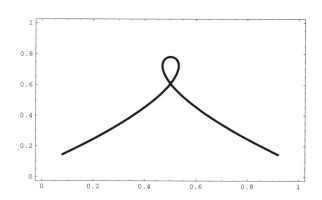

In most cases, a particular *Mathematica* graphics object always generates PostScript of a particular form. For Graphics3D objects, the option RenderAll allows you to choose between two different forms.

The main issue is how the polygons which make up three-dimensional objects should be rendered. With the default setting RenderAll -> True, all polygons you specify are drawn in full, but those behind are drawn first. When all the polygons are drawn, only those in front are visible. However, while an object is being drawn on a display, you can typically see the polygons inside it.

The problem with this approach is that for an object with many layers, you may generate a large amount of spurious PostScript code associated with polygons that are not visible in the final image. You can potentially avoid this by setting `RenderAll -> False`. In this case, *Mathematica* works out exactly which polygons or parts of polygons will actually be visible in your final image, and renders only these. So long as there are fairly few intersections between polygons, this approach will typically yield less PostScript code, though it may be much slower.

`RenderAll -> True`	draw all polygons, starting from the back (default)
`RenderAll -> False`	draw only those polygons or parts of polygons that are visible in the final image

An option for rendering three-dimensional pictures.

When you generate a PostScript representation of a three-dimensional object, you lose all information about the depths of the parts of the object. Sometimes, you may want to send to external programs a representation which includes depth information. Often, the original `Graphics3D` object in *Mathematica* form is then the appropriate representation. But some external programs cannot handle intersecting polygons. To deal with this, `Graphics3D` includes the option `PolygonIntersections`. If you set `PolygonIntersections -> False`, then `Show` will return not your original `Graphics3D` object, but rather one in which intersecting polygons have been broken into disjoint pieces, at least with the setting for `ViewPoint` and so on that you have given.

■ 2.9.15 Formats for Text in Graphics

+	`$TextStyle = `*value*	set the default text style for all graphics
+	`$FormatType = `*value*	set the default text format type for all graphics
+	`TextStyle -> `*value*	an option for the text style in a particular graphic
+	`FormatType -> `*value*	an option for the text format type in a particular graphic

Specifying formats for text in graphics.

Here is a plot with default settings for all formats.

In[1]:= `Plot[Sin[x]^2, {x, 0, 2 Pi}, PlotLabel->Sin[x]^2]`

Here is the same plot, but now using a 7-point italic font.

In[2]:= `Plot[Sin[x]^2, {x, 0, 2 Pi}, PlotLabel->Sin[x]^2,`
`TextStyle->{FontSlant->"Italic", FontSize->7}]`

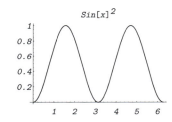

This uses `TraditionalForm` rather than `StandardForm`.

In[3]:= `Plot[Sin[x]^2, {x, 0, 2 Pi}, PlotLabel->Sin[x]^2,`
`FormatType -> TraditionalForm]`

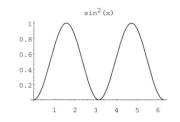

This tells *Mathematica* what default text style to use for all subsequent plots.

In[4]:= `$TextStyle = {FontFamily -> "Times", FontSize -> 7}`

Out[4]= {FontFamily → Times, FontSize → 7}

Now all the text is in 7-point Times font.

In[5]:= `Plot[Sin[x]^2, {x, 0, 2 Pi}, PlotLabel->Sin[x]^2]`

	"*style*"	a cell style in your current notebook
+	`FontSize -> `*n*	the size of font to use in printer's points
+	`FontSlant -> "Italic"`	use an italic font
+	`FontWeight -> "Bold"`	use a bold font
+	`FontFamily -> "`*name*`"`	specify the name of the font family to use (e.g. `"Times"`, `"Courier"`, `"Helvetica"`)

Typical elements used in the setting for `TextStyle` or `$TextStyle`.

If you use the standard notebook front end for *Mathematica*, then you can set `$TextStyle` or `TextStyle` to be the name of a cell style in your current notebook. This tells *Mathematica* to use that cell style as the default for formatting any text that appears in graphics.

You can also explicitly specify how text should be formatted by using options such as `FontSize` and `FontFamily`. Note that `FontSize` gives the absolute size of the font to use, measured in units of printer's points, with one point being $\frac{1}{72}$ inches. If you resize a plot, the text in it will not by default change size: to get text of a different size you must explicitly specify a new value for the `FontSize` option.

`StyleForm[`*expr*`, "style"]`	output *expr* in the specified cell style
`StyleForm[`*expr*`, `*options*`]`	output *expr* using the specified font and style options
`TraditionalForm[`*expr*`]`	output *expr* in `TraditionalForm`

Changing the formats of individual pieces of output.

This outputs the plot label using the section heading style in your current notebook.

In[6]:= `Plot[Sin[x]^2, {x, 0, 2 Pi},`
         `PlotLabel->StyleForm[Sin[x]^2, "Section"]]`

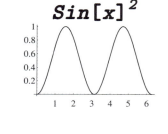

$$\mathtt{Sin[x]}^2$$

This uses the section heading style, but modified to be in italics.

In[7]:= `Plot[Sin[x]^2, {x, 0, 2 Pi},`
         `PlotLabel->StyleForm[Sin[x]^2, "Section",`
                 `FontSlant->"Italic"]]`

$$\mathit{Sin[x]}^2$$

This produces `TraditionalForm` output, with a 12-point font.

In[8]:= `Plot[Sin[x]^2, {x, 0, 2 Pi},`
         `PlotLabel->StyleForm[TraditionalForm[Sin[x]^2],`
                 `FontSize->12]]`

$$\sin^2(x)$$

You should realize that the ability to refer to cell styles such as "Section" depends on using the standard *Mathematica* notebook front end. Even if you are just using a text-based interface to *Mathematica*, however, you can still specify formatting of text in graphics using options such as `FontSize`. The complete collection of options that you can use is given on page 587.

■ 2.9.16 Graphics Primitives for Text

With the `Text` graphics primitive, you can insert text at any position in two- or three-dimensional *Mathematica* graphics. Unless you explicitly specify a style or font using `StyleForm`, the text will be given in your current default style.

`Text[`*expr*`, {`*x*`, `*y*`}]`	text centered at the point {*x*, *y*}
`Text[`*expr*`, {`*x*`, `*y*`}, {-1, 0}]`	text with its left-hand end at {*x*, *y*}
`Text[`*expr*`, {`*x*`, `*y*`}, {1, 0}]`	right-hand end at {*x*, *y*}
`Text[`*expr*`, {`*x*`, `*y*`}, {0, -1}]`	centered above {*x*, *y*}
`Text[`*expr*`, {`*x*`, `*y*`}, {0, 1}]`	centered below {*x*, *y*}
`Text[`*expr*`, {`*x*`, `*y*`}, {`*dx*`, `*dy*`}]`	text positioned so that {*x*, *y*} is at relative coordinates {*dx*, *dy*} within the box that bounds the text
`Text[`*expr*`, {`*x*`, `*y*`}, {`*dx*`, `*dy*`}, {0, 1}]`	text oriented vertically to read from bottom to top
`Text[`*expr*`, {`*x*`, `*y*`}, {`*dx*`, `*dy*`}, {0, -1}]`	text that reads from top to bottom
`Text[`*expr*`, {`*x*`, `*y*`}, {`*dx*`, `*dy*`}, {-1, 0}]`	text that is upside-down

Two-dimensional text.

This generates five pieces of text, and displays them in a plot.

```
In[1]:= Show[Graphics[
            Table[ Text[Expand[(1 + x)^n], {n, n}], {n, 5} ] ],
            PlotRange -> All]
```

$$1 + 5 x + 10 x^2 + 10 x^3 + 5 x^4 + x^5$$

$$1 + 4 x + 6 x^2 + 4 x^3 + x^4$$

$$1 + 3 x + 3 x^2 + x^3$$

$$1 + 2 x + x^2$$

$$1 + x$$

Here is some vertically oriented text with its left-hand side at the point {2, 2}.

```
In[2]:= Show[Graphics[Text[
            StyleForm["Some text", FontSize->14, FontWeight->"Bold"],
            {2, 2}, {-1, 0}, {0, 1}]], Frame -> True]
```

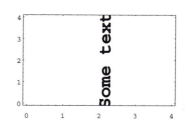

When you specify an offset for text, the relative coordinates that are used are taken to run from −1 to 1 in each direction across the box that bounds the text. The point {0, 0} in this coordinate system is defined to be center of the text. Note that the offsets you specify need not lie in the range −1 to 1.

Note that you can specify the color of a piece of text by preceding the Text graphics primitive with an appropriate RGBColor or other graphics directive.

Text[*expr*, {*x*, *y*, *z*}]	text centered at the point {*x*, *y*, *z*}
Text[*expr*, {*x*, *y*, *z*}, {*sdx*, *sdy*}]	text with a two-dimensional offset

Three-dimensional text.

This loads a package containing definitions of polyhedra.

```
In[3]:= <<Graphics`Polyhedra`
```

This puts text at the specified position in three dimensions.

```
In[4]:= Show[Graphics3D[{Dodecahedron[ ],
            Text["a point", {2, 2, 2}, {1, 1}]}]]
```

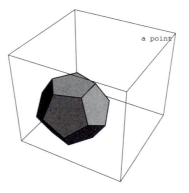

Note that when you use text in three-dimensional graphics, *Mathematica* assumes that the text is never hidden by any polygons or other objects.

option name	default value	
+ Background	None	background color
+ TextStyle	{}	style or font specification
+ FormatType	StandardForm	format type

Options for Text.

By default the text is just put straight on top of whatever graphics have already been drawn.

```
In[5]:= Show[Graphics[{{GrayLevel[0.5],
            Rectangle[{0, 0}, {1, 1}]},
            Text["Some text", {0.5, 0.5}]}]]
```

Now there is a rectangle with the background color of the whole plot enclosing the text.

```
In[6]:= Show[Graphics[{{GrayLevel[0.5],
            Rectangle[{0, 0}, {1, 1}]},
            Text["Some text", {0.5, 0.5},
                Background->Automatic]}]]
```

■ 2.9.17 Advanced Topic: Color Output

Monochrome displays	gray levels
Color displays	red, green and blue mixtures
Color printing	cyan, magenta, yellow and black mixtures

Specifications of color for different kinds of output devices.

When you generate graphics output in *Mathematica*, there are different specifications of color which are natural for different kinds of output devices. Sometimes output devices may automatically convert from one form of color specification to another. But *Mathematica* provides graphics directives which allow you directly to produce color specifications appropriate for particular devices.

GrayLevel[i]	gray level (setgray in PostScript)
RGBColor[r, g, b]	red, green and blue components for a display (setrgbcolor)
Hue[h, s, b]	hue, saturation and brightness components for a display (setrgbcolor)
CMYKColor[c, m, y, k]	cyan, magenta, yellow and black components for four-color process printing (setcmykcolor)

Color directives in *Mathematica*.

Each color directive in *Mathematica* yields a definite color directive in the PostScript code that *Mathematica* sends to your output device. Thus, for example, the RGBColor directive in *Mathematica* yields setrgbcolor in PostScript. The final treatment of the PostScript color directives is determined by your output device, and the PostScript interpreter that is used.

Nevertheless, in most cases, the parameters specified in the *Mathematica* color directives will be used fairly directly to set the intensities or densities of the components of the color output.

When this is done, it is important to realize that a given set of parameters in a *Mathematica* color directive may yield different perceived colors on different output devices. For example, the actual intensities of red, green and blue components will often differ between different color displays even when the settings for these components are the same. Such differences also occur when the brightness or contrast of a particular color display is changed.

In addition, you should realize that the complete "gamut" of colors that you can produce by varying parameters on a particular output device is smaller, often substantially so, than the gamut of colors which can be perceived by the human visual system. Even though the space of colors that we can perceive can be described with three parameters, it is not possible to reach all parts of this space with mixtures of a fixed number of "primary colors".

Different choices of primary colors are typically made for different types of output devices. Color displays, which work with emitted or transmitted light, typically use red, green and blue primary colors. However, color printing, which works with reflected light, typically uses cyan, magenta, yellow and black as primary colors. When a color image is printed, four separate passes are typically made, each time laying down one of these primary colors.

Thus, while `RGBColor` and `Hue` are natural color specifications for color displays, `CMYKColor` is the natural specification for color printing.

By default, *Mathematica* takes whatever color specifications you give, and uses them directly. The option `ColorOutput`, however, allows you to make *Mathematica* always convert the color specifications you give to ones appropriate for a particular kind of output device.

`ColorOutput -> Automatic`	use color specifications as given (default)
`ColorOutput -> None`	convert to monochrome
`ColorOutput -> GrayLevel`	convert all color specifications to gray levels
`ColorOutput -> RGBColor`	convert to RGBColor form
`ColorOutput -> CMYKColor`	convert to CMYKColor form
`ColorOutput -> f`	apply *f* to each color directive

Color output conversions.

One of the most complicated issues in color output is performing the "color separation" necessary to take a color specified using red, green and blue primaries, and render the color using cyan, magenta, yellow and black printing inks. *Mathematica* has a built-in algorithm for doing this conversion. The algorithm is based on an approximation to typical monitor colors and the standard set of four-color process printing inks. Note that the colors of these printing inks are not even close to complementary to typical monitor colors, and the actual transformation is quite nonlinear.

While *Mathematica* has built-in capabilities for various color conversions, you can also specify your own color conversions using `ColorOutput -> f`. With this option setting, the function *f* is automatically applied to each color directive generated by *Mathematica*.

Note that while any of the color directives given above can be used in setting up graphics objects, simulated lighting calculations in *Mathematica* are always done using `RGBColor`, and so all color directives are automatically converted to this form when simulated lighting is used.

This defines a transformation on `RGBColor` objects, which extracts the red component, and squares it.	*In[1]:=* `red[RGBColor[r_, g_, b_]] = GrayLevel[r^2]`
	Out[1]= GrayLevel[r^2]
This specifies that `red` should simply square any `GrayLevel` specification.	*In[2]:=* `red[GrayLevel[g_]] = GrayLevel[g^2]`
	Out[2]= GrayLevel[g^2]

This plots the squared red component, rather than using the usual transformation from color to black and white.

```
In[3]:= Plot3D[Sin[x + y], {x, -3, 3}, {y, -3, 3},
                            ColorOutput -> red]
```

Note that if you give your own `ColorOutput` transformation, you must specify how the transformation acts on every color directive that arises in the image you are producing. For three-dimensional plots shaded with simulated lighting, you must typically specify the transformation at least for `RGBColor` and `GrayLevel`.

■ 2.9.18 The Representation of Sound

Section 1.9.13 described how you can take functions and lists of data and produce sounds from them. This subsection discusses how sounds are represented in *Mathematica*.

Mathematica treats sounds much like graphics. In fact, *Mathematica* allows you to combine graphics with sound to create pictures with "sound tracks".

In analogy with graphics, sounds in *Mathematica* are represented by symbolic sound objects. The sound objects have head `Sound`, and contain a list of sound primitives, which represent sounds to be played in sequence.

Sound[{s_1, s_2, ... }]	a sound object containing a list of sound primitives

The structure of a sound object.

The functions `Play` and `ListPlay` discussed in Section 1.9.13 return `Sound` objects.

Play returns a Sound object. On appropriate computer systems, it also produces sound.

```
In[1]:= Play[Sin[300 t + 2 Sin[400 t]], {t, 0, 2}]
Out[1]= -Sound-
```

The Sound object contains a SampledSoundFunction primitive which uses a compiled function to generate amplitude samples for the sound.

```
In[2]:= Short[ InputForm[%] ]

Out[2]//Short= Sound[SampledSoundFunction[<<3>>]]
```

SampledSoundList[{a_1, a_2, ... }, r]	a sound with a sequence of amplitude levels, sampled at rate r
SampledSoundFunction[f, n, r]	a sound whose amplitude levels sampled at rate r are found by applying the function f to n successive integers

Mathematica sound primitives.

At the lowest level, all sounds in *Mathematica* are represented as a sequence of amplitude samples. In SampledSoundList, these amplitude samples are given explicitly in a list. In SampledSoundFunction, however, they are generated when the sound is output, by applying the specified function to a sequence of integer arguments. In both cases, all amplitude values obtained must be between −1 and 1.

ListPlay generates SampledSoundList primitives, while Play generates SampledSoundFunction primitives. With the default option setting Compiled -> True, Play will produce a SampledSoundFunction object containing a CompiledFunction.

Once you have generated a Sound object containing various sound primitives, you must then output it as a sound. Much as with graphics, the basic scheme is to take the *Mathematica* representation of the sound, and convert it to a lower-level form that can be handled by an external program, such as a *Mathematica* front end.

The low-level representation of sound used by *Mathematica* consists of a sequence of hexadecimal numbers specifying amplitude levels. Within *Mathematica*, amplitude levels are given as approximate real numbers between -1 and 1. In producing the low-level form, the amplitude levels are "quantized". You can use the option SampleDepth to specify how many bits should be used for each sample. The default is SampleDepth -> 8, which yields 256 possible amplitude levels, sufficient for most purposes.

You can use the option SampleDepth in any of the functions Play, ListPlay and PlaySound. In sound primitives, you can specify the sample depth by replacing the sample rate argument by the list {*rate*, *depth*}.

Since graphics and sound can be combined in *Mathematica*, their low-level representations must not conflict. As discussed in Section 2.9.14, all graphics in *Mathematica* are generated in the PostScript language. Sounds are also generated as a special PostScript function, which can be ignored by PostScript interpreters on devices which do not support sound output.

Display[*stream*, *sound*]	output sound to a stream
Display[*stream*, {*graphics*, *sound*}]	output graphics and sound to a stream

Sending sound to a stream.

Mathematica uses the same function Display to output sound, graphics, and combinations of the two.

In Play, ListPlay and Sound, the option DisplayFunction specifies how the sound should ultimately be output. The default for this option is the global variable $SoundDisplayFunction. Typically, this is set to an appropriate call to Display.

2.10 Manipulating Notebooks

+■ 2.10.1 Cells as *Mathematica* Expressions

Like other objects in *Mathematica*, the cells in a notebook, and in fact the whole notebook itself, are all ultimately represented as *Mathematica* expressions. With the standard notebook front end, you can use the command Show Expression to see the text of the *Mathematica* expression that corresponds to any particular cell.

Show Expression menu item	toggle between displayed form and underlying *Mathematica* expression
CTRL*✱ or CTRL 8 (between existing cells)	put up a dialog box to allow input of a cell in *Mathematica* expression form

Handling `Cell` expressions in the notebook front end.

Here is a cell displayed in its usual way in the front end.

> This is a text cell.

Here is the underlying *Mathematica* expression that corresponds to the cell.

```
Cell["This is a text cell.", "Text"]
```

`Cell[`*contents*`, "`*style*`"]`	a cell with a specific style
`Cell[`*contents*`, "`*style*`", `*options*`]`	a cell with additional options specified

Mathematica expressions corresponding to cells in notebooks.

Within a given notebook, there is always a collection of *styles* that can be used to determine the appearance and behavior of cells. Typically the styles are named so as to reflect what role cells which have them will play in the notebook.

`"Title"`	the title of the notebook
`"Section"`	a section heading
`"Subsection"`	a subsection heading
`"Text"`	ordinary text
`"Input"`	*Mathematica* input
`"Output"`	*Mathematica* output

Some typical cell styles defined in notebooks.

Here are several cells in different styles.

■ **This is in Section style.**

This is in Text style.

    `This is in Input style`.

Here are the expressions that correspond to these cells.

```
Cell["This is in Section style.", "Section"]
Cell["This is in Text style.", "Text"]
Cell["This is in Input style.", "Input"]
```

A particular style such as `"Section"` or `"Text"` defines various settings for the options associated with a cell. You can override these settings by explicitly setting options within a specific cell.

Here is the expression for a cell in which options are set to use a gray background and to put a frame around the cell.

```
Cell["This is some text.", "Text", CellFrame->True,
  Background->GrayLevel[.8]]
```

This is how the cell looks in a notebook.

This is some text.

option	default value	
CellFrame	False	whether to draw a frame around the cell
Background	GrayLevel[1]	what color to draw the background for the cell
Editable	True	whether to allow the contents of the cell to be edited
TextAlignment	Left	how to align text in the cell
FontSize	12	the point size of the font for text
CellTags	{ }	tags to be associated with the cell

A few of the large number of possible options for cells.

The standard notebook front end for *Mathematica* provides several ways to change the options of a cell. In simple cases, such as changing the size or color of text, there will often be a specific menu item for the purpose. But in general you can use the *option inspector* that is built into the front end. This is typically accessed using the Option Inspector menu item in the Format menu.

- Change settings for specific options with menus.
- Look at and modify all options with the option inspector.
- Edit the textual form of the expression corresponding to the cell.

- Change the settings for all cells with a particular style.

Ways to manipulate cells in the front end.

Sometimes you will want just to change the options associated with a specific cell. But often you may want to change the options associated with all cells in your notebook that have a particular style. You can do this by using the Edit Style Sheet command in the front end to open up the style sheet associated with your notebook, and then modifying the options for the cells in this style sheet that represent the style you want to change.

`CellPrint[Cell[... ]]`	insert a cell into your currently selected notebook
`CellPrint[{Cell[... ], Cell[... ], ... }]`	insert a sequence of cells into your currently selected notebook

Inserting cells into a notebook.

This inserts a section cell into the current notebook.

In[1]:= `CellPrint[Cell["The heading", "Section"]]`

■ **The heading**

This inserts a text cell with a frame around it.

In[2]:= `CellPrint[Cell["Some text", "Text", CellFrame->True]]`

■ **The heading**

Some text

`CellPrint` allows you to take a raw `Cell` expression and insert it into your current notebook. Sometimes, however, you may find it more convenient to give an ordinary *Mathematica* expression, and then have *Mathematica* convert it into a `Cell` of a certain style, and insert this cell into a notebook. You can do this using the function `StylePrint`.

`StylePrint[`*expr*`, "`*style*`"]`	create a new cell of the specified style, and write *expr* into it
`StylePrint[`*contents*`, "`*style*`", `*options*`]`	use the specified options for the new cell

Writing expressions into cells with specified styles.

This inserts a cell in section style into your current notebook.

In[3]:= `StylePrint["The heading", "Section"]`

■ **The heading**

This creates several cells in output style.

In[4]:= **Do[StylePrint[Factor[x^i - 1], "Output"], {i, 7, 10}]**

■ **The heading**

$(-1 + x) (1 + x + x^2 + x^3 + x^4 + x^5 + x^6)$

$(-1 + x) (1 + x) (1 + x^2) (1 + x^4)$

$(-1 + x) (1 + x + x^2) (1 + x^3 + x^6)$

$(-1 + x) (1 + x) (1 - x + x^2 - x^3 + x^4) (1 + x + x^2 + x^3 + x^4)$

You can use any cell options in StylePrint.

In[5]:= **StylePrint["Another heading", "Section", CellFrame->True, FontSize->28]**

■ **The heading**

$(-1 + x) (1 + x + x^2 + x^3 + x^4 + x^5 + x^6)$

$(-1 + x) (1 + x) (1 + x^2) (1 + x^4)$

$(-1 + x) (1 + x + x^2) (1 + x^3 + x^6)$

$(-1 + x) (1 + x) (1 - x + x^2 - x^3 + x^4) (1 + x + x^2 + x^3 + x^4)$

■ **Another heading**

CellPrint and StylePrint provide simple ways to modify open notebooks in the front end from within the kernel. Later in this section we will discuss more sophisticated and flexible ways to do this.

■ 2.10.2 Notebooks as *Mathematica* Expressions

Notebook[{*cell*$_1$, *cell*$_2$, ... }]	a notebook containing a sequence of cells
Notebook[*cells*, *options*]	a notebook with options specified

Expressions corresponding to notebooks.

Here is a simple *Mathematica* notebook.

■ **Section heading**

Some text.

More text.

Here is the expression that corresponds   `Notebook[{`
to this notebook.   `Cell["Section heading", "Section"],`
                                               `Cell["Some text.", "Text"],`
                                               `Cell["More text.", "Text"]}]`

Just like individual cells, notebooks in *Mathematica* can also have options. You can look at and modify these options using the options inspector in the standard notebook front end.

option	default value	
`WindowSize`	`{`*nx*`, `*ny*`}`	the size in pixels of the window used to display the notebook
`WindowFloating`	`False`	whether the window should float on top of others
`WindowToolbars`	`{ }`	what toolbars to include at the top of the window
`ShowPageBreaks`	`False`	whether to show where page breaks would occur if the notebook were printed
`CellGrouping`	`Automatic`	how to group cells in the notebook
`Evaluator`	`"Local"`	what kernel should be used to do evaluations in the notebook

A few of the large number of possible options for notebooks.

In addition to notebook options, you can also set any cell option at the notebook level. Doing this tells *Mathematica* to use that option setting as the default for all the cells in the notebook. You can override the default by explicitly setting the options within a particular cell.

Here is the expression corresponding to   `Notebook[{`
a notebook with a ruler displayed in   `Cell["Section heading", "Section"],`
the toolbar at the top of the window.   `Cell["Some text.", "Text"]},`
                                                  `WindowToolbars->{"RulerBar"}]`

This is what the notebook looks like in
the front end.

This sets the default background color for all cells in the notebook.

```
Notebook[{
    Cell["Section heading", "Section"],
    Cell["Some text.", "Text"]},
        Background->GrayLevel[.7]]
```

Now each cell has a gray background.

If you go outside of *Mathematica* and look at the raw text of the file that corresponds to a *Mathematica* notebook, you will find that what is in the file is just the textual form of the expression that represents the notebook. One way to create a *Mathematica* notebook is therefore to construct an appropriate expression and put it in a file.

In notebook files that are written out by *Mathematica*, some additional information is typically included to make it faster for *Mathematica* to read the file in again. The information is enclosed in *Mathematica* comments indicated by (∗ ... ∗) so that it does not affect the actual expression stored in the file.

NotebookOpen["*file*.nb"]	open a notebook file in the front end
NotebookPut[*expr*]	create a notebook corresponding to *expr* in the front end
NotebookGet[*obj*]	get the expression corresponding to an open notebook in the front end

Setting up notebooks in the front end from the kernel.

This writes a notebook expression out to the file `sample.nb`.

```
In[1]:= Notebook[{Cell["Section heading", "Section"],
            Cell["Some text.", "Text"]}] >> "sample.nb"
```

This reads the notebook expression back from the file.

```
In[2]:= <<sample.nb
Out[2]= Notebook[{Cell[Section heading, Section],
            Cell[Some text., Text]}]
```

This opens `sample.nb` as a notebook in the front end.

```
In[3]:= NotebookOpen["sample.nb"]
```

Once you have set up a notebook in the front end using `NotebookOpen`, you can then manipulate the notebook interactively just as you would any other notebook. But in order to use `NotebookOpen`, you have to explicitly have a notebook expression in a file. With `NotebookPut`, however, you can take a notebook expression that you have created in the kernel, and immediately display it as a notebook in the front end.

Here is a notebook expression in the kernel.

```
In[4]:= Notebook[{Cell["Section heading", "Section"],
            Cell["Some text.", "Text"]}]
```

```
Out[4]= Notebook[{Cell[Section heading, Section],
            Cell[Some text., Text]}]
```

This uses the expression to set up a notebook in the front end.

```
In[5]:= NotebookPut[%]
```

■ **Section heading**   ⌉

Some text.   ⌉

```
Out[5]= -NotebookObject-
```

You can use `NotebookGet` to get the notebook corresponding to a particular `NotebookObject` back into the kernel.

```
In[6]:= NotebookGet[%]
Out[6]= Notebook[{Cell[CellGroupData[
            {Cell[TextData[heading Section], Section],
             Cell[TextData[Some text.], Text]},
            Open]]}]
```

⁺■ 2.10.3 Manipulating Notebooks from the Kernel

If you want to do simple operations on *Mathematica* notebooks, then you will usually find it convenient just to use the interactive capabilities of the standard *Mathematica* front end. But if you want to do more complicated and systematic operations, then you will often find it better to use the kernel.

`Notebooks[ ]`	a list of all your open notebooks
`Notebooks["name"]`	a list of all open notebooks with the specified name
`SelectedNotebook[ ]`	the notebook that is currently selected
`InputNotebook[ ]`	the notebook into which typed input will go
`EvaluationNotebook[ ]`	the notebook in which this function is being evaluated
`ButtonNotebook[ ]`	the notebook containing the button (if any) which initiated this evaluation

Functions that give the notebook objects corresponding to particular notebooks.

Within the *Mathematica* kernel, notebooks that you have open in the front end are referred to by *notebook objects* of the form `NotebookObject[`*fe*`, `*id*`]`. The first argument of `NotebookObject` specifies the `FrontEndObject` for the front end in which the notebook resides, while the second argument gives a unique serial number for the notebook.

Here is a notebook set to be the currently selected one in the front end.

■ First Heading

■ Second Heading

This gives the notebook object corresponding to the selected notebook in the front end.

```
In[1]:= SelectedNotebook[ ]
Out[1]= -NotebookObject-
```

This gets the expression corresponding to the selected notebook into the kernel.

```
In[2]:= NotebookGet[%]
Out[2]= Notebook[
          {Cell[TextData[FirstHeading], Section],
           Cell[TextData[HeadingSecond], Section]}]
```

This replaces every occurrence of the string "Section" by "Text".

```
In[3]:= % /. "Section" -> "Text"
Out[3]= Notebook[{Cell[TextData[FirstHeading], Text],
          Cell[TextData[HeadingSecond], Text]}]
```

This replaces the currently selected notebook by the modified form.

```
In[4]:= NotebookPut[%, SelectedNotebook[ ]]
```

First Heading

Second Heading

`NotebookGet[`*obj*`]`	get the notebook expression corresponding to the notebook object *obj*
`NotebookPut[`*expr*`, `*obj*`]`	make *expr* the expression corresponding to the notebook object *obj*
`NotebookPut[`*expr*`]`	make *expr* the expression corresponding to the currently selected notebook

Exchanging whole notebook expressions between the kernel and front end.

If you want to do extensive manipulations on a particular notebook you will usually find it convenient to use `NotebookGet` to get the whole notebook into the kernel as a single expression. But if instead you want to do a sequence of small operations on a notebook, then it is often better to leave the notebook in the front end, and then to send specific commands from the kernel to the front end to tell it what operations to do.

Mathematica is set up so that anything you can do interactively to a notebook in the front end you can also do by sending appropriate commands to the front end from the kernel.

Options[*obj*]	give a list of all options set for the notebook corresponding to notebook object *obj*
Options[*obj*, *option*]	give the value of a specific option
FullOptions[*obj*, *option*]	give explicit option values even when the actual setting is Automatic
SetOptions[*obj*, *option->value*]	set the value of an option

Finding and setting options for notebooks.

This gives the setting of the WindowSize option for your currently selected notebook.

In[5]:= **Options[SelectedNotebook[ ], WindowSize]**

Out[5]= {WindowSize → {520., 600.}}

This changes the size of the currently selected notebook on the screen.

In[6]:= **SetOptions[SelectedNotebook[ ], WindowSize -> {250, 100}]**

First Heading

Second Heading

Out[6]= {WindowSize → {250., 100.}}

Within any open notebook, the front end always maintains a *current selection*. The selection can consist for example of a region of text within a cell or of a complete cell. Usually the selection is indicated on the screen by some form of highlighting. The selection can also be between two characters of text, or between two cells, in which case it is usually indicated on the screen by a vertical or horizontal insertion bar.

You can modify the current selection in an open notebook by issuing commands from the kernel.

SelectionMove[*obj*, Next, *unit*]	move the current selection to make it be the next unit of the specified type
SelectionMove[*obj*, Previous, *unit*]	move to the previous unit
SelectionMove[*obj*, After, *unit*]	move to just after the end of the present unit of the specified unit
SelectionMove[*obj*, Before, *unit*]	move to just before the beginning of the present unit
SelectionMove[*obj*, All, *unit*]	extend the current selection to cover the whole unit of the specified type

Moving the current selection in a notebook.

Character	individual character
Word	word or other token
Expression	complete subexpression
TextLine	line of text
TextParagraph	paragraph of text
CellContents	the contents of the cell
Cell	complete cell
CellGroup	cell group
EvaluationCell	cell associated with the current evaluation
ButtonCell	cell associated with any button that initiated the evaluation
GeneratedCell	cell generated by the current evaluation
Notebook	complete notebook

Units used in specifying selections.

Here is a simple notebook.

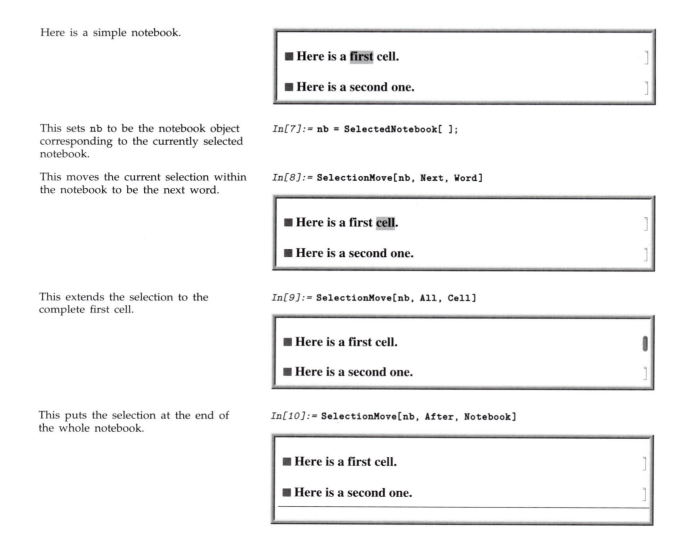

This sets nb to be the notebook object corresponding to the currently selected notebook.

In[7]:= **nb = SelectedNotebook[ ];**

This moves the current selection within the notebook to be the next word.

In[8]:= **SelectionMove[nb, Next, Word]**

This extends the selection to the complete first cell.

In[9]:= **SelectionMove[nb, All, Cell]**

This puts the selection at the end of the whole notebook.

In[10]:= **SelectionMove[nb, After, Notebook]**

NotebookFind[*obj*, *data*]	move the current selection to the next occurrence of the specified data in a notebook
NotebookFind[*obj*, *data*, Previous]	
	move to the previous occurrence
NotebookFind[*obj*, *data*, All]	make the current selection cover all occurrences
NotebookFind[*obj*, *data*, *dir*, *elems*]	
	search in the specified elements of each cell, going in direction *dir*
NotebookFind[*obj*, "*text*", IgnoreCase->True]	
	do not distinguish upper- and lower-case letters in text

Searching the contents of a notebook.

This moves the current selection to the position of the previous occurrence of the word cell.

In[11]:= **NotebookFind[nb, "cell", Previous]**

Out[11]= NotebookSelection[-NotebookObject-]

The letter α does not appear in the current notebook, so $Failed is returned, and the selection is not moved.

In[12]:= **NotebookFind[nb, "\[Alpha]", Next]**

■ Here is a first **cell.**

■ Here is a second one.

Out[12]= $Failed

CellContents	contents of each cell
CellStyle	the name of the style for each cell
CellLabel	the label for each cell
CellTags	tags associated with each cell
{$elem_1$, $elem_2$, ... }	several kinds of elements

Possible elements of cells to be searched by NotebookFind.

In setting up large notebooks, it is often convenient to insert tags which are not usually displayed, but which mark particular cells in such a way that they can be found using NotebookFind. You can set up tags for cells either interactively in the front end, or by explicitly setting the CellTags option for a cell.

NotebookLocate["*tag*"]	go to the next cell with the specified tag in the current notebook
NotebookLocate[{"*file*", "*tag*"}]	
	open another notebook if necessary

Globally locating cells in notebooks.

NotebookLocate is the underlying function that *Mathematica* calls when you follow a hyperlink in a notebook. The menu item Create Hyperlink sets up the appropriate NotebookLocate as part of the script for a particular hyperlink button.

NotebookWrite[*obj*, *data*]	write *data* into a notebook at the current selection
NotebookApply[*obj*, *data*]	write *data* into a notebook, inserting the current selection in place of the first ■ that appears in *data*
NotebookDelete[*obj*]	delete whatever is currently selected in a notebook
NotebookRead[*obj*]	get the expression that corresponds to the current selection in a notebook

Writing and reading in notebooks.

NotebookWrite[*obj*, *data*] is similar to a Paste operation in the front end: it replaces the current selection in your notebook by *data*. If the current selection is a cell NotebookWrite[*obj*, *data*] will replace the cell with *data*. If the current selection lies between two cells, however, then NotebookWrite[*obj*, *data*] will create an appropriate new cell or cells.

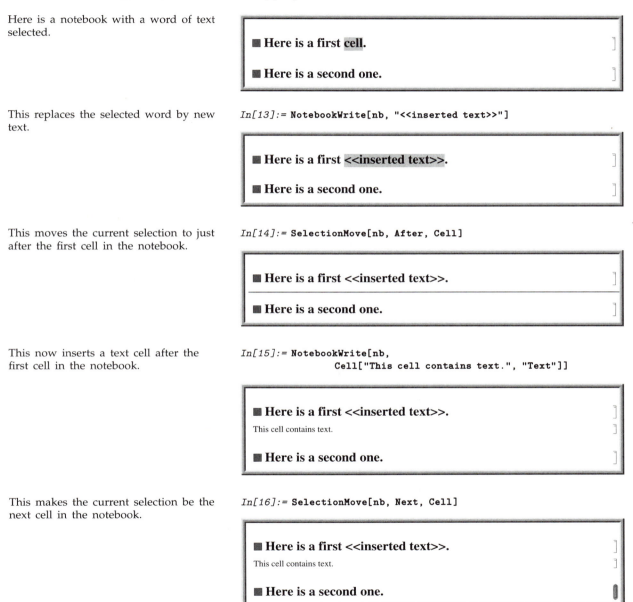

Here is a notebook with a word of text selected.

■ **Here is a first cell.**

■ **Here is a second one.**

This replaces the selected word by new text.

In[13]:= **NotebookWrite[nb, "<<inserted text>>"]**

■ **Here is a first <<inserted text>>.**

■ **Here is a second one.**

This moves the current selection to just after the first cell in the notebook.

In[14]:= **SelectionMove[nb, After, Cell]**

■ **Here is a first <<inserted text>>.**

■ **Here is a second one.**

This now inserts a text cell after the first cell in the notebook.

In[15]:= **NotebookWrite[nb,**
       Cell["This cell contains text.", "Text"]]

■ **Here is a first <<inserted text>>.**

This cell contains text.

■ **Here is a second one.**

This makes the current selection be the next cell in the notebook.

In[16]:= **SelectionMove[nb, Next, Cell]**

■ **Here is a first <<inserted text>>.**

This cell contains text.

■ **Here is a second one.**

This reads the current selection, returning it as an expression in the kernel.

In[17]:= **NotebookRead[nb]**

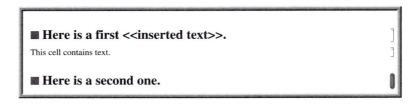

Out[17]= Cell[Here is a second one., Section]

NotebookWrite[*obj, data*] just discards the current selection and replaces it with *data*. But particularly if you are setting up palettes, it is often convenient first to modify *data* by inserting the current selection somewhere inside it. You can do this using *selection placeholders* and **NotebookApply**. The first time the character ■, entered as **\[SelectionPlaceholder]** or ESC spl ESC, appears anywhere in *data*, **NotebookApply** will replace this character by the current selection.

Here is a simple notebook with the current selection being the contents of a cell.

In[18]:= **nb = SelectedNotebook[ ] ;**

      Expand[(1 + x)⁴]

This replaces the current selection by a string that contains a copy of its previous form.

In[19]:= **NotebookApply[nb, "x + 1/■"]**

      x + 1 / Expand[(1 + x)⁴]

SelectionEvaluate[*obj*]	evaluate the current selection in place
SelectionCreateCell[*obj*]	create a new cell containing just the current selection
SelectionEvaluateCreateCell[*obj*]	
	evaluate the current selection and create a new cell for the result
SelectionAnimate[*obj*]	animate graphics in the current selection
SelectionAnimate[*obj, t*]	animate graphics for *t* seconds

Operations on the current selection.

This makes the current selection be the whole cell.

In[20]:= **SelectionMove[nb, All, CellContents]**

      x + 1 / Expand[(1 + x)⁴]

This evaluates the current selection in place.

In[21]:= **SelectionEvaluate[nb]**

$$x + \frac{1}{1 + 4x + 6x^2 + 4x^3 + x^4}$$

SelectionEvaluate allows you to take material from a notebook and send it through the kernel for evaluation. On its own, however, **SelectionEvaluate** always overwrites the material you took. But by using functions like **SelectionCreateCell** you can maintain a record of the sequence of forms that are generated—just like in a standard *Mathematica* session.

This makes the current selection be the whole cell.

In[22]:= **SelectionMove[nb, All, Cell]**

$$x + \frac{1}{1 + 4x + 6x^2 + 4x^3 + x^4}$$

This creates a new cell, and copies the current selection into it.

In[23]:= **SelectionCreateCell[nb]**

$$x + \frac{1}{1 + 4x + 6x^2 + 4x^3 + x^4}$$

$$x + \frac{1}{1 + 4x + 6x^2 + 4x^3 + x^4}$$

This wraps Factor around the contents of the current cell.

In[24]:= **NotebookApply[nb, "Factor[■]"]**

$$x + \frac{1}{1 + 4x + 6x^2 + 4x^3 + x^4}$$

$$\text{Factor}\left[x + \frac{1}{1 + 4x + 6x^2 + 4x^3 + x^4}\right]$$

This evaluates the contents of the current cell, and creates a new cell to give the result.

In[25]:= **SelectionEvaluateCreateCell[nb]**

$$x + \frac{1}{1 + 4x + 6x^2 + 4x^3 + x^4}$$

$$\text{Factor}\left[x + \frac{1}{1 + 4x + 6x^2 + 4x^3 + x^4}\right]$$

$$\frac{1 + x + 4x^2 + 6x^3 + 4x^4 + x^5}{(1 + x)^4}$$

Functions like **NotebookWrite** and **SelectionEvaluate** by default leave the current selection just after whatever material they insert into your notebook. You can then always move the selection by explicitly using **SelectionMove**. But functions like **NotebookWrite** and **SelectionEvaluate** can also take an additional argument which specifies where the current selection should be left after they do their work.

NotebookWrite[*obj*, *data*, *sel*]	write *data* into a notebook, leaving the current selection as specified by *sel*
NotebookApply[*obj*, *data*, *sel*]	write *data* replacing ■ by the previous current selection, then leaving the current selection as specified by *sel*
SelectionEvaluate[*obj*, *sel*]	evaluate the current selection, making the new current selection be as specified by *sel*
SelectionCreateCell[*obj*, *sel*]	create a new cell containing just the current selection, and make the new current selection be as specified by *sel*
SelectionEvaluateCreateCell[*obj*, *sel*]	
	evaluate the current selection, make a new cell for the result, and make the new current selection be as specified by *sel*

Performing operations and specifying what the new current selection should be.

After	immediately after whatever material is inserted (default)
Before	immediately before whatever material is inserted
All	the inserted material itself
Placeholder	the first ■ in the inserted material
None	leave the current selection unchanged

Specifications for the new current selection.

Here is a blank notebook.

In[26]:= **nb = SelectedNotebook[ ] ;**

This writes 10! into the notebook, making the current selection be what was written.

In[27]:= **NotebookWrite[nb, "10!", All]**

> 10!

This evaluates the current selection, creating a new cell for the result, and making the current selection be the whole of the result.

In[28]:= **SelectionEvaluateCreateCell[nb, All]**

> 10!
> 3628800

This wraps `FactorInteger` around the current selection.

In[29]:= `NotebookApply[nb, "FactorInteger[■]", All]`

```
10!
FactorInteger[3628800]
```

This evaluates the current selection, leaving the selection just before the result.

In[30]:= `SelectionEvaluate[nb, Before]`

```
10!
|{{2, 8}, {3, 4}, {5, 2}, {7, 1}}
```

This now inserts additional text at the position of the current selection.

In[31]:= `NotebookWrite[nb, "a = "]`

```
10!
a = {{2, 8}, {3, 4}, {5, 2}, {7, 1}}
```

`Options[`*obj, option*`]`	find the value of an option for a complete notebook
`Options[NotebookSelection[`*obj*`], `*option*`]`	
	find the value for the current selection
`SetOptions[`*obj, option->value*`]`	set the value of an option for a complete notebook
`SetOptions[NotebookSelection[`*obj*`], `*option->value*`]`	
	set the value for the current selection

Finding and setting options for whole notebooks and for the current selection.

Make the current selection be a complete cell.

In[32]:= `SelectionMove[nb, All, Cell]`

```
10!
a = {{2, 8}, {3, 4}, {5, 2}, {7, 1}}
```

Put a frame around the cell that is the current selection.

In[33]:= `SetOptions[NotebookSelection[nb], CellFrame->True]`

```
10!
a = {{2, 8}, {3, 4}, {5, 2}, {7, 1}}
```

NotebookCreate[ ]	create a new notebook
NotebookCreate[*options*]	create a notebook with specified options
NotebookOpen["*name*"]	open an existing notebook
NotebookOpen["*name*", *options*]	open a notebook with specified options
SetSelectedNotebook[*obj*]	make the specified notebook the selected one
NotebookPrint[*obj*]	send a notebook to your printer
NotebookPrint[*obj*, "*file*"]	send a PostScript version of a notebook to a file
NotebookPrint[*obj*, "!*command*"]	send a PostScript version of a notebook to an external command
NotebookSave[*obj*]	save the current version of a notebook in a file
NotebookSave[*obj*, "*file*"]	save the notebook in a file with the specified name
NotebookClose[*obj*]	close a notebook

Operations on whole notebooks.

If you call NotebookCreate[ ] a new empty notebook will appear on your screen.

By executing commands like SetSelectedNotebook and NotebookOpen, you tell the *Mathematica* front end to change the windows you see. Sometimes you may want to manipulate a notebook without ever having it displayed on the screen. You can do this by using the option setting Visible->False in NotebookOpen or NotebookCreate.

■ 2.10.4 Manipulating the Front End from the Kernel

$FrontEnd	the front end currently in use
Options[$FrontEnd, *option*]	the setting for a global option in the front end
FullOptions[$FrontEnd, *option*]	the explicit setting for an option
SetOptions[$FrontEnd, *option*->value*]	reset an option in the front end

Manipulating global options in the front end.

Just like cells and notebooks, the complete *Mathematica* front end has various options, which you can look at and manipulate from the kernel.

This gives the object corresponding to the front end currently in use.

```
In[1]:= $FrontEnd
Out[1]= FrontEndObject[LinkObject[ParentLink, 1, 1]]
```

This gives the current directory used by the front end for notebook files.

```
In[2]:= Options[$FrontEnd, NotebookDirectory]
Out[2]= {NotebookDirectory → ~$}
```

option	default value	
NotebookDirectory	"~$"	the current directory for notebook files
NotebookPath	(system dependent)	the path to search when trying to open notebooks
Language	"English"	language for system-generated text
MessageOptions	(list of settings)	how to handle various help and warning messages

A few global options for the *Mathematica* front end.

By using NotebookWrite you can effectively input to the front end any ordinary text that you can enter on the keyboard. FrontEndTokenExecute allows you to send from the kernel any command that the front end can execute. These commands include both menu items and control sequences.

FrontEndTokenExecute["*name*"]	execute a named command in the front end

Executing a named command in the front end.

`"Indent"`	indent all selected lines by one tab
`"NotebookStatisticsDialog"`	display statistics about the current notebook
`"OpenCloseGroup"`	toggle a cell group between open and closed
`"CellSplit"`	split a cell in two at the current insertion point
`"DuplicatePreviousInput"`	create a new cell which is a duplicate of the nearest input cell above
`"FindDialog"`	bring up the find dialog
`"ColorSelectorDialog"`	bring up the color selector dialog
`"GraphicsAlign"`	align selected graphics
`"CompleteSelection"`	complete the command name that is the current selection

A few named commands that can be given to the front end. These commands usually correspond to menu items.

■ 2.10.5 Advanced Topic: Executing Notebook Commands Directly in the Front End

When you execute a command like `NotebookWrite[`*obj*, *data*`]` the actual operation of inserting data into your notebook is performed in the front end. Normally, however, the kernel is needed in order to evaluate the original command, and to construct the appropriate request to send to the front end. But it turns out that the front end is set up to execute a limited collection of commands directly, without ever involving the kernel.

`NotebookWrite[`*obj*, *data*`]`	version of `NotebookWrite` to be executed in the kernel
`FrontEnd`NotebookWrite[`*obj*, *data*`]`	
	version of `NotebookWrite` to be executed directly in the front end

Distinguishing kernel and front end versions of commands.

The basic way that *Mathematica* distinguishes between commands to be executed in the kernel and to be executed directly in the front end is by using contexts. The kernel commands are in the usual `System`` context, but the front end commands are in the `FrontEnd`` context.

`FrontEndExecute[`*expr*`]`	send *expr* to be executed in the front end

Sending an expression to be executed in the front end.

Here is a blank notebook.

This uses kernel commands to write data into the notebook.

In[1]:= **NotebookWrite[SelectedNotebook[ ], "x + y + z"]**

In the kernel, these commands do absolutely nothing.

In[2]:= **FrontEnd`NotebookWrite[FrontEnd`SelectedNotebook[ ],**
        "a + b + c + d"]

Out[2]= FrontEnd`NotebookWrite[
        FrontEnd`SelectedNotebook[], a + b + c + d]

If they are sent to the front end, however, they cause data to be written into the notebook.

In[3]:= **FrontEndExecute[%]**

If you write sophisticated programs for manipulating notebooks, then you will have no choice but to execute these programs primarily in the kernel. But for the kinds of operations typically performed by simple buttons, you may find that it is possible to execute all the commands you need directly in the front end—without the kernel even needing to be running.

⊞ 2.10.6 Button Boxes and Active Elements in Notebooks

Within any cell in a notebook it is possible to set up ButtonBox objects that perform actions whenever you click on them. ButtonBox objects are the way that palette buttons, hyperlinks and other active elements are implemented in *Mathematica* notebooks.

When you first enter a ButtonBox object in a cell, it will behave just like any other expression, and by clicking on it you can select it, edit it, and so on. But if you set the Active option for the cell, say by choosing the Active item in the Cell Properties menu, then the ButtonBox will become active, and when you click on it, it will perform whatever action you have specified for it.

Here is a button.

In[1]:= **ButtonBox["Expand[■]"] // DisplayForm**

Out[1]//DisplayForm=   Expand[■]

When the button appears in an active cell, it will paste its contents whenever you click on it.

    Expand[■]

Here is a typical palette.

```
abc  xy
```

In the expression corresponding to the palette each button corresponds to a ButtonBox object.

```
Cell[BoxData[GridBox[{
    {
     ButtonBox["abc"],
     ButtonBox["xy"]}
    },
   ColumnSpacings->0]], "Input", Active->True]
```

ButtonBox[*boxes*]	a button that will paste its contents when it appears in an active cell
ButtonBox[*boxes*, Active->True]	
	a button that will always be active
ButtonBox[*boxes*, ButtonStyle->"*style*"]	
	a button whose properties are taken from the specified style

Basic ButtonBox objects.

By setting the ButtonStyle you can specify defaults both for how a button will be displayed, and what its action will be. The notebook front end provides a number of standard ButtonStyle settings, which you can access from the Create Button and Edit Button menu items.

"Paste"	paste the contents of the button (default)
"Evaluate"	paste then evaluate in place what has been pasted
"EvaluateCell"	paste then evaluate the whole cell
"CopyEvaluate"	copy the current selection into a new cell, then paste and evaluate in place
"CopyEvaluateCell"	copy the current selection into a new cell, then paste and evaluate the whole cell
"Hyperlink"	jump to a different location in the notebook

Standard settings for the ButtonStyle option.

Here is the expression corresponding to a CopyEvaluateCell button.

```
Cell[BoxData[
  ButtonBox[
   RowBox[{"Expand", "[", "\[SelectionPlaceholder]", "]"}],
   ButtonStyle->"CopyEvaluateCell"]], "Input",
  Active->True]
```

This is what the button looks like.

Here is a notebook with a selection made.

This is what happens when one then clicks on the button.

option	default value	
ButtonFunction	(pasting function)	the function to apply when the button is clicked
ButtonSource	Automatic	where to get the first argument of the button function from
ButtonData	Null	the second argument to supply to the button function
ButtonEvaluator	None	where to send the button function for evaluation
ButtonNote	ButtonData	what to display in the window status line when the cursor is over the button

Options that affect the action of buttons.

A particular `ButtonStyle` setting will specify defaults for all other button options. Some of these options will affect the display of the button, as discussed on page 431. Others affect the action it performs.

What ultimately determines the action of a button is the setting for the `ButtonFunction` option. This setting gives the *Mathematica* function which is to be executed whenever the button is clicked. Typically this function will be a combination of various notebook manipulation commands.

Thus, for example, in its most basic form, a `Paste` button will have a `ButtonFunction` given effectively by `NotebookApply[SelectedNotebook[ ], #]&`, while a `Hyperlink` button will have a `ButtonFunction` given effectively by `NotebookLocate[#2]&`.

When a button is clicked, two arguments are supplied to its `ButtonFunction`. The first is specified by `ButtonSource`, and the second by `ButtonData`.

Typically `ButtonData` is set to be a fixed expression, defined when the button was first created. `ButtonSource`, on the other hand, usually changes with the contents of the button, or the environment in which the button appears.

`Automatic`	`ButtonData` if it is set, otherwise `ButtonContents`
`ButtonContents`	the expression displayed on the button
`ButtonData`	the setting for the `ButtonData` option
`CellContents`	the contents of the cell in which the button appears
`Cell`	the whole cell in which the button appears
`Notebook`	the whole notebook in which the button appears
n	the expression n levels up from the button in the notebook

Possible settings for the `ButtonSource` option.

For a simple `Paste` button, the setting for `ButtonSource` is typically `ButtonContents`. This means that whatever is displayed in the button will be what is passed as the first argument of the button function. The button function can then take this argument and feed it to `NotebookApply`, thereby actually pasting it into the notebook.

By using settings other than `ButtonContents` for `ButtonSource`, you can create buttons which effectively pull in various aspects of their environment for processing. Thus, for example, with the setting `ButtonSource->Cell`, the first argument to the button function will be the expression that represents the whole cell in which the button appears. By having the button function manipulate this expression you can then make the button have a global effect on the whole cell, say by restructuring it in some specified way.

`None`	the front end
`Automatic`	the current kernel
`"name"`	a kernel with the specified name

Settings for the `ButtonEvaluator` option.

Once the arguments to a `ButtonFunction` have been found, and an expression has been constructed, there is then the question of where that expression should be sent for evaluation. The `ButtonEvaluator` option for a `ButtonBox` allows you to specify this.

In general, if the expression involves a range of *Mathematica* functions, then there will be no choice but to evaluate it in an actual *Mathematica* kernel. But if the expression involves only simple notebook manipulation commands, then it may be possible to execute the expression directly in the front end, without ever involving the kernel. You can specify that this should be done by setting the option `ButtonEvaluator->None`.

`FrontEndExecute[`*expr*`]`	execute an expression in the front end
`FrontEnd`NotebookApply[...], etc.`	
	front end versions of notebook commands

Expressions to be executed directly in the front end.

As discussed in the previous section, the standard notebook front end can handle only a limited set of commands, all identified as being in the `FrontEnd`` context. But these commands are sufficient to be able to implement all of the actions associated with standard button styles such as `Paste`, `EvaluateCell` and `Hyperlink`.

Note that even if an expression is sent to the front end, it will be executed only if it is wrapped in a `FrontEndExecute`.

■ 2.10.7 Advanced Topic: The Structure of Cells

`Cell[`*contents*`, "`*style*`"]`	a cell in a particular style
`Cell[`*contents*`, "`*style*`", `*options*`]`	a cell with additional options set

Expressions corresponding to cells.

Here is a notebook containing a text cell and a *Mathematica* input cell.

> Here is some ordinary text.
>
> x^α / y

Here are the expressions corresponding to these cells.

```
Cell["Here is some ordinary text.", "Text"]
Cell[BoxData[
  RowBox[{
    SuperscriptBox["x", "\[Alpha]"], "/", "y"}]], "Input"]
```

Here is a notebook containing a text cell with *Mathematica* input inside.

> Text with the formula xyz^α inside.

This is the expression corresponding to the cell. The *Mathematica* input is in a cell embedded inside the text.

```
Cell[TextData[{
  "Text with the formula ",
  Cell[BoxData[
    FormBox[
      SuperscriptBox["xyz", "\[Alpha]"], TraditionalForm]]],
  " inside."
}], "Text"]
```

`"text"`	plain text
`TextData[{text_1, text_2, ... }]`	text potentially in different styles, or containing cells
`BoxData[boxes]`	formatted *Mathematica* expressions
`GraphicsData["type", data]`	graphics or sounds
`OutputFormData["itext", "otext"]`	text as generated by `InputForm` and `OutputForm`
`RawData["data"]`	unformatted expressions as obtained using Show Expression
`CellGroupData[{cell_1, cell_2, ... }, Open]`	an open group of cells
`CellGroupData[{cell_1, cell_2, ... }, Closed]`	a closed group of cells
`StyleData["style"]`	a style definition cell

Expressions representing possible forms of cell contents.

■ 2.10.8 Styles and the Inheritance of Option Settings

Global	the complete front end and all open notebooks
Notebook	the current notebook
Style	the style of the current cell
Cell	the specific current cell
Selection	a selection within a cell

The hierarchy of levels at which options can be set.

option	typical default value	
CellDingbat	""	a dingbat to use to emphasize the cell
CellFrame	False	whether to draw a frame around the cell
Background	GrayLevel[1]	the background color for the cell
ShowCellBracket	True	whether to display the cell bracket
Magnification	1	the magnification at which to display the cell
CellOpen	True	whether to display the contents of the cell

Some basic cell display options.

This creates a cell in Section style with default settings for all options.

`In[1]:= CellPrint[Cell["A Heading", "Section"]]`

■ **A Heading**

This creates a cell with dingbat and background options modified.

`In[2]:= CellPrint[Cell["A Heading", "Section",`
`            CellDingbat->"\[FilledCircle]", Background->GrayLevel[.7]]]`

option	typical default value	
CellMargins	{7, 0}, {4, 4}	outer margins in printer's points to leave around the contents of the cell
CellFrameMargins	8	margins to leave inside the cell frame
CellElementSpacings	list of rules	details of the layout of cell elements
CellBaseline	Baseline	how to align the baseline of an inline cell with text around it

Options for cell positioning.

The option `CellMargins` allow you to specify both horizontal and vertical margins to put around a cell. You can set the horizontal margins interactively by using the margin stops in the ruler displayed when you choose the Show Ruler menu item in the front end.

Whenever an option can refer to all four edges of a cell, *Mathematica* follows the convention that the setting for the option takes the form {{*left*, *right*}, {*bottom*, *top*}}. By giving nonzero values for the *top* and *bottom* elements, `CellMargins` can specify gaps to leave above and below a particular cell. The values are always taken to be in printer's points.

This leaves 50 points of space on the left of the cell, and 20 points above and below.

```
In[3]:= CellPrint[Cell["First text", "Text",
          CellMargins->{{50, 0}, {20, 20}}]]
```

Almost every aspect of *Mathematica* notebooks can be controlled by some option or another. More detailed aspects are typically handled by "aggregate options" such as `CellElementSpacings`. The settings for these options are lists of *Mathematica* rules, which effectively give values for a sequence of suboptions. The names of these suboptions are usually strings rather than symbols.

This shows the settings for all the suboptions associated with `CellElementSpacings`.

```
In[4]:= Options[SelectedNotebook[ ], CellElementSpacings]

Out[4]= {CellElementSpacings →
            {CellMinHeight → 12., ClosedCellHeight → 19.,
             ClosedGroupTopMargin → 4.,
             GroupIconTopMargin → 3.,
             GroupIconBottomMargin → 12.}}
```

Mathematica allows you to embed cells inside pieces of text. The option `CellBaseline` determines how such "inline cells" will be aligned vertically with respect to the text around them. In direct analogy with the option `GridBaseline` for a `GridBox`, the option `CellBaseline` specifies what aspect of the cell should be considered its baseline.

Here is a cell containing an inline formula. The baseline of the formula is aligned with the baseline of the text around it.

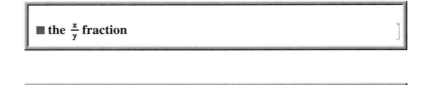

Here is a cell in which the bottom of the formula is aligned with the baseline of the text around it.

This alignment is specified using the
`CellBaseline->Bottom` setting.

```
Cell[TextData[{
  "the ",
  Cell[BoxData[
   RowBox[{
    FractionBox["x", "y"], " "}]],
   CellBaseline->Bottom],
  "fraction "
}], "Section"]
```

option	typical default value	
`CellLabel`	`""`	a label for a cell
`ShowCellLabel`	`True`	whether to show the label for a cell
`CellLabelAutoDelete`	`True`	whether to delete the label if the cell is modified
`CellTags`	`{ }`	tags for a cell
`ShowCellTags`	`False`	whether to show tags for a cell
`ConversionRules`	`{ }`	rules for external conversions

Options for ancillary data associated with cells.

In addition to the actual contents of a cell, it is often useful to associate various kinds of ancillary data with cells.

In a standard *Mathematica* session, cells containing successive lines of kernel input and output are given labels of the form `In[`n`]:=` and `Out[`n`]=`. The option `ShowCellLabel` determines whether such labels should be displayed. `CellLabelAutoDelete` determines whether the label on a cell should be removed if the contents of the cell are modified. Doing this ensures that `In[`n`]:=` and `Out[`n`]=` labels are only associated with unmodified pieces of kernel input and output.

Cell tags are typically used to associate keywords or other attributes with cells, that can be searched for using functions like `NotebookFind`. Destinations for hyperlinks in *Mathematica* notebooks are usually implemented using cell tags.

The option `ConversionRules` allows you to give a list containing entries such as `"TeX" -> `*data* which specify how the contents of a cell should be converted to external formats. This is particularly relevant if you want to keep a copy of the original form of a cell that has been converted in *Mathematica* notebook format from some external format.

option	typical default value	
Deletable	True	whether to allow a cell to be deleted interactively with the front end
Copyable	True	whether to allow a cell to be copied
Selectable	True	whether to allow the contents of a cell to be selected
Editable	True	whether to allow the contents of a cell to be edited
CellEditDuplicate	False	whether to make a copy of a cell if its contents are edited
Active	False	whether buttons in the cell are active

Options for controlling interactive operations on cells.

The options `Deletable`, `Copyable`, `Selectable` and `Editable` allow you to control what interactive operations should be allowed on cells. By setting these options to `False` at the notebook level, you can protect all the cells in a notebook.

Even if you allow a particular cell to be edited, you can set `CellEditDuplicate->True` to get *Mathematica* to make a copy of the contents of the cell before they are actually changed. Styles for cells that contain output from *Mathematica* kernel evaluations usually make use of this option.

option	typical default value	
Evaluator	"Local"	the name of the kernel to use for evaluations
Evaluatable	False	whether to allow the contents of a cell to be evaluated
CellEvaluationDuplicate	False	whether to make a copy of a cell if it is evaluated
CellAutoOverwrite	False	whether to overwrite previous output when new output is generated
GeneratedCell	False	whether this cell was generated from the kernel
InitializationCell	False	whether this cell should automatically be evaluated when the notebook is opened

Options for evaluation.

Mathematica makes it possible to specify a different evaluator for each cell in a notebook. But most often, the `Evaluator` option is set only at the notebook level, typically using the Kernel menu item in the front end.

The option `CellAutoOverwrite` is typically set to `True` for styles that represent *Mathematica* output. Doing this means that when you re-evaluate a particular piece of input, *Mathematica* will automatically delete the output that was previously generated from that input, and will overwrite it with new output.

The option `GeneratedCell` is set whenever a cell is generated by an external request to the front end rather than by an interactive operation within the front end. Thus, for example, any cell obtained as output from a kernel evaluation, or created using a function like `CellPrint` or `NotebookWrite`, will have `GeneratedCell->True`.

option	typical default value	
PageBreakAbove	Automatic	whether to put a page break just above a particular cell
PageBreakWithin	False	whether to allow a page break within a particular cell
PageBreakBelow	Automatic	whether to put a page break just below a particular cell
GroupPageBreakWithin	False	whether to allow a page break within a particular group of cells

Options for controlling page breaks when cells are printed.

When you display a notebook on the screen, you can scroll continuously through it. But if you print the notebook out, you have to decide where page breaks will occur. A setting of `Automatic` for a page break option tells *Mathematica* to make a page break if necessary; `True` specifies that a page break should always be made, while `False` specifies that it should never be.

+■ 2.10.10 Text and Font Options

option	typical default value	
PageWidth	WindowWidth	how wide to assume the page to be
TextAlignment	Left	how to align successive lines of text
TextJustification	0	how much to allow lines of text to be stretched to make them fit
ParagraphIndent	0	how many printer's points to indent the first line in each paragraph

General options for text formatting.

If you have a large block of text containing no explicit RETURN characters, then *Mathematica* will automatically break your text into a sequence of lines. The option `PageWidth` specifies how long each line should be allowed to be.

WindowWidth	the width of the window on the screen
PaperWidth	the width of the page as it would be printed
Infinity	an infinite width (no linebreaking)
n	explicit width given in ems

Settings for the PageWidth option.

The option `TextAlignment` allows you to specify how you want successive lines of text to be aligned. Since *Mathematica* normally breaks text only at space or punctuation characters, it is common to end up with lines of different lengths. Normally the variation in lengths will give your text a ragged boundary. But *Mathematica* allows you to adjust the spaces in successive lines of text so as to make the lines more nearly equal in length. The setting for `TextJustification` gives the fraction of extra space which *Mathematica* is allowed to add. `TextJustification->1` leads to "full justification" in which all complete lines of text are adjusted to be exactly the same length.

Left	aligned on the left
Right	aligned on the right
Center	centered
x	aligned at a position x running from −1 to +1 across the page

Settings for the `TextAlignment` option.

Here is text with
`TextAlignment->Left` and
`TextJustification->0`.

> Like other objects in *Mathematica*, the cells in a notebook, and in fact the whole notebook itself, are all ultimately represented as *Mathematica* expressions. With the standard notebook front end, you can use the command Show Expression to see the text of the *Mathematica* expression that corresponds to any particular cell.

With `TextAlignment->Center` the text
is centered.

> Like other objects in *Mathematica*, the cells in a notebook, and in fact the whole notebook itself, are all ultimately represented as *Mathematica* expressions. With the standard notebook front end, you can use the command Show Expression to see the text of the *Mathematica* expression that corresponds to any particular cell.

`TextJustification->1` adjusts word
spacing so that both the left and right
edges line up.

> Like other objects in *Mathematica*, the cells in a notebook, and in fact the whole notebook itself, are all ultimately represented as *Mathematica* expressions. With the standard notebook front end, you can use the command Show Expression to see the text of the *Mathematica* expression that corresponds to any particular cell.

`TextJustification->0.5` reduces the
degree of raggedness, but does not
force the left and right edges to be
precisely lined up.

> Like other objects in *Mathematica*, the cells in a notebook, and in fact the whole notebook itself, are all ultimately represented as *Mathematica* expressions. With the standard notebook front end, you can use the command Show Expression to see the text of the *Mathematica* expression that corresponds to any particular cell.

When you enter a block of text in a *Mathematica* notebook, *Mathematica* will treat any explicit RETURN characters that you type as paragraph breaks. The option `ParagraphIndent` allows you to specify how much you want to indent the first line in each paragraph. By giving a negative setting for `ParagraphIndent`, you can make the first line stick out to the left.

`LineSpacing->{c, 0}`	leave space so that the total height of each line is c times the height of its contents
`LineSpacing->{0, n}`	make the total height of each line exactly n printer's points
`LineSpacing->{c, n}`	make the total height c times the height of the contents plus n printer's points
`ParagraphSpacing->{c, 0}`	leave an extra space of c times the height of the font before the beginning of each paragraph
`ParagraphSpacing->{0, n}`	leave an extra space of exactly n printer's points before the beginning of each paragraph
`ParagraphSpacing->{c, n}`	leave an extra space of c times the height of the font plus n printer's points

Options for spacing between lines of text.

Here is some text with the default setting `LineSpacing->{1, 1}`, which inserts just 1 printer's point of extra space between successive lines.

> Like other objects in *Mathematica*, the cells in a notebook, and in fact the whole notebook itself, are all ultimately represented as *Mathematica* expressions. With the standard notebook front end, you can use the command Show Expression to see the text of the *Mathematica* expression that corresponds to any particular cell.

With `LineSpacing->{1, 5}` the text is "looser".

> Like other objects in *Mathematica*, the cells in a notebook, and in fact the whole notebook itself, are all ultimately represented as *Mathematica* expressions. With the standard notebook front end, you can use the command Show Expression to see the text of the *Mathematica* expression that corresponds to any particular cell.

`LineSpacing->{2, 0}` makes the text double-spaced.

> Like other objects in *Mathematica*, the cells in a notebook, and in fact the whole notebook itself, are all ultimately represented as *Mathematica* expressions. With the standard notebook front end, you can use the command Show Expression to see the text of the *Mathematica* expression that corresponds to any particular cell.

With `LineSpacing->{1, -2}` the text is tight.

> Like other objects in *Mathematica*, the cells in a notebook, and in fact the whole notebook itself, are all ultimately represented as *Mathematica* expressions. With the standard notebook front end, you can use the command Show Expression to see the text of the *Mathematica* expression that corresponds to any particular cell.

option	typical default value	
FontFamily	"Courier"	the family of font to use
FontSubstitutions	{ }	a list of substitutions to try for font family names
FontSize	12	the maximum height of characters in printer's points
FontWeight	"Bold"	the weight of characters to use
FontSlant	"Plain"	the slant of characters to use
FontTracking	"Plain"	the horizontal compression or expansion of characters
FontColor	GrayLevel[0]	the color of characters
Background	GrayLevel[1]	the color of the background for each character

Options for fonts.

"Courier"	text like this
"Times"	text like this
"Helvetica"	text like this

Some typical font family names.

FontWeight->"Plain"	text like this
FontWeight->"Bold"	**text like this**
FontWeight->"ExtraBold"	**text like this**
FontSlant->"Italic"	*text like this*
FontTracking->"Condensed"	text like this

Some settings of font options.

Mathematica allows you to specify the font that you want to use in considerable detail. Sometimes, however, the particular combination of font families and variations that you request may not be available on your computer system. In such cases, *Mathematica* will try to find the closest approximation it can. There are various additional options, such as `FontPostScriptName` and `FontNativeNames` that you can set to help *Mathematica* find an appropriate font. In addition, you can set `FontSubstitutions` to be a list of rules that give replacements to try for font family names.

There are a great many fonts available for ordinary text. But for special technical characters, and even for Greek letters, far fewer fonts are available. The *Mathematica* system includes fonts that were built to support all of the various special characters that are used by *Mathematica*. There are three versions of these fonts: ordinary (like Times), monospaced (like Courier), and sans serif (like Helvetica).

For a given text font, *Mathematica* tries to choose the special character font that matches it best. You can help *Mathematica* to make this choice by giving rules for "FontSerifed" and "FontMonospaced" in the setting for the `FontProperties` option. You can also give rules for "FontEncoding" to specify explicitly from what font each character is to be taken.

▪ 2.10.11 Advanced Topic: Options for Expression Input and Output

option	typical default value	
AutoIndent	True	whether to indent after an explicit RETURN character is entered
DelimiterFlashTime	0.3	the time in seconds to flash a delimiter when a matching one is entered
ShowSpecialCharacters	True	whether to replace \[*Name*] by a special character as soon as the] is entered
ShowStringCharacters	False	whether to display " when a string is entered
SingleLetterItalics	False	whether to put single-letter symbol names in italics
ZeroWidthTimes	False	whether to represent multiplication by a zero width character
AutoItalicWords	{"Mathematica", ... }	words to automatically put in italics

Options associated with the interactive entering of expressions.

The options `SingleLetterItalics` and `ZeroWidthTimes` are typically set whenever a cell uses `TraditionalForm`.

Here is an expression entered with default options for a StandardForm input cell.

$$x^6 + 6x^5y + 15x^4y^2 + 20x^3y^3 + 15x^2y^4 + 6xy^5 + y^6$$

Here is the same expression entered in a cell with SingleLetterItalics->True and ZeroWidthTimes->True.

$$x^6 + 6x^5y + 15x^4y^2 + 20x^3y^3 + 15x^2y^4 + 6xy^5 + y^6$$

option	typical default value	
StructuredSelection	False	whether to allow only complete subexpressions to be selected
DragAndDrop	False	whether to allow drag-and-drop editing

Options associated with interactive manipulation of expressions.

Mathematica normally allows you to select any part of an expression that you see on the screen. Occasionally, however, you may find it useful to get *Mathematica* to allow only selections which correspond to complete subexpressions. You can do this by setting the option StructuredSelection->True.

Here is an expression with a piece selected.

$$(-1+x)\,(1+x)\,(1-x+x^2-x^3+x^4)\,(1+x+x^2+x^3+x^4)$$

With StructuredSelection->True only complete subexpressions can ever be selected.

$$(-1+x)\,(1+x)\,(1-x+x^2-x^3+x^4)\,(1+x+x^2+x^3+x^4)$$
$$(-1+x)\,(1+x)\,(1-x+x^2-x^3+x^4)\,(1+x+x^2+x^3+x^4)$$
$$(-1+x)\,(1+x)\,(1-x+x^2-x^3+x^4)\,(1+x+x^2+x^3+x^4)$$

GridBox[*data*, *opts*]	give options that apply to a particular grid box
StyleBox[*boxes*, *opts*]	give options that apply to all boxes in *boxes*
Cell[*contents*, *opts*]	give options that apply to all boxes in *contents*
Cell[*contents*, GridBoxOptions->*opts*]	give default options settings for all GridBox objects in *contents*

Examples of specifying options for the display of expressions.

As discussed in Section 2.8, *Mathematica* provides many options for specifying how expressions should be displayed. By using StyleBox[*boxes*, *opts*] you can apply such options to collections of boxes. But *Mathematica* is set up so that any option that you can give to a StyleBox can also be given to a complete Cell object, or even a complete Notebook. Thus, for example, options like Background and LineIndent can be given to complete cells as well as to individual StyleBox objects.

There are some options that apply only to a particular type of box, such as GridBox. Usually these options are best given separately in each GridBox where they are needed. But sometimes you may want to specify default settings to be inherited by all GridBox objects that appear in a particular cell. You can do this by giving these default settings as the value of the option GridBoxOptions for the whole cell.

For each box type named *XXX*Box, *Mathematica* provides a cell option *XXX*BoxOptions that allows you to specify the default options settings for that type of box.

■ 2.10.12 Options for Graphics Cells

option	typical default value	
AspectRatioFixed	True	whether to keep a fixed aspect ratio if the image is resized
ImageSize	{288, 288}	the absolute width and height of the image in printer's points
ImageMargins	{{0, 0}, {0, 0}}	the widths of margins in printer's points to leave around the image

Options for displaying images in notebooks.

Here is a graphic displayed in a notebook.

With the default setting AspectRatioFixed->True resizing the graphic does not change its shape.

If you set `AspectRatioFixed->False` then you can change the shape.

Mathematica allows you to specify the final size of a graphic by setting the `ImageSize` option in kernel graphics functions such as `Plot` and `Display`. Once a graphic is in a notebook, you can then typically resize or move it just by using the mouse.

- Use the Animate Selected Graphics menu item in the front end.
- Use the kernel command `SelectionAnimate[`*obj*`]`.

Ways to generate animations in a notebook.

   Mathematica generates animated graphics by taking a sequence of graphics cells, and then treating them like frames in a movie. The option `AnimationDisplayTime` specifies how long a particular cell should be displayed as part of the movie.

option	typical default value	
`AnimationDisplayTime`	0	minimum time in seconds to display this cell during an animation
`AnimationDirection`	Forward	which direction to run an animation starting with this cell

Options for animations.

■ 2.10.13 Options for Notebooks

- Use the Option Inspector menu to change options interactively.
- Use `SetOptions[`*obj*, *options*`]` from the kernel.
- Use `NotebookCreate[`*options*`]` to create a new notebook with specified options.

Ways to change the overall options for a notebook.

This creates a notebook displayed in a 40 × 30 window with a thin frame.

```
In[1]:= NotebookCreate[WindowFrame->"ThinFrame",
                        WindowSize->{40, 30}]
```

option	typical default value	
StyleDefinitions	"DefaultStyles.nb"	the basic style sheet to use for the notebook
ScreenStyleEnvironment	"Working"	the style environment to use for screen display
PrintingStyleEnvironment	"Printout"	the style environment to use for printing

Style options for a notebook.

In giving style definitions for a particular notebook, *Mathematica* allows you either to reference another notebook, or explicitly to include the Notebook expression that defines the styles.

option	typical default value	
CellGrouping	Automatic	how to group cells in the notebook
ShowPageBreaks	False	whether to show where page breaks would occur if the notebook were printed
NotebookAutoSave	False	whether to automatically save the notebook after each evaluation

General options for notebooks.

Without CellGrouping->Automatic, cells are automatically grouped based on their style.

■ **Section heading**

First text cell.

Second text cell.

With CellGrouping->Manual, you have to group cells by hand.

■ **Section heading**

First text cell.

Second text cell.

option	typical default value	
DefaultNewCellStyle	"Input"	the default style for new cells created in the notebook
DefaultDuplicateCellStyle	"Input"	the default style for cells created by automatic duplication of existing cells

Options specifying default styles for cells created in a notebook.

Mathematica allows you to take any cell option and set it at the notebook level, thereby specifying a global default for that option throughout the notebook.

option	typical default value	
Editable	True	whether to allow cells in the notebook to be edited
Selectable	True	whether to allow cells to be selected
Deletable	True	whether to allow cells to be deleted
Background	GrayLevel[1]	what background color to use for the notebook
Magnification	1	at what magnification to display the notebook
PageWidth	WindowWidth	how wide to allow the contents of cells to be

A few cell options that are often set at the notebook level.

Here is a notebook with the Background option set at the notebook level.

Here is some text.

option	typical default value	
Visible	True	whether the window should be visible on the screen
WindowSize	{Automatic, Automatic}	the width and height of the window in printer's points
WindowMargins	Automatic	the margins to leave around the window when it is displayed on the screen
WindowFrame	"Normal"	the type of frame to draw around the window
WindowElements	{"StatusArea", ... }	elements to include in the window
WindowTitle	Automatic	what title should be displayed for the window
WindowToolbars	{ }	toolbars to display at the top of the window
WindowMovable	True	whether to allow the window to be moved around on the screen
WindowFloating	False	whether the window should always float on top of other windows
WindowClickSelect	True	whether the window should become selected if you click in it

Characteristics of the notebook window.

WindowSize allows you to specify how large you want a window to be; WindowMargins allows you to specify where you want the window to be placed on your screen. The setting WindowMargins->{{*left*, *right*}, {*bottom*, *top*}} gives the margins in printer's points to leave around your window on the screen. Often only two of the margins will be set explicitly; the others will be Automatic, indicating that these margins will be determined from the particular size of screen that you use.

`"Normal"`	an ordinary window
`"Palette"`	a palette window
`"ModelessDialog"`	a modeless dialog box window
`"ModalDialog"`	a modal dialog box window
`"MovableModalDialog"`	a modal dialog box window that can be moved around the screen
`"ThinFrame"`	an ordinary window with a thin frame
`"Frameless"`	an ordinary window with no frame at all
`"Generic"`	a window with a generic border, as used for the examples in this book

Typical possible settings for `WindowFrame`.

Mathematica allows many different types of windows. The details of how particular windows are rendered may differ slightly from one computer system to another, but their general form is always the same. `WindowFrame` specifies the type of frame to draw around the window. `WindowElements` gives a list of specific elements to include in the window.

`"StatusArea"`	an area used to display status messages, such as those from `ButtonNote` options
`"MagnificationPopUp"`	a pop-up menu of common magnifications
`"HorizontalScrollBar"`	a scroll bar for horizontal motion
`"VerticalScrollBar"`	a scroll bar for vertical motion

Some typical possible entries in the `WindowElements` list.

Here is a window with a status area and horizontal scroll bar, but no magnification pop-up or vertical scroll bar.

`"RulerBar"`	a ruler showing margin settings
`"EditBar"`	buttons for common editing operations
`"LinksBar"`	buttons for hyperlink operations

Some typical possible entries in the `WindowToolbars` list.

Here is a window with ruler and edit toolbars.

■ 2.10.14 Advanced Topic: Global Options for the Front End

In the standard notebook front end, *Mathematica* allows you to set a large number of global options. The values of all these options are by default saved in a "preferences file", and are automatically reused when you run *Mathematica* again.

style definitions	default style definitions to use for new notebooks
file locations	directories for finding notebooks and system files
data export options	how to export data in various formats
character encoding options	how to encode special characters
language options	what language to use for text
message options	how to handle messages generated by *Mathematica*
menu settings	items displayed in modifiable menus
dialog settings	choices made in dialog boxes
system configuration	private options for specific computer systems

Some typical categories of global options for the front end.

As discussed on page 566, you can access global front end options from the kernel by using Options[$FrontEnd, *name*]. But more often, you will want to access these options interactively using the Option Inspector in the front end.

2.11 Files and Streams

■ 2.11.1 Reading and Writing *Mathematica* Files

Particularly if you use a text-based *Mathematica* interface, you will often need to read and write files containing definitions and results from *Mathematica*. Section 1.11.1 gave a general discussion of how to do this. This section gives some more details.

`<<`*file* or `Get["`*file*`"]`	read in a file of *Mathematica* input, and return the last expression in the file
`!!`*file*	display the contents of a file

Reading files.

This shows the contents of the file factors.

```
In[1]:= !!factors

(* Factors of x^20 - 1 *)
 (-1 + x)*(1 + x)*(1 + x^2)*(1 - x + x^2 - x^3 + x^4)*
 (1 + x + x^2 + x^3 + x^4)*(1 - x^2 + x^4 - x^6 + x^8)
```

This reads in the file, and returns the last expression in it.

$$In[2]:= \text{<<}factors$$

$$Out[2]= (-1+x)\,(1+x)\,(1+x^2)\,(1-x+x^2-x^3+x^4)$$
$$(1+x+x^2+x^3+x^4)\,(1-x^2+x^4-x^6+x^8)$$

If *Mathematica* cannot find the file you ask it to read, it prints a message, then returns the symbol $Failed.

$$In[3]:= \text{<<}faxors$$

Get::noopen: Can't open faxors.

$$Out[3]= \$Failed$$

Mathematica input files can contain any number of expressions. Each expression, however, must start on a new line. The expressions may however continue for as many lines as necessary. Just as in a standard interactive *Mathematica* session, the expressions are processed as soon as they are complete. Note, however, that in a file, unlike an interactive session, you can insert a blank line at any point without effect.

When you read in a file with `<<`*file*, *Mathematica* returns the last expression it evaluates in the file. You can avoid getting any visible result from reading a file by ending the last expression in the file with a semicolon, or by explicitly adding `Null` after that expression.

If *Mathematica* encounters a syntax error while reading a file, it reports the error, skips the remainder of the file, then returns $Failed. If the syntax error occurs in the middle of a package which uses `BeginPackage` and other context manipulation functions, then *Mathematica* tries to restore the context to what it was before the package was read.

$expr \gg file$ or   `Put[`*expr*`, "`*file*`"]`
                                     write an expression to a file

$expr \ggg file$ or   `PutAppend[`*expr*`, "`*file*`"]`
                                       append an expression to a file

---

Writing expressions to files.

This writes an expression to the file tmp.	*In[4]:=* `Factor[x^6 - 1] >> tmp`
Here are the contents of the file.	*In[5]:=* `!!tmp`
	`(-1 + x)*(1 + x)*(1 - x + x^2)*(1 + x + x^2)`
This appends another expression to the same file.	*In[6]:=* `Factor[x^8 - 1] >>> tmp`
Both expressions are now in the file.	*In[7]:=* `!!tmp`
	`(-1 + x)*(1 + x)*(1 - x + x^2)*(1 + x + x^2)`
	`(-1 + x)*(1 + x)*(1 + x^2)*(1 + x^4)`

When you use *expr* $\ggg$ *file*, *Mathematica* appends each new expression you give to the end of your file. If you use *expr* $\gg$ *file*, however, then *Mathematica* instead wipes out anything that was in the file before, and then puts *expr* into the file.

When you use either $\gg$ or $\ggg$ to write expressions to files, the expressions are usually given in *Mathematica* input format, so that you can read them back into *Mathematica*. Sometimes, however, you may want to save expressions in other formats. You can do this by explicitly wrapping a format directive such as `OutputForm` around the expression you write out.

This writes an expression to the file tmp in output format.	*In[8]:=* `OutputForm[ Factor[x^6 - 1] ] >> tmp`
The expression in tmp is now in output format.	*In[9]:=* `!!tmp`
	$(-1 + x) (1 + x) (1 - x + x^2) (1 + x + x^2)$

One of the most common reasons for using files is to save definitions of *Mathematica* objects, to be able to read them in again in a subsequent *Mathematica* session. The operators $\gg$ and $\ggg$ allow you to save *Mathematica* expressions in files. You can use the function `Save` to save complete definitions of *Mathematica* objects, in a form suitable for execution in subsequent *Mathematica* sessions.

Save["*file*", *symbol*]	save the complete definitions for a symbol in a file
Save["*file*", "*form*"]	save definitions for symbols whose names match the string pattern *form*
Save["*file*", "*context*`"]	save definitions for all symbols in the specified context
Save["*file*", {*object*$_1$, *object*$_2$, ... }]	
	save definitions for several objects

Writing out definitions.

This assigns a value to the symbol a.

In[10]:= **a = 2 - x^2**

Out[10]= $2 - x^2$

You can use Save to write the definition of a to a file.

In[11]:= **Save["afile", a]**

Here is the definition of a that was saved in the file.

In[12]:= **!!afile**

a = 2 - x^2

When you define a new object in *Mathematica*, your definition will often depend on other objects that you defined before. If you are going to be able to reconstruct the definition of your new object in a subsequent *Mathematica* session, it is important that you store not only its own definition, but also the definitions of other objects on which it depends. The function Save looks through the definitions of the objects you ask it to save, and automatically also saves all definitions of other objects on which it can see that these depend. However, in order to avoid saving a large amount of unnecessary material, Save never includes definitions for symbols that have the attribute Protected. It assumes that the definitions for these symbols are also built in. Nevertheless, with such definitions taken care of, it should always be the case that reading the output generated by Save back into a new *Mathematica* session will set up the definitions of your objects exactly as you had them before.

This defines a function f which depends on the symbol a defined above.

In[13]:= **f[z_] := a^2 - 2**

This saves the complete definition of f in a file.

In[14]:= **Save["ffile", f]**

The file contains not only the definition of f itself, but also the definition of the symbol a on which f depends.

In[15]:= **!!ffile**

f[z_] := a^2 - 2

a = 2 - x^2

The function Save makes use of the output forms Definition and FullDefinition, which print as definitions of *Mathematica* symbols. In some cases, you may find it convenient to use these output forms directly.

The output form Definition[*f*] prints as the sequence of definitions that have been made for *f*.

In[16]:= **Definition[f]**

Out[16]= f[z_] := a² - 2

FullDefinition[*f*] includes definitions of the objects on which *f* depends.

In[17]:= **FullDefinition[f]**

Out[17]= f[z_] := a² - 2

$$a = 2 - x^2$$

When you create files for input to *Mathematica*, you usually want them to contain only "plain text", which can be read or modified directly. Sometimes, however, you may want the contents of a file to be "encoded" so that they cannot be read or modified directly as plain text, but can be loaded into *Mathematica*. You can create encoded files using the *Mathematica* function Encode.

Encode["*source*", "*dest*"]	write an encoded version of the file *source* to the file *dest*
<<*dest*	read in an encoded file
Encode["*source*", "*dest*", "*key*"]	encode with the specified key
Get["*dest*", "*key*"]	read in a file that was encoded with a key
Encode["*source*", "*dest*", MachineID -> "*ID*"]	create an encoded file which can only be read on a machine with a particular ID

Creating and reading encoded files.

This writes an expression in plain text to the file tmp.

In[18]:= **Factor[x^2 - 1] >> tmp**

This writes an encoded version of the file tmp to the file tmp.x.

In[19]:= **Encode["tmp", "tmp.x"]**

Here are the contents of the encoded file. The only recognizable part is the special *Mathematica* comment at the beginning.

In[20]:= **!!tmp.x**

(*!1N!*)mcm
_QZ9tcI1cfre*Wo8:) P

Even though the file is encoded, you can still read it into *Mathematica* using the << operator.

In[21]:= **<<tmp.x**

Out[21]= (-1 + x) (1 + x)

DumpSave["*file*.mx", *symbol*]	save definitions for a symbol in internal *Mathematica* format
DumpSave["*file*.mx", "*context*`"]	save definitions for all symbols in a context
DumpSave["*file*.mx", {*object*$_1$, *object*$_2$, ... }]	save definitions for several symbols or contexts
DumpSave["*package*`", *objects*]	save definitions in a file with a specially chosen name

Saving definitions in internal *Mathematica* format.

If you have to read in very large or complicated definitions, you will often find it more efficient to store these definitions in internal *Mathematica* format, rather than as text. You can do this using DumpSave.

This saves the definition for f in internal *Mathematica* format.

```
In[22]:= DumpSave["ffile.mx", f]

Out[22]= {f}
```

You can still use << to read the definition in.

```
In[23]:= <<ffile.mx
```

<< recognizes when a file contains definitions in internal *Mathematica* format, and operates accordingly. One subtlety is that the internal *Mathematica* format differs from one computer system to another. As a result, .mx files created on one computer cannot typically be read on another.

If you use DumpSave["*package*`", ...] then *Mathematica* will write out definitions to a file with a name like *package*.mx/*system*/*package*.mx, where *system* identifies your type of computer system.

This creates a file with a name that reflects the name of the computer system being used.

```
In[24]:= DumpSave["gffile`", f]

Out[24]= {f}
```

<< automatically picks out the file with the appropriate name for your computer system.

```
In[25]:= <<gffile`
```

DumpSave["*file*.mx"]	save all definitions in your current *Mathematica* session
DumpSave["*package*`"]	save all definitions in a file with a specially chosen name

Saving the complete state of a *Mathematica* session.

■ 2.11.2 External Programs

On most computer systems, you can execute external programs or commands from within *Mathematica*. Often you will want to take expressions you have generated in *Mathematica*, and send them to an external program, or take results from external programs, and read them into *Mathematica*.

Mathematica supports two basic forms of communication with external programs: *structured* and *unstructured*.

Structured communication	use *MathLink* to exchange expressions with *MathLink*-compatible external programs
Unstructured communication	use file reading and writing operations to exchange ordinary text

Two kinds of communication with external programs in *Mathematica*.

The idea of structured communication is to exchange complete *Mathematica* expressions to external programs which are specially set up to handle such objects. The basis for structured communication is the *MathLink* system, discussed in Section 2.12.

Unstructured communication consists in sending and receiving ordinary text from external programs. The basic idea is to treat an external program very much like a file, and to support the same kinds of reading and writing operations.

expr >> "!*command*"	send the text of an expression to an external program
<< "!*command*"	read in text from an external program as *Mathematica* input

Reading and writing to external programs.

In general, wherever you might use an ordinary file name, *Mathematica* allows you instead to give a *pipe*, written as an external command, prefaced by an exclamation point. When you use the pipe, *Mathematica* will execute the external command, and send or receive text from it.

This sends the result from `FactorInteger` to the external program `lpr`. On many Unix systems, this program generates a printout.

`In[1]:= FactorInteger[2^31 - 1] >> !lpr`

This executes the external command `echo $TERM`, then reads the result as *Mathematica* input.

`In[2]:= <<"!echo $TERM"`

`Out[2]= vt100`

One point to notice is that you can get away with dropping the double quotes around the name of a pipe on the right-hand side of << or >> if the name does not contain any spaces or other special characters.

Pipes in *Mathematica* provide a very general mechanism for unstructured communication with external programs. On many computer systems, *Mathematica* pipes are implemented using pipe mechanisms in the underlying operating system; in some cases, however, other interprocess communication mechanisms are used. One restriction of unstructured communication in *Mathematica* is that a given pipe can only be used for input or for output, and not for both at the same time. In order to do genuine two-way communication, you need to use *MathLink*.

Even with unstructured communication, you can nevertheless set up somewhat more complicated arrangements by using temporary files. The basic idea is to write data to a file, then to read it as needed.

`OpenTemporary[ ]`	open a temporary file with a unique name

Opening a temporary file.

Particularly when you work with temporary files, you may find it useful to be able to execute external commands which do not explicitly send or receive data from *Mathematica*. You can do this using the *Mathematica* function Run.

`Run["command", arg`$_1$`, ... ]`	run an external command from within *Mathematica*

Running external commands without input or output.

This executes the external Unix command `date`. The returned value is an "exit code" from the operating system.

```
In[3]:= Run["date"]

Wed Mar 27 16:51:55 CST 1996

Out[3]= 0
```

Note that when you use Run, you must not preface commands with exclamation points. Run simply takes the textual forms of the arguments you specify, then joins them together with spaces in between, and executes the resulting string as an external command.

It is important to realize that Run never "captures" any of the output from an external command. As a result, where this output goes is purely determined by your operating system. Similarly, Run does not supply input to external commands. This means that the commands can get input through any mechanism provided by your operating system. Sometimes external commands may be able to access the same input and output streams that are used by *Mathematica* itself. In some cases, this may be what you want. But particularly if you are using *Mathematica* with a front end, this can cause considerable trouble.

`!command`	intercept a line of *Mathematica* input, and run it as an external command

Shell escapes in *Mathematica*.

If you use *Mathematica* with a text-based interface, there is usually a special mechanism for executing external commands. With such an interface, *Mathematica* takes any line of input that starts with an exclamation point, and executes the text on the remainder of the line as an external command.

The way *Mathematica* uses !*command* is typical of the way "shell escapes" work in programs running under the Unix operating system. In most versions of *Mathematica*, you will be able to start an interactive shell from *Mathematica* simply by typing a single exclamation point on its own on a line.

This line is taken as a "shell escape", and executes the Unix command date.

```
In[4]:= !date
Wed Mar 27 16:52:00 CST 1996
Out[4]= 0
```

`RunThrough["command", expr]`	run *command*, using *expr* as input, and reading the output back into *Mathematica*

Running *Mathematica* expressions through external programs.

As discussed above, << and >> cannot be used to both send and receive data from an external program at the same time. Nevertheless, by using temporary files, you can effectively both send and receive data from an external program while still using unstructured communication.

The function `RunThrough` writes the text of an expression to a temporary file, then feeds this file as input to an external program, and captures the output as input to *Mathematica*. Note that in `RunThrough`, like `Run`, you should not preface the names of external commands with exclamation points.

This feeds the expression 789 to the external program cat, which in this case simply echoes the text of the expression. The output from cat is then read back into *Mathematica*.

```
In[5]:= RunThrough["cat", 789]
Out[5]= 789
```

■ 2.11.3 Advanced Topic: Streams and Low-Level Input and Output

Files and pipes are both examples of general *Mathematica* objects known as *streams*. A stream in *Mathematica* is a source of input or output. There are many operations that you can perform on streams.

You can think of >> and << as "high-level" *Mathematica* input-output functions. They are based on a set of lower-level input-output primitives that work directly with streams. By using these primitives, you can exercise more control over exactly how *Mathematica* does input and output. You will often need to do this, for example, if you write *Mathematica* programs which store and retrieve intermediate data from files or pipes.

The basic low-level scheme for writing output to a stream in *Mathematica* is as follows. First, you call `OpenWrite` or `OpenAppend` to "open the stream", telling *Mathematica* that you want to write output to a particular file or external program, and in what form the output should be written. Having opened a stream, you can then call `Write` or `WriteString` to write a sequence of expressions or strings to the stream. When you have finished, you call `Close` to "close the stream".

`"name"`	a file, specified by name
`"!name"`	a command, specified by name
`InputStream["name", n]`	an input stream
`OutputStream["name", n]`	an output stream

Streams in *Mathematica*.

When you open a file or a pipe, *Mathematica* creates a "stream object" that specifies the open stream associated with the file or pipe. In general, the stream object contains the name of the file or the external command used in a pipe, together with a unique number.

The reason that the stream object needs to include a unique number is that in general you can have several streams connected to the same file or external program at the same time. For example, you may start several different instances of the same external program, each connected to a different stream.

Nevertheless, when you have opened a stream, you can still refer to it using a simple file name or external command name so long as there is only one stream associated with this object.

This opens an output stream to the file `tmp`.	`In[1]:= stmp = OpenWrite["tmp"]`
	
	`Out[1]= OutputStream[tmp, 5]`

This writes a sequence of expressions to the file.	`In[2]:= Write[stmp, a, b, c]`
Since you only have one stream associated with file `tmp`, you can refer to it simply by giving the name of the file.	`In[3]:= Write["tmp", x]`

This closes the stream.	`In[4]:= Close[stmp]`
	
	`Out[4]= tmp`

Here is what was written to the file.	`In[5]:= !!tmp`
	
	`abc`
	`x`

■ 2.11.4 Naming and Finding Files

The precise details of the naming of files differ from one computer system to another. Nevertheless, *Mathematica* provides some fairly general mechanisms that work on all systems.

As mentioned in Section 1.11.2, *Mathematica* assumes that all your files are arranged in a hierarchy of *directories*. To find a particular file, *Mathematica* must know both what the name of the file is, and what sequence of directories it is in.

At any given time, however, you have a *current working directory*, and you can refer to files or other directories by specifying where they are relative to this directory. Typically you can refer to files or directories that are actually *in* this directory simply by giving their names, with no directory information.

`Directory[ ]`	your current working directory
`SetDirectory["dir"]`	set your current working directory
`ResetDirectory[ ]`	revert to your previous working directory

Manipulating directories.

This gives a string representing your current working directory.	`In[1]:= Directory[ ]` `Out[1]= /users/sw`
This sets your current working directory to be the Packages subdirectory.	`In[2]:= SetDirectory["Packages"]` `Out[2]= /users/sw/Packages`
Now your current working directory is different.	`In[3]:= Directory[ ]` `Out[3]= /users/sw/Packages`
This reverts to your previous working directory.	`In[4]:= ResetDirectory[ ]` `Out[4]= /users/sw`

When you call `SetDirectory`, you can give any directory name that is recognized by your operating system. Thus, for example, on Unix-based systems, you can specify a directory one level up in the directory hierarchy using the notation .., and you can specify your "home" directory as ~.

Whenever you go to a new directory using `SetDirectory`, *Mathematica* always remembers what the previous directory was. You can return to this previous directory using `ResetDirectory`. In general, *Mathematica* maintains a stack of directories, given by `DirectoryStack[ ]`. Every time you call `SetDirectory`, it adds a new directory to the stack, and every time you call `ResetDirectory` it removes a directory from the stack.

ParentDirectory[ ]	give the parent of your current working directory
$TopDirectory	the top-level directory in which *Mathematica* system files are installed
$LaunchDirectory	the directory in which the copy of *Mathematica* being run resides
$InitialDirectory	the current directory at the time *Mathematica* was started
$HomeDirectory	your home directory, if this is defined

Special directories.

Whenever you ask for a particular file, *Mathematica* in general goes through several steps to try and find the file you want. The first step is to use whatever standard mechanisms exist in your operating system or shell.

Mathematica scans the full name you give for a file, and looks to see whether it contains any of the "metacharacters" *, $, ~, ?, [, ", \ and '. If it finds such characters, then it passes the full name to your operating system or shell for interpretation. This means that if you are using a Unix-based system, then constructions like *name** and *$VAR* will be expanded at this point. But in general, *Mathematica* takes whatever was returned by your operating system or shell, and treats this as the full file name.

For output files, this is the end of the processing that *Mathematica* does. If *Mathematica* cannot find a unique file with the name you specified, then it will proceed to create the file.

If you are trying to get input from a file, however, then there is another round of processing that *Mathematica* does. What happens is that *Mathematica* looks at the value of the Path option for the function you are using to determine the names of directories relative to which it should search for the file. The default setting for the Path option is the global variable $Path.

$Path	a default list of directories relative to which to search for input files

Search path for files.

In general, the global variable $Path is defined to be a list of strings, with each string representing a directory. Every time you ask for an input file, what *Mathematica* effectively does is temporarily to make each of these directories in turn your current working directory, and then from that directory to try and find the file you have requested.

Here is a typical setting for $Path. The current directory (.) and your home directory (~) are listed first.

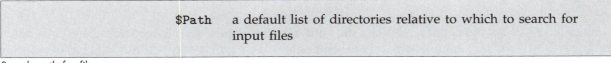

```
In[5]:= $Path

Out[5]= {., ~, /users/math/bin, /users/math/Packages}
```

FileNames[ ]	list all files in your current working directory
FileNames["*form*"]	list all files in your current working directory whose names match the string pattern *form*
FileNames[{"*form*$_1$", "*form*$_2$", ... }]	list all files whose names match any of the *form*$_i$
FileNames[*forms*, {"*dir*$_1$", "*dir*$_2$", ... }]	give the full names of all files whose names match *forms* in any of the directories *dir*$_i$
FileNames[*forms*, *dirs*, *n*]	include files that are in subdirectories up to *n* levels down
FileNames[*forms*, *dirs*, Infinity]	include files in all subdirectories
FileNames[*forms*, $Path, Infinity]	give all files whose names match *forms* in any subdirectory of the directories in $Path

Getting lists of files in particular directories.

Here is a list of all files in the current working directory whose names end with .m.

```
In[6]:= FileNames["*.m"]

Out[6]= {alpha.m, control.m, signals.m, test.m}
```

This lists files whose names start with a in the current directory, and in subdirectories with names that start with P.

```
In[7]:= FileNames["a*", {".", "P*"}]

Out[7]= {alpha.m, Packages/astrodata, Packages/astro.m,
              Previous/atmp}
```

FileNames returns a list of strings corresponding to file names. When it returns a file that is not in your current directory, it gives the name of the file relative to the current directory. Note that all names are given in the format appropriate for the particular computer system on which they were generated.

+	`DirectoryName["`*file*`"]`	extract the directory name from a file name
+	`ToFileName["`*directory*`", "`*name*`"]`	assemble a full file name from a directory name and a file name
	`ParentDirectory["`*directory*`"]`	give the parent of a directory
+	`ToFileName[{"`*dir₁*`", "`*dir₂*`", ... }, "`*name*`"]`	assemble a full file name from a hierarchy of directory names
+	`ToFileName[{"`*dir₁*`", "`*dir₂*`", ... }]`	assemble a single directory name from a hierarchy of directory names

Manipulating file names.

You should realize that different computer systems may give file names in different ways. Thus, for example, Unix systems typically give names in the form *dir/dir/name*, Macintosh systems in the form :*dir*:*dir*:*name*, and VMS systems in the form [*dir*]*name*. The function `ToFileName` assembles file names in the appropriate way for the particular computer system you are using.

This gives the directory portion of the file name.

```
In[8]:= DirectoryName["Packages/Math/test.m"]
Out[8]= Packages/Math/
```

This constructs the full name of another file in the same directory as `test.m`.

```
In[9]:= ToFileName[%, "abc.m"]
Out[9]= Packages/Math/abc.m
```

If you want to set up a collection of related files, it is often convenient to be able to refer to one file when you are reading another one. The global variable `$Input` gives the name of the file from which input is currently being taken. Using `DirectoryName` and `ToFileName` you can then conveniently specify the names of other related files.

`$Input`	the name of the file or stream from which input is currently being taken

Finding out how to refer to a file currently being read by *Mathematica*.

■ 2.11.5 Files for Packages

When you create or use *Mathematica* packages, you will often want to refer to files in a system-independent way. You can use contexts to do this.

The basic idea is that on every computer system there is a convention about how files corresponding to *Mathematica* contexts should be named. Then, when you refer to a file using a context, the particular version of *Mathematica* you are using converts the context name to the file name appropriate for the computer system you are on.

<<*context*\`	read in the file corresponding to the specified context

Using contexts to specify files.

This reads in one of the standard packages that come with *Mathematica*.

`In[1]:= <<Graphics`Colors` `

name.mx	file in DumpSave format
name.mx/$SystemID/*name*.mx	file in DumpSave format for your computer system
name.m	file in *Mathematica* source format
name/init.m	initialization file for a particular directory
dir/...	files in other directories specified by $Path

The typical sequence of files looked for by **<<***name*\`.

Mathematica is set up so that **<<***name*\` will automatically try to load the appropriate version of a file. It will first try to load a *name*.mx file that is optimized for your particular computer system. If it finds no such file, then it will try to load a *name*.m file containing ordinary system-independent *Mathematica* input.

If *name* is a directory, then *Mathematica* will try to load the initialization file init.m in that directory. The purpose of the init.m file is to provide a convenient way to set up *Mathematica* packages that involve many separate files.

The idea is to allow you to give just the command **<<***name*\`, but then to load init.m to initialize the whole package, reading in whatever other files are necessary.

This reads in the file Graphics/init.m, which initializes all standard *Mathematica* graphics packages.

`In[2]:= <<Graphics` `

■ 2.11.6 Manipulating Files and Directories

CopyFile["*file₁*", "*file₂*"]	copy *file₁* to *file₂*
RenameFile["*file₁*", "*file₂*"]	give *file₁* the name *file₂*
DeleteFile["*file*"]	delete a file
FileByteCount["*file*"]	give the number of bytes in a file
FileDate["*file*"]	give the modification date for a file
SetFileDate["*file*"]	set the modification date for a file to be the current date
FileType["*file*"]	give the type of a file as File, Directory or None

Functions for manipulating files.

Different operating systems have different commands for manipulating files. *Mathematica* provides a simple set of file manipulation functions, intended to work in the same way under all operating systems.

Notice that CopyFile and RenameFile give the final file the same modification date as the original one. FileDate returns modification dates in the {*year*, *month*, *day*, *hour*, *minute*, *second*} format used by Date.

CreateDirectory["*name*"]	create a new directory
DeleteDirectory["*name*"]	delete an empty directory
DeleteDirectory["*name*", DeleteContents -> True]	delete a directory and all files and directories it contains
RenameDirectory["*name₁*", "*name₂*"]	rename a directory
CopyDirectory["*name₁*", "*name₂*"]	copy a directory and all the files in it

Functions for manipulating directories.

■ 2.11.7 Reading Data

With <<, you can read files which contain *Mathematica* expressions given in input form. Sometimes, however, you may instead need to read files of *data* in other formats. For example, you may have data generated by an external program which consists of a sequence of numbers separated by spaces.

This data cannot be read directly as *Mathematica* input. However, the function `ReadList` can take such data from a file or input stream, and convert it to a *Mathematica* list.

`ReadList["`*file*`", Number]`	read a sequence of numbers from a file, and put them in a *Mathematica* list

Reading numbers from a file.

Here is a file of numbers.

```
In[1]:= !!numbers
11.1   22.2   33.3
44.4   55.5   66.6
```

This reads all the numbers in the file, and returns a list of them.

```
In[2]:= ReadList["numbers", Number]
Out[2]= {11.1, 22.2, 33.3, 44.4, 55.5, 66.6}
```

`ReadList["`*file*`", {Number, Number}]`	read numbers from a file, putting each successive pair into a separate list
`ReadList["`*file*`", Table[Number, {`*n*`}]]`	put each successive block of *n* numbers in a separate list
`ReadList["`*file*`", Number, RecordLists -> True]`	put all the numbers on each line of the file into a separate list

Reading blocks of numbers.

This puts each successive pair of numbers from the file into a separate list.

```
In[3]:= ReadList["numbers", {Number, Number}]
Out[3]= {{11.1, 22.2}, {33.3, 44.4}, {55.5, 66.6}}
```

This makes each line in the file into a separate list.

```
In[4]:= ReadList["numbers", Number, RecordLists -> True]
Out[4]= {{11.1, 22.2, 33.3}, {44.4, 55.5, 66.6}}
```

`ReadList` can handle numbers which are given in Fortran-like "E" notation. Thus, for example, `ReadList` will read 2.5E+5 as 2.5×10^5. Note that `ReadList` can handle numbers with any number of digits of precision.

Here is a file containing numbers in Fortran-like "E" notation.

```
In[5]:= !!bignum
4.5E-5     7.8E4
2.5E2      -8.9
```

`ReadList` can handle numbers in this form.

```
In[6]:= ReadList["bignum", Number]
Out[6]= {0.000045, 78000., 250., -8.9}
```

ReadList["*file*", *type*]	read a sequence of objects of a particular type
ReadList["*file*", *type*, *n*]	read at most *n* objects

Reading objects of various types.

ReadList can read not only numbers, but also a variety of other types of object. Each type of object is specified by a symbol such as Number.

Here is a file containing text.

In[7]:= **!!strings**

Here is text.
And more text.

This produces a list of the characters in the file, each given as a one-character string.

In[8]:= **ReadList["strings", Character]**

Out[8]= {H, e, r, e, , i, s, , t, e, x, t, ., ,
          , A, n, d, , m, o, r, e, , t, e, x, t, .,
          }

Here are the integer codes corresponding to each of the bytes in the file.

In[9]:= **ReadList["strings", Byte]**

Out[9]= {72, 101, 114, 101, 32, 105,
          115, 32, 116, 101, 120, 116, 46,
          32, 10, 65, 110, 100, 32, 109, 111, 114, 101,
          32, 116, 101, 120, 116, 46, 10}

This puts the data from each line in the file into a separate list.

In[10]:= **ReadList["strings", Byte, RecordLists -> True]**

Out[10]= {{72, 101, 114, 101, 32, 105,
           115, 32, 116, 101, 120, 116, 46, 32},
           {65, 110, 100, 32, 109, 111, 114,
           101, 32, 116, 101, 120, 116, 46}}

Byte	single byte of data, returned as an integer
Character	single character, returned as a one-character string
Real	approximate number in Fortran-like notation
Number	exact or approximate number in Fortran-like notation
Word	sequence of characters delimited by word separators
Record	sequence of characters delimited by record separators
String	string terminated by a newline
Expression	complete *Mathematica* expression
Hold[Expression]	complete *Mathematica* expression, returned inside Hold

Types of objects to read.

This returns a list of the "words" in the file strings.

In[11]:= **ReadList["strings", Word]**

Out[11]= {Here, is, text., And, more, text.}

ReadList allows you to read "words" from a file. It considers a "word" to be any sequence of characters delimited by word separators. You can set the option WordSeparators to specify the strings you want to treat as word separators. The default is to include spaces and tabs, but not to include, for example, standard punctuation characters. Note that in all cases successive words can be separated by any number of word separators. These separators are never taken to be part of the actual words returned by ReadList.

option name	default value	
RecordLists	False	whether to make a separate list for the objects in each record
RecordSeparators	{"\n"}	separators for records
WordSeparators	{" ", "\t"}	separators for words
NullRecords	False	whether to keep zero-length records
NullWords	False	whether to keep zero-length words
TokenWords	{}	words to take as tokens

Options for ReadList.

This reads the text in the file strings as a sequence of words, using the letter e and . as word separators.

In[12]:= **ReadList["strings", Word, WordSeparators -> {"e", "."}]**

Out[12]= {H, r, is t, xt, , And mor, t, xt}

Mathematica considers any data file to consist of a sequence of *records*. By default, each line is considered to be a separate record. In general, you can set the option RecordSeparators to give a list of separators for records. Note that words can never cross record separators. As with word separators, any number of record separators can exist between successive records, and these separators are not considered to be part of the records themselves.

By default, each line of the file is considered to be a record.

In[13]:= **ReadList["strings", Record] // InputForm**

Out[13]//InputForm= {"Here is text. ", "And more text."}

Here is a file containing three "sentences" ending with periods.

In[14]:= **!!sentences**

Here is text. And more.
And a second line.

This allows both periods and newlines as record separators.

In[15]:= **ReadList["sentences", Record,**
                    RecordSeparators -> {".", "\n"}]

Out[15]= {Here is text, And more, And a second line}

This puts the words in each "sentence" into a separate list.

```
In[16]:= ReadList["sentences", Word, RecordLists -> True,
                        RecordSeparators -> {".", "\n"}]
Out[16]= {{Here, is, text}, {And, more}, {And, a, second, line}}
```

```
ReadList["file", Record, RecordSeparators -> { }]
                read the whole of a file as a single string

ReadList["file", Record, RecordSeparators -> {{"lsep₁", ... }, {"rsep₁", ... }}]
                make a list of those parts of a file which lie between the lsepᵢ
                and the rsepᵢ
```

Settings for the RecordSeparators option.

Here is a file containing some text.

```
In[17]:= !!source

f[x] (: function f :)
g[x] (: function g :)
```

This reads all the text in the file source, and returns it as a single string.

```
In[18]:= InputForm[
                ReadList["source", Record, RecordSeparators -> { }]
                ]
Out[18]//InputForm=
        {"f[x] (: function f :)\ng[x] (: function g :)\n"}
```

This gives a list of the parts of the file that lie between (: and :) separators.

```
In[19]:= ReadList["source", Record,
                        RecordSeparators -> {{"(: "}, {" :)"}}]
Out[19]= {function f, function g}
```

By choosing appropriate separators, you can pick out specific parts of files.

```
In[20]:= ReadList[ "source", Record,
                RecordSeparators ->
                        {{"(: function ", "["}, {" :)", "]"}} ]
Out[20]= {x, f, x, g}
```

Mathematica usually allows any number of appropriate separators to appear between successive records or words. Sometimes, however, when several separators are present, you may want to assume that a "null record" or "null word" appears between each pair of adjacent separators. You can do this by setting the options NullRecords -> True or NullWords -> True.

Here is a file containing "words" separated by colons.

```
In[21]:= !!words

first:second::fourth:::seventh
```

Here the repeated colons are treated as single separators.

```
In[22]:= ReadList["words", Word, WordSeparators -> {":"}]
Out[22]= {first, second, fourth, seventh}
```

Now repeated colons are taken to have null words in between.

```
In[23]:= ReadList["words", Word, WordSeparators -> {":"},
                                NullWords -> True]
Out[23]= {first, second, , fourth, , , seventh}
```

In most cases, you want words to be delimited by separators which are not themselves considered as words. Sometimes, however, it is convenient to allow words to be delimited by special "token words", which are themselves words. You can give a list of such token words as a setting for the option `TokenWords`.

Here is some text.	*In[24]:=* **!!language**
	22*a*b+56*c+13*a*d
This reads the text, using the specified token words to delimit words in the text.	*In[25]:=* **ReadList["language", Word, TokenWords -> {"+", "*"}]**
	Out[25]= {22, *, a, *, b, +, 56, *, c, +, 13, *, a, *, d}

You can use `ReadList` to read *Mathematica* expressions from files. In general, each expression must end with a newline, although a single expression may go on for several lines.

Here is a file containing text that can be used as *Mathematica* input.	*In[26]:=* **!!exprs**
	x + y +
	z
	2^8
This reads the text in exprs as *Mathematica* expressions.	*In[27]:=* **ReadList["exprs", Expression]**
	Out[27]= {x + y + z, 256}
This prevents the expressions from being evaluated.	*In[28]:=* **ReadList["exprs", Hold[Expression]]**
	Out[28]= {Hold[x + y + z], Hold[2^8]}

`ReadList` can insert the objects it reads into any *Mathematica* expression. The second argument to `ReadList` can consist of any expression containing symbols such as `Number` and `Word` specifying objects to read. Thus, for example, `ReadList["file", {Number, Number}]` inserts successive pairs of numbers that it reads into lists. Similarly, `ReadList["file", Hold[Expression]]` puts expressions that it reads inside `Hold`.

If `ReadList` reaches the end of your file before it has finished reading a particular set of objects you have asked for, then it inserts the special symbol `EndOfFile` in place of the objects it has not yet read.

Here is a file of numbers.	*In[29]:=* **!!numbers**
	11.1 22.2 33.3
	44.4 55.5 66.6
The symbol EndOfFile appears in place of numbers that were needed after the end of the file was reached.	*In[30]:=* **ReadList["numbers", {Number, Number, Number, Number}]**
	Out[30]= {{11.1, 22.2, 33.3, 44.4},
	{55.5, 66.6, EndOfFile, EndOfFile}}

ReadList["!*command*", *type*]	execute a command, and read its output
ReadList[*stream*, *type*]	read any input stream

Reading from commands and streams.

This executes the Unix command date, and reads its output as a string.

In[31]:= **ReadList["!date", String]**

Out[31]= {Wed Mar 27 16:56:12 CST 1996}

OpenRead["*file*"]	open a file for reading
OpenRead["!*command*"]	open a pipe for reading
Read[*stream*, *type*]	read an object of the specified type from a stream
Skip[*stream*, *type*]	skip over an object of the specified type in an input stream
Skip[*stream*, *type*, *n*]	skip over *n* objects of the specified type in an input stream
Close[*stream*]	close an input stream

Functions for reading from input streams.

ReadList allows you to read *all* the data in a particular file or input stream. Sometimes, however, you want to get data a piece at a time, perhaps doing tests to find out what kind of data to expect next.

When you read individual pieces of data from a file, *Mathematica* always remembers the "current point" that you are at in the file. When you call OpenRead, *Mathematica* sets up an input stream from a file, and makes your current point the beginning of the file. Every time you read an object from the file using Read, *Mathematica* sets your current point to be just after the object you have read. Using Skip, you can advance the current point past a sequence of objects without actually reading the objects.

Here is a file of numbers.

In[32]:= **!!numbers**

```
11.1    22.2    33.3
44.4    55.5    66.6
```

This opens an input stream from the file.

In[33]:= **snum = OpenRead["numbers"]**

Out[33]= InputStream[numbers, 47]

This reads the first number from the file.

In[34]:= **Read[snum, Number]**

Out[34]= 11.1

This reads the second pair of numbers.

In[35]:= **Read[snum, {Number, Number}]**

Out[35]= {22.2, 33.3}

This skips the next number.

In[36]:= **Skip[snum, Number]**

And this reads the remaining numbers.

In[37]:= **ReadList[snum, Number]**

Out[37]= {55.5, 66.6}

This closes the input stream.

In[38]:= **Close[snum]**

Out[38]= numbers

This sets the stream position back.	*In[24]:=* **SetStreamPosition[stext, 5]**
	Out[24]= 5
Now Read returns the remainder of the first line.	*In[25]:=* **Read[stext, Record]**
	Out[25]= is the first line of text.
This closes the stream.	*In[26]:=* **Close[stext]**
	Out[26]= textfile

■ 2.11.9 Searching and Reading Strings

Functions like Read and Find are most often used for processing text and data from external files. In some cases, however, you may find it convenient to use these same functions to process strings within *Mathematica*. You can do this by using the function StringToStream, which opens an input stream that takes characters not from an external file, but instead from a *Mathematica* string.

StringToStream["*string*"]	open an input stream for reading from a string
Close[*stream*]	close an input stream

Treating strings as input streams.

This opens an input stream for reading from the string.	*In[1]:=* **str = StringToStream["A string of words."]**
	Out[1]= InputStream[String, 5]
This reads the first "word" from the string.	*In[2]:=* **Read[str, Word]**
	Out[2]= A
This reads the remaining words from the string.	*In[3]:=* **ReadList[str, Word]**
	Out[3]= {string, of, words.}
This closes the input stream.	*In[4]:=* **Close[str]**
	Out[4]= String

Input streams associated with strings work just like those with files. At any given time, there is a current position in the stream, which advances when you use functions like Read. The current position is given as the number of bytes from the beginning of the string by the function StreamPosition[*stream*]. You can explicitly set the current position using SetStreamPosition[*stream*, *n*].

Here is an input stream associated with a string.	*In[5]:=* **str = StringToStream["123 456 789"]**
	Out[5]= InputStream[String, 10]
The current position is initially 0 bytes from the beginning of the string.	*In[6]:=* **StreamPosition[str]**
	Out[6]= 0

This reads a number from the stream.	*In[7]:=* **Read[str, Number]** *Out[7]=* 123
The current position is now 3 bytes from the beginning of the string.	*In[8]:=* **StreamPosition[str]** *Out[8]=* 3
This sets the current position to be 1 byte from the beginning of the string.	*In[9]:=* **SetStreamPosition[str, 1]** *Out[9]=* 1
If you now read a number from the string, you get the 23 part of 123.	*In[10]:=* **Read[str, Number]** *Out[10]=* 23
This sets the current position to the end of the string.	*In[11]:=* **SetStreamPosition[str, Infinity]** *Out[11]=* 11
If you now try to read from the stream, you will always get EndOfFile.	*In[12]:=* **Read[str, Number]** *Out[12]=* EndOfFile
This closes the stream.	*In[13]:=* **Close[str]** *Out[13]=* String

Particularly when you are processing large volumes of textual data, it is common to read fairly long strings into *Mathematica*, then to use **StringToStream** to allow further processing of these strings within *Mathematica*. Once you have created an input stream using **StringToStream**, you can read and search the string using any of the functions discussed for files above.

This puts the whole contents of textfile into a string.	*In[14]:=* **s = First[ReadList["textfile", Record,**
	                             RecordSeparators -> {}]]
	Out[14]= Here is the first line of text.
	            And the second.
	            And the third. Here is the end.

This opens an input stream for the string.	*In[15]:=* **str = StringToStream[s]** *Out[15]=* InputStream[String, 22]
This gives the lines of text in the string that contain is.	*In[16]:=* **FindList[str, "is"]** *Out[16]=* {Here is the first line of text., And the third. Here is the end.}
This resets the current position back to the beginning of the string.	*In[17]:=* **SetStreamPosition[str, 0]** *Out[17]=* 0
This finds the first occurrence of the in the string, and leaves the current point just after it.	*In[18]:=* **Find[str, "the", RecordSeparators -> {" "}]** *Out[18]=* the

This reads the "word" which appears immediately after the.

In[19]:= **Read[str, Word]**

Out[19]= first

This closes the input stream.

In[20]:= **Close[str]**

Out[20]= String

2.12 *MathLink* and External Program Communication

+■ **2.12.1 How** *MathLink* **Is Used**

Most of this book has been concerned with how human users interact with *Mathematica*. *MathLink* provides a mechanism through which *programs* rather than human users can interact with *Mathematica*.

- Calling functions in an external program from within *Mathematica*.

- Calling *Mathematica* from within an external program.

- Setting up alternative front ends to *Mathematica*.

- Exchanging data between *Mathematica* and external programs.

- Exchanging data between concurrent *Mathematica* processes.

Some typical uses of *MathLink*.

MathLink provides a general interface for external programs to communicate with *Mathematica*. Many standard software systems now have *MathLink* compatibility either built in or available in add-on modules.

In addition, the *MathLink* Developer's Kit bundled with most versions of *Mathematica* provides the tools you need to create your own *MathLink*-compatible programs.

Once you have a *MathLink*-compatible program, you can transparently establish a link between it and *Mathematica*.

The link can either be on a single computer, or it can be over a network, potentially with a different type of computer at each end.

- Implementing inner loops in a low-level language.

- Handling large volumes of data external to *Mathematica*.

- Sending *Mathematica* graphics or other data for special processing.

- Connecting to a system with an existing user interface.

A few uses of *MathLink*-compatible programs.

MathLink-compatible programs range from very simple to very complex. A minimal *MathLink*-compatible program is just a few lines long. But it is also possible to build very large and sophisticated *MathLink*-compatible programs. Indeed, the *Mathematica* notebook front end is one example of a sophisticated *MathLink*-compatible program.

■ *MathLink* is a mechanism for exchanging *Mathematica* expressions between programs.

The basic idea of *MathLink*.

Much of the power of *MathLink* comes from its use of *Mathematica* expressions. The basic idea is that *MathLink* provides a way to exchange *Mathematica* expressions between programs, and such expressions can represent absolutely any kind of data.

■ An array of numbers.

■ A collection of geometrical objects.

■ A sequence of commands.

■ A stream of text.

■ Records in a database.

■ The cells of a *Mathematica* notebook.

A few examples of data represented by *Mathematica* expressions in *MathLink*.

The *MathLink* library consists of a collection of routines that allow external programs to send and receive *Mathematica* expressions.

The *MathLink* Developer's Kit provides utilities for incorporating these routines into external programs. The utilities are primarily intended for programs written in the C programming language, although by adding the appropriate links to the *MathLink* library it is possible to make any program *MathLink* compatible.

An important feature of the *MathLink* library is that it is completely platform independent: it can transparently use any interprogram communication mechanism that exists on your computer system.

■ 2.12.2 Installing Existing *MathLink*-Compatible Programs

One of the most common uses of *MathLink* is to allow you to call functions in an external program from within *Mathematica*. Once the external program has been set up, all you need do to be able to use it is to "install" it in your current *Mathematica* session.

`Install["`*prog*`"]`	install a *MathLink*-compatible external program
`Uninstall[`*link*`]`	uninstall the program

Setting up external programs with functions to be called from within *Mathematica*.

This installs a *MathLink*-compatible external program called `bitprog`.	`In[1]:= Install["bitprog"]` `Out[1]= LinkObject[bitprog, 4, 4]`
`BitAnd` is one of the functions inside `bitprog`.	`In[2]:= BitAnd[65535, 2047]` `Out[2]= 2047`
You can use it just as you would a function within *Mathematica*.	`In[3]:= Table[BitAnd[65535, i], {i, 2046, 2049}]` `Out[3]= {2046, 2047, 2048, 2049}`

When you have a package written in the *Mathematica* language a single version will run unchanged on any computer system. But external programs typically need to be compiled separately for every different type of computer.

Mathematica has a convention of keeping versions of external programs in directories that are named after the types of computers on which they will run. And assuming that this convention has been followed, `Install["`*prog*`"]` should always install the version of *prog* appropriate for the particular kind of computer that you are currently using.

`Install["`*name*``'``"]`	install a program found anywhere on `$Path`

Using context names to specify programs to install.

When you ask to read in a *Mathematica* language file using `<<`*name*``'``, *Mathematica* will automatically search all directories in the list `$Path` in order to find a file with the appropriate name. Similarly, if you use `Install["`*name*``'``"]` *Mathematica* will automatically search all directories in `$Path` in order to find an external program with the name *name*`.exe`. `Install["`*name*``'``"]` allows you to install programs that are stored in a central directory without explicitly having to specify their location.

■ 2.12.3 Setting Up External Functions to Be Called from *Mathematica*

If you have a function defined in an external program, then what you need to do in order to make it possible to call the function from within *Mathematica* is to add appropriate *MathLink* code that passes arguments to the function, and takes back the results it produces.

In simple cases, you can generate the necessary code just by giving an appropriate *MathLink template* for each external function.

```
:Begin:
:Function:      f
:Pattern:       f[x_Integer, y_Integer]
:Arguments:     {x, y}
:ArgumentTypes: {Integer, Integer}
:ReturnType:    Integer
:End:
```

A file `f.tm` containing a *MathLink* template for an external function `f`.

`:Begin:`	begin the template for a particular function
`:Function:`	the name of the function in the external program
`:Pattern:`	the pattern to be defined to call the function
`:Arguments:`	the arguments to the function
`:ArgumentTypes:`	the types of the arguments to the function
`:ReturnType:`	the type of the value returned by the function
`:End:`	end the template for a particular function
`:Evaluate:`	*Mathematica* input to evaluate when the function is installed

The elements of a *MathLink* template.

Once you have constructed a *MathLink* template for a particular external function, you have to combine this template with the actual source code for the function. Assuming that the source code is written in the C programming language, you can do this just by adding a line to include the standard *MathLink* header file, and then inserting a small `main` program.

Include the standard *MathLink* header file.	`#include "mathlink.h"`

Here is the actual source code for the function `f`.	`int f(int x, int y) {`
	`    return x+y;`
	`}`

This sets up the external program to be ready to take requests from *Mathematica*.	`int main(int argc, char *argv[]) {`
	`    return MLMain(argc, argv);`
	`}`

A file `f.c` containing C source code.

Note that the form of `main` required on different systems may be slightly different. The release notes included in the *MathLink* Developer's Kit on your particular computer system should give the appropriate form.

`mcc`	preprocess and compile *MathLink* source files
`mprep`	preprocess *MathLink* source files

Typical external programs for processing *MathLink* source files.

MathLink templates are conventionally put in files with names of the form *file*`.tm`. Such files can also contain C source code, interspersed between templates for different functions.

Once you have set up the appropriate files, you then need to process the *MathLink* template information, and compile all of your source code. Typically you do this by running various external programs, but the details will depend on your computer system.

Under Unix, for example, the *MathLink Developer's Kit* includes a program named `mcc` which will preprocess *MathLink* templates in any file whose name ends with `.tm`, and then call `cc` on the resulting C source code. `mcc` will pass command-line options and other files directly to `cc`.

This preprocesses `f.tm`, then compiles the resulting C source file.	`mcc -o f.exe f.tm`

This installs the binary in the current *Mathematica* session.	`In[1]:= Install["f.exe"]`
	`Out[1]= LinkObject[f.exe, 4, 4]`
Now `f[x, y]` calls the external function `f(int x, int y)` and adds two integers together.	`In[2]:= f[6, 9]`
	`Out[2]= 15`
The external program handles only machine integers, so this gives a peculiar result.	`In[3]:= f[2^31-1, 5]`
	`Out[3]= -2147483644`

On systems other than Unix, the *MathLink Developer's Kit* typically includes a program named `mprep`, which you have to call directly, giving as input all of the `.tm` files that you want to preprocess. `mprep` will generate C source code as output, which you can then feed to a C compiler.

Install["*prog*"]	install an external program
Uninstall[*link*]	uninstall an external program
Links["*prog*"]	show active links associated with "*prog*"
Links[ ]	show all active links
LinkPatterns[*link*]	show patterns that can be evaluated on a particular link

Handling links to external programs.

This finds the link to the f.exe program.

```
In[4]:= Links["f.exe"]
Out[4]= {LinkObject[./f.exe, 4, 4]}
```

This shows the *Mathematica* patterns that can be evaluated using the link.

```
In[5]:= LinkPatterns[%[[1]]]
Out[5]= {f[x_Integer, y_Integer]}
```

Install sets up the actual function f to execute an appropriate ExternalCall function.

```
In[6]:= ?f
Global`f

f[x_Integer, y_Integer] :=
    ExternalCall[LinkObject["./f.exe", 4, 4],
      CallPacket[0, {x, y}]]
```

When a *MathLink* template file is processed, two basic things are done. First, the :Pattern: and :Arguments: specifications are used to generate a *Mathematica* definition that calls an external function via *MathLink*. And second, the :Function:, :ArgumentTypes: and :ReturnType: specifications are used to generate C source code that calls your function within the external program.

	:Begin:	
This gives the name of the actual C function to call in the external program.	:Function:	prog_add
This gives the *Mathematica* pattern for which a definition should be set up.	:Pattern:	SkewAdd[x_Integer, y_Integer:1]
The values of the two list elements are the actual arguments to be passed to the external function.	:Arguments:	{x, If[x > 1, y, y + x - 2]}
This specifies that the arguments should be passed as integers to the C function.	:ArgumentTypes:	{Integer, Integer}
This specifies that the return value from the C function will be an integer.	:ReturnType:	Integer
	:End:	

Both the :Pattern: and :Arguments: specifications in a *MathLink* template can be any *Mathematica* expressions. Whatever you give as the :Arguments: specification will be evaluated every time you call the external function. The result of the evaluation will be used as the list of arguments to pass to the function.

Sometimes you may want to set up *Mathematica* expressions that should be evaluated not when an external function is called, but instead only when the external function is first installed.

You can do this by inserting :Evaluate: specifications in your *MathLink* template. The expression you give after :Evaluate: can go on for several lines: it is assumed to end when there is first a blank line, or a line that does not begin with spaces or tabs.

This specifies that a usage message for SkewAdd should be set up when the external program is installed.	`:Evaluate:    SkewAdd::usage = "SkewAdd[x, y] performs` `              a skew addition in an external program."`

When an external program is installed, the specifications in its *MathLink* template file are used in the order they were given. This means that any expressions given in :Evaluate: specifications that appear before :Begin: will have been evaluated before definitions for the external function are set up.

Here are *Mathematica* expressions to be evaluated before the definitions for external functions are set up.	`:Evaluate:    BeginPackage["XPack`"]` `:Evaluate: XF1::usage = "XF1[x, y] is one external function."` `:Evaluate: XF2::usage = "XF2[x] is another external function."` `:Evaluate: Begin["`Private`"]`

This specifies that the function XF1 in *Mathematica* should be set up to call the function f in the external C program.	`:Begin:`
	`:Function:       f`
	`:Pattern:        XF1[x_Integer, y_Integer]`
	`:Arguments:      {x, y}`
	`:ArgumentTypes:  {Integer, Integer}`
	`:ReturnType:     Integer`
	`:End:`

This specifies that XF2 in *Mathematica* should call g. Its argument and return value are taken to be approximate real numbers.	`:Begin:`
	`:Function:       g`
	`:Pattern:        XF2[x_?NumberQ]`
	`:Arguments:      {x}`
	`:ArgumentTypes:  {Real}`
	`:ReturnType:     Real`
	`:End:`

These *Mathematica* expressions are evaluated after the definitions for the external functions. They end the special context used for the definitions.	`:Evaluate:    End[ ]` `:Evaluate:    EndPackage[ ]`

Here is the actual source code for the function f. There is no need for the arguments of this function to have the same names as their *Mathematica* counterparts.	`int f(int i, int j) {`
	`    return i + j;`
	`}`

Here is the actual source code for g. Numbers that you give in *Mathematica* will automatically be converted into C double types before being passed to g.	`double g(double x) {`
	`    return x*x;`
	`}`

By using :Evaluate: specifications, you can evaluate *Mathematica* expressions when an external program is first installed. You can also execute code inside the external program at this time simply by inserting the code in main() before the call to MLMain(). This is sometimes useful if you need to initialize the external program before any functions in it are used.

`MLEvaluateString(stdlink, "string")`	evaluate a string as *Mathematica* input

Executing a command in *Mathematica* from within an external program.

This evaluates a *Mathematica* Print function if i < j.	`int diff(int i, int j) {`
	
	`    if (i < j) MLEvaluateString(stdlink, "Print[\"negative\"]");`
	
	`    return i - j;`
	`}`

This installs an external program containing the diff function defined above.	*In[7]:=* **Install["diffprog"]** *Out[7]=* LinkObject[diffprog, 5, 5]
Calling diff causes Print to be executed.	*In[8]:=* **diff[4, 7]** negative *Out[8]=* -3

Note that any results generated in the evaluation requested by MLEvaluateString() are ignored. To make use of such results requires full two-way communication between *Mathematica* and external programs, as discussed on page 660.

+■ 2.12.4 Handling Lists, Arrays and Other Expressions

MathLink allows you to exchange data of any type with external programs. For more common types of data, you simply need to give appropriate :ArgumentTypes: or :ReturnType: specifications in your *MathLink* template file.

Mathematica specification		C specification
Integer	integer	int
Real	floating-point number	double
IntegerList	list of integers	int *, long
RealList	list of floating-point numbers	double *, long
String	character string	char *
Symbol	symbol name	char *
Manual	call *MathLink* routines directly	void

Basic type specifications.

| Here is the *MathLink* template for a function that takes a list of integers as its argument. | ```
:Begin:
:Function:      h
:Pattern:       h[a_List]
:Arguments:     {a}
:ArgumentTypes: {IntegerList}
:ReturnType:    Integer
:End:
``` |
| Here is the C source code for the function. Note the extra argument alen which is used to pass the length of the list. | ```
int h(int *a, long alen) {

    int i, tot=0;

    for(i=0; i<alen; i++)
       tot += a[i];

    return tot;
}
``` |

This installs an external program containing the specifications for the function h.	*In[1]:=* **Install["hprog"]** *Out[1]=* LinkObject[hprog, 4, 4]

`MLPutIntegerArray()` and `MLPutRealArray()` allow you to send arrays which are laid out in memory in the one-dimensional way that C pre-allocates them. But if you create arrays during the execution of a C program, it is more common to set them up as nested collections of pointers. You can send such arrays to *Mathematica* by using a sequence of `MLPutFunction()` calls, ending with an `MLPutIntegerList()` call.

	`. . .`
This declares a to be a nested list of lists of lists of integers.	`int ***a;`
	`. . .`
This creates a *Mathematica* list with n1 elements.	`MLPutFunction(stdlink, "List", n1);`
	`for (i=0; i<n1; i++) {`
This creates a sublist with n2 elements.	`    MLPutFunction(stdlink, "List", n2);`
	`    for (j=0; j<n2; j++) {`
This writes out lists of integers.	`        MLPutIntegerList(stdlink, a[i][j], n3);`
	`    }`
	`}`
	`. . .`

It is important to realize that any expression you create using *MathLink* functions will be evaluated as soon as it is sent to *Mathematica*. This means, for example, that if you wanted to transpose an array that you were sending back to *Mathematica*, all you would need to do is to wrap a `Transpose` around the expression representing the array. You can then do this simply by calling `MLPutFunction(stdlink, "Transpose", 1);` just before you start creating the expression that represents the array.

The idea of post-processing data that you send back to *Mathematica* has many uses. One example is as a way of sending lists whose length you do not know in advance.

This creates a list in *Mathematica* by explicitly appending successive elements.	`In[7]:= t = {}; Do[t = Append[t, i^2], {i, 5}]; t` `Out[7]= {1, 4, 9, 16, 25}`
This creates a list in which each successive element is in a nested sublist.	`In[8]:= t = {}; Do[t = {t, i^2}, {i, 5}]; t` `Out[8]= {{{{{{}, 1}, 4}, 9}, 16}, 25}`
Flatten flattens out the list.	`In[9]:= Flatten[t]` `Out[9]= {1, 4, 9, 16, 25}`

Sequence automatically flattens itself.	*In[10]:=* **{Sequence[1, Sequence[4, Sequence[ ]]]}** *Out[10]=* {1, 4}

In order to call `MLPutIntegerList()`, you need to know the length of the list you want to send. But by creating a sequence of nested `Sequence` objects, you can avoid having to know the length of your whole list in advance.

This sets up the List around your result.	`MLPutFunction(stdlink, "List", 1);`
	`while(`*condition*`) {` *generate an element*
Create the next level Sequence object.	`MLPutFunction(stdlink, "Sequence", 2);`
Put the element.	`MLPutInteger(stdlink, `*i*`);`
	`}`
This closes off your last Sequence object.	`MLPutFunction(stdlink, "Sequence", 0);`

`MLGetInteger(stdlink, int *`*i*`)`	get an integer, storing it at address *i*
`MLGetReal(stdlink, double *`*x*`)`	get a floating-point number, storing it at address *x*

Basic functions for explicitly getting data from *Mathematica*.

Just as *MathLink* provides functions like `MLPutInteger()` to send data from an external program into *Mathematica*, so also *MathLink* provides functions like `MLGetInteger()` that allow you to get data from *Mathematica* into an external program.

The list that you give for `:ArgumentTypes:` in a *MathLink* template can end with `Manual`, indicating that after other arguments have been received, you will call *MathLink* functions to get additional expressions.

	`:Begin:`
	`:Function:` `f`
The function f in *Mathematica* takes 3 arguments.	`:Pattern:` `f[i_Integer, x_Real, y_Real]`
All these arguments are passed directly to the external program.	`:Arguments:` `{i, x, y}`
Only the first argument is sent directly to the external function.	`:ArgumentTypes:` `{Integer, Manual}`
	`:ReturnType:` `Real`
	`:End:`
The external function only takes one explicit argument.	`double f(int i) {`
This declares the variables x and y.	`    double x, y;`
MLGetReal() explicitly gets data from the link.	`    MLGetReal(stdlink, &x);`
	`    MLGetReal(stdlink, &y);`
	`    return i+x+y;`
	`}`

MathLink functions such as `MLGetInteger`(*link*, *pi*) work much like standard C library functions such as `fscanf`(*fp*, `"%d"`, *pi*). The first argument specifies the link from which to get data. The last argument gives the address at which the data that is obtained should be stored.

> `MLCheckFunction(stdlink, "`*name*`", long *`*n*`)`
> check the head of a function and store how many arguments it has

Getting a function via *MathLink*.

	`:Begin:`	
	`:Function:`	`f`
The function `f` in *Mathematica* takes a list of integers as an argument.	`:Pattern:`	`f[a:{___Integer}]`
The list is passed directly to the external program.	`:Arguments:`	`{a}`
The argument is to be retrieved manually by the external program.	`:ArgumentTypes:`	`{Manual}`
	`:ReturnType:`	`Integer`
	`:End:`	

```
The external function takes no explicit      int f(void) {
arguments.

This declares local variables.                  long n, i;
                                                int a[MAX];

This checks that the function being             MLCheckFunction(stdlink, "List", &n);
sent is a list, and stores how many
elements it has in n.

This gets each element in the list,          for (i=0; i<n; i++)
storing it in a[i].                              MLGetInteger(stdlink, a+i);

                                             ...
                                             }
```

In simple cases, it is usually possible to ensure on the *Mathematica* side that the data you send to an external program has the structure that is expected. But in general the return value from `MLCheckFunction()` will be non-zero only if the data consists of a function with the name you specify.

Note that if you want to get a nested collection of lists or other objects, you can do this by making an appropriate sequence of calls to `MLCheckFunction()`.

```
MLGetIntegerList(stdlink, int **a, long *n)
                get a list of integers, allocating the memory needed to
                store it
MLGetRealList(stdlink, double **a, long *n)
                get a list of floating-point numbers
```

```
MLDisownIntegerList(stdlink, int *a, long n)
                disown the memory associated with a list of integers
MLDisownRealList(stdlink, double *a, long n)
                disown the memory associated with a list of floating-point
                numbers
```

Getting lists of numbers.

When an external program gets data from *Mathematica*, it must set up a place to store the data. If the data consists of a single integer, as in MLGetInteger(stdlink, &n), then it suffices just to have declared this integer using int n.

But when the data consists of a list of integers of potentially any length, memory must be allocated to store this list at the time when the external program is actually called.

MLGetIntegerList(stdlink, &a, &n) will automatically do this allocation, setting a to be a pointer to the result. Note that memory allocated by functions like MLGetIntegerList() is always in a special reserved area, so you cannot modify or free it directly.

Here is an external program that will be sent a list of integers.	`int f(void) {`
This declares local variables. a is an array of integers.	`long n;` `int *a;`
This gets a list of integers, making a be a pointer to the result.	`MLGetIntegerList(stdlink, &a, &n);`
	`...`
This disowns the memory used to store the list of integers.	`MLDisownIntegerList(stdlink, a, n);`
	`...` `}`

If you use IntegerList as an :ArgumentTypes: specification, then *MathLink* will automatically disown the memory used for the list after your external function exits. But if you get a list of integers explicitly using `MLGetIntegerList()`, then you must not forget to disown the memory used to store the list after you have finished with it.

`MLGetIntegerArray(stdlink, int **`*a*`, long **`*dims*`, char ***`*heads*`, long *`*d*`)`
get an array of integers of any depth

`MLGetRealArray(stdlink, double **`*a*`, long **`*dims*`, char ***`*heads*`, long *`*d*`)`
get an array of floating-point numbers of any depth

`MLDisownIntegerArray(stdlink, int *`*a*`, long *`*dims*`, char **`*heads*`, long `*d*`)`
disown memory associated with an integer array

`MLDisownRealArray(stdlink, double *`*a*`, long *`*dims*`, char **`*heads*`, long `*d*`)`
disown memory associated with a floating-point array

Getting arrays of numbers.

`MLGetIntegerList()` extracts a one-dimensional array of integers from a single *Mathematica* list. `MLGetIntegerArray()` extracts an array of integers from a collection of lists or other *Mathematica* functions nested to any depth.

The name of the *Mathematica* function at level i in the structure is stored as a string in *heads*[i]. The size of the structure at level i is stored in *dims*[i], while the total depth is stored in d.

If you pass a list of complex numbers to your external program, then `MLGetRealArray()` will create a two-dimensional array containing a sequence of pairs of real and imaginary parts. In this case, *heads*[0] will be "List" while *heads*[1] will be "Complex".

Note that you can conveniently exchange arbitrary-precision numbers with external programs by converting them to lists of digits in *Mathematica* using `IntegerDigits` and `RealDigits`.

`MLGetString(stdlink, char **`*s*`)`   get a character string

`MLGetSymbol(stdlink, char **`*s*`)`   get a symbol name

`MLDisownString(stdlink, char *`*s*`)`   disown memory associated with a character string

`MLDisownSymbol(stdlink, char *`*s*`)`   disown memory associated with a symbol name

Getting character strings and symbol names.

If you use `String` as an `:ArgumentTypes:` specification, then *MathLink* will automatically disown the memory that is used to store the string after your function exits. This means that if you want to continue to refer to the string, you must allocate memory for it, and explicitly copy each character in it.

If you get a string using `MLGetString()`, however, then *MathLink* will not automatically disown the memory used for the string when your function exits. As a result, you can continue referring to the string. When you no longer need the string, you must nevertheless explicitly call `MLDisownString()` in order to disown the memory associated with it.

`MLGetFunction(stdlink, char **s, long *n)`	begin getting a function, storing the name of the head in s and the number of arguments in *n*
`MLDisownSymbol(stdlink, char *s)`	disown memory associated with a function name

Getting an arbitrary function.

If you know what function to expect in your external program, then it is usually simpler to call `MLCheckFunction()`. But if you do not know what function to expect, you have no choice but to call `MLGetFunction()`. If you do this, you need to be sure to call `MLDisownSymbol()` to disown the memory associated with the name of the function that is found by `MLGetFunction()`.

◼ 2.12.5 Special Topic: Portability of *MathLink* Programs

The *Mathematica* side of a *MathLink* connection is set up to work exactly the same on all computer systems. But inevitably there are differences between external programs on different computer systems.

For a start, different computer systems almost always require different executable binaries. When you call `Install["prog"]`, therefore, you must be sure that *prog* corresponds to a program that can be executed on your particular computer system.

`Install["file"]`	try to execute *file* directly
`Install["file", LinkProtocol->"type"]`	use the specified protocol for low-level data transport
`$SystemID`	identify the type of computer system being used
`Install["dir"]`	try to execute a file with a name of the form *dir*/`$SystemID`/*dir*

Installing programs on different computer systems.

Mathematica follows the convention that if *prog* is an ordinary file, then `Install["`*prog*`"]` will just try to execute it. But if *prog* is a directory, then *Mathematica* will look for a subdirectory of that directory whose name agrees with the current value of `$SystemID`, and will then try to execute a file named *prog* within that subdirectory.

`mcc -o` *prog* ...	put compiled code in the file *prog* in the current directory
`mcc -xo` *prog* ...	put compiled code in *prog*/`$SystemID`/*prog*

Typical Unix commands for compiling external programs.

Even though the executable binary of an external program is inevitably different on different computer systems, it can still be the case that the source code in a language such as C from which this binary is obtained can be essentially the same.

But to achieve portability in your C source code there are several points that you need to watch.

For a start, you should never make use of extra features of the C language or C run-time libraries that happen to be provided on a particular system, but are not part of standard C. In addition, you should try to avoid dealing with segmented or otherwise special memory models.

The include file `mathlink.h` contains standard C prototypes for all the functions in the *MathLink* library. If your compiler does not support such prototypes, you can ignore them by giving the directive `#define MLPROTOTYPES 0` before `#include "mathlink.h"`. But assuming that it does support prototypes, your compiler will always be able to check that the calls you make to functions in the *MathLink* library have arguments of appropriate types.

MLPutInteger()	MLGetInteger()	default integer of type `int`; sometimes 16 bits, sometimes 32 bits
MLPutShortInteger()	MLGetShortInteger()	short integer of type `short`; usually 16 bits
MLPutLongInteger()	MLGetLongInteger()	long integer of type `long`; usually 32 bits
MLPutReal()	MLGetReal()	default real number of type `double`; usually at least 64 bits
MLPutFloat()	MLGetFloat()	single-precision floating-point number of type `float`; often 32 bits
MLPutDouble()	MLGetDouble()	double-precision floating-point number of type `double`; usually at least 64 bits

MathLink functions that use specific C types.

On some computer systems and with some compilers, a C language `int` may be equivalent to a `long`. But the standard for the C language equally well allows `int` to be equivalent to `short`. And if you are going to call *MathLink* library functions in a portable way, it is essential that you use the same types as they do.

Once you have passed your data into the *MathLink* library functions, these functions then take care of all further issues associated with differences between data representations on different computer systems. Thus, for example, *MathLink* automatically swaps bytes when it sends data between big and little endian machines, and converts floating-point formats losing as little precision as possible.

```
MLPutString(stdlink, char *s)     put a string without special characters

MLPutUnicodeString(stdlink, unsigned short *s, long n)
                            put a string encoded in terms of 16-bit Unicode characters

MLPutByteString(stdlink, unsigned char *s, long n)
                            put a string containing only 8-bit character codes
```

```
MLGetString(stdlink, char **s)     get a string without special characters

MLGetUnicodeString(stdlink, unsigned short **s, long *n)
                            get a string encoded in terms of 16-bit Unicode characters

MLGetByteString(stdlink, unsigned char **s, long *n, long spec)
                            get a string containing only 8-bit character codes, using
                            spec as the code for all 16-bit characters
```

Manipulating general strings.

In simple C programs, it is typical to use strings that contain only ordinary ASCII characters. But in *Mathematica* it is possible to have strings containing all sorts of special characters. These characters are specified within *Mathematica* using Unicode character codes, as discussed on page 399.

C language `char *` strings typically use only 8 bits to store the code for each character. Unicode character codes, however, require 16 bits. As a result, the functions `MLPutUnicodeString()` and `MLGetUnicodeString()` work with arrays of `unsigned short` integers.

If you know that your program will not have to handle special characters, then you may find it convenient to use `MLPutByteString()` and `MLGetByteString()`. These functions represent all characters directly using 8-bit character codes. If a special character is sent from *Mathematica*, then it will be converted by `MLGetByteString()` to a fixed code that you specify.

■ `main()` may need to be different on different computer systems

A point to watch in creating portable *MathLink* programs.

Computer systems and compilers that have C run-time libraries based on the Unix model allow *MathLink* programs to have a main program of the form `main(argc, argv)` which simply calls `MLMain(argc, argv)`.

Some computer systems or compilers may however require main programs of a different form. You should realize that you can do whatever initialization you want inside `main()` before calling `MLMain()`. Once you have called `MLMain()`, however, your program will effectively go into an infinite loop, responding to requests from *Mathematica* until the link to it is closed.

⁺■ 2.12.6 Using *MathLink* to Communicate between *Mathematica* Sessions

LinkCreate["*name*"]	create a link for another program to connect to
LinkConnect["*name*"]	connect to a link created by another program
LinkClose[*link*]	close a *MathLink* connection
LinkWrite[*link, expr*]	write an expression to a *MathLink* connection
LinkRead[*link*]	read an expression from a *MathLink* connection
LinkRead[*link*, Hold]	read an expression and immediately wrap it with Hold
LinkReadyQ[*link*]	find out whether there is data ready to be read from a link

MathLink connections between *Mathematica* sessions.

<table>
<tr><td>This starts up a link on port number 5000.</td><td>Session A

In[1]:= link = LinkCreate["5000"]

Out[1]= LinkObject[5000@frog.wolfram.com, 4, 4]</td></tr>
<tr><td>This connects to the link on port 5000.</td><td>Session B

In[1]:= link = LinkConnect["5000"]

Out[1]= LinkObject[5000@frog.wolfram.com, 4, 4]</td></tr>
<tr><td>This evaluates 15! and writes it to the link.</td><td>Session A

In[2]:= LinkWrite[link, 15!]</td></tr>
<tr><td>This reads from the link, getting the 15! that was sent.</td><td>Session B

In[2]:= LinkRead[link]

Out[2]= 1307674368000</td></tr>
<tr><td>This writes data back on the link.</td><td>*In[3]:=* LinkWrite[link, N[%^6]]</td></tr>
<tr><td>And this reads the data written in session B.</td><td>Session A

In[3]:= LinkRead[link]

Out[3]= 5.00032×10^{72}</td></tr>
</table>

One use of *MathLink* connections between *Mathematica* sessions is simply as a way to transfer data without using intermediate files.

Another use is as a way to dispatch different parts of a computation to different sessions.

Session A

This writes the expression 2 + 2 without evaluating it.

```
In[4]:= LinkWrite[link, Unevaluated[2 + 2]]
```

Session B

This reads the expression from the link, immediately wrapping it in Hold.

```
In[4]:= LinkRead[link, Hold]
Out[4]= Hold[2 + 2]
```

This evaluates the expression.

```
In[5]:= ReleaseHold[%]
Out[5]= 4
```

When you call LinkWrite, it writes an expression to the *MathLink* connection and immediately returns. But when you call LinkRead, it will not return until it has read a complete expression from the *MathLink* connection.

You can tell whether anything is ready to be read by calling LinkReadyQ[*link*]. If LinkReadyQ returns True, then you can safely call LinkRead and expect immediately to start reading an expression. But if LinkReadyQ returns False, then LinkRead would block until an expression for it to read had been written by a LinkWrite in your other *Mathematica* session.

Session A

There is nothing waiting to be read on the link, so if LinkRead were to be called, it would block.

```
In[5]:= LinkReadyQ[link]
Out[5]= False
```

Session B

This writes an expression to the link.

```
In[6]:= LinkWrite[link, x + y]
```

Session A

Now there is an expression waiting to be read on the link.

```
In[6]:= LinkReadyQ[link]
Out[6]= True
```

LinkRead can thus be called without fear of blocking.

```
In[7]:= LinkRead[link]
Out[7]= x + y
```

LinkCreate[ ]	pick any unused port on your computer
LinkCreate["*number*"]	use a specific port
LinkConnect["*number*"]	connect to a port on the same computer
LinkConnect["*number@host*"]	connect a port on another computer

Ways to set up *MathLink* links.

MathLink can use whatever mechanism for interprogram communication your computer system supports. In setting up connections between concurrent *Mathematica* sessions, the most common mechanism is internet TCP ports.

Most computer systems have a few thousand possible numbered ports, some of which are typically allocated to standard system services.

You can use any of the unallocated ports for *MathLink* connections.

	Session on frog.wolfram.com
This finds an unallocated port on frog.wolfram.com.	*In[8]:=* **link = LinkCreate[ ]**
	Out[8]= LinkObject[2981@frog.wolfram.com, 5, 5]

	Session on toad.wolfram.com
This connects to the port on frog.wolfram.com.	*In[7]:=* **link = LinkConnect["2981@frog.wolfram.com"]**
	Out[7]= LinkObject[2981@frog.wolfram.com, 5, 5]
This sends the current machine name over the link.	*In[8]:=* **LinkWrite[link, $MachineName]**

	Session on frog.wolfram.com
This reads the expression written on toad.	*In[9]:=* **LinkRead[link]**
	Out[9]= toad

By using internet ports for *MathLink* connections, you can easily transfer data between *Mathematica* sessions on different machines. All that is needed is that an internet connection exists between the machines.

Note that because *MathLink* is completely system independent, the computers at each end of a *MathLink* connection do not have to be of the same type. *MathLink* nevertheless notices when they are, and optimizes data transmission in this case.

+■ 2.12.7 Calling Subsidiary *Mathematica* Processes

LinkLaunch["*prog*"]	start an external program and open a connection to it

Connecting to a subsidiary program via *MathLink*.

This starts a subsidiary *Mathematica* process on the computer system used here.	`In[1]:= link = LinkLaunch["math -mathlink"]` `Out[1]= LinkObject[math -mathlink, 4, 4]`
Here is a packet representing the first input prompt from the subsidiary *Mathematica* process.	`In[2]:= LinkRead[link]` `Out[2]= InputNamePacket[In[1]:= ]`
This writes a packet representing text to enter in the subsidiary *Mathematica* process.	`In[3]:= LinkWrite[link, EnterTextPacket["10!"]]`
Here is a packet representing the output prompt from the subsidiary *Mathematica* process.	`In[4]:= LinkRead[link]` `Out[4]= OutputNamePacket[Out[1]= ]`
And here is the actual result from the computation.	`In[5]:= LinkRead[link]` `Out[5]= ReturnTextPacket[3628800]`

The basic way that the various different objects involved in a *Mathematica* session are kept organized is by using *MathLink packets*. A *MathLink* packet is simply an expression with a definite head that indicates its role or meaning.

EnterTextPacket["*input*"]	text to enter corresponding to an input line
ReturnTextPacket["*output*"]	text returned corresponding to an output line
InputNamePacket["*name*"]	text returned for the name of an input line
OutputNamePacket["*name*"]	text returned for the name of an output line

Basic packets used in *Mathematica* sessions.

The fact that LinkRead returns an InputNamePacket indicates that the subsidiary *Mathematica* is now ready for new input.	`In[6]:= LinkRead[link]` `Out[6]= InputNamePacket[In[2]:= ]`
This enters two Print commands as input.	`In[7]:= LinkWrite[link, EnterTextPacket["Print[a]; Print[b];"]]`

Here is the text from the first Print.

```
In[8]:= LinkRead[link]
Out[8]= TextPacket[a
        ]
```

And here is the text from the second Print.

```
In[9]:= LinkRead[link]
Out[9]= TextPacket[b
        ]
```

No output line is generated, so the new packet is an InputNamePacket.

```
In[10]:= LinkRead[link]
Out[10]= InputNamePacket[In[3]:= ]
```

TextPacket["*string*"]	text from Print etc.
MessagePacket[*symb*, "*tag*", "*string*"]	a message
DisplayPacket["*string*"]	parts of PostScript graphics
DisplayEndPacket["*string*"]	the end of PostScript graphics

Some additional packets generated in *Mathematica* sessions.

If you enter input to *Mathematica* using EnterTextPacket["*input*"], then *Mathematica* will automatically generate a string version of your output, and will respond with ReturnTextPacket["*output*"]. But if you instead enter input using EnterExpressionPacket[*expr*] then *Mathematica* will respond with ReturnExpressionPacket[*expr*] and will not turn your output into a string.

EnterExpressionPacket[*expr*]	an expression to enter corresponding to an input line
ReturnExpressionPacket[*expr*]	an expression returned corresponding to an output line

Packets for representing input and output lines using expressions.

This enters an expression into the subsidiary *Mathematica* session without evaluating it.

```
In[11]:= LinkWrite[link, Unevaluated[EnterExpressionPacket[
            Factor[x^6 - 1]]]]
```

Here are the next 3 packets that come back from the subsidiary *Mathematica* session.

```
In[12]:= Table[LinkRead[link], {3}]
Out[12]= {OutputNamePacket[Out[3]= ],
          ReturnExpressionPacket[
            (-1 + x) (1 + x) (1 - x + x^2) (1 + x + x^2)],
          InputNamePacket[In[4]:= ]}
```

InputNamePacket and OutputNamePacket packets are often convenient for making it possible to tell the current state of a subsidiary *Mathematica* session. But you can suppress the generation of these

packets by calling the subsidiary *Mathematica* session with a string such as
`"math -mathlink -batchoutput"`.

Even if you suppress the explicit generation of `InputNamePacket` and `OutputNamePacket` packets, *Mathematica* will still process any input that you give with `EnterTextPacket` or `EnterExpressionPacket` as if you were entering an input line. This means for example that *Mathematica* will call `$Pre` and `$Post`, and will assign values to `In[$Line]` and `Out[$Line]`.

`EvaluatePacket[expr]`	an expression to be sent purely for evaluation
`ReturnPacket[expr]`	an expression returned from an evaluation

Evaluating expressions without explicit input and output lines.

This sends an `EvaluatePacket`. The `Unevaluated` prevents evaluation before the packet is sent.

```
In[13]:= LinkWrite[link, Unevaluated[EvaluatePacket[10!]]]
```

The result is a pure `ReturnPacket`.

```
In[14]:= LinkRead[link]

Out[14]= ReturnPacket[3628800]
```

This sends an `EvaluatePacket` requesting evaluation of `Print[x]`.

```
In[15]:= LinkWrite[link, Unevaluated[EvaluatePacket[Print[x]]]]
```

The first packet to come back is a `TextPacket` representing text generated by the `Print`.

```
In[16]:= LinkRead[link]

Out[16]= TextPacket[x
         ]
```

After that, the actual result of the `Print` is returned.

```
In[17]:= LinkRead[link]

Out[17]= ReturnPacket[Null]
```

In most cases, it is reasonable to assume that sending an `EvaluatePacket` to *Mathematica* will simply cause *Mathematica* to do a computation and to return various other packets, ending with a `ReturnPacket`. However, if the computation involves a function like `Input`, then *Mathematica* will have to request additional input before it can proceed with the computation.

This sends a packet whose evaluation involves an `Input` function.

```
In[18]:= LinkWrite[link,
              Unevaluated[EvaluatePacket[2 + Input["data ="]]]]
```

What comes back is an `InputPacket` which indicates that further input is required.

```
In[19]:= LinkRead[link]

Out[19]= InputPacket[data =]
```

There is nothing more to be read on the link at this point.

```
In[20]:= LinkReadyQ[link]

Out[20]= False
```

This enters more input.

```
In[21]:= LinkWrite[link, EnterTextPacket["x + y"]]
```

Now the Input function can be evaluated, and a `ReturnPacket` is generated.

```
In[22]:= LinkRead[link]
Out[22]= ReturnPacket[2 + x + y]
```

`LinkInterrupt[`*link*`]`	send an interrupt to a *MathLink*-compatible program

Interrupting a *MathLink*-compatible program.

This sends a very time-consuming calculation to the subsidiary process.

```
In[23]:= LinkWrite[link,
              EnterTextPacket["FactorInteger[2^777-1]"]]
```

The calculation is still going on.

```
In[24]:= LinkReadyQ[link]
Out[24]= False
```

This sends an interrupt.

```
In[25]:= LinkInterrupt[link]
```

Now the subsidiary process has stopped, and is sending back an interrupt menu.

```
In[26]:= LinkRead[link]
Out[26]= MenuPacket[1, Interrupt> ]
```

■ 2.12.8 Special Topic: Communication with *Mathematica* Front Ends

The *Mathematica* kernel uses *MathLink* to communicate with *Mathematica* front ends. If you start a *Mathematica* kernel from within a front end, therefore, the kernel will be controlled through a *MathLink* connection to this front end.

`$ParentLink`	the *MathLink* connection to use for kernel input and output

The link to the front end for a particular kernel.

The global variable `$ParentLink` specifies the *MathLink* connection that a particular kernel will use for input and output.

It is sometimes useful to reset `$ParentLink` in the middle of a *Mathematica* session, thereby effectively changing the front end to which the kernel is connected.

Session A

This creates a link on port 6000.

```
In[1]:= link = LinkCreate["6000"]
Out[1]= LinkObject[6000@frog.wolfram.com, 4, 4]
```

Session B

This connects to the link opened in session A.

```
In[1]:= LinkConnect["6000"]
Out[1]= LinkObject[6000@frog.wolfram.com, 4, 4]
```

This tells session B that it should use session A as a front end.	In[2]:= **$ParentLink = %**

Session A

Session A now acts as a front end to session B and gets all output from it.	In[2]:= **Table[LinkRead[link], 4]**
	Out[2]= {ResumePacket[LinkObject[ParentLink, 1, 1]],
	      OutputNamePacket[Out[2]=], ReturnTextPacket[
	      LinkObject[6000@frog.wolfram.com, 4, 4]],
	      InputNamePacket[In[3]:=]}

This releases session B again.	In[3]:= **LinkWrite[link, EnterTextPacket["$ParentLink=."]]**

Much like the *Mathematica* kernel, the standard notebook front end for *Mathematica* is set up to handle a certain set of *MathLink* packets.

Usually it is best to use functions like NotebookWrite and FrontEndExecute if you want to control the *Mathematica* front end from the kernel. But in some cases you may find it convenient to send packets directly to the front end using LinkWrite.

+■ 2.12.9 Two-Way Communication with External Programs

When you install a *MathLink*-compatible external program using Install, the program is set up to behave somewhat like a simplified *Mathematica* kernel. Every time you call a function in the external program, a CallPacket is sent to the program, and the program responds by sending back a result wrapped in a ReturnPacket.

This installs an external program, returning the LinkObject used for the connection to that program.	In[1]:= **link = Install["bitsprog"]** Out[1]= LinkObject[bitsprog, 4, 4]

The function ExternalCall sends a CallPacket to the external program.	In[2]:= **?bits**
	Global'bits
	
	bits[i_Integer] :=
	  ExternalCall[LinkObject["bitsprog", 4, 4],
	  CallPacket[0, {i}]]

You can send the CallPacket explicitly using LinkWrite. The first argument of the CallPacket specifies which function in the external program to call.	In[3]:= **LinkWrite[link, CallPacket[0, {67}]]**
Here is the response to the CallPacket from the external program.	In[4]:= **LinkRead[link]** Out[4]= {1, 1, 0, 0, 0, 0, 1}

If you use Install several times on a single external program, *Mathematica* will open several *MathLink* connections to the program. Each connection will however always correspond to a unique

LinkObject. Note that on some computer systems, you may need to make an explicit copy of the file containing the external program in order to be able to call it multiple times.

$CurrentLink	the *MathLink* connection to the external program currently being run

Identifying different instances of a single external program.

```
                                     :Begin:
                                     :Function:     addto

This gives $CurrentLink as an        :Pattern:      addto[$CurrentLink, n_Integer]
argument to addto.

                                     :Arguments:    {n}
                                     :ArgumentTypes: {Integer}
                                     :ReturnType:   Integer
                                     :End:

This zeros the global variable counter   int counter = 0;
every time the program is started.

                                     int addto(int n) {
                                         counter += n;
                                         return counter;
                                     }
```

This installs one instance of the external program containing addto.

In[5]:= **ct1 = Install["addtoprog"]**

Out[5]= LinkObject[addtoprog, 5, 5]

This installs another instance.

In[6]:= **ct2 = Install["addtoprog"]**

Out[6]= LinkObject[addtoprog, 6, 6]

This adds 10 to the counter in the first instance of the external program.

In[7]:= **addto[ct1, 10]**

Out[7]= 10

This adds 15 to the counter in the second instance of the external program.

In[8]:= **addto[ct2, 15]**

Out[8]= 15

This operates on the first instance of the program again.

In[9]:= **addto[ct1, 20]**

Out[9]= 30

If an external program maintains information about its state then you can use different instances of the program to represent different states. $CurrentLink then provides a way to refer to each instance of the program.

The value of $CurrentLink is temporarily set every time a particular instance of the program is called, as well as when each instance of the program is first installed.

MLEvaluateString(stdlink, "*string*")

> send input to *Mathematica* but return no results

Sending a string for evaluation by *Mathematica*.

The two-way nature of *MathLink* connections allows you not only to have *Mathematica* call an external program, but also to have that external program call back to *Mathematica*.

In the simplest case, you can use the *MathLink* function MLEvaluateString() to send a string to *Mathematica*. *Mathematica* will evaluate this string, producing whatever effects the string specifies, but it will not return any results from the evaluation back to the external program.

To get results back you need explicitly to send an EvaluatePacket to *Mathematica*, and then read the contents of the ReturnPacket that comes back.

. . .

This starts an EvaluatePacket.	`MLPutFunction(stdlink, "EvaluatePacket", 1);`
This constructs the expression Factorial[7] or 7!.	`MLPutFunction(stdlink, "Factorial", 1);` `  MLPutInteger(stdlink, 7);`
This specifies that the packet you are constructing is finished.	`MLEndPacket(stdlink);`
This checks the ReturnPacket that comes back.	`MLCheckFunction(stdlink, "ReturnPacket", &n);`
This extracts the integer result for 7! from the packet.	`MLGetInteger(stdlink, &ans);`

. . .

MLEndPacket(stdlink)   specify that a packet is finished and ready to be sent to *Mathematica*

Sending a packet to *Mathematica*.

At any stage in the execution of an external program, you can send EvaluatePacket[*input*] to *Mathematica*. In general, *Mathematica* may produce many packets in response, but the final packet should be ReturnPacket[*output*]. Page 668 will discuss how to handle sequences of packets and expressions whose structure you do not know in advance.

+■ 2.12.10 Special Topic: Running Programs on Remote Computers

MathLink allows you to call an external program from within *Mathematica* even when that program is running on a remote computer. Typically, you need to start the program directly from the operating system on the remote computer. But then you can connect to it using commands within your *Mathematica* session.

This starts the program `fprog` and tells it to create a new link.	⌐Operating system on `toad.wolfram.com` **`fprog -linkcreate`**
The program responds with the specification of the link it has created.	`Link created on: 2976@toad.wolfram.com`

This connects to the link that has been created.	⌐*Mathematica* session on `frog.wolfram.com` `In[1]:= `**`Install[LinkConnect["2976@toad.wolfram.com"]]`** `Out[1]= LinkObject[2976@toad.wolfram.com, 1]`
This now executes code in the external program on `toad.wolfram.com`.	`In[2]:= `**`f[16]`** `Out[2]= 561243`

External programs that are created using `mcc` or `mprep` always contain the code that is needed to set up *MathLink* connections. If you start such programs directly from your operating system, they will prompt you to specify what kind of connection you want. Alternatively, if your operating system supports it, you can also give this information as a command-line argument to the external program.

prog `-linkcreate`	operating system command to run a program and have it create a link
`Install[LinkConnect["`*port@host*`"]]`	*Mathematica* command to connect to the external program

Running an external program on a remote computer.

+■ 2.12.11 Special Topic: Running External Programs under a Debugger

MathLink allows you to run external programs under whatever debugger is provided in your software environment.

MathLink-compatible programs are typically set up to take arguments, usually on the command line, which specify what *MathLink* connections they should use.

| In debugger: | `run -linkcreate` |
| In *Mathematica*: | `Install[LinkConnect["port"]]` |

Running an external program under a debugger.

Note that in order to get a version of an external program that can be run under a debugger, you may need to specify -g or other flags when you compile the program.

	Debugger
Set a breakpoint in the C function f.	*(debug)* **break f** Breakpoint set: f: line 1
Start the external program.	*(debug)* **run -linkcreate**
The program responds with what port it is listening on.	Link created on: 2981@frog.wolfram.com

	Mathematica session
This connects to the program running under the debugger.	*In[1]:=* **Install[LinkConnect["2981@frog.wolfram.com"]]**
	Out[1]= LinkObject[2981@frog.wolfram.com, 1]
This calls a function which executes code in the external program.	*In[2]:=* **f[16]**

	Debugger
The external program stops at the breakpoint.	*(debug)* Breakpoint: f(16)
This tells the debugger to continue.	*(debug)* **continue**

	Mathematica session
Now f returns.	*Out[2]=* 561243

⁺■ 2.12.12 Manipulating Expressions in External Programs

Mathematica expressions provide a very general way to handle all kinds of data, and you may sometimes want to use such expressions inside your external programs. A language like C, however, offers no direct way to store general *Mathematica* expressions. But it is nevertheless possible to do this by using the *loopback links* provided by the *MathLink* library. A loopback link is a local *MathLink* connection inside your external program, to which you can write expressions that can later be read back.

```
MLINK MLLoopbackOpen(stdenv, long *errno)
                        open a loopback link

    void MLClose(MLINK link)    close a link
```

```
    int MLTransferExpression(MLINK dest, MLINK src)
                        get an expression from src and put it onto dest
```

Functions for manipulating loopback links.

	. . .
This opens a loopback link.	`ml = MLLoopbackOpen(stdenv, &errno);`

This puts the expression `Power[x, 3]` onto the loopback link.	`MLPutFunction(ml, "Power", 2);`
	`  MLPutSymbol(ml, "x");`
	`  MLPutInteger(ml, 3);`

	. . .

This gets the expression back from the loopback link.	`MLGetFunction(ml, &head, &n);`
	`  MLGetSymbol(ml, &sname);`
	`  MLGetInteger(ml, &k);`

	. . .
This closes the loopback link again.	`MLClose(ml);`

You can use `MLTransferExpression()` to take an expression that you get via `stdlink` from *Mathematica*, and save it in a local loopback link for later processing.

You can also use `MLTransferExpression()` to take an expression that you have built up on a local loopback link, and transfer it back to *Mathematica* via `stdlink`.

...

This puts 21! onto a local loopback link.	`MLPutFunction(ml, "Factorial", 1);` `  MLPutInteger(ml, 21);`
This sends the head `FactorInteger` to *Mathematica*.	`MLPutFunction(stdlink, "FactorInteger", 1);`
This transfers the 21! from the loopback link to `stdlink`.	`MLTransferExpression(stdlink, ml);`

You can put any sequence of expressions onto a loopback link. Usually you get the expressions off the link in the same order as you put them on.

And once you have got an expression off the link it is usually no longer saved. But by using `MLCreateMark()` you can mark a particular position in a sequence of expressions on a link, forcing *MathLink* to save every expression after the mark so that you can go back to it later.

`MLMARK MLCreateMark(MLINK link)`	create a mark at the current position in a sequence of expressions on a link
`MLSeekMark(MLINK link, MLMARK mark, long n)`	go back to a position *n* expressions after the specified mark on a link
`MLDestroyMark(MLINK link, MLMARK mark)`	destroy a mark in a link

Setting up marks in *MathLink* links.

. . .

This puts the integer 45 onto a loopback link.	`MLPutInteger(ml, 45);`
This puts 33 onto the link.	`MLPutInteger(ml, 33);`
And this puts 76.	`MLPutInteger(ml, 76);`
This will read 45 from the link. The 45 will no longer be saved.	`MLGetInteger(ml, &i);`
This creates a mark at the current position on the link.	`mark = MLCreateMark(ml);`
This will now read 33.	`MLGetInteger(ml, &i);`
And this will read 76.	`MLGetInteger(ml, &i);`
This goes back to the position of the mark.	`MLSeekMark(ml, mark, 0);`
Now this will read 33 again.	`MLGetInteger(ml, &i);`
It is important to destroy marks when you have finished with them, so no unnecessary expressions will be saved.	`MLDestroyMark(ml, mark);`

The way the *MathLink* library is implemented, it is very efficient to open and close loopback links, and to create and destroy marks in them. The only point to remember is that as soon as you create a mark on a particular link, *MathLink* will save subsequent expressions that are put on that link, and will go on doing this until the mark is destroyed.

`int MLGetNext(MLINK `*`link`*`)`	find the type of the next object on a link
`int MLGetArgCount(MLINK `*`link`*`, long *`*`n`*`)`	store in *n* the number of arguments for a function on a link
`int MLGetSymbol(MLINK `*`link`*`, char **`*`name`*`)`	get the name of a symbol
`int MLGetInteger(MLINK `*`link`*`, int *`*`i`*`)`	get a machine integer
`int MLGetReal(MLINK `*`link`*`, double *`*`x`*`)`	get a machine floating-point number
`int MLGetString(MLINK `*`link`*`, char **`*`string`*`)`	get a character string

Functions for getting pieces of expressions from a link.

MLTKFUNC	composite function—head and arguments
MLTKSYM	*Mathematica* symbol
MLTKINT	integer
MLTKREAL	floating-point number
MLTKSTR	character string

Constants returned by `MLGetNext()`.

```
                                     switch(MLGetNext(ml)) {

This reads a composite function.         case MLTKFUNC:
                                         MLGetArgCount(ml, &n);
                                         recurse for head
                                         for (i = 0; i < n; i++) {
                                             recurse for each argument
                                         }
                                         ...

This reads a single symbol.              case MLTKSYM:
                                         MLGetSymbol(ml, &name);
                                         ...

This reads a machine integer.            case MLTKINT:
                                         MLGetInteger(ml, &i);
                                         ...

                                     }
```

By using `MLGetNext()` it is straightforward to write programs that can read any expression. The way *MathLink* works, the head and arguments of a function appear as successive expressions on the link, which you read one after another.

Note that if you know that the head of a function will be a symbol, then you can use `MLGetFunction()` instead of `MLGetNext()`. In this case, however, you still need to call `MLDisownSymbol()` to disown the memory used to store the symbol name.

int MLPutNext(MLINK *link*, int *type*)	prepare to put an object of the specified type on a link
int MLPutArgCount(MLINK *link*, long *n*)	give the number of arguments for a composite function
int MLPutSymbol(MLINK *link*, char *name*)	put a symbol on the link
int MLPutInteger(MLINK *link*, int *i*)	put a machine integer
int MLPutReal(MLINK *link*, double *x*)	put a machine floating-point number
int MLPutString(MLINK *link*, char *string*)	put a character string

Functions for putting pieces of expressions onto a link.

MLPutNext() specifies types of expressions using constants such as MLTKFUNC from the mathlink.h header file—just like MLGetNext().

+■ 2.12.13 Advanced Topic: Error and Interrupt Handling

When you are putting and getting data via *MathLink* various kinds of errors can occur. Whenever any error occurs, *MathLink* goes into a completely inactive state, and all *MathLink* functions you call will return 0 immediately.

long MLError(MLINK *link*)	return a number identifying the current error, or 0 if none has occurred
char *MLErrorMessage(MLINK *link*)	return a character string describing the current error
int MLClearError(MLINK *link*)	clear the current error, returning *MathLink* if possible to an active state

Handling errors in *MathLink* programs.

When you do complicated operations, it is often convenient to check for errors only at the end. If you find that an error occurred, you must then call MLClearError() to activate *MathLink* again.

| `int MLNewPacket(MLINK` *link*`)` | skip to the end of the current packet |

Clearing out the remains of a packet.

After an error, it is common to want to discard the remainder of the packet or expression that you are currently processing. You can do this using `MLNewPacket()`.

In some cases, you may want to set it up so that if an error occurs while you are processing particular data, you can then later go back and reprocess the data in a different way. You can do this by calling `MLCreateMark()` to create a mark before you first process the data, and then calling `MLSeekMark()` to seek back to the mark if you need to reprocess the data. You should not forgot to call `MLDestroyMark()` when you have finally finished with the data—otherwise *MathLink* will continue to store it.

| `int MLAbort` | a global variable set when a program set up by `Install` is sent an abort interrupt |

Aborting an external program.

If you interrupt *Mathematica* while it is in the middle of executing an external function, it will typically give you the opportunity to try to abort the external function. If you choose to do this, what will happen is that the global variable `MLAbort` will be set to 1 inside your external program.

MathLink cannot automatically back out of an external function call that has been made. So if you have a function that can take a long time, you should explicitly check `MLAbort` every so often, returning from the function if you find that the variable has been set.

■ 2.12.14 Running *Mathematica* from Within an External Program

To run *Mathematica* from within an external program requires making use of many general features of *MathLink*. The first issue is how to establish a *MathLink* connection to *Mathematica*.

When you use *MathLink* templates to create external programs that can be called from *Mathematica*, source code to establish a *MathLink* connection is automatically generated, and all you have to do in your external program is to call `MLMain(`*argc*`, `*argv*`)`. But in general you need to call several functions to establish a *MathLink* connection.

2.13 Global Aspects of *Mathematica* Sessions

■ 2.13.1 The Main Loop

In any interactive session, *Mathematica* effectively operates in a loop. It waits for your input, processes the input, prints the result, then goes back to waiting for input again. As part of this "main loop", *Mathematica* maintains and uses various global objects. You will often find it useful to work with these objects.

You should realize, however, that if you use *Mathematica* through a special front end, your front end may set up its own main loop, and what is said in this section may not apply.

`In[n]`	the expression on the nth input line
`InString[n]`	the textual form of the nth input line
`%n` or `Out[n]`	the expression on the nth output line
`Out[{n_1, n_2, ... }]`	a list of output expressions
`%% ... %` (*n* times) or `Out[-n]`	the expression on the nth previous output line
`MessageList[n]`	a list of messages produced while processing the nth line
`$Line`	the current line number (resettable)

Input and output expressions.

In a standard interactive session, there is a sequence of input and output lines. *Mathematica* stores the values of the expressions on these lines in `In[n]` and `Out[n]`.

As indicated by the usual `In[n]:=` prompt, the input expressions are stored with delayed assignments. This means that whenever you ask for `In[n]`, the input expression will always be re-evaluated in your current environment.

This assigns a value to x.	*In[1]:=* **x = 7**
	Out[1]= 7
Now the value for x is used.	*In[2]:=* **x - x^2 + 5x - 1**
	Out[2]= -8
This removes the value assigned to x.	*In[3]:=* **x =.**
This is re-evaluated in your current environment, where there is no value assigned to x.	*In[4]:=* **In[2]**
	Out[4]= $-1 + 6x - x^2$

This gives the textual form of the second input line, appropriate for editing or other textual manipulation.	*In[5]:=* **InString[2] // InputForm**
	Out[5]//InputForm= "x - x^2 + 5x - 1"

	$HistoryLength	the number of previous lines of input and output to keep

Specifying the length of session history to keep.

Mathematica by default stores *all* your input and output lines for the duration of the session. In a very long session, this may take up a large amount of computer memory. You can nevertheless get rid of the input and output lines by explicitly clearing the values of In and Out, using Unprotect[In, Out], followed by Clear[In, Out]. You can also tell *Mathematica* to keep only a limited number of lines of history by setting the global variable $HistoryLength.

Note that at any point in a session, you can reset the line number counter $Line, so that for example new lines are numbered so as to overwrite previous ones.

$PreRead	a function applied to each input string before being fed to *Mathematica*
$Pre	a function applied to each input expression before evaluation
$Post	a function applied to each expression after evaluation
$PrePrint	a function applied after Out[n] is assigned, but before the result is printed
$SyntaxHandler	a function applied to any input line that yields a syntax error

Global functions used in the main loop.

Mathematica provides a variety of "hooks" that allow you to insert functions to be applied to expressions at various stages in the main loop. Thus, for example, any function you assign as the value of the global variable $Pre will automatically be applied before evaluation to any expression you give as input.

For a particular input line, the standard main loop begins by getting a text string of input. Particularly if you need to deal with special characters, you may want to modify this text string before it is further processed by *Mathematica*. You can do this by assigning a function as the value of the global variable $PreRead. This function will be applied to the text string, and the result will be used as the actual input string for the particular input line.

This tells *Mathematica* to replace << ... >> by { ... } in every input string.	`In[6]:= $PreRead = StringReplace[#, {"<<" -> "{", ">>" -> "}"}]&`
	
	`Out[6]= StringReplace[#1, {<< → {, >> → }}]&`

You can now enter braces as double angle brackets.	`In[7]:= <<4, 5, 6>>`
	
	`Out[7]= {4, 5, 6}`

You can remove the value for $PreRead like this, at least so long as your definition for $PreRead does not modify this very input string.	`In[8]:= $PreRead =.`

Once any `$PreRead` processing on an input string is finished, the string is read by *Mathematica*. At this point, *Mathematica* may find that there is a syntax error in the string. If this happens, then *Mathematica* calls whatever function you have specified as the value of `$SyntaxHandler`. It supplies two arguments: the input string, and the character position at which the syntax error was detected. With `$SyntaxHandler` you can, for example, generate an analysis of the syntax error, or call an editor. If your function returns a string, then *Mathematica* will use this string as a new input string.

This specifies what *Mathematica* should do when it gets a syntax error.	`In[9]:= $SyntaxHandler =`
	`        (Print[StringForm["Error at char `1` in `2`",`
	`                          #2, #1]]; $Failed)&`
	
	`Out[9]= (Print[Error at char #2 in #1];`
	`          $Failed)&`

This input generates a syntax error.	`In[10]:= 3 +/+ 5`
	
	`Syntax::sntxf: "3 +" cannot be followed by "/+ 5".`
	
	`Error at char 4 in 3 +/+ 5`

Once *Mathematica* has successfully read an input expression, it then evaluates this expression. Before doing the evaluation, *Mathematica* applies any function you have specified as the value of `$Pre`, and after the evaluation, it applies any function specified as the value of `$Post`. Note that unless the `$Pre` function holds its arguments unevaluated, the function will have exactly the same effect as `$Post`.

`$Post` allows you to specify arbitrary "post processing" to be done on results obtained from *Mathematica*. Thus, for example, to make *Mathematica* get a numerical approximation to every result it generates, all you need do is to set `$Post = N`.

This tells *Mathematica* to apply N to every result it generates.	`In[10]:= $Post = N`
	
	`Out[10]= N`

Now *Mathematica* gets a numerical approximation to anything you type in.	`In[11]:= Sqrt[7]`
	
	`Out[11]= 2.64575`

This removes the post-processing function you specified.	`In[12]:= $Post =.`

As soon as *Mathematica* has generated a result, and applied any `$Post` function you have specified, it takes the result, and assigns it as the value of `Out[$Line]`. The next step is for *Mathematica* to print the result. However, before doing this, it applies any function you have specified as the value of $PrePrint.

This tells *Mathematica* to shorten all output to two lines.

$In[13]:=$ **\$PrePrint = Short[#, 2]& ;**

Only a two-line version of the output is now shown.

$In[14]:=$ **Expand[(x + y)^40]**

$Out[14]= x^{40} + 40 x^{39} y + 780 x^{38} y^2 + 9880 x^{37} y^3 + \ll33\gg +$
$\qquad 9880 x^3 y^{37} + 780 x^2 y^{38} + 40 x y^{39} + y^{40}$

This removes the value you assigned to $PrePrint.

$In[15]:=$ **\$PrePrint =.**

There are various kinds of output generated in a typical *Mathematica* session. In general, each kind of output is sent to a definite *output channel*, as discussed on page 608. Associated with each output channel, there is a global variable which gives a list of the output streams to be included in that output channel.

\$Output	standard output and text generated by `Print`
\$Echo	an echo of each input line (as stored in `InString[`n`]`)
\$Urgent	input prompts and other urgent output
\$Messages	standard messages and output generated by `Message`
\$Display	graphics output generated by the default \$DisplayFunction
\$SoundDisplay	sound output generated by the default \$SoundDisplayFunction

Output channels in a standard *Mathematica* session.

By modifying the list of streams in a given output channel, you can redirect or copy particular kinds of *Mathematica* output. Thus, for example, by opening an output stream to a file, and including that stream in the $Echo list, you can get each piece of input you give to *Mathematica* saved in a file.

Streams[ ]	list of all open streams
Streams["*name*"]	list of all open streams with the specified name
\$Input	the name of the current input stream

Open streams in a *Mathematica* session.

The function `Streams` shows you all the input, output and other streams that are open at a particular point in a *Mathematica* session. The variable $Input gives the name of the current stream from which *Mathematica* input is being taken at a particular point. $Input is reset, for example, during the execution of a Get command.

$MessagePrePrint	a function to be applied to expressions that are given in messages
$Language	list of default languages to use for messages

Parameters for messages.

There are various global parameters which determine the form of messages generated by *Mathematica*.

As discussed in Section 2.8.21, typical messages include a sequence of expressions which are combined with the text of the message through StringForm. $MessagePrePrint gives a function to be applied to the expressions before they are printed. The default value of $MessagePrePrint is Short.

As discussed in Section 2.8.22, *Mathematica* allows you to specify the language in which you want messages to be produced. In a particular *Mathematica* session, you can assign a list of language names as the value of $Language.

Exit[ ] or Quit[ ]	terminate your *Mathematica* session
$Epilog	a global variable to be evaluated before termination

Terminating *Mathematica* sessions.

Mathematica will continue in its main loop until you explicitly tell it to exit. Most *Mathematica* interfaces provide special ways to do this. Nevertheless, you can always do it by explicitly calling Exit or Quit.

Mathematica allows you to give a value to the global variable $Epilog to specify operations to perform just before *Mathematica* actually exits. In this way, you can for example make *Mathematica* always save certain objects before exiting.

$IgnoreEOF	whether to ignore the end-of-file character

A global variable that determines the treatment of end-of-file characters.

As discussed in Section 2.7.5, *Mathematica* usually does not treat special characters in a special way. There is one potential exception, however. With the default setting $IgnoreEOF = False, *Mathematica* recognizes end-of-file characters. If *Mathematica* receives an end-of-file character as the only thing on a particular input line in a standard interactive *Mathematica* session, then it will exit the session.

Exactly how you enter an end-of-file character depends on the computer system you are using. Under Unix, for example, you typically press CONTROL-D.

Note that if you use *Mathematica* in a "batch mode", with all its input coming from a file, then it will automatically exit when it reaches the end of the file, regardless of the value of $IgnoreEOF.

■ 2.13.2 Dialogs

Within a standard interactive session, you can create "subsessions" or *dialogs* using the *Mathematica* command `Dialog`. Dialogs are often useful if you want to interact with *Mathematica* while it is in the middle of doing a calculation. As mentioned in Section 2.5.10, `TraceDialog` for example automatically calls `Dialog` at specified points in the evaluation of a particular expression. In addition, if you interrupt *Mathematica* during a computation, you can typically "inspect" its state using a dialog.

`Dialog[ ]`	initiate a *Mathematica* dialog
`Dialog[`*expr*`]`	initiate a dialog with *expr* as the current value of %
`Return[ ]`	return from a dialog, taking the current value of % as the return value
`Return[`*expr*`]`	return from a dialog, taking *expr* as the return value

Initiating and returning from dialogs.

This initiates a dialog.	*In[1]:=* `Dialog[ ]`
You can do computations in a dialog just as you would in any *Mathematica* session.	*In[2]:=* `2^41`
	Out[2]= 2199023255552
You can use `Return` to exit from a dialog.	*In[3]:=* `Return[ ]`
	Out[1]= 2199023255552

When you exit a dialog, you can return a value for the dialog using `Return[`*expr*`]`. If you do not want to return a value, and you have set `$IgnoreEOF = False`, then you can also exit a dialog simply by giving an end-of-file character, at least on systems with text-based interfaces.

To evaluate this expression, *Mathematica* initiates a dialog.	*In[2]:=* `1 + Dialog[ ]^2`
The value a + b returned from the dialog is now inserted in the original expression.	*In[3]:=* `Return[a + b]`
	Out[2]= $1 + (a + b)^2$

In starting a dialog, you will often find it useful to have some "initial expression". If you use `Dialog[`*expr*`]`, then *Mathematica* will start a dialog, using *expr* as the initial expression, accessible for example as the value of %.

This first starts a dialog with initial expression a^2.	*In[3]:=* **Map[Dialog, {a^2, b + c}]**
	Out[4]= a^2
% is the initial expression in the dialog.	*In[5]:=* **%^2 + 1**
	Out[5]= $1 + a^4$
This returns a value from the first dialog, and starts the second dialog, with initial expression b + c.	*In[6]:=* **Return[%]**
	Out[4]= $b + c$
This returns a value from the second dialog. The final result is the original expression, with values from the two dialogs inserted.	*In[5]:=* **Return[444]**
	Out[3]= $\{1 + a^4, 444\}$

Dialog effectively works by running a subsidiary version of the standard *Mathematica* main loop. Each dialog you start effectively "inherits" various values from the overall main loop. Some of the values are, however, local to the dialog, so their original values are restored when you exit the dialog.

Thus, for example, dialogs inherit the current line number **$Line** when they start. This means that the lines in a dialog have numbers that follow the sequence used in the main loop. Nevertheless, the value of **$Line** is local to the dialog. As a result, when you exit the dialog, the value of **$Line** reverts to what it was in the main loop.

If you start a dialog on line 10 of your *Mathematica* session, then the first line of the dialog will be labeled *In[11]*. Successive lines of the dialog will be labeled *In[12]*, *In[13]* and so on. Then, when you exit the dialog, the next line in your main loop will be labeled *In[11]*. At this point, you can still refer to results generated within the dialog as *Out[11]*, *Out[12]* and so on. These results will be overwritten, however, when you reach lines *In[12]*, *In[13]*, and so on in the main loop.

In a standard *Mathematica* session, you can tell whether you are in a dialog by seeing whether your input and output lines are indented. If you call a dialog from within a dialog, you will get two levels of indentation. In general, the indentation you get inside *d* nested dialogs is determined by the output form of the object **DialogIndent[*d*]**. By defining the format for this object, you can specify how dialogs should be indicated in your *Mathematica* session.

DialogSymbols :> {*x, y,* ... **}**	symbols whose values should be treated as local to the dialog
DialogSymbols :> {*x* = x_0, *y* = y_0, ... **}**	
	symbols with initial values
DialogProlog :> *expr*	an expression to evaluate before starting the dialog

Options for **Dialog**.

Whatever setting you give for DialogSymbols, Dialog will always treat the values of $Line, $Epilog and $MessageList as local. Note that if you give a value for $Epilog, it will automatically be evaluated when you exit the dialog.

When you call Dialog, its first step is to localize the values of variables. Then it evaluates any expression you have set for the option DialogProlog. If you have given an explicit argument to the Dialog function, this is then evaluated next. Finally, the actual dialog is started.

When you exit the dialog, you can explicitly specify the return value using Return[*expr*]. If you do not do this, the return value will be taken to be the last value generated in the dialog.

■ 2.13.3 Date and Time Functions

Date[ ]	give the current local date and time in the form {*year*, *month*, *day*, *hour*, *minute*, *second*}
Date[*z*]	give the current date and time in time zone *z*
TimeZone[ ]	give the time zone assumed by your computer system

Finding the date and time.

This gives the current date and time.

```
In[1]:= Date[ ]
Out[1]= {1996, 3, 27, 16, 38, 53}
```

The *Mathematica* Date function returns whatever your computer system gives as the current date and time. It assumes that any corrections for daylight saving time and so on have already been done by your computer system. In addition, it assumes that your computer system has been set for the appropriate time zone.

The function TimeZone[ ] returns the current time zone assumed by your computer system. The time zone is given as the number of hours which must be added to Greenwich mean time (GMT) to obtain the correct local time. Thus, for example, U.S. eastern standard time (EST) corresponds to time zone −5. Note that daylight saving time corrections must be included in the time zone, so U.S. eastern daylight time (EDT) corresponds to time zone −4.

This gives the current time zone assumed by your computer system.

```
In[2]:= TimeZone[ ]
Out[2]= -6
```

This gives the current date and time in time zone +9, the time zone for Japan.

```
In[3]:= Date[9]
Out[3]= {1996, 3, 28, 7, 38, 56}
```

$MachineName	the name of the computer on which *Mathematica* is running
$MachineDomain	the network domain for the computer
$MachineID	the unique ID assigned by *Mathematica* to the computer

Variables identifying the computer on which *Mathematica* is running.

$LicenseID	the ID for the license under which *Mathematica* is running
$LicenseExpirationDate	the date on which the license expires
$NetworkLicense	whether this is a network license
$LicenseServer	the full name of the machine serving the license
$LicenseProcesses	the number of *Mathematica* processes currently being run under the license
$MaxLicenseProcesses	the maximum number of processes provided by the license
$PasswordFile	password file used when the kernel was started

Variables associated with license management.

■ 2.13.6 Advanced Topic: Customizing Your *Mathematica* Configuration

- Load system-wide `init.m` initialization files
- Load `init.m`, `Kernel/init.m` and `FrontEnd/init.m` files in subdirectories of `Autoload` directories

Operations performed whenever *Mathematica* starts up.

You will often find it convenient to customize your copy of *Mathematica* by having *Mathematica* execute particular commands or load specific packages every time it starts up. You can do this by setting up system-wide `init.m` files, or by placing items in an `Autoload` directory.

- Load special or user-specific customization files
- Load customization files shared by all users of this copy of *Mathematica*

The order of loading customization files.

All versions of *Mathematica* allow shared customization files to be placed in a central `Configuration` directory. However, special or user-specific customization files are typically placed in directories that differ from one computer system to another.

Microsoft Windows	`Config` subdirectory of main *Mathematica* folder
Macintosh	`Mathematica 3.0 Prefs` folder in the `System Folder`
Unix	`.Mathematica3.0` subdirectory of each user's home directory
NeXT	`Library/Mathematica3.0` subdirectory of each user's home directory
all systems	`Configuration` subdirectory of the main *Mathematica* directory

Typical locations for customization files.

Section A.8 describes the arrangement of customization files for the *Mathematica* kernel and front end in more detail.

Part 3

Part 1 described how to do basic mathematics with Mathematica. For many kinds of calculations, you will need to know nothing more. But if you do want to use more advanced mathematics, this part discusses how to do it in Mathematica.

This part goes through the various mathematical functions and methods that are built into Mathematica. Some calculations can be done just by using these built-in mathematical capabilities. For many specific calculations, however, you will need to use application packages that have been written in Mathematica. These packages build on the mathematical capabilities discussed in this part, but add new functions for doing special kinds of calculations.

Much of what is said in this part assumes a knowledge of mathematics at an advanced undergraduate level. If you do not understand a particular section, then you can probably assume that you will not need to use that section.

Part 3

Advanced Mathematics in *Mathematica*

3.1 Numbers

■ 3.1.1 Types of Numbers

Four underlying types of numbers are built into *Mathematica*.

Integer	arbitrary-length exact integer
Rational	*integer*/*integer* in lowest terms
Real	approximate real number, with any specified precision
Complex	complex number of the form *number* + *number* I

Intrinsic types of numbers in *Mathematica*.

Rational numbers always consist of a ratio of two integers, reduced to lowest terms.

In[1]:= **12344/2222**

$$Out[1]= \frac{6172}{1111}$$

Approximate real numbers are distinguished by the presence of an explicit decimal point.

In[2]:= **5456.**

Out[2]= 5456.

An approximate real number can have any number of digits.

In[3]:= **4.5454352345454352345345234543**

Out[3]= 4.5454352345454352345345234543

Complex numbers can have integer or rational components.

In[4]:= **4 + 7/8 I**

$$Out[4]= 4 + \frac{7I}{8}$$

They can also have approximate real number components.

In[5]:= **4 + 5.6 I**

Out[5]= 4 + 5.6 I

123	an exact integer
123.	an approximate real number
123.0000000000000	an approximate real number with a certain precision
123. + 0. I	a complex number with approximate real number components

Several versions of the number 123.

You can distinguish different types of numbers in *Mathematica* by looking at their heads. (Although numbers in *Mathematica* have heads like other expressions, they do not have explicit elements which you can extract.)

The object 123 is taken to be an exact integer, with head Integer.

```
In[6]:= Head[123]
Out[6]= Integer
```

The presence of an explicit decimal point makes *Mathematica* treat 123. as an approximate real number, with head Real.

```
In[7]:= Head[123.]
Out[7]= Real
```

NumberQ[*x*]	test whether *x* is any kind of number
IntegerQ[*x*]	test whether *x* is an integer
EvenQ[*x*]	test whether *x* is even
OddQ[*x*]	test whether *x* is odd
PrimeQ[*x*]	test whether *x* is a prime integer
Head[*x*]===*type*	test the type of a number

Tests for different types of numbers.

NumberQ[*x*] tests for any kind of number.

```
In[8]:= NumberQ[5.6]
Out[8]= True
```

5. is treated as a Real, so IntegerQ gives False.

```
In[9]:= IntegerQ[5.]
Out[9]= False
```

If you use complex numbers extensively, there is one subtlety you should be aware of. When you enter a number like 123., *Mathematica* treats it as an approximate real number, but assumes that its imaginary part is exactly zero. Sometimes you may want to enter approximate complex numbers with imaginary parts that are zero, but only to a certain precision.

When the imaginary part is the exact integer 0, *Mathematica* simplifies complex numbers to real ones.

```
In[10]:= Head[ 123 + 0 I ]
Out[10]= Integer
```

Here the imaginary part is only zero to a certain precision, so *Mathematica* retains the complex number form.

```
In[11]:= Head[ 123. + 0. I ]
Out[11]= Complex
```

The distinction between complex numbers whose imaginary parts are exactly zero, or are only zero to a certain precision, may seem like a pedantic one. However, when we discuss, for example, the interpretation of powers and roots of complex numbers in Section 3.2.7, the distinction will become significant.

One way to find out the type of a number in *Mathematica* is just to pick out its head using Head[*expr*]. For many purposes, however, it is better to use functions like IntegerQ which explicitly test for particular types. Functions like this are set up to return True if their argument is manifestly of the required type, and to return False otherwise. As a result, IntegerQ[x] will give False, unless you have assigned x an explicit integer value.

In doing symbolic computations, however, you may sometimes want to treat x as an integer, even though you have not assigned an explicit integer value to it. You can override the assumption that the symbol x is not an integer by explicitly making an assignment of the form x/: IntegerQ[x] = True. This assignment specifies that whenever you specifically test x with IntegerQ, it will give the result True. You should realize, however, that the assignment does not actually change the head of x, so that, for example, x will still not match n_Integer. *Mathematica* also does not automatically make inferences based on the assignment. Thus, for example, it cannot determine solely on the basis of this assignment that IntegerQ[x^2] is also True.

x does not explicitly have head Integer, so IntegerQ returns False.	*In[12]:=* **IntegerQ[x]** *Out[12]=* False
This specifies that x is in fact an integer. The x/: specifies that the rule is associated with x, not IntegerQ.	*In[13]:=* **x/: IntegerQ[x] = True** *Out[13]=* True
The definition overrides the default assumption that x is not an integer.	*In[14]:=* **IntegerQ[x]** *Out[14]=* True

■ 3.1.2 Numeric Quantities

NumberQ[*expr*]	test whether *expr* is explicitly a number
NumericQ[*expr*]	test whether *expr* has a numerical value

Testing for numeric quantities.

Pi is a symbol, so Pi + 3 is not explicitly a number.	*In[1]:=* **NumberQ[Pi + 3]** *Out[1]=* False
It does however have a numerical value.	*In[2]:=* **NumericQ[Pi + 3]** *Out[2]=* True
This finds the explicit numerical value of Pi + 3.	*In[3]:=* **N[Pi + 3]** *Out[3]=* 6.14159

Mathematica knows that constants such as Pi are numeric quantities. It also knows that standard mathematical functions such as Log and Sin have numerical values when their arguments are numerical.

Log[2 + x] contains x, and is therefore not a numeric quantity.

In[4]:= **{NumericQ[Log[2]], NumericQ[Log[2 + x]]}**
Out[4]= {True, False}

Many functions implicitly use the numerical values of numeric quantities.

In[5]:= **Min[Exp[2], Log[2], Sqrt[2]]**
Out[5]= Log[2]

In general, *Mathematica* assumes that any function which has the attribute NumericFunction will yield numerical values when its arguments are numerical. All standard mathematical functions in *Mathematica* already have this attribute. But when you define your own functions, you can explicitly set the attribute to tell *Mathematica* to assume that these functions will have numerical values when their arguments are numerical.

■ 3.1.3 Converting between Different Forms of Numbers

N[x, n]	convert x to an approximate real number with n digits of precision
Rationalize[x]	give a rational number approximation to x
Rationalize[x, dx]	give a rational number approximation to within tolerance dx

Functions that convert between different types of numbers.

This gives a 30-digit real number approximation to 3/7.

In[1]:= **N[3/7, 30]**
Out[1]= 0.428571428571428571428571428571414285714285714

This takes the 30-digit number you have just generated, and reduces it to 20-digit precision.

In[2]:= **N[%, 20]**
Out[2]= 0.428571428571428571429

This converts the result back to a rational number.

In[3]:= **Rationalize[%]**
Out[3]= $\dfrac{3}{7}$

The numerical value of π is not "sufficiently close" to a rational number to be converted.

In[4]:= **Rationalize[N[Pi]]**
Out[4]= 3.14159

If you give a specific tolerance, Rationalize will give you a rational number approximation accurate to within that tolerance.

In[5]:= **Rationalize[N[Pi], 10^-5]**
Out[5]= $\dfrac{355}{113}$

With a tolerance of 0, Rationalize yields the best possible rational approximation given the precision of your input.

In[6]:= **Rationalize[N[Pi], 0]**

$$Out[6]= \frac{245850922}{78256779}$$

IntegerDigits[*n*]	a list of the decimal digits in the integer *n*
IntegerDigits[*n*, *b*]	the digits of *n* in base *b*
+ IntegerDigits[*n*, *b*, *len*]	the list of digits padded on the left with zeros to give total length *len*
RealDigits[*x*]	a list of the decimal digits in the approximate real number *x*, together with the number of digits to the left of the decimal point
RealDigits[*x*, *b*]	the digits of *x* in base *b*
+ RealDigits[*x*, *b*, *len*]	the first *len* digits of *x* in base *b*
+ RealDigits[*x*, *b*, *len*, *n*]	the first *len* digits starting with the coefficient of b^n
+ FromDigits[*list*]	reconstruct a number from its decimal digit sequence
+ FromDigits[*list*, *b*]	reconstruct a number from its digits sequence in base *b*

Converting between numbers and lists of digits.

Here is the list of base 16 digits for an integer.

In[7]:= **IntegerDigits[1234135634, 16]**

Out[7]= {4, 9, 8, 15, 6, 10, 5, 2}

This gives a list of digits, together with the number of digits that appear to the left of the decimal point.

In[8]:= **RealDigits[123.45678901234567890123 4567]**

Out[8]= {{1, 2, 3, 4, 5, 6, 7, 8, 9, 0, 1, 2, 3, 4, 5, 6, 7, 8, 9, 0, 1, 2, 3, 4, 5, 7}, 3}

Here is the binary digit sequence for 56, padded with zeros so that it is of total length 8.

In[9]:= **IntegerDigits[56, 2, 8]**

Out[9]= {0, 0, 1, 1, 1, 0, 0, 0}

This reconstructs the original number from its binary digit sequence.	*In[10]:=* **FromDigits[%, 2]** *Out[10]=* 56

b^^*nnnn*	a number in base b
BaseForm[x, b]	print with x in base b

Numbers in other bases.

When the base is larger than 10, extra digits are represented by letters a–z.

The number 100101_2 in base 2 is 37 in base 10.	*In[11]:=* **2^^100101** *Out[11]=* 37
This prints 37 in base 2.	*In[12]:=* **BaseForm[37, 2]** *Out[12]//BaseForm=* 100101_2
Here is a number in base 16.	*In[13]:=* **16^^ffffaa00** *Out[13]=* 4294945280
You can do computations with numbers in base 16. Here the result is given in base 10.	*In[14]:=* **16^^fffaa2 + 16^^ff - 1** *Out[14]=* 16776096
This gives the result in base 16.	*In[15]:=* **BaseForm[%, 16]** *Out[15]//BaseForm=* $fffba0_{16}$
You can give approximate real numbers, as well as integers, in other bases.	*In[16]:=* **2^^101.100101** *Out[16]=* 5.58
Here are the first few digits of $\sqrt{2}$ in octal.	*In[17]:=* **BaseForm[N[Sqrt[2], 30], 8]** *Out[17]//BaseForm=* $1.324047463177167462204262766115467_8$
This gives an explicit list of the first 15 octal digits.	*In[18]:=* **RealDigits[Sqrt[2], 8, 15]** *Out[18]=* {{1, 3, 2, 4, 0, 4, 7, 4, 6, 3, 1, 7, 7, 1, 6}, 1}
This gives 15 octal digits starting with the coefficient of 8^{-10}.	*In[19]:=* **RealDigits[Sqrt[2], 8, 15, -10]** *Out[19]=* {{1, 7, 7, 1, 6, 7, 4, 6, 2, 2, 0, 4, 2, 6, 2}, -9}

Section 2.8.7 describes how to print numbers in various formats. If you want to create your own formats, you will often need to use MantissaExponent to separate the pieces of approximate real numbers.

MantissaExponent[x]	give a list containing the mantissa and exponent of x
MantissaExponent[x, b]	give the mantissa and exponent in base b

Separating the mantissa and exponent of numbers.

This gives a list in which the mantissa and exponent of the number are separated.

```
In[20]:= MantissaExponent[3.45 10^125]
Out[20]= {0.345, 126}
```

■ 3.1.4 Numerical Precision

As discussed in Section 1.1.2, *Mathematica* can handle approximate real numbers with any number of digits. In general, the *precision* of an approximate real number is the number of decimal digits in it which are treated as significant for computations. The *accuracy* of an approximate real number is the number of these digits which appear to the right of the decimal point. Precision is thus a measure of the relative error in a number, while accuracy is a measure of absolute error.

Precision[x]	the total number of significant decimal digits in x
Accuracy[x]	the number of significant decimal digits to the right of the decimal point in x

Precision and accuracy of real numbers.

Here is an approximate real number.

```
In[1]:= xacc = 431.123145333555141444
Out[1]= 431.123145333555141444
```

This gives the total number of digits entered to specify the real number.

```
In[2]:= Precision[xacc]
Out[2]= 21
```

This gives the number of digits which appear to the right of the decimal point.

```
In[3]:= Accuracy[xacc]
Out[3]= 18
```

When you use N[*expr*, *n*], *Mathematica* tries to evaluate the expression *expr* to *n* digits of precision. And so long as your input has sufficient precision, *Mathematica* will usually succeed in getting a result with the requested precision.

This asks for Pi^25 to be evaluated to 30 digits of precision.

```
In[4]:= N[Pi^25, 30]
Out[4]= 2.68377941431776454900999928124395 × 10^{12}
```

The result indeed has 30 digits of precision.

```
In[5]:= Precision[%]
Out[5]= 30
```

N[*expr*, *n*]	evaluate *expr* numerically to *n*-digit precision using arbitrary-precision numbers if necessary
N[*expr*]	evaluate *expr* numerically using only machine-precision numbers

Numerical evaluation.

If you use N[*expr*], and do not explicitly specify the precision of numbers to use, *Mathematica* will use *machine-precision* numbers.

In general, *Mathematica* distinguishes two kinds of approximate real numbers: *arbitrary-precision* ones, and *machine-precision* ones. Arbitrary-precision numbers can contain any number of digits, and their precision is adjusted during computations. Machine-precision numbers, on the other hand, contain a fixed number of digits, and their precision remains unchanged throughout computations.

As discussed in more detail below, machine-precision numbers work by making direct use of the numerical capabilities of your underlying computer system. As a result, computations with them can be done quickly. However, machine-precision numbers are much less flexible than arbitrary-precision ones.

This evaluates Pi using machine precision.	*In[6]:=* **N[Pi]** *Out[6]=* 3.14159
On the computer system used to generate this example, the machine precision is 16 decimal digits.	*In[7]:=* **Precision[%]** *Out[7]=* 16
This gives the machine precision on the computer system.	*In[8]:=* **$MachinePrecision** *Out[8]=* 16

$MachinePrecision	the machine precision on your computer system
MachineNumberQ[*x*]	give True if *x* is a machine-precision number, and False otherwise

Machine-precision numbers.

When you enter an approximate real number, *Mathematica* has to decide whether to treat it as machine precision or arbitrary precision. Unless you specify otherwise, then if you give less than $MachinePrecision digits, *Mathematica* will treat the number as machine precision, and if you give more digits, it will treat the number as arbitrary precision.

123.4	a machine-precision number
123.45678901234567890	an arbitrary-precision number on some computer systems
123.45678901234567890`	a machine-precision number on all computer systems
123.456`200	an arbitrary-precision number with 200 digits of precision
123.456``200	an arbitrary-precision number with 200 digits of accuracy
1.234*^6	a machine-precision number in scientific notation (1.234×10^6)
1.234`200*^6	a number in scientific notation with 200 digits of precision
2^^101.111`200	a number in base 2 with 200 binary digits of precision
2^^101.111`200*^6	a number in base 2 scientific notation $(101.111_2 \times 2^6)$

Input forms for numbers.

When *Mathematica* prints out numbers, it usually tries to give them in a form that will be as easy as possible to read. But if you want to take numbers that are printed out by *Mathematica*, and then later use them as input to *Mathematica*, you need to make sure that no information gets lost.

In standard output form, *Mathematica* prints a number like this to six digits.

```
In[9]:= N[Pi]
Out[9]= 3.14159
```

In input form, *Mathematica* prints all the digits it knows.

```
In[10]:= InputForm[%]
Out[10]//InputForm= 3.141592653589793
```

Here is an arbitrary-precision number in standard output form.

```
In[11]:= N[Pi, 20]
Out[11]= 3.1415926535897932384646
```

In input form, *Mathematica* explicitly indicates the precision of the number, and gives extra digits to make sure the number can be reconstructed correctly.

```
In[12]:= InputForm[%]
Out[12]//InputForm= 3.14159265358979323846264338327950`20
```

This makes *Mathematica* not explicitly indicate precision.

```
In[13]:= InputForm[%, NumberMarks->False]
Out[13]//InputForm= 3.14159265358979323846
```

+ `InputForm[`*expr*`, NumberMarks->True]`

use ' marks in all approximate numbers

+ `InputForm[`*expr*`, NumberMarks->Automatic]`

use ' only in arbitrary-precision numbers

`InputForm[`*expr*`, NumberMarks->False]`

never use ' marks

Controlling printing of numbers.

The default setting for the `NumberMarks` option, both in `InputForm` and in functions such as `ToString` and `OpenWrite` is given by the value of `$NumberMarks`. By resetting `$NumberMarks`, therefore, you can globally change the way that numbers are printed in `InputForm`.

This makes *Mathematica* by default always include number marks in input form.

```
In[14]:= $NumberMarks = True
Out[14]= True
```

Even a machine-precision number is now printed with an explicit number mark.

```
In[15]:= InputForm[N[Pi]]
Out[15]//InputForm= 3.14159265358979311'
```

Even with no number marks, `InputForm` still uses *^ for scientific notation.

```
In[16]:= InputForm[N[Exp[600], 20], NumberMarks->False]
Out[16]//InputForm= 3.7730203009299398234*^260
```

In doing numerical computations, it is inevitable that you will sometimes end up with results that are less precise than you want. Particularly when you get numerical results that are very close to zero, you may well want to *assume* that the results should be exactly zero. The function Chop allows you to replace approximate real numbers that are close to zero by the exact integer 0.

`Chop[`*expr*`]`	replace all approximate real numbers in *expr* with magnitude less than 10^{-10} by 0
`Chop[`*expr*`, dx]`	replace numbers with magnitude less than *dx* by 0

Removing numbers close to zero.

This computation gives a small imaginary part.

```
In[17]:= Exp[ N[2 Pi I] ]
Out[17]= 1. - 2.44921×10⁻¹⁶ I
```

You can get rid of the imaginary part using Chop.

```
In[18]:= Chop[%]
Out[18]= 1.
```

■ 3.1.5 Arbitrary-Precision Numbers

When you do calculations with arbitrary-precision numbers, *Mathematica* keeps track of precision at all points. In general, *Mathematica* tries to give you results which have the highest possible precision, given the precision of the input you provided.

Mathematica treats arbitrary-precision numbers as representing the values of quantities where a certain number of digits are known, and the rest are unknown. In general, an arbitrary-precision number x is taken to have Precision[x] digits which are known exactly, followed by an infinite number of digits which are completely unknown.

When you do a computation, *Mathematica* keeps track of which digits in your result could be affected by unknown digits in your input. It sets the precision of your result so that no affected digits are ever included. This procedure ensures that all digits returned by *Mathematica* are correct, whatever the values of the unknown digits may be.

This evaluates Γ(1/7) trying to get 30-digit precision.	In[1]:= **N[Gamma[1/7], 30]** Out[1]= 6.548062940247824437714093349429
In this case, the result has a precision of exactly 30 digits.	In[2]:= **Precision[%]** Out[2]= 30
If you give input only to a few digits of precision, *Mathematica* cannot give you such high-precision output.	In[3]:= **N[Gamma[0.142], 30]** Out[3]= 6.589647294920398
If you want *Mathematica* to assume that 0.142 is *exactly* 142/1000, then you have to show this explicitly.	In[4]:= **N[Gamma[142/1000], 30]** Out[4]= 6.58964729492039788328481917496

In many computations, the precision of the results you get progressively degrades as a result of "roundoff error". A typical case of this occurs if you subtract two numbers that are close together. The result you get depends on high-order digits in each number, and typically has far fewer digits of precision than either of the original numbers.

Both input numbers have a precision of 20 digits, but the result has a precision of only 3 digits.	In[5]:= **1.11111111111111111111 −** **1.11111111111111111000** Out[5]= 1.11×10^{-18}
Adding extra digits in one number but not the other is not sufficient to allow extra digits to be found in the result.	In[6]:= **1.1111111111111111111345 −** **1.11111111111111111000** Out[6]= 1.11×10^{-18}

The precision of the output from a function can depend in a complicated way on the precision of the input. Functions that vary rapidly typically give less precise output, since the variation of the output associated with uncertainties in the input is larger. Functions that are close to constants can actually give output that is more precise than their input.

Functions like Sin that vary rapidly typically give output that is less precise than their input.	*In[7]:=* **Sin[111111111.0000000000000000]** *Out[7]=* -0.29753510333494323
Here is e^{-40} evaluated to 20-digit precision.	*In[8]:=* **N[Exp[-40], 20]** *Out[8]=* 4.2483542552915889953×10⁻¹⁸

Here is e^{-40} evaluated to 20-digit precision.

In[8]:= **N[Exp[-40], 20]**

Out[8]= $4.2483542552915889953 \times 10^{-18}$

The result you get by adding the exact integer 1 has a higher precision.

In[9]:= **1 + %**

Out[9]= 1.00000000000000000042483542552915889953

It is worth realizing that different ways of doing the same calculation can end up giving you results with very different precisions. Typically, if you once lose precision in a calculation, it is essentially impossible to regain it; in losing precision, you are effectively losing information about your result.

Here is a 40-digit number that is close to 1.

In[10]:= **x = N[1 - 10^-30, 40]**

Out[10]= 0.9999999999999999999999999999990000000000

Adding 1 to it gives another 40-digit number.

In[11]:= **1 + x**

Out[11]= 1.999999999999999999999999999999000000000

The original precision has been maintained.

In[12]:= **Precision[%]**

Out[12]= 40

This way of computing 1 + x loses precision.

In[13]:= **(x^2 - 1) / (x - 1)**

Out[13]= 2.

The result obtained in this way has quite low precision.

In[14]:= **Precision[%]**

Out[14]= 10

The fact that different ways of doing the same calculation can give you different numerical answers means, among other things, that comparisons between approximate real numbers must be treated with care. In testing whether two real numbers are "equal", *Mathematica* effectively finds their difference, and tests whether the result is "consistent with zero" to the precision given.

These numbers are equal to the precision given.

In[15]:= **3 == 3.00000000000000000000**

Out[15]= True

The internal algorithms that *Mathematica* uses to evaluate mathematical functions are set up to maintain as much precision as possible. In most cases, built-in *Mathematica* functions will give you results that have as much precision as can be justified on the basis of your input. In some cases, however, it is simply impractical to do this, and *Mathematica* will give you results that have lower precision. If you give higher-precision input, *Mathematica* will use higher precision in its internal calculations, and you will usually be able to get a higher-precision result.

N[*expr*]	evaluate *expr* numerically to give a machine-precision result
N[*expr*, *n*]	evaluate *expr* numerically trying to get a result with *n* digits of precision

Numerical evaluation.

If you start with an expression that contains only integers and other exact numeric quantities, then N[*expr*, *n*] will in almost all cases succeed in giving you a result to *n* digits of precision. You should realize, however, that to do this *Mathematica* sometimes has to perform internal intermediate calculations to much higher precision.

The global variable $MaxExtraPrecision specifies how many additional digits should be allowed in such intermediate calculations.

Mathematica automatically increases the precision that it uses internally in order to get the correct answer here.

```
In[16]:= N[Sin[10^40], 30]

Out[16]= -0.569633400953636327308034181815736
```

Using the default setting $MaxExtraPrecision=50 *Mathematica* cannot get the correct answer here.

```
In[17]:= N[Sin[10^100], 30]

$MaxExtraPrecision::mepr:
    In attempting to evaluate
    Sin[10000000000000000000<<71>>0000000000],
        $MaxExtraPrecision 50.
    was encountered. Increasing the value of
    $MaxExtraPrecision may help resolve the uncertainty.

Out[17]= 0.0
```

The precision is zero, indicating that no digits can be expected to be correct.

```
In[18]:= Precision[%]

Out[18]= 0
```

This tells *Mathematica* that it can use more digits in its internal calculations.

```
In[19]:= $MaxExtraPrecision = 100

Out[19]= 100
```

Now it gets the correct answer.

```
In[20]:= N[Sin[10^100], 30]

Out[20]= -0.372376123661276688262086955532
```

This resets $MaxExtraPrecision to its default value.

```
In[21]:= $MaxExtraPrecision = 50

Out[21]= 50
```

Mathematica saves its previous result, so still gives the correct answer here.

```
In[22]:= N[Sin[10^100], 30]

Out[22]= -0.372376123661276688262086955532
```

Even when you are doing computations that give exact results, *Mathematica* still occasionally uses approximate numbers for some of its internal calculations, so that the value of $MaxExtraPrecision can thus have an effect.

Mathematica works this out using bounds from approximate numbers.	`In[23]:= Sin[Exp[100]] > 0` `Out[23]= True`

With the default value of `$MaxExtraPrecision`, *Mathematica* cannot work this out.

`In[24]:= Sin[Exp[200]] > 0`

`$MaxExtraPrecision::mepr:`

In attempting to evaluate Sin[E^{200}], $MaxExtraPrecision 50. was encountered. Increasing the value of $MaxExtraPrecision may help resolve the uncertainty.

`Out[24]= Sin[E`^{200}`] > 0`

Temporarily resetting `$MaxExtraPrecision` allows *Mathematica* to get the result.

`In[25]:= Block[{$MaxExtraPrecision = 100},`
`          Sin[Exp[200]] > 0 ]`

`Out[25]= False`

variable	default value	
+ `$MaxExtraPrecision`	50	maximum additional precision to be used
+ `$MaxPrecision`	50000	maximum total precision to be used
+ `$MinPrecision`	0	minimum precision to be used

Global precision parameters.

When *Mathematica* works out the potential effect of unknown digits in arbitrary-precision numbers, it assumes by default that these digits are completely independent in different numbers. While this assumption will never yield too high a precision in a result, it may lead to unnecessary loss of precision.

In particular, if two numbers are generated in the same way in a computation, some of their unknown digits may be equal. Then, when these numbers are, for example, subtracted, the unknown digits may cancel. By assuming that the unknown digits are always independent, however, *Mathematica* will miss such cancellations.

Here is a number computed to 20-digit precision.	`In[26]:= delta = N[3^-30, 20]` `Out[26]= 4.85693574961886113791×10`$^{-15}$

The quantity 1 + delta has 34-digit precision.	`In[27]:= Precision[1 + delta]` `Out[27]= 34`

This quantity also has only 34-digit precision, since *Mathematica* assumes that the unknown digits in each number delta are independent.	`In[28]:= Precision[(1 + delta) - delta]` `Out[28]= 34`

Numerical algorithms sometimes rely on cancellations between unknown digits in different numbers yielding results of higher precision. If you can be sure that certain unknown digits will eventually cancel, then you can explicitly introduce arbitrary digits in place of the unknown ones. You can carry these arbitrary digits through your computation, then let them cancel, and get a result of higher precision.

SetPrecision[x, n]	create a number with n decimal digits of precision, padding with zeros if necessary
SetAccuracy[x, n]	create a number with n decimal digits of accuracy

Functions for modifying precision and accuracy.

This adds 10 arbitrary digits to delta.

$In[29]:=$ **delta = SetPrecision[delta, 30]**

$Out[29]=$ $4.85693574961886113790624264975 \times 10^{-15}$

The digits that were added cancel out here.

$In[30]:=$ **(1 + delta) - delta**

$Out[30]=$ $1.$

The precision of the result is now 44, rather than 34, digits.

$In[31]:=$ **Precision[%]**

$Out[31]=$ 44

SetPrecision works by adding digits which are zero in base 2. Sometimes, *Mathematica* stores slightly more digits in an arbitrary-precision number than it displays, and in such cases, SetPrecision will use these extra digits before introducing zeros.

This creates a number with a precision of 40 decimal digits. The extra digits come from conversion to base 10.

$In[32]:=$ **SetPrecision[0.300000000000000, 40]**

$Out[32]=$ $0.2999999999999999888977697537484345 9576368$

By making the global assignment \$MinPrecision = n, you can effectively apply SetPrecision[$expr$, n] at every step in a computation. This means that even when the number of correct digits in an arbitrary-precision number drops below n, the number will always be padded to have n digits.

If you set \$MaxPrecision = n as well as \$MinPrecision = n, then you can force all arbitrary-precision numbers to have a fixed precision of n digits. In effect, what this does is to make *Mathematica* treat arbitrary-precision numbers in much the same way as it treats machine numbers—but with more digits of precision.

Fixed-precision computation can make some calculations more efficient, but without careful analysis you can never be sure how many digits are correct in the results you get.

Here is a small number with 20-digit precision.

$In[33]:=$ **k = N[Exp[-60], 20]**

$Out[33]=$ $8.7565107626965203384 9 \times 10^{-27}$

With *Mathematica*'s usual arithmetic, this works fine.

$In[34]:=$ **Evaluate[1 + k] - 1**

$Out[34]=$ $8.7565107626965203384 9 \times 10^{-27}$

This tells *Mathematica* to use fixed-precision arithmetic.

```
In[35]:= $MinPrecision = $MaxPrecision = 20
Out[35]= 20
```

The first few digits are correct, but the rest are wrong.

```
In[36]:= Evaluate[1 + k] - 1
Out[36]= 8.7565107001277653351×10⁻²⁷
```

■ 3.1.6 Machine-Precision Numbers

Whenever machine-precision numbers appear in a calculation, the whole calculation is typically done in machine precision. *Mathematica* will then give machine-precision numbers as the result.

Whenever the input contains any machine-precision numbers, *Mathematica* does the computation to machine precision.

```
In[1]:= 1.444444444444444444 ^ 5.7
Out[1]= 8.13382
```

Zeta[5.6] yields a machine-precision result, so the N is irrelevant.

```
In[2]:= N[Zeta[5.6], 30]
Out[2]= 1.02337547922703
```

This gives a higher-precision result.

```
In[3]:= N[Zeta[56/10], 30]
Out[3]= 1.023375479227029910860417881026
```

When you do calculations with arbitrary-precision numbers, as discussed in the previous section, *Mathematica* always keeps track of the precision of your results, and gives only those digits which are known to be correct, given the precision of your input. When you do calculations with machine-precision numbers, however, *Mathematica* always gives you a machine-precision result, whether or not all the digits in the result can, in fact, be determined to be correct on the basis of your input.

This subtracts two machine-precision numbers.

```
In[4]:= diff = 1.11111111 - 1.11111000
Out[4]= 1.11×10⁻⁶
```

The result is taken to have machine precision.

```
In[5]:= Precision[diff]
Out[5]= 16
```

Here are all the digits in the result.

```
In[6]:= InputForm[diff]
Out[6]//InputForm= 1.109999999915345*^-6
```

The fact that you can get spurious digits in machine-precision numerical calculations with *Mathematica* is in many respects quite unsatisfactory. The ultimate reason, however, that *Mathematica* uses fixed precision for these calculations is a matter of computational efficiency.

Mathematica is usually set up to insulate you as much as possible from the details of the computer system you are using. In dealing with machine-precision numbers, you would lose too much, however, if *Mathematica* did not make use of some specific features of your computer.

The important point is that almost all computers have special hardware or microcode for doing floating-point calculations to a particular fixed precision. *Mathematica* makes use of these features when doing machine-precision numerical calculations.

The typical arrangement is that all machine-precision numbers in *Mathematica* are represented as "double-precision floating-point numbers" in the underlying computer system. On most current computers, such numbers contain a total of 64 binary bits, typically yielding 16 decimal digits of mantissa.

The main advantage of using the built-in floating-point capabilities of your computer is speed. Arbitrary-precision numerical calculations, which do not make such direct use of these capabilities, are usually many times slower than machine-precision calculations.

There are several disadvantages of using built-in floating-point capabilities. One already mentioned is that it forces all numbers to have a fixed precision, independent of what precision can be justified for them.

A second disadvantage is that the treatment of machine-precision numbers can vary slightly from one computer system to another. In working with machine-precision numbers, *Mathematica* is at the mercy of the floating-point arithmetic system of each particular computer. If floating-point arithmetic is done differently on two computers, you may get slightly different results for machine-precision *Mathematica* calculations on those computers.

$MachinePrecision	the number of decimal digits of precision
$MachineEpsilon	the minimum positive machine-precision number which can be added to 1.0 to give a result distinguishable from 1.0
$MaxMachineNumber	the maximum machine-precision number
$MinMachineNumber	the minimum positive machine-precision number
$MaxNumber	the maximum magnitude of an arbitrary-precision number
$MinNumber	the minimum magnitude of a positive arbitrary-precision number

Properties of numbers on a particular computer system.

Since machine-precision numbers on any particular computer system are represented by a definite number of binary bits, numbers which are too close together will have the same bit pattern, and so cannot be distinguished. The parameter $MachineEpsilon gives the distance between 1.0 and the closest number which has a distinct binary representation.

This gives the value of $MachineEpsilon for the computer system on which these examples are run.

In[7]:= **$MachineEpsilon**

Out[7]= 2.22045×10^{-16}

Although this prints as 1., *Mathematica* knows that the result is larger than 1.	*In[8]:=* **1. + \$MachineEpsilon** *Out[8]=* 1.
Subtracting 1 gives \$MachineEpsilon.	*In[9]:=* **% - 1.** *Out[9]=* 2.22045×10^{-16}
This again prints as 1.	*In[10]:=* **1. + \$MachineEpsilon/2** *Out[10]=* 1.
In this case, however, subtracting 1 yields 0, since 1 + \$MachineEpsilon/2 is not distinguished from 1. to machine precision.	*In[11]:=* **% - 1.** *Out[11]=* 0.

Machine-precision numbers have not only limited precision, but also limited magnitude. If you generate a number which lies outside the range specified by \$MinMachineNumber and \$MaxMachineNumber, *Mathematica* will automatically convert the number to arbitrary-precision form.

This is the maximum machine-precision number which can be handled on the computer system used for this example.	*In[12]:=* **\$MaxMachineNumber** *Out[12]=* 1.79769×10^{308}
Mathematica automatically converts the result of this computation to arbitrary precision.	*In[13]:=* **Exp[1000.]** *Out[13]=* $1.970071114017 \times 10^{434}$

■ 3.1.7 Advanced Topic: Interval Arithmetic

Interval[{*min*, *max*}]	the interval from *min* to *max*
Interval[{*min*₁, *max*₁}, {*min*₂, *max*₂}, ...]	
	the union of intervals from min_1 to max_1, min_2 to max_2, ...

Representations of real intervals.

This represents all numbers between −2 and +5.	*In[1]:=* **Interval[{-2, 5}]** *Out[1]=* Interval[{-2, 5}]
The square of any number between −2 and +5 is always between 0 and 25.	*In[2]:=* **Interval[{-2, 5}]^2** *Out[2]=* Interval[{0, 25}]
Taking the reciprocal gives two distinct intervals.	*In[3]:=* **1/Interval[{-2, 5}]** *Out[3]=* Interval$\left[\left\{-\infty, -\frac{1}{2}\right\}, \left\{\frac{1}{5}, \infty\right\}\right]$

Abs folds the intervals back together again.	$In[4]:=$ **Abs[%]** $Out[4]=$ $\text{Interval}\left[\left\{\dfrac{1}{5}, \infty\right\}\right]$
You can use intervals in many kinds of functions.	$In[5]:=$ **Solve[3 x + 2 == Interval[{-2, 5}], x]** $Out[5]=$ $\left\{\left\{x \to \text{Interval}\left[\left\{-\dfrac{4}{3}, 1\right\}\right]\right\}\right\}$
Some functions automatically generate intervals.	$In[6]:=$ **Limit[Sin[1/x], x -> 0]** $Out[6]=$ Interval[{-1, 1}]

+ **IntervalUnion[***interval***$_1$, *interval*$_2$, ...]**
  find the union of several intervals

+ **IntervalIntersection[***interval***$_1$, *interval*$_2$, ...]**
  find the intersection of several intervals

+ **IntervalMemberQ[***interval***, *x*]**   test whether the point *x* lies within an interval

+ **IntervalMemberQ[***interval***$_1$, *interval*$_2$]**
  test whether *interval*$_2$ lies completely within *interval*$_1$

Operations on intervals.

This finds the overlap of the two intervals.	$In[7]:=$ **IntervalIntersection[Interval[{3, 7}], Interval[{-2, 5}]]** $Out[7]=$ Interval[{3, 5}]
You can use Max and Min to find the end points of intervals.	$In[8]:=$ **Max[%]** $Out[8]=$ 5
This finds out which of a list of intervals contains the point 7.	$In[9]:=$ **IntervalMemberQ[** **Table[Interval[{i, i+1}], {i, 1, 20, 3}], 7]** $Out[9]=$ {False, False, True, False, False, False, False}

You can use intervals not only with exact quantities but also with approximate numbers. Even with machine-precision numbers, *Mathematica* always tries to do rounding in such a way as to preserve the validity of results.

This shows explicitly the interval treated by *Mathematica* as the machine-precision number 0.	$In[10]:=$ **Interval[0.]** $Out[10]=$ Interval[{-2.22507 $\times 10^{-308}$, 2.22507 $\times 10^{-308}$}]
This shows the corresponding interval around 100., shifted back to zero.	$In[11]:=$ **Interval[100.] - 100** $Out[11]=$ Interval[{-1.42108 $\times 10^{-14}$, 1.42108 $\times 10^{-14}$}]
The same kind of thing works with numbers of any precision.	$In[12]:=$ **Interval[N[Pi, 50]] - Pi** $Out[12]=$ Interval[{-8. $\times 10^{-50}$, 8. $\times 10^{-50}$}]

With ordinary machine-precision arithmetic, this computation gives an incorrect result.

In[13]:= `Sin[N[Pi]]`

Out[13]= 1.22461×10^{-16}

The interval generated here, however, includes the correct value of 0.

In[14]:= `Sin[Interval[N[Pi]]]`

Out[14]= `Interval[`$\{-3.21629 \times 10^{-16}, 5.6655 \times 10^{-16}\}$`]`

■ 3.1.8 Advanced Topic: Indeterminate and Infinite Results

If you type in an expression like 0/0, *Mathematica* prints a message, and returns the result Indeterminate.

In[1]:= `0/0`

Power::infy: Infinite expression $\frac{1}{0}$ encountered.

Infinity::indet:
    Indeterminate expression 0 ComplexInfinity encountered.

Out[1]= Indeterminate

An expression like 0/0 is an example of an *indeterminate numerical result*. If you type in 0/0, there is no way for *Mathematica* to know what answer you want. If you got 0/0 by taking the limit of x/x as $x \to 0$, then you might want the answer 1. On the other hand, if you got 0/0 instead as the limit of $2x/x$, then you probably want the answer 2. The expression 0/0 on its own does not contain enough information to choose between these and other cases. As a result, its value must be considered indeterminate.

Whenever an indeterminate result is produced in an arithmetic computation, *Mathematica* prints a warning message, and then returns Indeterminate as the result of the computation. If you ever try to use Indeterminate in an arithmetic computation, you always get the result Indeterminate. A single indeterminate expression effectively "poisons" any arithmetic computation. (The symbol Indeterminate plays a role in *Mathematica* similar to the "not a number" object in the IEEE Floating Point Standard.)

The usual laws of arithmetic simplification are suspended in the case of Indeterminate.

In[2]:= `Indeterminate - Indeterminate`

Out[2]= Indeterminate

Indeterminate "poisons" any arithmetic computation, and leads to an indeterminate result.

In[3]:= `2 Indeterminate - 7`

Out[3]= Indeterminate

When you do arithmetic computations inside *Mathematica* programs, it is often important to be able to tell whether indeterminate results were generated in the computations. You can do this by using the function Check discussed on page 461 to test whether any warning messages associated with indeterminate results were produced.

You can use `Check` inside a program to test whether warning messages are generated in a computation.

In[4]:= **Check[(7 - 7)/(8 - 8), meaningless]**

$$\text{Power::infy: Infinite expression } \frac{1}{0} \text{ encountered.}$$

Infinity::indet:
    Indeterminate expression 0 ComplexInfinity encountered.

Out[4]= meaningless

`Indeterminate`	an indeterminate numerical result
`Infinity`	a positive infinite quantity
`-Infinity`	a negative infinite quantity (`DirectedInfinity[-1]`)
`DirectedInfinity[r]`	an infinite quantity with complex direction *r*
`ComplexInfinity`	an infinite quantity with an undetermined direction
`DirectedInfinity[ ]`	equivalent to `ComplexInfinity`

Indeterminate and infinite quantities.

There are many situations where it is convenient to be able to do calculations with infinite quantities. The symbol `Infinity` in *Mathematica* represents a positive infinite quantity. You can use it to specify such things as limits of sums and integrals. You can also do some arithmetic calculations with it.

Here is an integral with an infinite limit.

In[5]:= **Integrate[1/x^3, {x, 1, Infinity}]**

$$Out[5]= \frac{1}{2}$$

Mathematica knows that $1/\infty = 0$.

In[6]:= **1/Infinity**

Out[6]= 0

If you try to find the difference between two infinite quantities, you get an indeterminate result.

In[7]:= **Infinity - Infinity**

Infinity::indet:
    Indeterminate expression (-Infinity) + (Infinity)
      encountered.

Out[7]= Indeterminate

There are a number of subtle points that arise in handling infinite quantities. One of them concerns the "direction" of an infinite quantity. When you do an infinite integral, you typically think of performing the integration along a path in the complex plane that goes to infinity in some direction. In this case, it is important to distinguish different versions of infinity that correspond to different directions in the complex plane. $+\infty$ and $-\infty$ are two examples, but for some purposes one also needs $i\infty$ and so on.

In *Mathematica*, infinite quantities can have a "direction", specified by a complex number. When you type in the symbol `Infinity`, representing a positive infinite quantity, this is converted internally to the form `DirectedInfinity[1]`, which represents an infinite quantity in the +1 direction. Similarly, `-Infinity` becomes `DirectedInfinity[-1]`, and `I Infinity` becomes `DirectedInfinity[I]`. Although the `DirectedInfinity` form is always used internally, the standard output format for `DirectedInfinity[r]` is r `Infinity`.

Infinity is converted internally to `DirectedInfinity[1]`.	`In[8]:= Infinity // FullForm`
	
	`Out[8]//FullForm= DirectedInfinity[1]`

Although the notion of a "directed infinity" is often useful, it is not always available. If you type in 1/0, you get an infinite result, but there is no way to determine the "direction" of the infinity. *Mathematica* represents the result of 1/0 as `DirectedInfinity[ ]`. In standard output form, this undirected infinity is printed out as `ComplexInfinity`.

1/0 gives an undirected form of infinity.

`In[9]:= 1/0`

```
                              1
Power::infy: Infinite expression - encountered.
                              0
```

`Out[9]= ComplexInfinity`

■ 3.1.9 Advanced Topic: Controlling Numerical Evaluation

+	`NHoldAll`	prevent any arguments of a function from being affected by N
+	`NHoldFirst`	prevent the first argument from being affected
+	`NHoldRest`	prevent all but the first argument from being affected

Attributes for controlling numerical evaluation.

Usually N goes inside functions and gets applied to each of their arguments.

`In[1]:= N[f[2/3, Pi]]`

`Out[1]= f[0.666667, 3.14159]`

This tells *Mathematica* not to apply N to the first argument of f.

`In[2]:= SetAttributes[f, NHoldFirst]`

Now the first argument of f is left in its exact form.

`In[3]:= N[f[2/3, Pi]]`

$$Out[3]= f\left[\frac{2}{3}, 3.14159\right]$$

3.2 Mathematical Functions

■ 3.2.1 Naming Conventions

Mathematical functions in *Mathematica* are given names according to definite rules. As with most *Mathematica* functions, the names are usually complete English words, fully spelled out. For a few very common functions, *Mathematica* uses the traditional abbreviations. Thus the modulo function, for example, is Mod, not Modulo.

Mathematical functions that are usually referred to by a person's name have names in *Mathematica* of the form *PersonSymbol*. Thus, for example, the Legendre polynomials $P_n(x)$ are denoted LegendreP[n, x]. Although this convention does lead to longer function names, it avoids any ambiguity or confusion.

When the standard notation for a mathematical function involves both subscripts and superscripts, the subscripts are given *before* the superscripts in the *Mathematica* form. Thus, for example, the associated Legendre polynomials $P_n^m(x)$ are denoted LegendreP[n, m, x].

■ 3.2.2 Numerical Functions

IntegerPart[x]	integer part of x
FractionalPart[x]	fractional part of x
Round[x]	integer $\langle x \rangle$ closest to x
Floor[x]	greatest integer $\lfloor x \rfloor$ not larger than x
Ceiling[x]	least integer $\lceil x \rceil$ not smaller than x
Sign[x]	1 for $x > 0$, −1 for $x < 0$
Abs[x]	absolute value $\|x\|$ of x
Max[x_1, x_2, ...] or Max[{x_1, x_2, ... }, ...]	the maximum of x_1, x_2, ...
Min[x_1, x_2, ...] or Min[{x_1, x_2, ... }, ...]	the minimum of x_1, x_2, ...

Some numerical functions of real variables.

x	IntegerPart[x]	FractionalPart[x]	Round[x]	Floor[x]	Ceiling[x]
2.4	2	0.4	2	2	3
2.5	2	0.5	2	2	3
2.6	2	0.6	3	2	3
-2.4	-2	-0.4	-2	-3	-2
-2.5	-2	-0.5	-2	-3	-2
-2.6	-2	-0.6	-3	-3	-2

Extracting integer and fractional parts.

IntegerPart[x] and FractionalPart[x] can be thought of as extracting digits to the left and right of the decimal point. Round[x] is often used for forcing numbers that are close to integers to be exactly integers. Floor[x] and Ceiling[x] often arise in working out how many elements there will be in sequences of numbers with non-integer spacings.

x + I y	the complex number $x + iy$
Re[z]	the real part $\mathrm{Re}\, z$
Im[z]	the imaginary part $\mathrm{Im}\, z$
Conjugate[z]	the complex conjugate z^* or $\bar{z}$
Abs[z]	the absolute value $|z|$
Arg[z]	the argument ϕ such that $z = |z|e^{i\phi}$

Numerical functions of complex variables.

■ 3.2.3 Pseudorandom Numbers

Random[ ]	a pseudorandom real between 0 and 1
Random[Real, *xmax*]	a pseudorandom real between 0 and *xmax*
Random[Real, {*xmin*, *xmax*}]	a pseudorandom real between *xmin* and *xmax*
Random[Complex]	a pseudorandom complex number in the unit square
Random[Complex, {*zmin*, *zmax*}]	a pseudorandom complex number in the rectangle defined by *zmin* and *zmax*
Random[*type*, *range*, *n*]	an *n*-digit pseudorandom number
Random[Integer]	0 or 1 with probability $\frac{1}{2}$
Random[Integer, {*imin*, *imax*}]	a pseudorandom integer between *imin* and *imax*, inclusive
SeedRandom[ ]	reseed the pseudorandom generator, with the time of day
SeedRandom[*s*]	reseed with the integer *s*
$RandomState	the current state of the pseudorandom generator

Pseudorandom number generation.

This gives a list of 3 pseudorandom numbers.	`In[1]:= Table[Random[ ], {3}]` `Out[1]= {0.0560708, 0.6303, 0.359894}`
Here is a 30-digit pseudorandom real number in the range 0 to 1.	`In[2]:= Random[Real, {0, 1}, 30]` `Out[2]= 0.748823044099679773836330229377`
This gives a list of 8 pseudorandom integers between 100 and 200 (inclusive).	`In[3]:= Table[Random[Integer, {100, 200}], {8}]` `Out[3]= {120, 108, 109, 147, 146, 189, 188, 187}`

If you call Random[ ] repeatedly, you should get a "typical" sequence of numbers, with no particular pattern. There are many ways to use such numbers.

One common way to use pseudorandom numbers is in making numerical tests of hypotheses. For example, if you believe that two symbolic expressions are mathematically equal, you can test this by plugging in "typical" numerical values for symbolic parameters, and then comparing the numerical results. (If you do this, you should be careful about numerical accuracy problems and about functions of complex variables that may not have unique values.)

Here is a symbolic equation.	*In[4]:=* `Sin[Cos[x]] == Cos[Sin[x]]`
	Out[4]= Sin[Cos[x]] == Cos[Sin[x]]
Substituting in a random numerical value shows that the equation is not always True.	*In[5]:=* `% /. x -> Random[ ]`
	Out[5]= False

Other common uses of pseudorandom numbers include simulating probabilistic processes, and sampling large spaces of possibilities. The pseudorandom numbers that *Mathematica* generates are always uniformly distributed over the range you specify.

Random is unlike almost any other *Mathematica* function in that every time you call it, you potentially get a different result. If you use Random in a calculation, therefore, you may get different answers on different occasions.

The sequences that you get from Random[ ] are not in most senses "truly random", although they should be "random enough" for practical purposes. The sequences are in fact produced by applying a definite mathematical algorithm, starting from a particular "seed". If you give the same seed, then you get the same sequence.

When *Mathematica* starts up, it takes the time of day (measured in small fractions of a second) as the seed for the pseudorandom number generator. Two different *Mathematica* sessions will therefore almost always give different sequences of pseudorandom numbers.

If you want to make sure that you always get the same sequence of pseudorandom numbers, you can explicitly give a seed for the pseudorandom generator, using SeedRandom.

This reseeds the pseudorandom generator.	*In[6]:=* `SeedRandom[143]`
Here are three pseudorandom numbers.	*In[7]:=* `Table[Random[ ], {3}]`
	Out[7]= {0.952311, 0.93591, 0.813754}
If you reseed the pseudorandom generator with the same seed, you get the same sequence of pseudorandom numbers.	*In[8]:=* `SeedRandom[143]; Table[Random[ ], {3}]`
	Out[8]= {0.952311, 0.93591, 0.813754}

Every single time Random is called, the internal state of the pseudorandom generator that it uses is changed. This means that calls to Random made in subsidiary calculations will have an effect on the numbers returned by Random in your main calculation. To avoid any problems associated with this, you can save the value of $RandomState before you do subsidiary calculations, and then restore it afterwards.

By localizing the value of $RandomState using Block, the internal state of the pseudorandom generator is restored after generating the first list.	*In[9]:=* `{Block[{$RandomState}, {Random[ ], Random[ ]}],` `{Random[ ], Random[ ]}}`
	Out[9]= {{0.1169, 0.783447}, {0.1169, 0.783447}}

■ 3.2.4 Integer and Number-Theoretical Functions

Mod[k, n]	k modulo n (remainder from dividing k by n)
Quotient[m, n]	the quotient of m and n (integer part of m/n)
GCD[n_1, n_2, ...]	the greatest common divisor of n_1, n_2, ...
LCM[n_1, n_2, ...]	the least common multiple of n_1, n_2, ...
IntegerDigits[n, b]	the digits of n in base b

Some integer functions.

The remainder on dividing 17 by 3.

```
In[1]:= Mod[17, 3]
Out[1]= 2
```

The integer part of 17/3.

```
In[2]:= Quotient[17, 3]
Out[2]= 5
```

Mod also works with real numbers.

```
In[3]:= Mod[5.6, 1.2]
Out[3]= 0.8
```

The result from Mod always has the same sign as the second argument.

```
In[4]:= Mod[-5.6, 1.2]
Out[4]= 0.4
```

For any integers a and b, it is always true that b*Quotient[a, b] + Mod[a, b] is equal to a.

The **greatest common divisor** function GCD[n_1, n_2, ...] gives the largest integer that divides all the n_i exactly. When you enter a ratio of two integers, *Mathematica* effectively uses GCD to cancel out common factors, and give a rational number in lowest terms.

The **least common multiple** function LCM[n_1, n_2, ...] gives the smallest integer that contains all the factors of each of the n_i.

The largest integer that divides both 24 and 15 is 3.

```
In[5]:= GCD[24, 15]
Out[5]= 3
```

FactorInteger[n]	a list of the prime factors of n, and their exponents
Divisors[n]	a list of the integers that divide n
Prime[k]	the kth prime number
PrimePi[x]	the number of primes less than or equal to x
PrimeQ[n]	give True if n is a prime, and False otherwise
FactorInteger[n, GaussianIntegers->True]	a list of the Gaussian prime factors of the Gaussian integer n, and their exponents
PrimeQ[n, GaussianIntegers->True]	give True if n is a Gaussian prime, and False otherwise

Integer factoring and related functions.

This gives the factors of 24 as 2^3, 3^1. The first element in each list is the factor; the second is its exponent.

```
In[6]:= FactorInteger[24]
Out[6]= {{2, 3}, {3, 1}}
```

Here are the factors of a larger integer.

```
In[7]:= FactorInteger[111111111111111111]
Out[7]= {{3, 2}, {7, 1}, {11, 1}, {13, 1}, {19, 1},
        {37, 1}, {52579, 1}, {333667, 1}}
```

You should realize that according to current mathematical thinking, integer factoring is a fundamentally difficult computational problem. As a result, you can easily type in an integer that *Mathematica* will not be able to factor in anything short of an astronomical length of time. As long as the integers you give are less than about 20 digits long, FactorInteger should have no trouble. Only in special cases, however, will it be able to deal with much longer integers. (You can make some factoring problems go faster by setting the option FactorComplete->False, so that FactorInteger[n] tries to pull out only easy factors from n.)

Here is a rather special long integer.

```
In[8]:= 30!
Out[8]= 265252859812191058636308480000000
```

Mathematica can easily factor this special integer.

```
In[9]:= FactorInteger[%]
Out[9]= {{2, 26}, {3, 14}, {5, 7}, {7, 4}, {11, 2}, {13, 2},
        {17, 1}, {19, 1}, {23, 1}, {29, 1}}
```

Although *Mathematica* may not be able to factor a large integer, it can often still test whether or not the integer is a prime. In addition, *Mathematica* has a fast way of finding the kth prime number.

It is often much faster to test whether a number is prime than to factor it.

```
In[10]:= PrimeQ[234242423]
Out[10]= False
```

Here is a plot of the first 100 primes.   *In[11]:=* **ListPlot[Table[Prime[n], {n, 100}]]**

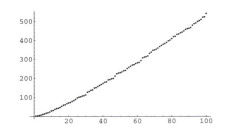

This is the millionth prime.   *In[12]:=* **Prime[1000000]**

                                           Out[12]= 15485863

Particularly in number theory, it is often more important to know the distribution of primes than their actual values. The function PrimePi[x] gives the number of primes $\pi(x)$ that are less than or equal to x.

This gives the number of primes less   *In[13]:=* **PrimePi[10^9]**
than a billion.
                                          Out[13]= 50847534

By default, FactorInteger allows only real integers. But with the option setting GaussianIntegers -> True, it also handles **Gaussian integers**, which are complex numbers with integer real and imaginary parts. Just as it is possible to factor uniquely in terms of real primes, it is also possible to factor uniquely in terms of Gaussian primes. There is nevertheless some potential ambiguity in the choice of Gaussian primes. In *Mathematica*, they are always chosen to have positive real parts, and non-negative imaginary parts, except for a possible initial factor of -1 or $\pm i$.

Over the Gaussian integers, 2 can be   *In[14]:=* **FactorInteger[2, GaussianIntegers -> True]**
factored as $(-i)(1+i)^2$.
                                          Out[14]= {{-I, 1}, {1 + I, 2}}

Here are the factors of a Gaussian   *In[15]:=* **FactorInteger[111 + 78 I, GaussianIntegers -> True]**
integer.
                                          Out[15]= {{2 + I, 1}, {3, 1}, {20 + 3 I, 1}}

PowerMod[a, b, n]	the power a^b modulo n
EulerPhi[n]	the Euler totient function $\phi(n)$
MoebiusMu[n]	the Möbius function $\mu(n)$
DivisorSigma[k, n]	the divisor function $\sigma_k(n)$
JacobiSymbol[n, m]	the Jacobi symbol $\left(\frac{n}{m}\right)$
ExtendedGCD[m, n]	the extended gcd of m and n
LatticeReduce[$\{v_1, v_2, \dots\}$]	the reduced lattice basis for the set of integer vectors v_i

Some functions from number theory.

The **modular power function** PowerMod[a, b, n] gives exactly the same results as Mod[$a \wedge b$, n] for $b > 0$. PowerMod is much more efficient, however, because it avoids generating the full form of $a \wedge b$.

You can use PowerMod not only to find positive modular powers, but also to find **modular inverses**. For negative b, PowerMod[a, b, n] gives, if possible, an integer k such that $ka^{-b} \equiv 1 \bmod n$. (Whenever such an integer exists, it is guaranteed to be unique modulo n.) If no such integer k exists, *Mathematica* leaves PowerMod unevaluated.

PowerMod is equivalent to using Power, then Mod, but is much more efficient.

In[16]:= **PowerMod[2, 13451, 3]**

Out[16]= 2

This gives the modular inverse of 3 modulo 7.

In[17]:= **PowerMod[3, -1, 7]**

Out[17]= 5

Multiplying the inverse by 3 modulo 7 gives 1, as expected.

In[18]:= **Mod[3 %, 7]**

Out[18]= 1

The **Euler totient function** $\phi(n)$ gives the number of integers less than n that are relatively prime to n. An important relation (Fermat's Little Theorem) is that $a^{\phi(n)} \equiv 1 \bmod n$ for all a relatively prime to n.

The **Möbius function** $\mu(n)$ is defined to be $(-1)^k$ if n is a product of k distinct primes, and 0 if n contains a squared factor (other than 1). An important relation is the Möbius inversion formula, which states that if $g(n) = \sum_{d|n} f(d)$ for all n, then $f(n) = \sum_{d|n} \mu(d) g(n/d)$, where the sums are over all positive integers d that divide n.

The **divisor function** $\sigma_k(n)$ is the sum of the kth powers of the divisors of n. The function $\sigma_0(n)$ gives the total number of divisors of n, and is often denoted $d(n)$. The function $\sigma_1(n)$, equal to the sum of the divisors of n, is often denoted $\sigma(n)$.

For prime n, $\phi(n) = n - 1$.

In[19]:= **EulerPhi[17]**

Out[19]= 16

The result is 1, as guaranteed by Fermat's Little Theorem.	$In[20]:=$ **PowerMod[3, %, 17]** $Out[20]=$ 1
This gives a list of all the divisors of 24.	$In[21]:=$ **Divisors[24]** $Out[21]=$ {1, 2, 3, 4, 6, 8, 12, 24}
$\sigma_0(n)$ gives the total number of distinct divisors of 24.	$In[22]:=$ **DivisorSigma[0, 24]** $Out[22]=$ 8

The **Jacobi symbol** JacobiSymbol[n, m] reduces to the **Legendre symbol** $\left(\frac{n}{m}\right)$ when m is an odd prime. The Legendre symbol is equal to zero if n is divisible by m, otherwise it is equal to 1 if n is a quadratic residue modulo the prime m, and to -1 if it is not. An integer n relatively prime to m is said to be a quadratic residue modulo m if there exists an integer k such that $k^2 \equiv n \bmod m$. The full Jacobi symbol is a product of the Legendre symbols $\left(\frac{n}{p_i}\right)$ for each of the prime factors p_i such that $m = \prod_i p_i$.

The **extended gcd** ExtendedGCD[m, n] gives a list $\{g, \{r, s\}\}$ where g is the greatest common divisor of m and n, and r and s are integers such that $g = rm + sn$. The extended gcd is important in finding integer solutions to linear (Diophantine) equations.

The first number in the list is the gcd of 105 and 196.	$In[23]:=$ **ExtendedGCD[105, 196]** $Out[23]=$ {7, {15, -8}}
The second pair of numbers satisfies $g = rm + sn$.	$In[24]:=$ **15 105 - 8 196** $Out[24]=$ 7

The lattice reduction function LatticeReduce[$\{v_1, v_2, \ldots\}$] is used in several kinds of modern algorithms. The basic idea is to think of the vectors v_k of integers as defining a mathematical *lattice*. The vector representing each point in the lattice can be written as a linear combination of the form $\sum c_k v_k$, where the c_k are integers. For a particular lattice, there are many possible choices of the "basis vectors" v_k. What LatticeReduce does is to find a reduced set of basis vectors $\bar{v}_k$ for the lattice, with certain special properties.

Three unit vectors along the three coordinate axes already form a reduced basis.	$In[25]:=$ **LatticeReduce[{{1,0,0},{0,1,0},{0,0,1}}]** $Out[25]=$ {{1, 0, 0}, {0, 1, 0}, {0, 0, 1}}
This gives the reduced basis for a lattice in four-dimensional space specified by three vectors.	$In[26]:=$ **LatticeReduce[{{1,0,0,12345}, {0,1,0,12435}, {0,0,1,12354}}]** $Out[26]=$ {{-1, 0, 1, 9}, {9, 1, -10, 0}, {85, -143, 59, 6}}

Notice that in the last example, LatticeReduce replaces vectors that are nearly parallel by vectors that are more perpendicular. In the process, it finds some quite short basis vectors.

■ 3.2.5 Combinatorial Functions

$n!$	factorial $n(n-1)(n-2) \times \ldots \times 1$
$n!!$	double factorial $n(n-2)(n-4) \times \ldots$
Binomial[n, m]	binomial coefficient $\binom{n}{m} = n!/[m!(n-m)!]$
Multinomial[n_1, n_2, ...]	multinomial coefficient $(n_1 + n_2 + \ldots)!/(n_1!n_2!\ldots)$
Fibonacci[n]	Fibonacci number F_n
Fibonacci[n, x]	Fibonacci polynomial $F_n(x)$
BernoulliB[n]	Bernoulli number B_n
BernoulliB[n, x]	Bernoulli polynomial $B_n(x)$
EulerE[n]	Euler number E_n
EulerE[n, x]	Euler polynomial $E_n(x)$
StirlingS1[n, m]	Stirling number of the first kind $S_n^{(m)}$
StirlingS2[n, m]	Stirling number of the second kind $S_n^{(m)}$
PartitionsP[n]	the number $p(n)$ of unrestricted partitions of the integer n
PartitionsQ[n]	the number $q(n)$ of partitions of n into distinct parts
Signature[{i_1, i_2, ... }]	the signature of a permutation

Combinatorial functions.

The **factorial function** $n!$ gives the number of ways of ordering n objects. For non-integer n, the numerical value of $n!$ is obtained from the gamma function, discussed in Section 3.2.10.

The **binomial coefficient** Binomial[n, m] can be written as $\binom{n}{m} = n!/[m!(n-m)!]$. It gives the number of ways of choosing m objects from a collection of n objects, without regard to order. The **Catalan numbers**, which appear in various tree enumeration problems, are given in terms of binomial coefficients as $c_n = \binom{2n}{n}/(n+1)$.

The **multinomial coefficient** Multinomial[n_1, n_2, ...], denoted $(N; n_1, n_2, \ldots, n_m) = N!/(n_1!n_2!\ldots n_m!)$, gives the number of ways of partitioning N distinct objects into m sets of sizes n_i (with $N = \sum_{i=1}^{m} n_i$).

Mathematica gives the exact integer result for the factorial of an integer.

```
In[1]:= 30!
Out[1]= 265252859812191058636308480000000
```

For non-integers, *Mathematica* evaluates factorials using the gamma function.

```
In[2]:= 3.6!
Out[2]= 13.3813
```

Mathematica can give symbolic results for some binomial coefficients.

```
In[3]:= Binomial[n, 2]
```

$$Out[3]= \frac{(-1+n)\,n}{2}$$

This gives the number of ways of partitioning $6 + 5 = 11$ objects into sets containing 6 and 5 objects.

```
In[4]:= Multinomial[6, 5]
Out[4]= 462
```

The result is the same as $\binom{11}{6}$.

```
In[5]:= Binomial[11, 6]
Out[5]= 462
```

The **Fibonacci numbers** Fibonacci[n] satisfy the recurrence relation $F_n = F_{n-1} + F_{n-2}$ with $F_1 = F_2 = 1$. They appear in a wide range of discrete mathematical problems. For large n, F_n/F_{n-1} approaches the golden ratio.

The **Fibonacci polynomials** Fibonacci[n, x] appear as the coefficients of t^n in the expansion of $t/(1 - xt - t^2) = \sum_{n=0}^{\infty} F_n(x)t^n/n!$.

The **Bernoulli polynomials** BernoulliB[n, x] satisfy the generating function relation $te^{xt}/(e^t - 1) = \sum_{n=0}^{\infty} B_n(x)t^n/n!$. The **Bernoulli numbers** BernoulliB[n] are given by $B_n = B_n(0)$. The B_n appear as the coefficients of the terms in the Euler-Maclaurin summation formula for approximating integrals.

Numerical values for Bernoulli numbers are needed in many numerical algorithms. You can always get these numerical values by first finding exact rational results using BernoulliB[n], and then applying N.

The **Euler polynomials** EulerE[n, x] have generating function $2e^{xt}/(e^t + 1) = \sum_{n=0}^{\infty} E_n(x)t^n/n!$, and the **Euler numbers** EulerE[n] are given by $E_n = 2^n E_n(\frac{1}{2})$. The Euler numbers are related to the **Genocchi numbers** by $G_n = 2^{2-2n}nE_{2n-1}$.

This gives the second Bernoulli polynomial $B_2(x)$.

```
In[6]:= BernoulliB[2, x]
```

$$Out[6]= \frac{1}{6} - x + x^2$$

You can also get Bernoulli polynomials by explicitly computing the power series for the generating function.

```
In[7]:= Series[t Exp[x t]/(Exp[t] - 1), {t, 0, 4}]
```

$$Out[7]= 1 + \left(-\frac{1}{2} + x\right)t + \left(\frac{1}{12} - \frac{x}{2} + \frac{x^2}{2}\right)t^2 + \left(\frac{x}{12} - \frac{x^2}{4} + \frac{x^3}{6}\right)$$

$$t^3 + \left(-\frac{1}{720} + \frac{x^2}{24} - \frac{x^3}{12} + \frac{x^4}{24}\right)t^4 + O[t]^5$$

BernoulliB[*n*] gives exact
rational-number results for Bernoulli
numbers.

In[8]:= **BernoulliB[20]**

$$Out[8]= -\frac{174611}{330}$$

Stirling numbers show up in many combinatorial enumeration problems. For **Stirling numbers of the first kind** StirlingS1[*n*, *m*], $(-1)^{n-m}S_n^{(m)}$ gives the number of permutations of *n* elements which contain exactly *m* cycles. These Stirling numbers satisfy the generating function relation $x(x-1)\ldots(x-n+1) = \sum_{m=0}^{n} S_n^{(m)}x^m$. Note that some definitions of the $S_n^{(m)}$ differ by a factor $(-1)^{n-m}$ from what is used in *Mathematica*.

Stirling numbers of the second kind StirlingS2[*n*, *m*] give the number of ways of partitioning a set of *n* elements into *m* non-empty subsets. They satisfy the relation $x^n = \sum_{m=0}^{n} S_n^{(m)}x(x-1)\ldots(x-m+1)$.

The **partition function** PartitionsP[*n*] gives the number of ways of writing the integer *n* as a sum of positive integers, without regard to order. PartitionsQ[*n*] gives the number of ways of writing *n* as a sum of positive integers, with the constraint that all the integers in each sum are distinct.

This gives a table of Stirling numbers
of the first kind.

In[9]:= **Table[StirlingS1[5, i], {i, 5}]**

Out[9]= {24, -50, 35, -10, 1}

The Stirling numbers appear as
coefficients in this product.

In[10]:= **Expand[Product[x - i, {i, 0, 4}]]**

$Out[10]= 24x - 50x^2 + 35x^3 - 10x^4 + x^5$

This gives the number of partitions of
100, with and without the constraint
that the terms should be distinct.

In[11]:= **{PartitionsQ[100], PartitionsP[100]}**

Out[11]= {444793, 190569292}

The partition function $p(n)$ increases
asymptotically like $e^{\sqrt{n}}$. Note that you
cannot simply use Plot to generate a
plot of a function like PartitionsP
because the function can only be
evaluated with integer arguments.

In[12]:= **ListPlot[Table[**
          N[Log[PartitionsP[n]]], {n, 100}]]

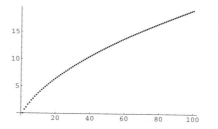

The functions in this section allow you to *enumerate* various kinds of combinatorial objects. Functions like Permutations, discussed in Section 1.8.13, allow you instead to *generate* lists of various combinations of elements.

The **signature function** Signature[{i_1, i_2, ... }] gives the signature of a permutation. It is equal to +1 for even permutations (composed of an even number of transpositions), and to −1 for odd permutations. The signature function can be thought of as a totally antisymmetric tensor, **Levi-Civita symbol** or **epsilon symbol**.

```
ClebschGordan[{j₁, m₁}, {j₂, m₂}, {j, m}]
                        Clebsch-Gordan coefficient

ThreeJSymbol[{j₁, m₁}, {j₂, m₂}, {j₃, m₃}]
                        Wigner 3-j symbol

SixJSymbol[{j₁, j₂, j₃}, {j₄, j₅, j₆}]
                        Racah 6-j symbol
```

Rotational coupling coefficients.

Clebsch-Gordan coefficients and n-j symbols arise in the study of angular momenta in quantum mechanics, and in other applications of the rotation group. The **Clebsch-Gordan coefficients** ClebschGordan[{j_1, m_1}, {j_2, m_2}, {j, m}] give the coefficients in the expansion of the quantum mechanical angular momentum state $|j, m\rangle$ in terms of products of states $|j_1, m_1\rangle |j_2, m_2\rangle$.

The **3-j symbols** or **Wigner coefficients** ThreeJSymbol[{j_1, m_1}, {j_2, m_2}, {j_3, m_3}] are a more symmetrical form of Clebsch-Gordan coefficients. In *Mathematica*, the Clebsch-Gordan coefficients are given in terms of 3-j symbols by $C^{j_1 j_2 j_3}_{m_1 m_2 m_3} = (-1)^{m_3 + j_1 - j_2} \sqrt{2j_3 + 1} \begin{pmatrix} j_1 & j_2 & j_3 \\ m_1 & m_2 & -m_3 \end{pmatrix}$.

The **6-j symbols** SixJSymbol[{j_1, j_2, j_3}, {j_4, j_5, j_6}] give the couplings of three quantum mechanical angular momentum states. The **Racah coefficients** are related by a phase to the 6-j symbols.

You can give symbolic parameters in 3-j symbols.

$In[13]:=$ **ThreeJSymbol[{j, m}, {j+1/2, -m-1/2}, {1/2, 1/2}]**

$Out[13]= -\dfrac{(-1)^{-j+m} \sqrt{1 + j + m}}{\sqrt{1 + 2j} \, \sqrt{2 + 2j}}$

■ 3.2.6 Elementary Transcendental Functions

Exp[z]	exponential function e^z
Log[z]	logarithm $\log_e(z)$
Log[b, z]	logarithm $\log_b(z)$ to base b

Sin[z], Cos[z], Tan[z], Csc[z], Sec[z], Cot[z]
trigonometric functions (with arguments in radians)

ArcSin[z], ArcCos[z], ArcTan[z], ArcCsc[z], ArcSec[z], ArcCot[z]
inverse trigonometric functions (giving results in radians)

ArcTan[x, y] the argument of $x + iy$

Sinh[z], Cosh[z], Tanh[z], Csch[z], Sech[z], Coth[z]
hyperbolic functions

ArcSinh[z], ArcCosh[z], ArcTanh[z], ArcCsch[z], ArcSech[z], ArcCoth[z]
inverse hyperbolic functions

Elementary transcendental functions.

Mathematica gives exact results for logarithms whenever it can. Here is $\log_2 1024$.

```
In[1]:= Log[2, 1024]
Out[1]= 10
```

You can find the numerical values of mathematical functions to any precision.

```
In[2]:= N[Log[2], 40]
Out[2]= 0.6931471805599453094172321214581765680755
```

This gives a complex number result.

```
In[3]:= N[ Log[-2] ]
Out[3]= 0.693147 + 3.14159 I
```

Mathematica can evaluate logarithms with complex arguments.

```
In[4]:= N[ Log[2 + 8 I] ]
Out[4]= 2.10975 + 1.32582 I
```

The arguments of trigonometric functions are always given in radians.

```
In[5]:= Sin[Pi/2]
Out[5]= 1
```

You can convert from degrees by explicitly multiplying by the constant Degree.

```
In[6]:= N[ Sin[30 Degree] ]
Out[6]= 0.5
```

Here is a plot of the hyperbolic tangent function. It has a characteristic "sigmoidal" form.

In[7]:= **Plot[Tanh[x], {x, -8, 8}]**

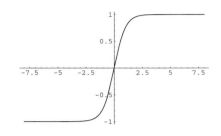

There are a number of additional trigonometric and hyperbolic functions that are sometimes used. The **versine** function is defined as $\text{vers}(z) = 1 - \cos(z)$. The **haversine** is simply $\text{hav}(z) = \frac{1}{2}\text{vers}(z)$. The complex exponential e^{ix} is sometimes written as $\text{cis}(x)$. The **gudermannian function** is defined as $\text{gd}(z) = 2\tan^{-1}(e^z) - \frac{\pi}{2}$. The **inverse gudermannian** is $\text{gd}^{-1}(z) = \log[\sec(z) + \tan(z)]$. The gudermannian satisfies such relations as $\sinh(z) = \tan[\text{gd}(x)]$.

■ 3.2.7 Functions That Do Not Have Unique Values

When you ask for the square root s of a number a, you are effectively asking for the solution to the equation $s^2 = a$. This equation, however, in general has two different solutions. Both $s = 2$ and $s = -2$ are, for example, solutions to the equation $s^2 = 4$. When you evaluate the "function" $\sqrt{4}$, however, you usually want to get a single number, and so you have to choose one of these two solutions. A standard choice is that $\sqrt{x}$ should be positive for $x > 0$. This is what the *Mathematica* function $\text{Sqrt}[x]$ does.

The need to make one choice from two solutions means that $\text{Sqrt}[x]$ cannot be a true *inverse function* for $x\char`^2$. Taking a number, squaring it, and then taking the square root can give you a different number than you started with.

$\sqrt{4}$ gives +2, not −2.

In[1]:= **Sqrt[4]**

Out[1]= 2

Squaring and taking the square root does not necessarily give you the number you started with.

In[2]:= **Sqrt[(-2)^2]**

Out[2]= 2

When you evaluate $\sqrt{-2i}$, there are again two possible answers: $-1 + i$ and $1 - i$. In this case, however, it is less clear which one to choose.

There is in fact no way to choose $\sqrt{z}$ so that it is continuous for all complex values of z. There has to be a "branch cut"—a line in the complex plane across which the function $\sqrt{z}$ is discontinuous. *Mathematica* adopts the usual convention of taking the branch cut for $\sqrt{z}$ to be along the negative real axis.

This gives $1 - i$, not $-1 + i$.

```
In[3]:= N[ Sqrt[-2 I] ]
Out[3]= 1. - 1. I
```

The branch cut in Sqrt along the negative real axis means that values of Sqrt[z] with z just above and below the axis are very different.

```
In[4]:= {Sqrt[-2 + 0.1 I], Sqrt[-2 - 0.1 I]}
Out[4]= {0.0353443 + 1.41465 I, 0.0353443 - 1.41465 I}
```

Their squares are nevertheless close.

```
In[5]:= %^2
Out[5]= {-2. + 0.1 I, -2. - 0.1 I}
```

The discontinuity along the negative real axis is quite clear in this three-dimensional picture of the imaginary part of the square root function.

```
In[6]:= Plot3D[ Im[Sqrt[x + I y]], {x, -4, 4}, {y, -4, 4} ]
```

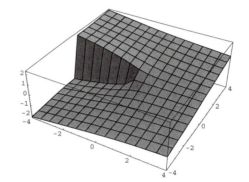

When you find an nth root using $z^{1/n}$, there are, in principle, n possible results. To get a single value, you have to choose a particular *principal root*. There is absolutely no guarantee that taking the nth root of an nth power will leave you with the same number.

This takes the tenth power of a complex number. The result is unique.

```
In[7]:= (2.5 + I)^10
Out[7]= -15781.1 - 12335.8 I
```

There are ten possible tenth roots. *Mathematica* chooses one of them. In this case it is not the number whose tenth power you took.

```
In[8]:= %^(1/10)
Out[8]= 2.61033 - 0.660446 I
```

There are many mathematical functions which, like roots, essentially give solutions to equations. The logarithm function and the inverse trigonometric functions are examples. In almost all cases, there are many possible solutions to the equations. Unique "principal" values nevertheless have to be chosen for the functions. The choices cannot be made continuous over the whole complex plane. Instead, lines of discontinuity, or branch cuts, must occur. The positions of these branch cuts are often quite arbitrary. *Mathematica* makes the most standard mathematical choices for them.

Sqrt[z] and z^s	$(-\infty, 0)$ for Re $s > 0$, $(-\infty, 0]$ for Re $s \leq 0$ (*s* not an integer)
Exp[z]	none
Log[z]	$(-\infty, 0]$
trigonometric functions	none
ArcSin[z] and ArcCos[z]	$(-\infty, -1)$ and $(+1, +\infty)$
ArcTan[z]	$(-i\infty, -i)$ and $[i, i\infty)$
ArcCsc[z] and ArcSec[z]	$(-1, +1)$
ArcCot[z]	$[-i, +i]$
hyperbolic functions	none
ArcSinh[z]	$(-i\infty, -i)$ and $(+i, +i\infty)$
ArcCosh[z]	$(-\infty, +1)$
ArcTanh[z]	$(-\infty, -1]$ and $[+1, +\infty)$
ArcCsch[z]	$(-i, i)$
ArcSech[z]	$(-\infty, 0]$ and $(+1, +\infty)$
ArcCoth[z]	$[-1, +1]$

Some branch-cut discontinuities in the complex plane.

ArcSin is a multiple-valued function, so there is no guarantee that it always gives the "inverse" of Sin.

```
In[9]:= ArcSin[Sin[4.5]]
Out[9]= -1.35841
```

Values of ArcSin[z] on opposite sides of the branch cut can be very different.

```
In[10]:= {ArcSin[2 + 0.1 I], ArcSin[2 - 0.1 I]}
Out[10]= {1.51316 + 1.31888 I, 1.51316 - 1.31888 I}
```

A three-dimensional picture, showing the two branch cuts for the function $\sin^{-1}(z)$.

In[11]:= `Plot3D[ Im[ArcSin[x + I y]], {x, -4, 4}, {y, -4, 4}]`

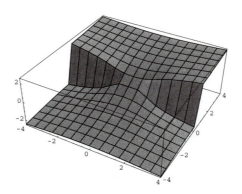

■ 3.2.8 Mathematical Constants

I	$i = \sqrt{-1}$
Infinity	∞
Pi	$\pi \simeq 3.14159$
Degree	$\pi/180$: degrees to radians conversion factor
GoldenRatio	$\phi = (1 + \sqrt{5})/2 \simeq 1.61803$
E	$e \simeq 2.71828$
EulerGamma	Euler's constant $\gamma \simeq 0.577216$
Catalan	Catalan's constant $\simeq 0.915966$

Mathematical constants.

Euler's constant `EulerGamma` is given by the limit $\gamma = \lim_{m \to \infty} \left(\sum_{k=1}^{m} \frac{1}{k} - \log m \right)$. It appears in many integrals, and asymptotic formulas. It is sometimes known as the **Euler-Mascheroni constant**, and denoted C.

Catalan's constant `Catalan` is given by the sum $\sum_{k=0}^{\infty} (-1)^k (2k + 1)^{-2}$. It often appears in asymptotic estimates of combinatorial functions.

Mathematical constants can be evaluated to arbitrary precision.

In[1]:= `N[EulerGamma, 40]`

Out[1]= `0.5772156649015328606065120900824024310421`

■ 3.2.9 Orthogonal Polynomials

`LegendreP[n, x]`	Legendre polynomials $P_n(x)$
`LegendreP[n, m, x]`	associated Legendre polynomials $P_n^m(x)$
`SphericalHarmonicY[l, m, θ, φ]`	spherical harmonics $Y_l^m(\theta, \phi)$
`GegenbauerC[n, m, x]`	Gegenbauer polynomials $C_n^{(m)}(x)$
`ChebyshevT[n, x], ChebyshevU[n, x]`	Chebyshev polynomials $T_n(x)$ and $U_n(x)$ of the first and second kinds
`HermiteH[n, x]`	Hermite polynomials $H_n(x)$
`LaguerreL[n, x]`	Laguerre polynomials $L_n(x)$
`LaguerreL[n, a, x]`	generalized Laguerre polynomials $L_n^a(x)$
`JacobiP[n, a, b, x]`	Jacobi polynomials $P_n^{(a,b)}(x)$

Orthogonal polynomials.

Legendre polynomials `LegendreP[n, x]` arise in studies of systems with three-dimensional spherical symmetry. They satisfy the differential equation $(1 - x^2)y'' - 2xy' + n(n + 1)y = 0$, and the orthogonality relation $\int_{-1}^{1} P_m(x)P_n(x)\,dx = 0$ for $m \neq n$.

The **associated Legendre polynomials** `LegendreP[n, m, x]` are obtained from derivatives of the Legendre polynomials according to $P_n^m(x) = (-1)^m(1 - x^2)^{m/2}\,d^m[P_n(x)]/dx^m$. Notice that for odd integers $m \leq n$, the $P_n^m(x)$ contain powers of $\sqrt{1 - x^2}$, and are therefore not strictly polynomials. The $P_n^m(x)$ reduce to $P_n(x)$ when $m = 0$.

The **spherical harmonics** `SphericalHarmonicY[l, m, θ, φ]` are related to associated Legendre polynomials. They satisfy the orthogonality relation $\int Y_l^m(\theta, \phi)\bar{Y}_{l'}^{m'}(\theta, \phi)\,d\omega = 0$ for $l \neq l'$ or $m \neq m'$, where $d\omega$ represents integration over the surface of the unit sphere.

This gives the algebraic form of the Legendre polynomial $P_8(x)$.

```
In[1]:= LegendreP[8, x]
```

$$Out[1]= \frac{35}{128} - \frac{315 x^2}{32} + \frac{3465 x^4}{64} - \frac{3003 x^6}{32} + \frac{6435 x^8}{128}$$

The integral $\int_{-1}^{1} P_7(x)\,P_8(x)\,dx$ gives zero by virtue of the orthogonality of the Legendre polynomials.

```
In[2]:= Integrate[LegendreP[7,x] LegendreP[8,x], {x, -1, 1}]
Out[2]= 0
```

Integrating the square of a single Legendre polynomial gives a non-zero result.

```
In[3]:= Integrate[LegendreP[8, x]^2, {x, -1, 1}]
```

$$Out[3]= \frac{2}{17}$$

High-degree Legendre polynomials oscillate rapidly.

$In[4]:=$ **Plot[LegendreP[10, x], {x, -1, 1}]**

The associated Legendre "polynomials" contain pieces proportional to $\sqrt{1-x^2}$.

$In[5]:=$ **LegendreP[8, 3, x]**

$Out[5]=\dfrac{3465}{8}\sqrt{1-x^2}\,(-1+x^2)\,(3x-26x^3+39x^5)$

Section 3.2.10 discusses the generalization of Legendre polynomials to Legendre functions, which can have non-integer degrees.

$In[6]:=$ **LegendreP[8.1, 0]**

$Out[6]=$ 0.268501

Gegenbauer polynomials GegenbauerC[n, m, x] can be viewed as generalizations of the Legendre polynomials to systems with ($m + 2$)-dimensional spherical symmetry. They are sometimes known as **ultraspherical polynomials**.

GegenbauerC[n, 0, x] is always equal to zero. GegenbauerC[n, x] is however given by the limit $\lim_{m\to 0} C_n^{(m)}(x)/m$. This form is sometimes denoted $C_n^{(0)}(x)$.

Series of Chebyshev polynomials are often used in making numerical approximations to functions. The **Chebyshev polynomials of the first kind** ChebyshevT[n, x] are defined by $T_n(\cos\theta) = \cos(n\theta)$. They are normalized so that $T_n(1) = 1$. They satisfy the orthogonality relation $\int_{-1}^{1} T_m(x)T_n(x)(1 - x^2)^{-1/2}\,dx = 0$ for $m \neq n$. The $T_n(x)$ also satisfy an orthogonality relation under summation at discrete points in x corresponding to the roots of $T_n(x)$.

The **Chebyshev polynomials of the second kind** ChebyshevU[n, z] are defined by $U_n(\cos\theta) = \sin[(n + 1)\theta]/\sin\theta$. With this definition, $U_n(1) = n + 1$. The U_n satisfy the orthogonality relation $\int_{-1}^{1} U_m(x)U_n(x)(1 - x^2)^{1/2}\,dx = 0$ for $m \neq n$.

The name "Chebyshev" is a transliteration from the Cyrillic alphabet; several other spellings, such as "Tschebyscheff", are sometimes used.

Hermite polynomials HermiteH[n, x] arise as the quantum-mechanical wave functions for a harmonic oscillator. They satisfy the differential equation $y'' - 2xy' + 2ny = 0$, and the orthogonality relation $\int_{-\infty}^{\infty} H_m(x)H_n(x)e^{-x^2}\,dx = 0$ for $m \neq n$. An alternative form of Hermite polynomials sometimes used is $He_n(x) = 2^{-n/2}H_n(x/\sqrt{2})$ (a different overall normalization of the $He_n(x)$ is also sometimes used).

The Hermite polynomials are related to the **parabolic cylinder functions** or **Weber functions** $D_n(x)$ by $D_n(x) = 2^{-n/2}e^{-x^2/4}H_n(x/\sqrt{2})$.

This gives the density for an excited state of a quantum-mechanical harmonic oscillator. The average of the wiggles is roughly the classical physics result.

$In[7]:=$ `Plot[(HermiteH[6, x] Exp[-x^2/2])^2, {x, -6, 6}]`

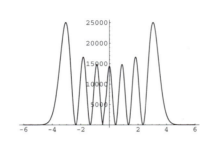

Generalized Laguerre polynomials `LaguerreL[n, a, x]` are related to hydrogen atom wave functions in quantum mechanics. They satisfy the differential equation $xy'' + (a + 1 - x)y' + ny = 0$, and the orthogonality relation $\int_0^\infty L_m^a(x)L_n^a(x)x^a e^{-x}\,dx = 0$ for $m \neq n$. The **Laguerre polynomials** `LaguerreL[n, x]` correspond to the special case $a = 0$.

Jacobi polynomials `JacobiP[n, a, b, x]` occur in studies of the rotation group, particularly in quantum mechanics. They satisfy the orthogonality relation $\int_{-1}^1 P_m^{(a,b)}(x)P_n^{(a,b)}(x)(1 - x)^a(1 + x)^b\,dx = 0$ for $m \neq n$. Legendre, Gegenbauer and Chebyshev polynomials can all be viewed as special cases of Jacobi polynomials. The Jacobi polynomials are sometimes given in the alternative form $G_n(p, q, x) = n!\,\Gamma(n + p)/\Gamma(2n + p)\ P_n^{(p-q,q-1)}(2x - 1)$.

You can get formulas for generalized Laguerre polynomials with arbitrary values of a.

$In[8]:=$ `LaguerreL[2, a, x]`

$Out[8]=$ $\dfrac{1}{2}(2 + 3a + a^2 - 4x - 2ax + x^2)$

◼ 3.2.10 Special Functions

Mathematica includes all the common special functions of mathematical physics found in standard handbooks. We will discuss each of the various classes of functions in turn.

One point you should realize is that in the technical literature there are often several conflicting definitions of any particular special function. When you use a special function in *Mathematica*, therefore, you should be sure to look at the definition given here to confirm that it is exactly what you want.

Mathematica gives exact results for some values of special functions.

$In[1]:=$ `Gamma[15/2]`

$Out[1]=$ $\dfrac{135135}{128}\sqrt{\pi}$

No exact result is known here.

$In[2]:=$ **Gamma[15/7]**

$Out[2]=$ Gamma$\left[\dfrac{15}{7}\right]$

A numerical result, to arbitrary precision, can nevertheless be found.

$In[3]:=$ **N[%, 40]**

$Out[3]=$ 1.069071500448624397994137689702693267 3667

You can give complex arguments to special functions.

$In[4]:=$ **Gamma[3 + 4I] //N**

$Out[4]=$ 0.00522554 − 0.172547 I

Special functions automatically get applied to each element in a list.

$In[5]:=$ **Gamma[{3/2, 5/2, 7/2}]**

$Out[5]=$ $\left\{\dfrac{1}{2}\sqrt{\pi}, \dfrac{3}{4}\sqrt{\pi}, \dfrac{15}{8}\sqrt{\pi}\right\}$

Mathematica knows analytical properties of special functions, such as derivatives.

$In[6]:=$ **D[Gamma[x], {x, 2}]**

$Out[6]=$ Gamma[x] PolyGamma[0, x]^2 + Gamma[x] PolyGamma[1, x]

You can use FindRoot to find roots of special functions.

$In[7]:=$ **FindRoot[BesselJ[0, x], {x, 1}]**

$Out[7]=$ {x → 2.40482}

Special functions in *Mathematica* can usually be evaluated for arbitrary complex values of their arguments. Often, however, the defining relations given below apply only for some special choices of arguments. In these cases, the full function corresponds to a suitable extension or "analytic continuation" of these defining relations. Thus, for example, integral representations of functions are valid only when the integral exists, but the functions themselves can usually be defined elsewhere by analytic continuation.

As a simple example of how the domain of a function can be extended, consider the function represented by the sum $\sum_{k=0}^{\infty} x^k$. This sum converges only when $|x| < 1$. Nevertheless, it is easy to show analytically that for any x, the complete function is equal to $1/(1 - x)$. Using this form, you can easily find a value of the function for any x, at least so long as $x \neq 1$.

Gamma and Related Functions

Beta[*a*, *b*]	Euler beta function B(a, b)
Beta[*z*, *a*, *b*]	incomplete beta function B$_z$(a, b)
BetaRegularized[*z*, *a*, *b*]	regularized incomplete beta function $I(z, a, b)$
Gamma[*z*]	Euler gamma function $\Gamma(z)$
Gamma[*a*, *z*]	incomplete gamma function $\Gamma(a, z)$
Gamma[*a*, z_0, z_1]	generalized incomplete gamma function $\Gamma(a, z_0) - \Gamma(a, z_1)$
GammaRegularized[*a*, *z*]	regularized incomplete gamma function $Q(a, z)$
InverseBetaRegularized[*s*, *a*, *b*]	
	inverse beta function
InverseGammaRegularized[*a*, *s*]	
	inverse gamma function
Pochhammer[*a*, *n*]	Pochhammer symbol $(a)_n$
PolyGamma[*z*]	digamma function $\psi(z)$
PolyGamma[*n*, *z*]	n^{th} derivative of the digamma function $\psi^{(n)}(z)$

Gamma and related functions.

The **Euler gamma function** Gamma[*z*] is defined by the integral $\Gamma(z) = \int_0^\infty t^{z-1} e^{-t} dt$. For positive integer n, $\Gamma(n) = (n-1)!$. $\Gamma(z)$ can be viewed as a generalization of the factorial function, valid for complex arguments z.

There are some computations, particularly in number theory, where the logarithm of the gamma function often appears. For positive real arguments, you can evaluate this simply as Log[Gamma[*z*]]. For complex arguments, however, this form yields spurious discontinuities. *Mathematica* therefore includes the separate function LogGamma[*z*], which yields the **logarithm of the gamma function** with a single branch cut along the negative real axis.

The **Euler beta function** Beta[*a*, *b*] is B(a, b) = $\Gamma(a)\Gamma(b)/\Gamma(a+b) = \int_0^1 t^{a-1}(1-t)^{b-1} dt$.

The **Pochhammer symbol** or **rising factorial** Pochhammer[*a*, *n*] is $(a)_n = a(a+1)\ldots(a+n-1) = \Gamma(a+n)/\Gamma(a)$. It often appears in series expansions for hypergeometric functions. Note that the Pochhammer symbol has a definite value even when the gamma functions which appear in its definition are infinite.

The **incomplete gamma function** Gamma[*a*, *z*] is defined by the integral $\Gamma(a, z) = \int_z^\infty t^{a-1} e^{-t} dt$. *Mathematica* includes a generalized incomplete gamma function Gamma[*a*, z_0, z_1] defined as $\int_{z_0}^{z_1} t^{a-1} e^{-t} dt$.

The alternative incomplete gamma function $\gamma(a, z)$ can therefore be obtained in *Mathematica* as Gamma[a, 0, z].

The **incomplete beta function** Beta[z, a, b] is given by $B_z(a, b) = \int_0^z t^{a-1}(1-t)^{b-1}dt$. Notice that in the incomplete beta function, the parameter z is an *upper* limit of integration, and appears as the *first* argument of the function. In the incomplete gamma function, on the other hand, z is a *lower* limit of integration, and appears as the *second* argument of the function.

In certain cases, it is convenient not to compute the incomplete beta and gamma functions on their own, but instead to compute *regularized forms* in which these functions are divided by complete beta and gamma functions. *Mathematica* includes the **regularized incomplete beta function** BetaRegularized[z, a, b] defined for most arguments by $I(z, a, b) = B(z, a, b)/B(a, b)$, but taking into account singular cases. *Mathematica* also includes the **regularized incomplete gamma function** GammaRegularized[a, z] defined by $Q(a, z) = \Gamma(a, z)/\Gamma(a)$, with singular cases taken into account.

The incomplete beta and gamma functions, and their inverses, are common in statistics. The **inverse beta function** InverseBetaRegularized[s, a, b] is the solution for z in $s = I(z, a, b)$. The **inverse gamma function** InverseGammaRegularized[a, s] is similarly the solution for z in $s = Q(a, z)$.

Derivatives of the gamma function often appear in summing rational series. The **digamma function** PolyGamma[z] is the logarithmic derivative of the gamma function, given by $\psi(z) = \Gamma'(z)/\Gamma(z)$. For integer arguments, the digamma function satisfies the relation $\psi(n) = -\gamma + \sum_{k=1}^{n-1} \frac{1}{k}$, where γ is Euler's constant (EulerGamma in *Mathematica*).

The **polygamma functions** PolyGamma[n, z] are given by $\psi^{(n)}(z) = d^n\psi(z)/dz^n$. Notice that the digamma function corresponds to $\psi^{(0)}(z)$. The general form $\psi^{(n)}(z)$ is the $(n+1)^{\text{th}}$, not the nth, logarithmic derivative of the gamma function. The polygamma functions satisfy the relation $\psi^{(n)}(z) = (-1)^{n+1} n! \sum_{k=0}^{\infty} 1/(z+k)^{n+1}$.

Many exact results for gamma and polygamma functions are built into *Mathematica*.

In[8]:= **PolyGamma[6]**

Out[8]= $\dfrac{137}{60}$ - EulerGamma

Here is a contour plot of the gamma function in the complex plane.

```
In[9]:= ContourPlot[ Abs[Gamma[x + I y]], {x, -3, 3},
                {y, -2, 2}, PlotPoints->40 ]
```

Zeta and Related Functions

LerchPhi[z, s, a]	Lerch's transcendent $\Phi(z, s, a)$
PolyLog[n, z]	polylogarithm function $\mathrm{Li}_n(z)$
RiemannSiegelTheta[t]	Riemann-Siegel function $\vartheta(t)$
RiemannSiegelZ[t]	Riemann-Siegel function $Z(t)$
StieltjesGamma[n]	Stieltjes constants γ_n
Zeta[s]	Riemann zeta function $\zeta(s)$
Zeta[s, a]	generalized Riemann zeta function $\zeta(s, a)$

Zeta and related functions.

The **Riemann zeta function** Zeta[s] is defined by the relation $\zeta(s) = \sum_{k=1}^{\infty} k^{-s}$ (for $s > 1$). Zeta functions with integer arguments arise in evaluating various sums and integrals. *Mathematica* gives exact results when possible for zeta functions with integer arguments.

There is an analytic continuation of $\zeta(s)$ for arbitrary complex $s \neq 1$. The zeta function for complex arguments is central to number-theoretical studies of the distribution of primes. Of particular importance are the values on the critical line $\mathrm{Re}\, s = \frac{1}{2}$.

In studying $\zeta(\frac{1}{2} + it)$, it is often convenient to define the two analytic **Riemann-Siegel functions** RiemannSiegelZ[t] and RiemannSiegelTheta[z] according to $Z(t) = e^{i\vartheta(t)}\zeta(\frac{1}{2} + it)$ and $\vartheta(t) =$

Im log $\Gamma(\frac{1}{4} + it/2) - t\log(\pi)/2$ (for t real). Note that the Riemann-Siegel functions are both real as long as t is real.

The **Stieltjes constants** StieltjesGamma[n] are generalizations of Euler's constant which appear in the series expansion of $\zeta(s)$ around its pole at $s = 1$; the coefficient of $(1 - s)^n$ is $\gamma_n/n!$. Euler's constant is γ_0.

The **generalized Riemann zeta function** or **Hurwitz zeta function** Zeta[s, a] is given by $\zeta(s, a) = \sum_{k=0}^{\infty}(k + a)^{-s}$, where any term with $k + a = 0$ is excluded.

Mathematica gives exact results for $\zeta(2n)$.

In[10]:= **Zeta[6]**

Out[10]= $\dfrac{\pi^6}{945}$

Here is a three-dimensional picture of the Riemann zeta function in the complex plane.

In[11]:= **Plot3D[Abs[Zeta[x + I y]], {x, -3, 3}, {y, 2, 35}, PlotPoints->30]**

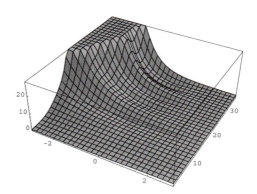

This is a plot of the absolute value of the Riemann zeta function on the critical line Re $z = \frac{1}{2}$. You can see the first few zeros of the zeta function.

In[12]:= **Plot[Abs[Zeta[1/2 + I y]], {y, 0, 40}]**

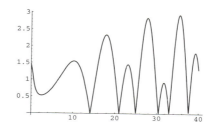

The **polylogarithm functions** PolyLog[n, z] are given by $\text{Li}_n(z) = \sum_{k=1}^{\infty} z^k/k^n$. The **dilogarithm** PolyLog[2, z] satisfies $\text{Li}_2(z) = \int_z^0 \log(1 - t)/t \, dt$. $\text{Li}_2(1 - z)$ is sometimes known as **Spence's integral**. Polylogarithms crop up in Feynman diagram integrals in elementary particle physics. The polylogarithm function is sometimes known as **Jonquière's function**.

The **Lerch transcendent** LerchPhi[z, s, a] is a generalization of the zeta and polylogarithm functions, given by $\Phi(z, s, a) = \sum_{k=0}^{\infty} z^k/(a + k)^s$, where any term with $a + k = 0$ is excluded. Many sums of reciprocal powers can be expressed in terms of the Lerch transcendent. For example, the **Catalan beta function** $\beta(s) = \sum_{k=0}^{\infty} (-1)^k (2k + 1)^{-s}$ can be obtained as $2^{-s}\Phi(-1, s, \frac{1}{2})$.

The Lerch transcendent is related to integrals of the **Fermi-Dirac** distribution in statistical mechanics by $\int_0^{\infty} k^s/(e^{k-\mu} + 1)\,dk = e^{\mu}\Gamma(s + 1)\Phi(-e^{\mu}, s + 1, 1)$.

The Lerch transcendent can also be used to evaluate **Dirichlet *L*-series** which appear in number theory. The basic *L*-series has the form $L(s, \chi) = \sum_{k=1}^{\infty} \chi(k)k^{-s}$, where the "character" $\chi(k)$ is an integer function with period m. *L*-series of this kind can be written as sums of Lerch functions with z a power of $e^{2\pi i/m}$.

LerchPhi[z, s, a, DoublyInfinite->True] gives the doubly infinite sum $\sum_{k=-\infty}^{\infty} z^k/(a + k)^s$.

Exponential Integral and Related Functions

CosIntegral[z]	cosine integral function Ci(z)
CoshIntegral[z]	hyperbolic cosine integral function Chi(z)
ExpIntegralE[n, z]	exponential integral $E_n(z)$
ExpIntegralEi[z]	exponential integral Ei(z)
LogIntegral[z]	logarithmic integral li(z)
SinIntegral[z]	sine integral function Si(z)
SinhIntegral[z]	hyperbolic sine integral function Shi(z)

Exponential integral and related functions.

Mathematica has two forms of exponential integral: ExpIntegralE and ExpIntegralEi.

The **exponential integral function** ExpIntegralE[n, z] is defined by $E_n(z) = \int_1^{\infty} e^{-zt}/t^n\,dt$.

The second **exponential integral function** ExpIntegralEi[z] is defined by $\mathrm{Ei}(z) = -\int_{-z}^{\infty} e^{-t}/t\,dt$ (for $z > 0$), where the principal value of the integral is taken.

The **logarithmic integral function** LogIntegral[z] is given by $\mathrm{li}(z) = \int_0^z dt/\log t$ (for $z > 1$), where the principal value of the integral is taken. li(z) is central to the study of the distribution of primes in number theory. The logarithmic integral function is sometimes also denoted by Li(z). In some number-theoretical applications, li(z) is defined as $\int_2^z dt/\log t$, with no principal value taken. This differs from the definition used in *Mathematica* by the constant li(2).

The **sine and cosine integral functions** `SinIntegral[z]` and `CosIntegral[z]` are defined by $\text{Si}(z) = \int_0^z \sin(t)/t\,dt$ and $\text{Ci}(z) = -\int_z^\infty \cos(t)/t\,dt$. The **hyperbolic sine and cosine integral functions** `SinhIntegral[z]` and `CoshIntegral[z]` are defined by $\text{Shi}(z) = \int_0^z \sinh(t)/t\,dt$ and $\text{Chi}(z) = \gamma + \log(z) + \int_0^z (\cosh(t) - 1)/t\,dt$.

Error Function and Related Functions

`Erf[z]`	error function erf(z)
`Erf[`z_0`, `z_1`]`	generalized error function erf(z_1) − erf(z_0)
`Erfc[z]`	complementary error function erfc(z)
`Erfi[z]`	imaginary error function erfi(z)
`FresnelC[z]`	Fresnel integral $C(z)$
`FresnelS[z]`	Fresnel integral $S(z)$
`InverseErf[s]`	inverse error function
`InverseErfc[s]`	inverse complementary error function

Error function and related functions.

The **error function** `Erf[z]` is the integral of the Gaussian distribution, given by $\text{erf}(z) = 2/\sqrt{\pi} \int_0^z e^{-t^2}\,dt$. The **complementary error function** `Erfc[z]` is given simply by $\text{erfc}(z) = 1 - \text{erf}(z)$. The **imaginary error function** `Erfi[z]` is given by $\text{erf}(iz)/i$. The generalized error function `Erf[`z_0`, `z_1`]` is defined by the integral $2/\sqrt{\pi} \int_{z_0}^{z_1} e^{-t^2}\,dt$. The error function is central to many calculations in statistics.

The **inverse error function** `InverseErf[s]` is defined as the solution for z in the equation $s = \text{erf}(z)$. The inverse error function appears in computing confidence intervals in statistics as well as in some algorithms for generating Gaussian random numbers.

Closely related to the error function are the **Fresnel integrals** `FresnelC[z]` defined by $C(z) = \int_0^z \cos(\pi t^2/2)\,dt$ and `FresnelS[z]` defined by $S(z) = \int_0^z \sin(\pi t^2/2)\,dt$. Fresnel integrals occur in diffraction theory.

Bessel Functions

`AiryAi[z]` and `AiryBi[z]`	Airy functions Ai(z) and Bi(z)
`AiryAiPrime[z]` and `AiryBiPrime[z]`	derivatives of Airy functions Ai′(z) and Bi′(z)
`BesselJ[n, z]` and `BesselY[n, z]`	Bessel functions $J_n(z)$ and $Y_n(z)$
`BesselI[n, z]` and `BesselK[n, z]`	modified Bessel functions $I_n(z)$ and $K_n(z)$

Bessel functions.

The **Bessel functions** `BesselJ[n, z]` and `BesselY[n, z]` are linearly independent solutions to the differential equation $z^2 y'' + z y' + (z^2 - n^2) y = 0$. For integer n, the $J_n(z)$ are regular at $z = 0$, while the $Y_n(z)$ have a logarithmic divergence at $z = 0$.

Bessel functions arise in solving differential equations for systems with cylindrical symmetry.

$J_n(z)$ is often called the **Bessel function of the first kind**, or simply *the* Bessel function. $Y_n(z)$ is referred to as the **Bessel function of the second kind**, the **Weber function**, or the **Neumann function** (denoted $N_n(z)$).

The **Hankel functions** (or **Bessel functions of the third kind**) $H_n^{(1,2)}(z) = J_n(z) \pm i Y_n(z)$ give an alternative pair of solutions to the Bessel differential equation.

In studying systems with spherical symmetry, **spherical Bessel functions** arise, defined by $f_n(z) = \sqrt{\pi/2z}\, F_{n+\frac{1}{2}}(z)$, where f and F can be j and J, y and Y, or h^i and H^i. For integer n, *Mathematica* gives exact algebraic formulas for spherical Bessel functions.

The **modified Bessel functions** `BesselI[n, z]` and `BesselK[n, z]` are solutions to the differential equation $z^2 y'' + z y' - (z^2 + n^2) y = 0$. For integer n, $I_n(z)$ is regular at $z = 0$; $K_n(z)$ always has a logarithmic divergence at $z = 0$. The $I_n(z)$ are sometimes known as **hyperbolic Bessel functions**.

Particularly in electrical engineering, one often defines the **Kelvin functions**, according to $\mathrm{ber}_n(z) + i\,\mathrm{bei}_n(z) = e^{n\pi i} J_n(z e^{-\pi i/4})$, $\mathrm{ker}_n(z) + i\,\mathrm{kei}_n(z) = e^{-n\pi i/2} K_n(z e^{\pi i/4})$.

The **Airy functions** `AiryAi[z]` and `AiryBi[z]` are the two independent solutions Ai(z) and Bi(z) to the differential equation $y'' - z y = 0$. Ai(z) tends to zero for large positive z, while Bi(z) increases unboundedly. The Airy functions are related to modified Bessel functions with one-third-integer orders. The Airy functions often appear as the solutions to boundary value problems in electromagnetic theory and quantum mechanics. In many cases the **derivatives of the Airy functions** `AiryAiPrime[z]` and `AiryBiPrime[z]` also appear.

Here is a plot of $J_0(\sqrt{x})$. This is a curve that an idealized chain hanging from one end can form when you wiggle it.

$In[13]:=$ **Plot[BesselJ[0, Sqrt[x]], {x, 0, 50}]**

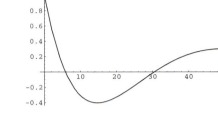

Mathematica generates explicit formulas for half-integer-order Bessel functions.

$In[14]:=$ **BesselK[3/2, x]**

$$Out[14]= \frac{E^{-x}\sqrt{\frac{\pi}{2}}\left(1+\frac{1}{x}\right)}{\sqrt{x}}$$

The Airy function plotted here gives the quantum-mechanical amplitude for a particle in a potential that increases linearly from left to right. The amplitude is exponentially damped in the classically inaccessible region on the right.

$In[15]:=$ **Plot[AiryAi[x], {x, -10, 10}]**

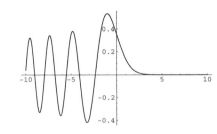

Legendre and Related Functions

LegendreP[n, z]	Legendre functions of the first kind $P_n(z)$
LegendreP[n, m, z]	associated Legendre functions of the first kind $P_n^m(z)$
LegendreQ[n, z]	Legendre functions of the second kind $Q_n(z)$
LegendreQ[n, m, z]	associated Legendre functions of the second kind $Q_n^m(z)$

Legendre and related functions.

The **Legendre functions** and **associated Legendre functions** satisfy the differential equation $(1-z^2)y'' - 2zy' + [n(n+1) - m^2/(1-z^2)]y = 0$. The **Legendre functions of the first kind**, LegendreP[n, z] and LegendreP[n, m, z], reduce to Legendre polynomials when n and m are integers. The **Legendre**

functions of the second kind LegendreQ[n, z] and LegendreQ[n, m, z] give the second linearly independent solution to the differential equation. For integer m they have logarithmic singularities at $z = \pm 1$. The $P_n(z)$ and $Q_n(z)$ solve the differential equation with $m = 0$.

Legendre functions arise in studies of quantum-mechanical scattering processes.

+   LegendreP[n, m, z] or LegendreP[n, m, 1, z]

                                 type 1 function containing $(1 - z^2)^{m/2}$

+   LegendreP[n, m, 2, z]   type 2 function containing $((1 + z)/(1 - z))^{m/2}$

+   LegendreP[n, m, 3, z]   type 3 function containing $((1 + z)/(-1 + z))^{m/2}$

Types of Legendre functions. Analogous types exist for LegendreQ.

Legendre functions of type 1 are defined only when z lies inside the unit circle in the complex plane. **Legendre functions of type 2** have the same numerical values as type 1 inside the unit circle, but are also defined outside. The type 2 functions have branch cuts from $-\infty$ to -1 and from $+1$ to $+\infty$. **Legendre functions of type 3**, sometimes denoted $\mathcal{P}_n^m(z)$ and $\mathcal{Q}_n^m(z)$, have a single branch cut from $-\infty$ to $+1$.

Toroidal functions or **ring functions**, which arise in studying systems with toroidal symmetry, can be expressed in terms of the Legendre functions $P_{\nu-\frac{1}{2}}^\mu(\cosh \eta)$ and $Q_{\nu-\frac{1}{2}}^\mu(\cosh \eta)$.

Conical functions can be expressed in terms of $P_{-\frac{1}{2}+ip}^\mu(\cos \theta)$ and $Q_{-\frac{1}{2}+ip}^\mu(\cos \theta)$.

When you use the function LegendreP[n, x] with an integer n, you get a Legendre polynomial. If you take n to be an arbitrary complex number, you get, in general, a Legendre function.

In the same way, you can use the functions GegenbauerC and so on with arbitrary complex indices to get **Gegenbauer functions**, **Chebyshev functions**, **Hermite functions**, **Jacobi functions** and **Laguerre functions**. Unlike for associated Legendre functions, however, there is no need to distinguish different types in such cases.

Confluent Hypergeometric Functions

HypergeometricOF1[*a*, *z*]	hypergeometric function $_0F_1(;a;z)$
+ HypergeometricOF1Regularized[*a*, *z*]	regularized hypergeometric function $_0F_1(;a;z)/\Gamma(a)$
Hypergeometric1F1[*a*, *b*, *z*]	Kummer confluent hypergeometric function $_1F_1(a;b;z)$
+ Hypergeometric1F1Regularized[*a*, *b*, *z*]	regularized confluent hypergeometric function $_1F_1(a;b;z)/\Gamma(b)$
HypergeometricU[*a*, *b*, *z*]	confluent hypergeometric function $U(a,b,z)$

Confluent hypergeometric functions.

Many of the special functions that we have discussed so far can be viewed as special cases of the **confluent hypergeometric function** Hypergeometric1F1[*a*, *b*, *z*].

The confluent hypergeometric function can be obtained from the series expansion $_1F_1(a;b;z) = 1 + az/b + a(a+1)/b(b+1) z^2/2! + \cdots = \sum_{k=0}^{\infty} (a)_k/(b)_k \, z^k/k!$. Some special results are obtained when a and b are both integers. If $a < 0$, and either $b > 0$ or $b < a$, the series yields a polynomial with a finite number of terms.

If b is zero or a negative integer, then $_1F_1(a;b;z)$ itself is infinite. But the **regularized confluent hypergeometric function** Hypergeometric1F1Regularized[*a*, *b*, *z*] given by $_1F_1(a;b;z)/\Gamma(b)$ has a finite value in all cases.

Among the functions that can be obtained from $_1F_1$ are the Bessel functions, error function, incomplete gamma function, and Hermite and Laguerre polynomials.

The function $_1F_1(a;b;z)$ is sometimes denoted $\Phi(a;b;z)$ or $M(a,b,z)$. It is often known as the **Kummer function**.

The $_1F_1$ function can be written in the integral representation $_1F_1(a;b;z) = \Gamma(b)/[\Gamma(b-a)\Gamma(a)] \int_0^1 e^{zt}t^{a-1}(1-t)^{b-a-1} \, dt$.

The $_1F_1$ confluent hypergeometric function is a solution to Kummer's differential equation $zy'' + (b-z)y' - ay = 0$, with the boundary conditions $_1F_1(a;b;0) = 1$ and $\partial[_1F_1(a;b;z)]/\partial z|_{z=0} = a/b$.

The function HypergeometricU[*a*, *b*, *z*] gives a second linearly independent solution to Kummer's equation. For Re $b > 1$ this function behaves like z^{1-b} for small z. It has a branch cut along the negative real axis in the complex z plane.

The function $U(a,b,z)$ has the integral representation $U(a,b,z) = 1/\Gamma(a) \int_0^{\infty} e^{-zt}t^{a-1}(1+t)^{b-a-1} \, dt$.

$U(a,b,z)$, like $_1F_1(a;b;z)$, is sometimes known as the **Kummer function**. The U function is sometimes denoted by Ψ.

The **Whittaker functions** give an alternative pair of solutions to Kummer's differential equation. The Whittaker function $M_{\kappa,\mu}$ is related to $_1F_1$ by $M_{\kappa,\mu}(z) = e^{-z/2}z^{1/2+\mu}{}_1F_1(\frac{1}{2}+\mu-\kappa; 1+2\mu; z)$. The second Whittaker function $W_{\kappa,\mu}$ obeys the same relation, with $_1F_1$ replaced by U.

The **parabolic cylinder functions** are related to Whittaker functions by $D_\nu(z) = 2^{1/4+\nu/2}z^{-1/2} \times W_{\frac{1}{4}+\frac{\nu}{2},-\frac{1}{4}}(z^2/2)$. For integer ν, the parabolic cylinder functions reduce to Hermite polynomials.

The **Coulomb wave functions** are also special cases of the confluent hypergeometric function. Coulomb wave functions give solutions to the radial Schrödinger equation in the Coulomb potential of a point nucleus. The regular Coulomb wave function is given by $F_L(\eta, \rho) = C_L(\eta)\rho^{L+1}e^{-i\rho}{}_1F_1(L+1-i\eta; 2L+2; 2i\rho)$, where $C_L(\eta) = 2^L e^{-\pi\eta/2}|\Gamma(L+1+i\eta)|/\Gamma(2L+2)$.

Other special cases of the confluent hypergeometric function include the **Toronto functions** $T(m,n,r)$, **Poisson-Charlier polynomials** $\rho_n(\nu, x)$, **Cunningham functions** $\omega_{n,m}(x)$ and **Bateman functions** $k_\nu(x)$.

A limiting form of the confluent hypergeometric function which often appears is HypergeometricOF1[a, z]. This function is obtained as the limit $_0F_1(; a; z) = \lim_{q\to\infty}{}_1F_1(q; a; z/q)$.

The $_0F_1$ function has the series expansion $_0F_1(; a; z) = \sum_{k=0}^\infty 1/(a)_k z^k/k!$ and satisfies the differential equation $zy'' + ay' - y = 0$.

Bessel functions of the first kind can be expressed in terms of the $_0F_1$ function.

Hypergeometric Functions and Generalizations

Hypergeometric2F1[a, b, c, z]   hypergeometric function $_2F_1(a,b;c;z)$

+ Hypergeometric2F1Regularized[a, b, c, z]
                    regularized hypergeometric function $_2F_1(a,b;c;z)/\Gamma(c)$

+ HypergeometricPFQ[{a_1, ... , a_p}, {b_1, ... , b_q}, z]
                    generalized hypergeometric function $_pF_q(\mathbf{a};\mathbf{b};z)$

+ HypergeometricPFQRegularized[{a_1, ... , a_p}, {b_1, ... , b_q}, z]
                    regularized generalized hypergeometric function

+ MeijerG[{{a_1, ... , a_n}, {a_{n+1}, ... , a_p}}, {{b_1, ... , b_m}, {b_{m+1}, ... , b_q}}, z]
                    Meijer G function

Hypergeometric functions and generalizations.

The **hypergeometric function** Hypergeometric2F1[a, b, c, z] has series expansion $_2F_1(a,b;c;z) = \sum_{k=0}^\infty (a)_k(b)_k/(c)_k z^k/k!$. The function is a solution of the hypergeometric differential equation $z(1-z)y'' + [c-(a+b+1)z]y' - aby = 0$.

The hypergeometric function can also be written as an integral: $_2F_1(a,b;c;z) = \Gamma(c)/[\Gamma(b)\Gamma(c-b)] \times \int_0^1 t^{b-1}(1-t)^{c-b-1}(1-tz)^{-a}\, dt$.

Elliptic Functions

JacobiAmplitude[u, m]	amplitude function am($u \mid m$)
JacobiSN[u, m], JacobiCN[u, m], etc.	
	Jacobi elliptic functions sn($u \mid m$), etc.
InverseJacobiSN[v, m], InverseJacobiCN[v, m], etc.	
	inverse Jacobi elliptic functions sn^{-1}($v \mid m$), etc.
EllipticTheta[a, u, q]	theta functions $\vartheta_a(u, q)$ ($a = 1, ..., 4$)
+ EllipticThetaPrime[a, u, q]	derivatives of theta functions $\vartheta'_a(u, q)$ ($a = 1, ..., 4$)
WeierstrassP[u, {g_2, g_3}]	Weierstrass elliptic function $\wp(u; g_2, g_3)$
WeierstrassPPrime[u, {g_2, g_3}]	
	derivative of Weierstrass elliptic function $\wp'(u; g_2, g_3)$
+ InverseWeierstrassP[p, {g_2, g_3}]	
	inverse Weierstrass elliptic function
+ WeierstrassSigma[u, {g_2, g_3}]	Weierstrass sigma function $\sigma(u; g_2, g_3)$
+ WeierstrassZeta[u, {g_2, g_3}]	Weierstrass zeta function $\zeta(u; g_2, g_3)$

Elliptic and related functions.

Rational functions involving square roots of quadratic forms can be integrated in terms of inverse trigonometric functions. The trigonometric functions can thus be defined as inverses of the functions obtained from these integrals.

By analogy, **elliptic functions** are defined as inverses of the functions obtained from elliptic integrals.

The **amplitude** for Jacobi elliptic functions JacobiAmplitude[u, m] is the inverse of the elliptic integral of the first kind. If $u = F(\phi \mid m)$, then $\phi = \text{am}(u \mid m)$. In working with Jacobi elliptic functions, the argument m is often dropped, so am($u \mid m$) is written as am(u).

The **Jacobi elliptic functions** JacobiSN[u, m] and JacobiCN[u, m] are given respectively by sn(u) = sin(ϕ) and cn(u) = cos(ϕ), where $\phi = \text{am}(u \mid m)$. In addition, JacobiDN[$u$, m] is given by dn(u) = $\sqrt{1 - m \sin^2(\phi)} = \Delta(\phi)$.

There are a total of twelve Jacobi elliptic functions JacobiPQ[u, m], with the letters P and Q chosen from the set S, C, D and N. Each Jacobi elliptic function JacobiPQ[u, m] satisfies the relation pq(u) = pn(u)/qn(u), where for these purposes nn(u) = 1.

There are many relations between the Jacobi elliptic functions, somewhat analogous to those between trigonometric functions. In limiting cases, in fact, the Jacobi elliptic functions reduce to trigonometric functions. So, for example, $sn(u|0) = \sin(u)$, $sn(u|1) = \tanh(u)$, $cn(u|0) = \cos(u)$, $cn(u|1) = sech(u)$, $dn(u|0) = 1$ and $dn(u|1) = sech(u)$.

The notation $Pq(u)$ is often used for the integrals $\int_0^u pq^2(t)\,dt$. These integrals can be expressed in terms of the Jacobi zeta function defined above.

One of the most important properties of elliptic functions is that they are *doubly periodic* in the complex values of their arguments. Ordinary trigonometric functions are singly periodic, in the sense that $f(z + s\omega) = f(z)$ for any integer s. The elliptic functions are doubly periodic, so that $f(z + r\omega + s\omega') = f(z)$ for any pair of integers r and s.

The Jacobi elliptic functions $sn(u|m)$, etc. are doubly periodic in the complex u plane. Their periods include $\omega = 4K(m)$ and $\omega' = 4iK(1 - m)$, where K is the complete elliptic integral of the first kind.

The choice of p and q in the notation $pq(u|m)$ for Jacobi elliptic functions can be understood in terms of the values of the functions at the quarter periods K and iK'.

This shows two complete periods in each direction of the absolute value of the Jacobi elliptic function $sn(u|\frac{1}{3})$.

```
In[4]:= ContourPlot[Abs[JacobiSN[ux + I uy, 1/3]],
                {ux, 0, 4 EllipticK[1/3]},
                {uy, 0, 4 EllipticK[2/3]},
                PlotPoints->40 ]
```

Also built into *Mathematica* are the **inverse Jacobi elliptic functions** InverseJacobiSN[v, m], InverseJacobiCN[v, m], etc. The inverse function $sn^{-1}(v|m)$, for example, gives the value of u for which $v = sn(u|m)$. The inverse Jacobi elliptic functions are related to elliptic integrals.

The four **theta functions** $\vartheta_a(u, q)$ are obtained from EllipticTheta[a, u, q] by taking a to be 1, 2, 3 or 4. The functions are defined by: $\vartheta_1(u, q) = 2q^{1/4} \sum_{n=0}^{\infty} (-1)^n q^{n(n+1)} \sin[(2n + 1)u]$, $\vartheta_2(u, q) = 2q^{1/4} \sum_{n=0}^{\infty} q^{n(n+1)} \cos[(2n+1)u]$, $\vartheta_3(u, q) = 1 + 2 \sum_{n=1}^{\infty} q^{n^2} \cos(2nu)$, $\vartheta_4(u, q) = 1 + 2 \sum_{n=1}^{\infty} (-1)^n q^{n^2} \cos(2nu)$. The theta functions are often written as $\vartheta_a(u)$ with the parameter q not explicitly given. The theta functions are sometimes written in the form $\vartheta(u|m)$, where m is related to q by $q = \exp[-\pi K(1 - m)/K(m)]$. In addition, q is sometimes replaced by τ, given by $q = e^{i\pi\tau}$. All the theta functions satisfy a diffusion-like differential equation $\partial^2\vartheta(u, \tau)/\partial u^2 = 4\pi i\,\partial\vartheta(u, \tau)/\partial\tau$.

The Jacobi elliptic functions can be expressed as ratios of the theta functions.

An alternative notation for theta functions is $\Theta(u \mid m) = \vartheta_4(v \mid m)$, $\Theta_1(u \mid m) = \vartheta_3(v \mid m)$, $H(u \mid m) = \vartheta_1(v)$, $H_1(u \mid m) = \vartheta_2(v)$, where $v = \pi u / 2K(m)$.

The **Neville theta functions** can be defined in terms of the theta functions as $\vartheta_s(u) = 2K(m)\vartheta_1(v \mid m)/\pi\vartheta_1'(0 \mid m)$, $\vartheta_c(u) = \vartheta_2(v \mid m)/\vartheta_2(0 \mid m)$, $\vartheta_d(u) = \vartheta_3(v \mid m)/\vartheta_3(0 \mid m)$, $\vartheta_n(u) = \vartheta_4(v \mid m)/\vartheta_4(0 \mid m)$, where $v = \pi u / 2K(m)$. The Jacobi elliptic functions can be represented as ratios of the Neville theta functions.

The **Weierstrass elliptic function** WeierstrassP[u, {g_2, g_3}] can be considered as the inverse of an elliptic integral. The Weierstrass function $\wp(u; g_2, g_3)$ gives the value of x for which $u = \int_\infty^x (4t^3 - g_2 t - g_3)^{-1/2} \, dt$. The function WeierstrassPPrime[u, {g_2, g_3}] is given by $\wp'(u; g_2, g_3) = \frac{\partial}{\partial u}\wp(u; g_2, g_3)$.

The Weierstrass functions are also sometimes written in terms of their *fundamental half-periods* ω and ω', obtained from the invariants g_2 and g_3 using WeierstrassHalfPeriods[{g_2, g_3}].

The function InverseWeierstrassP[p, {g_2, g_3}] finds one of the two values of u for which $p = \wp(u; g_2, g_3)$. This value always lies in the parallelogram defined by the complex number half-periods ω and ω'.

InverseWeierstrassP[{p, q}, {g_2, g_3}] finds the unique value of u for which $p = \wp(u; g_2, g_3)$ and $q = \wp'(u; g_2, g_3)$. In order for any such value of u to exist, p and q must be related by $q^2 = 4p^3 - g_2 p - g_3$.

The **Weierstrass zeta function** WeierstrassZeta[u, {g_2, g_3}] and **Weierstrass sigma function** WeierstrassSigma[u, {g_2, g_3}] are related to the Weierstrass elliptic functions by $\zeta'(z; g_2, g_3) = -\wp(z; g_2, g_3)$ and $\sigma'(z; g_2, g_3)/\sigma(z; g_2, g_3) = \zeta(z; g_2, g_3)$.

The Weierstrass zeta and sigma functions are not strictly elliptic functions since they are not periodic.

Elliptic Modular Functions

+	DedekindEta[τ]	Dedekind eta function $\eta(\tau)$
+	KleinInvariantJ[τ]	Klein invariant modular function $J(\tau)$
+	ModularLambda[τ]	modular lambda function $\lambda(\tau)$

Elliptic modular functions.

The **modular lambda function** ModularLambda[τ] relates the ratio of half-periods $\tau = \omega'/\omega$ to the parameter according to $m = \lambda(\tau)$.

The **Klein invariant modular function** KleinInvariantJ[τ] and the **Dedekind eta function** DedekindEta[τ] satisfy the relations $\Delta = g_2^3/J(\tau) = (2\pi)^{12}\eta^{24}(\tau)$.

Modular elliptic functions are defined to be invariant under certain fractional linear transformations of their arguments. Thus for example $\lambda(\tau)$ is invariant under any combination of the transformations $\tau \to \tau + 2$ and $\tau \to \tau/(1 - 2\tau)$.

Generalized Elliptic Integrals and Functions

`ArithmeticGeometricMean[a, b]`	
	the arithmetic-geometric mean of a and b
`EllipticExp[u, {a, b}]`	generalized exponential associated with the elliptic curve $y^2 = x^3 + ax^2 + bx$
`EllipticLog[{x, y}, {a, b}]`	generalized logarithm associated with the elliptic curve $y^2 = x^3 + ax^2 + bx$

Generalized elliptic integrals and functions.

The definitions for elliptic integrals and functions given above are based on traditional usage. For modern algebraic geometry, it is convenient to use slightly more general definitions.

The function `EllipticLog[{x, y}, {a, b}]` is defined as the value of the integral $\frac{1}{2}\int_{\infty}^{x}(t^3 + at^2 + bt)^{-1/2}\,dt$, where the sign of the square root is specified by giving the value of y such that $y = \sqrt{x^3 + ax^2 + bx}$. Integrals of the form $\int_{\infty}^{x}(t^2 + at)^{-1/2}\,dt$ can be expressed in terms of the ordinary logarithm (and inverse trigonometric functions). You can think of `EllipticLog` as giving a generalization of this, where the polynomial under the square root is now of degree three.

The function `EllipticExp[u, {a, b}]` is the inverse of `EllipticLog`. It returns the list $\{x, y\}$ that appears in `EllipticLog`. `EllipticExp` is an elliptic function, doubly periodic in the complex u plane.

`ArithmeticGeometricMean[a, b]` gives the **arithmetic-geometric mean (AGM)** of two numbers a and b. This quantity is central to many numerical algorithms for computing elliptic integrals and other functions. For positive reals a and b the AGM is obtained by starting with $a_0 = a$, $b_0 = b$, then iterating the transformation $a_{n+1} = \frac{1}{2}(a_n + b_n)$, $b_{n+1} = \sqrt{a_n b_n}$ until $a_n = b_n$ to the precision required.

+■ 3.2.12 Mathieu and Related Functions

+ `MathieuC[a, q, z]`	even Mathieu functions with characteristic value a and parameter q
+ `MathieuS[b, q, z]`	odd Mathieu function with characteristic value b and parameter q
+ `MathieuCPrime[a, q, z]` and `MathieuSPrime[b, q, z]`	
	z derivatives of Mathieu functions
+ `MathieuCharacteristicA[r, q]`	characteristic value a_r for even Mathieu functions with characteristic exponent r and parameter q
+ `MathieuCharacteristicB[r, q]`	characteristic value b_r for odd Mathieu functions with characteristic exponent r and parameter q
+ `MathieuCharacteristicExponent[a, q]`	
	characteristic exponent r for Mathieu functions with characteristic value a and parameter q

Mathieu and related functions.

The **Mathieu functions** `MathieuC[a, q, z]` and `MathieuS[a, q, z]` are solutions to the equation $y'' + [a - 2q\cos(2z)]y = 0$. This equation appears in many physical situations that involve elliptical shapes or periodic potentials. The function `MathieuC` is defined to be even in z, while `MathieuS` is odd.

When $q = 0$ the Mathieu functions are simply $\cos(\sqrt{a}z)$ and $\sin(\sqrt{a}z)$. For non-zero q, the Mathieu functions are only periodic in z for certain values of a. Such **Mathieu characteristic values** are given by `MathieuCharacteristicA[r, q]` and `MathieuCharacteristicB[r, q]` with r an integer or rational number. These values are often denoted by a_r and b_r.

For integer r, the even and odd Mathieu functions with characteristic values a_r and b_r are often denoted $ce_r(z, q)$ and $se_r(z, q)$, respectively. Note the reversed order of the arguments z and q.

According to Floquet's Theorem any Mathieu function can be written in the form $e^{irz}f(z)$, where $f(z)$ has period 2π and r is the **Mathieu characteristic exponent** `MathieuCharacteristicExponent[a, q]`. When the characteristic exponent r is an integer or rational number, the Mathieu function is therefore periodic. In general, however, when r is not a real integer, a_r and b_r turn out to be equal.

This shows the first five characteristic values a_r as functions of q.

```
In[1]:= Plot[Evaluate[Table[MathieuCharacteristicA[r, q],
            {r, 0, 4}]], {q, 0, 15}]
```

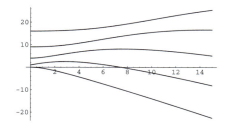

+■ **3.2.13 Working with Special Functions**

automatic evaluation	exact results for specific arguments
N[*expr*, *n*]	numerical approximations to any precision
D[*expr*, *x*]	exact results for derivatives
N[D[*expr*, *x*]]	numerical approximations to derivatives
Series[*expr*, {*x*, x_0, *n*}]	series expansions
Integrate[*expr*, *x*]	exact results for integrals
NIntegrate[*expr*, *x*]	numerical approximations to integrals
FindRoot[*expr*==0, {*x*, x_0}]	numerical approximations to roots

Some common operations on special functions.

Most special functions have simpler forms when given certain specific arguments. *Mathematica* will automatically simplify special functions in such cases.

Mathematica automatically writes this in terms of standard mathematical constants.

```
In[1]:= PolyLog[2, 1/2]
```

$$Out[1]= \frac{\pi^2}{12} - \frac{\text{Log}[2]^2}{2}$$

Here again *Mathematica* reduces a special case of the Airy function to an expression involving gamma functions.

$In[2]:=$ **AiryAi[0]**

$Out[2]=$ $\dfrac{1}{3^{2/3}\,\text{Gamma}\left[\frac{2}{3}\right]}$

For most choices of arguments, no exact reductions of special functions are possible. But in such cases, *Mathematica* allows you to find numerical approximations to any degree of precision. The algorithms that are built into *Mathematica* cover essentially all values of parameters—real and complex—for which the special functions are defined.

There is no exact result known here.

$In[3]:=$ **AiryAi[1]**

$Out[3]=$ AiryAi[1]

This gives a numerical approximation to 40 digits of precision.

$In[4]:=$ **N[AiryAi[1], 40]**

$Out[4]=$ 0.1352924163128814155241474235154663061749

The result here is a huge complex number, but *Mathematica* can still find it.

$In[5]:=$ **N[AiryAi[1000 I]]**

$Out[5]=$ $-4.780266637767 \times 10^{6472} + 3.67492090723 \times 10^{6472}\, I$

Most special functions have derivatives that can be expressed in terms of elementary functions or other special functions. But even in cases where this is not so, you can still use N to find numerical approximations to derivatives.

This derivative comes out in terms of elementary functions.

$In[6]:=$ **D[FresnelS[x], x]**

$Out[6]=$ $\text{Sin}\left[\dfrac{\pi x^2}{2}\right]$

This evaluates the derivative of the gamma function at the point 3.

$In[7]:=$ **Gamma'[3]**

$Out[7]=$ $2\left(\dfrac{3}{2} - \text{EulerGamma}\right)$

There is no exact formula for this derivative of the zeta function.

$In[8]:=$ **Zeta'[Pi]**

$Out[8]=$ Zeta'$[\pi]$

Applying N gives a numerical approximation.

$In[9]:=$ **N[%]**

$Out[9]=$ -0.167603

Mathematica incorporates a vast amount of knowledge about special functions—including essentially all the results that have been derived over the years. You access this knowledge whenever you do operations on special functions in *Mathematica*.

Here is a series expansion for a Fresnel function.

$In[10]:=$ **Series[FresnelS[x], {x, 0, 15}]**

$Out[10]=$ $\dfrac{\pi x^3}{6} - \dfrac{1}{336}\pi^3 x^7 + \dfrac{\pi^5 x^{11}}{42240} - \dfrac{\pi^7 x^{15}}{9676800} + O[x]^{18}$

Mathematica knows how to do a vast range of integrals involving special functions.

$In[11]:=$ **Integrate[AiryAi[x]^2, {x, 0, Infinity}]**

$Out[11]=$ $-\dfrac{\text{Gamma}\left[-\frac{1}{6}\right]}{12\, 2^{1/3}\, 3^{1/6}\, \pi^{3/2}}$

One feature of working with special functions is that there are a large number of relations between different functions, and these relations can often be used in simplifying expressions.

FullSimplify[*expr*]	try to simplify *expr* using a range of transformation rules

Simplifying expressions involving special functions.

This uses the reflection formula for the gamma function.

$In[12]:=$ **FullSimplify[Gamma[x] Gamma[1 - x]]**

$Out[12]=$ $\pi \, \text{Csc}[\pi x]$

This makes use of a representation for Chebyshev polynomials.

$In[13]:=$ **FullSimplify[ChebyshevT[n, z] - k Cos[n ArcCos[z]]]**

$Out[13]=$ $-(-1 + k) \text{Cos}[n \, \text{ArcCos}[z]]$

The Airy functions are related to Bessel functions.

$In[14]:=$ **FullSimplify[3 AiryAi[1] + Sqrt[3] AiryBi[1]]**

$Out[14]=$ $2 \, \text{BesselI}\left[-\frac{1}{3}, \frac{2}{3}\right]$

FunctionExpand[*expr*]	try to expand out special functions

Manipulating expressions involving special functions.

This expands out the PolyGamma, yielding a function with a simpler argument.

$In[15]:=$ **FunctionExpand[PolyGamma[2, 2 + x]]**

$Out[15]=$ $2\left(\dfrac{1}{x^3} + \dfrac{1}{(1 + x)^3}\right) + \text{PolyGamma}[2, x]$

Here is an example involving Bessel functions.

$In[16]:=$ **FunctionExpand[BesselY[n, I x]]**

$Out[16]=$ $-\dfrac{\dfrac{2 (I x)^{-n} x^n \, \text{BesselK}[n, x]}{\pi} + \text{BesselI}[n, x]}{(-(I x)^{-n} x^n + (I x)^n x^{-n} \text{Cos}[n\pi]) \text{Csc}[n\pi]}$

In this case the final result does not even involve PolyGamma.

$In[17]:=$ **FunctionExpand[Im[PolyGamma[0, 3 I]]]**

$Out[17]=$ $\dfrac{1}{6} + \dfrac{\pi \, \text{Coth}[3\pi]}{2}$

■ 3.2.14 Statistical Distributions and Related Functions

There are standard *Mathematica* packages for evaluating functions related to common statistical distributions. *Mathematica* represents the statistical distributions themselves in the symbolic form *name*[$param_1$, $param_2$, ...], where the $param_i$ are parameters for the distributions. Functions such as Mean, which give properties of statistical distributions, take the symbolic representation of the distribution as an argument.

`BetaDistribution[`α, β`]`	continuous beta distribution
`CauchyDistribution[`a, b`]`	Cauchy distribution with location parameter a and scale parameter b
`ChiSquareDistribution[`n`]`	chi-square distribution with n degrees of freedom
`ExponentialDistribution[`λ`]`	exponential distribution with scale parameter λ
`ExtremeValueDistribution[`α, β`]`	extreme value (Fisher-Tippett) distribution
`FRatioDistribution[`n_1, n_2`]`	F-ratio distribution with n_1 numerator and n_2 denominator degrees of freedom
`GammaDistribution[`α, λ`]`	gamma distribution with shape parameter α and scale parameter λ
`NormalDistribution[`μ, σ`]`	normal (Gaussian) distribution with mean μ and standard deviation σ
`LaplaceDistribution[`μ, β`]`	Laplace (double exponential) distribution with mean μ and variance parameter β
`LogNormalDistribution[`μ, σ`]`	lognormal distribution with mean parameter μ and variance parameter σ
`LogisticDistribution[`μ, β`]`	logistic distribution with mean μ and variance parameter β
`RayleighDistribution[`σ`]`	Rayleigh distribution
`StudentTDistribution[`n`]`	Student t distribution with n degrees of freedom
`UniformDistribution[`*min*, *max*`]`	uniform distribution on the interval {*min*, *max*}
`WeibullDistribution[`α, β`]`	Weibull distribution

Statistical distributions from the package `Statistics`ContinuousDistributions``.

Most of the continuous statistical distributions commonly used are derived from the **normal** or **Gaussian distribution** `NormalDistribution[`μ, σ`]`. This distribution has probability density $1/(\sqrt{2\pi}\sigma)\exp[-(x-\mu)^2/(2\sigma^2)]$. If you take random variables that follow any distribution with bounded variance, then the Central Limit Theorem shows that the mean of a large number of these variables always approaches a normal distribution.

The **logarithmic normal distribution** or **lognormal distribution** `LogNormalDistribution[`μ, σ`]` is the distribution followed by the exponential of a normal-distributed random variable. This distribution arises when many independent random variables are combined in a multiplicative fashion.

The **chi-square distribution** ChiSquareDistribution[n] is the distribution of the quantity $\sum_{i=1}^{n} x_i^2$, where the x_i are random variables which follow a normal distribution with mean zero and unit variance. The chi-square distribution gives the distribution of variances of samples from a normal distribution.

The **Student t distribution** StudentTDistribution[n] is the distribution followed by the ratio of a variable that follows the normal distribution to the square root of one that follows the chi-square distribution with n degrees of freedom. The t distribution characterizes the uncertainty in a mean when both the mean and variance are obtained from data.

The **F-ratio distribution**, **F-distribution** or **variance ratio distribution** FRatioDistribution[n_1, n_2] is the distribution of the ratio of two chi-square variables with n_1 and n_2 degrees of freedom. The F-ratio distribution is used in the analysis of variance for comparing variances from different models.

The **extreme value distribution** ExtremeValueDistribution[α, β] is the limiting distribution for the smallest or largest values in large samples drawn from a variety of distributions, including the normal distribution.

PDF[*dist*, x]	probability density function (frequency function) at x
CDF[*dist*, x]	cumulative distribution function at x
Quantile[*dist*, q]	q^{th} quantile
Mean[*dist*]	mean
Variance[*dist*]	variance
StandardDeviation[*dist*]	standard deviation
Skewness[*dist*]	coefficient of skewness
Kurtosis[*dist*]	coefficient of kurtosis
CharacteristicFunction[*dist*, t]	characteristic function $\phi(t)$
Random[*dist*]	pseudorandom number with specified distribution

Functions of statistical distributions.

The **cumulative distribution function** (cdf) CDF[*dist*, x] is given by the integral of the **probability density function** for the distribution up to the point x. For the normal distribution, the cdf is usually denoted $\Phi(x)$. Cumulative distribution functions are used in evaluating probabilities for statistical hypotheses. For discrete distributions, the cdf is given by the sum of the probabilities up to the point x. The cdf is sometimes called simply the **distribution function**. The cdf at a particular point x for a given distribution is often denoted $P(x|\theta_1, \theta_2, ...)$, where the θ_i are parameters of the distribution. The **upper tail area** is given in terms of the cdf by $Q(x|\theta_i) = 1 - P(x|\theta_i)$. Thus, for example, the upper tail area for a chi-square distribution with v degrees of freedom is denoted $Q(\chi^2 | v)$ and is given by `1 - CDF[ChiSquareDistribution[`*nu*`]`, *chi2*`]`.

The **quantile** `Quantile[`*dist*`, `*q*`]` is effectively the inverse of the cdf. It gives the value of x at which `CDF[`*dist*`, `*x*`]` reaches q. The median is given by `Quantile[`*dist*`, 1/2]`; quartiles, deciles and percentiles can also be expressed as quantiles. Quantiles are used in constructing confidence intervals for statistical parameter estimates.

The characteristic function `CharacteristicFunction[`*dist*`, `*t*`]` is given by $\phi(t) = \int p(x) \exp(itx)\, dx$, where $p(x)$ is the probability density for a distribution. The nth **central moment** of a distribution is given by the nth derivative $i^{-n}\phi^{(n)}(0)$.

`Random[`*dist*`]` gives pseudorandom numbers that follow the specified distribution. The numbers can be seeded as discussed in Section 3.2.3.

This loads the package which defines continuous statistical distributions.

```
In[1]:= <<Statistics`ContinuousDistributions`
```

This represents a normal distribution with mean zero and unit variance.

```
In[2]:= ndist = NormalDistribution[0, 1]

Out[2]= NormalDistribution[0, 1]
```

Here is a symbolic result for the cumulative distribution function of the normal distribution.

```
In[3]:= CDF[ndist, x]
```

$$Out[3]= \frac{1}{2}\left(1 + \text{Erf}\left[\frac{x}{\sqrt{2}}\right]\right)$$

This gives the value of x at which the cdf of the normal distribution reaches the value 0.9.

```
In[4]:= Quantile[ndist, 0.9] // N

Out[4]= 1.28155
```

Here is a list of five normal-distributed pseudorandom numbers.

```
In[5]:= Table[ Random[ndist], {5} ]

Out[5]= {-1.63994, 0.987641, -0.475946,
            -0.598517, -1.04913}
```

`BernoulliDistribution[p]`	discrete Bernoulli distribution with mean p
`BinomialDistribution[n, p]`	binomial distribution for n trials with probability p
`DiscreteUniformDistribution[n]`	
	discrete uniform distribution with n states
`GeometricDistribution[p]`	discrete geometric distribution with mean $1/p$
`HypergeometricDistribution[n, `n_{succ}`, `n_{tot}`]`	
	hypergeometric distribution for n trials with n_{succ} successes in a population of size n_{tot}
`NegativeBinomialDistribution[r, p]`	
	negative binomial distribution for failure count r and probability p
`PoissonDistribution[`mu`]`	Poisson distribution with mean μ

Statistical distributions from the package `Statistics'DiscreteDistributions'`.

Most of the common discrete statistical distributions can be derived by considering a sequence of "trials", each with two possible outcomes, say "success" and "failure".

The **Bernoulli distribution** `BernoulliDistribution[p]` is the probability distribution for a single trial in which success, corresponding to value 1, occurs with probability p, and failure, corresponding to value 0, occurs with probability $1 - p$.

The **binomial distribution** `BinomialDistribution[n, p]` is the distribution of the number of successes that occur in n independent trials when the probability for success in an individual trial is p. The distribution is given by $\binom{n}{k}p^k(1 - p)^{n-k}$.

The **negative binomial distribution** `NegativeBinomialDistribution[r, p]` gives the distribution of the number of failures that occur in a sequence of trials before r successes have occurred, given that the probability for success in each individual trial is p.

The **geometric distribution** `GeometricDistribution[p]` gives the distribution of the total number of trials before the first success occurs in a sequence of trials where the probability for success in each individual trial is p.

The **hypergeometric distribution** `HypergeometricDistribution[n, `n_{succ}`, `n_{tot}`]` is used in place of the binomial distribution for experiments in which the n trials correspond to sampling without replacement from a population of size n_{tot} with n_{succ} potential successes.

The **discrete uniform distribution** `DiscreteUniformDistribution[n]` represents an experiment with n outcomes that occur with equal probabilities.

3.3 Algebraic Manipulation

■ 3.3.1 Structural Operations on Polynomials

Expand[*poly*]	expand out products and powers
Factor[*poly*]	factor completely
FactorTerms[*poly*]	pull out any overall numerical factor
FactorTerms[*poly*, {*x*, *y*, ... }]	pull out any overall factor that does not depend on *x*, *y*, ...
Collect[*poly*, *x*]	arrange a polynomial as a sum of powers of *x*
Collect[*poly*, {*x*, *y*, ... }]	arrange a polynomial as a sum of powers of *x*, *y*, ...

Structural operations on polynomials.

Here is a polynomial in one variable.

$In[1]:=$ **(2 + 4 x^2)^2 (x - 1)^3**

$Out[1]= (-1 + x)^3 (2 + 4x^2)^2$

Expand expands out products and powers, writing the polynomial as a simple sum of terms.

$In[2]:=$ **t = Expand[%]**

$Out[2]= -4 + 12x - 28x^2 + 52x^3 - 64x^4 + 64x^5 - 48x^6 + 16x^7$

Factor performs complete factoring of the polynomial.

$In[3]:=$ **Factor[t]**

$Out[3]= 4(-1 + x)^3 (1 + 2x^2)^2$

FactorTerms pulls out the overall numerical factor from t.

$In[4]:=$ **FactorTerms[t]**

$Out[4]= 4(-1 + 3x - 7x^2 + 13x^3 - 16x^4 + 16x^5 - 12x^6 + 4x^7)$

There are several ways to write any polynomial. The functions Expand, FactorTerms and Factor give three common ways. Expand writes a polynomial as a simple sum of terms, with all products expanded out. FactorTerms pulls out common factors from each term. Factor does complete factoring, writing the polynomial as a product of terms, each of as low degree as possible.

When you have a polynomial in more than one variable, you can put the polynomial in different forms by essentially choosing different variables to be "dominant". Collect[*poly*, *x*] takes a polynomial in several variables and rewrites it as a sum of terms containing different powers of the "dominant variable" *x*.

Here is a polynomial in two variables.

$In[5]:=$ **Expand[(1 + 2x + y)^3]**

$Out[5]= 1 + 6x + 12x^2 + 8x^3 + 3y + 12xy + 12x^2y + 3y^2 + 6xy^2 + y^3$

Collect reorganizes the polynomial so that x is the "dominant variable".

$In[6]:=$ **Collect[%, x]**

$Out[6]= 1 + 8x^3 + 3y + 3y^2 + y^3 + x^2(12 + 12y) + x(6 + 12y + 6y^2)$

If you specify a list of variables, `Collect` will effectively write the expression as a polynomial in these variables.

$In[7]:=$ **Collect[Expand[(1 + x + 2y + 3z)^3], {x, y}]**

$Out[7]= 1 + x^3 + 8y^3 + 9z + 27z^2 + 27z^3 +$
$\qquad x^2 (3 + 6y + 9z) + y^2 (12 + 36z) + y (6 + 36z + 54z^2) +$
$\qquad x (3 + 12y^2 + 18z + 27z^2 + y (12 + 36z))$

`Expand[`*poly*`, `*patt*`]`	expand out *poly* avoiding those parts which do not contain terms matching *patt*

Controlling polynomial expansion.

This avoids expanding parts which do not contain x.

$In[8]:=$ **Expand[(x + 1)^2 (y + 1)^2, x]**

$Out[8]= (1 + y)^2 + 2x (1 + y)^2 + x^2 (1 + y)^2$

This avoids expanding parts which do not contain objects matching b[_].

$In[9]:=$ **Expand[(a[1] + a[2] + 1)^2 (1 + b[1])^2, b[_]]**

$Out[9]= (1 + a[1] + a[2])^2 + 2 (1 + a[1] + a[2])^2 b[1] +$
$\qquad (1 + a[1] + a[2])^2 b[1]^2$

`PowerExpand[`*expr*`]`	expand out $(ab)^c$ and $(a^b)^c$ in *expr*

Expanding powers.

Mathematica does not automatically expand out expressions of the form $(a\,b)\texttt{\^{}}c$ except when c is an integer. In general it is only correct to do this expansion if a and b are positive reals. Nevertheless, the function `PowerExpand` does the expansion, effectively assuming that a and b are indeed positive reals.

Mathematica does not automatically expand out this expression.

$In[10]:=$ **(x y)^n**

$Out[10]= (x y)^n$

`PowerExpand` does the expansion, effectively assuming that x and y are positive reals.

$In[11]:=$ **PowerExpand[%]**

$Out[11]= x^n y^n$

`Log` is not automatically expanded out.

$In[12]:=$ **Log[%]**

$Out[12]= Log[x^n y^n]$

`PowerExpand` does the expansion.

$In[13]:=$ **PowerExpand[%]**

$Out[13]= n\,Log[x] + n\,Log[y]$

+	`Collect[`*poly*`, `*patt*`]`	collect separately terms involving each object that matches *patt*
+	`Collect[`*poly*`, `*patt*`, `*h*`]`	apply *h* to each final coefficient obtained

Ways of collecting terms.

Here is an expression involving various functions f.

`In[14]:= t = 3 + x f[1] + x^2 f[1] + y f[2]^2 + z f[2]^2`

$Out[14]= 3 + x \, f[1] + x^2 \, f[1] + y \, f[2]^2 + z \, f[2]^2$

This collects terms that match f[_].

`In[15]:= Collect[t, f[_]]`

$Out[15]= 3 + (x + x^2) \, f[1] + (y + z) \, f[2]^2$

This applies `Factor` to each coefficient obtained.

`In[16]:= Collect[t, f[_], Factor]`

$Out[16]= 3 + x \, (1 + x) \, f[1] + (y + z) \, f[2]^2$

■ 3.3.2 Finding the Structure of a Polynomial

`PolynomialQ[`*expr*`, x]`	test whether *expr* is a polynomial in x
`PolynomialQ[`*expr*`, {`x_1`, `x_2`, ... }]`	
	test whether *expr* is a polynomial in the x_i
`Variables[`*poly*`]`	a list of the variables in *poly*
`Exponent[`*poly*`, x]`	the maximum exponent with which x appears in *poly*
`Coefficient[`*poly*`, `*expr*`]`	the coefficient of *expr* in *poly*
`Coefficient[`*poly*`, `*expr*`, n]`	the coefficient of *expr*^*n* in *poly*
`Coefficient[`*poly*`, `*expr*`, 0]`	the term in *poly* independent of *expr*
`CoefficientList[`*poly*`, {`x_1`, `x_2`, ... }]`	
	generate an array of the coefficients of the x_i in *poly*

Finding the structure of polynomials written in expanded form.

Here is a polynomial in two variables.

`In[1]:= t = (1 + x)^3 (1 - y - x)^2`

$Out[1]= (1 + x)^3 \, (1 - x - y)^2$

This is the polynomial in expanded form.

`In[2]:= Expand[t]`

$Out[2]= 1 + x - 2 x^2 - 2 x^3 + x^4 + x^5 - 2 y - 4 x y + 4 x^3 y +$
$\quad 2 x^4 y + y^2 + 3 x y^2 + 3 x^2 y^2 + x^3 y^2$

PolynomialQ reports that t is a
polynomial in x.

$In[3]:=$ **PolynomialQ[t, x]**

$Out[3]=$ True

This expression, however, is not a
polynomial in x.

$In[4]:=$ **PolynomialQ[x + Sin[x], x]**

$Out[4]=$ False

Variables gives a list of the variables
in the polynomial t.

$In[5]:=$ **Variables[t]**

$Out[5]=$ {x, y}

This gives the maximum exponent with
which x appears in the polynomial t.
For a polynomial in one variable,
Exponent gives the degree of the
polynomial.

$In[6]:=$ **Exponent[t, x]**

$Out[6]=$ 5

Coefficient[*poly*, *expr*] gives the
total coefficient with which *expr*
appears in *poly*. In this case, the result
is a sum of two terms.

$In[7]:=$ **Coefficient[t, x^2]**

$Out[7]=$ $-2 + 3y^2$

This is equivalent to
Coefficient[t, x^2].

$In[8]:=$ **Coefficient[t, x, 2]**

$Out[8]=$ $-2 + 3y^2$

This picks out the coefficient of x^0 in t.

$In[9]:=$ **Coefficient[t, x, 0]**

$Out[9]=$ $1 - 2y + y^2$

CoefficientList gives a list of the
coefficients of each power of x, starting
with x^0.

$In[10]:=$ **CoefficientList[1 + 3x^2 + 4x^4, x]**

$Out[10]=$ {1, 0, 3, 0, 4}

For multivariate polynomials,
CoefficientList gives an array of the
coefficients for each power of each
variable.

$In[11]:=$ **CoefficientList[t, {x, y}]**

$Out[11]=$ {{1, -2, 1}, {1, -4, 3}, {-2, 0, 3}, {-2, 4, 1},
         {1, 2, 0}, {1, 0, 0}}

It is important to notice that the functions in this section will work even on polynomials that are not
explicitly given in expanded form.

Many of the functions also work on expressions that are not strictly polynomials.

Without giving specific integer values
to a, b and c, this expression cannot
strictly be considered a polynomial.

$In[12]:=$ **x^a + x^b + y^c**

$Out[12]=$ $x^a + x^b + y^c$

Exponent[*expr*, x] still gives the
maximum exponent of x in *expr*, but
here has to write the result in symbolic
form.

$In[13]:=$ **Exponent[%, x]**

$Out[13]=$ Max[0, a, b]

■ 3.3.3 Structural Operations on Rational Expressions

For ordinary polynomials, `Factor` and `Expand` give the most important forms. For rational expressions, there are many different forms that can be useful.

`ExpandNumerator[`*expr*`]`	expand numerators only
`ExpandDenominator[`*expr*`]`	expand denominators only
`Expand[`*expr*`]`	expand numerators, dividing the denominator into each term
`ExpandAll[`*expr*`]`	expand numerators and denominators completely

Different kinds of expansion for rational expressions.

Here is a rational expression.

In[1]:= `t = (1 + x)^2 / (1 - x) + 3 x^2 / (1 + x)^2 + (2 - x)^2`

$$Out[1]= (2-x)^2 + \frac{3x^2}{(1+x)^2} + \frac{(1+x)^2}{1-x}$$

`ExpandNumerator` writes the numerator of each term in expanded form.

In[2]:= `ExpandNumerator[t]`

$$Out[2]= 4 - 4x + x^2 + \frac{3x^2}{(1+x)^2} + \frac{1+2x+x^2}{1-x}$$

`Expand` expands the numerator of each term, and divides all the terms by the appropriate denominators.

In[3]:= `Expand[t]`

$$Out[3]= 4 + \frac{1}{1-x} - 4x + \frac{2x}{1-x} + x^2 + \frac{x^2}{1-x} + \frac{3x^2}{(1+x)^2}$$

`ExpandDenominator` expands out the denominator of each term.

In[4]:= `ExpandDenominator[t]`

$$Out[4]= (2-x)^2 + \frac{(1+x)^2}{1-x} + \frac{3x^2}{1+2x+x^2}$$

`ExpandAll` does all possible expansions in the numerator and denominator of each term.

In[5]:= `ExpandAll[t]`

$$Out[5]= 4 + \frac{1}{1-x} - 4x + \frac{2x}{1-x} + x^2 + \frac{x^2}{1-x} + \frac{3x^2}{1+2x+x^2}$$

`ExpandAll[`*expr*`, `*patt*`]`, etc.	avoid expanding parts which contain no terms matching *patt*

Controlling expansion.

This avoids expanding the term which does not contain z.

In[6]:= `ExpandAll[(x + 1)^2/y^2 + (z + 1)^2/z^2, z]`

$$Out[6]= 1 + \frac{(1+x)^2}{y^2} + \frac{1}{z^2} + \frac{2}{z}$$

Together[*expr*]	combine all terms over a common denominator
Apart[*expr*]	write an expression as a sum of terms with simple denominators
Cancel[*expr*]	cancel common factors between numerators and denominators
Factor[*expr*]	perform a complete factoring

Structural operations on rational expressions.

Here is a rational expression.

$In[7]:=$ **u = (-4x + x^2)/(-x + x^2) + (-4 + 3x + x^2)/(-1 + x^2)**

$$Out[7]= \frac{-4x + x^2}{-x + x^2} + \frac{-4 + 3x + x^2}{-1 + x^2}$$

Together puts all terms over a common denominator.

$In[8]:=$ **Together[u]**

$$Out[8]= \frac{2(-4 + x^2)}{(-1 + x)(1 + x)}$$

You can use Factor to factor the numerator and denominator of the resulting expression.

$In[9]:=$ **Factor[%]**

$$Out[9]= \frac{2(-2 + x)(2 + x)}{(-1 + x)(1 + x)}$$

Apart writes the expression as a sum of terms, with each term having as simple a denominator as possible.

$In[10]:=$ **Apart[u]**

$$Out[10]= 2 - \frac{3}{-1 + x} + \frac{3}{1 + x}$$

Cancel cancels any common factors between numerators and denominators.

$In[11]:=$ **Cancel[u]**

$$Out[11]= \frac{-4 + x}{-1 + x} + \frac{4 + x}{1 + x}$$

Factor first puts all terms over a common denominator, then factors the result.

$In[12]:=$ **Factor[%]**

$$Out[12]= \frac{2(-2 + x)(2 + x)}{(-1 + x)(1 + x)}$$

In mathematical terms, Apart decomposes a rational expression into "partial fractions".

In expressions with several variables, you can use Apart[*expr*, *var*] to do partial fraction decompositions with respect to different variables.

Here is a rational expression in two variables.

$In[13]:=$ **v = (x^2+y^2)/(x + x y)**

$$Out[13]= \frac{x^2 + y^2}{x + x y}$$

This gives the partial fraction decomposition with respect to x.

$In[14]:=$ **Apart[v, x]**

$$Out[14]= \frac{x}{1+y} + \frac{y^2}{x\,(1+y)}$$

Here is the partial fraction decomposition with respect to y.

$In[15]:=$ **Apart[v, y]**

$$Out[15]= -\frac{1}{x} + \frac{y}{x} + \frac{1+x^2}{x\,(1+y)}$$

■ 3.3.4 Algebraic Operations on Polynomials

For many kinds of practical calculations, the only operations you will need to perform on polynomials are essentially the structural ones discussed in the preceding sections.

If you do more advanced algebra with polynomials, however, you will have to use the algebraic operations discussed in this section.

You should realize that most of the operations discussed in this section work only on ordinary polynomials, with integer exponents and rational-number coefficients for each term.

`PolynomialQuotient[`$poly_1$`, `$poly_2$`, `x`]`	find the result of dividing the polynomial $poly_1$ in x by $poly_2$, dropping any remainder term
`PolynomialRemainder[`$poly_1$`, `$poly_2$`, `x`]`	find the remainder from dividing the polynomial $poly_1$ in x by $poly_2$
`PolynomialGCD[`$poly_1$`, `$poly_2$`]`	find the greatest common divisor of two polynomials
`PolynomialLCM[`$poly_1$`, `$poly_2$`]`	find the least common multiple of two polynomials
`PolynomialMod[`$poly$`, `m`]`	reduce the polynomial $poly$ modulo m
`Resultant[`$poly_1$`, `$poly_2$`, `x`]`	find the resultant of two polynomials
`GroebnerBasis[{`$poly_1$`, `$poly_2$`, ... }, {`x_1`, `x_2`, ... }]`	find the Gröbner basis for the polynomials $poly_i$
`GroebnerBasis[{`$poly_1$`, `$poly_2$`, ... }, {`x_1`, `x_2`, ... }, {`y_1`, `y_2`, ... }]`	find the Gröbner basis eliminating the y_i
`+` `PolynomialReduce[`$poly$`, {`$poly_1$`, `$poly_2$`, ... }, {`x_1`, `x_2`, ... }]`	find a minimal representation of $poly$ in terms of the $poly_i$

Reduction of polynomials.

Given two polynomials $p(x)$ and $q(x)$, one can always uniquely write $\frac{p(x)}{q(x)} = a(x) + \frac{b(x)}{q(x)}$, where the degree of $b(x)$ is less than the degree of $q(x)$. PolynomialQuotient gives the quotient $a(x)$, and PolynomialRemainder gives the remainder $b(x)$.

This gives the remainder from dividing x^2 by $1 + x$.	`In[1]:= PolynomialRemainder[x^2, x+1, x]` `Out[1]= 1`
Here is the quotient of x^2 and $x + 1$, with the remainder dropped.	`In[2]:= PolynomialQuotient[x^2, x+1, x]` `Out[2]= -1 + x`
This gives back the original expression.	`In[3]:= Simplify[ (x+1) % + %% ]` `Out[3]= x^2`

Here the result depends on whether the polynomials are considered to be in x or y.	`In[4]:= {PolynomialRemainder[x+y, x-y, x],`
	`            PolynomialRemainder[x+y, x-y, y]}`
	`Out[4]= {2y, 2x}`

PolynomialGCD[$poly_1$, $poly_2$] finds the highest degree polynomial that divides the $poly_i$ exactly. It gives the analog for polynomials of the integer function GCD.

PolynomialGCD gives the greatest common divisor of the two polynomials.	`In[5]:= PolynomialGCD[ (1-x)^2 (1+x) (2+x), (1-x) (2+x) (3+x) ]` `Out[5]= (-1 + x) (2 + x)`

PolynomialMod is essentially the analog for polynomials of the function Mod for integers. When the modulus m is an integer, PolynomialMod[$poly$, m] simply reduces each coefficient in $poly$ modulo the integer m. If m is a polynomial, then PolynomialMod[$poly$, m] effectively tries to get as low degree a polynomial as possible by subtracting from $poly$ appropriate multiples $q\,m$ of m. The multiplier q can itself be a polynomial, but its degree is always less than the degree of $poly$. PolynomialMod yields a final polynomial whose degree and leading coefficient are both as small as possible.

This reduces x^2 modulo $x + 1$. The result is simply the remainder from dividing the polynomials.	`In[6]:= PolynomialMod[x^2, x+1]` `Out[6]= 1`

In this case, PolynomialMod and PolynomialRemainder do not give the same result.	`In[7]:= {PolynomialMod[x^2, 2x+1],`
	`            PolynomialRemainder[x^2, 2x+1, x]}`
	`Out[7]= $\left\{x^2, \dfrac{1}{4}\right\}$`

The main difference between PolynomialMod and PolynomialRemainder is that while the former works simply by multiplying and subtracting polynomials, the latter uses division in getting its results. In addition, PolynomialMod allows reduction by several moduli at the same time. A typical case is reduction modulo both a polynomial and an integer.

This reduces the polynomial $x^2 + 1$ modulo both $x + 1$ and 2.	`In[8]:= PolynomialMod[x^2 + 1, {x + 1, 2}]` `Out[8]= 0`

The function `Resultant[`$poly_1$`, `$poly_2$`, x]` is used in a number of classical algebraic algorithms. The resultant of two polynomials a and b, both with leading coefficient one, is given by the product of all the differences $a_i - b_j$ between the roots of the polynomials. It turns out that for any pair of polynomials, the resultant is always a polynomial in their coefficients. By looking at when the resultant is zero, one can tell for what values of their parameters two polynomials have a common root.

Here is the resultant with respect to y of two polynomials in x and y. The original polynomials have a common root in y only for values of x at which the resultant vanishes.

```
In[9]:= Resultant[(x-y)^2-2, y^2-3, y]

Out[9]= 1 - 10 x^2 + x^4
```

Gröbner bases appear in many modern algebraic algorithms and applications. The function `GroebnerBasis[{`$poly_1$`, `$poly_2$`, ... }, {`x_1`, `x_2`, ... }]` takes a set of polynomials, and reduces this set to a canonical form from which many properties can conveniently be deduced. An important feature is that the set of polynomials obtained from `GroebnerBasis` always has exactly the same collection of common roots as the original set.

The $(x + y)^2$ is effectively redundant, and so does not appear in the Gröbner basis.

```
In[10]:= GroebnerBasis[{(x+y), (x+y)^2}, {x, y}]

Out[10]= {x + y}
```

The polynomial 1 has no roots, showing that the original polynomials have no common roots.

```
In[11]:= GroebnerBasis[{x+y,x^2-1,y^2-2x}, {x, y}]

Out[11]= {1}
```

The polynomials are effectively unwound here, and can now be seen to have exactly five common roots.

```
In[12]:= GroebnerBasis[{x y^2+2 x y+x^2+1, x y+y^2+1}, {x, y}]

Out[12]= {-1 - y^2 + y^3 + y^4 + y^5, x + y^2 + y^3 + y^4}
```

`PolynomialReduce[`$poly$`, {`p_1`, `p_2`, ... }, {`x_1`, `x_2`, ... }]` yields a list $\{\{a_1, a_2, ... \}, b\}$ of polynomials with the property that b is minimal and $a_1 p_1 + a_2 p_2 + ... + b$ is exactly $poly$.

This writes $x^2 + y^2$ in terms of $x - y$ and $y + a$, leaving a remainder that depends only on a.

```
In[13]:= PolynomialReduce[x^2 + y^2, {x - y, y + a}, {x, y}]

Out[13]= {{x + y, -2a + 2y}, 2a^2}
```

`Factor[`*poly*`]`	factor a polynomial
`FactorSquareFree[`*poly*`]`	write a polynomial as a product of powers of square-free factors
`FactorTerms[`*poly*`, x]`	factor out terms that do not depend on x
`FactorList[`*poly*`]`, `FactorSquareFreeList[`*poly*`]`, `FactorTermsList[`*poly*`]`	
	give results as lists of factors

Functions for factoring polynomials.

`Factor`, `FactorTerms` and `FactorSquareFree` perform various degrees of factoring on polynomials. `Factor` does full factoring over the integers. `FactorTerms` extracts the "content" of the polynomial. `FactorSquareFree` pulls out any multiple factors that appear.

Here is a polynomial, in expanded form.	*In[14]:=* **t = Expand[2 (1 + x)^2 (2 + x) (3 + x)]**
	Out[14]= $12 + 34x + 34x^2 + 14x^3 + 2x^4$

`FactorTerms` pulls out only the factor of 2 that does not depend on x.	*In[15]:=* **FactorTerms[t, x]**
	Out[15]= $2(6 + 17x + 17x^2 + 7x^3 + x^4)$

`FactorSquareFree` factors out the 2 and the term (1 + x)^2, but leaves the rest unfactored.	*In[16]:=* **FactorSquareFree[t]**
	Out[16]= $2(1+x)^2(6 + 5x + x^2)$

`Factor` does full factoring, recovering the original form.	*In[17]:=* **Factor[t]**
	Out[17]= $2(1+x)^2(2+x)(3+x)$

Particularly when you write programs that work with polynomials, you will often find it convenient to pick out pieces of polynomials in a standard form. The function `FactorList` gives a list of all the factors of a polynomial, together with their exponents. The first element of the list is always the overall numerical factor for the polynomial.

The form that `FactorList` returns is the analog for polynomials of the form produced by `FactorInteger` for integers.

Here is a list of the factors of the polynomial in the previous set of examples. Each element of the list gives the factor, together with its exponent.	*In[18]:=* **FactorList[t]**
	Out[18]= {{2, 1}, {1 + x, 2}, {2 + x, 1}, {3 + x, 1}}

`Factor[`*poly*`, GaussianIntegers -> True]`
           factor a polynomial, allowing coefficients that are Gaussian integers

---

Factoring polynomials with complex coefficients.

`Factor` and related functions usually handle only polynomials with ordinary integer or rational-number coefficients. If you set the option `GaussianIntegers -> True`, however, then `Factor` will allow polynomials with coefficients that are complex numbers with rational real and imaginary parts. This often allows more extensive factorization to be performed.

This polynomial is irreducible when only ordinary integers are allowed.	*In[19]:=* **Factor[1 + x^2]**
	Out[19]= $1 + x^2$

When Gaussian integer coefficients are allowed, the polynomial factors.	*In[20]:=* **Factor[1 + x^2, GaussianIntegers -> True]**
	Out[20]= $(-I + x)(I + x)$

`Cyclotomic[n, x]`	give the cyclotomic polynomial of order n in x

Cyclotomic polynomials.

Cyclotomic polynomials arise as "elementary polynomials" in various algebraic algorithms. The cyclotomic polynomials are defined by $C_n(x) = \prod_k(x - e^{2\pi i k/n})$, where k runs over all positive integers less than n that are relatively prime to n.

This is the cyclotomic polynomial $C_6(x)$.

In[21]:= **Cyclotomic[6, x]**

Out[21]= $1 - x + x^2$

$C_6(x)$ appears in the factors of $x^6 - 1$.

In[22]:= **Factor[x^6 - 1]**

Out[22]= $(-1 + x) (1 + x) (1 - x + x^2) (1 + x + x^2)$

`Decompose[poly, x]`	decompose *poly*, if possible, into a composition of a list of simpler polynomials

Decomposing polynomials.

Factorization is one important way of breaking down polynomials into simpler parts. Another, quite different, way is *decomposition*. When one factors a polynomial $P(x)$, one writes it as a product $p_1(x)p_2(x)...$ of polynomials $p_i(x)$. Decomposing a polynomial $Q(x)$ consists of writing it as a *composition* of polynomials of the form $q_1(q_2(...(x)...))$.

Here is a simple example of Decompose. The original polynomial $x^4 + x^2 + 1$ can be written as the polynomial $\tilde{x}^2 + \tilde{x} + 1$, where $\tilde{x}$ is the polynomial x^2.

In[23]:= **Decompose[x^4 + x^2 + 1, x]**

Out[23]= $\{1 + x + x^2, x^2\}$

Here are two polynomial functions.

In[24]:= (**q1[x_] = 1 - 2x + x^4 ;**
            q2[x_] = 5x + x^3 ;)

This gives the composition of the two functions.

In[25]:= **Expand[q1[q2[x]]]**

Out[25]= $1 - 10x - 2x^3 + 625x^4 + 500x^6 + 150x^8 + 20x^{10} + x^{12}$

Decompose recovers the original functions.

In[26]:= **Decompose[%, x]**

Out[26]= $\{1 - 2x + x^4, 5x + x^3\}$

`Decompose[poly, x]` is set up to give a list of polynomials in x, which, if composed, reproduce the original polynomial. The original polynomial can contain variables other than x, but the sequence of polynomials that Decompose produces are all intended to be considered as functions of x.

Unlike factoring, the decomposition of polynomials is not completely unique. For example, the two sets of polynomials p_i and q_i, related by $q_1(x) = p_1(x - a)$ and $q_2(x) = p_2(x) + a$ give the same result on composition, so that $p_1(p_2(x)) = q_1(q_2(x))$. *Mathematica* follows the convention of absorbing any constant terms into the first polynomial in the list produced by `Decompose`.

> `InterpolatingPolynomial[{`f_1`, `f_2`, ... }, `x`]`
> give a polynomial in x which is equal to f_i when x is the integer i
>
> `InterpolatingPolynomial[{{`x_1`, `f_1`}, {`x_2`, `f_2`}, ... }, `x`]`
> give a polynomial in x which is equal to f_i when x is x_i

Generating interpolating polynomials.

This yields a quadratic polynomial which goes through the specified three points.

```
In[27]:= InterpolatingPolynomial[{{-1, 4}, {0, 2}, {1, 6}}, x]
Out[27]= 4 + (1 + x) (-2 + 3 x)
```

When x is 0, the polynomial has value 2.

```
In[28]:= % /. x -> 0
Out[28]= 2
```

◼ 3.3.5 Polynomials Modulo Primes

Mathematica can work with polynomials whose coefficients are in the finite field Z_p of integers modulo a prime p.

`PolynomialMod[`*poly*`, `*p*`]`	reduce the coefficients in a polynomial modulo p
`Expand[`*poly*`, Modulus -> `*p*`]`	expand *poly* modulo p
`Factor[`*poly*`, Modulus -> `*p*`]`	factor *poly* modulo p
`PolynomialGCD[`*poly*$_1$`, `*poly*$_2$`, Modulus -> `*p*`]`	find the GCD of the *poly*$_i$ modulo p
`GroebnerBasis[`*polys*`, `*vars*`, Modulus -> `*p*`]`	find the Gröbner basis modulo p

Functions for manipulating polynomials over finite fields.

Here is an ordinary polynomial.

```
In[1]:= Expand[ (1 + x)^6 ]
Out[1]= 1 + 6 x + 15 x^2 + 20 x^3 + 15 x^4 + 6 x^5 + x^6
```

This reduces the coefficients modulo 2.

```
In[2]:= PolynomialMod[%, 2]
Out[2]= 1 + x^2 + x^4 + x^6
```

Here are the factors of the resulting polynomial over the integers.

$In[3]:=$ **Factor[%]**

$Out[3]=$ $(1 + x^2) (1 + x^4)$

If you work modulo 2, further factoring becomes possible.

$In[4]:=$ **Factor[%, Modulus->2]**

$Out[4]=$ $(1 + x)^6$

+■ 3.3.6 Advanced Topic: Polynomials over Algebraic Number Fields

Functions like `Factor` usually assume that all coefficients in the polynomials they produce must involve only rational numbers. But by setting the option `Extension` you can extend the domain of coefficients that will be allowed.

+ `Factor[`*poly*`, Extension->{`a_1`, `a_2`, ... }]`
factor *poly* allowing coefficients that are rational combinations of the a_i

Factoring polynomials over algebraic number fields.

Allowing only rational number coefficients, this polynomial cannot be factored.

$In[1]:=$ **Factor[1 + x^4]**

$Out[1]=$ $1 + x^4$

With coefficients that can involve $\sqrt{2}$, the polynomial can now be factored.

$In[2]:=$ **Factor[1 + x^4, Extension -> {Sqrt[2]}]**

$Out[2]=$ $-\left(-1 + \sqrt{2}\,x - x^2\right)\left(1 + \sqrt{2}\,x + x^2\right)$

The polynomial can also be factored if one allows coefficients involving $\sqrt{-1}$.

$In[3]:=$ **Factor[1 + x^4, Extension -> {Sqrt[-1]}]**

$Out[3]=$ $(-I + x^2)(I + x^2)$

`GaussianIntegers->True` is equivalent to `Extension->Sqrt[-1]`.

$In[4]:=$ **Factor[1 + x^4, GaussianIntegers -> True]**

$Out[4]=$ $(-I + x^2)(I + x^2)$

If one allows coefficients that involve both $\sqrt{2}$ and $\sqrt{-1}$ the polynomial can be factored completely.

$In[5]:=$ **Factor[1 + x^4, Extension -> {Sqrt[2], Sqrt[-1]}]**

$Out[5]=$ $\frac{1}{4}\left(\sqrt{2} - (1 + I)\,x\right)\left(\sqrt{2} - (1 - I)\,x\right)$
$\left(\sqrt{2} + (1 - I)\,x\right)\left(\sqrt{2} + (1 + I)\,x\right)$

Expand gives the original polynomial back again.

$In[6]:=$ **Expand[%]**

$Out[6]=$ $1 + x^4$

+ `Factor[poly, Extension->Automatic]`
                                factor *poly* allowing algebraic numbers in *poly* to appear in
                                coefficients

Factoring polynomials with algebraic number coefficients.

Here is a polynomial with a coefficient involving $\sqrt{2}$.	*In[7]:=* `t = Expand[(Sqrt[2] + x)^2]` *Out[7]=* $2 + 2\sqrt{2}\, x + x^2$
By default, `Factor` will not factor this polynomial.	*In[8]:=* `Factor[t]` *Out[8]=* $2 + 2\sqrt{2}\, x + x^2$
But now the field of coefficients is extended by including $\sqrt{2}$, and the polynomial is factored.	*In[9]:=* `Factor[t, Extension -> Automatic]` *Out[9]=* $\left(\sqrt{2} + x\right)^2$

Other polynomial functions work much like `Factor`. By default, they treat algebraic number coefficients just like independent symbolic variables. But with the option `Extension->Automatic` they perform operations on these coefficients.

By default, `Cancel` does not reduce these polynomials.	*In[10]:=* `Cancel[t / (x^2 - 2)]` *Out[10]=* $\dfrac{2 + 2\sqrt{2}\, x + x^2}{-2 + x^2}$
But now it does.	*In[11]:=* `Cancel[t / (x^2 - 2), Extension->Automatic]` *Out[11]=* $\dfrac{-\sqrt{2} - x}{\sqrt{2} - x}$
By default, `PolynomialLCM` pulls out no common factors.	*In[12]:=* `PolynomialLCM[t, x^2 - 2]` *Out[12]=* $(-2 + x^2)\left(2 + 2\sqrt{2}\, x + x^2\right)$
But now it does.	*In[13]:=* `PolynomialLCM[t, x^2 - 2, Extension->Automatic]` *Out[13]=* $-2\sqrt{2} - 2x + \sqrt{2}\, x^2 + x^3$

+■ **3.3.7 Trigonometric Expressions**

+	TrigExpand[*expr*]	expand trigonometric expressions out into a sum of terms
+	TrigFactor[*expr*]	factor trigonometric expressions into products of terms
+	TrigFactorList[*expr*]	give terms and their exponents in a list
+	TrigReduce[*expr*]	reduce trigonometric expressions using multiple angles

Functions for manipulating trigonometric expressions.

This expands out a trigonometric expression.

$In[1]:=$ **TrigExpand[Sin[2 x] Cos[2 y]]**

$Out[1]= 2 \text{Cos}[x] \text{Cos}[y]^2 \text{Sin}[x] - 2 \text{Cos}[x] \text{Sin}[x] \text{Sin}[y]^2$

This factors the expression.

$In[2]:=$ **TrigFactor[%]**

$Out[2]= 2 \text{Cos}[x] \text{Sin}[x] (\text{Cos}[y] - \text{Sin}[y]) (\text{Cos}[y] + \text{Sin}[y])$

And this reduces the expression to a form linear in the trigonometric functions.

$In[3]:=$ **TrigReduce[%]**

$Out[3]= \frac{1}{2} \text{Sin}[2x - 2y] + \frac{1}{2} \text{Sin}[2x + 2y]$

TrigExpand works on hyperbolic as well as circular functions.

$In[4]:=$ **TrigExpand[Tanh[x + y]]**

$Out[4]= \frac{\text{Cosh}[y] \text{Sinh}[x]}{\text{Cosh}[x] \text{Cosh}[y] + \text{Sinh}[x] \text{Sinh}[y]} + \frac{\text{Cosh}[x] \text{Sinh}[y]}{\text{Cosh}[x] \text{Cosh}[y] + \text{Sinh}[x] \text{Sinh}[y]}$

TrigReduce reproduces the original form again.

$In[5]:=$ **TrigReduce[%]**

$Out[5]= \text{Tanh}[x + y]$

Mathematica automatically uses functions like Tan whenever it can.

$In[6]:=$ **Sin[x]^2/Cos[x]**

$Out[6]= \text{Sin}[x] \text{Tan}[x]$

With TrigFactorList, however, you can see the parts of functions like Tan.

$In[7]:=$ **TrigFactorList[%]**

$Out[7]= \{\{1, 1\}, \{\text{Sin}[x], 2\}, \{\text{Cos}[x], -1\}\}$

+	TrigToExp[*expr*]	write trigonometric functions in terms of exponentials
+	ExpToTrig[*expr*]	write exponentials in terms of trigonometric functions

Converting to and from exponentials.

TrigToExp writes trigonometric functions in terms of exponentials.

$In[8]:=$ **TrigToExp[Tan[x]]**

$Out[8]= \frac{I (E^{-Ix} - E^{Ix})}{E^{-Ix} + E^{Ix}}$

ExpToTrig does the reverse, getting rid of explicit complex numbers whenever possible.

```
In[9]:= ExpToTrig[%]
Out[9]= Tan[x]
```

ExpToTrig deals with hyperbolic as well as circular functions.

```
In[10]:= ExpToTrig[Exp[x] - Exp[-x]]
Out[10]= 2 Sinh[x]
```

You can also use ExpToTrig on purely numerical expressions.

```
In[11]:= ExpToTrig[(-1)^(1/17)]
```
$$Out[11]= \text{Cos}\left[\frac{\pi}{17}\right] + \text{I Sin}\left[\frac{\pi}{17}\right]$$

■ 3.3.8 Expressions Involving Complex Variables

Mathematica usually pays no attention to whether variables like x stand for real or complex numbers. Sometimes, however, you may want to make transformations which are appropriate only if particular variables are assumed to be either real or complex.

The function ComplexExpand expands out algebraic and trigonometric expressions, making definite assumptions about the variables that appear.

ComplexExpand[*expr*]	expand *expr* assuming that all variables are real
ComplexExpand[*expr*, {x_1, x_2, ... }]	
	expand *expr* assuming that the x_i are complex

Expanding complex expressions.

This expands the expression, assuming that x and y are both real.

```
In[1]:= ComplexExpand[Tan[x + I y]]
```
$$Out[1]= \frac{\text{Sin}[2x]}{\text{Cos}[2x] + \text{Cosh}[2y]} + \frac{\text{I Sinh}[2y]}{\text{Cos}[2x] + \text{Cosh}[2y]}$$

In this case, a is assumed to be real, but x is assumed to be complex, and is broken into explicit real and imaginary parts.

```
In[2]:= ComplexExpand[a + x^2, {x}]
```
$$Out[2]= a - \text{Im}[x]^2 + 2 \text{I Im}[x] \text{Re}[x] + \text{Re}[x]^2$$

With several complex variables, you quickly get quite complicated results.

```
In[3]:= ComplexExpand[Sin[x] Exp[y], {x, y}]
```
$$Out[3]= E^{\text{Re}[y]} \text{Cos}[\text{Im}[y]] \text{Cosh}[\text{Im}[x]] \text{Sin}[\text{Re}[x]] +$$
$$\quad \text{I} E^{\text{Re}[y]} \text{Cosh}[\text{Im}[x]] \text{Sin}[\text{Im}[y]] \text{Sin}[\text{Re}[x]] +$$
$$\quad \text{I} E^{\text{Re}[y]} \text{Cos}[\text{Im}[y]] \text{Cos}[\text{Re}[x]] \text{Sinh}[\text{Im}[x]] -$$
$$\quad E^{\text{Re}[y]} \text{Cos}[\text{Re}[x]] \text{Sin}[\text{Im}[y]] \text{Sinh}[\text{Im}[x]]$$

There are several ways to write a complex variable *z* in terms of real parameters. As above, for example, *z* can be written in the "Cartesian form" Re[z] + I Im[z]. But it can equally well be written in the "polar form" Abs[z] Exp[I Arg[z]].

The option `TargetFunctions` in `ComplexExpand` allows you to specify how complex variables should be written. `TargetFunctions` can be set to a list of functions from the set {`Re`, `Im`, `Abs`, `Arg`, `Conjugate`, `Sign`}. `ComplexExpand` will try to give results in terms of whichever of these functions you request. The default is typically to give results in terms of `Re` and `Im`.

This gives an expansion in Cartesian form.

In[4]:= `ComplexExpand[Re[z^2], {z}]`

Out[4]= $-\text{Im}[z]^2 + \text{Re}[z]^2$

Here is an expansion in polar form.

In[5]:= `ComplexExpand[Re[z^2], {z},`
               `                TargetFunctions -> {Abs, Arg}]`

Out[5]= $\text{Abs}[z]^2 \text{Cos}[\text{Arg}[z]]^2 - \text{Abs}[z]^2 \text{Sin}[\text{Arg}[z]]^2$

Here is another form of expansion.

In[6]:= `ComplexExpand[Re[z^2], {z}, TargetFunctions -> Conjugate]`

Out[6]= $\dfrac{z^2}{2} + \dfrac{\text{Conjugate}[z]^2}{2}$

■ 3.3.9 Simplification

`Simplify[`*expr*`]`	try various algebraic and trigonometric transformations to simplify an expression
`FullSimplify[`*expr*`]`	try a much wider range of transformations

Simplifying expressions.

Mathematica does not automatically simplify an algebraic expression like this.

In[1]:= `(1 - x)/(1 - x^2)`

Out[1]= $\dfrac{1 - x}{1 - x^2}$

`Simplify` performs the simplification.

In[2]:= `Simplify[%]`

Out[2]= $\dfrac{1}{1 + x}$

`Simplify` performs standard algebraic and trigonometric simplifications.

In[3]:= `Simplify[Sin[x]^2 + Cos[x]^2]`

Out[3]= 1

It does not however do more sophisticated transformations that involve for example special functions.

In[4]:= `Simplify[Gamma[1+n]/n]`

Out[4]= $\dfrac{\text{Gamma}[1 + n]}{n}$

FullSimplify does perform such
transformations.

```
In[5]:= FullSimplify[%]
Out[5]= Gamma[n]
```

+ **FullSimplify[*expr*, ExcludedForms -> *pattern*]**
try to simplify *expr*, without touching subexpressions that
match *pattern*

Controlling simplification.

Here is an expression involving
trigonometric functions and square
roots.

```
In[6]:= t = (1 - Sin[x]^2) Sqrt[Expand[(1 + Sqrt[2])^20]]
```

$$Out[6]= \sqrt{22619537 + 15994428\sqrt{2}}\ (1 - \text{Sin}[x]^2)$$

By default, FullSimplify will try to
simplify everything.

```
In[7]:= FullSimplify[t]
```

$$Out[7]= \left(3363 + 2378\sqrt{2}\right)\text{Cos}[x]^2$$

This makes FullSimplify avoid
simplifying the square roots.

```
In[8]:= FullSimplify[t, ExcludedForms->Sqrt[_]]
```

$$Out[8]= \sqrt{22619537 + 15994428\sqrt{2}}\ \text{Cos}[x]^2$$

+ **FullSimplify[*expr*, TimeConstraint->*t*]**
try to simplify *expr*, working for at most *t* seconds on each
transformation

+ **Simplify[*expr*, ComplexityFunction->*f*]** and **FullSimplify[*expr*, ComplexityFunction->*f*]**
simplify using *f* to determine what form is considered
simplest

Further control of simplification.

In both Simplify and FullSimplify there is always an issue of what counts as the "simplest" form of
an expression. You can use the option ComplexityFunction -> *f* to provide a function to determine
this. The function will be applied to each candidate form of the expression, and the one that gives
the smallest numerical value will be considered simplest.

With its default definition of simplicity,
Simplify leaves this unchanged.

```
In[9]:= Simplify[4 Log[10]]
Out[9]= 4 Log[10]
```

This now tries to minimize the number
of elements in the expression.

```
In[10]:= Simplify[4 Log[10], ComplexityFunction -> LeafCount]
Out[10]= Log[10000]
```

3.4 Manipulating Equations

■ 3.4.1 The Representation of Equations and Solutions

Mathematica treats equations as logical statements. If you type in an equation like x^2 + 3x == 2, *Mathematica* interprets this as a logical statement which asserts that x^2 + 3x is equal to 2. If you have assigned an explicit value to x, say x = 4, then *Mathematica* can explicitly determine that the logical statement x^2 + 3x == 2 is False.

If you have not assigned any explicit value to x, however, *Mathematica* cannot work out whether x^2 + 3x == 2 is True or False. As a result, it leaves the equation in the symbolic form x^2 + 3x == 2.

You can manipulate symbolic equations in *Mathematica* in many ways. One common goal is to rearrange the equations so as to "solve" for a particular set of variables.

Here is a symbolic equation.

In[1]:= **x^2 + 3x == 2**

Out[1]= $3x + x^2 == 2$

You can use the function Roots to rearrange the equation so as to give "solutions" for x. The result, like the original equation, can be viewed as a logical statement.

In[2]:= **Roots[%, x]**

Out[2]= $x == \frac{1}{2}\left(-3 - \sqrt{17}\right) \;||\; x == \frac{1}{2}\left(-3 + \sqrt{17}\right)$

The quadratic equation x^2 + 3x == 2 can be thought of as an implicit statement about the value of x. As shown in the example above, you can use the function Roots to get a more explicit statement about the value of x. The expression produced by Roots has the form x == r_1 || x == r_2. This expression is again a logical statement, which asserts that either x is equal to r_1, or x is equal to r_2. The values of x that are consistent with this statement are exactly the same as the ones that are consistent with the original quadratic equation. For many purposes, however, the form that Roots gives is much more useful than the original equation.

You can combine and manipulate equations just like other logical statements. You can use logical connectives such as || and && to specify alternative or simultaneous conditions. You can use functions like LogicalExpand to simplify collections of equations.

For many purposes, you will find it convenient to manipulate equations simply as logical statements. Sometimes, however, you will actually want to use explicit solutions to equations in other calculations. In such cases, it is convenient to convert equations that are stated in the form *lhs* == *rhs* into transformation rules of the form *lhs* -> *rhs*. Once you have the solutions to an equation in the form of explicit transformation rules, you can substitute the solutions into expressions by using the / . operator.

Roots produces a logical statement about the values of x corresponding to the roots of the quadratic equation.

In[3]:= **Roots[x^2 + 3x == 2, x]**

Out[3]= $x == \frac{1}{2}\left(-3 - \sqrt{17}\right) \;||\; x == \frac{1}{2}\left(-3 + \sqrt{17}\right)$

ToRules converts the logical statement into an explicit list of transformation rules.

$In[4]:=$ **{ToRules[%]}**

$Out[4]= \left\{\left\{x \to \frac{1}{2}\left(-3-\sqrt{17}\right)\right\}, \left\{x \to \frac{1}{2}\left(-3+\sqrt{17}\right)\right\}\right\}$

You can now use the transformation rules to substitute the solutions for x into expressions involving x.

$In[5]:=$ **x^2 + a x /. %**

$Out[5]= \left\{\frac{1}{4}\left(-3-\sqrt{17}\right)^2 + \frac{1}{2}\left(-3-\sqrt{17}\right)a,\right.$

$\left.\frac{1}{4}\left(-3+\sqrt{17}\right)^2 + \frac{1}{2}\left(-3+\sqrt{17}\right)a\right\}$

The function Solve produces transformation rules for solutions directly.

$In[6]:=$ **Solve[x^2 + 3x == 2, x]**

$Out[6]= \left\{\left\{x \to \frac{1}{2}\left(-3-\sqrt{17}\right)\right\}, \left\{x \to \frac{1}{2}\left(-3+\sqrt{17}\right)\right\}\right\}$

■ 3.4.2 Equations in One Variable

The main equations that Solve and related *Mathematica* functions deal with are *polynomial equations*.

It is easy to solve a linear equation in x.

$In[1]:=$ **Solve[a x + b == c , x]**

$Out[1]= \left\{\left\{x \to -\frac{b-c}{a}\right\}\right\}$

One can also solve quadratic equations just by applying a simple formula.

$In[2]:=$ **Solve[x^2 + a x + 2 == 0 , x]**

$Out[2]= \left\{\left\{x \to \frac{1}{2}\left(-a-\sqrt{-8+a^2}\right)\right\}, \left\{x \to \frac{1}{2}\left(-a+\sqrt{-8+a^2}\right)\right\}\right\}$

Mathematica can also find exact solutions to cubic equations. Here is the first solution to a comparatively simple cubic equation.

$In[3]:=$ **Solve[x^3 + 34 x + 1 == 0 , x] [[1]]**

$Out[3]= \left\{x \to 17\left(1+I\sqrt{3}\right)\left(\dfrac{2}{3\left(-9+\sqrt{471729}\right)}\right)^{1/3} - \right.$

$\left.\frac{1}{2}\left(1-I\sqrt{3}\right)\left(\frac{1}{18}\left(-9+\sqrt{471729}\right)\right)^{1/3}\right\}$

For cubic and quartic equations the results are often complicated, but for all equations with degrees up to four *Mathematica* is always able to give explicit formulas for the solutions.

An important feature of these formulas is that they involve only *radicals*: arithmetic combinations of square roots, cube roots and higher roots.

It is a fundamental mathematical fact, however, that for equations of degree five or higher, it is no longer possible in general to give explicit formulas for solutions in terms of radicals.

There are some specific equations for which this is still possible, but in the vast majority of cases it is not.

This constructs a degree six polynomial.

$In[4]:=$ **Expand[Product[x^2 - 2 i, {i, 3}]]**

$Out[4]= -48 + 44 x^2 - 12 x^4 + x^6$

For a polynomial that factors in the way this one does, it is straightforward for `Solve` to find the roots.

In[5]:= `Solve[% == 0, x]`

Out[5]= $\{\{x \to -2\}, \{x \to 2\}, \{x \to -\sqrt{2}\}, \{x \to \sqrt{2}\},$
$\{x \to -\sqrt{6}\}, \{x \to \sqrt{6}\}\}$

This constructs a polynomial of degree eight.

In[6]:= `Expand[x^2 - 2 /. x -> x^2 - 3 /. x -> x^2 - 5]`

Out[6]= $482 - 440 x^2 + 144 x^4 - 20 x^6 + x^8$

The polynomial does not factor, but it can be decomposed into nested polynomials, so `Solve` can again find explicit formulas for the roots.

In[7]:= `Solve[% == 0, x]`

Out[7]= $\left\{\left\{x \to -\sqrt{5 - \sqrt{3 - \sqrt{2}}}\right\}, \left\{x \to \sqrt{5 - \sqrt{3 - \sqrt{2}}}\right\},\right.$

$\left\{x \to -\sqrt{5 + \sqrt{3 - \sqrt{2}}}\right\}, \left\{x \to \sqrt{5 + \sqrt{3 - \sqrt{2}}}\right\},$

$\left\{x \to -\sqrt{5 - \sqrt{3 + \sqrt{2}}}\right\}, \left\{x \to \sqrt{5 - \sqrt{3 + \sqrt{2}}}\right\},$

$\left.\left\{x \to -\sqrt{5 + \sqrt{3 + \sqrt{2}}}\right\}, \left\{x \to \sqrt{5 + \sqrt{3 + \sqrt{2}}}\right\}\right\}$

✦	`Root[f, k]`	the kth root of the equation $f[x] == 0$

Implicit representation for roots.

No explicit formulas for the solution to this equation can be given in terms of radicals, so *Mathematica* uses an implicit symbolic representation.

In[8]:= `Solve[x^5 - x + 11 == 0, x]`

Out[8]= $\{\{x \to \text{Root}[11 - \#1 + \#1^5 \&, 1]\},$
$\{x \to \text{Root}[11 - \#1 + \#1^5 \&, 2]\},$
$\{x \to \text{Root}[11 - \#1 + \#1^5 \&, 3]\},$
$\{x \to \text{Root}[11 - \#1 + \#1^5 \&, 4]\},$
$\{x \to \text{Root}[11 - \#1 + \#1^5 \&, 5]\}\}$

This finds a numerical approximation to each root.

In[9]:= `N[%]`

Out[9]= $\{\{x \to -1.66149\}, \{x \to -0.46194 - 1.565 I\},$
$\{x \to -0.46194 + 1.565 I\}, \{x \to 1.29268 - 0.903032 I\},$
$\{x \to 1.29268 + 0.903032 I\}\}$

If what you want in the end is a numerical solution, it is usually much faster to use `NSolve` from the outset.

In[10]:= `NSolve[x^5 - x + 11 == 0, x]`

Out[10]= $\{\{x \to -1.66149\}, \{x \to -0.46194 - 1.565 I\},$
$\{x \to -0.46194 + 1.565 I\}, \{x \to 1.29268 - 0.903032 I\},$
$\{x \to 1.29268 + 0.903032 I\}\}$

`Root` objects provide an exact, though implicit, representation for the roots of a polynomial. You can work with them much as you would work with `Sqrt[2]` or any other expression that represents an exact numerical quantity.

Here is the Root object representing the first root of the polynomial discussed above.

In[11]:= **r = Root[#^5 - # + 11 &, 1]**

Out[11]= Root[11 - #1 + #1^5&, 1]

This is a numerical approximation to its value.

In[12]:= **N[r]**

Out[12]= -1.66149

Round does an exact computation to find the closest integer to the root.

In[13]:= **Round[r]**

Out[13]= -2

If you substitute the root into the original polynomial, and then simplify the result, you get zero.

In[14]:= **FullSimplify[x^5 - x + 11 /. x -> r]**

Out[14]= 0

This finds the product of all the roots of the original polynomial.

In[15]:= **FullSimplify[
            Product[Root[11 - # + #^5 &, k], {k, 5}]]**

Out[15]= -11

The complex conjugate of the third root is the second root.

In[16]:= **Conjugate[Root[11 - # + #^5 &, 3]]**

Out[16]= Root[11 - #1 + #1^5&, 2]

If the only symbolic parameter that exists in an equation is the variable that you are solving for, then all the solutions to the equation will just be numbers. But if there are other symbolic parameters in the equation, then the solutions will typically be functions of these parameters.

The solution to this equation can again be represented by Root objects, but now each Root object involves the parameter a.

In[17]:= **Solve[x^5 + x + a == 0, x]**

Out[17]= {{x → Root[a + #1 + #1^5&, 1]},
          {x → Root[a + #1 + #1^5&, 2]},
          {x → Root[a + #1 + #1^5&, 3]},
          {x → Root[a + #1 + #1^5&, 4]},
          {x → Root[a + #1 + #1^5&, 5]}}

When a is replaced with 1, the Root objects can be simplified, and some are given as explicit radicals.

In[18]:= **Simplify[% /. a -> 1]**

Out[18]= $\left\{\left\{x \to -\frac{1}{2} I\left(-I + \sqrt{3}\right)\right\}, \left\{x \to \frac{1}{2} I\left(I + \sqrt{3}\right)\right\},\right.$
          {x → Root[1 - #1^2 + #1^3&, 1]},
          {x → Root[1 - #1^2 + #1^3&, 2]},
          $\left.\{x \to \text{Root}[1 - \#1^2 + \#1^3\&, 3]\}\right\}$

This shows the behavior of the first root as a function of a.

$In[19]:=$ `Plot[Root[#^5 + # + a &, 1], {a, -2, 2}]`

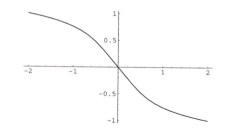

This finds the derivative of the first root with respect to a.

$In[20]:=$ `D[Root[#^5 + # + a &, 1], a]`

$$Out[20]= -\frac{1}{\left(1 + 5\,Root[a + \#1 + \#1^5 \&, 1]\right)^4}$$

If you give `Solve` any n^{th}-degree polynomial equation, then it will always return exactly n solutions, although some of these may be represented by `Root` objects. If there are degenerate solutions, then the number of times that each particular solution appears will be equal to its multiplicity.

`Solve` gives two identical solutions to this equation.

$In[21]:=$ `Solve[(x - 1)^2 == 0, x]`

$Out[21]=$ `{{x → 1}, {x → 1}}`

Here are the first four solutions to a tenth degree equation. The solutions come in pairs.

$In[22]:=$ `Take[Solve[(x^5 - x + 11)^2 == 0, x], 4]`

$Out[22]=$ `{{x → Root[11 - #1 + #1^5 &, 1]},`
`{x → Root[11 - #1 + #1^5 &, 1]},`
`{x → Root[11 - #1 + #1^5 &, 2]},`
`{x → Root[11 - #1 + #1^5 &, 2]}}`

Mathematica also knows how to solve equations which are not explicitly in the form of polynomials.

Here is an equation involving square roots.

$In[23]:=$ `Solve[ Sqrt[x] + Sqrt[1 + x] == a, x]`

$$Out[23]= \left\{\left\{x \to \frac{1 - 2a^2 + a^4}{4a^2}\right\}\right\}$$

And here is one involving logarithms.

$In[24]:=$ `Solve[ Log[x] + Log[1 - x] == a, x ]`

$$Out[24]= \left\{\left\{x \to \frac{1}{2}\left(1 - \sqrt{1 - 4E^a}\right)\right\}, \left\{x \to \frac{1}{2}\left(1 + \sqrt{1 - 4E^a}\right)\right\}\right\}$$

So long as an equation can be reduced to some kind of polynomial form, *Mathematica* will always be able to represent its solution in terms of `Root` objects, and will always be able to find accurate numerical approximations. However, with more general equations, involving say transcendental functions, there is no systematic way to use `Root` objects, or even to find numerical approximations. Section 3.9.6 discusses approaches to this problem in *Mathematica*.

This finds a numerical solution to the equation $x \sin(x) = \frac{1}{2}$, close to $x = 1$.

$In[25]:=$ `FindRoot[ x Sin[x] - 1/2 == 0 , {x, 1} ]`

$Out[25]=$ `{x → 0.740841}`

Plotting a graph of $x \sin(x) - \frac{1}{2}$ makes it fairly clear that there are, in fact, an infinite number of solutions to the equation.

$In[26]:=$ **Plot[x Sin[x] - 1/2 , {x, 0, 30}]**

+ ■ 3.4.3 Advanced Topic: Algebraic Numbers

| + | Root[f, k] | the kth root of the polynomial equation $f[x] == 0$ |

The representation of algebraic numbers.

When you enter a Root object, the polynomial that appears in it is automatically reduced to a minimal form.

$In[1]:=$ **Root[24 - 2 # + 4 #^5 &, 1]**

$Out[1]=$ Root[$12 - \#1 + 2\#1^5\&$, 1]

This extracts the pure function which represents the polynomial, and applies it to x.

$In[2]:=$ **First[%][x]**

$Out[2]=$ $12 - x + 2x^5$

Root objects are the way that *Mathematica* represents *algebraic numbers*. Algebraic numbers have the property that when you perform algebraic operations on them, you always get a single algebraic number as the result.

Here is the square root of an algebraic number.

$In[3]:=$ **Sqrt[Root[2 - # + #^5 &, 1]]**

$Out[3]=$ $\sqrt{\text{Root}[2 - \#1 + \#1^5\&, 1]}$

RootReduce reduces this to a single Root object.

$In[4]:=$ **RootReduce[%]**

$Out[4]=$ Root[$2 - \#1^2 + \#1^{10}\&$, 6]

Here is a more complicated expression involving an algebraic number.

$In[5]:=$ **Sqrt[2] + Root[2 - # + #^5 &, 1]^2**

$Out[5]=$ $\sqrt{2} + \text{Root}[2 - \#1 + \#1^5\&, 1]^2$

Again this can be reduced to a single Root object, albeit a fairly complicated one.

$In[6]:=$ **RootReduce[%]**

$Out[6]=$ Root[$14 - 72\#1 + 25\#1^2 - 144\#1^3 -$
$88\#1^4 - 8\#1^5 + 62\#1^6 - 14\#1^8 + \#1^{10}\&$,
2]

+	`RootReduce[expr]`	attempt to reduce *expr* to a single Root object
+	`ToRadicals[expr]`	attempt to transform Root objects to explicit radicals

Operations on algebraic numbers.

In this simple case the Root object is automatically expressed in terms of radicals.

$In[7]:=$ **Root[#^2 - # - 1 &, 1]**

$Out[7]= \dfrac{1}{2} \left(1 - \sqrt{5}\right)$

When cubic polynomials are involved, Root objects are not automatically expressed in terms of radicals.

$In[8]:=$ **Root[#^3 - 2 &, 1]**

$Out[8]= \mathrm{Root}[-2 + \#1^3 \&, 1]$

ToRadicals attempts to express all Root objects in terms of radicals.

$In[9]:=$ **ToRadicals[%]**

$Out[9]= 2^{1/3}$

If `Solve` and `ToRadicals` do not succeed in expressing the solution to a particular polynomial equation in terms of radicals, then it is a good guess that this fundamentally cannot be done. However, you should realize that there are some special cases in which a reduction to radicals is in principle possible, but *Mathematica* cannot find it. The simplest example is the equation $x^5 + 20x + 32 = 0$, but here the solution in terms of radicals is very complicated. The equation $x^6 - 9x^4 - 4x^3 + 27x^2 - 36x - 23$ is another example, where now $x = 2^{\frac{1}{3}} + 3^{\frac{1}{2}}$ is a solution.

This gives a Root object involving a degree six polynomial.

$In[10]:=$ **RootReduce[2^(1/3) + Sqrt[3]]**

$Out[10]= \mathrm{Root}[-23 - 36\,\#1 + 27\,\#1^2 - 4\,\#1^3 - 9\,\#1^4 + \#1^6 \&, 2]$

Even though a simple form in terms of radicals does exist, ToRadicals does not find it.

$In[11]:=$ **ToRadicals[%]**

$Out[11]= \mathrm{Root}[-23 - 36\,\#1 + 27\,\#1^2 - 4\,\#1^3 - 9\,\#1^4 + \#1^6 \&, 2]$

Beyond degree four, most polynomials do not have roots that can be expressed at all in terms of radicals. However, for degree five it turns out that the roots can always be expressed in terms of elliptic or hypergeometric functions. The results, however, are typically much too complicated to be useful in practice.

+	`RootSum[f, form]`	the sum of *form*[x] for all x satisfying the polynomial equation $f[x] == 0$
	`Normal[expr]`	the form of *expr* with RootSum replaced by explicit sums of Root objects

Sums of roots.

This computes the sum of the reciprocals of the roots of $1 + 2x + x^5$.

```
In[12]:= RootSum[(1 + 2 # + #^5)&, (1/#)&]
Out[12]= -2
```

Now no explicit result can be given in terms of radicals.

```
In[13]:= RootSum[(1 + 2 # + #^5)&, (# Log[1 + #])&]
Out[13]= RootSum[1 + 2#1 + #1^5&, Log[1 + #1] #1&]
```

This expands the RootSum into a explicit sum involving Root objects.

```
In[14]:= Normal[%]
```

$$Out[14]= Log[1 + Root[1 + 2\#1 + \#1^5\&, 1]]$$
$$Root[1 + 2\#1 + \#1^5\&, 1] +$$
$$Log[1 + Root[1 + 2\#1 + \#1^5\&, 2]]$$
$$Root[1 + 2\#1 + \#1^5\&, 2] +$$
$$Log[1 + Root[1 + 2\#1 + \#1^5\&, 3]]$$
$$Root[1 + 2\#1 + \#1^5\&, 3] +$$
$$Log[1 + Root[1 + 2\#1 + \#1^5\&, 4]]$$
$$Root[1 + 2\#1 + \#1^5\&, 4] +$$
$$Log[1 + Root[1 + 2\#1 + \#1^5\&, 5]]$$
$$Root[1 + 2\#1 + \#1^5\&, 5]$$

■ 3.4.4 Simultaneous Equations

You can give `Solve` a list of simultaneous equations to solve. `Solve` can find explicit solutions for a large class of simultaneous polynomial equations.

Here is a simple linear equation with two unknowns.

```
In[1]:= Solve[ { a x + b y == 1, x - y == 2 } , {x, y} ]
```
$$Out[1]= \left\{\left\{x \to -\frac{-1 - 2b}{a + b}, y \to -\frac{-1 + 2a}{a + b}\right\}\right\}$$

Here is a more complicated example. The result is a list of solutions, with each solution consisting of a list of transformation rules for the variables.

```
In[2]:= Solve[{x^2 + y^2 == 1, x + y == a}, {x, y}]
```
$$Out[2]= \left\{\left\{x \to \frac{1}{2}\left(a - \sqrt{2 - a^2}\right), y \to \frac{1}{2}\left(a + \sqrt{2 - a^2}\right)\right\},\right.$$
$$\left.\left\{x \to \frac{1}{2}\left(a + \sqrt{2 - a^2}\right), y \to \frac{1}{2}\left(a - \sqrt{2 - a^2}\right)\right\}\right\}$$

You can use the list of solutions with the `/.` operator.

```
In[3]:= x^3 + y^4 /. % /. a -> 0.7
Out[3]= {0.846576, 0.901873}
```

Even when `Solve` cannot find explicit solutions, it often can "unwind" simultaneous equations to produce a symbolic result in terms of `Root` objects.

In[4]:= **First[Solve[{x^2 + y^3 == x y, x + y + x y == 1},**
{x, y}]]

$$Out[4]= \left\{ x \rightarrow \right.$$
$$\frac{1}{2} \left(1 - \text{Root}[1 - 3\#1 + \#1^2 + 2\#1^3 + 2\#1^4 + \#1^5\&, 1]^2 - \right.$$
$$\text{Root}[1 - 3\#1 + \#1^2 + 2\#1^3 + 2\#1^4 + \#1^5\&, 1]^3 - $$
$$\left. \text{Root}[1 - 3\#1 + \#1^2 + 2\#1^3 + 2\#1^4 + \#1^5\&, 1]^4 \right),$$
$$\left. y \rightarrow \text{Root}[1 - 3\#1 + \#1^2 + 2\#1^3 + 2\#1^4 + \#1^5\&, 1] \right\}$$

You can then use `N` to get a numerical result.

In[5]:= **N[%]**

Out[5]= $\{x \rightarrow -3.4875, y \rightarrow -1.80402\}$

The variables that you use in `Solve` do not need to be single symbols. Often when you set up large collections of simultaneous equations, you will want to use expressions like $a[i]$ as variables.

Here is a list of three equations for the $a[i]$.

In[6]:= **Table[2 a[i] + a[i-1] == a[i+1], {i, 3}]**

Out[6]= $\{a[0] + 2a[1] == a[2],$
$a[1] + 2a[2] == a[3], a[2] + 2a[3] == a[4]\}$

This solves for some of the $a[i]$.

In[7]:= **Solve[% , {a[1], a[2], a[3]}]**

Out[7]= $\left\{ \left\{ a[1] \rightarrow \frac{1}{12} (-5a[0] + a[4]), \right. \right.$
$a[2] \rightarrow \frac{1}{6} (a[0] + a[4]),$
$\left. \left. a[3] \rightarrow \frac{1}{12} (-a[0] + 5a[4]) \right\} \right\}$

`Solve[`*eqns*`, {`x_1`, `x_2`, ... }]`	solve *eqns* for the specific objects x_i
`Solve[`*eqns*`]`	try to solve *eqns* for all the objects that appear in them

Solving simultaneous equations.

If you do not explicitly specify objects to solve for, `Solve` will try to solve for all the variables.

In[8]:= **Solve[{ x + y == 1, x - 3 y == 2 }]**

Out[8]= $\left\{ \left\{ x \rightarrow \frac{5}{4}, y \rightarrow -\frac{1}{4} \right\} \right\}$

- `Solve[{`*lhs₁*`==`*rhs₁*`, `*lhs₂*`==`*rhs₂*`, ... }, `*vars*`]`
- `Solve[`*lhs₁*`==`*rhs₁* `&& `*lhs₂*`==`*rhs₂* `&& ... , `*vars*`]`
- `Solve[{`*lhs₁*`, `*lhs₂*`, ... } == {`*rhs₁*`, `*rhs₂*`, ... }, `*vars*`]`

Ways to present simultaneous equations to `Solve`.

If you construct simultaneous equations from matrices, you typically get equations between lists of expressions.

```
In[9]:= {{3,1},{2,-5}}.{x,y}=={7,8}
Out[9]= {3x + y, 2x - 5y} == {7, 8}
```

Solve converts equations involving lists to lists of equations.

```
In[10]:= Solve[%, {x, y}]
```
$$Out[10]= \left\{\left\{x \to \frac{43}{17},\ y \to -\frac{10}{17}\right\}\right\}$$

You can use LogicalExpand to do the conversion explicitly.

```
In[11]:= LogicalExpand[%%]
Out[11]= 2x - 5y == 8 && 3x + y == 7
```

■ 3.4.5 Equations Involving Functions

Whenever equations can be reduced to a purely algebraic form, it is possible to solve them systematically using Solve. But at least with the default option setting InverseFunctions->True, Solve will also attempt to handle some other kinds of equations.

Here is a simple transcendental equation for x.

```
In[1]:= Solve[ArcSin[x] == a, x]
Out[1]= {{x → Sin[a]}}
```

There is no solution to this equation in terms of standard functions.

```
In[2]:= Solve[Cos[x] == x, x]

Solve::tdep:
    The equations appear to involve transcendental
      functions of the variables in an essentially
      non-algebraic way.

Out[2]= Solve[Cos[x] == x, x]
```

Mathematica can nevertheless find a numerical solution even in this case.

```
In[3]:= FindRoot[Cos[x] == x, {x, 0}]
Out[3]= {x → 0.739085}
```

In practice, a large fraction of equations involving transcendental functions cannot be solved exactly in symbolic form. And even in those cases where some solutions can be found, it is often impossible to get *all* the solutions.

Mathematica prints a warning indicating that solutions are lost in this case.

```
In[4]:= Solve[Sin[x] == a, x]

Solve::ifun:
    Inverse functions are being used by Solve, so some
      solutions may not be found.

Out[4]= {{x → ArcSin[a]}}
```

An equation like $\sin(x) = a$ in principle has an infinite number of solutions for x differing by multiples of 2π. However, even with the setting InverseFunctions -> True, Solve gives you only one of the possible solutions.

While all the solutions to this particular equation would be easy to parametrize, most such equations yield much more complicated sets of solutions. With simultaneous trigonometric equations, for example, it is common to end up needing solutions to arbitrary Diophantine equations, which cannot in general be found by any finite procedure.

The fact that *Mathematica* generates only some of the solutions to each equation means that if you try to solve several simultaneous equations, no solutions may be found, even though solutions do in fact exist.

With an unknown function f, *Mathematica* produces a warning, then gives a formal solution in terms of the inverse function of f.

```
In[5]:= Solve[f[x] == a, x]

InverseFunction::ifun:
   Warning: Inverse functions are being used. Values may
     be lost for multivalued inverses.

Out[5]= {{x → f^(-1)[a]}}
```

This shows the structure of the inverse function.

```
In[6]:= InputForm[%]

Out[6]//InputForm= {{x -> InverseFunction[f, 1, 1][a]}}
```

If you ask *Mathematica* to solve an equation involving an unknown function, it will try to construct a formal solution to the equation in terms of inverse functions. In doing this, *Mathematica* effectively assumes that the function indeed has a unique inverse. If there are several possible inverses, as in the case of a function like Sin, *Mathematica* will inevitably lose solutions in such a case.

InverseFunction[f]	the inverse function of f
InverseFunction[f, n]	the inverse function of f with respect to its nth argument
InverseFunction[f, n, tot]	the inverse function of f when the total number of arguments is tot

Inverse functions.

Here is the inverse function of f evaluated with argument a.

```
In[7]:= InverseFunction[f][a]

Out[7]= f^(-1)[a]
```

Applying f to the previous expression yields a warning, and then gives the result a.

```
In[8]:= f[%]

InverseFunction::ifun:
   Warning: Inverse functions are being used. Values may
     be lost for multivalued inverses.

Out[8]= a
```

■ 3.4.6 Getting Full Solutions

If you have an equation like 2 x == 0, it is perfectly clear that the only possible solution is x -> 0. However, if you have an equation like a x == 0, things are not so clear. If a is not equal to zero, then x -> 0 is again the only solution. However, if a is in fact equal to zero, then *any* value of x is a solution.

Solve implicitly assumes that the parameter a does not have the special value 0.

```
In[1]:= Solve[ a x == 0 , x ]

Out[1]= {{x → 0}}
```

Roots makes the same assumption.

```
In[2]:= Roots[ a x == 0 , x ]
Out[2]= x == 0
```

Reduce, on the other hand, gives you all the possibilities, without assuming anything about the value of a.

```
In[3]:= Reduce[ a x == 0 , x ]
Out[3]= a == 0 || x == 0
```

The results that Reduce gives are logical statements representing all possible solutions to an equation, allowing for special values of parameters. The || operator stands for OR, so that a == 0 || x == 0 means that either a is equal to 0 and there is no restriction on x, or x is equal to 0 and there is no restriction on a.

lhs == *rhs*	an equation asserting that two quantities are equal
lhs != *rhs*	an inequation asserting that two quantities are unequal
eqn_1 && eqn_2	equations that must simultaneously be satisfied
eqn_1 || eqn_2	alternative equations, only one of which need be satisfied

Logical forms associated with equations.

This is the solution to an arbitrary linear equation given by Roots and Solve.

```
In[4]:= Roots[a x + b == 0, x]
```
$$Out[4]= x == -\frac{b}{a}$$

Reduce gives the full version, which includes the possibility a==b==0. In reading the output, note that && has higher precedence than ||.

```
In[5]:= Reduce[a x + b == 0, x]
```
$$Out[5]= b == 0 \&\& a == 0 \;||\; a \neq 0 \&\& x == -\frac{b}{a}$$

Here is the full solution to a general quadratic equation. There are three alternatives. If a is non-zero, then there are two solutions for x, given by the standard quadratic formula. If a is zero, however, the equation reduces to a linear one. Finally, if a, b and c are all zero, there is no restriction on x.

```
In[6]:= Reduce[a x^2 + b x + c == 0, x]
```
$$Out[6]= a \neq 0 \&\& x == \frac{-b - \sqrt{b^2 - 4ac}}{2a} \;||$$
$$a \neq 0 \&\& x == \frac{-b + \sqrt{b^2 - 4ac}}{2a} \;||$$
$$c == 0 \&\& b == 0 \&\& a == 0 \;||\; b \neq 0 \&\& x == -\frac{c}{b} \&\& a == 0$$

The most important difference between Reduce and Solve is that Reduce gives *all* the possible solutions to a set of equations, while Solve gives only the *generic* ones. Solutions are considered "generic" if they involve conditions only on the variables that you explicitly solve for, and not on other parameters in the equations. Reduce and Solve also differ in that Reduce always returns combinations of equations, while Solve gives results in the form of transformation rules.

| Solve[*eqns*, *vars*] | find generic solutions to equations |
| Reduce[*eqns*, *vars*] | reduce equations, maintaining all solutions |

Solving equations.

■ 3.4.7 Advanced Topic: Existence of Solutions

Using Reduce, you can find out under exactly what conditions a particular set of equations has solutions. Solve tells you whether any generic solutions exist.

There is no value of x which solves these simultaneous equations. Reduce thus simplifies the logical statement x==1 && x==2 to the explicit value False.

```
In[1]:= Reduce[ x == 1 && x == 2 , x ]
Out[1]= False
```

There is a solution to these equations, but only when a has the special value 1.

```
In[2]:= Reduce[ x == 1 && x == a , x ]
Out[2]= x == 1 && a == 1
```

The solution is not generic, and is rejected by Solve.

```
In[3]:= Solve[ x == 1 && x == a , x ]
Out[3]= {}
```

But if a is constrained to have value 1, then Solve again returns a solution.

```
In[4]:= Solve[ x == 1 && x == a && a == 1, x ]
Out[4]= {{x → 1}}
```

This equation is true for any value of x.

```
In[5]:= Reduce[ x == x , x ]
Out[5]= True
```

This is the kind of result Solve returns when you give an equation that is always true.

```
In[6]:= Solve[ x == x , x ]
Out[6]= {{}}
```

When you work with systems of linear equations, you can use Solve to get generic solutions, and Reduce to find out for what values of parameters solutions exist.

Here is a matrix whose i, j^{th} element is $i + j$.

```
In[7]:= m = Table[i + j, {i, 3}, {j, 3}]
Out[7]= {{2, 3, 4}, {3, 4, 5}, {4, 5, 6}}
```

The matrix has determinant zero.

```
In[8]:= Det[ m ]
Out[8]= 0
```

This makes a set of three simultaneous equations.

```
In[9]:= eqn = m . {x, y, z} == {a, b, c}
Out[9]= {2x + 3y + 4z, 3x + 4y + 5z, 4x + 5y + 6z} == {a, b, c}
```

Solve reports that there are no generic solutions.

```
In[10]:= Solve[eqn, {x, y, z}]
Out[10]= {}
```

Reduce, however, shows that there
would be a solution if the parameters
satisfied the special condition
a == 2b − c.

In[11]:= **Reduce[eqn, {x, y, z}]**

Out[11]= $a == 2b - c \&\& x == -5b + 4c + z \&\& y == 4b - 3c - 2z$

For nonlinear equations, the conditions for the existence of solutions may be very complicated.

Here is a very simple pair of nonlinear
equations.

In[12]:= **eqn = {x y == a, x^2 y^2 == b}**

Out[12]= $\{xy == a, x^2 y^2 == b\}$

Solve shows that the equations have
no generic solutions.

In[13]:= **Solve[eqn, {x, y}]**

Out[13]= {}

Reduce gives the complete conditions
for a solution to exist.

In[14]:= **Reduce[eqn, {x, y}]**

Out[14]= $y == 0 \&\& a == 0 \&\& b == 0 \;||\; y \neq 0 \&\& a^2 == b \&\& x == \dfrac{a}{y}$

■ 3.4.8 Eliminating Variables

When you write down a set of simultaneous equations in *Mathematica*, you are specifying a collection of constraints between variables. When you use Solve, you are finding values for some of the variables in terms of others, subject to the constraints represented by the equations.

Solve[*eqns*, *vars*, *elims*]	find solutions for *vars*, eliminating the variables *elims*
Eliminate[*eqns*, *elims*]	rearrange equations to eliminate the variables *elims*

Eliminating variables.

Here are two equations involving x, y
and the "parameter" a.

In[1]:= **eqn = {x == 1 + 2 a, y == 9 + 2 x}**

Out[1]= $\{x == 1 + 2a, y == 9 + 2x\}$

If you solve for both x and y, you get
results in terms of a.

In[2]:= **Solve[eqn, {x, y}]**

Out[2]= $\{\{x \to 1 + 2a, y \to 11 + 4a\}\}$

Similarly, if you solve for x and a, you
get results in terms of y.

In[3]:= **Solve[eqn, {x, a}]**

Out[3]= $\left\{\left\{x \to \dfrac{-9+y}{2}, a \to \dfrac{-11+y}{4}\right\}\right\}$

If you only want to solve for x,
however, you have to specify whether
you want to eliminate y or a. This
eliminates y, and so gives the result in
terms of a.

In[4]:= **Solve[eqn, x, y]**

Out[4]= $\{\{x \to 1 + 2a\}\}$

If you eliminate a, then you get a
result in terms of y.

$In[5]:=$ **Solve[eqn, x, a]**

$Out[5]=$ $\left\{\left\{x \to \dfrac{-9+y}{2}\right\}\right\}$

In some cases, you may want to construct explicitly equations in which variables have been eliminated. You can do this using `Eliminate`.

This combines the two equations in the
list eqn, by eliminating the variable a.

$In[6]:=$ **Eliminate[eqn, a]**

$Out[6]=$ $y == 9 + 2 x$

This is what you get if you eliminate y
instead of a.

$In[7]:=$ **Eliminate[eqn, y]**

$Out[7]=$ $2 a == -1 + x$

As a more sophisticated example of `Eliminate`, consider the problem of writing $x^5 + y^5$ in terms of the "symmetric polynomials" $x + y$ and xy.

To solve the problem, we simply have
to write f in terms of a and b,
eliminating the original variables x
and y.

$In[8]:=$ **Eliminate[{f == x^5 + y^5, a == x + y, b == x y},**
            {x, y}]

$Out[8]=$ $a^5 - 5 a^3 b + 5 a b^2 == f$

~■ 3.4.9 Solving Equations with Subsidiary Conditions

In doing calculations with equations, you will often find it convenient to think of a particular set of equations as the "main" ones you are working with, and to think of other equations as "subsidiary conditions" that must also be satisfied.

A typical thing to do is to assign a name to the list of subsidiary conditions, and then to include them by name in each list of equations you give to `Solve`.

sincos is defined to be the equation
$\sin^2(x) + \cos^2(x) = 1$.

$In[1]:=$ **sincos = Sin[x]^2 + Cos[x]^2 == 1**

$Out[1]=$ $\text{Cos}[x]^2 + \text{Sin}[x]^2 == 1$

This solves the equation
$\sin(x) + 2 \cos(x) = 1$, with the
"subsidiary condition"
$\sin^2(x) + \cos^2(x) = 1$.

$In[2]:=$ **Solve[{ Sin[x] + 2 Cos[x] == 1, sincos } ,**
            { Sin[x], Cos[x] }]

$Out[2]=$ $\left\{\left\{\text{Sin}[x] \to -\dfrac{3}{5}, \text{Cos}[x] \to \dfrac{4}{5}\right\},\right.$

$\left.\{\text{Sin}[x] \to 1, \text{Cos}[x] \to 0\}\right\}$

Here is another equation, solved with
the same "subsidiary condition".

$In[3]:=$ **Solve[{ Sin[x] == Cos[x], sincos } ,**
            { Sin[x], Cos[x] }]

$Out[3]=$ $\left\{\left\{\text{Sin}[x] \to -\dfrac{1}{\sqrt{2}}, \text{Cos}[x] \to -\dfrac{1}{\sqrt{2}}\right\},\right.$

$\left.\left\{\text{Sin}[x] \to \dfrac{1}{\sqrt{2}}, \text{Cos}[x] \to \dfrac{1}{\sqrt{2}}\right\}\right\}$

When you are working with polynomials, there are ways to use `GroebnerBasis` and `PolynomialReduce` to reduce sets of polynomials subject to subsidiary conditions.

This sets up a Gröbner basis.	*In[4]:=* **g = GroebnerBasis[{x + y - a, x y - b}, {x, y}]** *Out[4]=* $\{b - ay + y^2, -a + x + y\}$
This gives a reduction of x^3+y^3 in terms of the elements of g.	*In[5]:=* **PolynomialReduce[x^3 + y^3, g, {x, y}]** *Out[5]=* $\{\{2a + x + y, a^2 - b + ax + x^2 - ay - xy\}, a^3 - 3ab\}$
This shows how x^3+y^3 can be reduced if x+y-a and x y-b are assumed to be zero.	*In[6]:=* **Last[%]** *Out[6]=* $a^3 - 3ab$
This reduces x^4+y^4 with the same subsidiary condition.	*In[7]:=* **Last[PolynomialReduce[x^4 + y^4, g, {x, y}]]** *Out[7]=* $a^4 - 4a^2b + 2b^2$

■ 3.4.10 Advanced Topic: Solving Logical Combinations of Equations

When you give a list of equations to `Solve`, it assumes that you want all the equations to be satisfied simultaneously. It is also possible to give `Solve` more complicated logical combinations of equations.

Solve assumes that the equations x + y == 1 and x - y == 2 are simultaneously valid.	*In[1]:=* **Solve[{x + y == 1, x - y == 2}, {x, y}]** *Out[1]=* $\left\{\left\{x \to \frac{3}{2}, y \to -\frac{1}{2}\right\}\right\}$
Here is an alternative form, using the logical connective && explicitly.	*In[2]:=* **Solve[x + y == 1 && x - y == 2, {x, y}]** *Out[2]=* $\left\{\left\{x \to \frac{3}{2}, y \to -\frac{1}{2}\right\}\right\}$
This specifies that *either* x + y == 1 *or* x - y == 2. Solve gives two solutions for x, corresponding to these two possibilities.	*In[3]:=* **Solve[x + y == 1 || x - y == 2, x]** *Out[3]=* $\{\{x \to 1 - y\}, \{x \to 2 + y\}\}$
Solve gives three solutions to this equation.	*In[4]:=* **Solve[x^3 == x, x]** *Out[4]=* $\{\{x \to -1\}, \{x \to 0\}, \{x \to 1\}\}$
If you explicitly include the assertion that x != 0, one of the previous solutions is suppressed.	*In[5]:=* **Solve[x^3 == x && x != 0, x]** *Out[5]=* $\{\{x \to -1\}, \{x \to 1\}\}$
Here is a slightly more complicated example. Note that the precedence of || is lower than the precedence of &&, so the equation is interpreted as (x^3 == x && x != 1) || x^2 == 2, not x^3 == x && (x != 1 || x^2 == 2).	*In[6]:=* **Solve[x^3 == x && x != 1 || x^2 == 2 , x]** *Out[6]=* $\left\{\{x \to -1\}, \{x \to 0\}, \left\{x \to -\sqrt{2}\right\}, \left\{x \to \sqrt{2}\right\}\right\}$

When you use `Solve`, the final results you get are in the form of transformation rules. If you use `Reduce` or `Eliminate`, on the other hand, then your results are logical statements, which you can manipulate further.

This gives a logical statement representing the solutions of the equation x^2 == x.

In[7]:= `Reduce[x^2 == x, x]`

Out[7]= $x == 0 \mid\mid x == 1$

This finds values of x which satisfy x^5 == x but do not satisfy the statement representing the solutions of x^2 == x.

In[8]:= `Reduce[x^5 == x && !%, x]`

Out[8]= $x == -1 \mid\mid x == -I \mid\mid x == I$

The logical statements produced by `Reduce` can be thought of as representations of the solution set for your equations. The logical connectives `&&`, `||` and so on then correspond to operations on these sets.

eqns$_1$ `||` *eqns*$_2$	union of solution sets
eqns$_1$ `&&` *eqns*$_2$	intersection of solution sets
`!`*eqns*	complement of a solution set
`Implies[`*eqns*$_1$`, `*eqns*$_2$`]`	the part of *eqns*$_1$ that contains *eqns*$_2$

Operations on solution sets.

In dealing with sets of equations, it is common to consider some of the objects that appear as true "variables", and others as "parameters". In some cases, you may need to know for what values of parameters a particular relation between the variables is *always* satisfied.

`SolveAlways[`*eqns*, *vars*`]`	solve for the values of parameters for which the *eqns* are satisfied for all values of the *vars*

Solving for parameters that make relations always true.

This finds the values of a, b and c for which the relation x + y == 1 implies a x^2 + b x y + c y^2 == 1 for all x and y.

In[9]:= `SolveAlways[`
      `Implies[ x + y == 1, a x^2 + b x y + c y^2 == 1 ],`
      `{ x, y } ]`

Out[9]= $\{\{a \to 1, b \to 2, c \to 1\}\}$

■ 3.4.11 Advanced Topic: Equations Modulo Integers

When you write an equation like *lhs* == *rhs*, you usually want to assert that the expressions *lhs* and *rhs* are exactly equal. For some purposes, however, it is convenient to use a weaker notion of equality, and to interpret *lhs* == *rhs* as meaning that two integer expressions are equal modulo some fixed integer. Solving equations that use this weaker notion of equality is important in many problems in number theory.

`Solve[`*eqns*`, `*vars*`, ... , Mode->Modular]`
solve equations with equality required only modulo an integer

`Modulus == `*p*   a special equation specifying the modulus used to determine equality

---

Solving equations modulo integers.

There are two ways to work with equations modulo integers. The first is explicitly to specify the modulus you want to use. The second is to let `Solve` find a modulus for which your equations are satisfied.

Mathematica cannot find a closed-form solution for this equation over complex numbers.

```
In[1]:= Solve[5 + 11x + 17x^2 + 7x^3 + 16x^4 + x^5==0, x]
```
$Out[1]= \{\{x \to \text{Root}[5 + 11\#1 + 17\#1^2 + 7\#1^3 + 16\#1^4 + \#1^5\&, 1]\},$
$\{x \to \text{Root}[5 + 11\#1 + 17\#1^2 + 7\#1^3 + 16\#1^4 + \#1^5\&, 2]\},$
$\{x \to \text{Root}[5 + 11\#1 + 17\#1^2 + 7\#1^3 + 16\#1^4 + \#1^5\&, 3]\},$
$\{x \to \text{Root}[5 + 11\#1 + 17\#1^2 + 7\#1^3 + 16\#1^4 + \#1^5\&, 4]\},$
$\{x \to \text{Root}[5 + 11\#1 + 17\#1^2 + 7\#1^3 + 16\#1^4 + \#1^5\&, 5]\}\}$

The equation does, however, have simple solutions over integers modulo 19. Notice that if you include an equation for Modulus, you do not have to set Mode->Modular explicitly.

```
In[2]:= Solve[5 + 11x + 17x^2 + 7x^3 + 16x^4 + x^5==0 &&
               Modulus==19, x]
```
$Out[2]= \{\{\text{Modulus} \to 19, x \to 1\}, \{\text{Modulus} \to 19, x \to 3\},$
$\{\text{Modulus} \to 19, x \to 7\}, \{\text{Modulus} \to 19, x \to 12\},$
$\{\text{Modulus} \to 19, x \to 18\}\}$

If you use `Mode->Modular`, but do not explicitly include an equation for the modulus you want to use, *Mathematica* will try to find a modulus for which your set of equations can be satisfied.

The result shows that these equations are satisfied modulo 2 when *x* is odd.

```
In[3]:= Solve[{x^2 + 1 == 0, x^3 + 1 == 0}, x, Mode->Modular]
```
$Out[3]= \{\{\text{Modulus} \to 2, x \to 1\}\}$

When you solve equations in the usual way over complex numbers, it takes *n* equations to determine the values of *n* complex variables. When you use `Mode->Modular` without specifying the modulus in advance, however, you can expect to get a finite number of solutions for *n* integer variables only by giving *n* + 1 equations. You can think of the extra equation as being what is needed to determine the modulus.

Here is a polynomial of degree three.

```
In[4]:= f = x^3 + 4x + 17
```
$Out[4]= 17 + 4x + x^3$

This finds the value of x and the modulus for which both f and its derivative vanish.

In[5]:= **Solve[f == D[f,x] == 0, x, Mode->Modular]**

Out[5]= {{Modulus → 8059, x → 1001}}

Here are the corresponding values of f and D[f,x].

In[6]:= **{f, D[f,x]} /. %**

Out[6]= {{1003007022, 3006007}}

They indeed do vanish modulo 8059.

In[7]:= **Mod[%, 8059]**

Out[7]= {{0, 0}}

Here is another example, based on a polynomial in two variables.

In[8]:= **f = y^2 - y - x^3 + x^2**

Out[8]= $x^2 - x^3 - y + y^2$

In the language of arithmetic geometry, this shows that the curve defined by $f = 0$ has a singular point modulo the prime number 11.

In[9]:= **Solve[f == D[f,x] == D[f,y] == 0, {x, y},
            Mode->Modular]**

Out[9]= {{Modulus → 11, y → 6, x → 8}}

3.5 Calculus

■ 3.5.1 Differentiation

D[*f*, *x*]	partial derivative $\frac{\partial}{\partial x} f$
D[*f*, x_1, x_2, ...]	multiple derivative $\frac{\partial}{\partial x_1} \frac{\partial}{\partial x_2} ... f$
D[*f*, {*x*, *n*}]	n^{th} derivative $\frac{\partial^n}{\partial x^n} f$
D[*f*, *x*, NonConstants -> {v_1, v_2, ... }]	
	$\frac{\partial}{\partial x} f$ with the v_i taken to depend on *x*

Partial differentiation operations.

This gives $\frac{\partial}{\partial x} x^n$.

```
In[1]:= D[x^n, x]
Out[1]= n x^{-1+n}
```

This gives the third derivative.

```
In[2]:= D[x^n, {x, 3}]
Out[2]= (-2 + n) (-1 + n) n x^{-3+n}
```

You can differentiate with respect to any expression that does not involve explicit mathematical operations.

```
In[3]:= D[ x[1]^2 + x[2]^2, x[1] ]
Out[3]= 2 x[1]
```

D does *partial differentiation*. It assumes here that y is independent of x.

```
In[4]:= D[x^2 + y^2, x]
Out[4]= 2 x
```

If *y* does in fact depend on *x*, you can use the explicit functional form y[x]. Section 3.5.4 describes how objects like y'[x] work.

```
In[5]:= D[x^2 + y[x]^2, x]
Out[5]= 2 x + 2 y[x] y'[x]
```

Instead of giving an explicit function y[x], you can tell D that y *implicitly* depends on x.
D[y, x, NonConstants->{y}] then represents $\frac{\partial y}{\partial x}$, with *y* implicitly depending on *x*.

```
In[6]:= D[x^2 + y^2, x, NonConstants -> {y}]
Out[6]= 2 x + 2 y D[y, x, NonConstants → {y}]
```

■ 3.5.2 Total Derivatives

$\texttt{Dt[}f\texttt{]}$	total differential df
$\texttt{Dt[}f, x\texttt{]}$	total derivative $\frac{df}{dx}$
$\texttt{Dt[}f, x_1, x_2, \ldots \texttt{]}$	multiple total derivative $\frac{d}{dx_1}\frac{d}{dx_2}\ldots f$
$\texttt{Dt[}f, x, \texttt{Constants} \texttt{->} \{c_1, c_2, \ldots \}\texttt{]}$	
	total derivative with c_i constant (i.e., $dc_i = 0$)
$\texttt{y/: Dt[y, x] = 0}$	set $\frac{dy}{dx} = 0$
$\texttt{SetAttributes[}c, \texttt{Constant]}$	define c to be a constant in all cases

Total differentiation operations.

When you find the derivative of some expression f with respect to x, you are effectively finding out how fast f changes as you vary x. Often f will depend not only on x, but also on other variables, say y and z. The results that you get then depend on how you assume that y and z vary as you change x.

There are two common cases. Either y and z are assumed to stay fixed when x changes, or they are allowed to vary with x. In a standard *partial derivative* $\frac{\partial f}{\partial x}$, all variables other than x are assumed fixed. On the other hand, in the *total derivative* $\frac{df}{dx}$, all variables are allowed to change with x.

In *Mathematica*, $\texttt{D[}f, x\texttt{]}$ gives a partial derivative, with all other variables assumed independent of x. $\texttt{Dt[}f, x\texttt{]}$ gives a total derivative, in which all variables are assumed to depend on x. In both cases, you can add an argument to give more information on dependencies.

This gives the *partial derivative* $\frac{\partial}{\partial x}(x^2 + y^2)$. y is assumed to be independent of x.

```
In[1]:= D[x^2 + y^2, x]
Out[1]= 2x
```

This gives the *total derivative* $\frac{d}{dx}(x^2 + y^2)$. Now y is assumed to depend on x.

```
In[2]:= Dt[x^2 + y^2, x]
Out[2]= 2x + 2y Dt[y, x]
```

You can make a replacement for $\frac{dy}{dx}$.

```
In[3]:= % /. Dt[y, x] -> yp
Out[3]= 2x + 2y yp
```

You can also make an explicit definition for $\frac{dy}{dx}$. You need to use $\texttt{y/:}$ to make sure that the definition is associated with $\texttt{y}$.

```
In[4]:= y/: Dt[y, x] = 0
Out[4]= 0
```

With this definition made, $\texttt{Dt}$ treats $\texttt{y}$ as independent of x.

```
In[5]:= Dt[x^2 + y^2 + z^2, x]
Out[5]= 2x + 2z Dt[z, x]
```

This removes your definition for the derivative of y.

$In[6]:=$ **Clear[y]**

This takes the total derivative, with z held fixed.

$In[7]:=$ **Dt[x^2 + y^2 + z^2, x, Constants->{z}]**

$Out[7]=$ $2x + 2y \, Dt[y, x, Constants \rightarrow \{z\}]$

This specifies that c is a constant under differentiation.

$In[8]:=$ **SetAttributes[c, Constant]**

The variable c is taken as a constant.

$In[9]:=$ **Dt[a^2 + c x^2, x]**

$Out[9]=$ $2cx + 2a \, Dt[a, x]$

The *function* c is also assumed to be a constant.

$In[10]:=$ **Dt[a^2 + c[x] x^2, x]**

$Out[10]=$ $2xc[x] + 2a \, Dt[a, x]$

This gives the total differential $d(x^2 + cy^2)$.

$In[11]:=$ **Dt[x^2 + c y^2]**

$Out[11]=$ $2x \, Dt[x] + 2cy \, Dt[y]$

You can make replacements and assignments for total differentials.

$In[12]:=$ **% /. Dt[y] -> dy**

$Out[12]=$ $2c \, dy \, y + 2x \, Dt[x]$

■ 3.5.3 Derivatives of Unknown Functions

Differentiating a known function gives an explicit result.

$In[1]:=$ **D[Log[x]^2, x]**

$Out[1]=$ $\dfrac{2 Log[x]}{x}$

Differentiating an unknown function f gives a result in terms of f'.

$In[2]:=$ **D[f[x]^2, x]**

$Out[2]=$ $2f[x] \, f'[x]$

Mathematica applies the chain rule for differentiation, and leaves the result in terms of f'.

$In[3]:=$ **D[x f[x^2], x]**

$Out[3]=$ $f[x^2] + 2x^2 f'[x^2]$

Differentiating again gives a result in terms of f, f' and f''.

$In[4]:=$ **D[%, x]**

$Out[4]=$ $6xf'[x^2] + 4x^3 f''[x^2]$

When a function has more than one argument, superscripts are used to indicate how many times each argument is being differentiated.

$In[5]:=$ **D[g[x^2, y^2], x]**

$Out[5]=$ $2x \, g^{(1,0)}[x^2, y^2]$

This represents $\frac{\partial}{\partial x}\frac{\partial}{\partial x}\frac{\partial}{\partial y}g(x, y)$. *Mathematica* assumes that the order in which derivatives are taken with respect to different variables is irrelevant.

$In[6]:=$ **D[g[x, y], x, x, y]**

$Out[6]=$ $g^{(2,1)}[x, y]$

You can find the value of the derivative
when $x = 0$ by replacing x with 0.

```
In[7]:= % /. x->0
Out[7]= g^(2,1)[0, y]
```

$f'[x]$	first derivative of a function of one variable
$f^{(n)}[x]$	n^{th} derivative of a function of one variable
$f^{(n_1, n_2, \ldots)}[x]$	derivative of a function of several variables, n_i times with respect to variable i

Output forms for derivatives of unknown functions.

■ 3.5.4 Advanced Topic: The Representation of Derivatives

Derivatives in *Mathematica* work essentially the same as in standard mathematics. The usual mathematical notation, however, often hides many details. To understand how derivatives are represented in *Mathematica*, we must look at these details.

The standard mathematical notation $f'(0)$ is really a shorthand for $\frac{d}{dt} f(t)|_{t=0}$, where t is a "dummy variable". Similarly, $f'(x^2)$ is a shorthand for $\frac{d}{dt} f(t)|_{t=x^2}$. As suggested by the notation f', the object $\frac{d}{dt} f(t)$ can in fact be viewed as a "pure function", to be evaluated with a particular choice of its parameter t. You can think of the operation of differentiation as acting on a *function f*, to give a new *function*, usually called f'.

With functions of more than one argument, the simple notation based on primes breaks down. You cannot tell for example whether $g'(0, 1)$ stands for $\frac{d}{dt} g(t, 1)|_{t=0}$ or $\frac{d}{dt} g(0, t)|_{t=1}$, and for almost any g, these will have totally different values. Once again, however, t is just a dummy variable, whose sole purpose is to show with respect to which "slot" g is to be differentiated.

In *Mathematica*, as in some branches of mathematics, it is convenient to think about a kind of differentiation that acts on *functions*, rather than expressions. We need an operation that takes the function f, and gives us the *derivative function* f'. Operations such as this that act on *functions*, rather than variables, are known in mathematics as *functionals*.

The object `f'` in *Mathematica* is the result of applying the differentiation functional to the function `f`. The full form of `f'` is in fact `Derivative[1][f]`. `Derivative[1]` is the *Mathematica* differentiation functional.

The arguments in the functional `Derivative[`n_1`, `n_2`, ... ]` specify how many times to differentiate with respect to each "slot" of the function on which it acts. By using functionals to represent differentiation, *Mathematica* avoids any need to introduce explicit "dummy variables".

This is the full form of the derivative
of the function f.

```
In[1]:= f' // FullForm
Out[1]//FullForm= Derivative[1][f]
```

Here an argument x is supplied.	*In[2]:=* **f'[x] // FullForm**
	Out[2]//FullForm= Derivative[1][f][x]
This is the second derivative.	*In[3]:=* **f''[x] // FullForm**
	Out[3]//FullForm= Derivative[2][f][x]
This gives a derivative of the function g with respect to its second "slot".	*In[4]:=* **D[g[x, y], y]**
	Out[4]= $g^{(0,1)}[x, y]$
Here is the full form.	*In[5]:=* **% // FullForm**
	Out[5]//FullForm= Derivative[0, 1][g][x, y]
Here is the second derivative with respect to the variable y, which appears in the second slot of g.	*In[6]:=* **D[g[x, y], {y, 2}] // FullForm**
	Out[6]//FullForm= Derivative[0, 2][g][x, y]
This is a mixed derivative.	*In[7]:=* **D[g[x, y], x, y, y] // FullForm**
	Out[7]//FullForm= Derivative[1, 2][g][x, y]
Since **Derivative** only specifies how many times to differentiate with respect to each slot, the order of the derivatives is irrelevant.	*In[8]:=* **D[g[x, y], y, y, x] // FullForm**
	Out[8]//FullForm= Derivative[1, 2][g][x, y]
Here is a more complicated case, in which both arguments of g depend on the differentiation variable.	*In[9]:=* **D[g[x, x], x]**
	Out[9]= $g^{(0,1)}[x, x] + g^{(1,0)}[x, x]$
This is the full form of the result.	*In[10]:=* **% // FullForm**
	Out[10]//FullForm= Plus[Derivative[0, 1][g][x, x],
	Derivative[1, 0][g][x, x]]

The object **f'** behaves essentially like any other function in *Mathematica*. You can evaluate the function with any argument, and you can use standard *Mathematica* **/.** operations to change the argument. (This would not be possible if explicit dummy variables had been introduced in the course of the differentiation.)

This is the *Mathematica* representation of the derivative of a function f, evaluated at the origin.	*In[11]:=* **f'[0] // FullForm**
	Out[11]//FullForm= Derivative[1][f][0]
The result of this derivative involves **f'** evaluated with the argument x^2.	*In[12]:=* **D[f[x^2], x]**
	Out[12]= $2 x f'[x^2]$
You can evaluate the result at the point $x = 2$ by using the standard *Mathematica* replacement operation.	*In[13]:=* **% /. x->2**
	Out[13]= $4 f'[4]$

There is some slight subtlety when you need to deduce the value of **f'** based on definitions for objects like **f[x_]**.

Here is a definition for a function h.	*In[14]:=* **h[x_] := x^4**

When you take the derivative of h[x], *Mathematica* first evaluates h[x], then differentiates the result.	*In[15]:=* **D[h[x], x]**
	Out[15]= $4x^3$

You can get the same result by applying the function h' to the argument x.	*In[16]:=* **h'[x]**
	Out[16]= $4x^3$

Here is the function h' on its own.	*In[17]:=* **h'**
	Out[17]= $4\#1^3$&

The function f' is completely determined by the form of the function f. Definitions for objects like f[x_] do not immediately apply however to expressions like f'[x]. The problem is that f'[x] has the full form Derivative[1][f][x], which nowhere contains anything that explicitly matches the pattern f[x_]. In addition, for many purposes it is convenient to have a representation of the function f' itself, without necessarily applying it to any arguments.

What *Mathematica* does is to try and find the explicit form of a *pure function* which represents the object f'. When *Mathematica* gets an expression like Derivative[1][f], it effectively converts it to the explicit form D[f[#], #]& and then tries to evaluate the derivative. In the explicit form, *Mathematica* can immediately use values that have been defined for objects like f[x_]. If *Mathematica* succeeds in doing the derivative, it returns the explicit pure-function result. If it does not succeed, it leaves the derivative in the original f' form.

This gives the derivative of Tan in pure-function form.	*In[18]:=* **Tan'**
	Out[18]= $\text{Sec}[\#1]^2$&

Here is the result of applying the pure function to the specific argument y.	*In[19]:=* **%[y]**
	Out[19]= $\text{Sec}[y]^2$

■ 3.5.5 Defining Derivatives

You can define the derivative in *Mathematica* of a function f of one argument simply by an assignment like f'[x_] = fp[x].

This defines the derivative of $f(x)$ to be $fp(x)$. In this case, you could have used = instead of :=.	*In[1]:=* **f'[x_] := fp[x]**

The rule for f'[x_] is used to evaluate this derivative.	*In[2]:=* **D[f[x^2], x]**
	Out[2]= $2x\,\text{fp}[x^2]$

Differentiating again gives derivatives of *fp*.	*In[3]:=* **D[%, x]**
	Out[3]= $2\,\text{fp}[x^2] + 4x^2\,\text{fp}'[x^2]$

This defines a value for the derivative of g at the origin.	*In[4]:=* **g'[0] = g0**
	Out[4]= g0
The value for g'[0] is used.	*In[5]:=* **D[g[x]^2, x] /. x->0**
	Out[5]= 2 g0 g[0]
This defines the second derivative of g, with any argument.	*In[6]:=* **g''[x_] = gpp[x]**
	Out[6]= gpp[x]
The value defined for the second derivative is used.	*In[7]:=* **D[g[x]^2, {x, 2}]**
	Out[7]= $2 g[x] gpp[x] + 2 g'[x]^2$

To define derivatives of functions with several arguments, you have to use the general representation of derivatives in *Mathematica*.

$f'[x\_] := rhs$	define the first derivative of f
Derivative[n][f][$x\_$] := rhs	define the nth derivative of f
Derivative[m, n, ...][g][$x\_$, $\_$, ...] := rhs	define derivatives of g with respect to various arguments

Defining derivatives.

This defines the second derivative of g with respect to its second argument.	*In[8]:=* **Derivative[0, 2][g][x_, y_] := g2p[x, y]**
This uses the definition just given.	*In[9]:=* **D[g[a^2, x^2], x, x]**
	Out[9]= $4 x^2 g2p[a^2, x^2] + 2 g^{(0,1)}[a^2, x^2]$

■ 3.5.6 Indefinite Integrals

The *Mathematica* function Integrate[f, x] gives you the *indefinite integral* $\int f \, dx$. You can think of the operation of indefinite integration as being an inverse of differentiation. If you take the result from Integrate[f, x], and then differentiate it, you always get a result that is mathematically equal to the original expression f.

In general, however, there is a whole family of results which have the property that their derivative is f. Integrate[f, x] gives you *an* expression whose derivative is f. You can get other expressions by adding an arbitrary constant of integration, or indeed by adding any function that is constant except at discrete points.

If you fill in explicit limits for your integral, any such constants of integration must cancel out. But even though the indefinite integral can have arbitrary constants added, it is still often very convenient to manipulate it without filling in the limits.

Mathematica applies standard rules to find indefinite integrals.

In[1]:= **Integrate[x^2, x]**

Out[1]= $\dfrac{x^3}{3}$

You can add an arbitrary constant to the indefinite integral, and still get the same derivative. **Integrate** simply gives you *an* expression with the required derivative.

In[2]:= **D[% + c , x]**

Out[2]= x^2

This gives the indefinite integral $\int \frac{dx}{x^2-1}$.

In[3]:= **Integrate[1/(x^2 - 1), x]**

Out[3]= $\dfrac{1}{2} \text{Log}[-1 + x] - \dfrac{1}{2} \text{Log}[1 + x]$

Differentiating should give the original function back again.

In[4]:= **D[%, x]**

Out[4]= $\dfrac{1}{2(-1+x)} - \dfrac{1}{2(1+x)}$

You need to manipulate it to get it back into the original form.

In[5]:= **Simplify[%]**

Out[5]= $\dfrac{1}{-1+x^2}$

The **Integrate** function assumes that any object that does not explicitly contain the integration variable is independent of it, and can be treated as a constant. As a result, **Integrate** is like an inverse of the *partial differentiation* function D.

The variable a is assumed to be independent of x.

In[6]:= **Integrate[a x^2, x]**

Out[6]= $\dfrac{a x^3}{3}$

The integration variable can be any expression that does not involve explicit mathematical operations.

In[7]:= **Integrate[x b[x]^2, b[x]]**

Out[7]= $\dfrac{1}{3} x b[x]^3$

Another assumption that **Integrate** implicitly makes is that all the symbolic quantities in your integrand have "generic" values. Thus, for example, *Mathematica* will tell you that $\int x^n \, dx$ is $\frac{x^{n+1}}{n+1}$ even though this is not true in the special case $n = -1$.

Mathematica gives the standard result for this integral, implicitly assuming that n is not equal to −1.

In[8]:= **Integrate[x^n, x]**

Out[8]= $\dfrac{x^{1+n}}{1+n}$

If you specifically give an exponent of −1, *Mathematica* produces a different result.

In[9]:= **Integrate[x^-1, x]**

Out[9]= $\text{Log}[x]$

You should realize that the result for any particular integral can often be written in many different forms. *Mathematica* tries to give you the most convenient form, following principles such as avoiding explicit complex numbers unless your input already contains them.

This integral is given in terms of ArcTan.

In[10]:= `Integrate[1/(1 + a x^2), x]`

$$Out[10]= \frac{\text{ArcTan}\left[\sqrt{a}\ x\right]}{\sqrt{a}}$$

This integral is given in terms of ArcTanh.

In[11]:= `Integrate[1/(1 - b x^2), x]`

$$Out[11]= \frac{\text{ArcTanh}\left[\sqrt{b}\ x\right]}{\sqrt{b}}$$

This is mathematically equal to the first integral, but is given in a somewhat different form.

In[12]:= `% /. b -> -a`

$$Out[12]= \frac{\text{ArcTanh}\left[\sqrt{-a}\ x\right]}{\sqrt{-a}}$$

The derivative is still correct.

In[13]:= `D[%, x]`

$$Out[13]= \frac{1}{1 + a x^2}$$

Even though they look quite different, both `ArcTan[x]` and `-ArcTan[1/x]` are indefinite integrals of $1/(1 + x^2)$.

In[14]:= `Simplify[D[{ArcTan[x], -ArcTan[1/x]}, x]]`

$$Out[14]= \left\{ \frac{1}{1 + x^2}, \frac{1}{1 + x^2} \right\}$$

Integrate chooses to use the simpler of the two forms.

In[15]:= `Integrate[1/(1 + x^2), x]`

Out[15]= `ArcTan[x]`

■ 3.5.7 Integrals That Can and Cannot Be Done

Evaluating integrals is much more difficult than evaluating derivatives. For derivatives, there is a systematic procedure based on the chain rule that effectively allows any derivative to be worked out. But for integrals, there is no such systematic procedure.

One of the main problems is that it is difficult to know what kinds of functions will be needed to evaluate a particular integral. When you work out a derivative, you always end up with functions that are of the same kind or simpler than the ones you started with. But when you work out integrals, you often end up needing to use functions that are much more complicated than the ones you started with.

This integral can be evaluated using the same kind of functions that appeared in the input.

In[1]:= `Integrate[Log[x]^2, x]`

$$Out[1]= 2x - 2x\,\text{Log}[x] + x\,\text{Log}[x]^2$$

But for this integral the special function `LogIntegral` is needed.

In[2]:= `Integrate[Log[Log[x]], x]`

Out[2]= `x Log[Log[x]] - LogIntegral[x]`

It is not difficult to find integrals that require all sorts of functions.

In[3]:= `Integrate[Sin[x^2], x]`

$$Out[3]= \sqrt{\frac{\pi}{2}}\ \text{FresnelS}\left[\sqrt{\frac{2}{\pi}}\ x\right]$$

Simple-looking integrals can give remarkably complicated results. Often it is convenient to apply `Simplify` to your answers.

In[4]:= `Simplify[ Integrate[Log[x] Exp[-x^2], x] ]`

Out[4]= $-\dfrac{1}{4\sqrt{x^2}}\left(x\left(2\,\text{Gamma}\left[\dfrac{1}{2}, x^2\right]\text{Log}[x] +\right.\right.$

$\left.\left.\text{MeijerG}\left[\{\{\}, \{1, 1\}\}, \left\{\left\{0, 0, \dfrac{1}{2}\right\}, \{\}\right\}, x^2\right]\right)\right)$

This integral involves an incomplete gamma function. Note that the power is carefully set up to allow any complex value of x.

In[5]:= `Integrate[Exp[-x^a], x]`

Out[5]= $-\dfrac{x\,(x^a)^{-1/a}\,\text{Gamma}\left[\frac{1}{a}, x^a\right]}{a}$

Mathematica includes a very wide range of mathematical functions, and by using these functions a great many integrals can be done. But it is still possible to find even fairly simple-looking integrals that just cannot be done in terms of any standard mathematical functions.

Here is a fairly simple-looking integral that cannot be done in terms of any standard mathematical functions.

In[6]:= `Integrate[Sin[x]/Log[x], x]`

Out[6]= $\displaystyle\int \dfrac{\text{Sin}[x]}{\text{Log}[x]}dx$

The main point of being able to do an integral in terms of standard mathematical functions is that it lets one use the known properties of these functions to evaluate or manipulate the result one gets.

In the most convenient cases, integrals can be done purely in terms of elementary functions such as exponentials, logarithms and trigonometric functions. In fact, if you give an integrand that involves only such elementary functions, then one of the important capabilities of `Integrate` is that if the corresponding integral can be expressed in terms of elementary functions, then `Integrate` will essentially always succeed in finding it.

Integrals of rational functions are straightforward to evaluate, and always come out in terms of rational functions, logarithms and inverse trigonometric functions.

In[7]:= `Integrate[x/((x - 1)(x + 2)), x]`

Out[7]= $\dfrac{1}{3}\text{Log}[-1 + x] + \dfrac{2}{3}\text{Log}[2 + x]$

The integral here is still of the same form, but now involves an implicit sum over the roots of a polynomial.

In[8]:= `Integrate[1/(1 + 2 x + x^3), x]`

Out[8]= $\text{RootSum}\left[1 + 2\#1 + \#1^3\,\&, \dfrac{\text{Log}[x - \#1]}{2 + 3\#1^2}\,\&\right]$

This finds numerical approximations to all the root objects.

In[9]:= `N[%]`

Out[9]= $(-0.19108 - 0.088541\,I)$

$\quad\quad\text{Log}[(-0.226699 - 1.46771\,I) + x] -$

$\quad\quad(0.19108 - 0.088541\,I)$

$\quad\quad\text{Log}[(-0.226699 + 1.46771\,I) + x] +$

$\quad\quad0.382159\,\text{Log}[0.453398 + x]$

Integrals of trigonometric functions usually come out in terms of other trigonometric functions.

In[10]:= `Integrate[Sin[x]^3 Cos[x]^2, x]`

Out[10]= $\dfrac{1}{240}\left(-30\,\text{Cos}[x] - 5\,\text{Cos}[3x] + 3\,\text{Cos}[5x]\right)$

Here is another form of the result.

$In[11]:=$ **Simplify[%]**

$Out[11]=$ $\dfrac{1}{30} \text{Cos}[x]^3 (-7 + 3\,\text{Cos}[2x])$

This is a fairly simple integral involving algebraic functions.

$In[12]:=$ **Integrate[Sqrt[x] Sqrt[1 + x], x]**

$Out[12]=$ $\sqrt{1+x}\left(\dfrac{\sqrt{x}}{4} + \dfrac{x^{3/2}}{2}\right) - \dfrac{\text{ArcSinh}\left[\sqrt{x}\right]}{4}$

Here is an integral involving nested square roots.

$In[13]:=$ **Integrate[Sqrt[x + Sqrt[x]], x]**

$Out[13]=$ $\dfrac{\sqrt{\sqrt{x}+x}\left(-\dfrac{x^{1/4}}{4} + \dfrac{x^{3/4}}{6} + \dfrac{2x^{5/4}}{3}\right)}{x^{1/4}} +$

$\dfrac{\sqrt{\sqrt{x}+x}\ \text{ArcSinh}[x^{1/4}]}{4\sqrt{1+\sqrt{x}}\ x^{1/4}}$

By nesting elementary functions you sometimes get integrals that can be done in terms of elementary functions.

$In[14]:=$ **Integrate[Cos[Log[x]], x]**

$Out[14]=$ $\dfrac{1}{2}(x\,\text{Cos}[\text{Log}[x]] + x\,\text{Sin}[\text{Log}[x]])$

But more often other kinds of functions are needed.

$In[15]:=$ **Integrate[Log[Cos[x]], x]**

$Out[15]=$ $\dfrac{I x^2}{2} - x\,\text{Log}[1 + E^{2Ix}] +$

$x\,\text{Log}[\text{Cos}[x]] + \dfrac{1}{2} I\,\text{PolyLog}[2, -E^{2Ix}]$

Integrals like this typically come out in terms of elliptic functions.

$In[16]:=$ **Integrate[Sqrt[Cos[x]], x]**

$Out[16]=$ $2\,\text{EllipticE}\left[\dfrac{x}{2}, 2\right]$

But occasionally one can get results in terms of elementary functions alone.

$In[17]:=$ **Integrate[Sqrt[Tan[x]], x]**

$Out[17]=$ $\dfrac{1}{2}\,\text{Csc}[x]\,(-\text{ArcSin}[\text{Cos}[x] - \text{Sin}[x]] -$

$\dfrac{\text{Log}\left[\text{Cos}[x] + \text{Sin}[x] + \sqrt{\text{Sin}[2x]}\,\right])}{\sqrt{\text{Sin}[2x]}\ \sqrt{\text{Tan}[x]}}$

Beyond working with elementary functions, **Integrate** includes a large number of algorithms for dealing with special functions. Sometimes it uses a direct generalization of the procedure for elementary functions. But more often its strategy is first to try to write the integrand in a form that can be integrated in terms of certain sophisticated special functions, and then having done this to try to find reductions of these sophisticated functions to more familiar functions.

To integrate this Bessel function requires a generalized hypergeometric function.

$In[18]:=$ **Integrate[BesselJ[0, x], x]**

$Out[18]=$ $x\,\text{HypergeometricPFQ}\left[\left\{\dfrac{1}{2}\right\}, \left\{1, \dfrac{3}{2}\right\}, -\dfrac{x^2}{4}\right]$

To integrate an elliptic integral also requires a generalized hypergeometric function.

$In[19]:=$ `Integrate[EllipticK[x], x]`

$Out[19]= \frac{1}{2} \pi x \, \text{HypergeometricPFQ}\left[\left\{\frac{1}{2}, \frac{1}{2}\right\}, \{2\}, x\right]$

Sometimes the integrals can be reduced to more familiar forms.

$In[20]:=$ `Integrate[x BesselJ[0, x], x]`

$Out[20]= \sqrt{x^2} \, \text{BesselJ}\left[1, \sqrt{x^2}\right]$

A large book of integral tables will list perhaps a few thousand indefinite integrals. *Mathematica* can do essentially all of these integrals. And because it contains general algorithms rather than just specific cases, *Mathematica* can actually do a vastly wider range of integrals.

You could expect to find this integral in any large book of integral tables.

$In[21]:=$ `Integrate[Log[1 - x]/x, x]`

$Out[21]= -\text{PolyLog}[2, x]$

To do this integral, however, requires a more general algorithm, rather than just a direct table look up.

$In[22]:=$ `Integrate[Log[1 + 3 x + x^2]/x, x] // Short`

$Out[22]//Short= \text{Log}[x] \left(\text{Log}\left[\frac{1}{2}\left(3 - \sqrt{5}\right) + x\right] - \text{Log}\left[1 + \frac{2x}{3 - \sqrt{5}}\right]\right) +$

$\ll 6 \gg$

Particularly if you introduce new mathematical functions of your own, you may want to teach *Mathematica* new kinds of integrals. You can do this by making appropriate definitions for `Integrate`.

In the case of differentiation, the chain rule allows one to reduce all derivatives to a standard form, represented in *Mathematica* using `Derivative`. But for integration, no such similar standard form exists, and as a result you often have to make definitions for several different versions of the same integral. Changes of variables and other transformations can rarely be done automatically by `Integrate`.

This integral cannot be done in terms of any of the standard mathematical functions built into *Mathematica*.

$In[23]:=$ `Integrate[Sin[Sin[x]], x]`

$Out[23]= \int \text{Sin}[\text{Sin}[x]] \, dx$

Before you add your own rules for integration, you have to remove write protection.

$In[24]:=$ `Unprotect[Integrate]`

$Out[24]= \{\text{Integrate}\}$

You can set up your own rule to define the integral to be, say, a "Jones" function.

$In[25]:=$ `Integrate[Sin[Sin[a_. + b_. x_]], x_] := Jones[a, x]/b`

Now *Mathematica* can do integrals that give Jones functions.

$In[26]:=$ `Integrate[Sin[Sin[3x]], x]`

$Out[26]= \frac{1}{3} \text{Jones}[0, x]$

As it turns out, the integral $\int \sin(\sin(x)) \, dx$ can in principle be represented as an infinite sum of $_2F_1$ hypergeometric functions, or as a suitably generalized Kampé de Fériet hypergeometric function of two variables.

◼ 3.5.8 Definite Integrals

Integrate[f, x]	the indefinite integral $\int f\, dx$
Integrate[f, {x, $xmin$, $xmax$}]	the definite integral $\int_{xmin}^{xmax} f\, dx$
Integrate[f, {x, $xmin$, $xmax$}, {y, $ymin$, $ymax$}]	the multiple integral $\int_{xmin}^{xmax} dx \int_{ymin}^{ymax} dy\, f$

Integration functions.

Here is the integral $\int_a^b x^2\, dx$.

```
In[1]:= Integrate[x^2, {x, a, b}]
```

$$Out[1]= -\frac{a^3}{3} + \frac{b^3}{3}$$

This gives the multiple integral $\int_0^a dx \int_0^b dy\,(x^2 + y^2)$.

```
In[2]:= Integrate[x^2 + y^2, {x, 0, a}, {y, 0, b}]
```

$$Out[2]= \frac{a^3 b}{3} + \frac{a b^3}{3}$$

The y integral is done first. Its limits can depend on the value of x. This ordering is the same as is used in functions like Sum and Table.

```
In[3]:= Integrate[x^2 + y^2, {x, 0, a}, {y, 0, x}]
```

$$Out[3]= \frac{a^4}{3}$$

In simple cases, definite integrals can be done by finding indefinite forms and then computing appropriate limits. But there is a vast range of integrals for which the indefinite form cannot be expressed in terms of standard mathematical functions, but the definite form still can be.

This indefinite integral cannot be done in terms of standard mathematical functions.

```
In[4]:= Integrate[Cos[Sin[x]], x]
```

$$Out[4]= \int Cos[Sin[x]]\,dx$$

This definite integral, however, can be done in terms of a Bessel function.

```
In[5]:= Integrate[Cos[Sin[x]], {x, 0, 2Pi}]
```

$$Out[5]= 2\pi\, BesselJ[0, 1]$$

Here is an integral where the indefinite form can be found, but it is much more efficient to work out the definite form directly.

```
In[6]:= Integrate[Log[x] Exp[-x^2], {x, 0, Infinity}]
```

$$Out[6]= -\frac{1}{4}\sqrt{\pi}\,(EulerGamma + Log[4])$$

Just because an integrand may contain special functions, it does not mean that the definite integral will necessarily be complicated.

```
In[7]:= Integrate[BesselK[0, x]^2, {x, 0, Infinity}]
```

$$Out[7]= \frac{\pi^2}{4}$$

Special functions nevertheless occur in this result.

```
In[8]:= Integrate[BesselK[0, x] BesselJ[0, x], {x, 0, Infinity}]
```

$$Out[8]= \frac{2\sqrt{2}\,Gamma\left[\frac{5}{4}\right]^2}{\sqrt{\pi}}$$

The integrand here is simple, but the definite integral is not.

$In[9]:=$ **Integrate[Sin[x^2] Exp[-x], {x, 0, Infinity}]**

$Out[9]= \dfrac{1}{2\sqrt{2}}\left(\sqrt{\pi}\,\text{Cos}\left[\dfrac{1}{4}\right] - \right.$

$\sqrt{2}\,\text{HypergeometricPFQ}\left[\{1\}, \left\{\dfrac{3}{4}, \dfrac{5}{4}\right\}, -\dfrac{1}{64}\right] +$

$\left.\sqrt{\pi}\,\text{Sin}\left[\dfrac{1}{4}\right]\right)$

Even when you can find the indefinite form of an integral, you will often not get the correct answer for the definite integral if you just subtract the values of the limits at each end point. The problem is that within the domain of integration there may be singularities whose effects are ignored if you follow this procedure.

Here is the indefinite integral of $1/x^2$.

$In[10]:=$ **Integrate[1/x^2, x]**

$Out[10]= -\dfrac{1}{x}$

This subtracts the limits at each end point.

$In[11]:=$ **Limit[%, x->2] - Limit[%, x->-2]**

$Out[11]= -1$

The true definite integral is divergent because of the double pole at $x = 0$.

$In[12]:=$ **Integrate[1/x^2, {x, -2, 2}]**

$Out[12]= \infty$

Here is a more subtle example, involving branch cuts rather than poles.

$In[13]:=$ **Simplify[Integrate[1/(1 + a Sin[x]), x]]**

$Out[13]= \dfrac{2\,\text{ArcTan}\left[\frac{a+\text{Tan}\left[\frac{x}{2}\right]}{\sqrt{1-a^2}}\right]}{\sqrt{1-a^2}}$

Taking limits in the indefinite integral gives 0.

$In[14]:=$ **Limit[%, x -> 2Pi] - Limit[%, x -> 0]**

$Out[14]= 0$

The definite integral, however, gives the correct result which depends on a.

$In[15]:=$ **Integrate[1/(1 + a Sin[x]), {x, 0, 2Pi}]**

$Out[15]= \dfrac{4\pi}{\sqrt{4 - 4a^2}}$

+ **Integrate[f, {x, $xmin$, $xmax$}, PrincipalValue -> True]**
  the Cauchy principal value of a definite integral

Principal value integrals.

Here is the indefinite integral of $1/x$.

$In[16]:=$ **Integrate[1/x, x]**

$Out[16]= \text{Log}[x]$

Substituting in the limits -1 and $+2$ yields a strange result involving $i\pi$.

$In[17]:=$ **Limit[%, x -> 2] - Limit[%, x -> -1]**

$Out[17]= -I\pi + \text{Log}[2]$

The ordinary Riemann definite integral is divergent.

`In[18]:= Integrate[1/x, {x, -1, 2}]`

`Integrate::idiv:`

   Integral of $\dfrac{1}{x}$ does not converge on {-1, 2}.

`Out[18]=` $\displaystyle\int_{-1}^{2} \frac{1}{x} dx$

The Cauchy principal value, however, is finite.

`In[19]:= Integrate[1/x, {x, -1, 2}, PrincipalValue->True]`

`Out[19]= Log[2]`

When parameters appear in an indefinite integral, it is essentially always possible to get results that are correct for almost all values of these parameters. But for definite integrals this is no longer the case. The most common problem is that a definite integral may converge only when the parameters that appear in it satisfy certain specific conditions.

This indefinite integral is correct for all $n \neq -1$.

`In[20]:= Integrate[x^n, x]`

`Out[20]=` $\dfrac{x^{1+n}}{1 + n}$

For the definite integral, however, n must satisfy a condition in order for the integral to be convergent.

`In[21]:= Integrate[x^n, {x, 0, 1}]`

`Out[21]=` $\text{If}\left[\text{Re}[n] > -1, \dfrac{1}{1+n}, \displaystyle\int_0^1 x^n dx\right]$

If n is replaced by 2, the condition is satisfied.

`In[22]:= % /. n -> 2`

`Out[22]=` $\dfrac{1}{3}$

option name	default value	
+ `GenerateConditions`	True	whether to generate explicit conditions
+ `Assumptions`	{}	what relations about parameters to assume

Options for `Integrate`.

With the assumption $n > 2$, the result is always $1/(1 + n)$.

`In[23]:= Integrate[x^n, {x, 0, 1}, Assumptions -> (n > 2)]`

`Out[23]=` $\dfrac{1}{1 + n}$

Even when a definite integral is convergent, the presence of singularities on the integration path can lead to discontinuous changes when the parameters vary. Sometimes a single formula containing functions like `Sign` can be used to summarize the result. In other cases, however, an explicit `If` is more convenient.

The If here gives the condition for the integral to be convergent.

$In[24]:=$ **Integrate[Sin[a x]/x, {x, 0, Infinity}]**

$Out[24]=$ $\mathrm{If}\left[\mathrm{Im[a]} == 0, \frac{1}{2} \pi \, \mathrm{Sign[a]}, \int_0^\infty \frac{\mathrm{Sin[a\,x]}}{x} dx\right]$

Here is the result assuming that a is real.

$In[25]:=$ **Integrate[Sin[a x]/x, {x, 0, Infinity},**
Assumptions -> Im[a] == 0]

$Out[25]=$ $\frac{1}{2} \pi \, \mathrm{Sign[a]}$

The result is discontinuous as a function of a. The discontinuity can be traced to the essential singularity of $\sin(x)$ at $x = \infty$.

$In[26]:=$ **Plot[%, {a, -5, 5}]**

There is no convenient way to represent this answer in terms of Sign, so *Mathematica* generates an explicit If.

$In[27]:=$ **Integrate[Sin[x] BesselJ[0, a x]/x, {x, 0, Infinity},**
Assumptions -> Im[a] == 0]

$Out[27]=$ $\mathrm{If}\left[\frac{1}{a} > -1 \ \&\& \ \frac{1}{a} < 1, \ \mathrm{ArcSin}\left[\frac{1}{a}\right] \mathrm{Sign[a]}, \ \frac{\pi}{2}\right]$

Here is a plot of the resulting function of a.

$In[28]:=$ **Plot[Evaluate[%], {a, -5, 5}]**

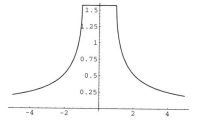

■ 3.5.9 Manipulating Integrals in Symbolic Form

When *Mathematica* cannot give you an explicit result for an integral, it leaves the integral in a symbolic form. It is often useful to manipulate this symbolic form.

Mathematica cannot give an explicit result for this integral, so it leaves the integral in symbolic form.	*In[1]:=* **Integrate[x^2 f[x], x]** *Out[1]=* $\int x^2 f[x] dx$
Differentiating the symbolic form gives the integrand back again.	*In[2]:=* **D[%, x]** *Out[2]=* $x^2 f[x]$
Here is a definite integral which cannot be done explicitly.	*In[3]:=* **Integrate[f[x], {x, a[x], b[x]}]** *Out[3]=* $\int_{a[x]}^{b[x]} f[x] dx$
This gives the derivative of the definite integral.	*In[4]:=* **D[%, x]** *Out[4]=* $-f[a[x]] a'[x] + f[b[x]] b'[x]$
Here is a definite integral with end points that do not explicitly depend on x.	*In[5]:=* **defint = Integrate[f[x], {x, a, b}]** *Out[5]=* $\int_{a}^{b} f[x] dx$
The partial derivative of this with respect to u is zero.	*In[6]:=* **D[defint, u]** *Out[6]=* 0
There is a non-trivial total derivative, however.	*In[7]:=* **Dt[defint, u]** *Out[7]=* $-Dt[a, u] f[a] + Dt[b, u] f[b]$

■ 3.5.10 Differential Equations

As discussed in Section 1.5.8, you can use the *Mathematica* function DSolve to find symbolic solutions to ordinary differential equations.

Solving a differential equation consists essentially in finding the form of an unknown function. In *Mathematica*, unknown functions are represented by expressions like y[x]. The derivatives of such functions are represented by y'[x], y''[x] and so on.

The *Mathematica* function DSolve returns as its result a list of rules for functions. There is a question of how these functions are represented. If you ask DSolve to solve for y[x], then DSolve will indeed return a rule for y[x]. In some cases, this rule may be all you need. But this rule, on its own, does not give values for y'[x] or even y[0]. In many cases, therefore, it is better to ask DSolve to solve not for y[x], but instead for y itself. In this case, what DSolve will return is a rule which gives y as a pure function, in the sense discussed in Section 2.2.5.

If you ask DSolve to solve for y[x], it will give a rule specifically for y[x].	*In[1]:=* **DSolve[y'[x] + y[x] == 1, y[x], x]** *Out[1]=* $\{\{y[x] \rightarrow 1 + E^{-x} C[1]\}\}$
The rule applies only to y[x] itself, and not, for example, to objects like y[0] or y'[x].	*In[2]:=* **y[x] + 2y'[x] + y[0] /. %** *Out[2]=* $\{1 + E^{-x} C[1] + y[0] + 2y'[x]\}$

If you ask DSolve to solve for y, it gives a rule for the object y on its own as a pure function.

$In[3]:=$ DSolve[y'[x] + y[x] == 1, y, x]

$Out[3]=$ {{y → (1 + E$^{-\#1}$ C[1] &)}}

Now the rule applies to all occurrences of y.

$In[4]:=$ y[x] + 2y'[x] + y[0] /. %

$Out[4]=$ {2 + C[1] − E^{-x} C[1]}

Substituting the solution into the original equation yields True.

$In[5]:=$ y'[x] + y[x] == 1 /. %%

$Out[5]=$ {True}

| DSolve[eqn, $y[x]$, x] | solve a differential equation for $y[x]$ |
| DSolve[eqn, y, x] | solve a differential equation for the function y |

Getting solutions to differential equations in different forms.

In standard mathematical notation, one typically represents solutions to differential equations by explicitly introducing "dummy variables" to represent the arguments of the functions that appear. If all you need is a symbolic form for the solution, then introducing such dummy variables may be convenient. However, if you actually intend to use the solution in a variety of other computations, then you will usually find it better to get the solution in pure-function form, without dummy variables. Notice that this form, while easy to represent in *Mathematica*, has no direct analog in standard mathematical notation.

DSolve[{eqn_1, eqn_2, ... }, {y_1, y_2, ... }, x]

solve a list of differential equations

Solving simultaneous differential equations.

This solves two simultaneous differential equations.

$In[6]:=$ DSolve[{y[x] == −z'[x], z[x] == −y'[x]}, {y, z}, x]

$Out[6]=$ {{y → (E$^{-\#1}$ C[1] − E$^{\#1}$ C[2] &),

z → (E$^{-\#1}$ C[1] + E$^{\#1}$ C[2] &)}}

Mathematica returns two distinct solutions for y in this case.

$In[7]:=$ DSolve[y[x] y'[x] == 1, y, x]

$Out[7]=$ {{y → (−$\sqrt{2 \#1 + 2 C[1]}$ &)}, {y → ($\sqrt{2 \#1 + 2 C[1]}$ &)}}

You can add constraints and boundary conditions for differential equations by explicitly giving additional equations such as y[0] == 0.

This asks for a solution which satisfies the condition y[0] == 1.

$In[8]:=$ DSolve[{y'[x] == a y[x], y[0] == 1}, y[x], x]

$Out[8]=$ {{y[x] → E$^{a x}$}}

If you ask *Mathematica* to solve a set of differential equations and you do not give any constraints or boundary conditions, then *Mathematica* will try to find a *general solution* to your equations. This general solution will involve various undetermined constants. One new constant is introduced for each order of derivative in each equation you give.

The default is that these constants are named C[n], where the index *n* starts at 1 for each invocation of DSolve. You can override this choice, by explicitly giving a setting for the option DSolveConstants. Any function you give is applied to each successive index value *n* to get the constants to use for each invocation of DSolve.

The general solution to this fourth-order equation involves four undetermined constants.	$In[9]:=$ **DSolve[y''''[x] == y[x], y[x], x]** $Out[9]=$ {{y[x] → $\qquad$ E^{-x} C[1] + E^x C[4] + C[3] Cos[x] − C[2] Sin[x]}}
Each independent initial or boundary condition you give reduces the number of undetermined constants by one.	$In[10]:=$ **DSolve[{y''''[x] == y[x], y[0] == y'[0] == 0}, y[x], x]** $Out[10]=$ {{y[x] → E^{-x} (−C[3] − C[4] + E^{2x} C[4] + $\qquad$ E^x C[3] Cos[x] − E^x (C[3] + 2 C[4]) Sin[x])}}

You should realize that finding exact formulas for the solutions to differential equations is a difficult matter. In fact, there are only fairly few kinds of equations for which such formulas can be found, at least in terms of standard mathematical functions.

The most widely investigated differential equations are linear ones, in which the functions you are solving for, as well as their derivatives, appear only linearly.

This is a homogeneous first-order linear differential equation, and its solution is quite simple.	$In[11]:=$ **DSolve[y'[x] − x y[x] == 0, y[x], x]** $Out[11]=$ $\left\{\left\{y[x] \rightarrow E^{\frac{x^2}{2}} C[1]\right\}\right\}$
Making the equation inhomogeneous leads to a significantly more complicated solution.	$In[12]:=$ **DSolve[y'[x] − x y[x] == 1, y[x], x]** $Out[12]=$ $\left\{\left\{y[x] \rightarrow E^{\frac{x^2}{2}} C[1] + E^{\frac{x^2}{2}} \sqrt{\frac{\pi}{2}}\ \text{Erf}\left[\frac{x}{\sqrt{2}}\right]\right\}\right\}$

If you have only a single linear differential equation, and it involves only a first derivative of the function you are solving for, then it turns out that the solution can always be found just by doing integrals.

But as soon as you have more than one differential equation, or more than a first-order derivative, this is no longer true. However, some simple second-order linear differential equations can nevertheless be solved using various special functions from Section 3.2.10. Indeed, historically many of these special functions were first introduced specifically in order to represent the solutions to such equations.

This is Airy's equation, which is solved in terms of Airy functions.	$In[13]:=$ **DSolve[y''[x] − x y[x] == 0, y[x], x]** $Out[13]=$ {{y[x] → AiryBi[x] C[1] + AiryAi[x] C[2]}}
This equation comes out in terms of Bessel functions.	$In[14]:=$ **DSolve[y''[x] − Exp[x] y[x] == 0, y[x], x]** $Out[14]=$ $\left\{\left\{y[x] \rightarrow \text{BesselI}\left[0, 2\sqrt{E^x}\right] C[1] + \text{BesselK}\left[0, 2\sqrt{E^x}\right] C[2]\right\}\right\}$

Occasionally second-order linear equations can be solved using only elementary functions.

$In[15]:=$ `DSolve[x^2 y''[x] + y[x] == 0, y[x], x]`

$Out[15]=$ $\{\{y[x] \to x^{(-1)^{1/3}} C[1] + x^{-(-1)^{2/3}} C[2]\}\}$

Beyond second order, the kinds of functions needed to solve even fairly simple linear differential equations become extremely complicated. At third order, the generalized Meijer G function `MeijerG` can sometimes be used, but at fourth order and beyond absolutely no standard mathematical functions are typically adequate, except in very special cases.

Here is a third-order linear differential equation which can be solved in terms of generalized hypergeometric functions.

$In[16]:=$ `DSolve[y'''[x] + x y[x] == 0, y[x], x]`

$Out[16]=$ $\Big\{\{y[x] \to$

$$C[1] \text{HypergeometricPFQ}\Big[\{\}, \Big\{\frac{1}{2}, \frac{3}{4}\Big\}, -\frac{x^4}{64}\Big] +$$

$$(x^4)^{1/4} C[2] \text{HypergeometricPFQ}\Big[$$

$$\{\}, \Big\{\frac{3}{4}, \frac{5}{4}\Big\}, -\frac{x^4}{64}\Big] + \sqrt{x^4} \, C[3]$$

$$\text{HypergeometricPFQ}\Big[\{\}, \Big\{\frac{5}{4}, \frac{3}{2}\Big\}, -\frac{x^4}{64}\Big]\}\Big\}$$

This requires more general Meijer G functions.

$In[17]:=$ `DSolve[y'''[x] + Exp[x] y[x] == 0, y[x], x]`

$Out[17]=$ `{{y[x] → C[1] HypergeometricPFQ[{}, {1, 1}, -E^x] +`
`C[2] MeijerG[{{}, {}}, {{0, 0}, {0}}, -E^x] +`
`C[3] MeijerG[{{}, {}}, {{0, 0, 0}, {}}, E^x]}}`

For nonlinear differential equations, only rather special cases can usually ever be solved in terms of standard mathematical functions. Nevertheless, `DSolve` includes fairly general procedures which allow it to handle almost all nonlinear differential equations whose solutions are found in standard reference books.

First-order nonlinear differential equations in which x does not appear on its own are fairly easy to solve.

$In[18]:=$ `DSolve[y'[x] - y[x]^2 == 0, y[x], x]`

$Out[18]=$ $\Big\{\Big\{y[x] \to \dfrac{1}{-x + C[1]}\Big\}\Big\}$

This Riccati equation already gives a significantly more complicated solution.

$In[19]:=$ `DSolve[y'[x] - y[x]^2 == x, y[x], x]`

$Out[19]=$ $\{\{y[x] \to -((-1)^{1/3} (\text{AiryAiPrime}[(-1)^{1/3} x] +$
$\text{AiryBiPrime}[(-1)^{1/3} x] C[1])) /$
$(\text{AiryAi}[(-1)^{1/3} x] + \text{AiryBi}[(-1)^{1/3} x] C[1])\}\}$

This Bernoulli equation, however, has a fairly simple solution.

$In[20]:=$ `DSolve[y'[x] - x y[x]^2 - y[x] == 0, y[x], x]`

$Out[20]=$ $\Big\{\Big\{y[x] \to -\dfrac{E^x}{-E^x + E^x x - C[1]}\Big\}\Big\}$

This Abel equation can be solved but only implicitly.

In[21]:= **DSolve[y'[x] + x y[x]^3 + y[x]^2 == 0, y[x], x]**

Solve::tdep:
    The equations appear to involve transcendental
    functions of the variables in an essentially
    non-algebraic way.

$$Out[21]= \text{Solve}\Big[\frac{\text{ArcTanh}\big[\frac{1+2xy[x]}{\sqrt{5}}\big]}{\sqrt{5}} - \text{Log}[x] + \text{Log}[xy[x]] -$$

$$\frac{1}{2}\text{Log}\big[-1 + xy[x] + x^2y[x]^2\big] == C[1],$$

$$\{y[x]\}\Big]$$

DSolve[*eqn*, $y[x_1, x_2, \ldots]$, $\{x_1, x_2, \ldots\}$]
    solve a partial differential equation for $y[x_1, x_2, \ldots]$

DSolve[*eqn*, $y[x_1, x_2, \ldots]$, $\{x_1, x_2, \ldots\}$]
    solve a partial differential equation for the function y

Solving partial differential equations.

DSolve is set up to handle not only *ordinary differential equations* in which just a single independent variable appears, but also *partial differential equations* in which two or more independent variables appear.

This finds the general solution to a simple partial differential equation with two independent variables.

In[22]:= **DSolve[D[y[x1, x2], x1] + D[y[x1, x2], x2] == 1/(x1 x2), y[x1, x2], {x1, x2}]**

$$Out[22]= \Big\{\Big\{y[x1, x2] \to$$
$$\frac{-\text{Log}[x1] + \text{Log}[x2] + (x1 - x2)\, C[1]\,[-x1 + x2]}{x1 - x2}\Big\}\Big\}$$

Here is the result represented as a pure function.

In[23]:= **DSolve[D[y[x1, x2], x1] + D[y[x1, x2], x2] == 1/(x1 x2), y, {x1, x2}]**

$$Out[23]= \Big\{\Big\{y \to$$
$$\Big(\frac{-\text{Log}[\#1] + \text{Log}[\#2] + (\#1 - \#2)\, C[1]\,[-\#1 + \#2]}{\#1 - \#2}\&\Big)\Big\}\Big\}$$

The basic mathematics of partial differential equations is considerably more complicated than that of ordinary differential equations. One feature is that whereas the general solution to an ordinary differential equation involves only arbitrary *constants*, the general solution to a partial differential equation, if it can be found at all, must involve arbitrary *functions*. Indeed, with m independent variables, arbitrary functions of $m-1$ variables must appear. DSolve by default names these functions C[n].

Here is a simple PDE involving three independent variables.	$In[24]:=$ `(D[#, x1] + D[#, x2] + D[#, x3])& [y[x1, x2, x3]] == 0` $Out[24]=$ $y^{(0,0,1)}[x1, x2, x3] +$ $\qquad y^{(0,1,0)}[x1, x2, x3] + y^{(1,0,0)}[x1, x2, x3] == 0$
The solution involves an arbitrary function of two variables.	$In[25]:=$ `DSolve[%, y[x1, x2, x3], {x1, x2, x3}]` $Out[25]=$ $\{\{y[x1, x2, x3] \to C[1][-x1 + x2, -x1 + x3]\}\}$
Here is the one-dimensional wave equation.	$In[26]:=$ `(c^2 D[#, x, x] - D[#, t, t])& [y[x, t]] == 0` $Out[26]=$ $-y^{(0,2)}[x, t] + c^2 y^{(2,0)}[x, t] == 0$
The solution to this second-order equation involves two arbitrary functions.	$In[27]:=$ `DSolve[%, y[x, t], {x, t}]` $Out[27]=$ $\left\{\left\{y[x, t] \to C[1]\left[t + \dfrac{x}{c}\right] + C[2]\left[t - \dfrac{x}{c}\right]\right\}\right\}$

For an ordinary differential equation, it is guaranteed that a general solution must exist, with the property that adding initial or boundary conditions simply corresponds to forcing specific choices for arbitrary constants in the solution. But for partial differential equations this is no longer true. Indeed, it is only for linear partial differential and a few other special types that such general solutions exist.

Other partial differential equations can be solved only when specific initial or boundary values are given, and in the vast majority of cases no solutions can be found as exact formulas in terms of standard mathematical functions.

Since y and its derivatives appear only linearly here, a general solution exists.	$In[28]:=$ `DSolve[x1 D[y[x1, x2], x1] + x2 D[y[x1, x2], x2]` $\qquad\qquad$ `== Exp[x1 x2], y[x1, x2], {x1, x2}]` $Out[28]=$ $\left\{\left\{y[x1, x2] \to\right.\right.$ $\qquad \dfrac{1}{2} \text{ExpIntegralEi}[x1\,x2] + C[1]\left[\dfrac{x2}{x1}\right]\left.\left.\right\}\right\}$
This weakly nonlinear PDE turns out to have a general solution.	$In[29]:=$ `DSolve[D[y[x1, x2], x1] + D[y[x1, x2], x2]` $\qquad\qquad$ `== Exp[y[x1, x2]], y[x1, x2], {x1, x2}]` $Out[29]=$ $\left\{\left\{y[x1, x2] \to \text{Log}\left[-\dfrac{1}{x1 - C[1][-x1 + x2]}\right]\right\}\right\}$
Here is a nonlinear PDE which has no general solution.	$In[30]:=$ `DSolve[D[y[x1, x2], x1] D[y[x1, x2], x2] == a,` $\qquad\qquad$ `y[x1, x2], {x1, x2}]` `DSolve::pde:` $\quad$ `Partial differential equation may not have a general` $\quad$ `solution. Try loading Calculus`DSolveIntegrals`\` to` $\quad$ `find special solutions.` $Out[30]=$ $\text{DSolve}[y^{(0,1)}[x1, x2]\, y^{(1,0)}[x1, x2] == a,$ $\qquad y[x1, x2], \{x1, x2\}]$

3.6 Series, Limits and Residues

■ 3.6.1 Making Power Series Expansions

Series[*expr*, {*x*, x_0, *n*}]	find the power series expansion of *expr* about the point $x = x_0$ to order at most $(x - x_0)^n$
Series[*expr*, {*x*, x_0, n_x}, {*y*, y_0, n_y}]	find series expansions with respect to *y* then *x*

Functions for creating power series.

Here is the power series expansion for exp(*x*) about the point $x = 0$ to order x^4.

$In[1]:=$ **Series[Exp[x], {x, 0, 4}]**

$Out[1]= 1 + x + \dfrac{x^2}{2} + \dfrac{x^3}{6} + \dfrac{x^4}{24} + O[x]^5$

Here is the series expansion of exp(*x*) about the point $x = 1$.

$In[2]:=$ **Series[Exp[x], {x, 1, 4}]**

$Out[2]= E + E (x - 1) + \dfrac{1}{2} E (x - 1)^2 + \dfrac{1}{6} E (x - 1)^3 +$

$\dfrac{1}{24} E (x - 1)^4 + O[x - 1]^5$

If *Mathematica* does not know the series expansion of a particular function, it writes the result symbolically in terms of derivatives.

$In[3]:=$ **Series[f[x], {x, 0, 3}]**

$Out[3]= f[0] + f'[0] x + \dfrac{1}{2} f''[0] x^2 + \dfrac{1}{6} f^{(3)}[0] x^3 + O[x]^4$

In mathematical terms, Series can be viewed as a way of constructing Taylor series for functions.

The standard formula for the Taylor series expansion about the point $x = x_0$ of a function $g(x)$ with k^{th} derivative $g^{(k)}(x)$ is $g(x) = \sum_{k=0}^{\infty} g^{(k)}(x_0) \frac{(x-x_0)^k}{k!}$. Whenever this formula applies, it gives the same results as Series. (For common functions, Series nevertheless internally uses somewhat more efficient algorithms.)

Series can also generate some power series that involve fractional and negative powers, not directly covered by the standard Taylor series formula.

Here is a power series that contains negative powers of *x*.

$In[4]:=$ **Series[Exp[x]/x^2, {x, 0, 4}]**

$Out[4]= \dfrac{1}{x^2} + \dfrac{1}{x} + \dfrac{1}{2} + \dfrac{x}{6} + \dfrac{x^2}{24} + \dfrac{x^3}{120} + \dfrac{x^4}{720} + O[x]^5$

Here is a power series involving fractional powers of *x*.

$In[5]:=$ **Series[Exp[Sqrt[x]], {x, 0, 2}]**

$Out[5]= 1 + \sqrt{x} + \dfrac{x}{2} + \dfrac{1}{6} x^{3/2} + \dfrac{x^2}{24} + O[x]^{5/2}$

Series can also handle series that involve logarithmic terms.	$In[6]:=$ **Series[Exp[2x] Log[x], {x, 0, 2}]**
	$Out[6]=$ $Log[x] + (2 Log[x]) x + (2 Log[x]) x^2 + O[x]^3$

There are, of course, mathematical functions for which no standard power series exist. *Mathematica* recognizes many such cases.

Series sees that $\exp(\frac{1}{x})$ has an essential singularity at $x = 0$, and does not produce a power series.	$In[7]:=$ **Series[Exp[1/x], {x, 0, 2}]**

Series::esss:

Essential singularity encountered in $Exp[\frac{1}{x} + O[x]^3]$.

$Out[7]=$ $Series\left[E^{\frac{1}{x}}, \{x, 0, 2\}\right]$

Series can nevertheless give you the power series for $\exp(\frac{1}{x})$ about the point $x = \infty$.	$In[8]:=$ **Series[Exp[1/x], {x, Infinity, 3}]**
	$Out[8]=$ $1 + \frac{1}{x} + \frac{1}{2}\left(\frac{1}{x}\right)^2 + \frac{1}{6}\left(\frac{1}{x}\right)^3 + O\left[\frac{1}{x}\right]^4$

Especially when negative powers occur, there is some subtlety in exactly how many terms of a particular power series the function **Series** will generate.

One way to understand what happens is to think of the analogy between power series taken to a certain order, and real numbers taken to a certain precision. Power series are "approximate formulas" in much the same sense as finite-precision real numbers are approximate numbers.

The procedure that **Series** follows in constructing a power series is largely analogous to the procedure that **N** follows in constructing a real-number approximation. Both functions effectively start by replacing the smallest pieces of your expression by finite-order, or finite-precision, approximations, and then evaluating the resulting expression. If there are, for example, cancellations, this procedure may give a final result whose order or precision is less than the order or precision that you originally asked for. Like **N**, however, **Series** has some ability to retry its computations so as to get results to the order you ask for. In cases where it does not succeed, you can usually still get results to a particular order by asking for a higher order than you need.

Series compensates for cancellations in this computation, and succeeds in giving you a result to order x^3.	$In[9]:=$ **Series[Sin[x]/x^2, {x, 0, 3}]**
	$Out[9]=$ $\frac{1}{x} - \frac{x}{6} + \frac{x^3}{120} + O[x]^4$

When you make a power series expansion in a variable x, *Mathematica* assumes that all objects that do not explicitly contain x are in fact independent of x. **Series** thus does partial derivatives (effectively using D) to build up Taylor series.

Both a and n are assumed to be independent of x.	$In[10]:=$ **Series[(a + x)^n , {x, 0, 2}]**
	$Out[10]=$ $a^n + (a^{-1+n} n) x + \frac{1}{2} (a^{-2+n} (-1 + n) n) x^2 + O[x]^3$

a[x] is now given as an explicit function of x.

$In[11]:=$ **Series[(a[x] + x)^n, {x, 0, 2}]**

$Out[11]=$ $a[0]^n + \left(n\,a[0]^{-1+n}\,(1 + a'[0])\right) x +$

$$\left(\frac{1}{2}\,(-1 + n)\,n\,a[0]^{-2+n}\,(1 + a'[0])^2 + \frac{1}{2}\,n\,a[0]^{-1+n}\,a''[0]\right)$$

$$x^2 + O[x]^3$$

You can use Series to generate power series in a sequence of different variables. Series works like Integrate, Sum and so on, and expands first with respect to the last variable you specify.

Series performs a series expansion successively with respect to each variable. The result in this case is a series in x, whose coefficients are series in y.

$In[12]:=$ **Series[Exp[x y], {x, 0, 3}, {y, 0, 3}]**

$Out[12]=$ $1 + \left(y + O[y]^4\right) x + \left(\frac{y^2}{2} + O[y]^4\right) x^2 +$

$$\left(\frac{y^3}{6} + O[y]^4\right) x^3 + O[x]^4$$

■ 3.6.2 Advanced Topic: The Representation of Power Series

Power series are represented in *Mathematica* as SeriesData objects.

The power series is printed out as a sum of terms, ending with O[x] raised to a power.

$In[1]:=$ **Series[Cos[x], {x, 0, 4}]**

$Out[1]=$ $1 - \dfrac{x^2}{2} + \dfrac{x^4}{24} + O[x]^5$

Internally, however, the series is stored as a SeriesData object.

$In[2]:=$ **InputForm[%]**

$Out[2]//InputForm=$ SeriesData[x, 0, {1, 0, -1/2, 0, 1/24}, 0, 5, 1]

By using SeriesData objects, rather than ordinary expressions, to represent power series, *Mathematica* can keep track of the order and expansion point, and do operations on the power series appropriately. You should not normally need to know the internal structure of SeriesData objects.

You can recognize a power series that is printed out in standard output form by the presence of an O[x] term. This term mimics the standard mathematical notation $O(x)$, and represents omitted terms of order x. For various reasons of consistency, *Mathematica* uses the notation O[x]^n for omitted terms of order x^n, corresponding to the mathematical notation $O(x)^n$, rather than the slightly more familiar, though equivalent, form $O(x^n)$.

Any time that an object like O[x] appears in a sum of terms, *Mathematica* will in fact convert the whole sum into a power series.

The presence of O[x] makes *Mathematica* convert the whole sum to a power series.

$In[3]:=$ **a x + Exp[x] + O[x]^3**

$Out[3]=$ $1 + (1 + a) x + \dfrac{x^2}{2} + O[x]^3$

■ 3.6.3 Operations on Power Series

Mathematica allows you to perform many operations on power series. In all cases, *Mathematica* gives results only to as many terms as can be justified from the accuracy of your input.

Here is a power series accurate to fourth order in *x*.

In[1]:= **Series[Exp[x], {x, 0, 4}]**

$Out[1]= 1 + x + \frac{x^2}{2} + \frac{x^3}{6} + \frac{x^4}{24} + O[x]^5$

When you square the power series, you get another power series, also accurate to fourth order.

In[2]:= **%^2**

$Out[2]= 1 + 2x + 2x^2 + \frac{4x^3}{3} + \frac{2x^4}{3} + O[x]^5$

Taking the logarithm gives you the result 2x, but only to order x^4.

In[3]:= **Log[%]**

$Out[3]= 2x + O[x]^5$

Mathematica keeps track of the orders of power series in much the same way as it keeps track of the precision of approximate real numbers. Just as with numerical calculations, there are operations on power series which can increase, or decrease, the precision (or order) of your results.

Here is a power series accurate to order x^10.

In[4]:= **Series[Cos[x], {x, 0, 10}]**

$Out[4]= 1 - \frac{x^2}{2} + \frac{x^4}{24} - \frac{x^6}{720} + \frac{x^8}{40320} - \frac{x^{10}}{3628800} + O[x]^{11}$

This gives a power series that is accurate only to order x^6.

In[5]:= **1 / (1 - %)**

$Out[5]= \frac{2}{x^2} + \frac{1}{6} + \frac{x^2}{120} + \frac{x^4}{3024} + \frac{x^6}{86400} + O[x]^7$

Mathematica also allows you to do calculus with power series.

Here is a power series for tan(*x*).

In[6]:= **Series[Tan[x], {x, 0, 10}]**

$Out[6]= x + \frac{x^3}{3} + \frac{2x^5}{15} + \frac{17x^7}{315} + \frac{62x^9}{2835} + O[x]^{11}$

Here is its derivative with respect to x.

In[7]:= **D[%, x]**

$Out[7]= 1 + x^2 + \frac{2x^4}{3} + \frac{17x^6}{45} + \frac{62x^8}{315} + O[x]^{10}$

Integrating with respect to x gives back the original power series.

In[8]:= **Integrate[%, x]**

$Out[8]= x + \frac{x^3}{3} + \frac{2x^5}{15} + \frac{17x^7}{315} + \frac{62x^9}{2835} + O[x]^{11}$

When you perform an operation that involves both a normal expression and a power series, *Mathematica* "absorbs" the normal expression into the power series whenever possible.

The 1 is automatically absorbed into the power series.

In[9]:= **1 + Series[Exp[x], {x, 0, 4}]**

$Out[9]= 2 + x + \frac{x^2}{2} + \frac{x^3}{6} + \frac{x^4}{24} + O[x]^5$

The x^2 is also absorbed into the power series.

$In[10]:= \% + x^2$

$Out[10]= 2 + x + \dfrac{3x^2}{2} + \dfrac{x^3}{6} + \dfrac{x^4}{24} + O[x]^5$

If you add Sin[x], *Mathematica* generates the appropriate power series for Sin[x], and combines it with the power series you have.

$In[11]:= \% + Sin[x]$

$Out[11]= 2 + 2x + \dfrac{3x^2}{2} + \dfrac{x^4}{24} + O[x]^5$

Mathematica also absorbs expressions that multiply power series. The symbol a is assumed to be independent of x.

$In[12]:= (a + x) \%^2$

$Out[12]= 4a + (4 + 8a)x + (8 + 10a)x^2 + (10 + 6a)x^3 +$
$\left(6 + \dfrac{29a}{12}\right)x^4 + O[x]^5$

Mathematica knows how to apply a wide variety of functions to power series. However, if you apply an arbitrary function to a power series, it is impossible for *Mathematica* to give you anything but a symbolic result.

Mathematica does not know how to apply the function f to a power series, so it just leaves the symbolic result.

$In[13]:= f[Series[Exp[x], \{x, 0, 3\}]]$

$Out[13]= f\left[1 + x + \dfrac{x^2}{2} + \dfrac{x^3}{6} + O[x]^4\right]$

■ 3.6.4 Advanced Topic: Composition and Inversion of Power Series

When you manipulate power series, it is sometimes convenient to think of the series as representing *functions*, which you can, for example, compose or invert.

+ ComposeSeries[*series*$_1$, *series*$_2$, ...]	
	compose power series
InverseSeries[*series*, *x*]	invert a power series

Composition and inversion of power series.

Here is the power series for exp(x) to order x^5.

$In[1]:= Series[Exp[x], \{x, 0, 5\}]$

$Out[1]= 1 + x + \dfrac{x^2}{2} + \dfrac{x^3}{6} + \dfrac{x^4}{24} + \dfrac{x^5}{120} + O[x]^6$

This replaces the variable x in the power series for exp(x) by a power series for sin(x).

$In[2]:= ComposeSeries[\%, Series[Sin[x], \{x, 0, 5\}]]$

$Out[2]= 1 + x + \dfrac{x^2}{2} - \dfrac{x^4}{8} - \dfrac{x^5}{15} + O[x]^6$

The result is the power series for exp(sin(x)).

$In[3]:= Series[Exp[Sin[x]], \{x, 0, 5\}]$

$Out[3]= 1 + x + \dfrac{x^2}{2} - \dfrac{x^4}{8} - \dfrac{x^5}{15} + O[x]^6$

The same is true here.	*In[5]:=* **Limit[(1 + 2 x) ^ (1/x), x -> 0]**
	Out[5]= E^2
The value of `Sign[x]` at *x*=0 is 0.	*In[6]:=* **Sign[0]**
	Out[6]= 0
Its *limit*, however, is 1. The limit is by default taken from above.	*In[7]:=* **Limit[Sign[x], x -> 0]**
	Out[7]= 1

Not all functions have definite limits at particular points. For example, the function $\sin(1/x)$ oscillates infinitely often near $x = 0$, so it has no definite limit there. Nevertheless, at least so long as x remains real, the values of the function near $x = 0$ always lie between -1 and 1. Limit represents values with bounded variation using `Interval` objects. In general, `Interval[{xmin, xmax}]` represents an uncertain value which lies somewhere in the interval *xmin* to *xmax*.

Limit returns an `Interval` object, representing the range of possible values of $\sin(1/x)$ near its essential singularity at $x = 0$.	*In[8]:=* **Limit[Sin[1/x], x -> 0]**
	Out[8]= Interval[{-1, 1}]
Mathematica can do arithmetic with `Interval` objects.	*In[9]:=* **(1 + %)^3**
	Out[9]= Interval[{0, 8}]
Mathematica represents this limit symbolically in terms of an `Interval` object.	*In[10]:=* **Limit[Exp[a Sin[x]], x -> Infinity]**
	Out[10]= $E^{a \, \text{Interval}[\{-1,1\}]}$

Some functions may have different limits at particular points, depending on the direction from which you approach those points. You can use the `Direction` option for `Limit` to specify the direction you want.

`Limit[`*expr*`, `*x*` -> `x_0`, Direction -> 1]`	find the limit as x approaches x_0 from below
`Limit[`*expr*`, `*x*` -> `x_0`, Direction -> -1]`	find the limit as x approaches x_0 from above

Directional limits.

The function $1/x$ has a different limiting value at $x = 0$, depending on whether you approach from above or below.

In[11]:= **Plot[1/x, {x, -1, 1}]**

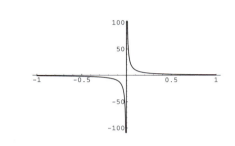

Approaching from below gives a limiting value of $-\infty$.

In[12]:= **Limit[1/x, x -> 0, Direction -> 1]**
Out[12]= $-\infty$

Approaching from above gives a limiting value of ∞.

In[13]:= **Limit[1/x, x -> 0, Direction -> -1]**
Out[13]= ∞

Limit makes no assumptions about functions like f[x] about which it does not have definite knowledge. As a result, Limit remains unevaluated in most cases involving symbolic functions.

Limit has no definite knowledge about f, so it leaves this limit unevaluated.

In[14]:= **Limit[x f[x], x -> 0]**
Out[14]= Limit[x f[x], x → 0]

■ 3.6.9 Residues

Limit[*expr*, x -> x_0] tells you what the value of *expr* is when x tends to x_0. When this value is infinite, it is often useful instead to know the *residue* of *expr* when x equals x_0. The residue is given by the coefficient of $(x - x_0)^{-1}$ in the power series expansion of *expr* about the point x_0.

Residue[*expr*, {x, x_0}]	the residue of *expr* when x equals x_0

Computing residues.

The residue here is equal to 1.

In[1]:= **Residue[1/x, {x, 0}]**
Out[1]= 1

The residue here is zero.

In[2]:= **Residue[1/x^2, {x, 0}]**
Out[2]= 0

3.7 Linear Algebra

■ 3.7.1 Constructing Matrices

Table[*f*, {*i*, *m*}, {*j*, *n*}]	build an $m \times n$ matrix where f is a function of i and j that gives the value of i, jth entry
Array[*f*, {*m*, *n*}]	build an $m \times n$ matrix whose i, jth entry is $f[i, j]$
DiagonalMatrix[*list*]	generate a diagonal matrix with the elements of *list* on the diagonal
IdentityMatrix[*n*]	generate an $n \times n$ identity matrix

Functions for constructing matrices.

This generates a 2×2 matrix whose i, jth entry is a[i, j].

```
In[1]:= Table[a[i, j], {i, 2}, {j, 2}]
Out[1]= {{a[1, 1], a[1, 2]}, {a[2, 1], a[2, 2]}}
```

Here is another way to produce the same matrix.

```
In[2]:= Array[a, {2, 2}]
Out[2]= {{a[1, 1], a[1, 2]}, {a[2, 1], a[2, 2]}}
```

DiagonalMatrix makes a matrix with zeros everywhere except on the leading diagonal.

```
In[3]:= DiagonalMatrix[{a, b, c}]
Out[3]= {{a, 0, 0}, {0, b, 0}, {0, 0, c}}
```

IdentityMatrix[*n*] produces an $n \times n$ identity matrix.

```
In[4]:= IdentityMatrix[3]
Out[4]= {{1, 0, 0}, {0, 1, 0}, {0, 0, 1}}
```

Of the functions for constructing matrices mentioned above, Table is the most general. You can use Table to produce many kinds of matrices.

Table[0, {*m*}, {*n*}]	a zero matrix
Table[Random[ ], {*m*}, {*n*}]	a matrix with random numerical entries
Table[If[*i* >= *j*, 1, 0], {*i*, *m*}, {*j*, *n*}]	a lower-triangular matrix
Table[If[*i* <= *j*, 1, 0], {*i*, *m*}, {*j*, *n*}]	an upper-triangular matrix
Table[Switch[*i*–*j*,–1,a[[*i*]],0,b[[*i*]],1,c[[*i*–1]],_,0], {*i*, *m*}, {*j*, *n*}]	a tridiagonal matrix

Some special types of matrices.

Table evaluates Random[ ] separately for each element, to give a different pseudorandom number in each case.

```
In[5]:= Table[Random[ ], {2}, {2}]
Out[5]= {{0.0560708, 0.6303}, {0.359894, 0.871377}}
```

This gives a tridiagonal matrix.

```
In[6]:= Table[Switch[i-j, -1, a, 0, b, 1, c, _, 0],
             {i, 5}, {j, 5}]
Out[6]= {{b, a, 0, 0, 0}, {c, b, a, 0, 0}, {0, c, b, a, 0},
        {0, 0, c, b, a}, {0, 0, 0, c, b}}
```

MatrixForm prints the matrix in a two-dimensional array, and makes the structure in this case clearer.

```
In[7]:= MatrixForm[%]
```

$$Out[7]//MatrixForm= \begin{pmatrix} b & a & 0 & 0 & 0 \\ c & b & a & 0 & 0 \\ 0 & c & b & a & 0 \\ 0 & 0 & c & b & a \\ 0 & 0 & 0 & c & b \end{pmatrix}$$

■ 3.7.2 Getting Pieces of Matrices

$m[[i, j]]$	the i, j^{th} entry
$m[[i]]$	the ith row
Transpose[m] [[i]] or Map[#[[i]]&, m]	the ith column
$m[[\{i_1, \ldots , i_r\}, \{j_1, \ldots , j_s\}]]$	the $r \times s$ submatrix of m with elements having row indices i_k and column indices j_k
$m[[\text{Range}[i_0, i_1], \text{Range}[j_0, j_1]]]$	a submatrix with elements having row and column indices respectively in the ranges i_0 through i_1 and j_0 through j_1

Ways to get pieces of matrices.

Matrices in *Mathematica* are represented as lists of lists. You can use all the standard *Mathematica* list-manipulation operations on matrices.

Here is a sample 3×3 matrix.

```
In[1]:= t = Array[a, {3, 3}]
Out[1]= {{a[1, 1], a[1, 2], a[1, 3]},
        {a[2, 1], a[2, 2], a[2, 3]},
        {a[3, 1], a[3, 2], a[3, 3]}}
```

This picks out the second row of the matrix.

```
In[2]:= t[[2]]
Out[2]= {a[2, 1], a[2, 2], a[2, 3]}
```

Here is the second column of the matrix.	*In[3]:=* `Map[#[[2]]&, t]` *Out[3]=* {a[1, 2], a[2, 2], a[3, 2]}
This picks out a submatrix.	*In[4]:=* `t[[ {1, 2}, {2, 3} ]]` *Out[4]=* {{a[1, 2], a[1, 3]}, {a[2, 2], a[2, 3]}}
Here is another way to specify the submatrix, convenient when you deal with bigger matrices.	*In[5]:=* `t[[ Range[1,2], Range[2,3] ]]` *Out[5]=* {{a[1, 2], a[1, 3]}, {a[2, 2], a[2, 3]}}

■ 3.7.3 Scalars, Vectors and Matrices

Mathematica represents matrices and vectors using lists. Anything that is not a list *Mathematica* considers as a scalar.

A vector in *Mathematica* consists of a list of scalars. A matrix consists of a list of vectors, representing each of its rows. In order to be a valid matrix, all the rows must be the same length, so that the elements of the matrix effectively form a rectangular array.

`VectorQ[`*expr*`]`	give `True` if *expr* has the form of a vector, and `False` otherwise
`MatrixQ[`*expr*`]`	give `True` if *expr* has the form of a matrix, and `False` otherwise
`Dimensions[`*expr*`]`	a list of the dimensions of a vector or matrix

Functions for testing the structure of vectors and matrices.

The list {a, b, c} has the form of a vector.	*In[1]:=* `VectorQ[ {a, b, c} ]` *Out[1]=* True
Anything that is not manifestly a list is treated as a scalar, so applying `VectorQ` gives False.	*In[2]:=* `VectorQ[ x + y ]` *Out[2]=* False
This is a 2×3 matrix.	*In[3]:=* `Dimensions[ {{a, b, c}, {ap, bp, cp}} ]` *Out[3]=* {2, 3}
For a vector, `Dimensions` gives a list with a single element equal to the result from `Length`.	*In[4]:=* `Dimensions[ {a, b, c} ]` *Out[4]=* {3}
This object does not count as a matrix because its rows are of different lengths.	*In[5]:=* `MatrixQ[ {{a, b, c}, {ap, bp}} ]` *Out[5]=* False

■ 3.7.4 Operations on Scalars, Vectors and Matrices

Most mathematical functions in *Mathematica* are set up to apply themselves separately to each element in a list. This is true in particular of all functions that carry the attribute `Listable`.

A consequence is that most mathematical functions are applied element by element to matrices and vectors.

The Log applies itself separately to each element in the vector.	*In[1]:=* **Log[{a, b, c}]** *Out[1]=* {Log[a], Log[b], Log[c]}
The same is true for a matrix, or, for that matter, for any nested list.	*In[2]:=* **Log[{{a, b}, {c, d}}]** *Out[2]=* {{Log[a], Log[b]}, {Log[c], Log[d]}}
The differentiation function D also applies separately to each element in a list.	*In[3]:=* **D[{x, x^2, x^3}, x]** *Out[3]=* {1, 2x, 3x^2}
The sum of two vectors is carried out element by element.	*In[4]:=* **{a, b} + {ap, bp}** *Out[4]=* {a + ap, b + bp}

If you try to add two vectors with different lengths, you get an error.

In[5]:= **{a, b, c} + {ap, bp}**

Thread::tdlen:
    Objects of unequal length in {a, b, c} + {ap, bp}
       cannot be combined.

Out[5]= {ap, bp} + {a, b, c}

This adds the scalar 1 to each element of the vector.	*In[6]:=* **1 + {a, b}** *Out[6]=* {1 + a, 1 + b}
Any object that is not manifestly a list is treated as a scalar. Here c is treated as a scalar, and added separately to each element in the vector.	*In[7]:=* **{a, b} + c** *Out[7]=* {a + c, b + c}
This multiplies each element in the vector by the scalar k.	*In[8]:=* **k {a, b}** *Out[8]=* {ak, bk}

It is important to realize that *Mathematica* treats an object as a vector in a particular operation only if the object is explicitly a list at the time when the operation is done. If the object is not explicitly a list, *Mathematica* always treats it as a scalar. This means that you can get different results, depending on whether you assign a particular object to be a list before or after you do a particular operation.

The object p is treated as a scalar, and added separately to each element in the vector.	*In[9]:=* **{a, b} + p** *Out[9]=* {a + p, b + p}
This is what happens if you now replace p by the list {c, d}.	*In[10]:=* **% /. p -> {c, d}** *Out[10]=* {{a + c, a + d}, {b + c, b + d}}

You would have got a different result if you had replaced p by {c, d} before you did the first operation.

```
In[11]:= {a, b} + {c, d}
Out[11]= {a + c, b + d}
```

■ 3.7.5 Multiplying Vectors and Matrices

$c\,v$, $c\,m$, etc.	multiply each element by a scalar
$v.v$, $v.m$, $m.v$, $m.m$, etc.	vector and matrix multiplication
Outer[Times, t, u]	outer product

Different kinds of vector and matrix multiplication.

This multiplies each element of the vector by the scalar k.

```
In[1]:= k {a, b, c}
Out[1]= {ak, bk, ck}
```

The "dot" operator gives the scalar product of two vectors.

```
In[2]:= {a, b, c} . {ap, bp, cp}
Out[2]= a ap + b bp + c cp
```

You can also use dot to multiply a matrix by a vector.

```
In[3]:= {{a, b}, {c, d}} . {x, y}
Out[3]= {a x + b y, c x + d y}
```

Dot is also the notation for matrix multiplication in *Mathematica*.

```
In[4]:= {{a, b}, {c, d}} . {{1, 2}, {3, 4}}
Out[4]= {{a + 3 b, 2 a + 4 b}, {c + 3 d, 2 c + 4 d}}
```

It is important to realize that you can use "dot" for both left- and right-multiplication of vectors by matrices. *Mathematica* makes no distinction between "row" and "column" vectors. Dot carries out whatever operation is possible. (In formal terms, $a.b$ contracts the last index of the tensor a with the first index of b.)

Here are definitions for a matrix m and a vector v.

```
In[5]:= m = {{a, b}, {c, d}} ;  v = {x, y}
Out[5]= {x, y}
```

This left-multiplies the vector v by m. The object v is effectively treated as a column vector in this case.

```
In[6]:= m . v
Out[6]= {a x + b y, c x + d y}
```

You can also use dot to right-multiply v by m. Now v is effectively treated as a row vector.

```
In[7]:= v . m
Out[7]= {a x + c y, b x + d y}
```

You can multiply m by v on both sides, to get a scalar.

```
In[8]:= v . m . v
Out[8]= x (a x + c y) + y (b x + d y)
```

For some purposes, you may need to represent vectors and matrices symbolically, without explicitly giving their elements. You can use dot to represent multiplication of such symbolic objects.

Dot effectively acts here as a non-commutative form of multiplication.	*In[9]:=* **a . b . a** *Out[9]=* a . b . a
It is, nevertheless, associative.	*In[10]:=* **(a . b) . (a . b)** *Out[10]=* a . b . a . b
Dot products of sums are not automatically expanded out.	*In[11]:=* **(a + b) . c . (d + e)** *Out[11]=* (a + b) . c . (d + e)
You can apply the distributive law in this case using the function Distribute, as discussed on page 253.	*In[12]:=* **Distribute[%]** *Out[12]=* a . c . d + a . c . e + b . c . d + b . c . e

The "dot" operator gives "inner products" of vectors, matrices, and so on. In more advanced calculations, you may also need to construct outer or Kronecker products of vectors and matrices. You can use the general function Outer to do this.

The outer product of two vectors is a matrix.	*In[13]:=* **Outer[Times, {a, b}, {c, d}]** *Out[13]=* {{a c, a d}, {b c, b d}}
The outer product of a matrix and a vector is a rank three tensor.	*In[14]:=* **Outer[Times, {{1, 2}, {3, 4}}, {x, y, z}]** *Out[14]=* {{{x, y, z}, {2x, 2y, 2z}}, {{3x, 3y, 3z}, {4x, 4y, 4z}}}

Outer products will be discussed in more detail in Section 3.7.11.

■ 3.7.6 Matrix Inversion

Inverse[m]	find the inverse of a square matrix

Matrix inversion.

Here is a simple 2×2 matrix.	*In[1]:=* **m = {{a, b}, {c, d}}** *Out[1]=* {{a, b}, {c, d}}
This gives the inverse of m. In producing this formula, *Mathematica* implicitly assumes that the determinant a d − b c is non-zero.	*In[2]:=* **Inverse[m]** *Out[2]=* $\left\{\left\{\dfrac{d}{-bc+ad}, -\dfrac{b}{-bc+ad}\right\}, \left\{-\dfrac{c}{-bc+ad}, \dfrac{a}{-bc+ad}\right\}\right\}$
Multiplying the inverse by the original matrix should give the identity matrix.	*In[3]:=* **% . m** *Out[3]=* $\left\{\left\{-\dfrac{bc}{-bc+ad} + \dfrac{ad}{-bc+ad}, 0\right\},\right.$ $\left.\left\{0, -\dfrac{bc}{-bc+ad} + \dfrac{ad}{-bc+ad}\right\}\right\}$

You have to use Together to clear the denominators, and get back a standard identity matrix.

```
In[4]:= Together[ % ]
Out[4]= {{1, 0}, {0, 1}}
```

Here is a matrix of rational numbers.

```
In[5]:= hb = Table[1/(i + j), {i, 4}, {j, 4}]
```

$$Out[5]= \left\{\left\{\frac{1}{2}, \frac{1}{3}, \frac{1}{4}, \frac{1}{5}\right\}, \left\{\frac{1}{3}, \frac{1}{4}, \frac{1}{5}, \frac{1}{6}\right\}, \left\{\frac{1}{4}, \frac{1}{5}, \frac{1}{6}, \frac{1}{7}\right\}, \left\{\frac{1}{5}, \frac{1}{6}, \frac{1}{7}, \frac{1}{8}\right\}\right\}$$

Mathematica finds the exact inverse of the matrix.

```
In[6]:= Inverse[hb]
Out[6]= {{200, -1200, 2100, -1120},
         {-1200, 8100, -15120, 8400},
         {2100, -15120, 29400, -16800},
         {-1120, 8400, -16800, 9800}}
```

Multiplying by the original matrix gives the identity matrix.

```
In[7]:= % . hb
Out[7]= {{1, 0, 0, 0}, {0, 1, 0, 0}, {0, 0, 1, 0},
         {0, 0, 0, 1}}
```

If you try to invert a singular matrix, *Mathematica* prints a warning message, and returns the inverse undone.

```
In[8]:= Inverse[ {{1, 2}, {1, 2}} ]
Inverse::sing: Matrix {{1, 2}, {1, 2}} is singular.
Out[8]= Inverse[{{1, 2}, {1, 2}}]
```

If you give a matrix with exact symbolic or numerical entries, *Mathematica* gives the exact inverse. If, on the other hand, some of the entries in your matrix are approximate real numbers, then *Mathematica* finds an approximate numerical result.

Here is a matrix containing approximate real numbers.

```
In[9]:= m = {{1.2, 5.7}, {4.2, 5.6}}
Out[9]= {{1.2, 5.7}, {4.2, 5.6}}
```

This finds the numerical inverse.

```
In[10]:= Inverse[ % ]
Out[10]= {{-0.325203, 0.33101}, {0.243902, -0.0696864}}
```

Multiplying by the original matrix gives you an identity matrix with small numerical errors.

```
In[11]:= % . m
```

$$Out[11]= \{\{1., 2.22045 \times 10^{-16}\}, \{0., 1.\}\}$$

You can get rid of the small off-diagonal terms using Chop.

```
In[12]:= Chop[ % ]
Out[12]= {{1., 0}, {0, 1.}}
```

When you try to invert a matrix with exact numerical entries, *Mathematica* can always tell whether or not the matrix is singular. When you invert an approximate numerical matrix, *Mathematica* can usually not tell for certain whether or not the matrix is singular: all it can tell is for example that the determinant is small compared to the entries of the matrix. When *Mathematica* suspects that you are trying to invert a singular numerical matrix, it prints a warning.

Mathematica prints a warning if you invert a numerical matrix that it suspects is singular.

```
In[13]:= Inverse[ {{1., 2.}, {1., 2.}} ]

Inverse::sing: Matrix {{1., 2.}, {1., 2.}} is singular.

Out[13]= Inverse[{{1., 2.}, {1., 2.}}]
```

If you work with high-precision approximate numbers, *Mathematica* will keep track of the precision of matrix inverses that you generate.

This generates a 6×6 numerical matrix with entries of 50-digit precision.

```
In[14]:= m = N [ Table[ GCD[i, j] + 1, {i, 6}, {j, 6} ], 50 ] ;
```

This takes the matrix, multiplies it by its inverse, and shows the first row of the result.

```
In[15]:= (m . Inverse[m]) [[1]]

Out[15]= {1., 0. × 10^{-46}, 0. × 10^{-47}, 0. × 10^{-57},
          0. × 10^{-58}, 0. × 10^{-47}}
```

This generates a 50-digit numerical approximation to a 6×6 Hilbert matrix. Hilbert matrices are notoriously hard to invert numerically.

```
In[16]:= m = N[Table[1/(i + j - 1), {i, 6}, {j, 6}], 50] ;
```

The result is still correct, but the zeros now have lower accuracy.

```
In[17]:= (m . Inverse[m]) [[1]]

Out[17]= {1., 0. × 10^{-37}, 0. × 10^{-37}, 0. × 10^{-36},
          0. × 10^{-36}, 0. × 10^{-36}}
```

Inverse works only on square matrices. Section 3.7.10 discusses the function **PseudoInverse**, which can also be used with non-square matrices.

■ 3.7.7 Basic Matrix Operations

Transpose[m]	transpose
Inverse[m]	matrix inverse
Det[m]	determinant
Minors[m, k]	a matrix of the $k \times k$ minors of m
Sum[m[[i, i]], {i, Length[m]}]	
	trace

Some basic matrix operations.

Transposing a matrix interchanges the rows and columns in the matrix. If you transpose an $m \times n$ matrix, you get an $n \times m$ matrix as the result.

Transposing a 2×3 matrix gives a 3×2 result.

```
In[1]:= Transpose[ {{a, b, c}, {ap, bp, cp}} ]

Out[1]= {{a, ap}, {b, bp}, {c, cp}}
```

Det[*m*] gives the determinant of a square matrix *m*. Minors[*m*, *k*] gives a matrix of the determinants of all the $k \times k$ submatrices of *m*. You can apply Minors to rectangular, as well as square, matrices.

Here is the determinant of a simple 2×2 matrix.

```
In[2]:= Det[ {{a, b}, {c, d}} ]
Out[2]= -b c + a d
```

This generates a 3×3 matrix, whose i, j^{th} entry is a[*i*, *j*].

```
In[3]:= m = Array[a, {3, 3}]
Out[3]= {{a[1, 1], a[1, 2], a[1, 3]},
         {a[2, 1], a[2, 2], a[2, 3]},
         {a[3, 1], a[3, 2], a[3, 3]}}
```

Here is the determinant of m.

```
In[4]:= Det[ m ]
Out[4]= -a[1, 3] a[2, 2] a[3, 1] + a[1, 2] a[2, 3] a[3, 1] +
        a[1, 3] a[2, 1] a[3, 2] - a[1, 1] a[2, 3] a[3, 2] -
        a[1, 2] a[2, 1] a[3, 3] + a[1, 1] a[2, 2] a[3, 3]
```

This gives the matrix of all 2×2 minors of m.

```
In[5]:= Minors[m, 2]
Out[5]= {{-a[1, 2] a[2, 1] + a[1, 1] a[2, 2],
          -a[1, 3] a[2, 1] + a[1, 1] a[2, 3],
          -a[1, 3] a[2, 2] + a[1, 2] a[2, 3]},
         {-a[1, 2] a[3, 1] + a[1, 1] a[3, 2],
          -a[1, 3] a[3, 1] + a[1, 1] a[3, 3],
          -a[1, 3] a[3, 2] + a[1, 2] a[3, 3]},
         {-a[2, 2] a[3, 1] + a[2, 1] a[3, 2],
          -a[2, 3] a[3, 1] + a[2, 1] a[3, 3],
          -a[2, 3] a[3, 2] + a[2, 2] a[3, 3]}}
```

You can use Det to find the characteristic polynomial for a matrix. Section 3.7.9 discusses ways to find eigenvalues and eigenvectors directly.

Here is a 3×3 matrix.

```
In[6]:= m = Table[ 1/(i + j), {i, 3}, {j, 3} ]
```

$$Out[6]= \left\{\left\{\frac{1}{2}, \frac{1}{3}, \frac{1}{4}\right\}, \left\{\frac{1}{3}, \frac{1}{4}, \frac{1}{5}\right\}, \left\{\frac{1}{4}, \frac{1}{5}, \frac{1}{6}\right\}\right\}$$

Following precisely the standard mathematical definition, this gives the characteristic polynomial for m.

```
In[7]:= Det[ m - x IdentityMatrix[3] ]
```

$$Out[7]= \frac{1}{43200} - \frac{131 x}{3600} + \frac{11 x^2}{12} - x^3$$

There are many other operations on matrices that can be built up from standard *Mathematica* functions. One example is the *trace* or *spur* of a matrix, given by the sum of the terms on the leading diagonal.

Here is a simple 2×2 matrix.

```
In[8]:= m = {{a, b}, {c, d}}
Out[8]= {{a, b}, {c, d}}
```

You can get the trace of the matrix by explicitly constructing a sum of the elements on its leading diagonal.

```
In[9]:= Sum[ m[[i, i]], {i, 2} ]
Out[9]= a + d
```

`MatrixPower[`*m*`, `*n*`]`	n^{th} matrix power
`MatrixExp[`*m*`]`	matrix exponential

Powers and exponentials of matrices.

Here is a 2×2 matrix.	*In[10]:=* `m = {{0.4, 0.6}, {0.525, 0.475}}`
	Out[10]= {{0.4, 0.6}, {0.525, 0.475}}
This gives the third matrix power of m.	*In[11]:=* `MatrixPower[m, 3]`
	Out[11]= {{0.465625, 0.534375}, {0.467578, 0.532422}}
It is equivalent to multiplying three copies of the matrix.	*In[12]:=* `m . m . m`
	Out[12]= {{0.465625, 0.534375}, {0.467578, 0.532422}}
Here is the millionth matrix power.	*In[13]:=* `MatrixPower[m, 10^6]`
	Out[13]= {{0.466667, 0.533333}, {0.466667, 0.533333}}
This gives the matrix exponential of m.	*In[14]:=* `MatrixExp[m]`
	Out[14]= {{1.7392, 0.979085}, {0.8567, 1.86158}}
Here is an approximation to the exponential of m, based on a power series approximation.	*In[15]:=* `Sum[MatrixPower[m, i]/i!, {i, 0, 5}]`
	Out[15]= {{1.73844, 0.978224}, {0.855946, 1.86072}}

■ 3.7.8 Solving Linear Systems

Many calculations involve solving systems of linear equations. In many cases, you will find it convenient to write down the equations explicitly, and then solve them using `Solve`.

In some cases, however, you may prefer to convert the system of linear equations into a matrix equation, and then apply matrix manipulation operations to solve it. This approach is often useful when the system of equations arises as part of a general algorithm, and you do not know in advance how many variables will be involved.

A system of linear equations can be stated in matrix form as **m**.**x** = **b**, where **x** is the vector of variables.

Note that if your system of equations is sparse, so that most of the entries in the matrix **m** are zero, then you will usually find it much more efficient to use `Solve` to work directly with your original equations, without ever converting them to matrix form.

LinearSolve[m, b]	give a vector x which solves the matrix equation $m.x == b$
NullSpace[m]	a list of basis vectors whose linear combinations satisfy the matrix equation $m.x == 0$
RowReduce[m]	a simplified form of m obtained by making linear combinations of rows

Functions for solving linear systems.

Here is a 2 × 2 matrix.

```
In[1]:= m = {{1, 5}, {2, 1}}
Out[1]= {{1, 5}, {2, 1}}
```

This gives two linear equations.

```
In[2]:= m . {x, y} == {a, b}
Out[2]= {x + 5 y, 2 x + y} == {a, b}
```

You can use Solve directly to solve these equations.

```
In[3]:= Solve[ %, {x, y} ]
```
$$Out[3]= \left\{\left\{x \to \frac{-a + 5b}{9}, \ y \to \frac{2a - b}{9}\right\}\right\}$$

You can also get the vector of solutions by calling LinearSolve. The result is equivalent to the one you get from Solve.

```
In[4]:= LinearSolve[m, {a, b}]
```
$$Out[4]= \left\{\frac{-a + 5b}{9}, \ \frac{2a - b}{9}\right\}$$

Another way to solve the equations is to invert the matrix m, and then multiply {a, b} by the inverse. This is not as efficient as using LinearSolve.

```
In[5]:= Inverse[m] . {a, b}
```
$$Out[5]= \left\{-\frac{a}{9} + \frac{5b}{9}, \ \frac{2a}{9} - \frac{b}{9}\right\}$$

RowReduce performs a version of Gaussian elimination and can also be used to solve the equations.

```
In[6]:= RowReduce[{{1, 5, a}, {2, 1, b}}]
```
$$Out[6]= \left\{\left\{1, 0, \frac{-a + 5b}{9}\right\}, \ \left\{0, 1, \frac{2a - b}{9}\right\}\right\}$$

If you have a square matrix **m** with a non-zero determinant, then you can always find a unique solution to the matrix equation **m.x = b** for any **b**. If, however, the matrix **m** has determinant zero, then there may be either no vector, or an infinite number of vectors **x** which satisfy **m.x = b** for a particular **b**. This occurs when the linear equations embodied in **m** are not independent.

When **m** has determinant zero, it is nevertheless always possible to find non-zero vectors **x** that satisfy **m.x = 0**. The set of vectors **x** satisfying this equation form the *null space* or *kernel* of the matrix **m**. Any of these vectors can be expressed as a linear combination of a particular set of basis vectors, which can be obtained using NullSpace[m].

Here is a simple matrix, corresponding to two identical linear equations.

```
In[7]:= m = {{1, 2}, {1, 2}}
Out[7]= {{1, 2}, {1, 2}}
```

The matrix has determinant zero.

In[8]:= **Det[m]**

Out[8]= 0

LinearSolve cannot find a solution to the equation **m.x** = **b** in this case.

In[9]:= **LinearSolve[m, {a, b}]**

```
LinearSolve::nosol:
    Linear equation encountered which has no solution.
```

Out[9]= LinearSolve[{{1, 2}, {1, 2}}, {a, b}]

There is a single basis vector for the null space of m.

In[10]:= **NullSpace[m]**

Out[10]= {{-2, 1}}

Multiplying the basis vector for the null space by m gives the zero vector.

In[11]:= **m . %[[1]]**

Out[11]= {0, 0}

Here is a simple symbolic matrix with determinant zero.

In[12]:= **m = {{a, b, c}, {2 a, 2 b, 2 c}, {3 a, 3 b, 3 c}}**

Out[12]= {{a, b, c}, {2a, 2b, 2c}, {3a, 3b, 3c}}

The basis for the null space of m contains two vectors. Any linear combination of these vectors gives zero when multiplied by m.

In[13]:= **NullSpace[m]**

$$Out[13]= \left\{\left\{-\frac{c}{a}, 0, 1\right\}, \left\{-\frac{b}{a}, 1, 0\right\}\right\}$$

An important feature of `LinearSolve` and `NullSpace` is that they work with *rectangular,* as well as *square,* matrices.

When you represent a system of linear equations by a matrix equation of the form **m.x** = **b**, the number of columns in **m** gives the number of variables, and the number of rows gives the number of equations. There are a number of cases.

Underdetermined	number of equations less than the number of variables; no solutions or many solutions may exist
Overdetermined	number of equations more than the number of variables; solutions may or may not exist
Nonsingular	number of independent equations equal to the number of variables, and determinant non-zero; a unique solution exists
Consistent	at least one solution exists
Inconsistent	no solutions exist

Classes of linear systems represented by rectangular matrices.

This asks for the solution to the inconsistent set of equations $x = 1$ and $x = 0$.

```
In[14]:= LinearSolve[{{1}, {1}}, {1, 0}]
LinearSolve::nosol:
   Linear equation encountered which has no solution.
Out[14]= LinearSolve[{{1}, {1}}, {1, 0}]
```

This matrix represents two equations, for three variables.

```
In[15]:= m = {{1, 3, 4}, {2, 1, 3}}
Out[15]= {{1, 3, 4}, {2, 1, 3}}
```

LinearSolve gives one of the possible solutions to this underdetermined set of equations.

```
In[16]:= v = LinearSolve[m, {1, 1}]
```

$$Out[16]= \left\{\frac{2}{5}, \frac{1}{5}, 0\right\}$$

When a matrix represents an underdetermined system of equations, the matrix has a non-trivial null space. In this case, the null space is spanned by a single vector.

```
In[17]:= NullSpace[m]
Out[17]= {{-1, -1, 1}}
```

If you take the solution you get from LinearSolve, and add any linear combination of the basis vectors for the null space, you still get a solution.

```
In[18]:= m . (v + 4 %[[1]])
Out[18]= {1, 1}
```

You can find out the number of redundant equations corresponding to a particular matrix by evaluating Length[NullSpace[*m*]]. Subtracting this quantity from the number of columns in *m* gives the *rank* of the matrix *m*.

+	LUDecomposition[*m*]	find the LU decomposition of a matrix
+	LUBackSubstitution[*data*, *b*]	use the LU decomposition to solve the equation **m.x = b**

Efficient repeated solution of linear systems.

If you have a large number of numerical matrix equations to solve of the form **m.x = b**, all with the same **m**, then you can often save time by first preprocessing **m** using LUDecomposition[*m*], and then taking the data you get and repeatedly applying LUBackSubstitution[*data*, *b*] for each **b**.

■ 3.7.9 Eigenvalues and Eigenvectors

Eigenvalues[m]	a list of the eigenvalues of m
Eigenvectors[m]	a list of the eigenvectors of m
Eigensystem[m]	a list of the form *{eigenvalues, eigenvectors}*
Eigenvalues[N[m]], etc.	numerical eigenvalues
Eigenvalues[N[m, k]], etc.	numerical eigenvalues, starting with k-digit precision

Eigenvalues and eigenvectors.

The eigenvalues of a matrix **m** are the values λ_i for which one can find non-zero vectors $\mathbf{x}_i$ such that $\mathbf{m}.\mathbf{x}_i = \lambda_i \mathbf{x}_i$. The eigenvectors are the vectors $\mathbf{x}_i$.

Finding the eigenvalues of an $n \times n$ matrix in principle involves solving an nth degree polynomial equation. For $n \geq 5$, therefore, the results cannot in general be expressed purely in terms of explicit radicals. Root objects can nevertheless always be used, although except for fairly sparse or otherwise simple matrices the expressions obtained are often unmanageably complex.

Even for a matrix as simple as this, the explicit form of the eigenvalues is quite complicated.

```
In[1]:= Eigenvalues[ {{a, b}, {-b, 2a}} ]
```
$$Out[1]= \left\{ \frac{1}{2} \left(3a - \sqrt{a-2b}\ \sqrt{a+2b}\ \right), \right.$$
$$\left. \frac{1}{2} \left(3a + \sqrt{a-2b}\ \sqrt{a+2b}\ \right) \right\}$$

If you give a matrix of approximate real numbers, *Mathematica* will find the approximate numerical eigenvalues and eigenvectors.

Here is a 2×2 numerical matrix.

```
In[2]:= m = {{2.3, 4.5}, {6.7, -1.2}}
Out[2]= {{2.3, 4.5}, {6.7, -1.2}}
```

The matrix has two eigenvalues, in this case both real.

```
In[3]:= Eigenvalues[ m ]
Out[3]= {6.31303, -5.21303}
```

Here are the two eigenvectors of m.

```
In[4]:= Eigenvectors[ m ]
Out[4]= {{0.746335, 0.66557}, {-0.513839, 0.857886}}
```

Eigensystem computes the eigenvalues and eigenvectors at the same time. The assignment sets vals to the list of eigenvalues, and vecs to the list of eigenvectors.

```
In[5]:= {vals, vecs} = Eigensystem[m]
Out[5]= {{6.31303, -5.21303},
           {{0.746335, 0.66557}, {-0.513839, 0.857886}}}
```

This verifies that the first eigenvalue and eigenvector satisfy the appropriate condition.

```
In[6]:= m . vecs[[1]] == vals[[1]] vecs[[1]]
Out[6]= True
```

This finds the eigenvalues of a random
4×4 matrix. For non-symmetric
matrices, the eigenvalues can have
imaginary parts.

```
In[7]:= Eigenvalues[ Table[Random[ ], {4}, {4}] ]
Out[7]= {2.30021, 0.319764 + 0.547199 I,
              0.319764 - 0.547199 I, 0.449291}
```

The function `Eigenvalues` always gives you a list of n eigenvalues for an $n \times n$ matrix. The eigenvalues correspond to the roots of the characteristic polynomial for the matrix, and may not necessarily be distinct. `Eigenvectors`, on the other hand, gives a list of eigenvectors which are guaranteed to be independent. If the number of such eigenvectors is less than n, then `Eigenvectors` appends zero vectors to the list it returns, so that the total length of the list is always n.

Here is a 3×3 matrix.

```
In[8]:= mz = {{0, 1, 0}, {0, 0, 1}, {0, 0, 0}}
Out[8]= {{0, 1, 0}, {0, 0, 1}, {0, 0, 0}}
```

The matrix has three eigenvalues, all
equal to zero.

```
In[9]:= Eigenvalues[mz]
Out[9]= {0, 0, 0}
```

There is, however, only one
independent eigenvector for the matrix.
`Eigenvectors` appends two zero
vectors to give a total of three vectors
in this case.

```
In[10]:= Eigenvectors[mz]
Out[10]= {{1, 0, 0}, {0, 0, 0}, {0, 0, 0}}
```

■ 3.7.10 Advanced Topic: Matrix Decompositions

`SingularValues[`m`]`	find the singular value decomposition of a numerical matrix
`PseudoInverse[`m`]`	compute the pseudoinverse of any matrix

Singular value decomposition and pseudoinverse.

Singular value decomposition is an important element of many numerical matrix algorithms. The basic idea is to write any matrix **m** in the form $\mathbf{u}^* \mathbf{m}_D \mathbf{v}$, where $\mathbf{m}_D$ is a diagonal matrix, **u** and **v** are row orthonormal matrices, and $\mathbf{u}^*$ is the Hermitian transpose of **u**.

The function `SingularValues[`m`]` returns a list containing the matrix **u**, the list of diagonal elements of $\mathbf{m}_D$, and the matrix **v**.

The diagonal elements of $\mathbf{m}_D$ are known as the *singular values* of the matrix **m**. One interpretation of the singular values is as follows. If you take a unit sphere in n-dimensional space, and multiply each vector in it by an $m \times n$ matrix **m**, you will get an ellipsoid in m-dimensional space. The singular values give the lengths of the principal axes of the ellipsoid. If the matrix **m** is singular in some way, this will be reflected in the shape of the ellipsoid. In fact, the ratio of the largest singular value of a matrix to the smallest one gives a *condition number* of the matrix, which determines, for example, the accuracy of numerical matrix inverses.

Very small singular values are usually numerically meaningless. `SingularValues` removes any singular values that are smaller than a certain *tolerance* multiplied by the largest singular value. The option `Tolerance` specifies the tolerance to use.

Here is the singular value decomposition for a non-singular 2×2 matrix.	`In[1]:= SingularValues[N[{{1, 3}, {-4, 3}}]]`
	`Out[1]= {{{-0.289784, -0.957092}, {-0.957092, 0.289784}},`
	`{5.14916, 2.91309},`
	`{{0.687215, -0.726454}, {-0.726454, -0.687215}}}`
Here is a convenient way to pick out the pieces of the result.	`In[2]:= {u, md, v} = %`
	`Out[2]= {{{-0.289784, -0.957092}, {-0.957092, 0.289784}},`
	`{5.14916, 2.91309},`
	`{{0.687215, -0.726454}, {-0.726454, -0.687215}}}`
This gives something close to the original matrix.	`In[3]:= Transpose[u] . DiagonalMatrix[md] . v`
	`Out[3]= {{1., 3.}, {-4., 3.}}`
Here is the singular value decomposition of a singular matrix. Only one singular value is given.	`In[4]:= SingularValues[N[{{1, 2}, {1, 2}}]]`
	`Out[4]= {{{-0.707107, -0.707107}}, {3.16228},`
	`{{-0.447214, -0.894427}}}`

The standard definition for the inverse of a matrix fails if the matrix is not square. Using singular value decomposition, however, it is possible to define a *pseudoinverse* even for non-square matrices, or for singular square ones. The pseudoinverse is defined in terms of the objects **u**, $\mathbf{m}_D$ and **v** as $\mathbf{m}^{(-1)} = \mathbf{v}^* \mathbf{m}_D^{-1} \mathbf{u}$. The pseudoinverse has the property that the sum of the squares of all the entries in $\mathbf{m}.\mathbf{m}^{(-1)} - \mathbf{I}$, where **I** is an identity matrix, is minimized. The pseudoinverse found in this way is important, for example, in carrying out fits to numerical data. The pseudoinverse is sometimes known as the generalized inverse, or the Moore-Penrose inverse.

`QRDecomposition[m]`	find the QR decomposition of a numerical matrix
`SchurDecomposition[m]`	find the Schur decomposition of a numerical matrix
+ `JordanDecomposition[m]`	find the Jordan decomposition of any matrix
+ `LUDecomposition[m]`	find the LU decomposition of any matrix

Other matrix decompositions.

Singular value decomposition writes any matrix as a product of a diagonal matrix with row and column orthonormal matrices. In some algorithms, it is also important to be able to decompose matrices as products involving *triangular matrices*.

QR decomposition writes any matrix **m** as a product $\mathbf{q}^*\mathbf{r}$, where **q** is an orthonormal matrix, $*$ denotes Hermitian transpose, and **r** is a triangular matrix, in which all entries below the leading diagonal are zero. The function `QRDecomposition[m]` returns a list containing the matrices **q** and **r**.

QR decomposition is often used in solving least-squares fitting problems, and is typically faster than singular value decomposition.

This computes the QR decomposition of a 2×2 matrix, then extracts the matrices **q** and **r**.

```
In[5]:= {q, r} = QRDecomposition[ N[{{1, 5}, {-7, 3}}] ]
Out[5]= {{{-0.141421, 0.989949}, {-0.989949, -0.141421}},
         {{-7.07107, 2.26274}, {0, -5.37401}}}
```

Since **q** is orthogonal, this gives the identity matrix.

```
In[6]:= Transpose[q] . q // Chop
Out[6]= {{1., 0}, {0, 1.}}
```

This gives the original matrix.

```
In[7]:= Transpose[q] . r
Out[7]= {{1., 5.}, {-7., 3.}}
```

Schur decomposition writes any matrix **m** in the form $\mathbf{qtq}^*$, where **q** is an orthogonal matrix, and **t** is block-upper triangular. The function SchurDecomposition[m] returns a list containing the matrices **q** and **t**. Schur decomposition is often used in evaluating functions of matrices.

The stability of numerical matrix algorithms is sometimes improved by "pivoting" or "balancing", in which the rows and columns of the matrix **m** are permuted and perhaps rescaled before QR or Schur decomposition is done. Setting the option Pivoting -> True tells *Mathematica* to perform such pivoting or balancing, and to give the matrix required as the last element of the list returned.

Jordan decomposition writes any square matrix **m** in the form $\mathbf{sjs}^{-1}$. The matrix **j** is usually just a diagonal matrix of eigenvalues, but in general it can also have ones directly above the diagonal. The function JordanDecomposition[m] returns a list containing the matrices **s** and **j**. Jordan decomposition is often used in evaluating functions of exact matrices.

LU decomposition is convenient for preprocessing matrices that will appear repeatedly in collections of linear equations, as discussed on page 849.

■ 3.7.11 Advanced Topic: Tensors

Tensors are mathematical objects that give generalizations of vectors and matrices. In *Mathematica*, a tensor is represented as a set of lists, nested to a certain number of levels. The nesting level is the *rank* of the tensor.

rank 0	scalar
rank 1	vector
rank 2	matrix
rank k	rank k tensor

Interpretations of nested lists.

A tensor of rank k is essentially a k-dimensional table of values. To be a true rank k tensor, it must be possible to arrange the elements in the table in a k-dimensional cuboidal array. There can be no holes or protrusions in the cuboid.

The *indices* that specify a particular element in the tensor correspond to the coordinates in the cuboid. The *dimensions* of the tensor correspond to the side lengths of the cuboid.

One simple way that a rank k tensor can arise is in giving a table of values for a function of k variables. In physics, the tensors that occur typically have indices which run over the possible directions in space or spacetime. Notice, however, that there is no built-in notion of covariant and contravariant tensor indices in *Mathematica*: you have to set these up explicitly using metric tensors.

`Table[f, {i`$_1$`, n`$_1$`}, {i`$_2$`, n`$_2$`}, ... , {i`$_k$`, n`$_k$`}]`	
	create an $n_1 \times n_2 \times ... \times n_k$ tensor whose elements are the values of f
`Array[a, {n`$_1$`, n`$_2$`, ... , n`$_k$`}]`	create an $n_1 \times n_2 \times ... \times n_k$ tensor with elements given by applying a to each set of indices
`Dimensions[t]`	give a list of the dimensions of a tensor
`TensorRank[t]`	find the rank of a tensor
`MatrixForm[t]`	print with the elements of t arranged in a two-dimensional array

Functions for creating and testing the structure of tensors.

Here is a $2 \times 3 \times 2$ tensor.

```
In[1]:= t = Table[i1+i2 i3, {i1, 2}, {i2, 3}, {i3, 2}]
Out[1]= {{{2, 3}, {3, 5}, {4, 7}}, {{3, 4}, {4, 6}, {5, 8}}}
```

This is another way to produce the same tensor.

```
In[2]:= Array[(#1 + #2 #3)&, {2, 3, 2}]
Out[2]= {{{2, 3}, {3, 5}, {4, 7}}, {{3, 4}, {4, 6}, {5, 8}}}
```

`MatrixForm` displays the elements of the tensor in a two-dimensional array. You can think of the array as being a 2×3 matrix of column vectors.

```
In[3]:= MatrixForm[ t ]
```

$$Out[3]//MatrixForm= \begin{pmatrix} \begin{pmatrix} 2 \\ 3 \end{pmatrix} & \begin{pmatrix} 3 \\ 5 \end{pmatrix} & \begin{pmatrix} 4 \\ 7 \end{pmatrix} \\ \begin{pmatrix} 3 \\ 4 \end{pmatrix} & \begin{pmatrix} 4 \\ 6 \end{pmatrix} & \begin{pmatrix} 5 \\ 8 \end{pmatrix} \end{pmatrix}$$

`Dimensions` gives the dimensions of the tensor.

```
In[4]:= Dimensions[ t ]
Out[4]= {2, 3, 2}
```

Here is the 111 element of the tensor.

```
In[5]:= t[[1, 1, 1]]
Out[5]= 2
```

TensorRank gives the rank of the tensor.	*In[6]:=* **TensorRank[t]** *Out[6]=* 3

The rank of a tensor is equal to the number of indices needed to specify each element. You can pick out subtensors by using a smaller number of indices.

Transpose[t]	transpose the first two indices in a tensor
Transpose[t, {p_1, p_2, ... }]	transpose the indices in a tensor so that the kth becomes the p_k^{th}
Outer[f, t_1, t_2]	form the generalized outer product of the tensors t_1 and t_2 with "multiplication operator" f
$t_1 \cdot t_2$	form the dot product of t_1 and t_2 (last index of t_1 contracted with first index of t_2)
Inner[f, t_1, t_2, g]	form the generalized inner product, with "multiplication operator" f and "addition operator" g

Tensor manipulation operations.

You can think of a rank k tensor as having k "slots" into which you insert indices. Applying Transpose is effectively a way of reordering these slots. If you think of the elements of a tensor as forming a k-dimensional cuboid, you can view Transpose as effectively rotating (and possibly reflecting) the cuboid.

In the most general case, Transpose allows you to specify an arbitrary reordering to apply to the indices of a tensor. The function Transpose[T, {p_1, p_2, ... , p_k}], gives you a new tensor T' such that the value of $T'_{i_1 i_2 ... i_k}$ is given by $T_{i_{p_1} i_{p_2} ... i_{p_k}}$.

If you originally had an $n_{p_1} \times n_{p_2} \times ... \times n_{p_k}$ tensor, then by applying Transpose, you will get an $n_1 \times n_2 \times ... \times n_k$ tensor.

Here is a matrix that you can also think of as a 2×3 tensor.	*In[7]:=* **m = {{a, b, c}, {ap, bp, cp}}** *Out[7]=* {{a, b, c}, {ap, bp, cp}}
Applying Transpose gives you a 3×2 tensor. Transpose effectively interchanges the two "slots" for tensor indices.	*In[8]:=* **mt = Transpose[m]** *Out[8]=* {{a, ap}, {b, bp}, {c, cp}}
The element m[[2, 3]] in the original tensor becomes the element m[[3, 2]] in the transposed tensor.	*In[9]:=* **{ m[[2, 3]], mt[[3, 2]] }** *Out[9]=* {cp, cp}

This produces a $2 \times 3 \times 1 \times 2$ tensor.

```
In[10]:= t = Array[a, {2, 3, 1, 2}]
Out[10]= {{{{a[1, 1, 1, 1], a[1, 1, 1, 2]}},
          {{a[1, 2, 1, 1], a[1, 2, 1, 2]}},
          {{a[1, 3, 1, 1], a[1, 3, 1, 2]}}},
         {{{a[2, 1, 1, 1], a[2, 1, 1, 2]}},
          {{a[2, 2, 1, 1], a[2, 2, 1, 2]}},
          {{a[2, 3, 1, 1], a[2, 3, 1, 2]}}}}
```

This transposes the first two levels of t.

```
In[11]:= tt1 = Transpose[t]
Out[11]= {{{{a[1, 1, 1, 1], a[1, 1, 1, 2]}},
          {{a[2, 1, 1, 1], a[2, 1, 1, 2]}}},
         {{{a[1, 2, 1, 1], a[1, 2, 1, 2]}},
          {{a[2, 2, 1, 1], a[2, 2, 1, 2]}}},
         {{{a[1, 3, 1, 1], a[1, 3, 1, 2]}},
          {{a[2, 3, 1, 1], a[2, 3, 1, 2]}}}}
```

The result is a $3 \times 2 \times 1 \times 2$ tensor.

```
In[12]:= Dimensions[ tt1 ]
Out[12]= {3, 2, 1, 2}
```

If you have a tensor that contains lists of the same length at different levels, then you can use Transpose to effectively collapse different levels.

This collapses all three levels, giving a list of the elements on the "main diagonal".

```
In[13]:= Transpose[Array[a, {3, 3, 3}], {1, 1, 1}]
Out[13]= {a[1, 1, 1], a[2, 2, 2], a[3, 3, 3]}
```

This collapses only the first two levels.

```
In[14]:= Transpose[Array[a, {2, 2, 2}], {1, 1}]
Out[14]= {{a[1, 1, 1], a[1, 1, 2]}, {a[2, 2, 1], a[2, 2, 2]}}
```

Outer products, and their generalizations, are a way of building higher-rank tensors from lower-rank ones. Outer products are also sometimes known as direct, tensor or Kronecker products.

From a structural point of view, the tensor you get from Outer[*f*, *t*, *u*] has a copy of the structure of *u* inserted at the "position" of each element in *t*. The elements in the resulting structure are obtained by combining elements of *t* and *u* using the function *f*.

This gives the "outer f" of two vectors. The result is a matrix.

```
In[15]:= Outer[ f, {a, b}, {ap, bp} ]
Out[15]= {{f[a, ap], f[a, bp]}, {f[b, ap], f[b, bp]}}
```

If you take the "outer f" of a length 3 vector with a length 2 vector, you get a 3×2 matrix.

```
In[16]:= Outer[ f, {a, b, c}, {ap, bp} ]
Out[16]= {{f[a, ap], f[a, bp]}, {f[b, ap], f[b, bp]},
          {f[c, ap], f[c, bp]}}
```

The result of taking the "outer f" of a 2×2 matrix and a length 3 vector is a $2 \times 2 \times 3$ tensor.

```
In[17]:= Outer[ f, {{m11, m12}, {m21, m22}}, {a, b, c} ]
Out[17]= {{{f[m11, a], f[m11, b], f[m11, c]},
           {f[m12, a], f[m12, b], f[m12, c]}},
          {{f[m21, a], f[m21, b], f[m21, c]},
           {f[m22, a], f[m22, b], f[m22, c]}}}
```

Here are the dimensions of the tensor.   *In[18]:=* **Dimensions[%]**

Out[18]= {2, 2, 3}

If you take the generalized outer product of an $m_1 \times m_2 \times ... \times m_r$ tensor and an $n_1 \times n_2 \times ... \times n_s$ tensor, you get an $m_1 \times ... \times m_r \times n_1 \times ... \times n_s$ tensor. If the original tensors have ranks r and s, your result will be a rank $r + s$ tensor.

In terms of indices, the result of applying Outer to two tensors $T_{i_1 i_2 ... i_r}$ and $U_{j_1 j_2 ... j_s}$ is the tensor $V_{i_1 i_2 ... i_r j_1 j_2 ... j_s}$ with elements $f[T_{i_1 i_2 ... i_r}, U_{j_1 j_2 ... j_s}]$.

In doing standard tensor calculations, the most common function f to use in Outer is Times, corresponding to the standard outer product.

Particularly in doing combinatorial calculations, however, it is often convenient to take f to be List. Using Outer, you can then get combinations of all possible elements in one tensor, with all possible elements in the other.

In constructing Outer[f, t, u] you effectively insert a copy of u at every point in t. To form Inner[f, t, u], you effectively combine and collapse the last dimension of t and the first dimension of u. The idea is to take an $m_1 \times m_2 \times ... \times m_r$ tensor and an $n_1 \times n_2 \times ... \times n_s$ tensor, with $m_r = n_1$, and get an $m_1 \times m_2 \times ... \times m_{r-1} \times n_2 \times ... \times n_s$ tensor as the result.

The simplest examples are with vectors. If you apply Inner to two vectors of equal length, you get a scalar. Inner[f, v_1, v_2, g] gives a generalization of the usual scalar product, with f playing the role of multiplication, and g playing the role of addition.

This gives a generalization of the standard scalar product of two vectors.

In[19]:= **Inner[f, {a, b, c}, {ap, bp, cp}, g]**

Out[19]= g[f[a, ap], f[b, bp], f[c, cp]]

This gives a generalization of a matrix product.

In[20]:= **Inner[f, {{1, 2}, {3, 4}}, {{a, b}, {c, d}}, g]**

Out[20]= {{g[f[1, a], f[2, c]], g[f[1, b], f[2, d]]},
{g[f[3, a], f[4, c]], g[f[3, b], f[4, d]]}}

Here is a $3 \times 2 \times 2$ tensor.

In[21]:= **a = Array[1&, {3, 2, 2}]**

Out[21]= {{{1, 1}, {1, 1}}, {{1, 1}, {1, 1}},
{{1, 1}, {1, 1}}}

Here is a $2 \times 3 \times 1$ tensor.

In[22]:= **b = Array[2&, {2, 3, 1}]**

Out[22]= {{{2}, {2}, {2}}, {{2}, {2}, {2}}}

This gives a $3 \times 2 \times 3 \times 1$ tensor.

In[23]:= **a . b**

Out[23]= {{{{4}, {4}, {4}}, {{4}, {4}, {4}}},
{{{4}, {4}, {4}}, {{4}, {4}, {4}}},
{{{4}, {4}, {4}}, {{4}, {4}, {4}}}}

Here are the dimensions of the result.

In[24]:= **Dimensions[%]**

Out[24]= {3, 2, 3, 1}

You can think of `Inner` as performing a "contraction" of the last index of one tensor with the first index of another. If you want to perform contractions across other pairs of indices, you can do so by first transposing the appropriate indices into the first or last position, then applying `Inner`, and then transposing the result back.

In many applications of tensors, you need to insert signs to implement antisymmetry. The function `Signature[{$i_1$, $i_2$, ... }]`, which gives the signature of a permutation, is often useful for this purpose.

`Outer[f, `t_1`, `t_2`, ... ]`	form a generalized outer product by combining the lowest-level elements of t_1, t_2, ...
+ `Outer[f, `t_1`, `t_2`, ... , n]`	treat only sublists at level n as separate elements
+ `Outer[f, `t_1`, `t_2`, ... , `n_1`, `n_2`, ... ]`	treat only sublists at level n_i in t_i as separate elements
`Inner[f, `t_1`, `t_2`, g]`	form a generalized inner product using the lowest-level elements of t_1
+ `Inner[f, `t_1`, `t_2`, g, n]`	treat only sublists at level n in t_1 as separate elements

Treating only certain sublists in tensors as separate elements.

Here every single symbol is treated as a separate element.

```
In[25]:= Outer[f, {{i, j}, {k, l}}, {x, y}]
Out[25]= {{{f[i, x], f[i, y]}, {f[j, x], f[j, y]}},
          {{f[k, x], f[k, y]}, {f[l, x], f[l, y]}}}
```

But here only sublists at level 1 are treated as separate elements.

```
In[26]:= Outer[f, {{i, j}, {k, l}}, {x, y}, 1]
Out[26]= {{f[{i, j}, x], f[{i, j}, y]},
          {f[{k, l}, x], f[{k, l}, y]}}
```

3.8 Numerical Operations on Data

■ 3.8.1 Curve Fitting

Built into *Mathematica* are various facilities for finding least-squares fits to data. The basic idea of the fits is to take a list of functions that you specify, and try to find a linear combination of them which approximates your data as well as possible. The goodness of fit is measured by the quantity $\chi^2 = \sum_i |F_i - f_i|^2$, where F_i is the value of your i^{th} data point, and f_i is the value obtained from the fit. The best fit is the one which minimizes χ^2.

`Fit[data, funs, vars]`	fit a list of data points using the functions *funs* of variables *vars*

The basic form of the `Fit` function.

`Fit[{f_1, f_2, ... }, {1, x}, x]`	linear fit
`Fit[{f_1, f_2, ... }, {1, x, x^2}, x]`	quadratic fit
`Fit[data, Table[x^i, {i, 0, n}], x]`	n^{th}-degree polynomial fit
`Exp[ Fit[Log[data], {1, x}, x] ]`	fit to e^{a+bx}

Some fits to lists of data.

Here is a table of the first 20 primes.

```
In[1]:= fp = Table[Prime[x], {x, 20}]
Out[1]= {2, 3, 5, 7, 11, 13, 17, 19, 23, 29, 31, 37,
         41, 43, 47, 53, 59, 61, 67, 71}
```

Here is a plot of this "data".

```
In[2]:= gp = ListPlot[ fp ]
```

This gives a linear fit to the list of primes. The result is the best linear combination of the functions 1 and x.

In[3]:= **Fit[fp, {1, x}, x]**

Out[3]= $-7.67368 + 3.77368\,x$

Here is a plot of the fit.

In[4]:= **Plot[%, {x, 0, 20}]**

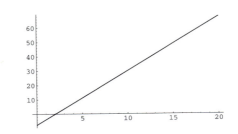

Here is the fit superimposed on the original data.

In[5]:= **Show[%, gp]**

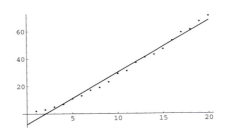

This gives a quadratic fit to the data.

In[6]:= **Fit[fp, {1, x, x^2}, x]**

Out[6]= $-1.92368 + 2.2055\,x + 0.0746753\,x^2$

Here is a plot of the quadratic fit.

In[7]:= **Plot[%, {x, 0, 20}]**

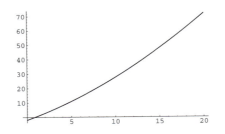

This shows the fit superimposed on the original data. The quadratic fit is better than the linear one.

In[8]:= **Show[%, gp]**

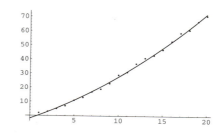

Polynomial fits are the most common kind to use. However, if you have a reason to believe that your data follows some other functional form, you can include the appropriate functions in the list you give to Fit.

This gives a table of the values of $1 + 2e^{-\frac{x}{3}}$ for x from 1 to 10 in steps of 1.

In[9]:= **ft = Table[N[1 + 2 Exp[-x/3]] , {x, 10}]**

Out[9]= {2.43306, 2.02683, 1.73576, 1.52719, 1.37775,
            1.27067, 1.19394, 1.13897, 1.09957, 1.07135}

This fit recovers the original functional form.

In[10]:= **Fit[ft, {1, Exp[-x/3]}, x]**

Out[10]= $1. + 2. E^{-x/3}$

If you include other functions in the list, Fit determines that they occur with small coefficients.

In[11]:= **Fit[ft, {1, Sin[x], Exp[-x/3], Exp[-x]}, x]**

Out[11]= $1. + 1.77636 \times 10^{-15} E^{-x} + 2. E^{-x/3} + 0. Sin[x]$

You can use Chop to get rid of the terms with small coefficients.

In[12]:= **Chop[%]**

Out[12]= $1. + 2. E^{-x/3}$

There are several common reasons for doing fits.

If you have a particular model for some data, you can do a fit to try and determine the parameters of the model.

Another common use of fits is in finding approximate formulas to describe a particular set of data. You can use the form you get from a Fit as a summary of your actual data.

In the examples of Fit so far, the data points you give are assumed to correspond to the results of evaluating a function of one variable when the variable successively takes on values 1, 2, ... You can also specify data that depends on several variables, each given an arbitrary sequence of values, not necessarily arranged in any kind of regular array.

$\{f_1, f_2, \dots \}$	data points obtained when a single coordinate takes on values 1, 2, …
$\{\{x_1, y_1, \dots, f_1\}, \{x_2, y_2, \dots, f_2\}, \dots \}$	data points obtained with values $x_i, y_i, \dots$ of a sequence of coordinates

Ways of specifying data in Fit.

This gives a table of the values of x, y and $1 + 5x - xy$. You need to use Flatten to get it in the right form for Fit.

```
In[13]:= Flatten[ Table[ {x, y, 1 + 5x - x y},
                {x, 0, 1, 0.4}, {y, 0, 1, 0.4} ], 1]
Out[13]= {{0, 0, 1}, {0, 0.4, 1}, {0, 0.8, 1}, {0.4, 0, 3.},
         {0.4, 0.4, 2.84}, {0.4, 0.8, 2.68}, {0.8, 0, 5.},
         {0.8, 0.4, 4.68}, {0.8, 0.8, 4.36}}
```

This produces a fit to a function of two variables.

```
In[14]:= Fit[ % , {1, x, y, x y}, {x, y} ]
Out[14]= 1. + 5. x - 4.44089×10^-16 y - 1. x y
```

Fit takes the list of functions you give, and finds the best fit to your data, according to the least-squares criterion, using these functions. There is absolutely no guarantee that the fit you get will in fact accurately reproduce your data. To find out whether it can, you should use statistical testing functions, such as those in the statistics packages available for *Mathematica*.

`InterpolatingPolynomial[{`$f_1, f_2, \dots, f_n$`}, x]`	find a polynomial in x which fits the values f_i exactly
`InterpolatingPolynomial[{{`x_1, f_1`}, {`x_2, f_2`}, ... }, x]`	find a polynomial which fits the points $\{x_i, f_i\}$ exactly
`InterpolatingPolynomial[{{`x_1`, {`$f_1, df_1, ddf_1, \dots$`}}, ... }]`	find a polynomial which fits the specified values and derivatives exactly

Finding exact fits.

If you have sufficiently few data points, then by including sufficiently many terms, you can construct a polynomial which fits your data exactly. In general, if you have n data points, you may need a polynomial of degree up to $n - 1$. The function `InterpolatingPolynomial` gives you such a polynomial. Such polynomials can in fact be useful not only in fitting numerical data, but also in various algebraic algorithms.

Here is the value at a particular position.	*In[19]:=* `%[6.5, 7.2]`
	Out[19]= `0.00360759`
Here is another array of values.	*In[20]:=* `tab = Table[1.5/(x^2 + y^3),`
	`{x, 5.5, 7.2, .2}, {y, 2.3, 8.9, .1}]` ;
To interpolate this array you explicitly have to tell *Mathematica* the domain it covers.	*In[21]:=* `ListInterpolation[tab, {{5.5, 7.2}, {2.3, 8.9}}]`
	Out[21]= `InterpolatingFunction[{{5.5, 7.2}, {2.3, 8.9}},`
	`<>]`

`ListInterpolation` works for arrays of any dimension, and in each case it produces an `InterpolatingFunction` object which takes the appropriate number of arguments.

This interpolates a three-dimensional array.	*In[22]:=* `ListInterpolation[`
	`Array[#1^2 + #2^2 - #3^2 &, {10, 10, 10}]]` ;
The resulting `InterpolatingFunction` object takes three arguments.	*In[23]:=* `%[3.4, 7.8, 2.6]`
	Out[23]= `65.64`

Mathematica can handle not only purely numerical approximate functions, but also ones which involve symbolic parameters.

This generates an `InterpolatingFunction` that depends on the parameters a and b.	*In[24]:=* `sfun = ListInterpolation[{1 + a, 2, 3, 4 + b, 5}]`
	Out[24]= `InterpolatingFunction[{{1, 5}}, <>]`
This shows how the interpolated value at 2.2 depends on the parameters.	*In[25]:=* `sfun[2.2] // Simplify`
	Out[25]= `2.2 - 0.048a - 0.032b`
With the default setting for `InterpolationOrder` used, the value at this point no longer depends on a.	*In[26]:=* `sfun[3.8] // Simplify`
	Out[26]= `3.8 + 0.864b`

In working with approximate functions, you can quite often end up with complicated combinations of `InterpolatingFunction` objects. You can always tell *Mathematica* to produce a single `InterpolatingFunction` object valid over a particular domain by using `FunctionInterpolation`.

This generates a new `InterpolatingFunction` object valid in the domain 0 to 1.	*In[27]:=* `FunctionInterpolation[x + sin[x^2], {x, 0, 1}]`
	Out[27]= `InterpolatingFunction[{{0, 1.}}, <>]`
This generates a nested `InterpolatingFunction` object.	*In[28]:=* `ListInterpolation[{3, 4, 5, sin[a], 6}]`
	Out[28]= `InterpolatingFunction[{{1, 5}}, <>]`
This produces a pure two-dimensional `InterpolatingFunction` object.	*In[29]:=* `FunctionInterpolation[a^2 + %[x], {x, 1, 3}, {a, 0, 1.5}]`
	Out[29]= `InterpolatingFunction[{{1., 3.}, {0, 1.5}}, <>]`

+	`FunctionInterpolation[`*expr*`, {`*x*`, `*xmin*`, `*xmax*`}]`
	construct an approximate function by evaluating *expr* with *x* ranging from *xmin* to *xmax*
+	`FunctionInterpolation[`*expr*`, {`*x*`, `*xmin*`, `*xmax*`}, {`*y*`, `*ymin*`, `*ymax*`}, ... ]`
	construct a higher-dimensional approximate function

Constructing approximate functions by evaluating expressions.

■ 3.8.3 Fourier Transforms

A common operation in analyzing various kinds of data is to find the Fourier transform, or spectrum, of a list of values. The idea is typically to pick out components of the data with particular frequencies, or ranges of frequencies.

`Fourier[{`a_1`, `a_2`, ... , `a_n`}]`	Fourier transform
`InverseFourier[{`b_1`, `b_2`, ... , `b_n`}]`	
	inverse Fourier transform

Fourier transforms.

There are several conventions that can be used in defining Fourier transforms. In *Mathematica*, the Fourier transform b_s of a list a_r of length n is taken to be $\frac{1}{\sqrt{n}} \sum_{r=1}^{n} a_r e^{2\pi i (r-1)(s-1)/n}$. Notice that the zero frequency term appears at position 1 in the resulting list.

Note that the convention for defining the Fourier transform used in *Mathematica* is the one common in the physical sciences. In electrical engineering, the sign of the exponent is typically reversed, leading to a list of values which is reversed.

The Fourier transform takes you from a time series of data to the frequency components of the data. You can use the inverse Fourier transform to get back to the time series. The inverse Fourier transform a_r of a list b_s of length n is defined to be $\frac{1}{\sqrt{n}} \sum_{s=1}^{n} b_s e^{-2\pi i (r-1)(s-1)/n}$.

Here is some data, corresponding to a square pulse.

```
In[1]:= {-1, -1, -1, -1, 1, 1, 1, 1}
Out[1]= {-1, -1, -1, -1, 1, 1, 1, 1}
```

Here is the Fourier transform of the data. It involves complex numbers.

```
In[2]:= Fourier[%]
Out[2]= {0. + 0. I, -0.707107 - 1.70711 I,
         0. + 0. I, -0.707107 - 0.292893 I,
         0. + 0. I, -0.707107 + 0.292893 I,
         0. + 0. I, -0.707107 + 1.70711 I}
```

Here is the inverse Fourier transform.

```
In[3]:= InverseFourier[%]
Out[3]= {-1. + 0. I, -1. + 0. I, -1. + 3.14018×10⁻¹⁶ I,
         -1. + 1.57009×10⁻¹⁶ I, 1. + 0. I, 1. + 0. I,
         1. - 3.14018×10⁻¹⁶ I, 1. - 1.57009×10⁻¹⁶ I}
```

After using Chop, this gives back exactly your original data.

```
In[4]:= Chop[%]
Out[4]= {-1., -1., -1., -1., 1., 1., 1., 1.}
```

Fourier works whether or not your list of data has a length which is a power of two. It is, however, significantly more efficient when the length is a power of two.

```
In[5]:= Fourier[{1, -1, 1}]
Out[5]= {0.57735 + 0. I, 0.57735 - 1. I, 0.57735 + 1. I}
```

This generates a length-256 list containing a periodic signal with random noise added.

```
In[6]:= data = Table[ N[Sin[30 2 Pi n/256] + (Random[ ] - 1/2)],
         {n, 256} ] ;
```

The data looks fairly random if you plot it directly.

```
In[7]:= ListPlot[ data, PlotJoined -> True ]
```

The Fourier transform, however, shows a strong peak at 30 + 1, and a symmetric peak at 257 − 30, reflecting the frequency 30 component of the original signal.

```
In[8]:= ListPlot[ Abs[Fourier[data]], PlotJoined -> True,
         PlotRange -> All ]
```

A common and important application of Fourier transforms is doing *convolutions*. The basic idea is that integrals of the form $\tilde{f}(x) = \int f(y)k(x - y)dy$ can be evaluated simply by multiplying the Fourier transforms of f and k. Convolutions are used extensively, for example, in smoothing data.

This generates some "data".

```
In[9]:= data = Table[ N[BesselJ[1, 10 n/256] +
                 0.2 (Random[ ] - 1/2)], {n, 256} ] ;
```

Here is a plot of the data.

```
In[10]:= ListPlot[data]
```

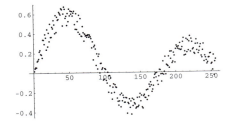

This generates a typical convolution kernel suitable for smoothing data.

```
In[11]:= kern = Table[Exp[-n^2/100.], {n, -128, 127}] ;
```

Here is a plot of the convolution kernel.

```
In[12]:= ListPlot[kern, PlotRange -> All]
```

This puts the convolution kernel in a form suitable for use in a discrete Fourier transform.

```
In[13]:= kern = RotateLeft[kern, 128]/Apply[Plus, kern] ;
```

The convolution is done by multiplying the Fourier transform of the data by the Fourier transform of the kernel, then taking the inverse Fourier transform of the result.

```
In[14]:= conv = InverseFourier[
               Sqrt[256] Fourier[data] Fourier[kern] ] ;
```

This plots the result. The Chop removes small imaginary parts that are generated in the Fourier transforms. The final plot is a smoothed version of the original data.

In[15]:= `ListPlot[ Chop[conv] ]`

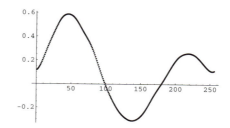

Fourier[{{a_{11}, a_{12}, ... }, {a_{21}, a_{22}, ... }, ... }]
                              two-dimensional Fourier transform

Two-dimensional Fourier transform.

Mathematica can find Fourier transforms for data in any number of dimensions. In *n* dimensions, the data is specified by a list nested *n* levels deep. Two-dimensional Fourier transforms are often used in image processing.

3.9 Numerical Operations on Functions

■ 3.9.1 Numerical Mathematics in *Mathematica*

One of the most important features of *Mathematica* is its ability to give you exact, symbolic, results for computations. There are, however, computations where it is just mathematically impossible to get exact "closed form" results. In such cases, you can still often get approximate numerical results.

There is no "closed form" result for $\int_0^1 \sin(\sin(x))\,dx$. *Mathematica* returns the integral in symbolic form.

```
In[1]:= Integrate[Sin[Sin[x]], {x, 0, 1}]
```
$$Out[1]= \int_0^1 \text{Sin}[\text{Sin}[x]]\,dx$$

You can now take the symbolic form of the integral, and ask for its approximate numerical value.

```
In[2]:= N[%]
```
$Out[2]= 0.430606$

When *Mathematica* cannot find an explicit result for something like a definite integral, it returns a symbolic form. You can take this symbolic form, and try to get an approximate numerical value by applying N.

By giving a second argument to N, you can specify the numerical precision to use.

```
In[3]:= N[ Integrate[Sin[Sin[x]], {x, 0, 1}], 40 ]
```
$Out[3]= 0.4306061031206906049123773552484658$

If you want to evaluate an integral numerically in *Mathematica*, then using Integrate and applying N to the result is not the most efficient way to do it. It is better instead to use the function NIntegrate, which immediately gives a numerical answer, without first trying to get an exact, symbolic, result. You should realize that even when Integrate does not in the end manage to give you an exact result, it may spend a lot of time trying to do so.

NIntegrate evaluates numerical integrals directly, without first trying to get a symbolic result.

```
In[4]:= NIntegrate[ Sin[Sin[x]], {x, 0, 1} ]
```
$Out[4]= 0.430606$

Integrate	NIntegrate	definite integrals
Sum	NSum	sums
Product	NProduct	products
Solve	NSolve	solutions of algebraic equations
DSolve	NDSolve	solutions of differential equations

Symbolic and numerical versions of some *Mathematica* functions.

■ 3.9.2 The Uncertainties of Numerical Mathematics

Mathematica does operations like numerical integration very differently from the way it does their symbolic counterparts.

When you do a symbolic integral, *Mathematica* takes the functional form of the integrand you have given, and applies a sequence of exact symbolic transformation rules to it, to try and evaluate the integral.

When you do a numerical integral, however, *Mathematica* does not look directly at the functional form of the integrand you have given. Instead, it simply finds a sequence of numerical values of the integrand at particular points, then takes these values and tries to deduce from them a good approximation to the integral.

An important point to realize is that when *Mathematica* does a numerical integral, the *only* information it has about your integrand is a sequence of numerical values for it. To get a definite result for the integral, *Mathematica* then effectively has to make certain assumptions about the smoothness and other properties of your integrand. If you give a sufficiently pathological integrand, these assumptions may not be valid, and as a result, *Mathematica* may simply give you the wrong answer for the integral.

This problem may occur, for example, if you try to integrate numerically a function which has a very thin spike at a particular position. *Mathematica* samples your function at a number of points, and then assumes that the function varies smoothly between these points. As a result, if none of the sample points come close to the spike, then the spike will go undetected, and its contribution to the numerical integral will not be correctly included.

Here is a plot of the function $\exp(-x^2)$.　　*In[1]:=* **Plot[Exp[-x^2], {x, -10, 10}, PlotRange->All]**

NIntegrate gives the correct answer for the numerical integral of this function from -10 to $+10$.

In[2]:= **NIntegrate[Exp[-x^2], {x, -10, 10}]**

Out[2]= 1.77245

If, however, you ask for the integral from −1000 to 1000, NIntegrate will miss the peak near $x = 0$, and give the wrong answer.

```
In[3]:= NIntegrate[Exp[-x^2], {x, -1000, 1000}]

NIntegrate::ploss:
    Numerical integration stopping due to loss of
    precision. Achieved neither the requested
    PrecisionGoal nor AccuracyGoal; suspect one of the
    following: highly oscillatory integrand or the true
    value of the integral is 0. If your integrand is
    oscillatory try using the option Method->Oscillatory
    in NIntegrate.
```

$Out[3]= 1.34946 \times 10^{-26}$

Although NIntegrate follows the principle of looking only at the numerical values of your integrand, it nevertheless tries to make the best possible use of the information that it can get. Thus, for example, if NIntegrate notices that the estimated error in the integral in a particular region is large, it will take more samples in that region. In this way, NIntegrate tries to "adapt" its operation to the particular integrand you have given.

The kind of adaptive procedure that NIntegrate uses is similar, at least in spirit, to what Plot does in trying to draw smooth curves for functions. In both cases, *Mathematica* tries to go on taking more samples in a particular region until it has effectively found a smooth approximation to the function in that region.

The kinds of problems that can appear in numerical integration can also arise in doing other numerical operations on functions.

For example, if you ask for a numerical approximation to the sum of an infinite series, *Mathematica* samples a certain number of terms in the series, and then does an extrapolation to estimate the contributions of other terms. If you insert large terms far out in the series, they may not be detected when the extrapolation is done, and the result you get for the sum may be incorrect.

A similar problem arises when you try to find a numerical approximation to the minimum of a function. *Mathematica* samples only a finite number of values, then effectively assumes that the actual function interpolates smoothly between these values. If in fact the function has a sharp dip in a particular region, then *Mathematica* may miss this dip, and you may get the wrong answer for the minimum.

If you work only with numerical values of functions, there is simply no way to avoid the kinds of problems we have been discussing. Exact symbolic computation, of course, allows you to get around these problems.

In many calculations, it is therefore worthwhile to go as far as you can symbolically, and then resort to numerical methods only at the very end. This gives you the best chance of avoiding the problems that can arise in purely numerical computations.

One might imagine that you could use symbolic methods to check for any features, say in the integrand of a numerical integral, that would give rise to problems in numerical computation. As soon as your integrand contains conditionals, control structures or nested function calls, there can be no general procedure, however, to do the tests that are needed. Nevertheless, for specific classes of integrands, it may be possible to perform some such tests. You can always implement these tests by defining special rules for `NIntegrate` in certain cases.

■ 3.9.3 Numerical Integration

`N[Integrate[`*expr*`, {`*x*`, `*xmin*`, `*xmax*`}]]`	try to perform an integral exactly, then find numerical approximations to the parts that remain
`NIntegrate[`*expr*`, {`*x*`, `*xmin*`, `*xmax*`}]`	find a numerical approximation to an integral
`NIntegrate[`*expr*`, {`*x*`, `*xmin*`, `*xmax*`}, {`*y*`, `*ymin*`, `*ymax*`}, ... ]`	multidimensional numerical integral $\int_{xmin}^{xmax} dx \int_{ymin}^{ymax} dy \ldots expr$
`NIntegrate[`*expr*`, {`*x*`, `*xmin*`, `*x*$_1$`, `*x*$_2$`, ... , `*xmax*`}]`	do a numerical integral along a line, starting at *xmin*, going through the points x_i, and ending at *xmax*

Numerical integration functions.

This finds a numerical approximation to the integral $\int_0^\infty e^{-x^3} dx$.	`In[1]:= NIntegrate[Exp[-x^3], {x, 0, Infinity}]` `Out[1]= 0.892979`
Here is the numerical value of the double integral $\int_{-1}^1 dx \int_{-1}^1 dy\,(x^2 + y^2)$.	`In[2]:= NIntegrate[x^2 + y^2, {x, -1, 1}, {y, -1, 1}]` `Out[2]= 2.66667`

An important feature of `NIntegrate` is its ability to deal with functions that "blow up" at known points. `NIntegrate` automatically checks for such problems at the end points of the integration region.

The function $1/\sqrt{x}$ blows up at $x = 0$, but `NIntegrate` still succeeds in getting the correct value for the integral.	`In[3]:= NIntegrate[1/Sqrt[x], {x, 0, 1}]` `Out[3]= 2.`
Mathematica can find the integral of $1/\sqrt{x}$ exactly.	`In[4]:= Integrate[1/Sqrt[x], {x, 0, 1}]` `Out[4]= 2`

NIntegrate detects that the singularity in $1/x$ at $x = 0$ is not integrable.

```
In[5]:= NIntegrate[1/x, {x, 0, 1}]

NIntegrate::slwcon:
    Numerical integration converging too slowly; suspect
    one of the following: singularity, oscillatory
    integrand, or insufficient WorkingPrecision. If your
    integrand is oscillatory try using the option
    Method->Oscillatory in NIntegrate.

NIntegrate::ncvb:
    NIntegrate failed to converge to prescribed accuracy
    after 7 recursive bisections in x near x =
                                 -57
            4.36999 10    .

Out[5]= 23953.1
```

NIntegrate does not automatically look for singularities except at the end points of your integration region. When other singularities are present, NIntegrate may not give you the right answer for the integral. Nevertheless, in following its adaptive procedure, NIntegrate will often detect the presence of potentially singular behavior, and will warn you about it.

NIntegrate does not handle the singularity in $1/\sqrt{|x|}$ in the middle of the integration region. However, it warns you of a possible problem. In this case, the final result is numerically quite close to the correct answer.

```
In[6]:= NIntegrate[1/Sqrt[Abs[x]], {x, -1, 2}]

NIntegrate::slwcon:
    Numerical integration converging too slowly; suspect
    one of the following: singularity, oscillatory
    integrand, or insufficient WorkingPrecision. If your
    integrand is oscillatory try using the option
    Method->Oscillatory in NIntegrate.

NIntegrate::ncvb:
    NIntegrate failed to converge to prescribed accuracy
    after 7 recursive bisections in x near x =
    -0.00390625.

Out[6]= 4.79343
```

If you know that your integrand has singularities at particular points, you can explicitly tell NIntegrate to deal with them. NIntegrate[*expr*, {x, *xmin*, x_1, x_2, ... , *xmax*}] integrates *expr* from *xmin* to *xmax*, looking for possible singularities at each of the intermediate points x_i.

This again gives the integral $\int_{-1}^{2} 1/\sqrt{|x|}\, dx$, but now explicitly deals with the singularity at $x = 0$.

```
In[7]:= NIntegrate[1/Sqrt[Abs[x]], {x, -1, 0, 2}]
Out[7]= 4.82843
```

You can also use the list of intermediate points x_i in NIntegrate to specify an integration contour to follow in the complex plane. The contour is taken to consist of a sequence of line segments, starting at *xmin*, going through each of the x_i, and ending at *xmax*.

This integrates $1/x$ around a closed contour in the complex plane, going from -1, through the points $-i$, 1 and i, then back to -1.

```
In[8]:= NIntegrate[1/x, {x, -1, -I, 1, I, -1}]
Out[8]= 1.11022×10⁻¹⁶ + 6.28318 I
```

The integral gives $2\pi i$, as expected from Cauchy's Theorem.

```
In[9]:= N[ 2 Pi I ]
Out[9]= 6.28318 I
```

There are a number of ways you can control the operation of NIntegrate. First, you may want to specify the accuracy of the answers you are trying to get. If you use Integrate, and then apply N to get numerical results, then the second argument you give to N specifies the precision to use in the internal computations used to do the numerical integral. You can also specify this precision using the option WorkingPrecision -> *n* for NIntegrate.

You should realize, however, that the option WorkingPrecision specifies only the precision to use for internal computations done by NIntegrate. The final answer that NIntegrate gives will almost always have a lower precision. You can nevertheless use NIntegrate to try and get an answer with a particular precision or accuracy by setting the options PrecisionGoal or AccuracyGoal. The default setting PrecisionGoal -> Automatic attempts to get answers with a precision equal to WorkingPrecision minus 10 digits. In general, NIntegrate continues until it achieves either of the goals specified by PrecisionGoal or AccuracyGoal.

This evaluates $\int_1^2 dx/x$ using 40-digit precision for internal computations. The precision goal in this case is automatically set to 30 digits.	*In[10]:=* **NIntegrate[1/x, {x, 1, 2}, WorkingPrecision->40]** *Out[10]=* 0.6931471805599453094172321214581766
The difference from the exact result is consistent with 0.	*In[11]:=* **% - N[Log[2], 40]** *Out[11]=* $0. \times 10^{-34}$
In fact, the result was correct to about 33 digits.	*In[12]:=* **Accuracy[%]** *Out[12]=* 33

option name	default value	
AccuracyGoal	Infinity	number of digits of accuracy to try and get in the final answer
PrecisionGoal	Automatic	number of digits of precision to try and get in the final answer
MinRecursion	0	minimum number of recursive subdivisions of the integration region
MaxRecursion	6	maximum number of recursive subdivisions of the integration region
SingularityDepth	4	number of recursive subdivisions to use before doing a change of variables at the end points
+ MaxPoints	Automatic	maximum total number of times to sample the integrand
WorkingPrecision	$MachinePrecision	number of digits to use in internal computations
Compiled	True	whether the integrand should be compiled

Options for NIntegrate.

When NIntegrate tries to evaluate a numerical integral, it samples the integrand at a sequence of points. If it finds that the integrand changes rapidly in a particular region, then it recursively takes more sample points in that region. The parameters MinRecursion and MaxRecursion specify the minimum and maximum number of levels of recursive subdivision to use. Increasing the value of MinRecursion guarantees that NIntegrate will use a larger number of sample points. MaxRecursion limits the number of sample points which NIntegrate will ever try to use. Increasing MinRecursion or MaxRecursion will make NIntegrate work more slowly. SingularityDepth specifies how many levels of recursive subdivision NIntegrate should try before it concludes that the integrand is "blowing up" at one of the endpoints, and does a change of variables.

With the default settings for all options, NIntegrate misses the peak in $\exp(-x^2)$ near $x = 0$, and gives the wrong answer for the integral.

```
In[13]:= NIntegrate[Exp[-x^2], {x, -1000, 1000}]

NIntegrate::ploss:
    Numerical integration stopping due to loss of
    precision. Achieved neither the requested
    PrecisionGoal nor AccuracyGoal; suspect one of the
    following: highly oscillatory integrand or the true
    value of the integral is 0. If your integrand is
    oscillatory try using the option Method->Oscillatory
    in NIntegrate.

Out[13]= 1.34946×10^-26
```

With the option MinRecursion->3, NIntegrate samples enough points that it notices the peak around $x = 0$. With the default setting of MaxRecursion, however, NIntegrate cannot use enough sample points to be able to expect an accurate answer.

```
In[14]:= NIntegrate[Exp[-x^2], {x, -1000, 1000},
                                        MinRecursion->3]
NIntegrate::ncvb:
    NIntegrate failed to converge to prescribed accuracy
        after 7 recursive bisections in x near x = 7.8125.
Out[14]= 0.991869
```

With this setting of MaxRecursion, NIntegrate can get an accurate answer for the integral.

```
In[15]:= NIntegrate[Exp[-x^2], {x, -1000, 1000},
                        MinRecursion->3, MaxRecursion->10]
Out[15]= 1.77245
```

Another way to solve the problem is to make NIntegrate break the integration region into several pieces, with a small piece that explicitly covers the neighborhood of the peak.

```
In[16]:= NIntegrate[Exp[-x^2], {x, -1000, -10, 10, 1000}]
Out[16]= 1.77245
```

For integrals in many dimensions, it can take a long time for NIntegrate to get a precise answer. However, by setting the option MaxPoints, you can tell NIntegrate to give you just a rough estimate, sampling the integrand only a limited number of times.

This gives an estimate of the volume of the unit sphere in three dimensions.

```
In[17]:= NIntegrate[If[x^2 + y^2 + z^2 < 1, 1, 0], {x, -1, 1},
                        {y, -1, 1}, {z, -1, 1}, MaxPoints->10000]
Out[17]= 4.2
```

Here is the precise result.

```
In[18]:= N[4/3 Pi]
Out[18]= 4.18879
```

■ 3.9.4 Numerical Evaluation of Sums and Products

NSum[f, {i, $imin$, $imax$}]	find a numerical approximation to the sum $\sum_{i=imin}^{imax} xf$
NSum[f, {i, $imin$, $imax$, di}]	use step di in the sum
NProduct[f, {i, $imin$, $imax$}]	find a numerical approximation to the product $\prod_{i=imin}^{imax} xf$

Numerical sums and products.

This gives a numerical approximation to $\sum_{i=1}^{\infty} \frac{1}{i^3+i!}$.

```
In[1]:= NSum[1/(i^3 + i!), {i, 1, Infinity}]
Out[1]= 0.64703
```

There is no exact result for this sum, so *Mathematica* leaves it in a symbolic form.

```
In[2]:= Sum[1/(i^3 + i!), {i, 1, Infinity}]
```
$$Out[2]= \sum_{i=1}^{\infty} \frac{1}{i^3 + i!}$$

You can apply N explicitly to get a numerical result.

In[3]:= **N[%]**

Out[3]= 0.64703

The way NSum works is to include a certain number of terms explicitly, and then to try and estimate the contribution of the remaining ones. There are two approaches to estimating this contribution. The first uses the Euler-Maclaurin method, and is based on approximating the sum by an integral. The second method, known as the Wynn epsilon method, samples a number of additional terms in the sum, and then tries to fit them to a polynomial multiplied by a decaying exponential.

option name	default value	
AccuracyGoal	Infinity	number of digits of accuracy to try and get in the Euler-Maclaurin method
PrecisionGoal	Automatic	number of digits of precision to try and get in the Euler-Maclaurin method
WorkingPrecision	$MachinePrecision	number of digits of precision to use in internal computations
Method	Automatic	Integrate (Euler-Maclaurin method) or Fit (Wynn epsilon method)
NSumTerms	15	number of terms to include explicitly
NSumExtraTerms	12	number of terms to use for extrapolation in the Wynn epsilon method
Compiled	True	whether to compile the summand

Options for NSum.

If you do not explicitly specify the method to use, NSum will try to choose between the methods it knows. In any case, some implicit assumptions about the functions you are summing have to be made. If these assumptions are not correct, you may get inaccurate answers.

The most common place to use NSum is in evaluating sums with infinite limits. You can, however, also use it for sums with finite limits. By making implicit assumptions about the objects you are evaluating, NSum can often avoid doing as many function evaluations as an explicit Sum computation would require.

This finds the numerical value of $\sum_{n=0}^{100} e^{-n}$ by extrapolation techniques.

In[4]:= **NSum[Exp[-n], {n, 0, 100}]**

Out[4]= 1.58198

You can also get the result, albeit much less efficiently, by constructing the symbolic form of the sum, then evaluating it numerically.

In[5]:= **Sum[Exp[-n], {n, 0, 100}] //N**

Out[5]= 1.58198

NProduct works in essentially the same way as NSum, with analogous options.

■ 3.9.5 Numerical Solution of Polynomial Equations

When Solve cannot find explicit solutions to polynomial equations, it returns a symbolic form of the result in terms of Root objects.

```
In[1]:= Solve[x^5 + 7x + 1 == 0, x]
```
$Out[1]= \{\{x \to \text{Root}[1 + 7\#1 + \#1^5\&, 1]\},$
$\qquad \{x \to \text{Root}[1 + 7\#1 + \#1^5\&, 2]\},$
$\qquad \{x \to \text{Root}[1 + 7\#1 + \#1^5\&, 3]\},$
$\qquad \{x \to \text{Root}[1 + 7\#1 + \#1^5\&, 4]\},$
$\qquad \{x \to \text{Root}[1 + 7\#1 + \#1^5\&, 5]\}\}$

You can get numerical solutions by applying N.

```
In[2]:= N[%]
```
$Out[2]= \{\{x \to -0.142849\}, \{x \to -1.11308 - 1.15173\,I\},$
$\qquad \{x \to -1.11308 + 1.15173\,I\}, \{x \to 1.1845 - 1.15139\,I\},$
$\qquad \{x \to 1.1845 + 1.15139\,I\}\}$

This gives the numerical solutions to 25-digit precision.

```
In[3]:= N[%%, 25]
```
$Out[3]= \{\{x \to -0.1428486455250044341134 1155\},$
$\qquad \{x \to -1.113077976547710735600 3979 -$
$\qquad\qquad 1.1517343621516743050467702\,I\},$
$\qquad \{x \to -1.113077976547710735600 3979 +$
$\qquad\qquad 1.1517343621516743050467702\,I\},$
$\qquad \{x \to 1.1845022993102129526571037 -$
$\qquad\qquad 1.1513900754088370746991467\,I\},$
$\qquad \{x \to 1.1845022993102129526571037 +$
$\qquad\qquad 1.1513900754088370746991467\,I\}\}$

You can use NSolve to get numerical solutions to polynomial equations directly, without first trying to find exact results.

```
In[4]:= NSolve[x^7 + x + 1 == 0, x]
```
$Out[4]= \{\{x \to -0.796544\}, \{x \to -0.705298 - 0.637624\,I\},$
$\qquad \{x \to -0.705298 + 0.637624\,I\},$
$\qquad \{x \to 0.123762 - 1.05665\,I\},$
$\qquad \{x \to 0.123762 + 1.05665\,I\},$
$\qquad \{x \to 0.979808 - 0.516677\,I\},$
$\qquad \{x \to 0.979808 + 0.516677\,I\}\}$

NSolve[*poly*==0, *x*]	get approximate numerical solutions to a polynomial equation
NSolve[*poly*==0, *x*, *n*]	get solutions to *n*-digit precision

Numerical solution of polynomial equations.

NSolve will always give you the complete set of numerical solutions to any polynomial equation in one variable.

You can also get numerical solutions to sets of simultaneous polynomial equations. You can use Solve to "unwind" the simultaneous equations, and then apply N to get numerical results.

Solve writes the solution in terms of roots of a polynomial in one variable.

In[5]:= **First[**
       Solve[{x^2 + y^2 == 1, x^3 + y^3 == 2}, {x, y}]]

$Out[5]= \left\{ x \rightarrow \frac{1}{3} \text{Root}[3 + 3\#1^2 - 4\#1^3 - 3\#1^4 + 2\#1^6 \&, 1] \right.$

$\left(-3 - 6\,\text{Root}[3 + 3\#1^2 - 4\#1^3 - 3\#1^4 + 2\#1^6 \&, 1] - \right.$

$\text{Root}[3 + 3\#1^2 - 4\#1^3 - 3\#1^4 + 2\#1^6 \&, 1]^2 +$

$4\,\text{Root}[3 + 3\#1^2 - 4\#1^3 - 3\#1^4 + 2\#1^6 \&, 1]^3 +$

$\left. 2\,\text{Root}[3 + 3\#1^2 - 4\#1^3 - 3\#1^4 + 2\#1^6 \&, 1]^4 \right),$

$\left. y \rightarrow \text{Root}[3 + 3\#1^2 - 4\#1^3 - 3\#1^4 + 2\#1^6 \&, 1] \right\}$

You can apply N to get a numerical result.

In[6]:= **N[%]**

$Out[6]= \{x \rightarrow -1.09791 + 0.839887\,I, y \rightarrow -1.09791 - 0.839887\,I\}$

■ 3.9.6 Numerical Root Finding

NSolve gives you a general way to find numerical approximations to the solutions of polynomial equations. Finding numerical solutions to more general equations, however, can be much more difficult, as discussed in Section 3.4.2. FindRoot gives you a way to search for a numerical solution to an arbitrary equation, or set of equations.

FindRoot[*lhs*==*rhs*, {*x*, x_0}]	search for a numerical solution to the equation *lhs*==*rhs*, starting with $x=x_0$
FindRoot[*lhs*==*rhs*, {*x*, {x_0, x_1}}]	search for a solution using x_0 and x_1 as the first two values of x (this form must be used if symbolic derivatives of the equation cannot be found)
FindRoot[*lhs*==*rhs*, {*x*, *xstart*, *xmin*, *xmax*}]	search for a solution, stopping the search if x ever gets outside the range *xmin* to *xmax*
FindRoot[{eqn_1, eqn_2, ... }, {*x*, x_0}, {*y*, y_0}, ...]	search for a numerical solution to the simultaneous equations eqn_i

Numerical root finding.

The curves for cos(*x*) and *x* intersect at one point.

In[1]:= **Plot[{Cos[x], x}, {x, -1, 1}]**

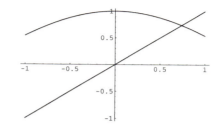

This finds a numerical approximation to the value of *x* at which the intersection occurs. The 0 tells FindRoot what value of *x* to try first.

In[2]:= **FindRoot[Cos[x] == x, {x, 0}]**

Out[2]= {x → 0.739085}

In trying to find a solution to your equation, FindRoot starts at the point you specify, and then progressively tries to get closer and closer to a solution. Even if your equations have several solutions, FindRoot always returns the first solution it finds. Which solution this is will depend on what starting point you chose. So long as you start sufficiently close to a particular solution, FindRoot will always return that solution.

The equation sin(*x*) = 0 has an infinite number of solutions of the form $x = n\pi$. If you start sufficiently close to a particular solution, FindRoot will give you that solution.

In[3]:= **FindRoot[Sin[x] == 0, {x, 3}]**

Out[3]= {x → 3.14159}

If you start with *x* = 6, you get a numerical approximation to the solution $x = 2\pi$.

In[4]:= **FindRoot[Sin[x] == 0, {x, 6}]**

Out[4]= {x → 6.28318}

This is what happens if FindRoot cannot find a solution to your equation.

In[5]:= **FindRoot[Sin[x] == 2, {x, 1}]**

FindRoot::cvnwt:
    Newton's method failed to converge to the prescribed
      accuracy after 15 iterations.

Out[5]= {x → -10.3883}

If you want FindRoot to search for complex solutions to this equation, then you have to give a complex starting value.

In[6]:= **FindRoot[Sin[x] == 2, {x, I}]**

Out[6]= {x → 1.5708 + 1.31696 I}

You can give FindRoot bounds on the region in which you want it to look for solutions.

This tells FindRoot to try values of x starting at 1, but never going outside the region 0.5 to 1.5. In this case, FindRoot finds no solutions in the region you specified.

In[7]:= **FindRoot[Sin[x] == 0, {x, 1, 0.5, 1.5}]**

FindRoot::regex:
    Reached the point {-0.557408}
      which is outside the region {{0.5, 1.5}}.

Out[7]= {x → -0.557408}

Picking good starting points is crucial in getting useful answers from FindRoot. To know how to pick good starting points, you need to understand a little about how FindRoot actually works.

In the simplest case, FindRoot uses *Newton's method*. To find a solution to an equation of the form $f(x) = 0$, the method starts at x_0, then uses knowledge of the derivative f' to take a sequence of steps toward a solution. Each new point x_n that it tries is found from the previous point x_{n-1} by the formula $x_n = x_{n-1} - f(x_{n-1})/f'(x_{n-1})$.

One important limitation of Newton's method is that it "gets stuck" if it ever gets to a point where the derivative of the function vanishes. You can usually avoid this problem by choosing starting points that have no special properties with respect to the equations you are trying to solve.

The derivative of $x^2 - 1$ is zero at the starting point $x = 0$. As a result FindRoot cannot decide whether to take its first step in the positive or the negative direction.

```
In[8]:= FindRoot[x^2 - 1 == 0, {x, 0}]

FindRoot::jsing:
    Encountered a singular Jacobian at the point
        x = 0.. Try perturbing the initial point(s).

Out[8]= FindRoot[x^2 - 1 == 0, {x, 0}]
```

If you start at a random point, however, FindRoot will usually succeed in finding a solution.

```
In[9]:= FindRoot[x^2 - 1 == 0, {x, Random[ ]}]
Out[9]= {x → 1.}
```

FindRoot uses versions of Newton's method in many cases. Especially when there are several variables, the precise set of starting points which lead to a particular solution can become extremely complicated. The best policy is to try and start as close to the solution as possible, and to avoid any "special points".

This finds a solution to a set of simultaneous equations. It is a good idea to avoid taking the starting values for x and y to be equal, or in any other way "special".

```
In[10]:= FindRoot[{Sin[x] == Cos[y], x + y == 1},
                  {x, .1}, {y, .2}]
Out[10]= {x → 1.2854, y → -0.285398}
```

If the functions that appear in your equations are sufficiently simple, then *Mathematica* will be able to find their derivatives symbolically. In all the examples of FindRoot that we have used so far, this is possible. As a result, FindRoot can use the formula for Newton's method directly.

If, on the other hand, FindRoot has to estimate the derivative of your functions numerically, then it must take another approach. In simple cases, the approach it uses is based on the "secant method". One feature of this method is that to get it started, you have to specify not just the first value to try, but rather the first *two* values.

This specifies the first two values of x to try.

```
In[11]:= FindRoot[Cos[x] == x, {x, {0, 1}}]
Out[11]= {x → 0.739085}
```

If *Mathematica* cannot get an explicit formula for the derivative of what appears in your equation, you must specify the first two values to try. Here FindRoot finds a zero of the Riemann zeta function.	*In[12]:=* **FindRoot[Zeta[1/2 + I t] == 0, {t, {12, 13}}]** *Out[12]=* {t → 14.1347 − 4.42626×10⁻⁷ I}

If you are finding a root of a function of one variable, and the first two points you tell FindRoot to try give values of the function with opposite signs, then FindRoot is guaranteed to find a root. (This is true so long as your function is real and satisfies some basic continuity conditions.)

option name	default value	
AccuracyGoal	Automatic	the accuracy with which functions must be zero in order to be accepted as a solution
WorkingPrecision	$MachinePrecision	the number of digits of precision to keep in internal computations
MaxIterations	15	the maximum number of steps to take in trying to find a solution
Compiled	True	whether to compile the function

Options for FindRoot.

There are several options you can use to control the operation of FindRoot. First, you can set MaxIterations to specify the maximum number of steps that FindRoot should use in attempting to find a solution. Even if FindRoot does not successfully find a solution in the number of steps you specify, it returns the most recent values it has tried. If you want to continue the search, you can then give these values as starting points.

To work out whether it has found an acceptable root, FindRoot evaluates your function and sees whether the result is zero to within the accuracy specified by the option AccuracyGoal. FindRoot will always print a warning message if it does not find a solution to within the specified accuracy. In doing internal computations, FindRoot uses the precision specified by the option WorkingPrecision. The default AccuracyGoal is 10 digits less than WorkingPrecision.

This specifies that the zeta function needs to be zero to 10-digit accuracy at the solution. The Riemann hypothesis asserts that the imaginary part of t should be exactly zero.	*In[13]:=* **FindRoot[Zeta[1/2 + I t] == 0, {t, {12, 13}},** **AccuracyGoal -> 10]** *Out[13]=* {t → 14.1347 + 1.79054×10⁻¹¹ I}

■ 3.9.7 Numerical Solution of Differential Equations

The function NDSolve discussed in Section 1.6.4 allows you to find numerical solutions to differential equations. NDSolve handles both single differential equations, and sets of simultaneous differential equations. It can handle a wide range of *ordinary differential equations* as well as some *partial differential equations*. In a system of ordinary differential equations there can be any number of unknown functions y_i, but all of these functions must depend on a single "independent variable" x, which is the same for each function. Partial differential equations involve two or more independent variables.

NDSolve[{eqn_1, eqn_2, ... }, y, {x, $xmin$, $xmax$}]	find a numerical solution for the function y with x in the range $xmin$ to $xmax$
NDSolve[{eqn_1, eqn_2, ... }, {y_1, y_2, ... }, {x, $xmin$, $xmax$}]	find numerical solutions for several functions y_i

Finding numerical solutions to ordinary differential equations.

NDSolve represents solutions for the functions y_i as InterpolatingFunction objects. The InterpolatingFunction objects provide approximations to the y_i over the range of values $xmin$ to $xmax$ for the independent variable x.

NDSolve finds solutions iteratively. It starts at a particular value of x, then takes a sequence of steps, trying eventually to cover the whole range $xmin$ to $xmax$.

In order to get started, NDSolve has to be given appropriate initial or boundary conditions for the y_i and their derivatives. These conditions specify values for $y_i[x]$, and perhaps derivatives $y_i'[x]$, at particular points x. In general, at least for ordinary differential equations, the conditions you give can be at any x: NDSolve will automatically cover the range $xmin$ to $xmax$.

This finds a solution for y with x in the range 0 to 2, using an initial condition for y[0].

```
In[1]:= NDSolve[{y'[x] == y[x], y[0] == 1}, y, {x, 0, 2}]
Out[1]= {{y → InterpolatingFunction[{{0., 2.}}, <>]}}
```

This still finds a solution with x in the range 0 to 2, but now the initial condition is for y[3].

```
In[2]:= NDSolve[{y'[x] == y[x], y[3] == 1}, y, {x, 0, 2}]
Out[2]= {{y → InterpolatingFunction[{{0., 2.}}, <>]}}
```

Here is a simple boundary value problem.

```
In[3]:= NDSolve[{y''[x] + x y[x] == 0, y[0] == 1, y[1] == -1},
          y, {x, 0, 1}]
Out[3]= {{y → InterpolatingFunction[{{0., 1.}}, <>]}}
```

When you use NDSolve, the initial or boundary conditions you give must be sufficient to determine the solutions for the y_i completely. When you use DSolve to find symbolic solutions to differential equations, you can get away with specifying fewer initial conditions. The reason is that DSolve automatically inserts arbitrary constants C[i] to represent degrees of freedom associated with initial conditions that you have not specified explicitly. Since NDSolve must give a numerical solution, it cannot represent these kinds of additional degrees of freedom. As a result, you must explicitly give all the initial or boundary conditions that are needed to determine the solution.

In a typical case, if you have differential equations with up to n^{th} derivatives, then you need to give initial conditions for up to $(n-1)^{th}$ derivatives, or give boundary conditions at n points.

With a third-order equation, you need to give initial conditions for up to second derivatives.

```
In[4]:= NDSolve[
            { y'''[x] + 8 y''[x] + 17 y'[x] + 10 y[x] == 0,
              y[0] == 6, y'[0] == -20, y''[0] == 84},
              y, {x, 0, 1} ]

Out[4]= {{y → InterpolatingFunction[{{0., 1.}}, <>]}}
```

This plots the solution obtained.

```
In[5]:= Plot[Evaluate[ y[x] /. % ], {x, 0, 1}]
```

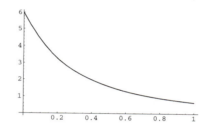

With a third-order equation, you can also give boundary conditions at three points.

```
In[6]:= NDSolve[
            { y'''[x] + Sin[x] == 0,
              y[0] == 4, y[1] == 7, y[2] == 0 }, y, {x, 0, 2}]

Out[6]= {{y → InterpolatingFunction[{{0., 2.}}, <>]}}
```

Mathematica allows you to use any appropriate linear combination of function values and derivatives as boundary conditions.

```
In[7]:= NDSolve[{ y''[x] + y[x] == 12 x,
            2 y[0] - y'[0] == -1, 2 y[1] + y'[1] == 9},
              y, {x, 0, 1}]

Out[7]= {{y → InterpolatingFunction[{{0., 1.}}, <>]}}
```

In most cases, all the initial conditions you give must involve the same value of x, say x_0. As a result, you can avoid giving both *xmin* and *xmax* explicitly. If you specify your range of x as $\{x, x_1\}$, then *Mathematica* will automatically generate a solution over the range x_0 to x_1.

This generates a solution over the range 0 to 2.

```
In[8]:= NDSolve[{y'[x] == y[x], y[0] == 1}, y, {x, 2}]

Out[8]= {{y → InterpolatingFunction[{{0., 2.}}, <>]}}
```

You can give initial conditions as equations of any kind. In some cases, these equations may have multiple solutions. In such cases, NDSolve will correspondingly generate multiple solutions.

The initial conditions in this case lead to multiple solutions.

```
In[9]:= NDSolve[{y'[x]^2 - y[x]^2 == 0, y[0]^2 == 4},
                 y[x], {x, 1}]

Out[9]= {{y[x] →
            InterpolatingFunction[{{0., 1.}}, <>][x]},
         {y[x] →
            InterpolatingFunction[{{0., 1.}}, <>][x]},
         {y[x] →
            InterpolatingFunction[{{0., 1.}}, <>][x]},
         {y[x] →
            InterpolatingFunction[{{0., 1.}}, <>][x]}}
```

Here is a plot of all the solutions.

```
In[10]:= Plot[Evaluate[ y[x] /. % ], {x, 0, 1}]
```

You can use NDSolve to solve systems of coupled differential equations.

This finds a numerical solution to a pair of coupled equations.

```
In[11]:= sol = NDSolve[
             {x'[t] == -y[t] - x[t]^2, y'[t] == 2 x[t] - y[t],
              x[0] == y[0] == 1}, {x, y}, {t, 10}]

Out[11]= {{x → InterpolatingFunction[{{0., 10.}}, <>],
           y → InterpolatingFunction[{{0., 10.}}, <>]}}
```

This plots the solution for y from these equations.

```
In[12]:= Plot[Evaluate[y[t] /. sol], {t, 0, 10}]
```

This generates a parametric plot using both x and y.

In[13]:= **ParametricPlot[Evaluate[{x[t], y[t]} /. sol],
                    {t, 0, 10}, PlotRange -> All]**

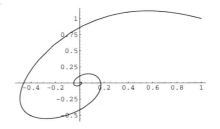

Unknown functions in differential equations do not necessarily have to be represented by single symbols. If you have a large number of unknown functions, you will often find it more convenient, for example, to give the functions names like *y[i]*.

This constructs a set of five coupled differential equations and initial conditions.

In[14]:= **eqns = Join[
            Table[y[i]'[x] == y[i-1][x] - y[i][x], {i, 2, 4}],
            {y[1]'[x] == -y[1][x], y[5]'[x] == y[4][x],
                                        y[1][0] == 1},
            Table[y[i][0] == 0, {i, 2, 5}]
            ]**

Out[14]= {(y[2])'[x] == y[1][x] - y[2][x],
          (y[3])'[x] == y[2][x] - y[3][x],
          (y[4])'[x] == y[3][x] - y[4][x],
          (y[1])'[x] == -y[1][x],
          (y[5])'[x] == y[4][x], y[1][0] == 1, y[2][0] == 0,
          y[3][0] == 0, y[4][0] == 0, y[5][0] == 0}

This solves the equations.

In[15]:= **NDSolve[eqns, Table[y[i], {i, 5}], {x, 10}]**

Out[15]= {{y[1] → InterpolatingFunction[{{0., 10.}}, <>],
          y[2] → InterpolatingFunction[{{0., 10.}}, <>],
          y[3] → InterpolatingFunction[{{0., 10.}}, <>],
          y[4] → InterpolatingFunction[{{0., 10.}}, <>],
          y[5] → InterpolatingFunction[{{0., 10.}}, <>]}}

Here is a plot of the solutions.

$In[16]:=$ **Plot[Evaluate[Table[y[i][x], {i, 5}] /. %],**
{x, 0, 10}]

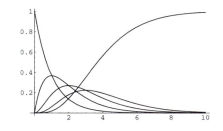

option name	default value	
AccuracyGoal	Automatic	number of digits of accuracy to try and get in the solution
PrecisionGoal	Automatic	number of digits of precision to try and get in the solution
WorkingPrecision	$MachinePrecision	number of digits to use in internal computations
+ InterpolationPrecision	Automatic	number of digits to use in the data for the InterpolationFunction returned
MaxSteps	Automatic	maximum number of steps in x to take
StartingStepSize	Automatic	starting size of step in x to use
+ MaxStepSize	Infinity	maximum size of step in x to use
Compiled	True	whether to compile the equations

Options for NDSolve.

NDSolve allows you to specify the precision or accuracy of result you want. In general, NDSolve makes the steps it takes smaller and smaller until the solution it gets satisfies either the AccuracyGoal *or* the PrecisionGoal you give. The setting for AccuracyGoal effectively determines the absolute error to allow in the solution, while the setting for PrecisionGoal determines the relative error. If you need to track a solution whose value comes close to zero, then you will typically need to increase the setting for AccuracyGoal. By setting AccuracyGoal -> Infinity, you tell NDSolve to use PrecisionGoal only.

NDSolve uses the setting you give for WorkingPrecision to determine the total number of digits to use in its internal computations. If you specify large values for AccuracyGoal or PrecisionGoal, then you typically need to give a somewhat larger value for WorkingPrecision. With the default setting of Automatic, AccuracyGoal and PrecisionGoal are both equal to the setting for WorkingPrecision minus 10 digits.

This generates a high-precision solution to a complex differential equation.

In[17]:= **NDSolve[{y'[x] == I/4 y[x], y[0] == 1}, y, {x, 1},**
        AccuracyGoal -> 20, PrecisionGoal -> 20,
            WorkingPrecision -> 25]

Out[17]= {{y → InterpolatingFunction[{{0, 1.}}, <>]}}

Here is an approximation to $e^{i/4}$ found from the solution.

In[18]:= **y[1] /. %**

Out[18]= {0.96891242171064478411851855 +
    0.24740395925452292962341091I}

As mentioned above, NDSolve works by taking a sequence of steps in the independent variable x. NDSolve uses an adaptive procedure to determine the size of these steps. In general, if the solution appears to be varying rapidly in a particular region, then NDSolve will reduce the step size so as to be able to track the solution better.

This solves a differential equation in which the derivative has a discontinuity.

In[19]:= **NDSolve[**
    {y'[x] == If[x < 0, 1/(x-1), 1/(x+1)],
     y[-5] == 5},
   y, {x, -5, 5}]

Out[19]= {{y → InterpolatingFunction[{{-5., 5.}}, <>]}}

NDSolve reduced the step size around $x = 0$ so as to reproduce the kink accurately.

In[20]:= **Plot[Evaluate[y[x] /. %], {x, -5, 5}]**

Through its adaptive procedure, NDSolve is able to solve "stiff" differential equations in which there are several components which vary with x at very different rates.

In these equations, y varies much more rapidly than z.

In[21]:= **sol = NDSolve[**
    {y'[x] == -40 y[x], z'[x] == -z[x]/10,
               y[0] == z[0] == 1},
   {y, z}, {x, 0, 1}]

Out[21]= {{y → InterpolatingFunction[{{0., 1.}}, <>],
    z → InterpolatingFunction[{{0., 1.}}, <>]}}

NDSolve nevertheless tracks both components successfully.

$In[22]:=$ **Plot[Evaluate[{y[x], z[x]} /. sol], {x, 0, 1},**
                                        PlotRange -> All]

NDSolve follows the general procedure of reducing step size until it tracks solutions accurately. There is a problem, however, when the true solution has a singularity. In this case, NDSolve might go on reducing the step size forever, and never terminate. To avoid this problem, the option MaxSteps specifies the maximum number of steps that NDSolve will ever take in attempting to find a solution. For ordinary differential equations the default setting is MaxSteps -> 1000.

NDSolve stops after taking 1000 steps.

$In[23]:=$ **NDSolve[{y'[x] == -1/x^2, y[-1] == -1}, y[x], {x, -1, 0}]**

NDSolve::mxst:
   Maximum number of 1000 steps reached at the point x ==
                        -22
      -7.57086 10   .

$Out[23]=$ {{y[x] → InterpolatingFunction[
                  {{-1., -7.57086×10^{-22}}}, <>][x]}}

There is in fact a singularity in the solution at $x = 0$.

$In[24]:=$ **Plot[Evaluate[y[x] /. %], {x, -1, 0}]**

The default setting MaxSteps -> 1000 should be sufficient for most equations with smooth solutions. When solutions have a complicated structure, however, you may sometimes have to choose larger settings for MaxSteps. With the setting MaxSteps -> Infinity there is no upper limit on the number of steps used.

To reproduce the full structure of the solution to the Lorenz equations, you need to give a larger setting for MaxSteps.

```
In[25]:= NDSolve[ {x'[t] == -3 (x[t] - y[t]),
                   y'[t] == -x[t] z[t] + 26.5 x[t] - y[t],
                   z'[t] == x[t] y[t] - z[t],
                   x[0] == z[0] == 0, y[0] == 1},
                   {x, y, z}, {t, 0, 20}, MaxSteps->3000 ]

Out[25]= {{x -> InterpolatingFunction[{{0., 20.}}, <>],
           y -> InterpolatingFunction[{{0., 20.}}, <>],
           z -> InterpolatingFunction[{{0., 20.}}, <>]}}
```

Here is a parametric plot of the solution in three dimensions.

```
In[26]:= ParametricPlot3D[Evaluate[{x[t], y[t], z[t]} /. %],
                   {t, 0, 20}, PlotPoints -> 1000]
```

When NDSolve solves a particular set of differential equations, it always tries to choose a step size appropriate for those equations. In some cases, the very first step that NDSolve makes may be too large, and it may miss an important feature in the solution. To avoid this problem, you can explicitly set the option StartingStepSize to specify the size to use for the first step.

NDSolve[{eqn$_1$, eqn$_2$, ... }, y, {x, xmin, xmax}, {t, tmin, tmax}]   solve a system of partial differential equations for y
NDSolve[{eqn$_1$, eqn$_2$, ... }, {y$_1$, y$_2$, ... }, {x, xmin, xmax}, {t, tmin, tmax}]   solve a system of partial differential equations for several functions y$_i$

Finding numerical solutions to partial differential equations.

This finds a numerical solution to the wave equation. The result is a two-dimensional interpolation function.

```
In[27]:= NDSolve[{D[y[x, t], t, t] == D[y[x, t], x, x],
                  y[x, 0] == Exp[-x^2], Derivative[0,1][y][x, 0] == 0,
                  y[-5, t] == y[5, t]}, y, {x, -5, 5}, {t, 0, 5}]

Out[27]= {{y -> InterpolatingFunction[
                  {{-5, 5.}, {0., 5.}}, <>]}}
```

This generates a plot of the result.

```
In[28]:= Plot3D[Evaluate[y[x, t] /. First[%]],
           {x, -5, 5}, {t, 0, 5}, PlotPoints->30]
```

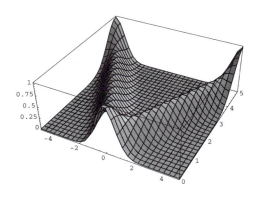

This finds a numerical solution to the nonlinear sine-Gordon equation.

```
In[29]:= NDSolve[{D[y[x, t], t, t] == D[y[x, t], x, x] + Sin[y[x, t]],
           y[x, 0] == Exp[-x^2], Derivative[0,1][y][x, 0] == 0,
           y[-5, t] == y[5, t]}, y, {x, -5, 5}, {t, 0, 5}]

Out[29]= {{y -> InterpolatingFunction[
           {{-5, 5.}, {0., 5.}}, <>]}}
```

Here is a plot of the result.

```
In[30]:= Plot3D[Evaluate[y[x, t] /. First[%]],
           {x, -5, 5}, {t, 0, 5}, PlotPoints->30]
```

■ 3.9.8 Numerical Minimization

FindRoot gives you a way to find points at which a particular function is equal to zero. It is also often important to be able to find points at which a function has its minimum value. In principle, you could do this by applying `FindRoot` to the derivative of the function. In practice, however, there are much more efficient approaches.

`FindMinimum` gives you a way to find a minimum value for a function. As in `FindRoot`, you specify the first one or two points to try, and then `FindMinimum` tries to get progressively more accurate approximations to a minimum. If `FindMinimum` returns a definite result, then the result is guaranteed to correspond to at least a local minimum of your function. However, it is important to understand that the result may not be the global minimum point.

You can understand something about how `FindMinimum` works by thinking of the values of your function as defining the height of a surface. What `FindMinimum` does is essentially to start at the points you specify, then follow the path of steepest descent on the surface. Except in pathological cases, this path always leads to at least a local minimum on the surface. In many cases, however, the minimum will not be a global one. As a simple analogy which illustrates this point, consider a physical mountain. Any water that falls on the mountain takes the path of steepest descent down the side of the mountain. Yet not all the water ends up at the bottom of the valleys; much of it gets stuck in mountain lakes which correspond to local minima of the mountain height function.

You should also realize that because `FindMinimum` does not take truly infinitesimal steps, it is still possible for it to overshoot even a local minimum.

This finds the value of x which minimizes $\Gamma(x)$, starting from $x = 2$.	`In[1]:= FindMinimum[Gamma[x], {x, 2}]`
	
	`Out[1]= {0.885603, {x → 1.46163}}`

Here is a function with many local minima.	`In[2]:= Plot[Sin[x] + x/5, {x, -10, 10}]`

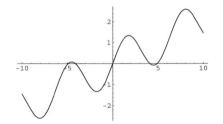

`FindMinimum` finds the local minimum closest to $x = 1$. This is not the global minimum for the function.	`In[3]:= FindMinimum[Sin[x] + x/5, {x, 1}]`
	
	`Out[3]= {-1.33423, {x → -1.77215}}`

This finds the local minimum of a function of two variables. As in `FindRoot`, it is a good idea to choose starting values that are not too "special".	`In[4]:= FindMinimum[x^4 + 3 x^2 y + 5 y^2 + x + y,`
	`                    {x, 0.1}, {y, 0.2}]`
	
	`Out[4]= {-0.832579, {x → -0.886326, y → -0.335672}}`

FindMinimum[*f*, {*x*, *x*₀}]	search for a local minimum in the function *f*, starting from the point $x = x_0$
FindMinimum[*f*, {*x*, {*x*₀, *x*₁}}]	search for a local minimum using x_0 and x_1 as the first two values of *x* (this form must be used if symbolic derivatives of *f* cannot be found)
FindMinimum[*f*, {*x*, *xstart*, *xmin*, *xmax*}]	search for a local minimum, stopping the search if *x* ever gets outside the range *xmin* to *xmax*
FindMinimum[*f*, {*x*, *x*₀}, {*y*, *y*₀}, ...]	search for a local minimum in a function of several variables

Numerical minimization.

■ 3.9.9 Linear Programming

FindMinimum can find local minima for arbitrary functions. In solving optimization problems, it is however often important to be able to find *global* maxima and minima.

Linear programming provides a way to do this for linear functions. In general, linear programming allows you to find the global minimum or maximum of any linear function subject to a set of constraints defined by linear inequalities.

For a function of *n* variables, the constraints effectively define a region in *n*-dimensional space. Each linear inequality gives a plane in *n*-dimensional space which forms one of the sides of the region.

ConstrainedMax[*f*, {*inequalities*}, {*x*, *y*, ... }]	find the global maximum of *f* in the region specified by the inequalities
ConstrainedMin[*f*, {*inequalities*}, {*x*, *y*, ... }]	find the global minimum of *f* in the region specified by the inequalities

Solving linear optimization problems.

The functions ConstrainedMax and ConstrainedMin allow you to specify an "objective function" to maximize or minimize, together with a set of linear constraints on variables. *Mathematica* assumes in all cases that the variables are constrained to have non-negative values.

The maximum value of $x + y$ in this case is attained when $x = 1$ and $y = 2$.

```
In[1]:= ConstrainedMax[x + y, {x < 1, y < 2}, {x, y}]
Out[1]= {3, {x → 1, y → 2}}
```

Mathematica assumes that x and y are constrained to be non-negative.	`In[2]:= ConstrainedMin[x + y, {x < 1, y < 2}, {x, y}]`
	
	`Out[2]= {0, {x → 0, y → 0}}`

Here is a slightly more complicated linear programming problem.	`In[3]:= ConstrainedMax[17x - 20y + 18z,`
	`        {x - y + z < 10, x < 5, x + z > 20}, {x, y, z}]`
	
	`Out[3]= {160, {x → 0, y → 10, z → 20}}`

You can give both exact and approximate numbers as coefficients in linear programming problems. When the numbers you give are exact, *Mathematica* will always generate results in terms of exact rational numbers.

If the coefficients in your input are exact, *Mathematica* will give exact rational numbers in the output.	`In[4]:= ConstrainedMin[x + 3 y + 7 z,`
	`        {x - 3 y < 7, 2 x + 3 z >= 5, x + y + z < 10},`
	`                              {x, y, z}]`
	
	`Out[4]= {`$\frac{5}{2}$`, {x → `$\frac{5}{2}$`, y → 0, z → 0}}`

Mathematica allows you to use both strict inequalities of the form $a < b$ and non-strict inequalities of the form $a <= b$ in specifying linear programming problems. If you work with approximate numbers, then these types of inequalities cannot be distinguished. However, if you work with exact numbers, then these types of inequalities could in principle yield different results.

It turns out that the solution to any linear programming problem always corresponds to a point which lies at the boundary of the region defined for that problem. With non-strict inequalities, the solution point lies actually *on* the boundary. With strict inequalities, however, the solution point in principle lies infinitesimally within the boundary. *Mathematica* ignores this issue when giving exact results for linear programming problems. Thus *Mathematica* may yield a result like x -> 1 when in fact x must in principle be infinitesimally smaller than 1.

As a result of this phenomenon, exact results you get from functions like `ConstrainedMax` may have the property that they do not satisfy strict inequalities that appear in the constraints you specify. The results would however satisfy non-strict versions of the same inequalities.

The result x -> 1 satisfies x <= 1 but not x < 1.	`In[5]:= ConstrainedMax[x, {x < 1}, {x}]`
	
	`Out[5]= {1, {x → 1}}`

`ConstrainedMax` and `ConstrainedMin` allow you to give an arbitrary list of inequalities, as well as equations, to specify constraints between variables. In some cases, these constraints may turn out to be inconsistent. In such cases, `ConstrainedMax` and `ConstrainedMin` return unevaluated.

The constraints given here are inconsistent.	`In[6]:= ConstrainedMax[x, {x < 1, x > 2}, {x}]`
	
	`ConstrainedMax::nsat:`
	`    The specified constraints cannot be satisfied.`
	
	`Out[6]= ConstrainedMax[x, {x < 1, x > 2}, {x}]`

In most practical linear optimization problems, the region corresponding to the constraints you specify is finite in all directions. It is however possible to give inequalities which specify infinite regions. In such cases, there may be no bound on the objective function, and *Mathematica* will return infinite or indeterminate results.

The region specified in this case is unbounded.

```
In[7]:= ConstrainedMax[x, {x > 1}, {x}]
ConstrainedMax::nbdd: Specified domain appears unbounded.
Out[7]= {∞, {x → Indeterminate}}
```

In `ConstrainedMax` and `ConstrainedMin` the objective functions and constraints are specified in symbolic form. Sometimes, however, it is more convenient to handle linear programming problems simply by setting up vectors and matrices which represent the appropriate coefficients of the linear functions that appear. You can do this using `LinearProgramming`.

`LinearProgramming[c, m, b]`	find the vector **x** which minimizes **c.x** subject to the constraints **m.x** ≥ **b** and **x** ≥ 0

Linear programming in matrix form.

Here is a linear programming problem given in symbolic form.

```
In[8]:= ConstrainedMin[2x - 3y,
            {x + y < 10, x - y > 2, x > 1}, {x, y}]
Out[8]= {0, {x → 6, y → 4}}
```

Here is the same problem given in matrix form.

```
In[9]:= LinearProgramming[{2, -3},
            {{-1, -1}, {1, -1}, {1, 0}}, {-10, 2, 1}]
Out[9]= {6, 4}
```

■ 3.9.10 Advanced Topic: Functions with Sensitive Dependence on Their Input

Functions that are specified by simple algebraic formulas tend to be such that when their input is changed only slightly, their output also changes only slightly. But functions that are instead based on executing procedures quite often show almost arbitrarily sensitive dependence on their input. Typically the reason this happens is that the procedure "excavates" progressively less and less significant digits in the input.

This shows successive steps in a simple iterative procedure with input 0.1111.

```
In[1]:= NestList[FractionalPart[2 #]&, 0.1111, 10]
Out[1]= {0.1111, 0.2222, 0.4444, 0.8888, 0.7776, 0.5552,
            0.1104, 0.2208, 0.4416, 0.8832, 0.7664}
```

Here is the result with input 0.1112. Progressive divergence from the result with input 0.1111 is seen.

```
In[2]:= NestList[FractionalPart[2 #]&, 0.1112, 10]
Out[2]= {0.1112, 0.2224, 0.4448, 0.8896, 0.7792, 0.5584,
            0.1168, 0.2336, 0.4672, 0.9344, 0.8688}
```

The action of `FractionalPart[2 x]` is particularly simple in terms of the binary digits of the number x: it just drops the first one, and shifts the remaining ones to the left. After several steps, this means that the results one gets are inevitably sensitive to digits that are far to the right, and have an extremely small effect on the original value of x.

This shows the shifting process achieved by `FractionalPart[2 x]` in the first 8 binary digits of x.	*In[3]:=* `RealDigits[Take[%, 5], 2, 8, -1]` *Out[3]=* {{{0, 0, 0, 1, 1, 1, 0, 0}, 0}, {{0, 0, 1, 1, 1, 0, 0, 0}, 0}, {{0, 1, 1, 1, 0, 0, 0, 1}, 0}, {{1, 1, 1, 0, 0, 0, 1, 1}, 0}, {{1, 1, 0, 0, 0, 1, 1, 1}, 0}}

If you give input only to a particular precision, you are effectively specifying only a certain number of digits. And once all these digits have been "excavated" you can no longer get accurate results, since to do so would require knowing more digits of your original input. So long as you use arbitrary-precision numbers, *Mathematica* automatically keeps track of this kind of degradation in precision.

Successive steps yield numbers of progressively lower precision, and eventually no precision at all is left.	*In[4]:=* `NestList[FractionalPart[40 #]&, N[1/9, 20], 20]` *Out[4]=* {0.11111111111111111111, 0.44444444444444444444, 0.7777777777777778, 0.1111111111111111, 0.444444444444444, 0.77777777777778, 0.11111111111, 0.4444444444, 0.777777778, 0.1111111, 0.444444, 0.7778, 0.11, 0.0, 0., 0., 0., 0., 0.0, 0.}

This asks for the precision of each number. *Mathematica* generates a warning for numbers where no precision is left.	*In[5]:=* `Map[Precision, %]`
	
	Precision::mnprc:
	  Value 0 would be inconsistent with \$MinPrecision;
	    bounding by \$MinPrecision instead.
	
	Precision::mnprc:
	  Value -1 would be inconsistent with \$MinPrecision;
	    bounding by \$MinPrecision instead.
	
	Precision::mnprc:
	  Value -2 would be inconsistent with \$MinPrecision;
	    bounding by \$MinPrecision instead.
	
	General::stop:
	  Further output of Precision::mnprc
	    will be suppressed during this calculation.
	
	Out[5]= {20, 19, 18, 15, 14, 13, 10, 9, 8, 6, 5, 3,
	1, 0, 0, 0, 0, 0, 0, 0, 0}

This shows that the exact result is a periodic sequence.	*In[6]:=* `NestList[FractionalPart[40 #]&, 1/9, 10]` *Out[6]=* $\left\{\frac{1}{9}, \frac{4}{9}, \frac{7}{9}, \frac{1}{9}, \frac{4}{9}, \frac{7}{9}, \frac{1}{9}, \frac{4}{9}, \frac{7}{9}, \frac{1}{9}, \frac{4}{9}\right\}$

It is important to realize that if you use approximate numbers of any kind, then in an example like the one above you will always eventually run out of precision. But so long as you use arbitrary-precision numbers, *Mathematica* will explicitly show you any decrease in precision that is occurring. However, if you use machine-precision numbers, then *Mathematica* will not keep track of precision, and you cannot tell when your results become meaningless.

If you use machine-precision numbers, *Mathematica* will no longer keep track of any degradation in precision.

```
In[7]:= NestList[FractionalPart[40 #]&, N[1/9], 20]
Out[7]= {0.111111, 0.444444, 0.777778,
          0.111111, 0.444444, 0.777778, 0.111111,
          0.444445, 0.77781, 0.112405, 0.496185,
          0.847383, 0.89534, 0.813599, 0.543945,
          0.757812, 0.3125, 0.5, 0., 0., 0.}
```

By iterating the operation `FractionalPart[2 x]` you extract successive binary digits in whatever number you start with. And if these digits are apparently random—as in a number like π—then the results will be correspondingly random. But if the digits have a simple pattern—as in any rational number—then the results you get will be correspondingly simple.

By iterating an operation such as `FractionalPart[3/2 x]` it turns out however to be possible to get seemingly random sequences even from very simple input. This is an example of a very general phenomenon first identified by me in the mid-1980s, which has nothing directly to do with sensitive dependence on input.

This generates a seemingly random sequence, even starting from simple input.

```
In[8]:= NestList[FractionalPart[3/2 #]&, 1, 15]
```
$$Out[8]= \left\{1, \frac{1}{2}, \frac{3}{4}, \frac{1}{8}, \frac{3}{16}, \frac{9}{32}, \frac{27}{64}, \frac{81}{128}, \frac{243}{256}, \frac{217}{512}, \right.$$
$$\left. \frac{651}{1024}, \frac{1953}{2048}, \frac{1763}{4096}, \frac{5289}{8192}, \frac{15867}{16384}, \frac{14833}{32768} \right\}$$

After the values have been computed, one can safely find numerical approximations to them.

```
In[9]:= N[%]
Out[9]= {1., 0.5, 0.75, 0.125, 0.1875,
          0.28125, 0.421875, 0.632812, 0.949219,
          0.423828, 0.635742, 0.953613, 0.43042,
          0.64563, 0.968445, 0.452667}
```

Here are last 5 results after 1000 iterations, computed using exact numbers.

```
In[10]:= Take[N[NestList[FractionalPart[3/2 #]&, 1, 1000]], -5]
Out[10]= {0.0218439, 0.0327659, 0.0491488,
           0.0737233, 0.110585}
```

Using machine-precision numbers gives completely incorrect results.

```
In[11]:= Take[NestList[FractionalPart[3/2 #]&, 1., 1000], -5]
Out[11]= {0.670664, 0.0059966, 0.0089949,
           0.0134924, 0.0202385}
```

Many kinds of iterative procedures yield functions that depend sensitively on their input. Such functions also arise when one looks at solutions to differential equations. In effect, varying the independent parameter in the differential equation is a continuous analog of going from one step to the next in an iterative procedure.

This finds a solution to the Duffing equation with initial condition 1.

```
In[12]:= NDSolve[{x''[t] + 0.15 x'[t] - x[t] + x[t]^3 == 0.3 Cos[t],
          x[0] == -1, x'[0] == 1}, x, {t, 0, 50}]
Out[12]= {{x → InterpolatingFunction[{{0., 50.}}, <>]}}
```

Here is a plot of the solution.

In[13]:= `Plot[Evaluate[x[t] /. %], {t, 0, 50}]`

Here is the same equation with initial condition 1.001.

In[14]:= `NDSolve[{x''[t] + 0.15 x'[t] - x[t] + x[t]^3 == 0.3 Cos[t],`
                       `x[0] == -1, x'[0] == 1.001}, x, {t, 0, 50}]`

Out[14]= `{{x → InterpolatingFunction[{{0., 50.}}, <>]}}`

The solution progressively diverges from the one shown above.

In[15]:= `Plot[Evaluate[x[t] /. %], {t, 0, 50}]`

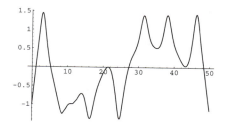

3.10 Mathematical and Other Notation

■ 3.10.1 Special Characters

Built into *Mathematica* are a large number of special characters intended for use in mathematical and other notation. Pages 1270–1316 give a complete listing.

Each special character is assigned a full name such as \[Infinity]. More common special characters are also assigned aliases, such as ⎋inf⎋, where ⎋ stands for the [ESC] key.

For special characters that are supported in standard dialects of T_EX, *Mathematica* also allows you to use aliases based on T_EX names. Thus, for example, you can enter \[Infinity] using the alias ⎋\infty⎋. *Mathematica* also supports aliases such as ⎋&infin⎋ based on names used in SGML and HTML.

Standard system software on many computer systems also supports special key combinations for entering certain special characters. On a Macintosh, for example, OPTION-5 will produce ∞ in most fonts. With the notebook front end *Mathematica* automatically allows you to use special key combinations when these are available, and with a text-based interface you can get *Mathematica* to accept such key combinations if you set an appropriate value for $CharacterEncoding.

- Use a full name such as \[Infinity]

- Use an alias such as [ESC]inf[ESC]

- Use a T_EX alias such as [ESC]\infty[ESC]

- Use an SGML or HTML alias such as [ESC]&infin[ESC]

- Click on a button in a palette

- Use a special key combination supported by your computer system

Ways to enter special characters.

In a *Mathematica* notebook, you can use special characters just like you use standard keyboard characters. You can include special characters both in ordinary text and in input that you intend to give to *Mathematica*.

Some special characters are set up to have an immediate meaning to *Mathematica*. Thus, for example, π is taken to be the symbol Pi. Similarly, $\geq$ is taken to be the operator >=, while $\cup$ is equivalent to the function Union.

π and $\geq$ have immediate meanings in *Mathematica*.

```
In[1]:= π ≥ 3

Out[1]= True
```

∪ or \[Union] is immediately interpreted as the Union function.	*In[2]:=* {a, b, c} ∪ {c, d, e} *Out[2]=* {a, b, c, d, e}
⊔ or \[SquareUnion] has no immediate meaning to *Mathematica*.	*In[3]:=* {a, b, c} ⊔ {c, d, e} *Out[3]=* {a, b, c} ⊔ {c, d, e}

Among ordinary characters such as E and i, some have an immediate meaning to *Mathematica*, but most do not. And the same is true of special characters.

Thus, for example, while π and ∞ have an immediate meaning to *Mathematica*, λ and $\mathcal{L}$ do not.

This allows you to set up your own definitions for λ and $\mathcal{L}$.

λ has no immediate meaning in *Mathematica*.	*In[4]:=* λ[2] + λ[3] *Out[4]=* λ[2] + λ[3]
This defines a meaning for λ.	*In[5]:=* λ[x_] := $\sqrt{x^2 - 1}$
Now *Mathematica* evaluates λ just as it would any other function.	*In[6]:=* λ[2] + λ[3] *Out[6]=* $2\sqrt{2} + \sqrt{3}$

Characters such as λ and $\mathcal{L}$ are treated by *Mathematica* as letters—just like ordinary keyboard letters like a or b.

But characters such as ⊕ and ⊔ are treated by *Mathematica* as *operators*. And although these particular characters are not assigned any built-in meaning by *Mathematica*, they are nevertheless required to follow a definite *syntax*.

⊔ is an infix operator.	*In[7]:=* {a, b, c} ⊔ {c, d, e} *Out[7]=* {a, b, c} ⊔ {c, d, e}
The definition assigns a meaning to the ⊔ operator.	*In[8]:=* x_ ⊔ y_ := Join[x, y]
Now ⊔ can be evaluated by *Mathematica*.	*In[9]:=* {a, b, c} ⊔ {c, d, e} *Out[9]=* {a, b, c, c, d, e}

The details of how input you give to *Mathematica* is interpreted depends on whether you are using StandardForm or TraditionalForm, and on what additional information you supply in InterpretationBox and similar constructs.

But unless you explicitly override its built-in rules by giving your own definitions for MakeExpression, *Mathematica* will always assign the same basic syntactic properties to any particular special character.

These properties not only affect the interpretation of the special characters in *Mathematica* input, but also determine the structure of expressions built with these special characters. They also affect various aspects of formatting; operators, for example, have extra space left around them, while letters do not.

Letters	a, E, π, Ξ, $\mathcal{L}$, etc.
Letter-like forms	∞, $\emptyset$, $\mho$, £, etc.
Operators	$\oplus$, ∂, $\approx$, $\rightleftharpoons$, etc.

Types of special characters.

In using special characters, it is important to make sure that you have the correct character for a particular purpose. There are quite a few examples of characters that look similar, yet are in fact quite different.

A common issue is operators whose forms are derived from letters. An example is $\sum$ or \[Sum], which looks very similar to Σ or \[CapitalSigma].

As is typical, however, the operator form $\sum$ is slightly less elaborate and more stylized than the letter form Σ. In addition, $\sum$ is an extensible character which grows depending on the summand, while Σ has a size determined only by the current font.

$\sum$	Σ	\[Sum], \[CapitalSigma]	μ	μ	\[Micro], \[Mu]
$\prod$	Π	\[Product], \[CapitalPi]	Å	Å	\[Angstrom], \[CapitalARing]
$\cup$	U	\[Union], keyboard U	$\emptyset$	$\emptyset$	\[EmptySet], \[CapitalOSlash]
$\in$	ϵ	\[Element], \[Epsilon]	A	A	\[CapitalAlpha], keyboard A
$\mathtext{d}$	d	\[DifferentialD], keyboard d	i	i	\[ImaginaryI], keyboard i

Different characters that look similar.

In cases such as \[CapitalAlpha] versus A, both characters are letters. However, *Mathematica* treats these characters as different, and in some fonts, for example, they may look quite different.

The result contains four distinct characters.

```
In[10]:= Union[ {\[CapitalAlpha], A, A, \[Mu], \[Mu], \[Micro]} ]
Out[10]= {A, A, μ, μ}
```

Traditional mathematical notation occasionally uses ordinary letters as operators. An example is the d in a differential such as dx that appears in an integral.

To make *Mathematica* have a precise and consistent syntax, it is necessary at least in StandardForm to distinguish between an ordinary d and the $\mathtext{d}$ used as a differential operator.

The way *Mathematica* does this is to use a special character $\mathtext{d}$ or \[DifferentialD] as the differential operator. This special character can be entered using the alias :dd:.

Mathematica uses a special character for the differential operator, so there is no conflict with an ordinary d.

$In[11]:= \int x^d \, dx$

$Out[11]= \dfrac{x^{1+d}}{1+d}$

When letters and letter-like forms appear in *Mathematica* input, they are typically treated as names of symbols. But when operators appear, functions must be constructed that correspond to these operators. In almost all cases, what *Mathematica* does is to create a function whose name is the full name of the special character that appears as the operator.

Mathematica constructs a `CirclePlus` function to correspond to the operator ⊕, whose full name is \[CirclePlus].

$In[12]:= $ `a ⊕ b ⊕ c // FullForm`

$Out[12]//FullForm=$ `CirclePlus[a, b, c]`

This constructs an `And` function, which happens to have built-in evaluation rules in *Mathematica*.

$In[13]:= $ `a ∧ b ∧ c // FullForm`

$Out[13]//FullForm=$ `And[a, b, c]`

Following the correspondence between operator names and function names, special characters such as ∪ that represent built-in *Mathematica* functions have names that correspond to those functions. Thus, for example, ÷ is named \[Divide] to correspond to the built-in *Mathematica* function `Divide`, and ⇒ is named \[Implies] to correspond to the built-in function `Implies`.

In general, however, special characters in *Mathematica* are given names that are as generic as possible, so as not to prejudice different uses. Most often, characters are thus named mainly according to their appearance. The character ⊕ is therefore named \[CirclePlus], rather than, say, \[DirectSum], and ≈ is named \[TildeTilde] rather than, say, \[ApproximatelyEqual].

× ×	\[Times], \[Cross]		* *	\[Star], keyboard *	
∧ ∧	\[And], \[Wedge]		\ \	\[Backslash], keyboard \	
∨ ∨	\[Or], \[Vee]		· .	\[CenterDot], keyboard .	
→ →	\[Rule], \[RightArrow]		∧ ^	\[Wedge], keyboard ^	
⇒ ⇒	\[Implies], \[DoubleRightArrow]		ı |	\[VerticalBar], keyboard |	

Different operator characters that look similar.

There are sometimes characters that look similar but which are used to represent different operators. An example is \[Times] and \[Cross]. \[Times] corresponds to the ordinary `Times` function for multiplication; \[Cross] corresponds to the `Cross` function for vector cross products. The × for \[Cross] is drawn slightly smaller than × for `Times`, corresponding to usual careful usage in mathematical typography.

The \[Times] operator represents ordinary multiplication.

$In[14]:= $ `{5, 6, 7} \[Times] {2, 3, 1}`

$Out[14]= $ `{10, 18, 7}`

The \[Cross] operator represents vector cross products.	*In[15]:=* **{5, 6, 7} \[Cross] {2, 3, 1}** *Out[15]=* {-15, 9, 3}

The two operators display in a similar way—with \[Times] slightly larger than \[Cross].	*In[16]:=* **{a × b, a × b}** *Out[16]=* {ab, a×b}

In the example of \[And] and \[Wedge], the \[And] operator—which happens to be drawn slightly larger—corresponds to the built-in *Mathematica* function And, while the \[Wedge] operator has a generic name based on the appearance of the character and has no built-in meaning.

You can mix \[Wedge] and \[And] operators. Each has a definite precedence.	*In[17]:=* **a \[Wedge] b \[And] c \[Wedge] d // FullForm** *Out[17]//FullForm=* And[Wedge[a, b], Wedge[c, d]]

Some of the special characters commonly used as operators in mathematical notation look similar to ordinary keyboard characters. Thus, for example, ∧ or \[Wedge] looks similar to the ^ character on a standard keyboard.

Mathematica interprets a raw ^ as a power. But it interprets ∧ as a generic Wedge function. In cases such as this where there is a special character that looks similar to an ordinary keyboard character, the convention is to use the ordinary keyboard character as the alias for the special character. Thus, for example, :^: is the alias for \[Wedge].

The raw ^ is interpreted as a power, but the :^: is a generic wedge operator.	*In[18]:=* **{x ^ y, x :^: y}** *Out[18]=* {x^y, x∧y}

A related convention is that when a special character is used to represent an operator that can be typed using ordinary keyboard characters, those characters are used in the alias for the special character. Thus, for example, :->: is the alias for → or \[Rule], while :&&: is the alias for ∧ or \[And].

:->: is the alias for \[Rule], and :&&: for \[And].	*In[19]:=* **{x :->: y, x :&&: y} // FullForm** *Out[19]//FullForm=* List[Rule[x, y], And[x, y]]

The most extreme case of characters that look alike but work differently occurs with vertical bars.

form	character name	alias	interpretation
$x \mid y$	keyboard			Alternatives[x, y]
$x \mid y$	\[VerticalSeparator]	⦂|⦂	VerticalSeparator[x, y]
$x \mid y$	\[VerticalBar]	⦂␣|⦂	VerticalBar[x, y]
$\mid x \mid$	\[LeftBracketingBar]	⦂l|⦂	BracketingBar[x]
	\[RightBracketingBar]	⦂r|⦂	

Different types of vertical bars.

Notice that the alias for \[VerticalBar] is ⦂␣|⦂, while the alias for the somewhat more common \[VerticalSeparator] is ⦂|⦂. *Mathematica* often gives similar-looking characters similar aliases; it is a general convention that the aliases for the less commonly used characters are distinguished by having spaces at the beginning.

⦂*nnn*⦂	built-in alias for a common character
⦂␣*nnn*⦂	built-in alias for similar but less common character
⦂.*nnn*⦂	alias globally defined in a *Mathematica* session
⦂,*nnn*⦂	alias defined in a specific notebook

Conventions for special character aliases.

The notebook front end for *Mathematica* often allows you to set up your own aliases for special characters. If you want to, you can overwrite the built-in aliases. But the convention is to use aliases that begin with a dot or comma.

Note that whatever aliases you may use to enter special characters, the full names of the characters will always be used when the characters are stored in files.

■ 3.10.2 Names of Symbols and Mathematical Objects

Mathematica by default interprets any sequence of letters or letter-like forms as the name of a symbol.

All these are treated by *Mathematica* as symbols.

```
In[1]:= {ξ, Σα, R∞, ℋ, ℵ, ∠ABC, ■X, m…n}

Out[1]= {ξ, Σα, R∞, ℋ, ℵ, ∠ABC, ■X, m…n}
```

form	character name	alias	interpretation
π	\[Pi]	⁞p⁞, ⁞pi⁞	equivalent to Pi
∞	\[Infinity]	⁞inf⁞	equivalent to Infinity
e	\[ExponentialE]	⁞ee⁞	equivalent to E
i	\[ImaginaryI]	⁞ii⁞	equivalent to I
j	\[ImaginaryJ]	⁞jj⁞	equivalent to I

Symbols with built-in meanings whose names do not start with capital English letters.

Essentially all symbols with built-in meanings in *Mathematica* have names that start with capital English letters. Among the exceptions are e and i, which are provided to let you enter what would normally be E and I as more familiar lower-case letters.

You can use forms such as e for input in StandardForm, but they are not used for output.

```
In[2]:= {e ^ (2 π i), e ^ π}
Out[2]= {1, E^π}
```

In TraditionalForm they are also used for output.

```
In[3]:= TraditionalForm[%]
Out[3]//TraditionalForm= {1, e^π}
```

In written material, it is standard to use very short names—often single letters—for most of the mathematical objects that one considers. But in *Mathematica*, it is usually better to use longer and more explicit names.

In written material you can always explain that a particular single-letter name means one thing in one place and another in another place. But in *Mathematica*, unless you use different contexts, a global symbol with a particular name will always be assumed to mean the same thing.

As a result, it is typically better to use longer names, which are more likely to be unique, and which describe more explicitly what they mean.

For variables to which no value will be assigned, or for local symbols, it is nevertheless convenient and appropriate to use short, often single-letter, names.

It is sensible to give the global function LagrangianL a long and explicit name. The local variables can be given short names.

```
In[4]:= LagrangianL[ϕ_, μ_] = (□ϕ)^2 + μ^2 ϕ^2
Out[4]= μ^2 ϕ^2 + (□ϕ)^2
```

form	input	interpretation
x_n	x `CTRL` `_` n `CTRL` `␣` or x_n	`Subscript[x, n]`
x_+	x `CTRL` `_` $+$ `CTRL` `␣` or x_+	`SubPlus[x]`
x_-	x `CTRL` `_` $-$ `CTRL` `␣` or x_-	`SubMinus[x]`
x_*	x `CTRL` `_` $*$ `CTRL` `␣` or x_*	`SubStar[x]`
x^+	x `CTRL` `^` $+$ `CTRL` `␣` or x\^+	`SuperPlus[x]`
x^-	x `CTRL` `^` $-$ `CTRL` `␣` or x\^-	`SuperMinus[x]`
x^*	x `CTRL` `^` $*$ `CTRL` `␣` or x\^*	`SuperStar[x]`
$x^\dagger$	x `CTRL` `^` `dg` `CTRL` `␣` or x\^\[Dagger]	`SuperDagger[x]`
$\overline{x}$	x `CTRL` `&` `_` `CTRL` `␣` or x\&_	`OverBar[x]`
$\vec{x}$	x `CTRL` `&` `vec` `CTRL` `␣` or x\&\[RightVector]	`OverVector[x]`
$\tilde{x}$	x `CTRL` `&` $\sim$ `CTRL` `␣` or x\&~	`OverTilde[x]`
$\hat{x}$	x `CTRL` `&` `^` `CTRL` `␣` or x\&^	`OverHat[x]`
$\dot{x}$	x `CTRL` `&` `.` `CTRL` `␣` or x\&.	`OverDot[x]`
$\underline{x}$	x `CTRL` `+` `_` `CTRL` `␣` or x\+_	`UnderBar[x]`
$\mathbf{x}$	`StyleBox[x, FontWeight->"Bold"]`	x

Creating objects with annotated names.

Note that with a notebook front end, you can typically change the style of text using menu items. Internally the result will be to insert `StyleBox` objects, but you do not need to do this explicitly.

option	typical default value	
`SingleLetterItalics`	`Automatic`	whether to use italics for single-letter symbol names

An option for cells in a notebook.

It is conventional in traditional mathematical notation that names consisting of single ordinary English letters are normally shown in italics, while other names are not. If you use `TraditionalForm`, then *Mathematica* will by default follow this convention. You can explicitly specify whether you want the convention followed by setting the `SingleLetterItalics` option for particular cells or cell styles.

■ 3.10.3 Letters and Letter-like Forms

Greek Letters

form	full name	aliases
α	\[Alpha]	:a:, :alpha:
β	\[Beta]	:b:, :beta:
γ	\[Gamma]	:g:, :gamma:
δ	\[Delta]	:d:, :delta:
ε	\[Epsilon]	:e:, :epsilon:
ε	\[CurlyEpsilon]	:ce:, :cepsilon:
ζ	\[Zeta]	:z:, :zeta:
η	\[Eta]	:h:, :et:, :eta:
θ	\[Theta]	:q:, :th:, :theta:
ϑ	\[CurlyTheta]	:cq:, :cth:, :ctheta:
ι	\[Iota]	:i:, :iota:
κ	\[Kappa]	:k:, :kappa:
χ	\[CurlyKappa]	:ck:, :ckappa:
λ	\[Lambda]	:l:, :lambda:
μ	\[Mu]	:m:, :mu:
ν	\[Nu]	:n:, :nu:
ξ	\[Xi]	:x:, :xi:
o	\[Omicron]	:om:, :omicron:
π	\[Pi]	:p:, :pi:
ϖ	\[CurlyPi]	:cp:, :cpi:
ρ	\[Rho]	:r:, :rho:
ϱ	\[CurlyRho]	:cr:, :crho:
σ	\[Sigma]	:s:, :sigma:
ς	\[FinalSigma]	:fs:
τ	\[Tau]	:t:, :tau:
υ	\[Upsilon]	:u:, :upsilon:
φ	\[Phi]	:f:, :ph:, :phi:
φ	\[CurlyPhi]	:j:, :cph:, :cphi:
χ	\[Chi]	:c:, :ch:, :chi:
ψ	\[Psi]	:y:, :ps:, :psi:
ω	\[Omega]	:o:, :w:, :omega:
ϝ	\[Digamma]	:di:, :digamma:
ϙ	\[Koppa]	:ko:, :koppa:
ϛ	\[Stigma]	:sti:, :stigma:
ϡ	\[Sampi]	:sa:, :sampi:

form	full name	aliases
A	\[CapitalAlpha]	:A:, :Alpha:
B	\[CapitalBeta]	:B:, :Beta:
Γ	\[CapitalGamma]	:G:, :Gamma:
Δ	\[CapitalDelta]	:D:, :Delta:
E	\[CapitalEpsilon]	:E:, :Epsilon:
Z	\[CapitalZeta]	:Z:, :Zeta:
H	\[CapitalEta]	:H:, :Et:, :Eta:
Θ	\[CapitalTheta]	:Q:, :Th:, :Theta:
I	\[CapitalIota]	:I:, :Iota:
K	\[CapitalKappa]	:K:, :Kappa:
Λ	\[CapitalLambda]	:L:, :Lambda:
M	\[CapitalMu]	:M:, :Mu:
N	\[CapitalNu]	:N:, :Nu:
Ξ	\[CapitalXi]	:X:, :Xi:
O	\[CapitalOmicron]	:Om:, :Omicron:
Π	\[CapitalPi]	:P:, :Pi:
P	\[CapitalRho]	:R:, :Rho:
Σ	\[CapitalSigma]	:S:, :Sigma:
T	\[CapitalTau]	:T:, :Tau:
Υ	\[CapitalUpsilon]	:U:, :Upsilon:
Υ	\[CurlyCapitalUpsilon]	:cU:, :cUpsilon:
Φ	\[CapitalPhi]	:F:, :Ph:, :Phi:
X	\[CapitalChi]	:C:, :Ch:, :Chi:
Ψ	\[CapitalPsi]	:Y:, :Ps:, :Psi:
Ω	\[CapitalOmega]	:O:, :W:, :Omega:
Ϝ	\[CapitalDigamma]	:Di:, :Digamma:
Ϙ	\[CapitalKoppa]	:Ko:, :Koppa:
Ϛ	\[CapitalStigma]	:Sti:, :Stigma:
ϡ	\[CapitalSampi]	:Sa:, :Sampi:

The complete collection of Greek letters in *Mathematica*.

You can use Greek letters as the names of symbols. The only Greek letter with a built-in meaning in StandardForm is π, which *Mathematica* takes to stand for the symbol Pi.

Note that even though π on its own is assigned a built-in meaning, combinations such as $\pi 2$ or $x\pi$ have no built-in meanings.

The Greek letters Σ and Π look very much like the operators for sum and product. But as discussed above, these operators are different characters, entered as \[Sum] and \[Product] respectively.

Similarly, ϵ is different from the $\in$ operator \[Element], and μ is different from µ or \[Micro].

Some capital Greek letters such as \[CapitalAlpha] look essentially the same as capital English letters. *Mathematica* however treats them as different characters, and in TraditionalForm it uses \[CapitalBeta], for example, to denote the built-in function Beta.

Following common convention, lower-case Greek letters are rendered slightly slanted in the standard fonts provided with *Mathematica*, while capital Greek letters are unslanted.

Almost all Greek letters that do not look similar to English letters are widely used in science and mathematics. The **capital xi** Ξ is rare, though it is used to denote the cascade hyperon particles, the grand canonical partition function and regular language complexity. The **capital upsilon** Υ is also rare, though it is used to denote $b\bar{b}$ particles, as well as the vernal equinox.

Curly Greek letters are often assumed to have different meanings from their ordinary counterparts. Indeed, in pure mathematics a single formula can sometimes contain both curly and ordinary forms of a particular letter. The curly pi ϖ is rare, except in astronomy.

The **final sigma** ς is used for sigmas that appear at the ends of words in written Greek; it is not commonly used in technical notation.

The **digamma** $\digamma$, **koppa** $\koppa$, **stigma** ς and **sampi** $\sampi$ are archaic Greek letters. These letters provide a convenient extension to the usual set of Greek letters. They are sometimes needed in making correspondences with English letters. The digamma corresponds to an English w, and koppa to an English q. Digamma is occasionally used to denote the digamma function PolyGamma[x].

Variants of English Letters

form	full name	alias		form	full name	alias
ℓ	\[ScriptL]	:scl:		$\mathbb{C}$	\[DoubleStruckCapitalC]	:dsC:
$\mathcal{E}$	\[ScriptCapitalE]	:scE:		$\mathbb{R}$	\[DoubleStruckCapitalR]	:dsR:
$\mathcal{H}$	\[ScriptCapitalH]	:scH:		$\mathbb{Q}$	\[DoubleStruckCapitalQ]	:dsQ:
$\mathcal{L}$	\[ScriptCapitalL]	:scL:		$\mathbb{Z}$	\[DoubleStruckCapitalZ]	:dsZ:
$\mathfrak{C}$	\[GothicCapitalC]	:goC:		$\mathbb{N}$	\[DoubleStruckCapitalN]	:dsN:
$\mathfrak{H}$	\[GothicCapitalH]	:goH:		ı	\[DotlessI]	
$\mathfrak{I}$	\[GothicCapitalI]	:goI:		ȷ	\[DotlessJ]	
$\mathfrak{R}$	\[GothicCapitalR]	:goR:		$\wp$	\[WeierstrassP]	:wp:

Some commonly used variants of English letters.

By using menu items in the notebook front end, or explicit StyleBox objects, you can make changes in the font and style of ordinary text. However, such changes are usually discarded whenever you send input to the *Mathematica* kernel.

Script, gothic and double-struck characters are however treated as fundamentally different from their ordinary forms. This means that even though a C that is italic or a different size will be considered equivalent to an ordinary C when fed to the kernel, a double-struck $\mathbb{C}$ will not.

Different styles and sizes of C are treated as the same by the kernel. But gothic and double-struck characters are treated as different.

```
In[1]:= c + c + C + c + ℂ
Out[1]= 3 c + ℭ + ℂ
```

In standard mathematical notation, capital script and gothic letters are sometimes used interchangeably. The double-struck letters, sometimes called blackboard or openface letters, are conventionally used to denote specific sets. Thus, for example, $\mathbb{C}$ conventionally denotes the set of complex numbers, and $\mathbb{Z}$ the set of integers.

Dotless i and j are not usually taken to be different in meaning from ordinary i and j; they are simply used when overscripts are being placed on the ordinary characters.

\[WeierstrassP] is a notation specifically used for the Weierstrass P function WeierstrassP.

full names	*aliases*	
\[ScriptA] – \[ScriptZ]	:sca: – :scz:	lower-case script letters
\[ScriptCapitalA] – \[ScriptCapitalZ]	:scA: – :scZ:	upper-case script letters
\[GothicA] – \[GothicZ]	:goa: – :goz:	lower-case gothic letters
\[GothicCapitalA] – \[GothicCapitalZ]	:goA: – :goZ:	upper-case gothic letters
\[DoubleStruckA] – \[DoubleStruckZ]	:dsa: – :dsz:	lower-case double-struck letters
\[DoubleStruckCapitalA] – \[DoubleStruckCapitalZ]	:dsA: – :dsZ:	upper-case double-struck letters

Complete alphabets of variant English letters.

Hebrew Letters

form	*full name*	*alias*		*form*	*full name*
א	\[Aleph]	:al:		ג	\[Gimel]
ב	\[Bet]			ד	\[Dalet]

Hebrew characters.

Hebrew characters are used in mathematics in the theory of transfinite sets; $\aleph_0$ is for example used to denote the total number of integers.

Units and Letter-like Mathematical Symbols

form	full name	alias		form	full name	alias
°	\[Degree]	:deg:		∅	\[EmptySet]	:es:
μ	\[Micro]	:mi:		∞	\[Infinity]	:inf:
℧	\[Mho]	:mho:		e	\[ExponentialE]	:ee:
Å	\[Angstrom]	:Ang:		i	\[ImaginaryI]	:ii:
ℏ	\[HBar]	:hb:		j	\[ImaginaryJ]	:jj:
¢	\[Cent]	:cent:		π	\[DoubledPi]	:pp:
£	\[Sterling]			γ	\[DoubledGamma]	:gg:
¥	\[Yen]					

Units and letter-like mathematical symbols.

Mathematica treats ° or \[Degree] as the symbol Degree, so that, for example, 30° is equivalent to 30 Degree.

Note that μ, Å and ∅ are all distinct from the ordinary letters μ (\[Mu]), Å (\[CapitalARing]) and ∅ (\[CapitalOSlash]).

Mathematica interprets ∞ as Infinity, e as E, and both i and j as I. The characters e, i and j are provided as alternatives to the usual upper-case letters E and I.

π and γ are not by default assigned meanings in StandardForm. You can therefore use π to represent a pi that will not automatically be treated as Pi. In TraditionalForm γ is interpreted as EulerGamma.

form	full name	alias		form	full name	alias
∂	\[PartialD]	:pd:		∇	\[Del]	:del:
d	\[DifferentialD]	:dd:		Σ	\[Sum]	:sum:
D	\[CapitalDifferentialD]	:DD:		∏	\[Product]	:prod:

Operators that look like letters.

∇ is an operator while ℏ, ° and ¥ are ordinary symbols.

```
In[1]:= {∇ f, ℏ^2, 45°, 5000¥} // FullForm
Out[1]//FullForm= List[Del[f], Power[ℏ, 2], Times[45, Degree],
                        Times[5000, ¥]]
```

Shapes, Icons and Geometrical Constructs

form	full name	alias		form	full name	alias
▪	\[FilledVerySmallSquare]	:fvssq:		○	\[EmptySmallCircle]	:esci:
▫	\[EmptySmallSquare]	:essq:		●	\[FilledSmallCircle]	:fsci:
◼	\[FilledSmallSquare]	:fssq:		○	\[EmptyCircle]	:eci:
☐	\[EmptySquare]	:esq:		⬤	\[GrayCircle]	:gci:
◼	\[GraySquare]	:gsq:		●	\[FilledCircle]	:fci:
◼	\[FilledSquare]	:fsq:		△	\[EmptyUpTriangle]	
⸬	\[DottedSquare]			▲	\[FilledUpTriangle]	
☐	\[EmptyRectangle]			▽	\[EmptyDownTriangle]	
◼	\[FilledRectangle]			▼	\[FilledDownTriangle]	
◇	\[EmptyDiamond]			★	\[FivePointedStar]	:*5:
◆	\[FilledDiamond]			✶	\[SixPointedStar]	:*6:

Shapes.

Shapes are most often used as "dingbats" to emphasize pieces of text. But *Mathematica* treats them as letter-like forms, and also allows them to appear in the names of symbols.

In addition to shapes such as \[EmptySquare], there are characters such as \[Square] which are treated by *Mathematica* as operators rather than letter-like forms.

form	full name	alias		form	full name	aliases
✻	\[MathematicaIcon]	:math:		☺	\[HappySmiley]	:): , :-):
⊛	\[KernelIcon]			☺	\[NeutralSmiley]	:-|:
♡	\[LightBulb]			☹	\[SadSmiley]	:-(:
⚠	\[WarningSign]			☹	\[FreakedSmiley]	:-@:
⊕	\[WatchIcon]			𝔸	\[Wolf]	:wf: , :wolf:

Icons.

You can use icon characters just like any other letter-like forms.

$In[2]:= \textbf{Expand[(☺ + 𝔸)\^4]}$

$Out[2]= ☺^4 + 4☺^3\,𝔸 + 6☺^2\,𝔸^2 + 4☺\,𝔸^3 + 𝔸^4$

form	full name		form	full name
∟	\[Angle]		∢	\[SphericalAngle]
∟	\[RightAngle]		△	\[EmptyUpTriangle]
∡	\[MeasuredAngle]		⌀	\[Diameter]

Notation for geometrical constructs.

Since *Mathematica* treats characters like ∟ as letter-like forms, constructs like ∟BC are treated in *Mathematica* as single symbols.

Textual Elements

form	full name	alias		form	full name	alias
–	\[Dash]	:-:		′	\[Prime]	:':
—	\[LongDash]	:--:		″	\[DoublePrime]	:'':
•	\[Bullet]	:bu:		‵	\[ReversePrime]	:`:
¶	\[Paragraph]			‶	\[ReverseDoublePrime]	:``:
§	\[Section]			«	\[LeftGuillemet]	:g<<:
¿	\[DownQuestion]	:d?:		»	\[RightGuillemet]	:g>>:
¡	\[DownExclamation]	:d!:		…	\[Ellipsis]	:...:

Characters used for punctuation and annotation.

form	full name		form	full name	alias
©	\[Copyright]		†	\[Dagger]	:dg:
®	\[RegisteredTrademark]		‡	\[DoubleDagger]	:ddg:
™	\[Trademark]		♣	\[ClubSuit]	
♭	\[Flat]		◇	\[DiamondSuit]	
♮	\[Natural]		♡	\[HeartSuit]	
♯	\[Sharp]		♠	\[SpadeSuit]	

Other characters used in text.

form	full name	alias	form	full name	alias
—	\[HorizontalLine]	:hline:	⌣	\[UnderParenthesis]	:u(:
|	\[VerticalLine]	:vline:	⌢	\[OverParenthesis]	:o(:
...	\[Ellipsis]	:...:	—	\[UnderBracket]	:u[:
...	\[CenterEllipsis]		—	\[OverBracket]	:o[:
⋮	\[VerticalEllipsis]		⌣	\[UnderBrace]	:u{:
.·	\[AscendingEllipsis]		⌢	\[OverBrace]	:o{:
·.	\[DescendingEllipsis]				

Characters used in building sequences and arrays.

The under and over braces grow to enclose the whole expression.

In[3]:= **Underoverscript[Expand[(1 + x)^4],**
\[UnderBrace], \[OverBrace]]

Out[3]= $\overbrace{1 + 4x + 6x^2 + 4x^3 + x^4}$

Extended Latin Letters

Mathematica supports all the characters commonly used in Western European languages based on Latin scripts.

form	full name	alias		form	full name	alias
à	\[AGrave]	:a`:		À	\[CapitalAGrave]	:A`:
á	\[AAcute]	:a':		Á	\[CapitalAAcute]	:A':
â	\[AHat]	:a^:		Â	\[CapitalAHat]	:A^:
ã	\[ATilde]	:a~:		Ã	\[CapitalATilde]	:A~:
ä	\[ADoubleDot]	:a":		Ä	\[CapitalADoubleDot]	:A":
å	\[ARing]	:ao:		Å	\[CapitalARing]	:Ao:
ā	\[ABar]	:a-:		Ā	\[CapitalABar]	:A-:
ă	\[ACup]	:au:		Ă	\[CapitalACup]	:Au:
æ	\[AE]	:ae:		Æ	\[CapitalAE]	:AE:
ć	\[CAcute]	:c':		Ć	\[CapitalCAcute]	:C':
ç	\[CCedilla]	:c,:		Ç	\[CapitalCCedilla]	:C,:
č	\[CHacek]	:cv:		Č	\[CapitalCHacek]	:Cv:
è	\[EGrave]	:e`:		È	\[CapitalEGrave]	:E`:
é	\[EAcute]	:e':		É	\[CapitalEAcute]	:E':
ē	\[EBar]	:e-:		Ē	\[CapitalEBar]	:E-:
ê	\[EHat]	:e^:		Ê	\[CapitalEHat]	:E^:
ë	\[EDoubleDot]	:e":		Ë	\[CapitalEDoubleDot]	:E":
ě	\[ECup]	:eu:		Ě	\[CapitalECup]	:Eu:
ì	\[IGrave]	:i`:		Ì	\[CapitalIGrave]	:I`:
í	\[IAcute]	:i':		Í	\[CapitalIAcute]	:I':
î	\[IHat]	:i^:		Î	\[CapitalIHat]	:I^:
ï	\[IDoubleDot]	:i":		Ï	\[CapitalIDoubleDot]	:I":
ĭ	\[ICup]	:iu:		Ĭ	\[CapitalICup]	:Iu:
ð	\[Eth]	:d-:		Ð	\[CapitalEth]	:D-:
ł	\[LSlash]	:l/:		Ł	\[CapitalLSlash]	:L/:
ñ	\[NTilde]	:n~:		Ñ	\[CapitalNTilde]	:N~:
ò	\[OGrave]	:o`:		Ò	\[CapitalOGrave]	:O`:
ó	\[OAcute]	:o':		Ó	\[CapitalOAcute]	:O':
ô	\[OHat]	:o^:		Ô	\[CapitalOHat]	:O^:
õ	\[OTilde]	:o~:		Õ	\[CapitalOTilde]	:O~:
ö	\[ODoubleDot]	:o":		Ö	\[CapitalODoubleDot]	:O":
ő	\[ODoubleAcute]	:o'':		Ő	\[CapitalODoubleAcute]	:O'':
ø	\[OSlash]	:o/:		Ø	\[CapitalOSlash]	:O/:
š	\[SHacek]	:sv:		Š	\[CapitalSHacek]	:Sv:
ù	\[UGrave]	:u`:		Ù	\[CapitalUGrave]	:U`:
ú	\[UAcute]	:u':		Ú	\[CapitalUAcute]	:U':
û	\[UHat]	:u^:		Û	\[CapitalUHat]	:U^:
ü	\[UDoubleDot]	:u":		Ü	\[CapitalUDoubleDot]	:U":
ű	\[UDoubleAcute]	:u'':		Ű	\[CapitalUDoubleAcute]	:U'':
ý	\[YAcute]	:y':		Ý	\[CapitalYAcute]	:Y':
þ	\[Thorn]	:thn:		Þ	\[CapitalThorn]	:Thn:
ß	\[SZ]	:sz:, :ss:				

Variants of English letters.

Most of the characters shown are formed by adding diacritical marks to ordinary English letters. Exceptions include \[SZ] ß, used in German, and \[Thorn] þ and \[Eth] ð, used primarily in Old English.

You can make additional characters by explicitly adding diacritical marks yourself.

char CTRL+& *mark* CTRL+␣ or \(*char*\&*mark*\)

 add a mark above a character

char CTRL++ *mark* CTRL+␣ or \(*char*\+*mark*\)

 add a mark below a character

Adding marks above and below characters.

form	alias	full name	
´	(keyboard character)	\[RawQuote]	acute accent
´	⁝´⁝	\[Prime]	acute accent
`	(keyboard character)	\[RawBackquote]	grave accent
`	⁝`⁝	\[ReversePrime]	grave accent
..	(keyboard characters)		umlaut or diaeresis
^	(keyboard character)	\[RawWedge]	circumflex or hat
o	⁝esc i⁝	\[EmptySmallCircle]	ring
.	(keyboard character)	\[RawDot]	dot
~	(keyboard character)	\[RawTilde]	tilde
‾	(keyboard character)	\[RawUnderscore]	bar or macron
ˇ	⁝hc⁝	\[Hacek]	hacek or check
˘	⁝bv⁝	\[Breve]	breve
⁀	⁝dbv⁝	\[DownBreve]	tie accent
"	⁝''⁝	\[DoublePrime]	long umlaut
¸	⁝cd⁝	\[Cedilla]	cedilla

Diacritical marks to add to characters.

+■ 3.10.4 Operators

Basic Mathematical Operators

form	full name	alias
×	\[Times]	:*:
÷	\[Divide]	:div:
√	\[Sqrt]	:sqrt:

form	full name	alias
×	\[Cross]	:cross:
±	\[PlusMinus]	:+-:
∓	\[MinusPlus]	:-+:

Some operators used in basic arithmetic and algebra.

Note that the × for \[Cross] is distinguished by being drawn slightly smaller than the × for \[Times].

$x \times y$	Times[x, y]	multiplication
$x \div y$	Divide[x, y]	division
$\sqrt{x}$	Sqrt[x]	square root
$x \times y$	Cross[x, y]	vector cross product
$\pm x$	PlusMinus[x]	(no built-in meaning)
$x \pm y$	PlusMinus[x, y]	(no built-in meaning)
$\mp x$	MinusPlus[x]	(no built-in meaning)
$x \mp y$	MinusPlus[x, y]	(no built-in meaning)

Interpretation of some operators in basic arithmetic and algebra.

Operators in Calculus

form	full name	alias
∇	\[Del]	:del:
∂	\[PartialD]	:pd:
d	\[DifferentialD]	:dd:
∑	\[Sum]	:sum:
∏	\[Product]	:prod:

form	full name	alias
∫	\[Integral]	:int:
∮	\[ContourIntegral]	:cint:
∯	\[DoubleContourIntegral]	
∮	\[CounterClockwiseContourIntegral]	:cccint:
∮	\[ClockwiseContourIntegral]	:ccint:

Operators used in calculus.

Logical and Other Connectives

form	full name	aliases		form	full name	alias
∧	\[And]	:&&:, :and:		⇒	\[Implies]	:=>:
∨	\[Or]	:||:, :or:		⇒	\[RoundImplies]	
¬	\[Not]	:!:, :not:		∴	\[Therefore]	:tf:
∀	\[ForAll]	:fa:		∵	\[Because]	
∃	\[Exists]	:ex:		⊢	\[RightTee]	
∄	\[NotExists]	:!ex:		⊣	\[LeftTee]	
∋	\[SuchThat]	:st:		⊨	\[DoubleRightTee]	
|	\[VerticalSeparator]	:|:		⫤	\[DoubleLeftTee]	
:	\[Colon]	:::				

Operators used as logical connectives.

The operators ∧, ∨ and ¬ are interpreted as corresponding to the built-in functions And, Or and Not, and are equivalent to the keyboard operators &&, || and !. Note that ¬ is a prefix operator.

$x \Rightarrow y$ and $x \Rightarrow y$ are both taken to give the built-in function Implies[x, y].

This is interpreted using the built-in functions And and Implies.

In[1]:= **3 < 4 ∧ x > 5 ⇒ y < 7**

Out[1]= Implies[x > 5, y < 7]

Mathematica supports most of the standard syntax used in mathematical logic. In *Mathematica*, however, the variables that appear in the quantifiers ∀, ∃ and ∄ must appear as subscripts. If they appeared directly after the quantifier symbols then there could be a conflict with multiplication operations.

∀ and ∃ are essentially prefix operators like ∂.

In[2]:= **∀$_x$ ∃$_y$ ϕ[x, y] // FullForm**

Out[2]//FullForm= ForAll[x, Exists[y, ϕ[x, y]]]

Operators Used to Represent Actions

form	full name	alias		form	full name	alias
∘	\[SmallCircle]	⦂sc⦂		∧	\[Wedge]	⦂^⦂
⊕	\[CirclePlus]	⦂c+⦂		∨	\[Vee]	⦂v⦂
⊖	\[CircleMinus]	⦂c-⦂		∪	\[Union]	⦂un⦂
⊗	\[CircleTimes]	⦂c*⦂		⊎	\[UnionPlus]	
⊙	\[CircleDot]	⦂c.⦂		∩	\[Intersection]	⦂inter⦂
◇	\[Diamond]	⦂dia⦂		⊓	\[SquareIntersection]	
·	\[CenterDot]	⦂.⦂		⊔	\[SquareUnion]	
*	\[Star]	⦂star⦂		∐	\[Coproduct]	⦂coprod⦂
≀	\[VerticalTilde]			⌢	\[Cap]	
\	\[Backslash]	⦂\⦂		⌣	\[Cup]	
				□	\[Square]	⦂sq⦂

Operators typically used to represent actions. All the operators except \[Square] are infix.

Following *Mathematica*'s usual convention, all the operators in the table above are interpreted to give functions whose names are exactly the names of the characters that appear in the operators.

The operators are interpreted as functions with corresponding names.

```
In[3]:= x ⊕ y ⌢ z // FullForm
Out[3]//FullForm= CirclePlus[x, Cap[y, z]]
```

All the operators in the table above, except for □, are infix, so that they must appear in between their operands.

Bracketing Operators

form	full name	alias		form	full name	alias
⌊	\[LeftFloor]	⦂lf⦂		⟨	\[LeftAngleBracket]	⦂<⦂
⌋	\[RightFloor]	⦂rf⦂		⟩	\[RightAngleBracket]	⦂>⦂
⌈	\[LeftCeiling]	⦂lc⦂		⦀	\[LeftBracketingBar]	⦂l⦂
⌉	\[RightCeiling]	⦂rc⦂		⦀	\[RightBracketingBar]	⦂r⦂
⟦	\[LeftDoubleBracket]	⦂[[⦂		⦀	\[LeftDoubleBracketingBar]	⦂l|⦂
⟧	\[RightDoubleBracket]	⦂]]⦂		⦀	\[RightDoubleBracketingBar]	⦂r|⦂

Characters used as bracketing operators.

$\lfloor x \rfloor$	Floor[x]
$\lceil x \rceil$	Ceiling[x]
$m[\![i,j, \ldots]\!]$	Part[m, i, j, ...]
$\langle x,y, \ldots \rangle$	AngleBracket[x, y, ...]
$\vert x,y, \ldots \vert$	BracketingBar[x, y, ...]
$\Vert x,y, \ldots \Vert$	DoubleBracketingBar[x, y, ...]

Interpretations of bracketing operators.

Operators Used to Represent Relations

form	full name	alias		form	full name	alias
==	\[Equal]	:==:		$\neq$	\[NotEqual]	:!=:
$\equiv$	\[Congruent]	:===:		$\not\equiv$	\[NotCongruent]	:!===:
~	\[Tilde]	:~:		$\nsim$	\[NotTilde]	:!~:
$\approx$	\[TildeTilde]	:~~:		$\napprox$	\[NotTildeTilde]	:!~~:
$\simeq$	\[TildeEqual]	:~=:		$\not\simeq$	\[NotTildeEqual]	:!~=:
$\cong$	\[TildeFullEqual]	:~==:		$\ncong$	\[NotTildeFullEqual]	:!~==:
$\approx$	\[EqualTilde]	:=~:		$\not\approx$	\[NotEqualTilde]	:!=~:
$\doteqdot$	\[HumpEqual]	:h=:		$\neq$	\[NotHumpEqual]	:!h=:
$\asymp$	\[HumpDownHump]			$\not\asymp$	\[NotHumpDownHump]	
$\asymp$	\[CupCap]			$\nasymp$	\[NotCupCap]	
$\doteq$	\[DotEqual]			$::$	\[Proportion]	
$\propto$	\[Proportional]	:prop:				

Operators usually used to represent similarity or equivalence.

The special character = (or \[Equal]) is an alternative input form for ==. $\neq$ is used both for input and output.

$In[4]:= \{a == b, a = b, a != b, a \neq b\}$

$Out[4]= \{a == b, a == b, a \neq b, a \neq b\}$

form	full name	alias		form	full name	alias
≥	\[GreaterEqual]	`⋮>=⋮`		≱	\[NotGreaterEqual]	`⋮!>=⋮`
≤	\[LessEqual]	`⋮<=⋮`		≰	\[NotLessEqual]	`⋮!<=⋮`
⩾	\[GreaterSlantEqual]	`⋮>/⋮`		⪈	\[NotGreaterSlantEqual]	`⋮!>/⋮`
⩽	\[LessSlantEqual]	`⋮</⋮`		⪇	\[NotLessSlantEqual]	`⋮!</⋮`
≧	\[GreaterFullEqual]			≩	\[NotGreaterFullEqual]	
≦	\[LessFullEqual]			≨	\[NotLessFullEqual]	
≳	\[GreaterTilde]	`⋮>~⋮`		≴	\[NotGreaterTilde]	`⋮!>~⋮`
≲	\[LessTilde]	`⋮<~⋮`		≵	\[NotLessTilde]	`⋮!<~⋮`
≫	\[GreaterGreater]			≫̸	\[NotGreaterGreater]	
≪	\[LessLess]			≪̸	\[NotLessLess]	
⋙	\[NestedGreaterGreater]			⋙̸	\[NotNestedGreaterGreater]	
⋘	\[NestedLessLess]			⋘̸	\[NotNestedLessLess]	
≷	\[GreaterLess]			≹	\[NotGreaterLess]	
≶	\[LessGreater]			≸	\[NotLessGreater]	
⋛	\[GreaterEqualLess]			≯	\[NotGreater]	`⋮!>⋮`
⋚	\[LessEqualGreater]			≮	\[NotLess]	`⋮!<⋮`

Operators usually used for ordering by magnitude.

form	full name	alias		form	full name	alias
⊂	\[Subset]	`⋮sub⋮`		⊄	\[NotSubset]	`⋮!sub⋮`
⊃	\[Superset]	`⋮sup⋮`		⊅	\[NotSuperset]	`⋮!sup⋮`
⊆	\[SubsetEqual]	`⋮sub=⋮`		⊈	\[NotSubsetEqual]	`⋮!sub=⋮`
⊇	\[SupersetEqual]	`⋮sup=⋮`		⊉	\[NotSupersetEqual]	`⋮!sup=⋮`
∈	\[Element]	`⋮elem⋮`		∉	\[NotElement]	`⋮!elem⋮`
∋	\[ReverseElement]	`⋮mem⋮`		∌	\[NotReverseElement]	`⋮!mem⋮`

Operators used for relations in sets.

form	full name		form	full name
>	\[Succeeds]		⊁	\[NotSucceeds]
<	\[Precedes]		⊀	\[NotPrecedes]
≥	\[SucceedsEqual]		≱	\[NotSucceedsEqual]
≤	\[PrecedesEqual]		⋨	\[NotPrecedesTilde]
≽	\[SucceedsSlantEqual]		⋡	\[NotSucceedsSlantEqual]
≼	\[PrecedesSlantEqual]		⋠	\[NotPrecedesSlantEqual]
≿	\[SucceedsTilde]		⋣	\[NotSucceedsTilde]
≾	\[PrecedesTilde]		⋬	\[NotPrecedesEqual]
▷	\[RightTriangle]		⋫	\[NotRightTriangle]
◁	\[LeftTriangle]		⋪	\[NotLeftTriangle]
⊵	\[RightTriangleEqual]		⋭	\[NotRightTriangleEqual]
⊴	\[LeftTriangleEqual]		⋬	\[NotLeftTriangleEqual]
⫐	\[RightTriangleBar]		⫑	\[NotRightTriangleBar]
⫏	\[LeftTriangleBar]		⫐	\[NotLeftTriangleBar]
⊐	\[SquareSuperset]		⊐̸	\[NotSquareSuperset]
⊏	\[SquareSubset]		⊏̸	\[NotSquareSubset]
⊒	\[SquareSupersetEqual]		⋣	\[NotSquareSupersetEqual]
⊑	\[SquareSubsetEqual]		⋢	\[NotSquareSubsetEqual]

Operators usually used for other kinds of orderings.

form	full name	alias		form	full name	alias
∣	\[VerticalBar]	⬚|⬚		∤	\[NotVerticalBar]	⬚!⬚
∥	\[DoubleVerticalBar]	⬚||⬚		∦	\[NotDoubleVerticalBar]	⬚!|⬚

Relational operators based on vertical bars.

Operators Based on Arrows and Vectors

Operators based on arrows are often used in pure mathematics and elsewhere to represent various kinds of transformations or changes.

$\rightarrow$ is equivalent to ->.

```
In[5]:= x + y /. x → 3
Out[5]= 3 + y
```

form	full name	alias		form	full name	alias
$\rightarrow$	\[Rule]	:->:		$\Rightarrow$	\[Implies]	:=>:
$\mapsto$	\[RuleDelayed]	::>:		$⇒$	\[RoundImplies]	

Arrow-like operators with built-in meanings in *Mathematica*.

form	full name	alias		form	full name
$\rightarrow$	\[RightArrow]	:_->:		$\uparrow$	\[UpArrow]
$\leftarrow$	\[LeftArrow]	:<-:		$\downarrow$	\[DownArrow]
$\leftrightarrow$	\[LeftRightArrow]	:<->:		$\updownarrow$	\[UpDownArrow]
$\longrightarrow$	\[LongRightArrow]	:-->:		$\Uparrow$	\[UpTeeArrow]
$\longleftarrow$	\[LongLeftArrow]	:<--:		$\Downarrow$	\[DownTeeArrow]
$\longleftrightarrow$	\[LongLeftRightArrow]	:<-->:		$\overline{\uparrow}$	\[UpArrowBar]
$\rightarrow$	\[ShortRightArrow]			$\underline{\downarrow}$	\[DownArrowBar]
$\leftarrow$	\[ShortLeftArrow]			$\Uparrow$	\[DoubleUpArrow]
$\mapsto$	\[RightTeeArrow]			$\Downarrow$	\[DoubleDownArrow]
$\leftarrowtail$	\[LeftTeeArrow]			$\Updownarrow$	\[DoubleUpDownArrow]
$\twoheadrightarrow$	\[RightArrowBar]			$\rightleftarrows$	\[RightArrowLeftArrow]
$\twoheadleftarrow$	\[LeftArrowBar]			$\leftrightarrows$	\[LeftArrowRightArrow]
$\Rightarrow$	\[DoubleRightArrow]	:_=>:		$\upharpoonright$	\[UpArrowDownArrow]
$\Leftarrow$	\[DoubleLeftArrow]	:_<=:		$\downharpoonright$	\[DownArrowUpArrow]
$\Leftrightarrow$	\[DoubleLeftRightArrow]	:<=>:		$\searrow$	\[LowerRightArrow]
$\Longrightarrow$	\[DoubleLongRightArrow]	:==>:		$\swarrow$	\[LowerLeftArrow]
$\Longleftarrow$	\[DoubleLongLeftArrow]	:<==:		$\nwarrow$	\[UpperLeftArrow]
$\Longleftrightarrow$	\[DoubleLongLeftRightArrow]	:<==>:		$\nearrow$	\[UpperRightArrow]

Ordinary arrows.

form	full name	alias	form	full name
→	\[RightVector]	:vec:	↿	\[LeftUpVector]
←	\[LeftVector]		⇃	\[LeftDownVector]
↔	\[LeftRightVector]		↕	\[LeftUpDownVector]
⇁	\[DownRightVector]		↾	\[RightUpVector]
↽	\[DownLeftVector]		⇂	\[RightDownVector]
⇀⇁	\[DownLeftRightVector]		↿⇂	\[RightUpDownVector]
↦	\[RightTeeVector]		⊥	\[LeftUpTeeVector]
↤	\[LeftTeeVector]		⊤	\[LeftDownTeeVector]
↦	\[DownRightTeeVector]		⊥	\[RightUpTeeVector]
↤	\[DownLeftTeeVector]		⊤	\[RightDownTeeVector]
⇥	\[RightVectorBar]		⊼	\[LeftUpVectorBar]
⇤	\[LeftVectorBar]		↧	\[LeftDownVectorBar]
⇥	\[DownRightVectorBar]		⊼	\[RightUpVectorBar]
⇤	\[DownLeftVectorBar]		↧	\[RightDownVectorBar]
⇌	\[Equilibrium]	:equi:	⇅	\[UpEquilibrium]
⇋	\[ReverseEquilibrium]		⇵	\[ReverseUpEquilibrium]

Vectors and related arrows.

All the arrow and vector-like operators
in *Mathematica* are infix.

$In[6]:=$ x ⇌ y ⇅ z

$Out[6]=$ x ⇌ y‖z

form	full name	alias	form	full name
⊢	\[RightTee]	:rT:	⊨	\[DoubleRightTee]
⊣	\[LeftTee]	:lT:	⊨	\[DoubleLeftTee]
⊥	\[UpTee]	:uT:		
⊤	\[DownTee]	:dT:		

Tees.

■ 3.10.5 Structural Elements and Keyboard Characters

full name	alias		full name	alias
\[InvisibleComma]	:,:		\[AlignmentMarker]	:am:
\[InvisibleSpace]	:is:		\[NoBreak]	:nb:
\[Null]	:null:			

Invisible characters.

In the input there is an invisible comma between the 1 and 2.

```
In[1]:= m₁₂
Out[1]= m_{1,2}
```

Here there is an invisible space between the x and y, interpreted as multiplication.

```
In[2]:= FullForm[xy]
Out[2]//FullForm= Times[x, y]
```

\[Null] does not display, but can take modifications such as superscripts.

```
In[3]:= \!\(f[x, \[Null]\^a]\)
Out[3]= f[x, ᵃ]
```

The \[AlignmentMarker] does not display, but shows how to line up the elements of the column.

```
In[4]:= GridBox[{{"b \[AlignmentMarker]+ c + d"},
            {"a + b \[AlignmentMarker]+ c"}},
        ColumnAlignments->"\[AlignmentMarker]"] // DisplayForm

Out[4]//DisplayForm=    b + c + d
                      a + b + c
```

full name	alias		full name	alias
\[VeryThinSpace]	:␣:		\[NegativeVeryThinSpace]	:⁻␣:
\[ThinSpace]	:␣␣:		\[NegativeThinSpace]	:⁻␣␣:
\[MediumSpace]	:␣␣␣:		\[NegativeMediumSpace]	:⁻␣␣␣:
\[ThickSpace]	:␣␣␣␣:		\[NegativeThickSpace]	:⁻␣␣␣␣:
\[InvisibleSpace]	:is:		\[NonBreakingSpace]	:nbs:
\[NewLine]			\[IndentingNewLine]	:nl:

Spacing and newline characters.

form	full name	alias	form	full name	alias
■	\[SelectionPlaceholder]	:spl:	□	\[Placeholder]	:pl:

Characters used in buttons.

In the buttons in a palette, you often want to set up a template with placeholders to indicate where expressions should be inserted. \[SelectionPlaceholder] marks the position where an expression that is currently selected should be inserted when the contents of the button are pasted. \[Placeholder] marks other positions where subsequent expressions can be inserted. The TAB key will take you from one such position to the next.

form	full name	alias		form	full name	alias
␣	\[SpaceIndicator]	⣉space⣉		CTRL	\[ControlKey]	⣉ctrl⣉
⌣	\[RoundSpaceIndicator]			CMD	\[CommandKey]	⣉cmd⣉
↵	\[ReturnIndicator]	⣉ret⣉		{	\[LeftModified]	⣉[⣉
RET	\[ReturnKey]	⣉␣ret⣉		]	\[RightModified]	⣉]⣉
ESC	\[EscapeKey]	⣉␣esc⣉		⌘	\[CloverLeaf]	⣉cl⣉
⣉	\[AliasIndicator]	⣉esc⣉				

Representations of keys on a keyboard.

In describing how to enter input into *Mathematica*, it is sometimes useful to give explicit representations for keys you should press. You can do this using characters like ↵ and ESC. Note that ␣ and ⌣ are actually treated as spacing characters by *Mathematica*.

This string shows how to type α^2.

```
In[5]:= "\[EscapeKey]a\[EscapeKey]
          \[ControlKey]\[LeftModified]^\[RightModified]2
          \[ControlKey]\[LeftModified]
                  \[SpaceIndicator]\[RightModified]"
```

Out[5]= ESC a ESC CTRL{^}2 CTRL{␣}

form	full name		form	full name
⋱	\[Continuation]		▪	\[SkeletonIndicator]
≪	\[LeftSkeleton]		◹	\[ErrorIndicator]
≫	\[RightSkeleton]			

Characters generated in *Mathematica* output.

Mathematica uses a \[Continuation] character to indicate that the number continues onto the next line.

```
In[6]:= 60!
Out[6]= 832098711274139014427634118322336438075417260636⋱
          12459524492776964096000000000000
```

form	full name		form	full name
	\[NewLine]		/	\[RawSlash]
	\[RawReturn]		<	\[RawLess]
	\[RawTab]		=	\[RawEqual]
	\[RawSpace]		>	\[RawGreater]
,	\[RawComma]		?	\[RawQuestion]
.	\[RawDot]		@	\[RawAt]
!	\[RawExclamation]		[	\[RawLeftBracket]
"	\[RawDoubleQuote]		\	\[RawBackslash]
#	\[RawNumberSign]		]	\[RawRightBracket]
%	\[RawPercent]		^	\[RawWedge]
&	\[RawAmpersand]		:	\[RawColon]
'	\[RawQuote]		_	\[RawUnderscore]
(	\[RawLeftParenthesis]		`	\[RawBackquote]
)	\[RawRightParenthesis]		{	\[RawLeftBrace]
*	\[RawStar]		|	\[RawVerticalBar]
+	\[RawPlus]		}	\[RawRightBrace]
−	\[RawDash]		~	\[RawTilde]

Raw keyboard characters.

The fonts that are distributed with *Mathematica* contain their own renderings of many ordinary keyboard characters. The reason for this is that standard system fonts often do not contain appropriate renderings. For example, ^ and ~ are often drawn small and above the centerline, while for clarity in *Mathematica* they must be drawn larger and centered on the centerline.

Formula Gallery

Mathematica has sophisticated built-in capabilities for formatting mathematical formulas. This Formula Gallery shows a few examples of what it can do. The examples are mostly default output from Mathematica, with no adjustments made. Some examples are in `TraditionalForm` while others are in `StandardForm`. `TraditionalForm` is intended to mimic as closely as possible the format of traditional mathematical documents; `StandardForm` is set up to provide input with unambiguous meaning, and to maximize the clarity of interactive presentation on a computer screen. `TraditionalForm` by default uses fonts with variable width characters, while `StandardForm` by default uses fonts with fixed width characters. All the special characters in this Formula Gallery and throughout this book are rendered using special Mathematica fonts.

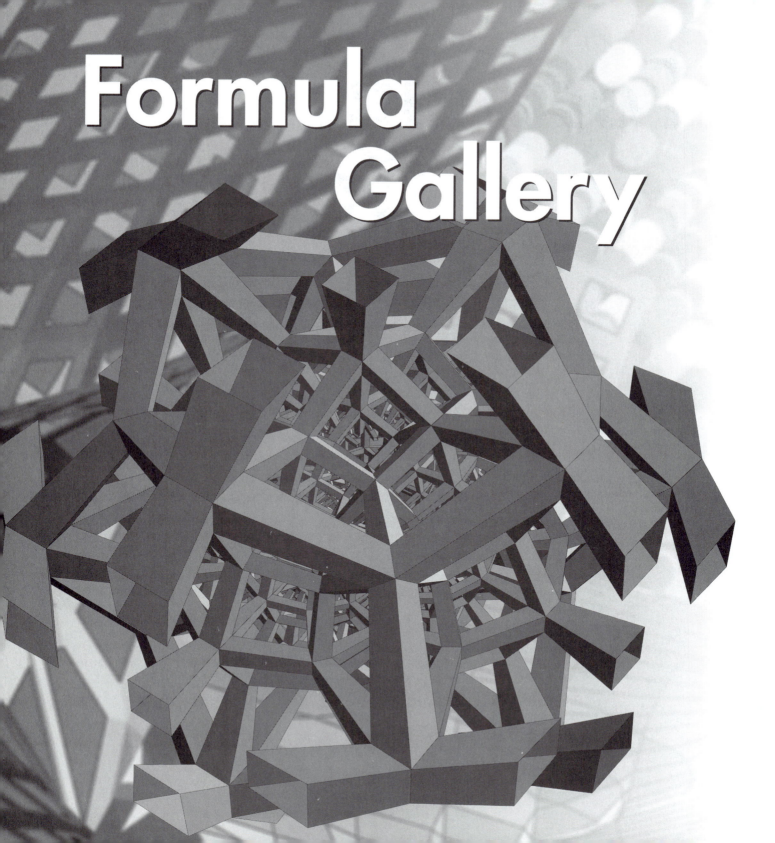

Formula Gallery

A definite integral (TraditionalForm)

$$\int_0^1 \frac{\log(t)^{16}}{\sqrt{1-t^2}}\, dt = \frac{1}{131072}\pi \log^{16}(4) + \frac{5}{16384}\pi^3 \log^{14}(4) + \frac{105}{2048}\pi \log^{13}(4)\,\zeta(3) +$$

$$\frac{1729}{98304}\pi^5 \log^{12}(4) + \frac{1365}{1024}\log^{11}(4)\,(\pi^3\,\zeta(3) + 18\,\pi\,\zeta(5)) + \frac{715}{49152}\log^{10}(4)\,(55\pi^7 + 6048\,\pi\,\zeta(3)^2) +$$

$$\frac{5005}{2048}\log^9(4)\,(19\,\pi^5\,\zeta(3) + 180\,\pi^3\,\zeta(5) + 3240\,\pi\,\zeta(7)) + \frac{143}{65536}\log^8(4)\,(11813\pi^9 + 604800\,\pi^3\,\zeta(3)^2 + 21772800\,\pi\,\zeta(3)\,\zeta(5)) +$$

$$\frac{2145}{512}\log^7(4)\,(275\,\pi^7\,\zeta(3) + 10080\,\pi\,\zeta(3)^3 + 2394\,\pi^5\,\zeta(5) + 22680\,\pi^3\,\zeta(7) + 428400\,\pi\,\zeta(9)) +$$

$$\frac{4095}{16384}\log^6(4)\,(2117\pi^{11} + 93632\,\pi^5\,\zeta(3)^2 + 1774080\,\pi^3\,\zeta(3)\,\zeta(5) + 15966720\,\pi\,\zeta(5)^2 + 31933440\,\pi\,\zeta(3)\,\zeta(7)) +$$

$$\frac{3003}{2048}\log^5(4)\,(11813\,\pi^9\,\zeta(3) + 201600\,\pi^3\,\zeta(3)^3 + 99000\,\pi^7\,\zeta(5) + 10886400\,\pi\,\zeta(3)^2\,\zeta(5) + 861840\,\pi^5\,\zeta(7) +$$
$$8568000\,\pi^3\,\zeta(9) + 168739200\,\pi\,\zeta(11)) +$$

$$\frac{3}{32768}\log^4(4)\,(64604977\pi^{13} + 2642640000\,\pi^7\,\zeta(3)^2 + 48432384000\,\pi\,\zeta(3)^4 + 46010764800\,\pi^5\,\zeta(3)\,\zeta(5) +$$
$$217945728000\,\pi^3\,\zeta(5)^2 + 435891456000\,\pi^3\,\zeta(3)\,\zeta(7) + 7846046208000\,\pi\,\zeta(5)\,\zeta(7) + 8233505280000\,\pi\,\zeta(3)\,\zeta(9)) +$$

$$\frac{4095}{1024}\log^3(4)\,(31755\,\pi^{11}\,\zeta(3) + 468160\,\pi^5\,\zeta(3)^3 + 259886\,\pi^9\,\zeta(5) + 13305600\,\pi^3\,\zeta(3)^2\,\zeta(5) + 239500800\,\pi\,\zeta(3)\,\zeta(5)^2 +$$
$$2178000\,\pi^7\,\zeta(7) + 239500800\,\pi\,\zeta(3)^2\,\zeta(7) + 19896800\,\pi^5\,\zeta(9) + 206236800\,\pi^3\,\zeta(11) + 4191264000\,\pi\,\zeta(13)) +$$

$$\frac{5}{49152}\log^2(4)\,(263101079\pi^{15} + 10216638432\,\pi^9\,\zeta(3)^2 + 87178291200\,\pi^3\,\zeta(3)^4 + 171243072000\,\pi^7\,\zeta(3)\,\zeta(5) +$$
$$6276836966400\,\pi\,\zeta(3)^3\,\zeta(5) + 745374389760\,\pi^5\,\zeta(5)^2 + 1490748779520\,\pi^5\,\zeta(3)\,\zeta(7) + 14122883174400\,\pi^3\,\zeta(5)\,\zeta(7) +$$
$$127105948569600\,\pi\,\zeta(7)^2 + 14820309504000\,\pi^3\,\zeta(3)\,\zeta(9) + 266765571072000\,\pi\,\zeta(5)\,\zeta(9) + 291872918937600\,\pi\,\zeta(3)\,\zeta(11)) +$$

$$\frac{9}{2048}\log(4)\,(64604977\,\pi^{13}\,\zeta(3) + 880880000\,\pi^7\,\zeta(3)^3 + 9686476800\,\pi\,\zeta(3)^5 +$$
$$520146900\,\pi^{11}\,\zeta(5) + 23005382400\,\pi^5\,\zeta(3)^2\,\zeta(5) + 217945728000\,\pi^3\,\zeta(3)\,\zeta(5)^2 + 1307674368000\,\pi\,\zeta(5)^3 +$$
$$4256932680\,\pi^9\,\zeta(7) + 217945728000\,\pi^3\,\zeta(3)^2\,\zeta(7) + 7846046208000\,\pi\,\zeta(3)\,\zeta(5)\,\zeta(7) + 37437400000\,\pi^7\,\zeta(9) +$$
$$4116752640000\,\pi\,\zeta(3)^2\,\zeta(9) + 356583427200\,\pi^5\,\zeta(11) + 3814050240000\,\pi^3\,\zeta(13) + 79346774707200\,\pi\,\zeta(15)) +$$

$$\frac{7}{6684672}(19449462373\pi^{17} + 727611206400\,\pi^{11}\,\zeta(3)^2 + 5363540582400\,\pi^5\,\zeta(3)^4 +$$
$$11909681372160\,\pi^9\,\zeta(3)\,\zeta(5) + 203249958912000\,\pi^3\,\zeta(3)^3\,\zeta(5) + 49905123840000\,\pi^7\,\zeta(5)^2 +$$
$$5487748890624000\,\pi\,\zeta(3)^2\,\zeta(5)^2 + 99810247680000\,\pi^7\,\zeta(3)\,\zeta(7) + 3658499260416000\,\pi\,\zeta(3)^3\,\zeta(7) +$$
$$868893574348800\,\pi^5\,\zeta(5)\,\zeta(7) + 4115811667968000\,\pi^3\,\zeta(7)^2 +$$
$$911801899008000\,\pi^5\,\zeta(3)\,\zeta(9) + 8638123253760000\,\pi^3\,\zeta(5)\,\zeta(9) + 155486218567680000\,\pi\,\zeta(7)\,\zeta(9) +$$
$$9451123089408000\,\pi^3\,\zeta(3)\,\zeta(11) + 170120215609344000\,\pi\,\zeta(5)\,\zeta(11) + 192071211171840000\,\pi\,\zeta(3)\,\zeta(13))$$

A Pisot number (TraditionalForm)

$$\left(\sqrt[3]{\frac{2}{27 + 3\sqrt{69}}} + \frac{1}{3}\sqrt[3]{\frac{27 + 3\sqrt{69}}{2}} \right)^{30000} =$$

50431659606566549321505946924275748107761027468089350316784446771287571822648621061039807658193406827538578254082133094787003547777871766946859877182545765655157863751804030841080877201973602630453775992992526007874643437115478340662656654242263167137970470876460028676595720882553729941413991192954257293905515987341623164931728987789298548218169139563816353624128215994510253193649036511102215152338143645279048930913371354240272588991921619868232355282955810598732001078755504975632193024344987469732081489429513875050815089544676150938253329884107629370887783660465530686857728553866459504826468144393019990165743377364065922255679117090517971285407731191277888144108736659703862174018641106917574995202365941964030217895956126590152078242574779075678185904725211878343979501048953268614290340265384707905146487735500216875475845252225041904360870681078279227104457227362368796693241733784161166959198410304677682964919409043870523002732003770237480443431032331691094261441144380298348751920199059562790511888049750265002682883521913896858496289686123578807667253851478579344449553914415375194372851217961223158428624231899492121175279814486360858048056575120864817906982359465546791033345570306144306889182376593558188718231183975111872409211627286291267138116086580374089300715168761587253411276229688666052103626113997282152567942245999124318525312272054453231352062266379427243641875073599561819112180689917957773267962616087523437758046684223813614460906815885942316844499056313085691439816110464143597646450582731053204235727780550415107612874413316609704003435615559435569931037256700736284601124392438005172117946648151586517714791609426531867375357616728998278915676581991850146147039469698790005505782180436742773778553079652925731007044050355286577065658891134133678171929347960975134996519924167215688582041932369782649567521678584676130166501497508373554704845376808917106579182046296637409148513289873712928793514345917581372183082138176837444493669698475749155502722721819149673730689452542949330172497476348802878923380972880989819941626981662787664453931670154635431610660994478782022049824681885420029046846763098262298893067982085873006027223547673545004480573914810092491101933870588744990654481144456437881423922057266818027803279734701366817533469290959062710889715842108254898313134138767612788549048657824912624883639420318879265232485613570477399709046710448077813242383525775842418033574517057365270541979506919519088585109853839062549850746730941961116578083869871331034408636054845107081922257029648252724270305699507491876725741414282227189033471727764395434254185950990747290625952762962184681171936790178602417989512006492961330651781076337449499729308205550243207661846458602761611981567677373636018999149195717505734613349483793082747826653826109388871646107637707669952322121063841012111950272802819214732121339193913851711740180545436004534753223529995802192329202767788406529942228608625210506805680779347684445472832022947989505073864225065042453778536680082426933681881662317694955672636170867065177268568641882560696136399378938092363061534206649910677121667830726528065065115430787822086187067816894109743170406015960678013961777060204838325510730464182561678677867776664114588829507728845970964346546857260085067375205588321834061968066477136954754650582659722182787527038013350885360773847158970095196369406644986845955931896822762457057294441289666846719625035790435931009430361335058057283719525424750533492243401220689154316788170873900884991490588279135076804550682803394454230822114888818737649635439941364151152126830053340927532304714488156842955217262531239581967894186558682010795291845929630207675781253001308948114465174795123603548945492907...

Product of two five-dimensional totally antisymmetric tensors (StandardForm)

$$\varepsilon_{\alpha\beta\rho\sigma\tau}\,\varepsilon_{\kappa\lambda\mu\nu\xi} =$$

$$\delta_{\alpha\xi}\delta_{\beta\nu}\delta_{\rho\mu}\delta_{\sigma\lambda}\delta_{\tau\kappa} - \delta_{\alpha\nu}\delta_{\beta\xi}\delta_{\rho\mu}\delta_{\sigma\lambda}\delta_{\tau\kappa} - \delta_{\alpha\xi}\delta_{\beta\mu}\delta_{\rho\nu}\delta_{\sigma\lambda}\delta_{\tau\kappa} + \delta_{\alpha\mu}\delta_{\beta\xi}\delta_{\rho\nu}\delta_{\sigma\lambda}\delta_{\tau\kappa} +$$
$$\delta_{\alpha\nu}\delta_{\beta\mu}\delta_{\rho\xi}\delta_{\sigma\lambda}\delta_{\tau\kappa} - \delta_{\alpha\mu}\delta_{\beta\nu}\delta_{\rho\xi}\delta_{\sigma\lambda}\delta_{\tau\kappa} - \delta_{\alpha\xi}\delta_{\beta\nu}\delta_{\rho\lambda}\delta_{\sigma\mu}\delta_{\tau\kappa} + \delta_{\alpha\nu}\delta_{\beta\xi}\delta_{\rho\lambda}\delta_{\sigma\mu}\delta_{\tau\kappa} +$$
$$\delta_{\alpha\xi}\delta_{\beta\lambda}\delta_{\rho\nu}\delta_{\sigma\mu}\delta_{\tau\kappa} - \delta_{\alpha\lambda}\delta_{\beta\xi}\delta_{\rho\nu}\delta_{\sigma\mu}\delta_{\tau\kappa} - \delta_{\alpha\nu}\delta_{\beta\lambda}\delta_{\rho\xi}\delta_{\sigma\mu}\delta_{\tau\kappa} + \delta_{\alpha\lambda}\delta_{\beta\nu}\delta_{\rho\xi}\delta_{\sigma\mu}\delta_{\tau\kappa} +$$
$$\delta_{\alpha\xi}\delta_{\beta\mu}\delta_{\rho\lambda}\delta_{\sigma\nu}\delta_{\tau\kappa} - \delta_{\alpha\mu}\delta_{\beta\xi}\delta_{\rho\lambda}\delta_{\sigma\nu}\delta_{\tau\kappa} - \delta_{\alpha\xi}\delta_{\beta\lambda}\delta_{\rho\mu}\delta_{\sigma\nu}\delta_{\tau\kappa} + \delta_{\alpha\lambda}\delta_{\beta\xi}\delta_{\rho\mu}\delta_{\sigma\nu}\delta_{\tau\kappa} +$$
$$\delta_{\alpha\mu}\delta_{\beta\lambda}\delta_{\rho\xi}\delta_{\sigma\nu}\delta_{\tau\kappa} - \delta_{\alpha\lambda}\delta_{\beta\mu}\delta_{\rho\xi}\delta_{\sigma\nu}\delta_{\tau\kappa} - \delta_{\alpha\nu}\delta_{\beta\mu}\delta_{\rho\lambda}\delta_{\sigma\xi}\delta_{\tau\kappa} + \delta_{\alpha\mu}\delta_{\beta\nu}\delta_{\rho\lambda}\delta_{\sigma\xi}\delta_{\tau\kappa} +$$
$$\delta_{\alpha\nu}\delta_{\beta\lambda}\delta_{\rho\mu}\delta_{\sigma\xi}\delta_{\tau\kappa} - \delta_{\alpha\lambda}\delta_{\beta\nu}\delta_{\rho\mu}\delta_{\sigma\xi}\delta_{\tau\kappa} - \delta_{\alpha\mu}\delta_{\beta\lambda}\delta_{\rho\nu}\delta_{\sigma\xi}\delta_{\tau\kappa} + \delta_{\alpha\lambda}\delta_{\beta\mu}\delta_{\rho\nu}\delta_{\sigma\xi}\delta_{\tau\kappa} -$$
$$\delta_{\alpha\xi}\delta_{\beta\nu}\delta_{\rho\mu}\delta_{\sigma\kappa}\delta_{\tau\lambda} + \delta_{\alpha\nu}\delta_{\beta\xi}\delta_{\rho\mu}\delta_{\sigma\kappa}\delta_{\tau\lambda} + \delta_{\alpha\xi}\delta_{\beta\mu}\delta_{\rho\nu}\delta_{\sigma\kappa}\delta_{\tau\lambda} - \delta_{\alpha\mu}\delta_{\beta\xi}\delta_{\rho\nu}\delta_{\sigma\kappa}\delta_{\tau\lambda} -$$
$$\delta_{\alpha\nu}\delta_{\beta\mu}\delta_{\rho\xi}\delta_{\sigma\kappa}\delta_{\tau\lambda} + \delta_{\alpha\mu}\delta_{\beta\nu}\delta_{\rho\xi}\delta_{\sigma\kappa}\delta_{\tau\lambda} + \delta_{\alpha\xi}\delta_{\beta\nu}\delta_{\rho\kappa}\delta_{\sigma\mu}\delta_{\tau\lambda} - \delta_{\alpha\nu}\delta_{\beta\xi}\delta_{\rho\kappa}\delta_{\sigma\mu}\delta_{\tau\lambda} -$$
$$\delta_{\alpha\xi}\delta_{\beta\kappa}\delta_{\rho\nu}\delta_{\sigma\mu}\delta_{\tau\lambda} + \delta_{\alpha\kappa}\delta_{\beta\xi}\delta_{\rho\nu}\delta_{\sigma\mu}\delta_{\tau\lambda} + \delta_{\alpha\nu}\delta_{\beta\kappa}\delta_{\rho\xi}\delta_{\sigma\mu}\delta_{\tau\lambda} - \delta_{\alpha\kappa}\delta_{\beta\nu}\delta_{\rho\xi}\delta_{\sigma\mu}\delta_{\tau\lambda} -$$
$$\delta_{\alpha\xi}\delta_{\beta\mu}\delta_{\rho\kappa}\delta_{\sigma\nu}\delta_{\tau\lambda} + \delta_{\alpha\mu}\delta_{\beta\xi}\delta_{\rho\kappa}\delta_{\sigma\nu}\delta_{\tau\lambda} + \delta_{\alpha\xi}\delta_{\beta\kappa}\delta_{\rho\mu}\delta_{\sigma\nu}\delta_{\tau\lambda} - \delta_{\alpha\kappa}\delta_{\beta\xi}\delta_{\rho\mu}\delta_{\sigma\nu}\delta_{\tau\lambda} -$$
$$\delta_{\alpha\mu}\delta_{\beta\kappa}\delta_{\rho\xi}\delta_{\sigma\nu}\delta_{\tau\lambda} + \delta_{\alpha\kappa}\delta_{\beta\mu}\delta_{\rho\xi}\delta_{\sigma\nu}\delta_{\tau\lambda} + \delta_{\alpha\nu}\delta_{\beta\mu}\delta_{\rho\kappa}\delta_{\sigma\xi}\delta_{\tau\lambda} - \delta_{\alpha\mu}\delta_{\beta\nu}\delta_{\rho\kappa}\delta_{\sigma\xi}\delta_{\tau\lambda} -$$
$$\delta_{\alpha\nu}\delta_{\beta\kappa}\delta_{\rho\mu}\delta_{\sigma\xi}\delta_{\tau\lambda} + \delta_{\alpha\kappa}\delta_{\beta\nu}\delta_{\rho\mu}\delta_{\sigma\xi}\delta_{\tau\lambda} + \delta_{\alpha\mu}\delta_{\beta\kappa}\delta_{\rho\nu}\delta_{\sigma\xi}\delta_{\tau\lambda} - \delta_{\alpha\kappa}\delta_{\beta\mu}\delta_{\rho\nu}\delta_{\sigma\xi}\delta_{\tau\lambda} +$$
$$\delta_{\alpha\xi}\delta_{\beta\nu}\delta_{\rho\lambda}\delta_{\sigma\kappa}\delta_{\tau\mu} - \delta_{\alpha\nu}\delta_{\beta\xi}\delta_{\rho\lambda}\delta_{\sigma\kappa}\delta_{\tau\mu} - \delta_{\alpha\xi}\delta_{\beta\lambda}\delta_{\rho\nu}\delta_{\sigma\kappa}\delta_{\tau\mu} + \delta_{\alpha\lambda}\delta_{\beta\xi}\delta_{\rho\nu}\delta_{\sigma\kappa}\delta_{\tau\mu} +$$
$$\delta_{\alpha\nu}\delta_{\beta\lambda}\delta_{\rho\xi}\delta_{\sigma\kappa}\delta_{\tau\mu} - \delta_{\alpha\lambda}\delta_{\beta\nu}\delta_{\rho\xi}\delta_{\sigma\kappa}\delta_{\tau\mu} - \delta_{\alpha\xi}\delta_{\beta\nu}\delta_{\rho\kappa}\delta_{\sigma\lambda}\delta_{\tau\mu} + \delta_{\alpha\nu}\delta_{\beta\xi}\delta_{\rho\kappa}\delta_{\sigma\lambda}\delta_{\tau\mu} +$$
$$\delta_{\alpha\xi}\delta_{\beta\kappa}\delta_{\rho\nu}\delta_{\sigma\lambda}\delta_{\tau\mu} - \delta_{\alpha\kappa}\delta_{\beta\xi}\delta_{\rho\nu}\delta_{\sigma\lambda}\delta_{\tau\mu} - \delta_{\alpha\nu}\delta_{\beta\kappa}\delta_{\rho\xi}\delta_{\sigma\lambda}\delta_{\tau\mu} + \delta_{\alpha\kappa}\delta_{\beta\nu}\delta_{\rho\xi}\delta_{\sigma\lambda}\delta_{\tau\mu} +$$
$$\delta_{\alpha\xi}\delta_{\beta\lambda}\delta_{\rho\kappa}\delta_{\sigma\nu}\delta_{\tau\mu} - \delta_{\alpha\lambda}\delta_{\beta\xi}\delta_{\rho\kappa}\delta_{\sigma\nu}\delta_{\tau\mu} - \delta_{\alpha\xi}\delta_{\beta\kappa}\delta_{\rho\lambda}\delta_{\sigma\nu}\delta_{\tau\mu} + \delta_{\alpha\kappa}\delta_{\beta\xi}\delta_{\rho\lambda}\delta_{\sigma\nu}\delta_{\tau\mu} +$$
$$\delta_{\alpha\lambda}\delta_{\beta\kappa}\delta_{\rho\xi}\delta_{\sigma\nu}\delta_{\tau\mu} - \delta_{\alpha\kappa}\delta_{\beta\lambda}\delta_{\rho\xi}\delta_{\sigma\nu}\delta_{\tau\mu} - \delta_{\alpha\nu}\delta_{\beta\lambda}\delta_{\rho\kappa}\delta_{\sigma\xi}\delta_{\tau\mu} + \delta_{\alpha\lambda}\delta_{\beta\nu}\delta_{\rho\kappa}\delta_{\sigma\xi}\delta_{\tau\mu} +$$
$$\delta_{\alpha\nu}\delta_{\beta\kappa}\delta_{\rho\lambda}\delta_{\sigma\xi}\delta_{\tau\mu} - \delta_{\alpha\kappa}\delta_{\beta\nu}\delta_{\rho\lambda}\delta_{\sigma\xi}\delta_{\tau\mu} - \delta_{\alpha\lambda}\delta_{\beta\kappa}\delta_{\rho\nu}\delta_{\sigma\xi}\delta_{\tau\mu} + \delta_{\alpha\kappa}\delta_{\beta\lambda}\delta_{\rho\nu}\delta_{\sigma\xi}\delta_{\tau\mu} -$$
$$\delta_{\alpha\xi}\delta_{\beta\mu}\delta_{\rho\lambda}\delta_{\sigma\kappa}\delta_{\tau\nu} + \delta_{\alpha\mu}\delta_{\beta\xi}\delta_{\rho\lambda}\delta_{\sigma\kappa}\delta_{\tau\nu} + \delta_{\alpha\xi}\delta_{\beta\lambda}\delta_{\rho\mu}\delta_{\sigma\kappa}\delta_{\tau\nu} - \delta_{\alpha\lambda}\delta_{\beta\xi}\delta_{\rho\mu}\delta_{\sigma\kappa}\delta_{\tau\nu} -$$
$$\delta_{\alpha\mu}\delta_{\beta\lambda}\delta_{\rho\xi}\delta_{\sigma\kappa}\delta_{\tau\nu} + \delta_{\alpha\lambda}\delta_{\beta\mu}\delta_{\rho\xi}\delta_{\sigma\kappa}\delta_{\tau\nu} + \delta_{\alpha\xi}\delta_{\beta\mu}\delta_{\rho\kappa}\delta_{\sigma\lambda}\delta_{\tau\nu} - \delta_{\alpha\mu}\delta_{\beta\xi}\delta_{\rho\kappa}\delta_{\sigma\lambda}\delta_{\tau\nu} -$$
$$\delta_{\alpha\xi}\delta_{\beta\kappa}\delta_{\rho\mu}\delta_{\sigma\lambda}\delta_{\tau\nu} + \delta_{\alpha\kappa}\delta_{\beta\xi}\delta_{\rho\mu}\delta_{\sigma\lambda}\delta_{\tau\nu} + \delta_{\alpha\mu}\delta_{\beta\kappa}\delta_{\rho\xi}\delta_{\sigma\lambda}\delta_{\tau\nu} - \delta_{\alpha\kappa}\delta_{\beta\mu}\delta_{\rho\xi}\delta_{\sigma\lambda}\delta_{\tau\nu} -$$
$$\delta_{\alpha\xi}\delta_{\beta\lambda}\delta_{\rho\kappa}\delta_{\sigma\mu}\delta_{\tau\nu} + \delta_{\alpha\lambda}\delta_{\beta\xi}\delta_{\rho\kappa}\delta_{\sigma\mu}\delta_{\tau\nu} + \delta_{\alpha\xi}\delta_{\beta\kappa}\delta_{\rho\lambda}\delta_{\sigma\mu}\delta_{\tau\nu} - \delta_{\alpha\kappa}\delta_{\beta\xi}\delta_{\rho\lambda}\delta_{\sigma\mu}\delta_{\tau\nu} -$$
$$\delta_{\alpha\lambda}\delta_{\beta\kappa}\delta_{\rho\xi}\delta_{\sigma\mu}\delta_{\tau\nu} + \delta_{\alpha\kappa}\delta_{\beta\lambda}\delta_{\rho\xi}\delta_{\sigma\mu}\delta_{\tau\nu} + \delta_{\alpha\mu}\delta_{\beta\lambda}\delta_{\rho\kappa}\delta_{\sigma\xi}\delta_{\tau\nu} - \delta_{\alpha\lambda}\delta_{\beta\mu}\delta_{\rho\kappa}\delta_{\sigma\xi}\delta_{\tau\nu} -$$
$$\delta_{\alpha\mu}\delta_{\beta\kappa}\delta_{\rho\lambda}\delta_{\sigma\xi}\delta_{\tau\nu} + \delta_{\alpha\kappa}\delta_{\beta\mu}\delta_{\rho\lambda}\delta_{\sigma\xi}\delta_{\tau\nu} + \delta_{\alpha\lambda}\delta_{\beta\kappa}\delta_{\rho\mu}\delta_{\sigma\xi}\delta_{\tau\nu} - \delta_{\alpha\kappa}\delta_{\beta\lambda}\delta_{\rho\mu}\delta_{\sigma\xi}\delta_{\tau\nu} +$$
$$\delta_{\alpha\nu}\delta_{\beta\mu}\delta_{\rho\lambda}\delta_{\sigma\kappa}\delta_{\tau\xi} - \delta_{\alpha\mu}\delta_{\beta\nu}\delta_{\rho\lambda}\delta_{\sigma\kappa}\delta_{\tau\xi} - \delta_{\alpha\nu}\delta_{\beta\lambda}\delta_{\rho\mu}\delta_{\sigma\kappa}\delta_{\tau\xi} + \delta_{\alpha\lambda}\delta_{\beta\nu}\delta_{\rho\mu}\delta_{\sigma\kappa}\delta_{\tau\xi} +$$
$$\delta_{\alpha\mu}\delta_{\beta\lambda}\delta_{\rho\nu}\delta_{\sigma\kappa}\delta_{\tau\xi} - \delta_{\alpha\lambda}\delta_{\beta\mu}\delta_{\rho\nu}\delta_{\sigma\kappa}\delta_{\tau\xi} - \delta_{\alpha\nu}\delta_{\beta\mu}\delta_{\rho\kappa}\delta_{\sigma\lambda}\delta_{\tau\xi} + \delta_{\alpha\mu}\delta_{\beta\nu}\delta_{\rho\kappa}\delta_{\sigma\lambda}\delta_{\tau\xi} +$$
$$\delta_{\alpha\nu}\delta_{\beta\kappa}\delta_{\rho\mu}\delta_{\sigma\lambda}\delta_{\tau\xi} - \delta_{\alpha\kappa}\delta_{\beta\nu}\delta_{\rho\mu}\delta_{\sigma\lambda}\delta_{\tau\xi} - \delta_{\alpha\mu}\delta_{\beta\kappa}\delta_{\rho\nu}\delta_{\sigma\lambda}\delta_{\tau\xi} + \delta_{\alpha\kappa}\delta_{\beta\mu}\delta_{\rho\nu}\delta_{\sigma\lambda}\delta_{\tau\xi} +$$
$$\delta_{\alpha\nu}\delta_{\beta\lambda}\delta_{\rho\kappa}\delta_{\sigma\mu}\delta_{\tau\xi} - \delta_{\alpha\lambda}\delta_{\beta\nu}\delta_{\rho\kappa}\delta_{\sigma\mu}\delta_{\tau\xi} - \delta_{\alpha\nu}\delta_{\beta\kappa}\delta_{\rho\lambda}\delta_{\sigma\mu}\delta_{\tau\xi} + \delta_{\alpha\kappa}\delta_{\beta\nu}\delta_{\rho\lambda}\delta_{\sigma\mu}\delta_{\tau\xi} +$$
$$\delta_{\alpha\lambda}\delta_{\beta\kappa}\delta_{\rho\nu}\delta_{\sigma\mu}\delta_{\tau\xi} - \delta_{\alpha\kappa}\delta_{\beta\lambda}\delta_{\rho\nu}\delta_{\sigma\mu}\delta_{\tau\xi} - \delta_{\alpha\mu}\delta_{\beta\lambda}\delta_{\rho\kappa}\delta_{\sigma\nu}\delta_{\tau\xi} + \delta_{\alpha\lambda}\delta_{\beta\mu}\delta_{\rho\kappa}\delta_{\sigma\nu}\delta_{\tau\xi} +$$
$$\delta_{\alpha\mu}\delta_{\beta\kappa}\delta_{\rho\lambda}\delta_{\sigma\nu}\delta_{\tau\xi} - \delta_{\alpha\kappa}\delta_{\beta\mu}\delta_{\rho\lambda}\delta_{\sigma\nu}\delta_{\tau\xi} - \delta_{\alpha\lambda}\delta_{\beta\kappa}\delta_{\rho\mu}\delta_{\sigma\nu}\delta_{\tau\xi} + \delta_{\alpha\kappa}\delta_{\beta\lambda}\delta_{\rho\mu}\delta_{\sigma\nu}\delta_{\tau\xi}$$

Trigonometric formulas (TraditionalForm)

$$-\frac{\sin(\frac{\pi}{7})}{\sin^2(\frac{2\pi}{7})} + \frac{\sin(\frac{3\pi}{7})}{\sin^2(\frac{\pi}{7})} + \frac{\sin(\frac{2\pi}{7})}{\sin^2(\frac{3\pi}{7})} = 2\sqrt{7}$$

$$\frac{\sin^2(\frac{\pi}{7})}{\sin^4(\frac{2\pi}{7})} + \frac{\sin^2(\frac{3\pi}{7})}{\sin^4(\frac{\pi}{7})} + \frac{\sin^2(\frac{2\pi}{7})}{\sin^4(\frac{3\pi}{7})} = 28$$

$$\frac{\sin^2(\frac{\pi}{7})}{\sin^4(\frac{2\pi}{7})}\left(\frac{4\sin(\frac{\pi}{7})}{\sin(\frac{2\pi}{7})} - \frac{2\sin(\frac{3\pi}{7})}{\sin(\frac{\pi}{7})}\right) + \frac{\sin^2(\frac{3\pi}{7})}{\sin^4(\frac{\pi}{7})}\left(\frac{2\sin(\frac{2\pi}{7})}{\sin(\frac{3\pi}{7})} + \frac{4\sin(\frac{3\pi}{7})}{\sin(\frac{\pi}{7})}\right) - \frac{\sin^2(\frac{2\pi}{7})}{\sin^4(\frac{3\pi}{7})}\left(\frac{2\sin(\frac{\pi}{7})}{\sin(\frac{2\pi}{7})} + \frac{4\sin(\frac{2\pi}{7})}{\sin(\frac{3\pi}{7})}\right) = 280$$

$$\cos\left(\frac{\pi}{17}\right) = \frac{1}{8}\sqrt{2\left(2\sqrt{\sqrt{\frac{17(17-\sqrt{17})}{2}} - \sqrt{\frac{17-\sqrt{17}}{2}} - 4\sqrt{34+2\sqrt{17}} + 3\sqrt{17} + 17} + \sqrt{34-2\sqrt{17}} + \sqrt{17} + 15\right)}$$

$$\tan\left(\frac{\pi}{120}\right) = \sqrt{\frac{8-\sqrt{2(2-\sqrt{3})(3-\sqrt{5})} - \sqrt{2(2+\sqrt{3})(5+\sqrt{5})}}{8+\sqrt{2(2-\sqrt{3})(3-\sqrt{5})} + \sqrt{2(2+\sqrt{3})(5+\sqrt{5})}}}$$

$$\cos\left(\frac{\pi}{240}\right) = \frac{1}{16}\left(\sqrt{2-\sqrt{2+\sqrt{2}}}\left(\sqrt{2(5+\sqrt{5})} + \sqrt{3} - \sqrt{15}\right) + \sqrt{\sqrt{2+\sqrt{2}} + 2\left(\sqrt{6(5+\sqrt{5})} + \sqrt{5} - 1\right)}\right)$$

$\frac{\pi}{4} = \cot^{-1}(2) + \cot^{-1}(3)$

$\frac{\pi}{4} = 2\cot^{-1}(3) + \cot^{-1}(7)$

$\frac{\pi}{4} = 4\cot^{-1}(5) - \cot^{-1}(239)$

$\frac{\pi}{4} = 5\cot^{-1}(6) - \cot^{-1}(\frac{503}{16}) - \cot^{-1}(117)$

$\frac{\pi}{4} = 6\cot^{-1}(8) + \cot^{-1}(\frac{99}{5}) - 3\cot^{-1}(268)$

$\frac{\pi}{4} = 8\cot^{-1}(10) - 2\cot^{-1}(\frac{452761}{2543}) - \cot^{-1}(1393)$

$\frac{\pi}{4} = 12\cot^{-1}(18) + 3\cot^{-1}(70) + 5\cot^{-1}(99) + 8\cot^{-1}(307)$

$\frac{\pi}{4} = \cot^{-1}(2) + \cot^{-1}(5) + \cot^{-1}(8)$

$\frac{\pi}{4} = 3\cot^{-1}(4) + \cot^{-1}(\frac{99}{5})$

$\frac{\pi}{4} = 4\cot^{-1}(5) - \cot^{-1}(70) + \cot^{-1}(99)$

$\frac{\pi}{4} = 5\cot^{-1}(7) + 2\cot^{-1}(\frac{79}{3})$

$\frac{\pi}{4} = 8\cot^{-1}(10) - \cot^{-1}(239) - 4\cot^{-1}(515)$

$\frac{\pi}{4} = 8\cot^{-1}(10) - \cot^{-1}(100) - \cot^{-1}(515) - \cot^{-1}(\frac{371498882}{3583})$

$\frac{\pi}{4} = 12\cot^{-1}(18) + 8\cot^{-1}(99) + 3\cot^{-1}(239) + 8\cot^{-1}(307)$

Some definite integrals (TraditionalForm)

$$\int_0^1 \log(x)^3 \sqrt{1-x}\, dx = -\frac{2}{27}\left(640 - 24\pi^2 - 312\log(4) + 9\pi^2\log(4) + 72\log(4)^2 - 9\log(4)^3 - 108\,\zeta(3)\right)$$

$$\int_0^1 \frac{\sin^{-1}(x)^5}{x}\, dx = \frac{\pi}{64}\left(2\pi^4\log(2) - 30\,\pi^2\,\zeta(3) + 225\,\zeta(5)\right)$$

$$\int_0^1 \frac{1}{x^2}\left(\frac{1}{x}\ln\left(\frac{1+x}{1-x}\right) - 2\right)^2 dx = \frac{2}{9}(\pi^2 - 6)$$

$$\int_0^\infty \frac{1}{(x^2 + 2y\cos(t)\,x + y^2)^2}\, dy = \frac{1}{4x^3}\csc^3(t)\left(2\tan^{-1}\left(\tan\left(\frac{t}{2}\right)\right) + \tan^{-1}(\tan(t)) - \sin(2t)\right)$$

$$\int_0^{\frac{\pi}{2}} (\log(\sin(x))\,x^2 + \log(\cos(x))\,x)\,dx = \frac{1}{48}\left(-6\,\pi^2\log(2) - \pi^3\log(4) - 21\,\zeta(3) + 9\,\pi\,\zeta(3)\right)$$

$$\int_0^1 \sqrt{1-x}\,\cos(2x)\,e^x dx = \frac{1}{100}i\,e^{-2i}\left(20i\,e^{2i} + (4+3i)\sqrt{1-2i}\,e\,\sqrt{\pi}\,\mathrm{erf}\left(\sqrt{1-2i}\right) - (4-3i)\sqrt{1+2i}\,e^{1+4i}\,\sqrt{\pi}\,\mathrm{erf}\left(\sqrt{1+2i}\right)\right)$$

$$\int_0^\infty J_2(x)^2\,e^{-x} dx = \frac{3}{8}\,_2F_1\left(\frac{5}{2}, \frac{5}{2}; 5; -4\right)$$

$$\int_0^\infty e^{-x^3}\sin(x)\,dx = \frac{1}{3}\Gamma\left(\frac{2}{3}\right)\,_0F_3\left(; \frac{1}{2}, \frac{2}{3}, \frac{7}{6}; -\frac{1}{11664}\right) - \frac{1}{54}\Gamma\left(\frac{1}{3}\right)\,_0F_3\left(; \frac{5}{6}, \frac{4}{3}, \frac{3}{2}; -\frac{1}{11664}\right) + \frac{1}{360}\,_1F_4\left(1; \frac{7}{6}, \frac{4}{3}, \frac{5}{3}, \frac{11}{6}; -\frac{1}{11664}\right)$$

$$\int_0^\infty e^{-x\sinh(u)}J_m(x)\,dx = \mathrm{If}\Big[\mathrm{Re}[m] > -1 \wedge \mathrm{Re}[\sinh(u)] > 0,$$

$$-\frac{2e^u\,(e^u\,(1 - e^{-2u}))^{-m}}{1 - e^{2u}}\,_2F_1\left(\frac{m}{2} + \frac{1}{2}, \frac{m}{2} + 1; m+1; -\frac{4e^{-2u}}{(1 - e^{-2u})^2}\right), \int_0^\infty e^{-x\sinh(u)}J_m(x)\,dx\Big]$$

$$\int_0^\infty \mathrm{Ai}(x)^2\,\mathrm{Ai}(-x)^2 dx = \frac{1}{24\pi}$$

$$\int_0^\infty t\,Y_0(t)\,J_0(t)\,I_2(t)\,K_2(t)\,dt = \frac{1}{8}\pi(16\log(2) + \pi - 8)$$

Generating functions for partitions (StandardForm)

$$\prod_{n=1}^{\infty} (1 - x^n) = \sum_{k=-\infty}^{\infty} (-1)^k x^{\frac{3k^2+k}{2}}$$

$$\prod_{n=1}^{\infty} (1 - x^n)^3 = \sum_{k=-\infty}^{\infty} (4k + 1) x^{2k^2+k}$$

$$\frac{\prod_{n=1}^{\infty} (1 - x^n)^2}{\prod_{n=1}^{\infty} (1 - x^{2n})} = \sum_{k=-\infty}^{\infty} (-1)^k x^{k^2}$$

$$\frac{\prod_{n=1}^{\infty} (1 - x^{2n})^2}{\prod_{n=1}^{\infty} (1 - x^n)} = \sum_{k=-\infty}^{\infty} x^{2k^2+k}$$

Surface area of an ellipsoid (StandardForm)

$$\int_0^{2\pi} \int_0^{\pi} \text{Sin}[\theta] \sqrt{b^2 c^2 \, \text{Sin}[\theta]^2 \, \text{Cos}[\phi]^2 + a^2 c^2 \, \text{Sin}[\theta]^2 \, \text{Sin}[\phi]^2 + a^2 b^2 \, \text{Cos}[\theta]^2} \, d\theta d\phi$$

$$= 2\pi \left(c^2 + \frac{bc^2}{\sqrt{a^2 - c^2}} \text{EllipticE}[\theta, m] + b \sqrt{a^2 - c^2} \, \text{EllipticF}[\theta, m] \right)$$

$$m = \frac{a^2 (b^2 - c^2)}{b^2 (a^2 - c^2)}; \quad \theta = \text{ArcSin}\left[1 - \frac{c^2}{a^2} \right] \; / ; \; a \geq b \geq c$$

Iterated radical identities (StandardForm)

$$\sqrt{6 + \sqrt{6 + \sqrt{6 + \sqrt{6 + \sqrt{6 + \sqrt{6 + \sqrt{6 + \ldots}}}}}}} = 3$$

$$\frac{2}{\sqrt{2}} \frac{2}{\sqrt{2 + \sqrt{2}}} \frac{2}{\sqrt{2 + \sqrt{2 + \sqrt{2}}}} \frac{2}{\sqrt{2 + \sqrt{2 + \sqrt{2 + \sqrt{2}}}}} \ldots = \frac{\pi}{2}$$

$$\sqrt{1 + \sqrt{1 + \sqrt{1 + \sqrt{1 + \sqrt{1 + \ldots}}}}} = 1 + \cfrac{1}{1 + \cfrac{1}{1 + \cfrac{1}{1 + \cfrac{1}{1 + \ldots}}}}$$

Polylogarithm identities (StandardForm)

$$2 \, \text{PolyLog}\left[2, \frac{5 - \sqrt{5}}{5 + \sqrt{5}} \right] + \text{Log}\left[\frac{5 - \sqrt{5}}{5 + \sqrt{5}} \right] \text{Log}\left[1 - \frac{5 - \sqrt{5}}{5 + \sqrt{5}} \right] - \frac{2\pi^2}{15} = 0$$

$$\text{PolyLog}\left[2, \frac{1}{4} \right] + 2 \, \text{PolyLog}\left[2, \frac{1}{3} \right] + \text{Log}\left[\frac{4}{3} \right] \text{Log}[2] + \text{Log}\left[\frac{3}{2} \right] \text{Log}[3] - \frac{\pi^2}{6} = 0$$

Heisenberg-Euler Lagrangian from quantum electrodynamics (TraditionalForm)

$$\mathcal{L}_{\text{eff}} = \frac{1}{2}(E^2 - B^2) - \frac{1}{8\pi^2}\int_\Gamma \frac{e^{-m^2 u}}{u^3}\left(e^2\, u^2\, |E \cdot B|\, \frac{\text{Re}\left[\cosh\left(e\,u\,\sqrt{2(B^2 - E^2 + i\,E \cdot B)}\right)\right]}{\text{Im}\left[\cosh\left(e\,u\,\sqrt{2(B^2 - E^2 + i\,E \cdot B)}\right)\right]} - 1 + \frac{2}{3}\,e^2\,u^2\,(E^2 - B^2)\right) du$$

Diagram from homological algebra (TraditionalForm)

$$
\begin{array}{ccccccccc}
X^{p-1} & \xrightarrow{\xi^p} & X^p & \xrightarrow{\nu^p} & X & \overset{\eta_p}{\Longrightarrow} & X_p & \overset{\xi_p}{\Longrightarrow} & X_{p+1} \\
\downarrow{\scriptstyle \kappa^{p-1}} & & \downarrow{\scriptstyle \kappa^p} & & \downarrow{\scriptstyle \kappa} & & \| & & \| \\
X^{p-1}_{-\infty} & \longrightarrow & X^p_{-\infty} & \xrightarrow{\nu^p_{-\infty}} & X_{-\infty} & \overset{\eta_{-\infty,p}}{\Longrightarrow} & X_p & \overset{\xi_p}{\Longrightarrow} & X_{p+1} \\
\| & & \| & & \uparrow{\scriptstyle \overline{\lambda}} & & \uparrow{\scriptstyle \lambda_p} & & \uparrow{\scriptstyle \lambda_{p+1}} \\
X^{p-1}_{-\infty} & \xrightarrow{\xi^p_{-\infty}} & X^p_{-\infty} & \xrightarrow{\nu^{\infty,p}_{-\infty}} & (X_{-\infty})^\infty & \overset{\eta^\infty_{-\infty,p}}{\Longrightarrow} & X^\infty_p & \overset{\xi^\infty_p}{\Longrightarrow} & X^\infty_{p+1}
\end{array}
$$

Sums involving zeta functions (TraditionalForm)

$$\sum_{k=2}^{\infty}(\zeta(k) - 1)\,x^k = -x\,(\psi(2 - x) + \gamma - 1) \qquad \sum_{k=2}^{\infty}\frac{(-1)^k}{2^k}\,\zeta(k) = 1 - \log(2)$$

Green's function for the Laplace operator on a rectangle with homogeneous Dirichlet boundary conditions (TraditionalForm)

$$G(x, x', y, y') = \frac{1}{2\pi}\text{Re}\left[\log\left(\frac{\vartheta_1(\frac{\pi}{4a}(x + iy + x' - iy'),\, e^{-\frac{a}{b}\pi})\,\vartheta_1(\frac{\pi}{4a}(x + iy - x' + iy'),\, e^{-\frac{a}{b}\pi})}{\vartheta_1(\frac{\pi}{4a}(x + iy - x' - iy'),\, e^{-\frac{a}{b}\pi})\,\vartheta_1(\frac{\pi}{4a}(x + iy + x' + iy'),\, e^{-\frac{a}{b}\pi})}\right)\right]$$

Nontrivial square root of an identity matrix (TraditionalForm)

$$\sqrt{\begin{pmatrix} 1 & 0 & 0 & 0 & 0 & 0 & 0 & 0 & 0 \\ 0 & 1 & 0 & 0 & 0 & 0 & 0 & 0 & 0 \\ 0 & 0 & 1 & 0 & 0 & 0 & 0 & 0 & 0 \\ 0 & 0 & 0 & 1 & 0 & 0 & 0 & 0 & 0 \\ 0 & 0 & 0 & 0 & 1 & 0 & 0 & 0 & 0 \\ 0 & 0 & 0 & 0 & 0 & 1 & 0 & 0 & 0 \\ 0 & 0 & 0 & 0 & 0 & 0 & 1 & 0 & 0 \\ 0 & 0 & 0 & 0 & 0 & 0 & 0 & 1 & 0 \\ 0 & 0 & 0 & 0 & 0 & 0 & 0 & 0 & 1 \end{pmatrix}} = \begin{pmatrix} \gamma & \beta & \delta & \epsilon & \alpha & \epsilon & \delta & \beta & \gamma \\ \beta & \epsilon & \epsilon & \beta & 0 & -\beta & -\epsilon & -\epsilon & -\beta \\ \delta & \epsilon & \gamma & -\beta & -\alpha & -\beta & \gamma & \epsilon & \delta \\ \epsilon & \beta & -\beta & -\epsilon & 0 & \epsilon & \beta & -\beta & -\epsilon \\ \alpha & 0 & -\alpha & 0 & \alpha & 0 & -\alpha & 0 & \alpha \\ \epsilon & -\beta & -\beta & \epsilon & 0 & -\epsilon & \beta & \beta & -\epsilon \\ \delta & -\epsilon & \gamma & \beta & -\alpha & \beta & \gamma & -\epsilon & \delta \\ \beta & -\epsilon & \epsilon & -\beta & 0 & \beta & -\epsilon & \epsilon & -\beta \\ \gamma & -\beta & \delta & -\epsilon & \alpha & -\epsilon & \delta & -\beta & \gamma \end{pmatrix}$$

$$\alpha = \frac{1}{\sqrt{5}}, \quad \beta = \frac{1}{2}\sqrt{\frac{5 - \sqrt{5}}{10}}, \quad \gamma = \frac{-1 + \sqrt{5}}{4\sqrt{5}}, \quad \delta = \frac{1 + \sqrt{5}}{4\sqrt{5}}, \quad \epsilon = \frac{1}{2}\sqrt{\frac{5 + \sqrt{5}}{10}}$$

Some indefinite integrals (StandardForm)

$$\int \frac{\text{Log}[-1+x]\,\text{Log}[1+x]}{x^4}\,dx =$$

$$\frac{1}{6x^3}\left(x\left(2x - \text{Log}[-1+x] + 2x\,\text{Log}[-1+x] - x^2\,\text{Log}[-1+x] - x^2\,\text{Log}[-x] + x^2\,\text{Log}[x] - \right.\right.$$

$$\left.2x^2\,\text{Log}[1-x]\,\text{Log}[x] + 2x^2\,\text{Log}[-1+x]\,\text{Log}[x] - 2x^2\,\text{Log}[-1+x]\,\text{Log}\left[\frac{1+x}{2}\right]\right) +$$

$$\left(x(1+x)^2 + 2x^3\,\text{Log}\left[\frac{1-x}{2}\right] - 2\,\text{Log}[-1+x]\right)\text{Log}[1+x] +$$

$$\left.2x^3\left(-\text{PolyLog}\left[2,\;\frac{1}{2}-\frac{x}{2}\right] + \text{PolyLog}[2,\,-x] - \text{PolyLog}[2,\,x] + \text{PolyLog}\left[2,\;\frac{1+x}{2}\right]\right)\right)$$

$$\int \text{Tan}[x]^a\,dx =$$

$$-\frac{1}{2}\,\text{Beta}\left[\text{Cos}[x]^2,\;\frac{1-a}{2},\;\frac{1+a}{2}\right]\text{Cos}[x]\,(\text{Cos}[x]^2)^{\frac{-1+a}{2}}\,\text{Sin}[x]\,(\text{Sin}[x]^2)^{\frac{-1-a}{2}}\,\text{Tan}[x]^a$$

$$\int \text{Log}[\text{Sin}[x] + \text{Tan}[x]]\,dx = \frac{I}{2}x^2 - x\,\text{Log}[1 - E^{Ix}] - 3x\,\text{Log}[1 + E^{Ix}] + x\,\text{Log}[1 + E^{2Ix}] +$$

$$x\,\text{Log}[\text{Sin}[x] + \text{Tan}[x]] + 3I\,\text{PolyLog}[2,\,-E^{Ix}] + I\,\text{PolyLog}[2,\,E^{Ix}] - \frac{I}{2}\text{PolyLog}[2,\,-E^{2Ix}]$$

$$\int \frac{1+x}{x\sqrt{(x-a)\,(x-b)\,(x-c)}}\,dx = \frac{2\,(b-c)\,\sqrt{\frac{a-x}{a-c}}\,\sqrt{\frac{(b-x)\,(-c+x)}{(b-c)^2}}}{c\,\sqrt{(-a+x)\,(-b+x)\,(-c+x)}}$$

$$\left(c\,\text{EllipticF}\left[\text{ArcSin}\left[\sqrt{\frac{-c+x}{b-c}}\right],\;\frac{b-c}{a-c}\right] + \text{EllipticPi}\left[1 - \frac{b}{c},\;\text{ArcSin}\left[\sqrt{\frac{-c+x}{b-c}}\right],\;\frac{b-c}{a-c}\right]\right)$$

$$\int x^p\,\text{Sin}[x]\,dx = -\frac{I}{2}\left(-(-Ix)^{-1-p}\,x^{1+p}\,\text{Gamma}[1+p,\,-Ix] + (Ix)^{-1-p}\,x^{1+p}\,\text{Gamma}[1+p,\,Ix]\right)$$

$$\int \frac{x\,\text{ArcTan}[x]}{x^2+1}\,dx = \frac{1}{2}\left(I\,\text{ArcTan}[x]^2 - 2\,\text{ArcTan}[x]\,\text{Log}[1 + E^{2I\,\text{ArcTan}[x]}] + I\,\text{PolyLog}[2,\,-E^{2I\,\text{ArcTan}[x]}]\right)$$

$$\int \frac{\text{Cos}[x]}{\text{Sin}[x]^6\,\text{Sin}[2x]^{\frac{3}{2}}}\,dx = \frac{1}{390}\text{Csc}[x]^7\,\sqrt{\text{Sin}[2x]}\,(-77 + 86\,\text{Cos}[2x] - 28\,\text{Cos}[4x] + 4\,\text{Cos}[6x])$$

$$\int \frac{x\,\text{ArcSec}[x]}{\sqrt{x^2-1}}\,dx = \sqrt{x^2-1}\,\text{ArcSec}[x] - \frac{x\,\sqrt{\frac{x^2-1}{x^2}}\,\text{Log}[x]}{\sqrt{x^2-1}}$$

$$\int x^2\,\text{Tan}[x]\,dx = \frac{I}{3}x^3 - x^2\,\text{Log}[1 + E^{2Ix}] + I\,x\,\text{PolyLog}[2,\,-E^{2Ix}] - \frac{1}{2}\text{PolyLog}[3,\,-E^{2Ix}]$$

Graphics Gallery

Mathematica incorporates powerful capabilities for making graphics. This Graphics Gallery shows a few examples of images created by Mathematica users around the world. Some of the images are generated by fairly simple Mathematica programs; others are the output of much more complex programs. The images illustrate the use of Mathematica in creating a wide range of graphics—from direct representations of physical objects to highly abstract mathematical and artistic forms.

For further information about the graphics in this gallery visit http://www.wolfram.com/graphics-gallery. A series of books containing more extensive Mathematica graphics will be available from Wolfram Media, Inc. Visit http://www.graphica.com for more information.

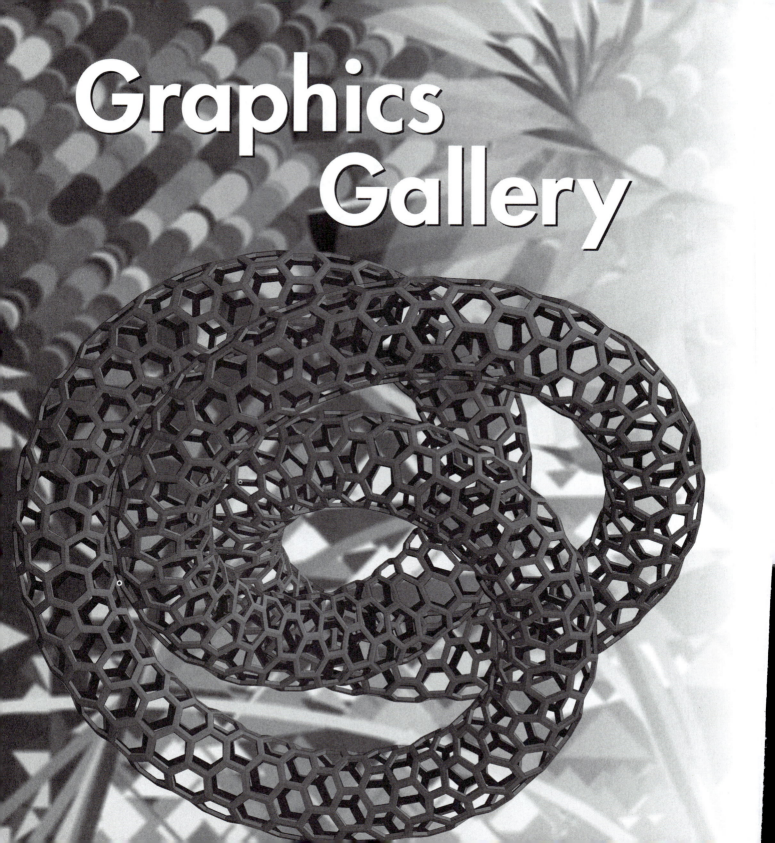

Graphics Gallery

Foreground: random rotation of triangles on the faces of a cube.

Background: iterations of random trigonometric mappings (both by M. Trott).

This page: random smooth interpolation from a hexagonal to a square lattice; zeros of the generalized Riemann zeta function $\zeta($a, s$)$ as a function of a (both by M. Trott).

Facing page, reading from top left: voltage regulator circuit (J. Novak); McPherson strut suspension (R. Beretta); Archimedean spiral (M. Trott); Gallium arsenide crystal structure with bismuth overlayer (A. McLean); Cassegranian optics telescope (D. Barnhart); February 26, 1998 total solar eclipse (T. Robb).

2

8

9

10

1–6 Multiple stellations and truncations of dodecahedra (all by J. Adams).

7–13 Stellations and truncations of polyhedra (all by R. Maeder).

11

6

Successive inversions of five circles.

Facing page, reading from top left: Voderberg spiral of identical nonagons; inversion of a checker-board; superposition of sine waves; phyllotaxis spiral; Brillouin zones of a square lattice; nested disks in a triangle; curve generated by an L system; Koch curve approximations; smooth areas produced by overlapping disks (all by M. Trott).

Foreground, left to right: smooth
connection of cylinders (M. Trott);
simultaneous rotation and shrinking of
the faces of an icosahedron (M. Trott);
bookshelf design (R. Jakschewitz);
flapping bird origami (L. Zamiatina);
chain of extruded icosahedra
(M. Trott); Beethoven (T. Robb);
iterated random tangential reflections
of a curve (M. Trott).

Background, from left: planisphere for
the Southern Hemisphere (T. Robb);
random tree of arcs (M. Trott).

Effects of Two-Dimensional Colored Noise

Mathematica art images generated by simple programs based on two-dimensional colored noise (all by I. Bakshee).

Foreground, clockwise from left: twisted torus; Klein bottle; surface generated by random rotation and contraction of a space curve; inversion of a cube; Riemann surface of the function $(z^4)^{-1/4}$.

Background: the Riemann surface of the functions $(z^2-1)^{1/4}$ (all by M. Trott).

Hue[h]

0.25

0.375   0.125

0.625   0.875

0.75

0

This page: charts of colors generated with color directives GrayLevel, Hue, RGBColor and CMYKColor for a sample of fixed and varied arguments.

Facing page: effect of light source positions and colors and surface color on a Klein bottle. First row—light sources vary; second row—diffuse reflection property of the surface varies; third row—specular reflection property of the surface varies; last row—no light sources are applied; polygons and their edges are explicitly colored.

GrayLevel[s]

Hue[h, s, 1]

Hue[h, 1, b]

Hue[1, s, b]

RGBColor[r, g, 0]

RGBColor[r, 0, b]

RGBColor[0, g, b]

CMYKColor[c, m, 1, 0]

CMYKColor[c, 1, y, 0]

CMYKColor[1, m, y, 0]

LightSources ->
{{{1, 0, 1}, RGBColor[1, 0, 0]},
 {{1, 1, 1}, RGBColor[0, 1, 0]},
 {{0, 1, 1}, RGBColor[0, 0, 1]}}

(default light sources)

LightSources ->
{{{0, 0, 1}, RGBColor[1, 0, 0]},
 {{1, 0, 0}, RGBColor[0, 1, 0]},
 {{0, 1, 0}, RGBColor[0, 0, 1]}}

LightSources ->
{{{0, 0, 1}, RGBColor[0, 1, 0]},
 {{1, 0, 0.4}, RGBColor[1, 0, 0]},
 {{0, 1, 0.4}, RGBColor[0, 0, 1]}}

LightSources ->
{{{0, 0, 1}, RGBColor[0, 0, 1]},
 {{1, 0, 0.4}, RGBColor[1, 0, 0]},
 {{0, 1, 0.4}, RGBColor[0, 1, 0]}}

SurfaceColor[RGBColor[1, 0.5, 0.5]],
LightSources ->
{{{1, 0, 1}, RGBColor[1, 0, 0]},
 {{-0.2, 0.9, 1}, RGBColor[0, 1, 0]},
 {{-0.2, -0.9, 1}, RGBColor[0, 0, 1]}}

SurfaceColor[RGBColor[0, 1, 0]],
LightSources ->
{{{1, 0, 1}, RGBColor[1, 0, 0]},
 {{1, 1, 1}, RGBColor[0, 1, 0]},
 {{0, 1, 1}, RGBColor[0, 0, 1]}}

SurfaceColor[RGBColor[0, 0, 1]],
LightSources ->
{{{1, 0, 1}, RGBColor[1, 0, 0]},
 {{1, 1, 1}, RGBColor[0, 1, 0]},
 {{0, 1, 1}, RGBColor[0, 0, 1]}}

SurfaceColor[RGBColor[0.5, 0.5, 1]],
LightSources ->
{{{1, 0, 1}, RGBColor[1, 0, 0]},
 {{-0.2, 0.9, 1}, RGBColor[0, 1, 0]},
 {{-0.2, -0.9, 1}, RGBColor[0, 0, 1]}}

SurfaceColor[GrayLevel[0],
  GrayLevel[1], 5],
LightSources ->
{{{0, 0, 1}, RGBColor[1, 0, 0]},
 {{1, 0, 0.3}, RGBColor[0, 1, 0]},
 {{-1, 0, 0.3}, RGBColor[0, 1, 0]},
 {{0, 1, 0.3}, RGBColor[0, 0, 1]}}

SurfaceColor[GrayLevel[0],
  GrayLevel[1], 3],
LightSources ->
{{{2, 3, 4}, RGBColor[1, 0, 0]},
 {{1, -5, 6}, RGBColor[0, 1, 0]},
 {{2, 6, -12}, RGBColor[0, 0, 1]}}

SurfaceColor[GrayLevel[0],
  RGBColor[0.25, 1, 0.25], 3],
LightSources ->
{{{2, 3, 4}, RGBColor[1, 0, 0]},
 {{1, -5, 6}, RGBColor[0, 1, 0]},
 {{2, 6, -12}, RGBColor[0, 0, 1]}}

SurfaceColor[GrayLevel[0],
  RGBColor[0.33, 1, 0.33], 3],
LightSources ->
{{{0, 0, 1}, RGBColor[1, 0, 0]},
 {{1, 0, 0.3}, RGBColor[0, 1, 0]},
 {{-1, 0, 0.3}, RGBColor[0, 1, 0]},
 {{0, 1, 0.3}, RGBColor[0, 0, 1]}}

polygons colored with Hue[h], no
edges shown

polygons colored with GrayLevel[0.7],
edges colored with Hue[h]

polygons colored with RGBColor[1,0,0]
or RGBColor[0,0,1], edges colored
with GrayLevel[1]

polygons colored with Hue[h], no
edges shown

Animations

Clockwise from top left: square
rolling on catenaries (S. Wagon and
L. Hall); cam-follower mechanism
(R. Beretta); golf swing (H. Murrell);
interlocking tori (W. Gosper); noise
texture model of fire (T. Robb).

Appendix

This appendix gives a definitive summary of the complete Mathematica system. Most of what it contains you will never need to know for any particular application of Mathematica.

You should realize that this appendix describes all the features of Mathematica, independent of their importance in typical usage.

Other parts of this book are organized along pedagogical lines, emphasizing important points, and giving details only when they are needed.

This appendix gives all the details of every feature. As a result, you will often find obscure details discussed alongside very common and important functions. Just remember that this appendix is intended for reference purposes, not for sequential reading. Do not be put off by the complexity of some of what you see; you will almost certainly never have to use it. But if you do end up having to use it, you will probably be happy that it is there.

By experimenting with Mathematica, you may find features that go beyond what is described in this appendix. You should not use any such features: there is no certainty that features which are not documented will continue to be supported in future versions of Mathematica.

Appendix

Mathematica Reference Guide

A.1 Basic Objects

■ A.1.1 Expressions

Expressions are the main type of data in *Mathematica*.

Expressions can be written in the form $h[e_1, e_2, \ldots]$. The object h is known generically as the *head* of the expression. The e_i are termed the *elements* of the expression. Both the head and the elements may themselves be expressions.

The *parts* of an expression can be referred to by numerical indices. The head has index 0; element e_i has index i. $\mathtt{Part}[expr, i]$ or $expr[[i]]$ gives the part of *expr* with index i. Negative indices count from the end.

$\mathtt{Part}[expr, i_1, i_2, \ldots]$, $expr[[i_1, i_2, \ldots]]$ or $\mathtt{Extract}[expr, \{i_1, i_2, \ldots\}]$ gives the piece of *expr* found by successively extracting parts of subexpressions with indices $i_1, i_2, \ldots$. If you think of expressions as trees, the indices specify which branch to take at each node as you descend from the root.

The pieces of an expression that are specified by giving a sequence of exactly n indices are defined to be at *level* n in the expression. You can use levels to determine the domain of application of functions like $\mathtt{Map}$. Level 0 corresponds to the whole expression.

The *depth* of an expression is defined to be the maximum number of indices needed to specify any part of the expression, plus one. A negative level number $-n$ refers to all parts of an expression that have depth n.

■ A.1.2 Symbols

Symbols are the basic named objects in *Mathematica*.

The name of a symbol must be a sequence of letters, letter-like forms and digits, not starting with a digit. Upper- and lower-case letters are always distinguished in *Mathematica*.

aaaaa	user-defined symbol
Aaaaa	system-defined symbol
$Aaaa	global or internal system-defined symbol
aaaa$	symbol renamed in a scoping construct
aa$nn	unique local symbol generated in a module

Conventions for symbol names.

Essentially all system-defined symbols have names that contain only ordinary English letters, together with numbers and $. The exceptions are π, ∞, e, i and j.

System-defined symbols conventionally have names that consist of one or more complete English words. The first letter of each word is capitalized, and the words are run together.

Once created, an ordinary symbol in *Mathematica* continues to exist unless it is explicitly removed using `Remove`. However, symbols created automatically in scoping constructs such as `Module` carry the attribute `Temporary` which specifies that they should automatically be removed as soon as they no longer appear in any expression.

When a new symbol is to be created, *Mathematica* first applies any value that has been assigned to `$NewSymbol` to strings giving the name of the symbol, and the context in which the symbol would be created.

If the message `General::newsym` is switched on, then *Mathematica* reports new symbols that are created. This message is switched off by default. Symbols created automatically in scoping constructs are not reported.

If the message `General::spell` is switched on, then *Mathematica* prints a warning if the name of a new symbol is close to the names of one or more existing symbols.

■ A.1.3 Contexts

The full name of any symbol in *Mathematica* consists of two parts: a *context*, and a *short name*. The full name is written in the form *context*`*name*. The context *context*` can contain the same characters as the short name. It may also contain any number of context mark characters `, and must end with a context mark.

At any point in a *Mathematica* session, there is a *current context* `$Context` and a *context search path* `$ContextPath` consisting of a list of contexts. Symbols in the current context, or in contexts on the context search path can be specified by giving only their short names.

name	search `$Context`, then `$ContextPath`; create in `$Context` if necessary
`*name*	search `$Context` only; create there if necessary
context`*name*	search *context* only; create there if necessary
`*context*`*name*	search `$Context`*context* only; create there if necessary

Contexts used for various specifications of symbols.

With *Mathematica* packages, it is conventional to associate contexts whose names correspond to the names of the packages. Packages typically use `BeginPackage` and `EndPackage` to define objects in the appropriate context, and to add the context to the global $ContextPath. EndPackage prints a warning about any symbols that were created in a package but which are "shadowed" by existing symbols on the context search path.

The context is included in the printed form of a symbol only if it would be needed to specify the symbol *at the time of printing*.

■ A.1.4 Atomic Objects

All expressions in *Mathematica* are ultimately made up from a small number of basic or atomic types of objects.

These objects have heads which are symbols that can be thought of as "tagging" their types. The objects contain "raw data", which can usually be accessed only by functions specific to the particular type of object. You can extract the head of the object using Head, but you cannot directly extract any of its other parts.

Symbol	symbol (extract name using SymbolName)
String	character string "*cccc*" (extract characters using Characters)
Integer	integer (extract digits using IntegerDigits)
Real	approximate real number (extract digits using RealDigits)
Rational	rational number (extract parts using Numerator and Denominator)
Complex	complex number (extract parts using Re and Im)

Atomic objects.

Atomic objects in *Mathematica* are considered to have depth 0 and yield True when tested with AtomQ.

As an optimization for some special kinds of computations, the raw data in *Mathematica* atomic objects can be given explicitly using Raw[*head*, "*hexstring*"]. The data is specified as a string of hexadecimal digits, corresponding to an array of bytes. When no special output form exists, InputForm prints special objects using Raw. *The behavior of* Raw *differs from one implementation of Mathematica to another; its general use is strongly discouraged.*

■ A.1.5 Numbers

Integer	integer *nnnn*
Real	approximate real number *nnn.nnn*
Rational	rational number *nnn/nnn*
Complex	complex number *nnn* + *nnn* I

Basic types of numbers.

All numbers in *Mathematica* can contain any number of digits. *Mathematica* does exact computations when possible with integers and rational numbers, and with complex numbers whose real and imaginary parts are integers or rational numbers.

There are two types of approximate real numbers in *Mathematica*: *arbitrary precision* and *machine precision*. In manipulating arbitrary-precision numbers, *Mathematica* always tries to modify the precision so as to ensure that all digits actually given are correct.

With machine-precision numbers, all computations are done to the same fixed precision, so some digits given may not be correct.

Unless otherwise specified, *Mathematica* treats as machine-precision numbers all approximate real numbers that lie between $MinMachineNumber and $MaxMachineNumber and that are input with less than $MachinePrecision digits.

In InputForm, *Mathematica* prints machine-precision numbers with $MachinePrecision digits, except when trailing digits are zero.

In any implementation of *Mathematica*, the magnitudes of numbers (except 0) must lie between $MinNumber and $MaxNumber. Numbers with magnitudes outside this range are represented by Underflow[ ] and Overflow[ ].

■ A.1.6 Character Strings

Character strings in *Mathematica* can contain any sequence of characters. They are input in the form "*ccccc*".

The individual characters can be printable ASCII (with character codes between 32 and 126), or in general any 8- or 16-bit characters. *Mathematica* uses the Unicode character encoding for 16-bit characters.

In input form, 16-bit characters are represented when possible in the form \[*name*], and otherwise as \:*nnnn*.

Null bytes can appear at any point within *Mathematica* strings.

A.2 Input Syntax

∼■ A.2.1 Entering Characters

■ Enter it directly (e.g. +)

■ Enter it by full name (e.g. \[Alpha])

■ Enter it by alias (e.g. ⌐a⌐) (notebook front end only)

■ Enter it by choosing from a palette (notebook front end only)

■ Enter it by character code (e.g. \053)

Typical ways to enter characters.

All printable ASCII characters can be entered directly. Those that are not alphanumeric are assigned explicit names in *Mathematica*, allowing them to be entered even on keyboards where they do not explicitly appear.

	\[RawSpace]	<	\[RawLess]
!	\[RawExclamation]	=	\[RawEqual]
"	\[RawDoubleQuote]	>	\[RawGreater]
#	\[RawNumberSign]	?	\[RawQuestion]
%	\[RawPercent]	@	\[RawAt]
&	\[RawAmpersand]	[	\[RawLeftBracket]
'	\[RawQuote]	\	\[RawBackslash]
(	\[RawLeftParenthesis]	]	\[RawRightBracket]
)	\[RawRightParenthesis]	^	\[RawWedge]
*	\[RawStar]	_	\[RawUnderscore]
+	\[RawPlus]	`	\[RawBackquote]
,	\[RawComma]	{	\[RawLeftBrace]
–	\[RawDash]	|	\[RawVerticalBar]
.	\[RawDot]	}	\[RawRightBrace]
/	\[RawSlash]	~	\[RawTilde]
:	\[RawColon]		

Full names for non-alphanumeric printable ASCII characters.

All characters which are entered into the *Mathematica* kernel are interpreted according to the setting for the `CharacterEncoding` option for the stream from which they came.

In the *Mathematica* front end, characters entered on the keyboard are interpreted according to the current setting of the `CharacterEncoding` option for the current notebook.

\[*Name*]	a character with the specified full name
nnn	a character with octal code *nnn*
\.*nn*	a character with hexadecimal code *nn*
\:*nnnn*	a character with hexadecimal code *nnnn*

Ways to enter characters.

Codes for characters can be generated using `ToCharacterCode`. The Unicode standard is followed, with various extensions.

8-bit characters have codes less than 256; 16-bit characters have codes between 256 and 65535. Approximately 600 characters are assigned explicit names in *Mathematica*. Other characters must be entered using their character codes.

\\	single backslash (decimal code 92)
\b	backspace or Control-H (decimal code 8)
\t	tab or Control-I (decimal code 9)
\n	newline or Control-J (decimal code 10; full name \[NewLine])
\f	form feed or Control-L (decimal code 12)
\r	carriage return or Control-M (decimal code 13)
\000	null byte (code 0)

Some special 8-bit characters.

■ A.2.2 Types of Input Syntax

This appendix describes the standard input syntax used by *Mathematica*. This input syntax is the one used by default in `InputForm` and `StandardForm`. You can modify the syntax by making definitions for `MakeExpression[`*expr*`, `*form*`]`.

Options can be set to specify what form of input should be accepted by a particular cell in a notebook or from a particular stream.

The input syntax in `TraditionalForm`, for example, is different from that in `InputForm` and `StandardForm`.

In general, what input syntax does is to determine how a particular string or collection of boxes should be interpreted as an expression. When boxes are set up, say with the notebook front end, there can be hidden `InterpretationBox` or `TagBox` objects which modify the interpretation of the boxes.

■ A.2.3 Character Strings

"characters"	a character string
\"	a literal " in a character string
\\	a literal \ in a character string
\< ... \>	a substring in which newlines are interpreted literally
\!\(... \)	a substring representing two-dimensional boxes

Entering character strings.

Character strings can contain any sequence of 8- or 16-bit characters. Characters entered by name or character code are stored the same as if they were entered directly.

Single newlines followed by spaces or tabs are converted to a single space when a string is entered, unless these characters occur within \< ... \>, in which case they are left unchanged.

Within \!\(... \) any box structures represented using backslash sequences can be used.

■ A.2.4 Symbol Names and Contexts

name	symbol name
`*name*	symbol name in current context
context`*name*	symbol name in specified context

Symbol names and contexts.

Symbol names and contexts can contain any characters that are treated by *Mathematica* as letters or letter-like forms. They can contain digits but cannot start with them.

■ A.2.5 Numbers

digits	integer
digits.*digits*	approximate number
base^^*digits*	integer in specified base
base^^*digits*.*digits*	approximate number in specified base
mantissa*^*n*	scientific notation ($mantissa \times 10^n$)
base^^*mantissa**^*n*	scientific notation in specified base ($mantissa \times base^n$)
number`	machine-precision approximate number
number`*p*	arbitrary-precision number with *p* digits of precision
number``*p*	arbitrary-precision number with *p* digits of accuracy

Input forms for numbers.

Numbers can be entered with the notation *base*^^*digits* in any base from 2 to 36. The base itself is given in decimal. For bases larger than 10, additional digits are chosen from the letters a–z or A–Z. Upper- and lower-case letters are equivalent for these purposes. Floating-point numbers can be specified by including . in the *digits* sequence.

In scientific notation, *mantissa* can contain ` marks. The exponent *n* must always be an integer, specified in decimal.

The precision or accuracy *p* can be any real number; it does not need to be an integer.

In the form *base*^^*number*`*p* the precision *p* is given in decimal, but it gives the number of digits of precision in the specified base, not in base 10.

■ A.2.6 Bracketed Objects

Bracketed objects use explicit left and right delimiters to indicate their extent. They can appear anywhere within *Mathematica* input, and can be nested in any way.

The delimiters in bracketed objects are *matchfix operators*. But since these delimiters explicitly enclose all operands, no precedence need be assigned to such operators.

(* *any text* *)	comment
(*expr*)	parenthesization: grouping of input

Bracketed objects without comma-separated elements.

Comments can be nested, and can continue for any number of lines. They can contain any 8- or 16-bit characters.

Parentheses must enclose a single complete expression; neither (e, e) nor $( )$ are allowed.

$\{e_1, e_2, \ldots\}$	$\texttt{List}[e_1, e_2, \ldots]$
$\langle e_1, e_2, \ldots \rangle$	$\texttt{AngleBracket}[e_1, e_2, \ldots]$
$\lfloor expr \rfloor$	$\texttt{Floor}[expr]$
$\lceil expr \rceil$	$\texttt{Ceiling}[expr]$
$\mid e_1, e_2, \ldots \mid$	$\texttt{BracketingBar}[e_1, e_2, \ldots]$
$\parallel e_1, e_2, \ldots \parallel$	$\texttt{DoubleBracketingBar}[e_1, e_2, \ldots]$
$\backslash(input\backslash)$	input or grouping of boxes

Bracketed objects that allow comma-separated elements.

Throughout this book the notation … is used to stand for any sequence of expressions.

$\{e_1, e_2, \ldots\}$ can include any number of elements, with successive elements separated by commas.

$\{ \}$ is $\texttt{List}[\ ]$, a list with zero elements.

$\langle e_1, e_2, \ldots \rangle$ can be entered as $\backslash[\texttt{LeftAngleBracket}]\ e_1, e_2, \ldots \backslash[\texttt{RightAngleBracket}]$.

The character $\backslash[\texttt{InvisibleComma}]$ can be used interchangeably with ordinary commas; the only difference is that $\backslash[\texttt{InvisibleComma}]$ will not be displayed.

When the delimiters are special characters, it is a convention that they are named $\backslash[\texttt{Left}Name]$ and $\backslash[\texttt{Right}Name]$.

$\backslash(\ldots \backslash)$ is used to enter boxes using one-dimensional strings. Note that within the outermost $\backslash(\ldots \backslash)$ in a piece of input the syntax used is slightly different from outside, as described on page 984.

$h[e_1, e_2, \ldots]$	standard expression
$e[[i_1, i_2, \ldots]]$	$\texttt{Part}[e, i_1, i_2, \ldots]$
$e[\![i_1, i_2, \ldots]\!]$	$\texttt{Part}[e, i_1, i_2, \ldots]$

Bracketed objects with heads.

Bracketed objects with heads explicitly delimit all their operands except the head. A precedence must be assigned to define the extent of the head.

The precedence of $h[e]$ is high enough that $!h[e]$ is interpreted as $\text{Not}[h[e]]$. However, $h\_s[e]$ is instead interpreted as $(h\_s)[e]$.

■ A.2.7 Operator Input Forms

Characters that are not letters, letter-like forms or structural elements are treated by *Mathematica* as *operators*. *Mathematica* has built-in rules for interpreting all operators. The functions to which these operators correspond may or may not, however, have built-in evaluation or other rules. Cases in which built-in meanings are by default defined are indicated by ◁ in the tables below.

Operators that construct two-dimensional boxes—all of which have names beginning with back-slash—can only be used inside \(... \). The table below gives the interpretations of these operators within \!\(... \). Page 985 gives interpretations when no \! is included.

expr and *expr*$_i$	any expression
symb	any symbol
patt	any pattern object
string and *string*$_i$	"*cccc*" or a sequence of letters, letter-like forms and digits
filename	like *string*, but can include additional characters described below
◁	built-in meanings exist
+	new in *Mathematica* Version 3

Objects used in the tables of operator input forms.

operator form	full form	grouping	
forms representing numbers (see page 969)			◁
forms representing symbols (see page 968)			◁
forms representing character strings (see page 968)			◁
expr::*string*	`MessageName[`*expr*`, "`*string*`"]`		◁
expr::*string*$_1$::*string*$_2$	`MessageName[`*expr*`, "`*string*$_1$`", "`*string*$_2$`"]`		◁
forms containing `#` *(see page 978))*			◁
forms containing `%` *(see page 978)*			◁
forms containing `_` *(see page 978)*			◁
`<<` *filename*	`Get["`*filename*`"]`		◁
+ $\overset{expr_2}{expr_1}$	`Overscript[`*expr*$_1$`, `*expr*$_2$`]`	$\binom{e}{e}$ e	
+ *expr*$_1$ `\&` *expr*$_2$	`Overscript[`*expr*$_1$`, `*expr*$_2$`]`	e`\&`$(e$`\&`$e)$	
+ $\underset{expr_2}{expr_1}$	`Underscript[`*expr*$_1$`, `*expr*$_2$`]`	e $\binom{e}{e}$	
+ *expr*$_1$ `\+` *expr*$_2$	`Underscript[`*expr*$_1$`, `*expr*$_2$`]`	e`\+`$(e$`\+`$e)$	
+ $\overset{expr_3}{\underset{expr_2}{expr_1}}$	`Underoverscript[`*expr*$_1$`, `*expr*$_2$`, `*expr*$_3$`]`		
+ *expr*$_1$ `\+` *expr*$_2$ `\%` *expr*$_3$	`Underoverscript[`*expr*$_1$`, `*expr*$_2$`, `*expr*$_3$`]`		
+ *expr*$_1$ `\&` *expr*$_2$ `\%` *expr*$_3$	`Underoverscript[`*expr*$_1$`, `*expr*$_3$`, `*expr*$_2$`]`		
+ *expr*$_{1}$$_{expr_2}$	`Subscript[`*expr*$_1$`, `*expr*$_2$`]`	$e_{(e_e)}$	
+ *expr*$_1$ `\_` *expr*$_2$	`Subscript[`*expr*$_1$`, `*expr*$_2$`]`	e`\_`$(e$`\_`$e)$	
+ *expr*$_1$ `\_` *expr*$_2$ `\%` *expr*$_3$	`Power[Subscript[`*expr*$_1$`, `*expr*$_2$`], `*expr*$_3$`]`		◁
+ `\!`*boxes*	(interpreted version of *boxes*)		
expr$_1$`?`*expr*$_2$	`PatternTest[`*expr*$_1$`, `*expr*$_2$`]`		◁
expr$_1$`[`*expr*$_2$`, ... ]`	*expr*$_1$`[`*expr*$_2$`, ... ]`	$(e[e])[e]$	◁
expr$_1$`[[`*expr*$_2$`, ... ]]`	`Part[`*expr*$_1$`, `*expr*$_2$`, ... ]`	$(e[[e]])[[e]]$	◁
+ *expr*$_1$`⟦`*expr*$_2$`, ... ⟧`	`Part[`*expr*$_1$`, `*expr*$_2$`, ... ]`	$(e⟦e⟧)⟦e⟧$	◁
+ `\*`*expr*	(boxes constructed from *expr*)		

Operator input forms, in order of decreasing precedence, part one.

operator form	full form	grouping	
expr++	`Increment[`*expr*`]`		◁
expr--	`Decrement[`*expr*`]`		◁
++*expr*	`PreIncrement[`*expr*`]`		◁
--*expr*	`PreDecrement[`*expr*`]`		◁
expr$_1$ @ *expr*$_2$	*expr*$_1$`[`*expr*$_2$`]`	*e* @ (*e* @ *e*)	◁
expr$_1$ ~ *expr*$_2$ ~ *expr*$_3$	*expr*$_2$`[`*expr*$_1$`, `*expr*$_3$`]`	(*e* ~ *e* ~ *e*) ~ *e* ~ *e*	◁
expr$_1$ /@ *expr*$_2$	`Map[`*expr*$_1$`, `*expr*$_2$`]`	*e* /@ (*e* /@ *e*)	◁
expr$_1$ //@ *expr*$_2$	`MapAll[`*expr*$_1$`, `*expr*$_2$`]`	*e* //@ (*e* //@ *e*)	◁
expr$_1$ @@ *expr*$_2$	`Apply[`*expr*$_1$`, `*expr*$_2$`]`	*e* @@ (*e* @@ *e*)	◁
expr!	`Factorial[`*expr*`]`		◁
expr!!	`Factorial2[`*expr*`]`		◁
expr'	`Derivative[1][`*expr*`]`		◁
expr$_1$ <> *expr*$_2$ <> *expr*$_3$	`StringJoin[`*expr*$_1$`, `*expr*$_2$`, `*expr*$_3$`]`	*e* <> *e* <> *e*	◁
expr$_1$ ^ *expr*$_2$	`Power[`*expr*$_1$`, `*expr*$_2$`]`	*e*^(*e*^*e*)	◁
+ *expr*$_1^{expr_2}$	`Power[`*expr*$_1$`, `*expr*$_2$`]`	$e^{(e^e)}$	◁
+ *expr*$_{1expr_2}^{expr_3}$	`Power[Subscript[`*expr*$_1$`, `*expr*$_2$`], `*expr*$_3$`]`		◁
+ *expr*$_1$ \^ *expr*$_2$ \% *expr*$_3$	`Power[Subscript[`*expr*$_1$`, `*expr*$_3$`], `*expr*$_2$`]`		◁
+ *vertical arrow and vector operators*			
+ $\sqrt{}$*expr*	`Sqrt[`*expr*`]`	$\sqrt{}(\sqrt{}e)$	◁
+ \@ *expr*	`Sqrt[`*expr*`]`	\@(\@*e*)	◁
+ \@ *expr* \% *n*	`Power[`*expr*`, 1/`*n*`]`		◁
+ ∫ *expr*$_1$ d*expr*$_2$	`Integrate[`*expr*$_1$`, `*expr*$_2$`]`	∫ (∫ *e* d *e*) d *e*	◁
+ $\int_{e_1}^{e_2} e_3 \mathrm{d} e_4$	`Integrate[`*e*$_3$`, {`*e*$_4$`, `*e*$_1$`, `*e*$_2$`}]`	∫ (∫ *e* d *e*) d *e*	◁
+ *other integration operators: see page 979*			
+ ∂$_{expr_1}$ *expr*$_2$	`D[`*expr*$_2$`, `*expr*$_1$`]`	∂$_e$ (∂$_e$ *e*)	◁
+ ∇ *expr*	`Del[`*expr*`]`	∇ (∇ *e*)	
+ □ *expr*	`Square[`*expr*`]`	□ (□ *e*)	
+ *expr*$_1$ ∘ *expr*$_2$ ∘ *expr*$_3$	`SmallCircle[`*expr*$_1$`, `*expr*$_2$`, `*expr*$_3$`]`	*e* ∘ *e* ∘ *e*	
+ *expr*$_1$ ⊙ *expr*$_2$ ⊙ *expr*$_3$	`CircleDot[`*expr*$_1$`, `*expr*$_2$`, `*expr*$_3$`]`	*e* ⊙ *e* ⊙ *e*	

Operator input forms, in order of decreasing precedence, part two.

operator form	full form	grouping	
$expr_1$ ** $expr_2$ ** $expr_3$	NonCommutativeMultiply[$expr_1$, $expr_2$, $expr_3$]	e ** e ** e	
+ $expr_1$ × $expr_2$ × $expr_3$	Cross[$expr_1$, $expr_2$, $expr_3$]	e × e × e	◁
$expr_1$. $expr_2$. $expr_3$	Dot[$expr_1$, $expr_2$, $expr_3$]	e . e . e	◁
$-expr$	Times[-1, $expr$]		◁
$+expr$	$expr$		◁
+ ± $expr$	PlusMinus[$expr$]		
+ ∓ $expr$	MinusPlus[$expr$]		
$expr_1$ / $expr_2$	$expr_1$ ($expr_2$)^-1	$(e / e) / e$	◁
+ $expr_1$ ÷ $expr_2$	Divide[$expr_1$, $expr_2$]	$(e ÷ e) ÷ e$	◁
+ $expr_1$ \/ $expr_2$	Divide[$expr_1$, $expr_2$]	$(e\backslash/e)\backslash/e$	◁
+ $expr_1$ \ $expr_2$ \ $expr_3$	Backslash[$expr_1$, $expr_2$, $expr_3$]	$e \backslash e \backslash e$	
+ $expr_1$ ◇ $expr_2$ ◇ $expr_3$	Diamond[$expr_1$, $expr_2$, $expr_3$]	$e ◇ e ◇ e$	
+ $expr_1$ ∧ $expr_2$ ∧ $expr_3$	Wedge[$expr_1$, $expr_2$, $expr_3$]	$e ∧ e ∧ e$	
+ $expr_1$ ∨ $expr_2$ ∨ $expr_3$	Vee[$expr_1$, $expr_2$, $expr_3$]	$e ∨ e ∨ e$	
+ $expr_1$ ⊗ $expr_2$ ⊗ $expr_3$	CircleTimes[$expr_1$, $expr_2$, $expr_3$]	$e ⊗ e ⊗ e$	
+ $expr_1$ · $expr_2$ · $expr_3$	CenterDot[$expr_1$, $expr_2$, $expr_3$]	$e · e · e$	
$expr_1$ $expr_2$ $expr_3$	Times[$expr_1$, $expr_2$, $expr_3$]	$e\ e\ e$	◁
$expr_1$ * $expr_2$ * $expr_3$	Times[$expr_1$, $expr_2$, $expr_3$]	$e * e * e$	◁
+ $expr_1$ × $expr_2$ × $expr_3$	Times[$expr_1$, $expr_2$, $expr_3$]	$e × e × e$	◁
+ $expr_1$ * $expr_2$ * $expr_3$	Star[$expr_1$, $expr_2$, $expr_3$]	$e * e * e$	
+ $\prod_{e_1=e_2}^{e_3} e_4$	Product[e_4, {e_1, e_2, e_3}]	$\prod (\prod e)$	◁
+ $expr_1$ ≀ $expr_2$ ≀ $expr_3$	VerticalTilde[$expr_1$, $expr_2$, $expr_3$]	$e ≀ e ≀ e$	
+ $expr_1$ ⅠⅠ $expr_2$ ⅠⅠ $expr_3$	Coproduct[$expr_1$, $expr_2$, $expr_3$]	e ⅠⅠ e ⅠⅠ e	
+ $expr_1$ ⌢ $expr_2$ ⌢ $expr_3$	Cap[$expr_1$, $expr_2$, $expr_3$]	$e ⌢ e ⌢ e$	
+ $expr_1$ ⌣ $expr_2$ ⌣ $expr_3$	Cup[$expr_1$, $expr_2$, $expr_3$]	$e ⌣ e ⌣ e$	

Operator input forms, in order of decreasing precedence, part three.

operator form	full form	grouping	
+ $expr_1 \oplus expr_2 \oplus expr_3$	CirclePlus[$expr_1$, $expr_2$, $expr_3$]	$e \oplus e \oplus e$	
+ $expr_1 \ominus expr_2$	CircleMinus[$expr_1$, $expr_2$]	$(e \ominus e) \ominus e$	
+ $\displaystyle\sum_{e_1=e_2}^{e_3} e_4$	Sum[e_4, {e_1, e_2, e_3}]	$\sum \left(\sum e \right)$	◁
$expr_1 + expr_2 + expr_3$	Plus[$expr_1$, $expr_2$, $expr_3$]	$e + e + e$	◁
$expr_1 - expr_2$	$expr_1 + (-1\ expr_2)$	$(e - e) - e$	◁
+ $expr_1 \pm expr_2$	PlusMinus[$expr_1$, $expr_2$]	$(e \pm e) \pm e$	
+ $expr_1 \mp expr_2$	MinusPlus[$expr_1$, $expr_2$]	$(e \mp e) \mp e$	
+ $expr_1 \cap expr_2$	Intersection[$expr_1$, $expr_2$]	$e \cap e \cap e$	◁
+ other intersection operators			
+ $expr_1 \cup expr_2$	Union[$expr_1$, $expr_2$]	$e \cup e \cup e$	◁
+ other union operators			
$expr_1 == expr_2$	Equal[$expr_1$, $expr_2$]	$e == e == e$	◁
+ $expr_1 \equiv expr_2$	Equal[$expr_1$, $expr_2$]	$e \equiv e \equiv e$	◁
$expr_1 \mathrel{!=} expr_2$	Unequal[$expr_1$, $expr_2$]	$e \mathrel{!=} e \mathrel{!=} e$	◁
+ $expr_1 \neq expr_2$	Unequal[$expr_1$, $expr_2$]	$e \neq e \neq e$	◁
+ other equality and similarity operators			
$expr_1 > expr_2$	Greater[$expr_1$, $expr_2$]	$e > e > e$	◁
$expr_1 >= expr_2$	GreaterEqual[$expr_1$, $expr_2$]	$e >= e >= e$	◁
+ $expr_1 \geq expr_2$	GreaterEqual[$expr_1$, $expr_2$]	$e \geq e \geq e$	◁
+ $expr_1 \geqslant expr_2$	GreaterEqual[$expr_1$, $expr_2$]	$e \geqslant e \geqslant e$	◁
$expr_1 < expr_2$	Less[$expr_1$, $expr_2$]	$e < e < e$	◁
$expr_1 <= expr_2$	LessEqual[$expr_1$, $expr_2$]	$e <= e <= e$	◁
+ $expr_1 \leq expr_2$	LessEqual[$expr_1$, $expr_2$]	$e \leq e \leq e$	◁
+ $expr_1 \leqslant expr_2$	LessEqual[$expr_1$, $expr_2$]	$e \leqslant e \leqslant e$	◁
+ other ordering operators			
+ $expr_1 \mid expr_2$	VerticalBar[$expr_1$, $expr_2$]	$e \mid e \mid e$	
+ $expr_1 \nmid expr_2$	NotVerticalBar[$expr_1$, $expr_2$]	$e \nmid e \nmid e$	
+ $expr_1 \parallel expr_2$	DoubleVerticalBar[$expr_1$, $expr_2$]	$e \parallel e \parallel e$	
+ $expr_1 \nparallel expr_2$	NotDoubleVerticalBar[$expr_1$, $expr_2$]	$e \nparallel e \nparallel e$	
+ horizontal arrow and vector operators			
+ diagonal arrow operators			

Operator input forms, in order of decreasing precedence, part four.

operator form	full form	grouping	
$expr_1$ === $expr_2$	SameQ[$expr_1$, $expr_2$]	e === e === e	◁
$expr_1$ =!= $expr_2$	UnsameQ[$expr_1$, $expr_2$]	e =!= e =!= e	◁
+ $expr_1 \subset expr_2$	Subset[$expr_1$, $expr_2$]	$e \subset e \subset e$	
+ $expr_1 \supset expr_2$	Superset[$expr_1$, $expr_2$]	$e \supset e \supset e$	
+ $expr_1 \in expr_2$	Element[$expr_1$, $expr_2$]	$e \in e \in e$	
+ other set relation operators			
+ $\forall_{expr_1} expr_2$	ForAll[$expr_1$, $expr_2$]	$\forall_e$ ($\forall_e$ e)	
+ $\exists_{expr_1} expr_2$	Exists[$expr_1$, $expr_2$]	$\exists_e$ ($\exists_e$ e)	
+ $\nexists_{expr_1} expr_2$	NotExists[$expr_1$, $expr_2$]	$\nexists_e$ ($\nexists_e$ e)	
!$expr$	Not[$expr$]	!(!e)	◁
+ $\neg$ $expr$	Not[$expr$]	$\neg$ ($\neg$ e)	◁
$expr_1$ && $expr_2$ && $expr_3$	And[$expr_1$, $expr_2$, $expr_3$]	e && e && e	◁
+ $expr_1 \wedge expr_2 \wedge expr_3$	And[$expr_1$, $expr_2$, $expr_3$]	$e \wedge e \wedge e$	◁
$expr_1$ || $expr_2$ || $expr_3$	Or[$expr_1$, $expr_2$, $expr_3$]	e || e || e	◁
+ $expr_1 \vee expr_2 \vee expr_3$	Or[$expr_1$, $expr_2$, $expr_3$]	$e \vee e \vee e$	◁
+ $expr_1 \Rightarrow expr_2$	Implies[$expr_1$, $expr_2$]	$e \Rightarrow (e \Rightarrow e)$	◁
+ $expr_1 \Rightarrow expr_2$	Implies[$expr_1$, $expr_2$]	$e = (e = e)$	◁
+ $expr_1 \vdash expr_2$	RightTee[$expr_1$, $expr_2$]	$e \vdash (e \vdash e)$	
+ $expr_1 \vDash expr_2$	DoubleRightTee[$expr_1$, $expr_2$]	$e \vDash (e \vDash e)$	
+ $expr_1 \dashv expr_2$	LeftTee[$expr_1$, $expr_2$]	$(e \dashv e) \dashv e$	
+ $expr_1 \dashv expr_2$	DoubleLeftTee[$expr_1$, $expr_2$]	$(e \dashv e) \dashv e$	
+ $expr_1 \ni expr_2$	SuchThat[$expr_1$, $expr_2$]	$e \ni (e \ni e)$	
$expr$..	Repeated[$expr$]		◁
$expr$...	RepeatedNull[$expr$]		◁
$expr_1$ | $expr_2$	Alternatives[$expr_1$, $expr_2$]	e | e | e	◁
$symb$:$expr$	Pattern[$symb$, $expr$]		◁
$patt$:$expr$	Optional[$patt$, $expr$]		◁
$expr_1$ /; $expr_2$	Condition[$expr_1$, $expr_2$]	$(e/;e)/;e$	◁

Operator input forms, in order of decreasing precedence, part five.

operator form	full form	grouping	
$expr_1$ -> $expr_2$	`Rule[`$expr_1$`, `$expr_2$`]`	$e \to (e \to e)$	◁
+ $expr_1$ → $expr_2$	`Rule[`$expr_1$`, `$expr_2$`]`	$e \to (e \to e)$	◁
$expr_1$:> $expr_2$	`RuleDelayed[`$expr_1$`, `$expr_2$`]`	$e :> (e :> e)$	◁
+ $expr_1$:→ $expr_2$	`RuleDelayed[`$expr_1$`, `$expr_2$`]`	$e :\to (e :\to e)$	◁
$expr_1$ /. $expr_2$	`ReplaceAll[`$expr_1$`, `$expr_2$`]`	$(e / . e) / . e$	◁
$expr_1$ //. $expr_2$	`ReplaceRepeated[`$expr_1$`, `$expr_2$`]`	$(e // . e) // . e$	◁
$expr_1$ += $expr_2$	`AddTo[`$expr_1$`, `$expr_2$`]`		◁
$expr_1$ -= $expr_2$	`SubtractFrom[`$expr_1$`, `$expr_2$`]`		◁
$expr_1$ *= $expr_2$	`TimesBy[`$expr_1$`, `$expr_2$`]`		◁
$expr_1$ /= $expr_2$	`DivideBy[`$expr_1$`, `$expr_2$`]`		◁
$expr$ &	`Function[`$expr$`]`		◁
+ $expr_1$: $expr_2$	`Colon[`$expr_1$`, `$expr_2$`]`	$e : e : e$	
$expr_1$ // $expr_2$	$expr_2$`[`$expr_1$`]`	$(e // e) // e$	
+ $expr_1$ | $expr_2$	`VerticalSeparator[`$expr_1$`, `$expr_2$`]`	$e \| e \| e$	
+ $expr_1$ ∴ $expr_2$	`Therefore[`$expr_1$`, `$expr_2$`]`	$e \therefore (e \therefore e)$	
+ $expr_1$ ∵ $expr_2$	`Because[`$expr_1$`, `$expr_2$`]`	$(e \because e) \because e$	
$expr_1$ = $expr_2$	`Set[`$expr_1$`, `$expr_2$`]`	$e = (e = e)$	◁
$expr_1$:= $expr_2$	`SetDelayed[`$expr_1$`, `$expr_2$`]`		◁
$expr_1$ ^= $expr_2$	`UpSet[`$expr_1$`, `$expr_2$`]`		◁
$expr_1$ ^:= $expr_2$	`UpSetDelayed[`$expr_1$`, `$expr_2$`]`		◁
$symb$/: $expr_1$ = $expr_2$	`TagSet[`$symb$`, `$expr_1$`, `$expr_2$`]`		◁
$symb$/: $expr_1$:= $expr_2$	`TagSetDelayed[`$symb$`, `$expr_1$`, `$expr_2$`]`		◁
$expr$ =.	`Unset[`$expr$`]`		◁
$symb$/: $expr$ =.	`TagUnset[`$symb$`, `$expr$`]`		◁
$expr$ >> $filename$	`Put[`$expr$`, "`*filename*`"]`		◁
$expr$ >>> $filename$	`PutAppend[`$expr$`, "`*filename*`"]`		◁
$expr_1$;$expr_2$;$expr_3$	`CompoundExpression[`$expr_1$`, `$expr_2$`, `$expr_3$`]`		◁
$expr_1$;$expr_2$;	`CompoundExpression[`$expr_1$`, `$expr_2$`, Null]`		◁
+ $expr_1$ \` $expr_2$	`FormBox[`$expr_2$`, `$expr_1$`]`		

Operator input forms, in order of decreasing precedence, part six.

special input form	full form
#	Slot[1]
#*n*	Slot[*n*]
##	SlotSequence[1]
##*n*	SlotSequence[*n*]
%	Out[ ]
%%	Out[-2]
%% ... % (*n* times)	Out[-*n*]
%*n*	Out[*n*]
_	Blank[ ]
_*expr*	Blank[*expr*]
__	BlankSequence[ ]
__*expr*	BlankSequence[*expr*]
___	BlankNullSequence[ ]
___*expr*	BlankNullSequence[*expr*]
_.	Optional[Blank[ ]]
*symb*_	Pattern[*symb*, Blank[ ]]
*symb*_*expr*	Pattern[*symb*, Blank[*expr*]]
*symb*__	Pattern[*symb*, BlankSequence[ ]]
*symb*__*expr*	Pattern[*symb*, BlankSequence[*expr*]]
*symb*___	Pattern[*symb*, BlankNullSequence[ ]]
*symb*___*expr*	Pattern[*symb*, BlankNullSequence[*expr*]]
*symb*_.	Optional[Pattern[*symb*, Blank[ ]]]

Additional input forms, in order of decreasing precedence.

Special Characters

Special characters that appear in operators usually have names that correspond to the names of the functions they represent. Thus the character ⊕ has name \[CirclePlus] and yields the function CirclePlus. Exceptions are \[GreaterSlantEqual], \[LessSlantEqual] and \[RoundImplies].

The delimiters in matchfix operators have names \[Left*Name*] and \[Right*Name*].

Pages 1270–1316 give a complete listing of special characters that appear in operators.

keyboard characters	special character	keyboard characters	special character
->	\[Rule] →	>=	\[GreaterEqual] ≥
:>	\[RuleDelayed] :→	>=	\[GreaterSlantEqual] ⩾
==	\[Equal] ==	>=	\[LessEqual] ≤
!=	\[NotEqual] ≠	>=	\[LessSlantEqual] ⩽

Keyboard and special characters with the same interpretations.

keyboard character	special character	keyboard character	special character
\[RawColon] :	\[Colon] :	\[RawDot] .	\[CenterDot] ·
\[RawTilde] ~	\[Tilde] ~	\[RawVerticalBar] |	\[VerticalBar] ❘
\[RawWedge] ^	\[Wedge] ∧	\[RawVerticalBar] |	\[VerticalSeparator] ❘
\[RawWedge] ^	\[And] ∧	\[RawVerticalBar] |	\[LeftBracketingBar] ❘
\[RawStar] *	\[Star] ⋆	\[RawDash] -	\[Dash] -
\[RawBackslash] \	\[Backslash] \	...	\[Ellipsis] …

Some keyboard and special characters with different interpretations.

Precedence and the Ordering of Input Forms

The tables of input forms are arranged in decreasing order of precedence. Input forms in the same box have the same precedence. Each page in the table begins a new box. As discussed in Section 2.1.3, precedence determines how *Mathematica* groups terms in input expressions. The general rule is that if $\otimes$ has higher precedence than $\oplus$, then $a \oplus b \otimes c$ is interpreted as $a \oplus (b \otimes c)$, and $a \otimes b \oplus c$ is interpreted as $(a \otimes b) \oplus c$.

Grouping of Input Forms

The third columns in the tables show how multiple occurrences of a single input form, or of several input forms with the same precedence, are grouped. For example, a/b/c is grouped as (a/b)/c ("left associative"), while a^b^c is grouped as a^(b^c) ("right associative"). No grouping is needed in an expression like a + b + c, since Plus is fully associative, as represented by the attribute Flat.

Precedence of Integration Operators

Forms such as $\int expr_1 \, \mathrm{d} \, expr_2$ have an "outer" precedence just below Power, as indicated in the table above, but an "inner" precedence just above $\sum$. The outer precedence determines when $expr_2$ needs to be parenthesized; the inner precedence determines when $expr_1$ needs to be parenthesized.

\[ContourIntegral], \[ClockwiseContourIntegral] and \[DoubleContourIntegral] work the same as \[Integral].

See page 982 for two-dimensional input forms associated with integration operators.

Spaces and Multiplication

Spaces in *Mathematica* denote multiplication, just as they do in standard mathematical notation. In addition, *Mathematica* takes complete expressions that are adjacent, not necessarily separated by spaces, to be multiplied together.

- x y z $\longrightarrow$ x*y*z
- 2x $\longrightarrow$ 2*x
- 2(x+1) $\longrightarrow$ 2*(x+1)
- c(x+1) $\longrightarrow$ c*(x+1)
- (x+1)(y+2) $\longrightarrow$ (x+1)*(y+2)
- x! y $\longrightarrow$ x!*y
- x!y $\longrightarrow$ x!*y

Alternative forms for multiplication.

An expression like x!y could potentially mean either (x!)*y or x*(!y). The first interpretation is chosen because Factorial has higher precedence than Not.

Spaces within single input forms are ignored. Thus, for example, a + b is equivalent to a+b. You will often want to insert spaces around lower precedence operators to improve readability.

You can give a "coefficient" for a symbol by preceding it with any sequence of digits. When you use numbers in bases larger than 10, the digits can include letters. (In bases other than 10, there must be a space between the end of the coefficient, and the beginning of the symbol name.)

- x^2y, like x^2 y, means (x^2) y
- x/2y, like x/2 y, means (x/2) y
- xy is a single symbol, not x*y

Some cases to be careful about.

Spaces to Avoid

You should avoid inserting any spaces between the different characters in composite operators such as /., =. and >=. Although in some cases such spaces are allowed, they are liable to lead to confusion.

Another case where spaces must be avoided is between the characters of the pattern object x_. If you type x _, *Mathematica* will interpret this as x*_, rather than the single named pattern object x_.

Similarly, you should not insert any spaces inside pattern objects like *x_:value*.

Spacing Characters

- Ordinary keyboard space (\[RawSpace])

- \[VeryThinSpace], \[ThinSpace], ..., \[ThickSpace]

- \[NegativeVeryThinSpace], \[NegativeThinSpace], ..., \[NegativeThickSpace]

- ␣ (\[SpaceIndicator])

Spacing characters equivalent to an ordinary keyboard space.

Relational Operators

Relational operators can be mixed. An expression like a > b >= c is converted to Inequality[a, Greater, b, GreaterEqual, c], which effectively evaluates as (a > b) && (b >= c). (The reason for the intermediate Inequality form is that it prevents objects from being evaluated twice when input like a > b >= c is processed.)

File Names

Any file name can be given in quotes after <<, >> and >>>. File names can also be given without quotes if they contain only alphanumeric characters, special characters and the characters `, /, ., \, !, -, _, :, $, *, ~ and ?, together with matched pairs of square brackets enclosing any characters other than spaces, tabs and newlines. Note that file names given without quotes can be followed only by spaces, tabs or newlines, or by the characters),], } as well as semicolon and comma.

⁺■ A.2.8 Two-Dimensional Input Forms

Two-dimensional input forms with built-in evaluation rules.

Any array of expressions represented by a `GridBox` is interpreted as a list of lists. Even if the `GridBox` has only one row, the interpretation is still $\{\{a_1, a_2, \dots\}\}$.

In the form $\int_{xmin}^{xmax} yw\frac{dx}{z}$ the limits $xmin$ and $xmax$ can be omitted, as can y and w.

x_y	`Subscript[x, y]`	$\overset{y}{x}$	`Overscript[x, y]`
		$\underset{y}{x}$	`Underscript[x, y]`
x_+	`SubPlus[x]`		
x_-	`SubMinus[x]`	$\overline{x}$	`OverBar[x]`
x_*	`SubStar[x]`	$\vec{x}$	`OverVector[x]`
		$\tilde{x}$	`OverTilde[x]`
x^+	`SuperPlus[x]`	$\hat{x}$	`OverHat[x]`
x^-	`SuperMinus[x]`	$\dot{x}$	`OverDot[x]`
x^*	`SuperStar[x]`		
$x^\dagger$	`SuperDagger[x]`	$\underline{x}$	`UnderBar[x]`

Two-dimensional input forms without built-in evaluation rules.

There is no issue of precedence for forms such as $\sqrt{x}$ and $\hat{x}$ in which operands are effectively spanned by the operator. For forms such as x_y and $x^\dagger$ a left precedence does need to be specified, so such forms are included in the main table of precedences above.

A.3 Some General Notations and Conventions

■ A.3.1 Function Names

The names of built-in functions follow some general guidelines.

- The name consists of complete English words, or standard mathematical abbreviations. American spelling is used.

- The first letter of each word is capitalized.

- Functions whose names end with Q usually "ask a question", and return either `True` or `False`.

- Mathematical functions that are named after people usually have names in *Mathematica* of the form *PersonSymbol*.

■ A.3.2 Function Arguments

The main expression or object on which a built-in function acts is usually given as the first argument to the function. Subsidiary parameters appear as subsequent arguments.

The following are exceptions:

- In functions like `Map` and `Apply`, the function to apply comes before the expression it is to be applied to.

- In scoping constructs such as `Module` and `Function`, local variables and parameter names come before bodies.

- In functions like `Write` and `Display`, the name of the file is given before the objects to be written to it.

For mathematical functions, arguments that are written as subscripts in standard mathematical notation are given before those that are written as superscripts.

■ A.3.3 Options

Some built-in functions can take *options*. Each option has a name, represented as a symbol. Options are set by giving rules of the form *name->value* or *name:>value*. Such rules must appear after all the other arguments in a function. Rules for different options can be given in any order. If you do not explicitly give a rule for a particular option, a default setting for that option is used.

Options[*f*]	give the default rules for all options associated with *f*
Options[*expr*]	give the options set in a particular expression
Options[*expr*, *name*]	give the setting for the option *name* in an expression
FullOptions[*expr*, *name*]	give the full setting for *name*, even if its actual setting is Automatic
SetOptions[*f*, *name*->*value*, ...]	
	set default rules for options associated with *f*

Operations on options.

■ A.3.4 Part Numbering

n	element *n* (starting at 1)
−*n*	element *n* from the end
0	head

Numbering of parts.

■ A.3.5 Sequence Specifications

n	elements 1 through *n*
−*n*	last *n* elements
{*n*}	element *n* only
{*m*, *n*}	elements *m* through *n* (inclusive)

Specifications for sequences of parts.

Sequence specifications are used in the functions Drop, StringDrop, StringTake, Subscripted, Take and Thread.

■ A.3.6 Level Specifications

n	levels 1 through n
Infinity	levels 1 through Infinity
{n}	level n only
{n_1, n_2}	levels n_1 through n_2
Heads -> True	include heads of expressions
Heads -> False	do not include heads of expressions

Level specifications.

The level in an expression corresponding to a non-negative integer n is defined to consist of parts specified by n indices. A negative level number $-n$ represents all parts of an expression that have depth n. The depth of an expression, Depth[*expr*], is the maximum number of indices needed to specify any part, plus one. Levels *do not* include heads of expressions, except with the option setting Heads -> True. Level 0 is the whole expression. Level -1 contains all symbols and other objects that have no subparts.

Ranges of levels specified by {n_1, n_2} contain all parts that are neither above level n_1, nor below level n_2 in the tree. The n_i need not have the same sign. Thus, for example, {2, -2} specifies subexpressions which occur anywhere below the top level, but above the leaves, of the expression tree.

Level specifications are used by functions such as Apply, Cases, Count, FreeQ, Level, Map, MapIndexed, Position, and Scan. Note, however, that the default level specifications are not the same for all of these functions.

Functions with level specifications visit different subexpressions in an order that corresponds to depth-first traversal of the expression tree, with leaves visited before roots. The subexpressions visited have part specifications which occur in an order which is lexicographic, except that longer sequences appear before shorter ones.

■ A.3.7 Iterators

{imax}	iterate *imax* times
{i, imax}	*i* goes from 1 to *imax* in steps of 1
{i, imin, imax}	*i* goes from *imin* to *imax* in steps of 1
{i, imin, imax, di}	*i* goes from *imin* to *imax* in steps of *di*
{i, imin, imax}, *{j, jmin, jmax}*, ...	*i* goes from *imin* to *imax*, and for each value of *i*, *j* goes from *jmin* to *jmax*, etc.

Iterator notation.

Iterators are used in such functions as Sum, Table, Do and Range.

The iteration parameters *imin*, *imax* and *di* do not need to be integers. The variable *i* is given a sequence of values starting at *imin*, and increasing in steps of *di*, stopping when the next value of *i* would be greater than *imax*. The iteration parameters can be arbitrary symbolic expressions, so long as (*imax*−*imin*)/*di* is a number.

When several iteration variables are used, the limits for the later ones can depend on the values of earlier ones.

The variable *i* can be any symbolic expression; it need not be a single symbol. The value of *i* is automatically set up to be local to the iteration function. This is effectively done by wrapping a Block construct containing *i* around the iteration function.

The procedure for evaluating iteration functions is described on page 994.

■ A.3.8 Scoping Constructs

Function[{*x*, ... }, *body*]	local parameters
lhs -> *rhs* and *lhs* :> *rhs*	local pattern names
lhs = *rhs* and *lhs* := *rhs*	local pattern names
With[{*x* = x_0, ... }, *body*]	local constants
Module[{*x*, ... }, *body*]	local variables

Scoping constructs in *Mathematica*.

Scoping constructs allow the names of certain symbols to be local.

When nested scoping constructs are evaluated, new symbols are automatically generated in the inner scoping constructs so as to avoid name conflicts with symbols in outer scoping constructs.

In general, symbols with names of the form *xxx* are renamed *xxx$*.

When a transformation rule or definition is used, `ReplaceAll` (`/.`) is effectively used to replace the pattern names that appear on the right-hand side. Nevertheless, new symbols are generated when necessary to represent other objects that appear in scoping constructs on the right-hand side.

Each time it is evaluated, `Module` generates symbols with unique names of the form *xxx$nnn* as replacements for all local variables that appear in its body.

■ A.3.9 Ordering of Expressions

The canonical ordering of expressions used automatically with the attribute `Orderless` and in functions such as `Sort` satisfies the following rules:

- Integers, rational and approximate real numbers are ordered by their numerical values.

- Complex numbers are ordered by their real parts, and in the event of a tie, by the absolute values of their imaginary parts.

- Symbols are ordered according to their names, and in the event of a tie, by their contexts.

- Expressions are usually ordered by comparing their parts in a depth-first manner. Shorter expressions come first.

- Powers and products are treated specially, and are ordered to correspond to terms in a polynomial.

- Strings are ordered as they would be in a dictionary, with the upper-case versions of letters coming after lower-case ones. Ordinary letters appear first, followed in order by script, Gothic, double-struck, Greek and Hebrew. Mathematical operators appear in order of decreasing precedence.

■ A.3.10 Mathematical Functions

The mathematical functions such as `Log[x]` and `BesselJ[n, x]` that are built into *Mathematica* have a number of features in common.

- They carry the attribute `Listable`, so that they are automatically "threaded" over any lists that appear as arguments.

- They carry the attribute `NumericFunction`, so that they are assumed to give numerical values when their arguments are numerical.

- They give exact results in terms of integers, rational numbers and algebraic expressions in special cases.

- Except for functions whose arguments are always integers, mathematical functions in *Mathematica* can be evaluated to any numerical precision, with any complex numbers as arguments. If a function is undefined for a particular set of arguments, it is returned in symbolic form in this case.

- Numerical evaluation leads to results of a precision no higher than can be justified on the basis of the precision of the arguments. Thus `N[Gamma[27/10], 100]` yields a high-precision result, but `N[Gamma[2.7], 100]` cannot.

- When possible, symbolic derivatives, integrals and series expansions of built-in mathematical functions are evaluated in terms of other built-in functions.

■ A.3.11 Mathematical Constants

Mathematical constants such as `E` and `Pi` that are built into *Mathematica* have the following properties:

- They do not have values as such.

- They have numerical values that can be found to any precision.

- They are treated as numeric quantities in `NumericQ` and elsewhere.

- They carry the attribute `Constant`, and so are treated as constants in derivatives.

■ A.3.12 Protection

Mathematica allows you to make assignments that override the standard operation and meaning of built-in *Mathematica* objects.

To make it difficult to make such assignments by mistake, most built-in *Mathematica* objects have the attribute `Protected`. If you want to make an assignment for a built-in object, you must first remove this attribute. You can do this by calling the function `Unprotect`.

There are a few fundamental *Mathematica* objects to which you absolutely cannot assign your own values. These objects carry the attribute `Locked`, as well as `Protected`. The `Locked` attribute prevents you from changing any of the attributes, and thus from removing the `Protected` attribute.

■ A.3.13 String Patterns

Functions such as `StringMatchQ`, `Names` and `Remove` allow you to give *string patterns*. String patterns can contain *metacharacters*, which can stand for sequences of ordinary characters.

*	zero or more characters
@	one or more characters excluding upper-case letters
* etc.	literal *, etc.

Metacharacters used in string patterns.

A.4 Evaluation

■ A.4.1 The Standard Evaluation Sequence

The following is the sequence of steps that *Mathematica* follows in evaluating an expression like $h[e_1, e_2, \ldots]$. Every time the expression changes, *Mathematica* effectively starts the evaluation sequence over again.

- If the expression is a raw object (e.g., `Integer`, `String`, etc.), leave it unchanged.

- Evaluate the head h of the expression.

- Evaluate each element e_i of the expression in turn. If h is a symbol with attributes `HoldFirst`, `HoldRest`, `HoldAll` or `HoldAllComplete`, then skip evaluation of certain elements.

- Unless h has attribute `HoldAllComplete` strip the outermost of any `Unevaluated` wrappers that appear in the e_i.

- Unless h has attribute `SequenceHold`, flatten out all `Sequence` objects that appear among the e_i.

- If h has attribute `Flat`, then flatten out all nested expressions with head h.

- If h has attribute `Listable`, then thread through any e_i that are lists.

- If h has attribute `Orderless`, then sort the e_i into order.

- Unless h has attribute `HoldAllComplete`, use any applicable transformation rules associated with f that you have defined for objects of the form $h[f[e_1, \ldots], \ldots]$.

- Use any built-in transformation rules associated with f for objects of the form $h[f[e_1, \ldots], \ldots]$.

- Use any applicable transformation rules that you have defined for $h[e_1, e_2, \ldots]$ or for $h[\ldots][\ldots]$.

- Use any built-in transformation rules for $h[e_1, e_2, \ldots]$ or for $h[\ldots][\ldots]$.

■ A.4.2 Non-Standard Argument Evaluation

There are a number of built-in *Mathematica* functions that evaluate their arguments in special ways. The control structure `While` is an example. The symbol `While` has the attribute `HoldAll`. As a result, the arguments of `While` are not evaluated as part of the standard evaluation process. Instead, the internal code for `While` evaluates the arguments in a special way. In the case of `While`, the code evaluates the arguments repeatedly, so as to implement a loop.

Control structures	arguments evaluated in a sequence determined by control flow (e.g., `CompoundExpression`)
Conditionals	arguments evaluated only when they correspond to branches that are taken (e.g., `If`, `Which`)
Logical operations	arguments evaluated only when they are needed in determining the logical result (e.g., `And`, `Or`)
Iteration functions	first argument evaluated for each step in the iteration (e.g., `Do`, `Sum`, `Plot`)
Tracing functions	form never evaluated (e.g., `Trace`)
Assignments	first argument only partially evaluated (e.g., `Set`, `AddTo`)
Pure functions	function body not evaluated (e.g., `Function`)
Scoping constructs	variable specifications not evaluated (e.g., `Module`, `Block`)
Holding functions	argument maintained in unevaluated form (e.g., `Hold`, `HoldPattern`)

Built-in functions that evaluate their arguments in special ways.

Logical Operations

In an expression of the form e_1`&&`e_2`&&`e_3 the e_i are evaluated in order. As soon as any e_i is found to be `False`, evaluation is stopped, and the result `False` is returned. This means that you can use the e_i to represent different "branches" in a program, with a particular branch being evaluated only if certain conditions are met.

The `Or` function works much like `And`; it returns `True` as soon as it finds any argument that is `True`. `Xor`, on the other hand, always evaluates *all* its arguments.

Iteration Functions

An iteration function such as `Do[`f`, {`i`, `*imin*`, `*imax*`}]` is evaluated as follows:

- The iteration specification is evaluated. If it is not found to be of the form {i, *imin*, *imax*}, the evaluation stops.

- The value of the iteration variable i is made local, effectively using `Block`.

- *imin* and *imax* are used to determine the sequence of values to be assigned to the iteration variable i.

- The iteration variable is successively set to each value, and *f* is evaluated in each case.

- The local values assigned to *i* are cleared.

    If there are several iteration variables, the same procedure is followed for each variable in turn.

    Unless otherwise specified, *f* is not evaluated until a specific value has been assigned to *i*, and is then evaluated for each value of *i* chosen. You can use `Evaluate[f]` to make *f* be evaluated immediately, rather than only after a specific value has been assigned to *i*.

Assignments

The left-hand sides of assignments are only partially evaluated.

- If the left-hand side is a symbol, no evaluation is performed.

- If the left-hand side is a function without hold attributes, the arguments of the function are evaluated, but the function itself is not evaluated.

    The right-hand side is evaluated for immediate (=), but not for delayed (:=), assignments.

    Any subexpression of the form `HoldPattern[`*expr*`]` that appears on the left-hand side of an assignment is not evaluated, but is replaced by the unevaluated form of *expr* before the assignment is done.

■ A.4.3 Overriding Non-Standard Argument Evaluation

> *f*`[`*expr*$_1$`, ... , Evaluate[`*expr*$_n$`], ... ]`
>
>   evaluates the argument *expr*$_n$, whether or not the attributes of *f* specify that it should be held

Overriding holding of arguments.

By using `Evaluate`, you can get any argument of a function evaluated immediately, even if the argument would usually be evaluated later under the control of the function.

■ A.4.4 Preventing Evaluation

Mathematica provides various functions which act as "wrappers" to prevent the expressions they contain from being evaluated.

	Hold[*expr*]	treated as Hold[*expr*] in all cases
+	HoldComplete[*expr*]	treated as HoldComplete[*expr*] with upvalues disabled
	HoldForm[*expr*]	treated as *expr* for printing
+	HoldPattern[*expr*]	treated as *expr* in rules, definitions and patterns
	Unevaluated[*expr*]	treated as *expr* when arguments are passed to a function

Wrappers that prevent expressions from being evaluated.

■ A.4.5 Global Control of Evaluation

In the evaluation procedure described above, two basic kinds of steps are involved:

- Iteration: evaluate a particular expression until it no longer changes.

- Recursion: evaluate subsidiary expressions needed to find the value of a particular expression.

Iteration leads to evaluation chains in which successive expressions are obtained by the application of various transformation rules.

Trace shows evaluation chains as lists, and shows subsidiary evaluations corresponding to recursion in sublists.

The expressions associated with the sequence of subsidiary evaluations which lead to an expression currently being evaluated are given in the list returned by Stack[ ].

$RecursionLimit	maximum recursion depth
$IterationLimit	maximum number of iterations

Global variables controlling the evaluation of expressions.

■ A.4.6 Aborts

You can ask *Mathematica* to abort at any point in a computation, either by calling the function Abort[ ], or by typing appropriate interrupt keys.

When asked to abort, *Mathematica* will terminate the computation as quickly as possible. If the answer obtained would be incorrect or incomplete, then *Mathematica* returns $Aborted instead of giving that answer.

Aborts can be caught using CheckAbort, and can be postponed using AbortProtect.

A.5 Patterns and Transformation Rules

■ A.5.1 Patterns

Patterns stand for classes of expressions. They contain *pattern objects* which represent sets of possible expressions.

_	any expression
$x\_$	any expression, given the name x
$x : pattern$	a pattern, given the name x
pattern ? *test*	a pattern that yields True when *test* is applied to its value
$\_h$	any expression with head h
x_h	any expression with head h, given the name x
__	any sequence of one or more expressions
___	any sequence of zero or more expressions
$x\_\_$ and $x\_\_\_$	sequences of expressions, given the name x
$\_\_h$ and $\_\_\_h$	sequences of expressions, each with head h
$x\_\_h$ and $x\_\_\_h$	sequences of expressions with head h, given the name x
$x\_:v$	an expression with default value v
$x\_h:v$	an expression with head h and default value v
$x\_.$	an expression with a globally defined default value
Optional[x_h]	an expression that must have head h, and has a globally defined default value
pattern..	a pattern repeated one or more times
pattern...	a pattern repeated zero or more times
pattern$_1$	*pattern*$_2$	...	a pattern which matches at least one of the *pattern*$_i$
pattern /; *cond*	a pattern for which *cond* evaluates to True
HoldPattern[*pattern*]	a pattern not evaluated
Verbatim[*expr*]	an expression to be matched verbatim

Pattern objects.

When several pattern objects with the same name occur in a single pattern, all the objects must stand for the same expression. Thus f[x_, x_] can stand for f[2, 2] but not f[2, 3].

In a pattern object such as _h, the head h can be any expression, but cannot itself be a pattern.

A pattern object such as x__ stands for a *sequence* of expressions. So, for example, f[x__] can stand for f[a, b, c], with x being Sequence[a, b, c]. If you use x, say in the result of a transformation rule, the sequence will be spliced into the function in which x appears. Thus g[u, x, u] would become g[u, a, b, c, u].

When the pattern objects x_:v and x_. appear as arguments of functions, they represent arguments which may be omitted. When the argument corresponding to x_:v is omitted, x is taken to have value v. When the argument corresponding to x_. is omitted, x is taken to have a *default value* that is associated with the function in which it appears. You can specify this default value by making assignments for Default[*f*] and so on.

Default[*f*]	default value for $x\_.$ when it appears as any argument of the function f
Default[*f*, *n*]	default value for $x\_.$ when it appears as the nth argument (negative n count from the end)
Default[*f*, *n*, *tot*]	default value for the nth argument when there are a total of *tot* arguments

Default values.

A pattern like f[x__, y__, z__] can match an expression like f[a, b, c, d, e] with several different choices of x, y and z. The choices with x and y of minimum length are tried first. In general, when there are multiple __ or ___ in a single function, the case that is tried first takes all the __ and ___ to stand for sequences of minimum length, except the last one, which stands for "the rest" of the arguments.

When x_:v or x_. are present, the case that is tried first is the one in which none of them correspond to omitted arguments. Cases in which later arguments are dropped are tried next.

Orderless	$f[x, y]$ and $f[y, x]$ are equivalent
Flat	$f[f[x], y]$ and $f[x, y]$ are equivalent
OneIdentity	$f[x]$ and x are equivalent

Attributes used in matching patterns.

- If `name.mx` is a directory, then *name*.`mx/$SystemID/`*name*.`mx` is used if it exists.

  In `Install`, *name*` is taken to refer to a file or directory named *name*.`exe`.

■ A.6.2 Streams

`InputStream["`*name*`", `*n*`]`	input from a file or pipe
`OutputStream["`*name*`", `*n*`]`	output to a file or pipe

Types of streams.

option name	default value	
+ `CharacterEncoding`	`$CharacterEncoding`	encoding to use for special characters
+ `DOSTextFormat`	`False`	whether to output files with MS-DOS text-mode conventions
`FormatType`	`InputForm`	default format for expressions
`PageWidth`	`78`	number of characters per line
`StringConversion`	`Identity`	function applied to convert strings containing special characters
`TotalWidth`	`Infinity`	maximum number of characters in a single expression

Options for output streams.

You can test options for streams using `Options`, and reset them using `SetOptions`.

A.7 *Mathematica* Sessions

⁺■ A.7.1 Command-Line Options and Environment Variables

-password	*Mathematica* password
-pwfile	*Mathematica* password file
-pwpath	path to search for a *Mathematica* password file
-run	*Mathematica* input to run (kernel only)
-initfile	*Mathematica* initialization file
-initpath	path to search for initialization files
-noinit	do not run initialization files
-mathlink	communicate only via *MathLink* (kernel only)

Typical command-line options for *Mathematica* executables.

If the *Mathematica* front end is called with a notebook file as a command-line argument, then this notebook will be made the initial selected notebook. Otherwise, a new notebook will be created for this purpose.

Mathematica kernels and front ends can also take additional command-line options specific to particular window environments.

$MATHINIT	command-line environment for the *Mathematica* front end, as well as *MathReader*
$MATHKERNELINIT	command-line environment for the *Mathematica* kernel

Environment variables.

If no command-line options are explicitly given, *Mathematica* will read the values of operating system environment variables, and will use these values like command lines.

■ A.7.2 Initialization

On startup, the *Mathematica* kernel does the following:

■ Perform license management operations.

- Run *Mathematica* commands specified in any -runfirst options passed to the kernel executable.

- Run *Mathematica* commands specified in any -run options passed to the kernel executable.

- Run the *Mathematica* commands in the user-specific or special location file init.m.

- Run the *Mathematica* commands in the site-wide or central location file init.m.

- Load init.m and Kernel/init.m files in Autoload directories.

- Begin running the main loop.

■ A.7.3 The Main Loop

All *Mathematica* sessions repeatedly execute the following main loop:

- Read in input.

- Apply $PreRead function, if defined, to the input string.

- Print syntax warnings if necessary.

- Apply $SyntaxHandler function if there is a syntax error.

- Assign InString[*n*].

- Apply $Pre function, if defined, to the input expression.

- Assign In[*n*].

- Evaluate expression.

- Apply $Post function, if defined.

- Assign Out[*n*], stripping off any formatting wrappers.

- Apply $PrePrint function, if defined.

- Assign MessageList[*n*] and clear $MessageList.

- Print expression, if it is not Null.

- Increment $Line.

- Clear any pending aborts.

Note that if you call *Mathematica* via *MathLink* from within an external program, then you must effectively create your own main loop, which will usually differ from the one described above.

■ A.7.4 Messages

During a *Mathematica* session messages can be generated either by explicit calls to `Message`, or in the course of executing other built-in functions.

f::*name*::*lang*	a message in a specific language
f::*name*	a message in a default language
`General`::*name*	a general message with a given name

Message names.

If no language is specified for a particular message, text for the message is sought in each of the languages specified by `$Language`. If *f*::*name* is not defined, a definition for `General`::*name* is sought. If still no message is found, any value defined for `$NewMessage` is applied to *f* and "*name*".

`Off[`*message*`]` prevents a specified message from ever being printed. `Check` allows you to determine whether particular messages were generated during the evaluation of an expression. `$MessageList` and `MessageList[`*n*`]` record all the messages that were generated during the evaluation of a particular line in a *Mathematica* session.

Messages are specified as strings to be used as the first argument of `StringForm`. `$MessagePrePrint` is applied to each expression to be spliced into the string.

■ A.7.5 Termination

`Exit[ ]` or `Quit[ ]`	terminate *Mathematica*
`$Epilog`	symbol to evaluate before *Mathematica* exits
`$IgnoreEOF`	whether to exit an interactive *Mathematica* session when an end-of-file character is received
`end.m`	file to read when *Mathematica* terminates

Mathematica termination.

There are several ways to end a *Mathematica* session. If you are using *Mathematica* interactively, typing `Exit[ ]` or `Quit[ ]` on an input line will always terminate *Mathematica*.

If you are taking input for *Mathematica* from a file, *Mathematica* will exit when it reaches the end of the file. If you are using *Mathematica* interactively, it will still exit if it receives an end-of-file character (typically CTRL-d). You can stop *Mathematica* from doing this by setting `$IgnoreEOF=True`.

■ A.7.6 Network License Management

single-machine license	a process must always run on a specific machine
network license	a process can run on any machine on a network

Single-machine and network licenses.

Copies of *Mathematica* can be set up with either single-machine or network licenses. A network license is indicated by a line in the `mathpass` file starting with `!`*name*, where *name* is the name of the server machine for the network license.

Under the Unix operating system, network licenses are controlled by the *Mathematica* license management program `mathlm`. This program must be running whenever a *Mathematica* with a network license is being used. Typically you will want to set up your system so that `mathlm` is started whenever the system boots.

- Type `./mathlm` directly on the Unix command line
- Add a line to start `mathlm` in your central `/etc/rc.local` boot file
- Add a `crontab` entry to start `mathlm`

Ways to start the network license manager.

When `mathlm` is started, it normally sets itself up as a background process, and continues running until it is explicitly terminated. Note that if one `mathlm` process is running, any other `mathlm` processes you try to start will automatically exit immediately.

`-logfile` *file*	write a log of license requests to *file*
`-syslog`	write the log to the `syslog` daemon
`-pwfile` *file*	use the specified `mathpass` file (default `./mathpass`)
`-timeout` *n*	suspend authorization on stopped *Mathematica* jobs after *n* hours
`-restrict` *prog*	authorize a session only if executing *prog* yields a nonzero exit code

Command-line switches for `mathlm`.

You can use the `mathlm -restrict` *prog* to tell the network license manager to authorize only certain sessions. The program *prog* is passed as arguments the user ID and machine name for the session to be started, together with sequences *i*, UID, name for sessions 1, 2, ... already started.

Note that as an alternative to `-restrict`, you can insert commands in `init.m` that exit unless `$UserName`, `$MachineName` and so on have appropriate values.

`monitorlm`	print the current status of the network license manager
`mathlm -verbose`	run `mathlm` in the foreground, printing actions that it takes
`math -lmverbose`	run `math`, printing information on interactions with `mathlm`

Ways to debug network license setups.

A.8 Installation and Organization of System Files

+■ A.8.1 Running and Installing *Mathematica*

> ■ Directly from the CD-ROM distribution medium.
>
> ■ Installed on a disk accessible from your computer.

Two ways to run *Mathematica*.

Mathematica is normally distributed on CD-ROM. Typically a single CD-ROM will contain the files needed for versions of *Mathematica* on all computer systems.

The CD-ROM is set up so that if you have the appropriate authorization and license, you will usually be able to run *Mathematica* directly from the CD-ROM.

If you want to install *Mathematica* on a hard disk or other mass storage device, you will need to copy the necessary files from the CD-ROM. You can do this using the installation programs that are provided on the CD-ROM.

These programs allow you to install *Mathematica* both for operation on a single type of computer, and for operation across different types of computers.

In addition to *Mathematica* itself, there are also standard ways to install *Mathematica* application packs, as discussed on page 1015.

+■ A.8.2 Overall Organization of the CD-ROM

Macintosh	HFS partition visible only on Macintosh systems
PC	ISO 9660 level 1 partition intended for PCs
General	ISO 9660 level 2 partition with RRIP containing versions for all systems

Basic partitions on a typical *Mathematica* distribution CD-ROM.

In the PC partition, all file names follow 8.3 DOS conventions, and CRLF newlines are included in text files. Note that *Mathematica* itself works the same regardless of how newlines are specified.

The General partition contains versions for all computer systems—including Macintosh and PC.

`Executables`	executables for each computer system to be run directly from the CD-ROM
`Installation`	installation programs for each computer system
`Registration`	material associated with registration and getting passwords
`SystemFiles`	files needed to run the *Mathematica* system
`Configuration`	default configuration files
`Documentation`	documentation for *Mathematica*, including the on-line version of this book
`AddOns`	packages and other add-ons to *Mathematica*

Typical elements of each partition.

In the `General` partition, `Executables` contains subdirectories for each type of computer system, as specified by `$SystemID`. These subdirectories then contain command files that invoke the actual executable programs.

In the `Macintosh` and `PC` partitions, the executable programs are included directly at the top level, and there is no separate `Executables` directory.

■ A.8.3 Running the Executable Programs

`Mathematica`	*Mathematica* front end
`MathKernel`	*Mathematica* kernel, usually with its own text-based front end
`MathReader`	*Mathematica* notebook reader
`math`	*Mathematica* kernel to run in a terminal window
`mcc`	script for preprocessing and compiling *MathLink* source files

Typical names of command files that invoke the executable programs.

If you install *Mathematica* onto your hard disk, there are various conventions for where executable programs are placed. The basic idea is that it should be possible to start up the programs directly by clicking on icons or by typing appropriate command names.

Microsoft Windows, Windows 95 and Windows NT

- `Mathematica`, `MathKernel` and `MathReader` are all placed in the main *Mathematica* folder.

- Under Windows 95, the executables can be run from the *Start* menu by going to `Programs`, `Wolfram Research`.

- `math` and `mcc` can be run in a DOS shell. The `PATH` variable is set up to make these programs be found.

Macintosh

- `Mathematica`, `MathKernel` and `MathReader` are all placed in the main *Mathematica* folder.

- Aliases are often created and placed on the desk top.

- `math` and `mcc` are not provided.

- `mprep` is provided for preprocessing *MathLink* template files, and is placed in the `Binaries` folder in the *MathLink* Developer's Kit.

Unix

- All the executable programs listed are shell scripts.

- Symbolic links to the programs are typically placed in `/usr/local/bin`.

- `math` simply calls `MathKernel` and does not bring up any front end.

- Under the X Window System the notebook front end can be started by typing `Mathematica` in a terminal window.

NEXTSTEP

- The *Mathematica* front end executable is called `Mathematica.app` and is typically placed in `/LocalApps`.

- The *MathReader* executable is called `MathReader.app` and is typically placed in `/LocalApps`.

- Other programs and files are organized as for standard Unix systems.

■ A.8.4 The Installation Process

You can install *Mathematica* locally on your computer system by running an installation program from the distribution CD-ROM.

Before you will be able to run *Mathematica*, you will usually have to set up an appropriate password. Your installation program will tell you how to do this.

minimal	the minimal files necessary to run *Mathematica* on a particular system
default	the complete set of files for a particular system
custom	custom-chosen sets of files

Typical types of installation available in the installation program.

Steps in the automatic installation process typically include:

- Copying files from the CD-ROM to your hard disk.

- Installing executable programs or aliases in a central place on your system.

- Installing *Mathematica* fonts in a central place on your system.

- Installing man pages on Unix systems.

- Optionally installing on-line documentation, add-on packages and *Mathematica* examples.

- Setting up appropriate custom configuration files.

■ A.8.5 File Organization after Installation

`C:\MATH30`	Microsoft Windows 3.1
`C:\PROGRAM_FILES\WOLFRAM_RESEARCH\Mathematica\3.0`	Windows 95 and Windows NT
`Mathematica 3.0`	Macintosh
`/usr/local/Mathematica3.0`	Unix and NeXT

Typical names for the main *Mathematica* folder.

Within the main *Mathematica* folder, files are arranged in a way that mirrors their organization on the CD-ROM.

The name of the directory corresponding to the main *Mathematica* folder is given in the kernel by `$TopDirectory`.

System Files

System files are typically stored in the `SystemFiles` subdirectory of the main *Mathematica* folder. The installation procedure will copy the files needed for your particular setup.

`Kernel/Binaries/`*system*	kernel binaries or elements for each computer system
`Kernel/SystemResources/`*system*	system-specific `.mx` files used by the kernel
`Kernel/TextResources`	message and text files used by the kernel
`FrontEnd/Binaries/`*system*	front end binaries or elements for each computer system
`FrontEnd/SystemResources`	files used by the front end in each window system environment
`FrontEnd/Caches`	caches used by the front end
`FrontEnd/TextResources`	message and text files used by the front end
`FrontEnd/StyleSheets`	default notebook style sheets
`FrontEnd/Palettes`	default palette notebooks
`MathReader/Binaries/`*system*	*MathReader* binaries and libraries
`MathLink/`*system*	*MathLink* libraries and related material
`Fonts`	*Mathematica* fonts, often copied to a central directory
`CharacterEncodings`	specifications of character encodings
`SystemDocumentation/`*env*	Unix man pages and other environment-specific documentation
`Graphics/Binaries/`*system*	PostScript interpreters and graphics programs
`Graphics/SystemResources`	PostScript definitions and other resources for graphics
`Graphics/Packages`	packages for setting up graphics
`Installation`	various auxiliary programs used in installation, called automatically by the main installer program
`Templates`	templates for configuration files

Typical subdirectories of the `SystemFiles` directory.

Some resource directories may contain files specific to particular languages or computing environments. These files are given in subdirectories such as `Japanese/Windows`.

■ A.8.6 Configuration Files

Templates for configurations are typically stored in the `Templates` subdirectory of the `SystemFiles` directory. Either at installation, or when *Mathematica* is first run, configuration files are then automatically set up in specific directories.

Microsoft Windows	`Config` subdirectory of main *Mathematica* folder
Macintosh	`Mathematica:3.0` folder in the `Preferences` folder inside `System Folder`
Unix	`.Mathematica/3.0` subdirectory of each user's home directory
NeXT	`Library/Mathematica/3.0` subdirectory of each user's home directory
all systems	`Configuration` subdirectory of the main *Mathematica* directory

Typical locations for configuration files.

Mathematica will first use files that are in the general `Configuration` directory, then will use files that are in specific per-user directories. On multi-user systems, putting files in the general `Configuration` directory allows for site-wide configuration. *Mathematica* password files are typically in the `Configuration` directory.

`Kernel/init.m`	run when the kernel is started
`Kernel/end.m`	run when the kernel is terminated
`FrontEnd/init.m`	read when the front end is started
`FrontEnd/StyleSheets/`	customized notebook style sheets
`FrontEnd/Caches/`	caches used by the front end
`Palettes/`	additional palettes to appear in the front end menu

Some typical configuration files.

Kernel configuration files can contain any *Mathematica* commands. These commands can test global variables such as $SystemID and $MachineName to determine what operations to perform. Front end configuration files can contain only certain special commands, as described on page 986.

◼ A.8.7 Documentation Files

RefGuide	reference guide and examples for built-in functions
MainBook	the complete text of this book
AddOns	documentation for packages and other add-ons
GettingStarted/*env*	introductory documentation for specific systems
OtherResources	additional *Mathematica* information
Index	master index of all documentation

Typical subdirectories of the Documentation directory.

All the elements of the Documentation directory can be accessed through the help browser in the front end. BrowserCategories files in each subdirectory set up the categories used in the help browser. BrowserIndex files provide data for the master index.

Note that the complete Documentation directory is over 50 megabytes in size. Any parts that are not installed will be indicated as unavailable in the help browser.

◼ A.8.8 Add-ons

AddOns/StandardPackages/	standard add-on packages distributed with *Mathematica*
AddOns/Applications/*name*/	named add-on applications
AddOns/Autoload/*name*/	add-ons to be loaded automatically when *Mathematica* is started
AddOns/MathLink/	*MathLink* development material

Typical files for add-ons.

The main *Mathematica* distribution CD-ROM typically includes certain standard add-ons. Many further add-ons are also available. All add-ons are typically installed in the **AddOns** subdirectory of your main *Mathematica* folder.

`init.m` or `Kernel/init.m`	an initialization file to be loaded by the kernel
`FrontEnd/init.m`	an initialization file to be loaded by the front end
`Documentation/`	documentation to be found by the front end
`Packages/`	*Mathematica* package files used
`Binaries/`	binaries used

Typical possible contents of the directory for an add-on.

With the default setting for the kernel `$Path` variable, an add-on can be loaded from within a *Mathematica* session simply by using the command `<<`*name*`'`. This will load the `init.m` file for the add-on, which should in turn be set up to load other necessary files or packages.

By placing the directory for an add-on in `AddOns/Autoload/`, you can have *Mathematica* automatically load the add-on whenever you start the kernel or the front end.

Note that with the default setting for the front end documentation path, all documentation in `Documentation` directories will automatically show up in the front end help browser.

`MathLink/Documentation/`	general *MathLink* documentation
`MathLink/DevelopersKits/`*system*`/`	
	MathLink Developer's Kits for specific systems

MathLink development material.

Note that on some systems you may need to copy files from the `DevelopersKits` directory into the actual directories that you are using for software development.

Microsoft Windows, Windows 95 and Windows NT

- Shared libraries are used.

Macintosh

- Fat shared libraries are used.

- Example projects are provided for CodeWarrior, MPW and ThinkC integrated development environments.

Unix

- Statically linked libraries are provided for all systems.
- Dynamically linked libraries are provided whenever systems support them.
- Makefiles are provided for the example programs.

A.9 Some Notes on Internal Implementation

▪ A.9.1 Introduction

General issues about the internal implementation of *Mathematica* are discussed on pages 215–223. Given here are brief notes on particular features.

These notes apply to Version 3.0. Algorithms and other aspects of implementation are subject to change in future versions.

It should be emphasized that these notes give only a rough indication of basic methods and algorithms used. The actual implementation usually involves many substantial additional elements.

Thus, for example, the notes simply say that DSolve solves second-order linear differential equations using the Kovacic algorithm. But the internal code which achieves this is over 60 pages long, includes a number of other algorithms, and involves a great many subtleties.

▪ A.9.2 Data Structures and Memory Management

A *Mathematica* expression internally consists of a contiguous array of pointers, the first to the head, and the rest to its successive elements.

Each expression contains a special form of hash code which is used both in pattern matching and evaluation.

For every symbol there is a central *symbol table entry* which stores all information about the symbol.

Most raw objects such as strings and numbers are allocated separately; unique copies are however maintained of small integers and of certain approximate numbers generated in computations.

Every piece of memory used by *Mathematica* maintains a count of how many times it is referenced. Memory is automatically freed when this count reaches zero.

The contiguous storage of elements in expressions reduces memory fragmentation and swapping. However, it can lead to the copying of a complete array of pointers when a single element in a long expression is modified. Many optimizations based on reference counts and pre-allocation are used to avoid such copying.

▪ A.9.3 Basic System Features

Mathematica is fundamentally an interpreter which scans through expressions calling internal code pointed to by the symbol table entries of heads that it encounters.

Any transformation rule—whether given as x -> y or in a definition—is automatically compiled into a form which allows for rapid pattern matching. Many different types of patterns are distinguished and are handled by special code.

A form of hashing that takes account of blanks and other features of patterns is used in pattern matching.

The internal code associated with pattern matching is approximately 250 pages long.

When a large number of definitions are given for a particular symbol, a hash table is automatically built using a version of Dispatch so that appropriate rules can quickly be found.

■ A.9.4 Numerical and Related Functions

Basic arithmetic

Large integer multiplication uses the Karatsuba algorithm. ■ Integer powers are found by an algorithm based on Horner's rule. ■ Exact roots start from numerical estimates. ■ Significance arithmetic is used for arithmetic with approximate numbers. ■ Basic arithmetic uses approximately 400 pages of C source code.

Pseudorandom numbers

Random uses the Wolfram rule 30 cellular automaton generator for integers. ■ It uses a Marsaglia-Zaman subtract-with-borrow generator for real numbers.

Number-theoretical functions

GCD uses the Jebelean-Weber accelerated GCD algorithm, together with a combination of Euclid's algorithm and an algorithm based on iterative removal of powers of 2. ■ PrimeQ first tests for divisibility using small primes, then uses the Miller-Rabin strong pseudoprime test base 2 and base 3, and then uses the Lucas test. ■ As of 1995, this procedure is known to be correct only for $n < 2.5 \times 10^{10}$, and it is conceivable that for larger n it could claim a composite number to be prime. ■ The package NumberTheory`PrimeQ` contains a much slower algorithm which has been proved correct for all n. It can return an explicit certificate of primality. ■ FactorInteger switches between removing small primes by trial division and using the Pollard $p - 1$, Pollard rho and continued fraction algorithm. ■ The package NumberTheory`FactorIntegerECM` contains an elliptic curve algorithm suitable for factoring some very large integers. ■ Prime and PrimePi use sparse caching and sieving. For large n, the Lagarias-Miller-Odlyzko algorithm for PrimePi is used, based on asymptotic estimates of the density of primes, and is inverted to give Prime. ■ LatticeReduce uses the Lenstra-Lenstra-Lovasz lattice reduction algorithm.

Combinatorial functions

Most of the combinatorial functions use sparse caching and recursion. ■ Fibonacci[n] uses an iterative method based on the binary digit sequence of n. ■ PartitionsP[n] uses Euler's pentagonal formula for small n, and the non-recursive Hardy-Ramanujan-Rademacher method for larger n. ■ ClebschGordan and related functions use generalized hypergeometric series.

Elementary transcendental functions

Exponential and trigonometric functions use Taylor series, stable recursion by argument doubling, and functional relations. ■ Log and inverse trigonometric functions use Taylor series and functional relations.

Mathematical constants

Values of constants are cached once computed. ■ Pi uses the Chudnovsky formula (roughly 14 digits per step). ■ E is computed from its continued fraction expansion. ■ EulerGamma uses the Brent-McMillan algorithm.

Special functions

For machine precision most special functions use *Mathematica*-derived rational minimax approximations. The notes that follow apply mainly to arbitrary precision. ■ Orthogonal polynomials use stable recursion formulas for polynomial cases and hypergeometric functions in general. ■ Gamma uses recursion, functional equations and the Binet asymptotic formula. ■ Incomplete gamma and beta functions use hypergeometric series and continued fractions. ■ PolyGamma uses Euler-Maclaurin summation, functional equations and recursion. ■ PolyLog uses Euler-Maclaurin summation, expansions in terms of incomplete gamma functions and numerical quadrature. ■ Zeta and related functions use Euler-Maclaurin summation and functional equations. Near the critical strip they also use the Riemann-Siegel formula. ■ StieltjesGamma uses Keiper's algorithm based on numerical quadrature of an integral representation of the zeta function. ■ The error function and functions related to exponential integrals are all evaluated using incomplete gamma functions. ■ The inverse error functions use binomial search and a high-order generalized Newton's method. ■ Bessel functions use series and asymptotic expansions. For integer orders, some also use stable forward recursion. ■ The hypergeometric functions use functional equations, stable recurrence relations, series expansions and asymptotic series. Methods from NSum and NIntegrate are also sometimes used. ■ ProductLog uses high-order Newton's method starting from rational approximations and asymptotic expansions. ■ Elliptic integrals are evaluated using the descending Gauss transformation. ■ Elliptic theta functions use series summation with recursive evaluation of series terms. ■ Other elliptic functions mostly use arithmetic-geometric mean methods. ▪ Mathieu functions use Fourier series. The Mathieu characteristic functions use generalizations of Blanch's Newton method.

Numerical integration

With `Method->Automatic`, `NIntegrate` uses `GaussKronrod` in one dimension, and `MultiDimensional` otherwise. ▪ If an explicit setting for `MaxPoints` is given, `NIntegrate` by default uses `Method->QuasiMonteCarlo`. ▪ `GaussKronrod`: adaptive Gaussian quadrature with error estimation based on evaluation at Kronrod points. ▪ `DoubleExponential`: non-adaptive double-exponential quadrature. ▪ `Trapezoidal`: elementary trapezoidal method. ▪ `Oscillatory`: transformation to handle integrals containing trigonometric and Bessel functions. ▪ `MultiDimensional`: adaptive Genz-Malik algorithm. ▪ `MonteCarlo`: non-adaptive Monte Carlo. ▪ `QuasiMonteCarlo`: non-adaptive Halton-Hammersley-Wozniakowski algorithm.

Numerical sums and products

If the ratio test does not give 1, the Wynn epsilon algorithm is applied to a sequence of partial sums or products. ▪ Otherwise Euler-Maclaurin summation is used with `Integrate` or `NIntegrate`.

Numerical differential equations

With `Method->Automatic`, `NDSolve` switches between a non-stiff Adams method and a stiff Gear method. Based on LSODE. ▪ `Adams`: implicit Adams method with order between 1 and 12. ▪ `Gear`: backward difference formula method with order between 1 and 5. ▪ `RungeKutta`: Fehlberg order 4–5 Runge-Kutta method for non-stiff equations. ▪ For linear boundary value problems the Gel'fand-Lokutsiyevskii chasing method is used. ▪ For 1+1-dimensional PDEs the method of lines is used. ▪ The code for `NDSolve` is about 500 pages long.

Approximate equation solving and minimization

Polynomial root finding is done based on the Jenkins-Traub algorithm. ▪ For sparse linear systems, `Solve` and `NSolve` use several efficient numerical methods, mostly based on Gauss factoring with Markowitz products (approximately 250 pages of code). ▪ `FindRoot` uses a damped Newton's method, the secant method and Brent's method. ▪ With `Method->Automatic`, `FindMinimum` uses various methods due to Brent: the conjugate gradient in one dimension, and a modification of Powell's method in several dimensions. ▪ With `Method->Newton` `FindMinimum` uses Newton's method. With `Method->QuasiNewton` `FindMinimum` uses the BFGS version of the quasi-Newton method. ▪ `ConstrainedMax` and related functions use an enhanced version of the simplex algorithm.

Data manipulation

`Fourier` uses the FFT algorithm with decomposition of the length into prime factors. ▪ `InterpolatingFunction` uses divided differences to construct Lagrange or Hermite interpolating polynomials. ▪ `Fit` works by computing the product of the response vector with the pseudoinverse of the design matrix.

Approximate numerical linear algebra

Machine-precision matrices are typically converted to a special internal representation for processing. ▪ Algorithms similar to those of LINPACK, EISPACK and LAPACK are used when appropriate. ▪ `LUDecomposition`, `Inverse`, `RowReduce` and `Det` use Gaussian elimination with partial pivoting. `LinearSolve` uses the same methods, together with iterative improvement for high-precision numbers. ▪ `SingularValues` uses the QR algorithm with Givens rotations. `PseudoInverse` and `NullSpace` are based on `SingularValues`. ▪ `QRDecomposition` uses Householder transformations. ▪ `SchurDecomposition` uses QR iteration. ▪ `MatrixExp` uses Schur decomposition.

Exact numerical linear algebra

`Inverse` and `LinearSolve` use efficient row reduction based on numerical approximation. ▪ With `Modulus->`n, modular Gaussian elimination is used. ▪ `Det` uses modular methods and row reduction, constructing a result using the Chinese Remainder Theorem. ▪ `Eigenvalues` works by interpolating the characteristic polynomial. ▪ `MatrixExp` uses Putzer's method or Jordan decomposition.

+■ A.9.5 Algebra and Calculus

Polynomial manipulation

For univariate polynomials, `Factor` uses a variant of the Cantor-Zassenhaus algorithm to factor modulo a prime, then uses Hensel lifting and recombination to build up factors over the integers. ▪ Factoring over algebraic number fields is done by finding a primitive element over the rationals and then using Trager's algorithm. ▪ For multivariate polynomials `Factor` works by substituting appropriate choices of integers for all but one variable, then factoring the resulting univariate polynomials, and reconstructing multivariate factors using Wang's algorithm. ▪ The internal code for `Factor` exclusive of general polynomial manipulation is about 250 pages long. ▪ `FactorSquareFree` works by finding a derivative and then iteratively computing GCDs. ▪ `Resultant` uses either explicit subresultant polynomial remainder sequences or modular sequences accompanied by the Chinese Remainder Theorem. ▪ `Apart` uses either a version of the Padé technique or the method of undetermined coefficients. ▪ `PolynomialGCD` usually uses modular algorithms, including Zippel's sparse modular algorithm, but in some cases uses subresultant polynomial remainder sequences.

Symbolic linear algebra

`RowReduce`, `LinearSolve` and `NullSpace` are based on Gaussian elimination. ▪ `Inverse` uses cofactor expansion and row reduction. Pivots are chosen heuristically by looking for simple expressions. ▪ `Det` uses direct cofactor expansion for small matrices, and Gaussian elimination for larger ones. ▪ `MatrixExp` finds eigenvalues and then uses Putzer's method. ▪ Zero testing for various functions is done using symbolic transformations and interval-based numerical approximations after random numerical values have been substituted for variables.

Exact equation solving

For linear equations Gaussian elimination and other methods of linear algebra are used. ▪ `Root` objects representing algebraic numbers are usually isolated and manipulated using validated numerical methods. With `ExactRootIsolation->True`, `Root` uses for real roots a continued fraction version of an algorithm based on Descartes' rule of signs, and for complex roots the Collins-Krandick algorithm. ▪ For single polynomial equations, `Solve` uses explicit formulas up to degree four, attempts to reduce polynomials using `Factor` and `Decompose`, and recognizes cyclotomic and other special polynomials. ▪ For systems of polynomial equations, `Solve` constructs a Gröbner basis. ▪ `Solve` and `GroebnerBasis` use an efficient version of the Buchberger algorithm. ▪ For non-polynomial equations, `Solve` attempts to change variables and add polynomial side conditions. ▪ The code for `Solve` is about 500 pages long.

Simplification

`FullSimplify` automatically applies about 40 types of general algebraic transformations, as well as about 100 types of rules for specific mathematical functions. ▪ Generalized hypergeometric functions are simplified using about 70 pages of *Mathematica* transformation rules. These functions are fundamental to many calculus operations in *Mathematica*.

Integration

For indefinite integrals, an extended version of the Risch algorithm is used whenever both the integrand and integral can be expressed in terms of elementary functions, exponential integral functions, polylogarithms and other related functions. ▪ For other indefinite integrals, heuristic simplification followed by pattern matching is used. ▪ The algorithms in *Mathematica* cover all of the indefinite integrals in standard reference books such as Gradshteyn-Ryzhik. ▪ Definite integrals that involve no singularities are mostly done by taking limits of the indefinite integrals. ▪ Many other definite integrals are done using Marichev-Adamchik Mellin transform methods. The results are often initially expressed in terms of Meijer G functions, which are converted into hypergeometric functions using Slater's Theorem and then simplified. ▪ `Integrate` uses about 500 pages of *Mathematica* code and 600 pages of C code.

Differential equations

Linear equations with constant coefficients are solved using matrix exponentiation. ▪ Second-order linear equations with variable coefficients whose solutions can be expressed in terms of elementary functions and their integrals are solved using the Kovacic algorithm. ▪ Linear equations with polynomial coefficients are solved in terms of special functions by using Mellin transforms. ▪ When possible, nonlinear equations are solved by symmetry reduction techniques. For first-order equations classical techniques are used; for second-order equations and systems Bocharov techniques are used. ▪ For partial differential equations, separation of variables and symmetry reduction are used. ▪ `DSolve` uses about 300 pages of *Mathematica* code and 200 pages of C code.

Sums and products

Polynomial series are summed using Bernoulli and Euler polynomials. ■ Series involving rational and factorial functions are summed using Adamchik techniques in terms of generalized hypergeometric functions, which are then simplified. ■ Series involving polygamma functions are summed using integral representations. ■ Dirichlet and related series are summed using pattern matching. ■ For infinite series, d'Alembert and Raabe convergence tests are used. ■ The algorithms in *Mathematica* cover at least 90% of the sums in standard reference books such as Gradshteyn-Ryzhik. ■ Products are done primarily using pattern matching. ■ Sum and Product use about 100 pages of *Mathematica* code.

Series and limits

Series works by recursively composing series expansions of functions with series expansions of their arguments. ■ Limits are found from series and using other methods.

■ A.9.6 Output and Interfacing

Graphics

Hidden-surface elimination for 3D graphics is done so as to be independent of display resolution. ■ A custom-written PostScript interpreter is used to render graphics in the front end. ■ Notebooks use a custom platform-independent bitmap image format.

Front end

The front end uses *MathLink* both for communication with the kernel, and for communication between its different internal components. ■ All menu items and other functions in the front end are specified using *Mathematica* expressions. ■ Configuration and preference files use *Mathematica* language format. ■ The help browser is based on *Mathematica* notebooks generated from the same source code as this book.

Notebooks

Notebooks are represented as *Mathematica* expressions. ■ Notebook files contain additional cached outline information in the form of *Mathematica* comments. This information makes possible efficient random access. ■ Incremental saving of notebooks is done so as to minimize rewriting of data, moving data already written out whenever possible. ■ All special characters are represented platform-independently using Unicode. Mapping tables are set up for specific Kanji and other fonts.

MathLink

In OSI terms, *MathLink* is a presentation-level protocol, which can be layered on top of any transport medium, both message-based and stream-based. ■ *MathLink* encodes data in a compressed format when it determines that both ends of a link are on compatible computer systems. ■ *MathLink* can transmit out-of-band data such as interrupts as well as *Mathematica* expressions. ■ When possible *MathLink* is implemented using dynamically linked shared libraries.

Expression formatting

The front end uses a directed acyclic graph to represent the box structure of formatted expressions. ■ Boxes are interpreted using a two-dimensional generalization of an operator precedence parser. ■ Incremental parsing is used to minimize structure and display updating. ■ Character spacing and positioning are determined from font data and operator tables. ■ Line breaking is globally optimized throughout expressions, based on a method similar to the one used for text layout in TEX. ■ Expression formatting uses about 2000 pages of C code.

A.10 Listing of Major Built-in *Mathematica* Objects

■ Introduction

This section gives an alphabetical list of built-in objects which are supported in *Mathematica* Version 3.0.

The list does not include objects such as `CirclePlus` that are associated with operators such as ⊕, but which have no built-in values.

The list also does not include objects that are defined in *Mathematica* packages, even those distributed as a standard part of the *Mathematica* system.

Note also that options which appear only in a single built-in *Mathematica* function are sometimes not given as separate entries in the list.

A few objects in the list, mostly ones related to external operations, are not available on some computer systems.

> +■   object or feature completely new after Version 2.0
>
> ~■   object or feature whose functionality was extensively changed after Version 2.0

New objects and features in the listing.

Note that between Version 2.0 and Version 3.0, the internal code for a large fraction of all functions in *Mathematica* has been modified in one way or another. Even if an object is not indicated by +■ or ~■ in this listing, therefore, it may well have changed in its efficiency or in the details of the results it gives.

In a typical version of *Mathematica* there are various additional objects present which are not included in this listing. You should avoid using such objects. Some may be provided for compatibility with older *Mathematica* systems; others may be preliminary or experimental. In general, however, the specifications of such objects can be expected to change.

In many versions of *Mathematica*, you can access the text given in this section directly, typically using the Help Browser (see page 56). Typing ?*F* to the *Mathematica* kernel will also give you the main description of the object *F* from this section.

More information on related packages mentioned in this listing can be found using the Help Browser, or by looking at *Standard Add-on Packages* published by Wolfram Research. Note that the specifications of functions in packages are subject to incompatible changes in future versions of *Mathematica*.

Many functions listed below are implemented using *Mathematica* programs which are distributed in source code form with most versions of *Mathematica*. Information on the location of these programs can be found in on-line documentation.

There are a total of 1130 objects in this listing.

■ Conventions in This Listing

text in this style	literal *Mathematica* input that you type in as it is printed (e.g., function names)
text in this style	expressions that you fill in (e.g., function arguments)
object$_1$, *object$_2$*, ...	a sequence of any number of expressions
+	new since *Mathematica* Version 2.0
~	modified since *Mathematica* Version 2.0

Conventions used in the list of built-in objects.

■ Abort

`Abort[ ]` generates an interrupt to abort a computation.

You can call `Abort` anywhere within a computation. It has the same effect as an interactive interrupt in which you select the abort option. ■ You can use `Abort` as an "emergency stop" in a computation. ■ Once `Abort` has been called, *Mathematica* functions currently being evaluated return as quickly as possible. ■ In an interactive session, the final result from an aborted computation is `$Aborted`. ■ You can use `CheckAbort` to "catch" returns from an abort. ■ See page 350. ■ See also: `Throw`, `TimeConstrained`, `MemoryConstrained`, `Return`.

■ AbortProtect

`AbortProtect[expr]` evaluates *expr*, saving any aborts until the evaluation is complete.

Aborts that are generated during an `AbortProtect` take effect as soon as the execution of the `AbortProtect` is over. ■ `CheckAbort` can be used inside `AbortProtect` to catch and absorb any aborts that occur. ■ `AbortProtect` also protects against aborts generated by `TimeConstrained` and `MemoryConstrained`. ■ See page 350.

■ Abs

`Abs[z]` gives the absolute value of the real or complex number *z*.

For complex numbers *z*, `Abs[z]` gives the modulus $|z|$. ■ `Abs[z]` is left unevaluated if *z* is not a numeric quantity. ■ See pages 718 and 719. ■ See also: `Re`, `Im`, `Arg`, `Mod`, `ComplexExpand`.

■ AbsoluteDashing

`AbsoluteDashing[{$d_1$, $d_2$, ... }]` is a graphics directive which specifies that lines which follow are to be drawn dashed, with successive segments having absolute lengths d_1, d_2, ... (repeated cyclically).

The absolute lengths are measured in units of printer's points, approximately equal to $\frac{1}{72}$ of an inch. ■ `AbsoluteDashing[{ }]` specifies that lines should be solid. ■ `AbsoluteDashing` can be used in both two- and three-dimensional graphics. ■ See page 481. ■ See also: `AbsoluteThickness`, `Offset`, `Thickness`, `GrayLevel`, `Hue`, `RGBColor`.

■ AbsolutePointSize

`AbsolutePointSize[d]` is a graphics directive which specifies that points which follow are to be shown if possible as circular regions with absolute diameter *d*.

The absolute diameter is measured in units of printer's points, approximately equal to $\frac{1}{72}$ of an inch. ■ `AbsolutePointSize` can be used in both two- and three-dimensional graphics. ■ See page 480. ■ See also: `Offset`, `PointSize`, `Thickness`.

■ AbsoluteThickness

`AbsoluteThickness[d]` is a graphics directive which specifies that lines which follow are to be drawn with absolute thickness *d*.

The absolute thickness is measured in units of printer's points, approximately equal to $\frac{1}{72}$ of an inch. ■ `AbsoluteThickness` can be used in both two- and three-dimensional graphics. ■ See page 481. ■ See also: `Offset`, `AbsoluteDashing`, `PointSize`, `Dashing`.

■ AbsoluteTime

AbsoluteTime[ ] gives the total number of seconds since the beginning of January 1, 1900, in your time zone.

AbsoluteTime[ ] uses whatever date and time have been set on your computer system. It performs no corrections for time zones, daylight saving time, etc. ■ AbsoluteTime[z] gives the date in time zone z. This is inferred by knowing your local date and time, and local time zone. The time zone is given as the number of hours to be added to Greenwich mean time to obtain local time. ■ AbsoluteTime[ ] is accurate only down to a granularity of at least $TimeUnit seconds. ■ There are 2208988800 seconds from the beginning of January 1, 1900 to the beginning of January 1, 1970 and 2840140800 seconds to the beginning of January 1, 1990. ■ See page 683. ■ See also: Date, SessionTime, TimeUsed, Timing, TimeZone, ToDate, FromDate. ■ Related package: Miscellaneous`Calendar`.

■ AccountingForm

AccountingForm[*expr*] prints with all numbers in *expr* given in standard accounting notation.

AccountingForm never uses scientific notation. ■ AccountingForm uses parentheses to indicate negative numbers. ■ AccountingForm takes the same options as NumberForm, but uses a different default function for ExponentFunction, and a different default for NumberSigns. ■ AccountingForm acts as a "wrapper", which affects printing, but not evaluation. ■ See page 414. ■ See also: PaddedForm, NumberForm.

■ Accuracy

Accuracy[x] gives the number of digits to the right of the decimal point in the number x.

If x is not a number, Accuracy[x] gives the minimum value of Accuracy for all the numbers that appear in x. ■ Accuracy gives Infinity when applied to exact numbers, such as integers. ■ Accuracy assumes a precision of $MachinePrecision when applied to machine-precision numbers. ■ Accuracy can yield a negative result. ■ See page 702. ■ See also: Precision, N, Chop, SetAccuracy.

■ AccuracyGoal

AccuracyGoal is an option for various numerical operations which specifies how many digits of accuracy should be sought in the final result.

AccuracyGoal is an option for such functions as NIntegrate, NDSolve and FindRoot. ■ AccuracyGoal -> Automatic yields an accuracy goal equal to 10 digits less than the setting for WorkingPrecision. ■ AccuracyGoal -> Infinity specifies that accuracy should not be used as the criterion for terminating the numerical procedure. PrecisionGoal is typically used in this case. ■ Even though you may specify AccuracyGoal->n, the results you get may have much less than n-digit accuracy. ■ In most cases, you must set WorkingPrecision to be at least as large as AccuracyGoal. ■ AccuracyGoal effectively specifies the absolute error allowed in a numerical procedure. ■ With AccuracyGoal->a and PrecisionGoal->p *Mathematica* attempts to make the numerical error in a result of size x be less than $10^{-a} + |x|10^{-p}$. ■ See page 877. ■ See also: PrecisionGoal, WorkingPrecision.

+■ Active

Active is an option for ButtonBox, Cell and Notebook which specifies whether a button should be active.

With Active->False the contents of a button can be edited. ■ With Active->True a button will perform an action when it is clicked. ■ Active cells are indicated by an A in their cell bracket. ■ See page 582. ■ See also: ButtonStyle, Evaluator.

■ **AddTo**

x += dx adds dx to x and returns the new value of x.

`AddTo` has the attribute `HoldFirst`. ▪ x += dx is equivalent to $x = x + dx$. ▪ See page 285. ▪ See also: `Increment`, `PreIncrement`, `Set`, `PrependTo`.

+■ **AdjustmentBox**

`AdjustmentBox[`*box*`, `*opts*`]` displays with the placement of *box* adjusted using the options given.

In the notebook front end, `AdjustmentBox` objects can typically be inserted and modified using [CTRL][←], [CTRL][→], [CTRL][↑] and [CTRL][↓]. These keys move your current selection by one pixel at the current screen magnification. ▪ The following options can be given:

`BoxMargins`	{{*left*, *right*}, {*bottom*, *top*}}	margins to leave around the contents of the box
`BoxBaselineShift`	*up*	how much the baseline should be shifted relative to those of neighboring boxes

▪ Horizontal motion specifications are in ems; vertical ones in x-heights. ▪ Motion specifications can be either positive or negative numbers. ▪ Positive margin specifications increase the spacing around *box*; negative ones decrease it. ▪ Moving the baseline affects for example vertical alignment in a `RowBox`. ▪ Top and bottom margins affect for example placement in a `FractionBox` or an `OverscriptBox`. ▪ In `StandardForm` and `InputForm` input, `AdjustmentBox` is by default ignored, so that `AdjustmentBox[`*box*`, `*opts*`]` is interpreted just as *box* would be. ▪ Inserting an explicit spacing character such as \[ThinSpace] can have the same effect for display as `AdjustmentBox`, but the spacing character by default affects interpretation. ▪ `AdjustmentBox[`*box*`, `*opts*`]` uses the options given only to adjust the position of *box* itself. Unlike `StyleBox`, it does not propagate the options to subboxes. ▪ See page 434. ▪ See also: `StyleBox`, `GridBox`, `ScriptBaselineShifts`.

■ **AiryAi**

`AiryAi[`*z*`]` gives the Airy function Ai(z).

Mathematical function (see Section A.3.10). ▪ The Airy function Ai(z) is a solution to the differential equation $y'' - xy = 0$. ▪ Ai(z) tends to zero as $z \to \infty$. ▪ `AiryAi[`*z*`]` is an entire function of z with no branch cut discontinuities. ▪ See page 746.

■ **AiryAiPrime**

`AiryAiPrime[`*z*`]` gives the derivative of the Airy function Ai′(z).

Mathematical function (see Section A.3.10). ▪ See notes for `AiryAi`. ▪ See page 746.

■ **AiryBi**

`AiryBi[`*z*`]` gives the Airy function Bi(z).

Mathematical function (see Section A.3.10). ▪ The Airy function Bi(z) is a solution to the differential equation $y'' - xy = 0$. ▪ Bi(z) increases exponentially as $z \to \infty$. ▪ `AiryBi[`*z*`]` is an entire function of z with no branch cut discontinuities. ▪ See page 746.

■ **AiryBiPrime**

`AiryBiPrime[`*z*`]` gives the derivative of the Airy function Bi′(z).

Mathematical function (see Section A.3.10). ▪ See notes for `AiryBi`. ▪ See page 746.

■ **All**

All is a setting used for certain options.

For example, PlotRange -> All specifies that all points are to be included in a plot. ■ See page 135. ■ See also: Automatic, None.

■ **Alternatives**

p_1 | p_2 | ... is a pattern object which represents any of the patterns p_i.

Example: _Integer | _Real represents an object with head either Integer or Real. ■ Unless the same set of pattern names appears in all of the p_i, you cannot use these pattern names on the right-hand side of transformation rules for the pattern. Thus, for example, you can use x in a[x_] | b[x_], but you can use neither x nor y in a[x_] | b[y_]. ■ See page 266. ■ See also: Optional.

■ **AmbientLight**

AmbientLight is an option for Graphics3D and related functions that gives the level of simulated ambient illumination in a three-dimensional picture.

The setting for AmbientLight must be a GrayLevel, Hue or RGBColor directive. ■ See page 524. ■ See also: Lighting, LightSources, SurfaceColor.

■ **AnchoredSearch**

AnchoredSearch is an option for Find and FindList which specifies whether the text searched for must be at the beginning of a record.

With the default setting RecordSeparators -> {"\n"}, AnchoredSearch -> True specifies that the text must appear at the beginning of a line. ■ See page 624.

~■ **And**

e_1 && e_2 && ... is the logical AND function. It evaluates its arguments in order, giving False immediately if any of them are False, and True if they are all True.

+■ And[e_1, e_2, ...] can be input in StandardForm and InputForm as $e_1 \wedge e_2 \wedge$ ... . The character $\wedge$ can be entered as :&&:, :and: or \[And]. ■ And evaluates its arguments in a non-standard way (see page 994). ■ And gives symbolic results when necessary. It applies no simplification rules, except removing initial arguments that are True. ■ See page 85. ■ See also: LogicalExpand.

+■ **AnimationDirection**

AnimationDirection is an option for Cell which specifies the direction to run an animation which starts with the cell.

The setting AnimationDirection->Forward specifies that the animation should run through successive selected graphics cells in the order that they appear in the notebook, and should then start again at the first cell. ■ AnimationDirection->Backward specifies that the reverse order should be used. ■ AnimationDirection->ForwardBackward specifies that the animation should run from the first cell to the last, and should then reverse back to the first cell again. ■ It is the setting of AnimationDirection for the first graphics cell in the sequence selected that determines the animation direction for the whole sequence. ■ See page 591. ■ See also: AnimationDisplayTime.

+■ **AnimationDisplayTime**

> `AnimationDisplayTime` is an option for `Cell` which specifies the minimum time in seconds for which a cell should be displayed in the course of an animation.
>
> The default setting of `AnimationDisplayTime->0` specifies that the animation should be run as fast as your computer can. ▪ See page 591. ▪ See also: `AnimationDirection`.

■ **Apart**

> `Apart[`*expr*`]` rewrites a rational expression as a sum of terms with minimal denominators.
>
> `Apart[`*expr*`,` *var*`]` treats all variables other than *var* as constants.
>
> Example: `Apart[(x^2+1)/(x-1)]` ⟶ `1 + 2/(-1 + x) + x`. ▪ `Apart` gives the partial fraction decomposition of a rational expression. ▪ `Apart[`*expr*`,` *var*`]` writes *expr* as a polynomial in *var* together with a sum of ratios of polynomials, where the degree in *var* of each numerator polynomial is less than that of the corresponding denominator polynomial. ▪ `Apart[(x + y)/(x - y), x]` ⟶ `1 + (2*y)/(x - y)`. ▪ `Apart[(x + y)/(x - y), y]` ⟶ `-1 - (2*x)/(-x + y)`. ▪ `Apart[`*expr*`, Trig -> True]` treats trigonometric functions as rational functions of exponentials, and manipulates them accordingly. ▪ See page 772. ▪ See also: `Together, Cancel, PolynomialQuotient`.

■ **Append**

> `Append[`*expr*`,` *elem*`]` gives *expr* with *elem* appended.
>
> Examples: `Append[{a,b}, c]` ⟶ `{a, b, c}`; `Append[f[a], b+c]` ⟶ `f[a, b + c]`. ▪ In iteratively building a structure, it is usually more efficient to use {*list*, *new*} at each step, followed by `Flatten` at the end, than to use `Append[`*list*`,` *new*`]` at each step. ▪ See page 121. ▪ See also: `Prepend, Insert, AppendTo`.

■ **AppendTo**

> `AppendTo[`*s*`,` *elem*`]` appends *elem* to the value of *s*, and resets *s* to the result.
>
> `AppendTo[`*s*`,` *elem*`]` is equivalent to *s* = `Append[`*s*`,` *elem*`]`. ▪ `AppendTo[`*s*`,` *elem*`]` does not evaluate *s*. ▪ You can use `AppendTo` repeatedly to build up a list. ▪ An alternative and often more efficient way to build up a list is to use a sequence of assignments of the form *s* = {*s*, *elem*}, and then to call `Flatten` on the resulting structure. ▪ See page 287. ▪ See also: `PrependTo`.

■ **Apply**

> `Apply[`*f*`,` *expr*`]` or *f* `@@` *expr* replaces the head of *expr* by *f*.
>
> `Apply[`*f*`,` *expr*`,` *levelspec*`]` replaces heads in parts of *expr* specified by *levelspec*.
>
> Examples: `Apply[f, {a, b, c}]` ⟶ `f[a, b, c]`; `Apply[Plus, g[a, b]]` ⟶ `a + b`. ▪ Level specifications are described on page 989. ▪ The default value for *levelspec* in `Apply` is {0}. ▪ Examples: `Apply[f, {{a,b},{c,d}}]` ⟶ `f[{a, b}, {c, d}]`. ▪ `Apply[f, {{a,b},{c,d}}, {1}]` ⟶ `{f[a, b], f[c, d]}`. ▪ `Apply[f, {{{{a}}}}, -2]` ⟶ `{f[f[f[a]]]}`. ▪ See page 241. ▪ See also: `Map, Scan, Level, Operate, MapThread`.

■ **ArcCos**

> `ArcCos[`*z*`]` gives the arc cosine $\cos^{-1}(z)$ of the complex number *z*.
>
> Mathematical function (see Section A.3.10). ▪ All results are given in radians. ▪ For real *z* between -1 and 1, the results are always in the range 0 to π. ▪ `ArcCos[`*z*`]` has branch cut discontinuities in the complex *z* plane running from $-\infty$ to -1 and $+1$ to $+\infty$. ▪ See page 731.

■ **ArcCosh**

ArcCosh[z] gives the inverse hyperbolic cosine $\cosh^{-1}(z)$ of the complex number z.

Mathematical function (see Section A.3.10). ■ ArcCosh[z] has a branch cut discontinuity in the complex z plane running from $-\infty$ to $+1$. ■ See page 731. ■ See also: ArcSech.

■ **ArcCot**

ArcCot[z] gives the arc cotangent $\cot^{-1}(z)$ of the complex number z.

Mathematical function (see Section A.3.10). ■ All results are given in radians. ■ For real z, the results are always in the range $-\pi/2$ to $\pi/2$, excluding 0. ■ ArcCot[z] has a branch cut discontinuity in the complex z plane running from $-i$ to $+i$. ■ See page 731.

■ **ArcCoth**

ArcCoth[z] gives the inverse hyperbolic cotangent $\coth^{-1}(z)$ of the complex number z.

Mathematical function (see Section A.3.10). ■ ArcCoth[z] has a branch cut discontinuity in the complex z plane running from -1 to $+1$. ■ See page 731.

■ **ArcCsc**

ArcCsc[z] gives the arc cosecant $\csc^{-1}(z)$ of the complex number z.

Mathematical function (see Section A.3.10). ■ All results are given in radians. ■ For real z outside the interval -1 to 1, the results are always in the range $-\pi/2$ to $\pi/2$, excluding 0. ■ ArcCsc[z] has a branch cut discontinuity in the complex z plane running from -1 to $+1$. ■ See page 731.

■ **ArcCsch**

ArcCsch[z] gives the inverse hyperbolic cosecant $\operatorname{csch}^{-1}(z)$ of the complex number z.

Mathematical function (see Section A.3.10). ■ ArcCsch[z] has a branch cut discontinuity in the complex z plane running from $-i$ to $+i$. ■ See page 731.

■ **ArcSec**

ArcSec[z] gives the arc secant $\sec^{-1}(z)$ of the complex number z.

Mathematical function (see Section A.3.10). ■ All results are given in radians. ■ For real z outside the interval -1 to 1, the results are always in the range 0 to π, excluding $\pi/2$. ■ ArcSec[z] has a branch cut discontinuity in the complex z plane running from -1 to $+1$. ■ See page 731.

■ **ArcSech**

ArcSech[z] gives the inverse hyperbolic secant $\operatorname{sech}^{-1}(z)$ of the complex number z.

Mathematical function (see Section A.3.10). ■ ArcSech[z] has branch cut discontinuities in the complex z plane running from $-\infty$ to 0 and $+1$ to $+\infty$. ■ See page 731.

■ **ArcSin**

ArcSin[z] gives the arc sine $\sin^{-1}(z)$ of the complex number z.

Mathematical function (see Section A.3.10). ■ All results are given in radians. ■ For real z between -1 and 1, the results are always in the range $-\pi/2$ to $\pi/2$. ■ ArcSin[z] has branch cut discontinuities in the complex z plane running from $-\infty$ to -1 and $+1$ to $+\infty$. ■ See page 731.

■ AxesStyle

AxesStyle is an option for graphics functions which specifies how axes should be rendered.

AxesStyle can be used in both two- and three-dimensional graphics. ■ **AxesStyle -> *style*** specifies that all axes are to be generated with the specified graphics directive, or list of graphics directives. ■ **AxesStyle -> {{*xstyle*}, {*ystyle*}, ... }** specifies that axes should use graphics directives *xstyle*, ... The styles must be enclosed in lists, perhaps of length one. ■ Styles can be specified using graphics directives such as **Dashing**, **Hue** and **Thickness**. ■ The default color of axes is specified by the option **DefaultColor**. ■ See pages 492 and 529. ■ See also: **Prolog**, **Epilog**, **PlotStyle**, **FrameStyle**.

■ Background

~ **Background** is an option which specifies the background color to use.

~■ **Background** is an option for graphics functions, **Text**, **Cell** and **ButtonBox**. ~■ The setting for **Background** in graphics functions must be a **CMYKColor**, **GrayLevel**, **Hue** or **RGBColor** directive. ~■ The default setting in graphics functions is **Background->Automatic**, which produces a white background on most output devices. +■ In **Text**, **Background->None** draws no background rectangle around the text and **Background->Automatic** draws a background rectangle in the same color as the background for the whole plot. +■ In a cell, the background is used only for the region inside any cell frame. ■ See pages 484 and 579. ■ See also: **Prolog**, **DefaultColor**, **PlotRegion**, **FontColor**.

■ BaseForm

BaseForm[*expr*, *n*] prints with the numbers in *expr* given in base *n*.

The maximum allowed base is 36. For bases larger than 10, additional digits are chosen from the letters a–z. ■ You can enter a number in an arbitrary base using *base^^digits*. ■ When a number in an arbitrary base is given in scientific notation, the exponent is still given in base 10. ■ You can mix **BaseForm** with **NumberForm** and related functions. ■ **BaseForm** acts as a "wrapper", which affects printing, but not evaluation. ■ See pages 417 and 701. ■ See also: **IntegerDigits**, **RealDigits**.

■ Begin

Begin["*context*`"] resets the current context.

Begin resets the value of **$Context**. ■ The interpretation of symbol names depends on context. **Begin** thus affects the parsing of input expressions. ■ See page 377. ■ See also: **BeginPackage**, **End**, **$ContextPath**.

■ BeginPackage

BeginPackage["*context*`"]** makes *context*` and **System` the only active contexts.

BeginPackage["*context*`", {"*need$_1$*`", "*need$_2$*`", ... }] calls **Needs** on the *need$_i$*.

BeginPackage is typically used at the beginning of a *Mathematica* package. ■ **BeginPackage** resets the values of both **$Context** and **$ContextPath**. ■ The interpretation of symbol names depends on context. **BeginPackage** thus affects the parsing of input expressions. ■ See page 377. ■ See also: **EndPackage**.

■ BernoulliB

BernoulliB[*n*] gives the Bernoulli number B_n.

BernoulliB[*n*, *x*] gives the Bernoulli polynomial $B_n(x)$.

Mathematical function (see Section A.3.10). ■ The Bernoulli polynomials satisfy the generating function relation $te^{xt}/(e^t - 1) = \sum_{n=0}^{\infty} B_n(x)(t^n/n!)$. ■ The Bernoulli numbers are given by $B_n = B_n(0)$. ■ See page 727.

■ **BesselI**

BesselI[n, z] gives the modified Bessel function of the first kind $I_n(z)$.

Mathematical function (see Section A.3.10). ■ $I_n(z)$ satisfies the differential equation $z^2 y'' + zy' - (z^2 + n^2)y = 0$.
■ BesselI[n, z] has a branch cut discontinuity in the complex z plane running from $-\infty$ to 0. ■ See page 746.

■ **BesselJ**

BesselJ[n, z] gives the Bessel function of the first kind $J_n(z)$.

Mathematical function (see Section A.3.10). ■ $J_n(z)$ satisfies the differential equation $z^2 y'' + zy' + (z^2 - n^2)y = 0$.
■ BesselJ[n, z] has a branch cut discontinuity in the complex z plane running from $-\infty$ to 0. ■ See page 746.
■ Related package: NumericalMath`BesselZeros`.

■ **BesselK**

BesselK[n, z] gives the modified Bessel function of the second kind $K_n(z)$.

Mathematical function (see Section A.3.10). ■ $K_n(z)$ satisfies the differential equation $z^2 y'' + zy' - (z^2 + n^2)y = 0$.
■ BesselK[n, z] has a branch cut discontinuity in the complex z plane running from $-\infty$ to 0. ■ See page 746.

■ **BesselY**

BesselY[n, z] gives the Bessel function of the second kind $Y_n(z)$.

Mathematical function (see Section A.3.10). ■ $Y_n(z)$ satisfies the differential equation $z^2 y'' + zy' + (z^2 - n^2)y = 0$.
■ BesselY[n, z] has a branch cut discontinuity in the complex z plane running from $-\infty$ to 0. ■ See page 746.
■ Related package: NumericalMath`BesselZeros`.

■ **Beta**

Beta[a, b] gives the Euler beta function B(a, b).

Beta[z, a, b] gives the incomplete beta function B$_z(a, b)$.

Mathematical function (see Section A.3.10). ■ $B(a, b) = \Gamma(a)\Gamma(b)/\Gamma(a + b) = \int_0^1 t^{a-1}(1 - t)^{b-1}dt$.
■ $B_z(a, b) = \int_0^z t^{a-1}(1 - t)^{b-1}dt$. ■ Beta[$z$, a, b] has a branch cut discontinuity in the complex z plane running from $-\infty$ to 0. ■ Beta[z_0, z_1, a, b] gives the generalized incomplete beta function $\int_{z_0}^{z_1} t^{a-1}(1 - t)^{b-1}dt$. ■ Note that the arguments in the incomplete form of Beta are arranged differently from those in the incomplete form of Gamma.
+■ In TraditionalForm, Beta is output using \[CapitalBeta]. ■ See page 740. ■ See also: InverseBetaRegularized.

■ **BetaRegularized**

BetaRegularized[z, a, b] gives the regularized incomplete beta function $I_z(a, b)$.

Mathematical function (see Section A.3.10). ■ For non-singular cases, $I(z, a, b) = B(z, a, b)/B(a, b)$.
■ BetaRegularized[z_0, z_1, a, b] gives the generalized regularized incomplete beta function defined in non-singular cases as Beta[z_0, z_1, a, b]/Beta[a, b]. ■ Note that the arguments in BetaRegularized are arranged differently from those in GammaRegularized. ■ See page 740. ■ See also: Beta, InverseBetaRegularized.

■ Binomial

Binomial[n, m] gives the binomial coefficient $\binom{n}{m}$.

Integer mathematical function (see Section A.3.10). ■ Binomial is evaluated symbolically when possible. ■ Example: Binomial[x+2, x] $\longrightarrow$ ((1 + x) * (2 + x)) / 2. ■ In general, $\binom{n}{m}$ is defined by $\Gamma(n+1)/(\Gamma(m+1)\Gamma(n-m+1))$ or suitable limits of this. ■ See page 727. ■ See also: Multinomial, Pochhammer.

■ Blank

_ or Blank[ ] is a pattern object that can stand for any *Mathematica* expression.

_h or Blank[h] can stand for any expression with head h.

The head h in _h cannot itself contain pattern objects. ■ See page 256. ■ See also: Pattern, Optional.

■ BlankNullSequence

___ (three _ characters) or BlankNullSequence[ ] is a pattern object that can stand for any sequence of zero or more *Mathematica* expressions.

___h or BlankNullSequence[h] can stand for any sequence of expressions, all of which have head h.

Blank sequences work slightly differently depending on whether or not the head of the expression in which they appear is a symbol with the attribute Flat. ■ Consider matching the pattern $f[a_1, a_2, \ldots, \_\_\_, c_1, \ldots]$ against the expression $f[a_1, a_2, \ldots, b_1, \ldots, c_1, \ldots]$. If f is a symbol with attribute Flat, then the ___ will be taken to stand for the expression $f[b_1, \ldots]$. If f is not a symbol with attribute Flat, then ___ will be taken to stand for the sequence of expressions $b_1, \ldots$. With a named pattern, such as $x\_\_\_$, x can be used only as an element in an expression. The sequence of expressions $b_1, \ldots$ is "spliced in" to replace x, thereby usually increasing the length of the expression. ■ If ___ matches a sequence of length more than one, then the sequence will be represented by a Sequence object. In most uses of ___, however, the Sequence object will automatically be spliced into another expression, and will never appear explicitly. ■ See page 270. ■ See also: Pattern, SlotSequence.

■ BlankSequence

__ (two _ characters) or BlankSequence[ ] is a pattern object that can stand for any sequence of one or more *Mathematica* expressions.

__h or BlankSequence[h] can stand for any sequence of one or more expressions, all of which have head h.

See notes for BlankNullSequence. ■ See page 270.

■ Block

Block[{x, y, ... }, *expr*] specifies that *expr* is to be evaluated with local values for the symbols x, y, ...

Block[{$x = x_0$, ... }, *expr*] defines initial local values for x, ...

Block allows you to set up an environment in which the values of variables can temporarily be changed. ■ When you execute a block, values assigned to x, y, ... are cleared. When the execution of the block is finished, the original values of these symbols are restored. ■ Block affects only the *values* of symbols, not their names. ■ Initial values specified for x, y, ... are evaluated before x, y, ... are cleared. ■ You can use Block[{*vars*}, *body* /; *cond*] as the right-hand side of a transformation rule with a condition attached. ■ Block has attribute HoldAll. ■ Block implements dynamic scoping of variables. ■ Block is automatically used to localize values of iterators in iteration constructs such as Do, Sum and Table. ■ See page 368. ■ See also: Module, With, CompoundExpression.

■ Boxed

Boxed is an option for Graphics3D which specifies whether to draw the edges of the bounding box in a three-dimensional picture.

Boxed -> True draws the box; Boxed -> False does not. ■ See pages 149 and 528.

■ BoxRatios

BoxRatios is an option for Graphics3D and SurfaceGraphics which gives the ratios of side lengths for the bounding box of the three-dimensional picture.

BoxRatios -> {s_x, s_y, s_z} gives the side-length ratios. ■ See page 510.

■ BoxStyle

BoxStyle is an option for three-dimensional graphics functions which specifies how the bounding box should be rendered.

BoxStyle can be set to a list of graphics directives such as Dashing, Thickness, GrayLevel and RGBColor. ■ See pages 483 and 529. ■ See also: AxesStyle, Prolog, Epilog, DisplayFunction.

■ Break

Break[ ] exits the nearest enclosing Do, For or While.

+■ Break[ ] takes effect as soon as it is evaluated, even if it appears inside other functions. ■ After a Break the value Null is returned from the enclosing control structure. ■ The function of Break can also be achieved using Throw and Catch. ■ See page 333. ■ See also: Continue, Return, Goto, Abort.

+■ **ButtonBox**

ButtonBox[*boxes*] represents a button in a notebook, displaying *boxes* and performing an action when it is clicked on.

The default action is to paste *boxes* at your current insertion point.

Other actions can be specified using options.

ButtonBox objects are used to implement palette buttons, hyperlinks and other active elements in notebooks.
■ ButtonBox objects are active when either they or the cell that contains them has the option Active->True.
■ When ButtonBox objects are active, they perform an action whenever they are clicked on. Otherwise, clicking on them simply selects them or their contents. ■ ButtonBox[*boxes*, ButtonStyle->"*style*"] takes the properties of the ButtonBox from the specified style. The style for a ButtonBox can specify both its appearance and its action. ■ The following options affecting button appearance can be given:

Background	GrayLevel[0.8]	button background color
ButtonFrame	"Palette"	the type of frame for the button
ButtonExpandable	True	whether a button should expand to fill a position in a GridBox
ButtonMargins	3	the margin in printer's points around the contents of a button
ButtonMinHeight	1	the minimum total height of a button in units of font size

■ The following options affecting button action can be given:

Active	False	make the button always active
ButtonData	Null	the second argument to supply to the button function
ButtonEvaluator	None	where to send the button function expression for evaluation
ButtonFunction	(pasting function)	the function to apply when the button is clicked
ButtonNote	ButtonData	what to display in the window status line when the cursor is over the button
ButtonSource	Automatic	where to get the first argument of the button function from

■ ButtonBox[...] is by default interpreted as Button[...] if it is given as input to the *Mathematica* kernel. ■ See pages 427 and 569. ■ See also: Dialog, Input.

+■ **ButtonData**

ButtonData is an option for ButtonBox which specifies the second argument to give to the ButtonFunction for the button when the button is active and is clicked on.

The default is ButtonData->Null. ■ ButtonData provides a convenient way to associate additional data with a button that does not affect the display of the button. ■ See page 571. ■ See also: ButtonSource, ButtonNote, ButtonStyle.

+■ **ButtonEvaluator**

ButtonEvaluator is an option for ButtonBox which specifies where the expression constructed from ButtonFunction should be sent for evaluation.

The default setting is ButtonEvaluator->None. ■ Possible settings are:

None	the front end
Automatic	the kernel used by default in the current notebook
"*name*"	a kernel referred to by a specific name

■ With ButtonEvaluator->Automatic the expression to be evaluated can contain any *Mathematica* objects. ■ With ButtonEvaluator->None the expression can contain only the specific notebook commands supported by the front end. All these commands are in the context FrontEnd`. Expressions intended for processing purely by the front end must be wrapped with FrontEndExecute. ■ See page 571. ■ **See also:** ButtonFunction, ButtonStyle, SelectionEvaluate, ButtonNotebook.

+■ **ButtonExpandable**

ButtonExpandable is an option for ButtonBox which specifies whether the button should expand to fill any GridBox position in which it appears.

The default setting is ButtonExpandable->True. ■ This setting is usually used for all buttons that appear in palettes. ■ With ButtonExpandable->False the size of a button is determined purely by its contents, independent of its environment. ■ With ButtonExpandable->False, gutters will often be left between buttons in a GridBox. ■ See page 431. ■ See also: ButtonMargins, ButtonMinHeight, TextJustification.

+■ **ButtonFrame**

ButtonFrame is an option for ButtonBox which specifies the type of frame to display around a button.

Typical settings supported include:

"Palette"	a button in a palette
"DialogBox"	a button in a dialog box
"Hyperlink"	a hyperlink

■ Button frames generated by ButtonFrame are set up to follow the conventions for particular computer systems. ■ A button with a particular setting for ButtonFrame may look slightly different on different computer systems. ■ See page 431. ■ See also: ButtonStyle, WindowFrame.

+■ **ButtonFunction**

ButtonFunction is an option for ButtonBox which specifies the function to execute when the button is active and is clicked on.

The default setting for ButtonFunction causes the button to paste its contents at your current notebook selection. ■ ButtonFunction is used only with the setting Active->True either for the individual button, or for the cell which contains it. ■ With ButtonFunction->f the first argument supplied to f is specified by the setting for ButtonSource, and the second argument by the setting for ButtonData. ■ Standard *Mathematica* precedence rules require parentheses in ButtonFunction->(*body* &). ■ Settings for ButtonFunction are often inherited from button styles via the ButtonStyle option. ■ See page 571. ■ See also: ButtonEvaluator, ButtonNote, NotebookApply, ButtonNotebook.

+■ **ButtonMargins**

ButtonMargins is an option for ButtonBox which specifies how much space in printer's points to leave around the contents of a button when the button is displayed.

The default setting is ButtonMargins->3. ■ See page 431. ■ See also: ButtonExpandable, ButtonMinHeight.

+■ **ButtonMinHeight**

ButtonMinHeight is an option for ButtonBox which specifies the minimum total height in units of font size that should be allowed for the button.

The default setting ButtonMinHeight->1 forces a button to have a total height which at least accommodates all the characters in the current font. ■ ButtonMinHeight->0 reduces the total height of a button as much as possible, allowing buttons containing characters such as x and X to be different heights. ■ See page 431. ■ See also: ButtonMargins, ButtonExpandable, RowMinHeight.

+■ **ButtonNote**

ButtonNote is an option for ButtonBox which specifies what should be displayed in the status line of the current notebook window when the button is active and the cursor is placed on top of it.

The default is to display whatever setting is given for ButtonData. ■ Any expression can be specified as the setting for ButtonNote, though most windows will only allow a single character height to be displayed. ■ ButtonNote can be used to display keyboard equivalents for buttons in a palette. ■ See page 571. ■ See also: ButtonData, ButtonFunction, ButtonStyle.

+■ **ButtonNotebook**

ButtonNotebook[ ] gives the notebook, if any, that contains the button which initiated the current evaluation.

ButtonNotebook returns a NotebookObject. ■ If a button in a palette initiates evaluation in another notebook, then ButtonNotebook[ ] will be the palette, but EvaluationNotebook[ ] will be the other notebook. ■ If the current evaluation was not initiated by a button, then ButtonNotebook[ ] will return $Failed. ■ See page 554. ■ See also: Notebooks, EvaluationNotebook, SelectedNotebook, InputNotebook.

+■ **ButtonSource**

ButtonSource is an option for ButtonBox which specifies the first argument to give to the ButtonFunction for the button when the button is active and is clicked on.

The default is ButtonSource->Automatic. ■ Possible settings are:

Automatic	ButtonData if it is set, otherwise ButtonContents
ButtonContents	the first argument of the ButtonBox
ButtonData	the setting for the ButtonData option
Cell	the whole cell in which the button appears
CellContents	the contents of the cell in which the button appears
Notebook	the whole notebook in which the button appears
n	the expression *n* levels up from the button in the notebook

■ See page 571. ■ See also: ButtonFunction, ButtonData, ButtonStyle, NotebookRead.

+■ **ButtonStyle**

ButtonStyle is an option for ButtonBox which specifies the default properties for the button.

Typical styles defined in the standard notebook front end are:

"Paste"	paste the contents of the button (default)
"Evaluate"	paste then evaluate in place what has been pasted
"EvaluateCell"	paste then evaluate the whole cell
"CopyEvaluate"	copy the current selection into a new cell, then paste and evaluate in place
"CopyEvaluateCell"	copy the current selection into a new cell, then paste and evaluate the whole cell
"Hyperlink"	jump to a different location in the notebook

■ The properties specified by a button style can affect both the appearance and action of a button. ■ The properties can be overriden by explicit settings for ButtonBox options. ■ See page 570. ■ See also: ButtonFrame, ButtonFunction.

■ **Byte**

Byte represents a single byte of data in Read.

See page 618. ▪ Related package: Utilities`BinaryFiles`.

■ **ByteCount**

ByteCount[*expr*] gives the number of bytes used internally by *Mathematica* to store *expr*.

ByteCount does not take account of any sharing of subexpressions. The results it gives assume that every part of the expression is stored separately. ByteCount will therefore often give an overestimate of the amount of memory currently needed to store a particular expression. When you manipulate the expression, however, subexpressions will often stop being shared, and the amount of memory needed will be close to the value returned by ByteCount. ▪ See page 687. ▪ See also: LeafCount, MemoryInUse, MaxMemoryUsed, Length, StringLength, Depth.

■ **C**

C[*i*] is the default form for the ith constant of integration produced in solving a differential equation with DSolve.

The indices *i* are chosen to be successive integers, starting at 1 every time DSolve is called. ▪ The function applied to the index *i* to produce the ith constant of integration is determined by the setting for the option DSolveConstants in DSolve. The default is DSolveConstants->C. ▪ See pages 89 and 822. ▪ See also: Unique.

~■ **Cancel**

Cancel[*expr*] cancels out common factors in the numerator and denominator of *expr*.

Example: Cancel[(x^2-1)/(x-1)] ⟶ 1 + x. ▪ Cancel is Listable. ▪ Cancel cancels out the greatest common divisor of the numerator and denominator. +▪ Cancel[*expr*, Modulus->*p*] generates a result modulo *p*. +▪ Cancel[*expr*, Extension->Automatic] allows operations to be performed on algebraic numbers in *expr*. ~■ Cancel[*expr*, Trig -> True] treats trigonometric functions as rational functions of exponentials, and manipulates them accordingly. ▪ See page 772. ▪ See also: Apart, GCD.

■ **Cases**

Cases[{e_1, e_2, ... }, *pattern*] gives a list of the e_i that match the pattern.

Cases[{e_1, ... }, *pattern* -> *rhs*] gives a list of the values of *rhs* corresponding to the e_i that match the pattern.

Cases[*expr*, *pattern*, *levspec*] gives a list of all parts of *expr* on levels specified by *levspec* which match the pattern.

Cases[*expr*, *pattern* -> *rhs*, *levspec*] gives the values of *rhs* which match the pattern.

Example: Cases[{2, x, 4}, _Integer] ⟶ {2, 4}. ▪ The first argument to Cases need not have head List. ▪ Cases[*expr*, *pattern*, *levspec*, *n*] gives the first *n* parts in *expr* which match the pattern. ▪ Level specifications are described on page 989. ▪ See page 258. ▪ See also: Select, Position, ReplaceList, Collect. ▪ Related package: Statistics`DataManipulation`.

■ **Catalan**

Catalan is Catalan's constant, with numerical value ≃ 0.915966.

Mathematical constant (see Section A.3.11). ▪ Catalan's constant is given by the sum $\sum_{k=0}^{\infty}(-1)^k(2k+1)^{-2}$. ▪ See page 735.

~■ Catch

Catch[*expr*] returns the argument of the first Throw generated in the evaluation of *expr*.

+ Catch[*expr*, *form*] returns *value* from the first Throw[*value*, *tag*] for which *form* matches *tag*.

+ Catch[*expr*, *form*, *f*] returns *f*[*value*, *tag*].

~■ Catch[*expr*, ...] always returns the value of *expr* if no Throw was generated during the evaluation. ~■ *form* can be any expression, and is often a pattern. ~■ *tag* in Throw[*value*, *tag*] is re-evaluated every time it is compared to *form*. ■ See page 330. ■ See also: Check, CheckAbort.

~■ Ceiling

Ceiling[*x*] gives the smallest integer greater than or equal to *x*.

Mathematical function (see Section A.3.10). ■ Examples: Ceiling[2.4] $\longrightarrow$ 3; Ceiling[2.6] $\longrightarrow$ 3; Ceiling[-2.4] $\longrightarrow$ -2; Ceiling[-2.6] $\longrightarrow$ -2. +■ Ceiling[*x*] can be entered in StandardForm and InputForm as ⌈ *x* ⌉, ⌈lc⌉ *x* ⌈rc⌉ or \[LeftCeiling] *x* \[RightCeiling]. +■ Ceiling[*x*] returns an integer when *x* is any numeric quantity, whether or not it is an explicit number. ■ Example: Ceiling[Pi^2] $\longrightarrow$ 10. +■ For exact numeric quantities, Ceiling internally uses numerical approximations to establish its result. This process can be affected by the setting of the global variable $MaxExtraPrecision. ■ See page 718. ■ See also: Floor, IntegerPart, Round, Chop.

+■ Cell

Cell[*contents*, "*style*"] represents a cell in a *Mathematica* notebook.

A *Mathematica* notebook consists of a list of cells. ■ You can see the form of a cell as an expression by using the Show Expression command in the standard *Mathematica* front end. ■ You can access cells in a notebook directly using the front end. You can also access the cells from the kernel using NotebookRead and NotebookWrite, or using Options and SetOptions on NotebookSelection[*obj*]. ■ The contents of cells can be the following:

"*text*"	plain text
TextData[{*text*₁, *text*₂, ... }]	general text objects
BoxData[*boxes*]	formatted *Mathematica* expressions
GraphicsData["*type*", *data*]	graphics or sounds
OutputFormData["*itext*", "*otext*"]	text as generated by InputForm and OutputForm
RawData["*data*"]	unformatted expressions
CellGroupData[{*cell*₁, *cell*₂, ... }, Open]	open group of cells
CellGroupData[{*cell*₁, *cell*₂, ... }, Closed]	closed group of cells
StyleData["*style*"]	sample cell for a particular style

■ In any given notebook, a collection of possible cell styles are defined, typically with names such as "Title", "Section", "Input" and "Output". ■ Cells can have many options, including:

Active	whether buttons in cell should be active
Background	the color of the background for the cell
Editable	whether to allow the contents of the cell to be edited
CellFrame	whether to draw a frame around the cell
CellTags	tags for the cell
FontSize	the default size of text in the cell
TextAlignment	how to align text in the cell

■ See page 573. ■ See also: Notebook, CellPrint.

+■ **CellAutoOverwrite**

CellAutoOverwrite is an option for Cell which specifies whether new output obtained by evaluating this cell should overwrite old output.

Any sequence of cells with GeneratedCell->True which follow the given cell are assumed to correspond to output. ■ The output is deleted only when new output is ready to be inserted in its place. ■ CellAutoOverwrite is typically set for cells in "Input" style. ■ See page 582. ■ See also: GeneratedCell, CellEvaluationDuplicate, Deletable.

+■ **CellBaseline**

CellBaseline is an option for Cell which specifies where the baseline of the cell should be assumed to be when it appears inside another cell.

CellBaseline is used to determine the vertical alignment of cells that are embedded in text, typically in TextData objects. ■ CellBaseline->*pos* specifies that position *pos* in the Cell should be assumed to be the baseline of the Cell and should therefore be aligned with baselines of other boxes. ■ Possible settings are:

Axis	axis of the expression in the cell
Baseline	baseline of the expression in the cell (default)
Bottom	bottom of the expression in the cell
Center	center of the expression in the cell
Top	top of the expression in the cell

■ See page 579. ■ See also: CellMargins, GridBaseline.

+■ **CellDingbat**

CellDingbat is an option for Cell which specifies what dingbat to use to emphasize a cell.

The setting CellDingbat->"" displays no dingbat. ■ Dingbats are placed to the left of the main contents of a cell, aligned with the first line of the contents. ■ Dingbats are placed outside of any cell frame. ■ The setting for CellDingbat can be any string. A typical setting is "\[FilledSquare]". ■ CellDingbat is often set for styles of cells rather than for individual cells. ■ See page 579. ■ See also: CellFrame, Background.

+■ **CellEditDuplicate**

CellEditDuplicate is an option for Cell which specifies whether the front end should make a copy of the cell before actually applying any changes in its contents that you request.

CellEditDuplicate is by default set to True for cells that are generated as *Mathematica* output. ■ New cells generated when CellEditDuplicate->True have styles specified by the setting for DefaultDuplicateCellStyle for the notebook. ■ CellEditDuplicate is typically set for styles of cells rather than for individual cells. ■ See page 582. ■ See also: CellEvaluationDuplicate, Editable.

+■ **CellEvaluationDuplicate**

CellEvaluationDuplicate is an option for Cell which specifies whether the front end should make a copy of the cell before performing any evaluation of its contents that you request.

New cells generated when CellEvaluationDuplicate->True have styles specified by the setting for DefaultDuplicateCellStyle for the notebook. ■ CellEvaluationDuplicate is typically set for styles of cells rather than for individual cells. ■ See page 582. ■ See also: CellEditDuplicate, Evaluatable, CellAutoOverwrite.

+■ CellFrame

CellFrame is an option for Cell which specifies whether a frame should be drawn around a cell.

The space left between the frame and the cell contents is determined by CellFrameMargins. ■ Dingbats go outside the frame. ■ See page 579. ■ See also: Background, CellDingbat, FrameBox.

+■ CellFrameMargins

CellFrameMargins is an option for Cell which specifies the absolute margins in printer's points to leave inside a frame that is drawn around a cell.

Possible settings are:

dist	the same margins on all sides
{{*left*, *right*}, {*bottom*, *top*}}	different margins on different sides

■ See page 579. ■ See also: CellMargins.

+■ CellGroupData

CellGroupData[{*cell*$_1$, *cell*$_2$, ... }, Open] represents an open group of cells in a notebook.

CellGroupData[{*cell*$_1$, *cell*$_2$, ... }, Closed] represents a closed group of cells.

When a group of cells is closed, only the first member of the group is visible. ■ When cells are entered into a notebook, they are automatically placed in groups unless CellGrouping->Manual is set. ■ See page 574. ■ See also: Cell, BoxFormData, CellGrouping, CellOpen.

+■ CellGrouping

CellGrouping is an option for Notebook which specifies how cells in the notebook should be assembled into groups.

The default setting is typically CellGrouping->Automatic. ■ With CellGrouping->Automatic, cells are automatically grouped in a hierarchical way based on their styles. ■ With CellGrouping->Manual, cells must be grouped manually, either by setting up explicit CellGroupData expressions, or by using the Group Cells menu item in the notebook front end. ■ See page 592. ■ See also: CellGroupData.

+■ CellLabel

CellLabel is an option for Cell which gives the label to use for a particular cell.

CellLabel->"" specifies that no label should be used for a cell. ■ Cell labels are displayed when the setting ShowCellLabels->True is made. ■ Cell labels are typically generated automatically when cells appear as input or output to the *Mathematica* kernel. ■ Cell labels are automatically deleted when a cell is modified if CellLabelAutoDelete->True. ■ See page 581. ■ See also: CellTags.

+■ CellLabelAutoDelete

CellLabelAutoDelete is an option for Cell which specifies whether a label for the cell should be automatically deleted if the contents of the cell are modified or the notebook containing the cell is saved in a file.

Cells that represent *Mathematica* input and output typically have CellLabelAutoDelete->False. ■ CellLabelAutoDelete is more often set for styles of cells than for individual cells. ■ See page 581. ■ See also: CellLabel, ShowCellLabel, CellTags, CellAutoOverwrite.

+■ **CellMargins**

> CellMargins is an option for Cell which specifies the absolute margins in printer's points to leave around a cell.

Possible settings are:

dist	the same margins on all sides
{{*left*, *right*}, {*bottom*, *top*}}	different margins on different sides

■ The left margin gives the distance from the edge of the window to the left-hand side of the cell. ■ The right margin gives the distance from the inside of the cell bracket to the right-hand side of the cell. ■ The left and right margins can be set interactively in the front end using the Show Ruler ruler. ■ The top and bottom margins determine the amount of space to leave above and below the cell. ■ The margins go to the edge of any cell frame that is present. ■ Cell dingbats are placed to the left of the left-hand side of the cell, and extend into the left cell margin. ■ See page 579. ■ See also: CellFrameMargins, CellBaseline, ImageMargins, WindowMargins.

+■ **CellOpen**

> CellOpen is an option for Cell which specifies whether the contents of a cell should be explicitly displayed.

With CellOpen->False, a small cell bracket is still shown to indicate the presence of a cell. ■ Cells which are not open can still be evaluated automatically if you set CellAutoEvaluate->True. ■ See page 579. ■ See also: Visible, CellGroupData, CellEditable, ConversionRules.

+■ **CellPrint**

> CellPrint[*cell*] inserts *cell* at the current selection in your currently selected notebook.
>
> CellPrint[{*cell*$_1$, *cell*$_2$, ... }] inserts a sequence of cells.

CellPrint creates a new cell directly after the current selection in your currently selected notebook. ■ The *cell*$_i$ must all have head Cell. ■ CellPrint is a special case of NotebookWrite. ■ With a text-based front end, CellPrint[*cell*] does the same as applying Print to the contents of *cell*. ■ Cells generated by CellPrint by default have GeneratedCell->True. ■ See page 550. ■ See also: StylePrint, Print, NotebookWrite, NotebookPrint.

+■ **CellTags**

> CellTags is an option for Cell which gives a list of tags to associate with a cell.

Cell tags are typically used to allow searching for cells. ■ The tags are usually strings. ■ Cell tags are displayed when the setting ShowCellTags->True is made. ■ See page 581. ■ See also: CellLabel, ConversionRules.

■ **CForm**

> CForm[*expr*] prints as a C language version of *expr*.

Standard arithmetic functions and certain control structures are translated. ■ No declarations are generated. ■ CForm acts as a "wrapper", which affects printing, but not evaluation. ■ See pages 207 and 404. ■ See also: FortranForm, Compile.

■ **Character**

> Character represents a single character in Read.

See page 618. ■ Related package: Utilities`BinaryFiles`.

⁺■ ColumnAlignments

`ColumnAlignments` is an option for `GridBox` which specifies how entries in each column should be aligned.

The following settings can be given:

`Center`	centered (default)
`Left`	left justified (aligned on left edge)
`Right`	right justified (aligned on right edge)
`"."`	aligned at decimal points
`"c"`	aligned at the first occurrence of the character c
$\{pos_1, pos_2, \dots\}$	separate settings for each column in the grid

■ Lists of settings are used cyclically if there are more columns in the grid than elements in the list. ■ With the setting `ColumnAlignments->"c"` a column will be right justified if the character c appears nowhere in it. ■ You can insert invisible `\[AlignmentMarker]` characters in the entries in a grid to specify how these entries should be aligned. ■ See page 428. ■ See also: `RowAlignments`, `ColumnsEqual`, `TableAlignments`, `TextAlignment`.

■ ColumnForm

`ColumnForm[{`e_1`, `e_2`, ... }]` prints as a column with e_1 above e_2, etc.

`ColumnForm[`*list*`, `*horiz*`]` specifies the horizontal alignment of each element.

`ColumnForm[`*list*`, `*horiz*`, `*vert*`]` also specifies the vertical alignment of the whole column.

Possible horizontal alignments are:

`Center`	centered
`Left`	left justified (default case)
`Right`	right justified

Possible vertical alignments are:

`Above`	the bottom element of the column is aligned with the baseline
`Below`	the top element is aligned with the baseline (default case)
`Center`	the column is centered on the baseline

■ The first argument of `ColumnForm` can have any head, not necessarily `List`. ■ `ColumnForm` acts as a "wrapper", which affects printing, but not evaluation. ■ See pages 395 and 416. ■ See also: `TableForm`, `MatrixForm`, `SequenceForm`, `GridBox`.

⁺■ ColumnLines

`ColumnLines` is an option for `GridBox` which specifies whether lines should be drawn between adjacent columns.

The default setting is `ColumnLines->False`. ■ `ColumnLines->{`v_{12}`, `v_{23}`, ... }` specifies whether lines should be drawn between successive pairs of columns. The v_{ij} can be `True` or `False`. ■ If there are more columns than entries in the list, the last element is used repeatedly for remaining pairs of columns. ■ Lines can be drawn around the outside of a `GridBox` using `FrameBox`. ■ See page 425. ■ See also: `RowLines`, `FrameBox`, `GridLines`.

+■ **ColumnsEqual**

ColumnsEqual is an option for GridBox which specifies whether all columns in the grid should be assigned equal width.

The default setting ColumnsEqual->False determines the width of each column from the widest entry in that column. ■ ColumnsEqual->True makes all columns the same width, with the width determined by the widest entry in the whole GridBox. ■ See page 428. ■ See also: ColumnWidths, ColumnAlignments, ColumnSpacings, RowsEqual, MatrixForm.

+■ **ColumnSpacings**

ColumnSpacings is an option for GridBox which specifies the spaces in ems that should be inserted between adjacent columns.

The default setting is ColumnSpacings->1. ■ ColumnSpacings effectively specifies the minimum distance between entries in adjacent columns; individual entries will often not fill their columns and will therefore be further apart. ■ ColumnSpacings->n uses a column spacing equal to n times the current font size—usually about n times the width of an M in the current font. ■ ColumnSpacings->$\{s_{12}, s_{23}, \dots\}$ can be used to specify different spacings between different columns. If there are more columns than entries in this list, then the last element of the list is used repeatedly for the remaining columns. ■ See page 428. ■ See also: ColumnAlignments, ColumnWidths, ColumnsEqual, RowSpacings, TableSpacing.

+■ **ColumnWidths**

ColumnWidths is an option for GridBox which specifies the widths of columns in ems.

The default setting is ColumnWidths->Automatic, specifying that all columns should be made wide enough to fit their contents without breaking onto multiple lines. ■ ColumnWidths->n uses column widths equal to n times the current font size—usually about n times the width of an M in the current font. ■ ColumnWidths->$\{w_1, w_2, \dots\}$ can be used to specify different widths for different columns. If there are more columns than entries in this list, then the last element of the list is used repeatedly for the remaining columns. ■ An explicit setting for ColumnWidths overrides ColumnsEqual->True. ■ See page 428. ■ See also: ColumnsEqual, ColumnSpacings.

■ Compile

Compile[{x_1, x_2, ... }, *expr*] creates a compiled function which evaluates *expr* assuming numerical values of the x_i.

Compile[{{x_1, t_1}, ... }, *expr*] assumes that x_i is of a type which matches t_i.

+ Compile[{{x_1, t_1, n_1}, ... }, *expr*] assumes that x_i is a rank n_i array of objects each of a type which matches t_i.

Compile[*vars*, *expr*, {{p_1, pt_1}, ... }] assumes that subexpressions in *expr* which match p_i are of types which match pt_i.

The types handled by Compile are:

_Integer   machine-size integer
_Real   machine-precision approximate real number (default)
_Complex   machine-precision approximate complex number
True | False   logical variable

+■ Nested lists given as input to a compiled function must be full arrays of numbers. +■ Compile handles numerical functions, matrix operations, procedural programming constructs, list manipulation functions, functional programming constructs, etc. ■ Compile generates a CompiledFunction object. ■ Compiled code does not handle numerical precision and local variables in the same way as ordinary *Mathematica* code. ■ If a compiled function cannot be evaluated with particular arguments using compiled code, ordinary *Mathematica* code is used instead. ■ Ordinary *Mathematica* code can be called from within compiled code. Results obtained from the *Mathematica* code are assumed to be approximate real numbers, unless specified otherwise by the third argument of Compile. ■ The number of times and the order in which objects are evaluated by Compile may be different from ordinary *Mathematica* code. ■ Compile has attribute HoldAll, and does not by default do any evaluation before compilation. ■ You can use Compile[... , Evaluate[*expr*]] to specify that *expr* should be evaluated symbolically before compilation. ■ See page 352. ■ See also: Dispatch, Function, InterpolatingFunction, CForm.

■ Compiled

Compiled is an option for various numerical and plotting functions which specifies whether the expressions they work with should automatically be compiled.

Compiled -> True automatically creates compiled functions. ■ You should set Compiled -> False if you need to use high-precision numbers. ■ See pages 353 and 878.

■ CompiledFunction

CompiledFunction[*args*, *nregs*, *instr*, *func*] represents compiled code for evaluating a compiled function.

args is a list giving a pattern for the type of each argument to the function. The types are specified as in Compile. ■ *nregs* is a list giving the number of integer, real, complex and logical registers required to evaluate the compiled code. ■ *instr* is a list of actual compiled code instructions. ■ *func* is a *Mathematica* pure function to be used if no result can be obtained from the compiled code for any reason. ■ Compile generates a CompiledFunction object which can be executed by applying it to appropriate arguments. ■ CompiledFunction objects that are constructed explicitly can also be executed. Basic consistency checks are done when such objects are first evaluated by *Mathematica*. ■ The code in a CompiledFunction object is based on an idealized register machine. ■ See page 356. ■ See also: InterpolatingFunction.

■ Complement

Complement[*eall*, e_1, e_2, ...] gives the elements in *eall* which are not in any of the e_i.

The list returned by Complement is sorted into standard order. ■ Example:
Complement[{a,b,c,d,e}, {a,c}, {d}] ⟶ {b, e}. +■ Complement[*eall*, e_1, ... , SameTest->*test*] applies *test* to each pair of elements in *eall* and the e_i to determine whether they should be considered the same. ■ See page 123.
■ See also: Intersection, Union.

■ Complex

Complex is the head used for complex numbers.

You can enter a complex number in the form *x* + I *y*. ■ _Complex can be used to stand for a complex number in a pattern. ■ You have to use Re and Im to extract parts of Complex numbers. ■ See page 696. ■ See also: Real, Re, Im.

■ ComplexExpand

ComplexExpand[*expr*] expands *expr* assuming that all variables are real.

ComplexExpand[*expr*, {x_1, x_2, ... }] expands *expr* assuming that variables matching any of the x_i are complex.

Example: ComplexExpand[Sin[x + I y]] ⟶ Cosh[y] Sin[x] + I Cos[x] Sinh[y]. ■ The variables given in the second argument of ComplexExpand can be patterns. ■ Example:
ComplexExpand[Sin[x], x] ⟶ Cosh[Im[x]] Sin[Re[x]] + I Cos[Re[x]] Sinh[Im[x]]. ■ The option TargetFunctions can be given as a list of functions from the set {Re, Im, Abs, Arg, Conjugate, Sign}. ComplexExpand will try to give results in terms of functions specified.
■ ComplexExpand[*expr*, *vars*, TargetFunctions -> {Abs, Arg}] converts to polar coordinates. ■ See page 782.
■ See also: GaussianIntegers, TrigToExp, ExpToTrig, TrigExpand, FunctionExpand.

■ ComplexInfinity

ComplexInfinity represents a quantity with infinite magnitude, but undetermined complex phase.

ComplexInfinity is converted to DirectedInfinity[ ]. ■ In OutputForm, DirectedInfinity[ ] is printed as ComplexInfinity. ■ See page 716. ■ See also: Infinity, Indeterminate.

■ ComplexityFunction

ComplexityFunction is an option for Simplify and FullSimplify which gives a function to rank the complexity of different forms of an expression.

With the default setting ComplexityFunction->Automatic, forms are ranked primarily according to their LeafCount, with corrections to treat integers with more digits as more complex.
■ Simplify[*expr*, ComplexityFunction->*f*] applies *f* to each intermediate expression generated by Simplify, treating the one which yields the smallest numerical value as simplest. ■ See page 784. ■ See also: Length, StringLength, TimeConstraint, ExcludedForms.

■ ComposeList

ComposeList[{f_1, f_2, ... }, *x*] generates a list of the form {x, $f_1[x]$, $f_2[f_1[x]]$, ... }.

Example: ComposeList[{a, b, c}, x] ⟶ {x, a[x], b[a[x]], c[b[a[x]]]}. ■ See page 247. ■ See also: NestList, FoldList.

■ ComposeSeries

`ComposeSeries[series`$_1$`, series`$_2$`, ... ]` composes several power series.

`ComposeSeries[series`$_1$`, series`$_2$`, ... ]` effectively replaces the variable in *series*$_1$ by *series*$_2$ and so on. ■ Two series can only meaningfully be composed when the point about which the first series is expanded corresponds to the limiting value of the second series at its expansion point. ■ See page 830. ■ See also: `InverseSeries`.

■ Composition

`Composition[f`$_1$`, f`$_2$`, f`$_3$`, ... ]` represents a composition of the functions $f_1, f_2, f_3, \dots$.

Composition allows you to build up compositions of functions which can later be applied to specific arguments. ■ Example: `Composition[a, b, c][x]` $\longrightarrow$ `a[b[c[x]]]`. ■ Composition objects containing `Identity` or `InverseFunction[f]` are automatically simplified when possible. ■ Composition has the attributes `Flat` and `OneIdentity`. ■ *a* @ *b* @ *c* gives *a*[*b*[*c*]]. ■ *a* // *b* // *c* gives *c*[*b*[*a*]]. ■ See page 250. ■ See also: `Nest`, `Function`.

■ CompoundExpression

expr$_1$; *expr*$_2$; ... evaluates the *expr*$_i$ in turn, giving the last one as the result.

`CompoundExpression` evaluates its arguments in a sequence corresponding to the control flow. ■ The returned value can be the result of `Return[expr]`. ■ The evaluation of the *expr*$_i$ can be affected by `Return`, `Throw` and `Goto`. ■ *expr*$_1$; *expr*$_2$; returns value `Null`. If it is given as input, the resulting output will not be printed. `Out[n]` will nevertheless be assigned to be the value of *expr*$_2$. ■ See pages 43 and 977. ■ See also: `Block`.

■ Condition

patt /; *test* is a pattern which matches only if the evaluation of *test* yields `True`.

lhs :> *rhs* /; *test* represents a rule which applies only if the evaluation of *test* yields `True`.

lhs := *rhs* /; *test* is a definition to be used only if *test* yields `True`.

Example: The pattern `x_` /; `x > 0` represents an expression which must be positive. ■ All pattern variables used in *test* must also appear in *patt*. ■ Example: `f[x_] := fp[x]` /; `x > 1` defines a function in the case when $x > 1$. ■ *lhs* := `Module[{`*vars*`}`, *rhs* /; *test*`]` allows local variables to be shared between *test* and *rhs*. You can use the same construction with `Block` and `With`. ■ See pages 262 and 325. ■ See also: `If`, `Switch`, `Which`, `PatternTest`.

■ Conjugate

`Conjugate[z]` gives the complex conjugate z^* of the complex number z.

Mathematical function (see Section A.3.10). ■ See page 719. ■ See also: `ComplexExpand`.

■ Constant

`Constant` is an attribute which indicates zero derivative of a symbol with respect to all parameters.

`Constant` is used by `Dt`. ■ Functions *f*[...] are taken to have zero total derivative if *f* has attribute `Constant`. ■ Mathematical constants such as `Pi` have attribute `Constant`. ■ See pages 309 and 805.

■ Constants

`Constants` is an option for `Dt` which gives a list of objects to be taken as constants.

If *f* appears in the list of `Constants`, then both `Dt[f]` and `Dt[f[ ... ]]` are taken to be zero. ■ See page 805. ■ See also: `D`.

■ **ConstrainedMax**

ConstrainedMax[*f*, {*inequalities*}, {*x*, *y*, ... }] finds the global maximum of *f* in the domain specified by the inequalities. The variables *x*, *y*, ... are all assumed to be non-negative.

ConstrainedMax returns a list of the form {*f*$_{max}$, {*x*->*x*$_{max}$, *y*->*y*$_{max}$, ... }}, where *f*$_{max}$ is the maximum value of *f* in the specified domain, and *x*$_{max}$, *y*$_{max}$, ... give the point at which the maximum is attained. ■ ConstrainedMax implements linear programming. It can always get a result so long as *f* and the inequalities you specify depend only linearly on the variables *x*, *y*, ... The inequalities can contain no parameters other than the explicit variables you specify. The inequalities cannot involve complex numbers. ■ ConstrainedMax returns unevaluated if the inequalities are inconsistent. ■ ConstrainedMax returns an infinite result if the value of *f* is unbounded in the domain specified by the inequalities. ■ ConstrainedMax yields exact rational number results if *f* and the inequalities are specified exactly. ■ ConstrainedMax accepts both strict inequalities of the form *lhs* < *rhs*, and non-strict ones of the form *lhs* <= *rhs*. It also accepts equalities of the form *lhs* == *rhs*. ■ When ConstrainedMax returns rational number results, it assumes that all inequalities are not strict. Thus, for example, ConstrainedMax may return x->1/2, even though strict inequalities allow only $\frac{1}{2} - \epsilon$. ■ ConstrainedMax finds approximate numerical results if its input contains approximate numbers. The option Tolerance specifies the tolerance to be used for internal comparisons. The default is Tolerance->Automatic, which does exact comparisons for exact numbers, and uses tolerance 10^{-6} for approximate numbers. ■ See page 896. ■ Implementation notes: see page 1020. ■ See also: LinearProgramming, FindMinimum. ■ Related package: Statistics`NonlinearFit`.

■ **ConstrainedMin**

ConstrainedMin[*f*, {*inequalities*}, {*x*, *y*, ... }] finds the global minimum of *f* in the domain specified by the inequalities. The variables *x*, *y*, ... are all assumed to be non-negative.

See notes for ConstrainedMax. ■ See page 896.

■ **Context**

Context[ ] gives the current context.

Context[*symbol*] gives the context in which a symbol appears.

The current context is the value of $Context. ■ See page 373. ■ See also: Begin, $ContextPath, Remove.

■ **Contexts**

Contexts[ ] gives a list of all contexts.

Contexts["*string*"] gives a list of the contexts which match the string.

The string can contain metacharacters such as * and @, as described on page 992. ■ See pages 373 and 382. ■ See also: $Packages, $ContextPath.

~■ **Continue**

Continue[ ] exits to the nearest enclosing Do, For or While in a procedural program.

+■ Continue[ ] takes effect as soon as it is evaluated, even if it appears inside other functions. ■ The function of Continue can also be achieved using Throw and Catch. ■ See page 333. ■ See also: Break, Goto.

■ ContourGraphics

ContourGraphics[*array*] is a representation of a contour plot.

array must be a rectangular array of real numbers, representing *z* values. ~■ The following options can be given:

AspectRatio	1	ratio of height to width
Axes	False	whether to draw axes
AxesLabel	None	axes labels
AxesOrigin	Automatic	where axes should cross
AxesStyle	{}	graphics directives to specify the style for axes
Background	Automatic	background color for the plot
ColorFunction	Automatic	function specifying the color of regions between contour lines
ColorOutput	Automatic	type of color output to produce
ContourLines	True	whether to draw explicit contour lines
Contours	10	what contours to use
ContourShading	True	whether to shade the regions between contours
ContourStyle	Automatic	the style for contour lines
DefaultColor	Automatic	the default color for plot elements
DisplayFunction	$DisplayFunction	function for generating output
Epilog	{}	graphics primitives to be rendered after the main plot
FormatType	$FormatType	the default format type for text
Frame	True	whether to put a frame around the plot
FrameLabel	None	frame labels
FrameStyle	Automatic	graphics directives giving the style for the frame
FrameTicks	Automatic	frame tick marks
ImageSize	Automatic	the absolute size at which to render the graphic in a notebook
MeshRange	Automatic	ranges of *x* and *y* coordinates
PlotLabel	None	a label for the plot
PlotRange	Automatic	range of *z* values to include
PlotRegion	Automatic	the final display region to be filled
Prolog	{}	graphics primitives to be rendered before the main plot
RotateLabel	True	whether to rotate *y* labels on the frame
TextStyle	$TextStyle	the default style for text
Ticks	Automatic	tick marks

■ ContourGraphics[*g*] converts DensityGraphics and SurfaceGraphics objects to ContourGraphics. The resulting graphics can be rendered using Show. ■ Graphics[ContourGraphics[...]] generates a representation in terms of an ordinary Graphics object. ■ ContourGraphics is generated by ContourPlot and ListContourPlot. ■ See page 497. ■ See also: ListContourPlot, DensityGraphics.

■ ContourLines

ContourLines is an option for contour plots which specifies whether to draw explicit contour lines.

ContourLines -> True draws contour lines. ContourLines -> False does not. ■ See page 498. ■ See also: ContourStyle, Contours.

■ ContourPlot

ContourPlot[*f*, {*x*, *xmin*, *xmax*}, {*y*, *ymin*, *ymax*}] generates a contour plot of *f* as a function of *x* and *y*.

ContourPlot evaluates its arguments in a non-standard way (see page 994). You should use Evaluate to evaluate the function to be plotted if this can safely be done before specific numerical values are supplied. ■ ContourPlot has the same options as ContourGraphics, with the following additions:

| Compiled | True | whether to compile the function to plot |
| PlotPoints | 15 | the number of points in each direction at which to sample the function |

■ ContourPlot has the default option setting Frame -> True. ■ ContourPlot returns a ContourGraphics object, with the MeshRange option set. ■ See page 145. ■ See also: DensityPlot. ■ Related packages: Graphics`ContourPlot3D`, Graphics`ImplicitPlot`, Graphics`PlotField`, Graphics`ComplexMap`.

■ Contours

Contours is an option for ContourGraphics specifying the contours to use.

Contours -> *n* chooses *n* equally spaced contours between the minimum and maximum *z* values. ■ Contours -> {z_1, z_2, ... } specifies the explicit *z* values of contours to use. ■ See pages 146 and 498.

■ ContourShading

ContourShading is an option for contour plots which specifies whether the regions between contour lines should be shaded.

With ContourShading -> False, regions between contour lines are left blank. ■ With ContourShading -> True, regions are colored based on the setting for the option ColorFunction. The default is to color the regions with gray levels running from black to white with increasing height. ■ The value given as the argument for the ColorFunction function is the average of the values of the contour lines bounding a particular region, scaled so that it lies between 0 and 1. ■ See page 499.

■ ContourStyle

ContourStyle is an option for contour plots that specifies the style in which contour lines should be drawn.

ContourStyle -> *style* specifies that all contour lines are to be generated with the specified graphics directive, or list of graphics directives. ■ ContourStyle -> {{$style_1$}, {$style_2$}, ... } specifies that successive contour lines should use graphics directives $style_1$, ... The styles must be enclosed in lists, perhaps of length one. ■ The $style_i$ are used cyclically. ■ Styles can be specified using graphics directives such as Dashing, Hue and Thickness. ■ See page 498. ■ See also: PlotStyle.

+■ ConversionRules

ConversionRules is an option for Cell which can be set to a list of rules specifying how the contents of the cell are to be converted to external formats.

Typical elements in the list have the form "TeX" -> *data*. ■ Settings for ConversionRules do not affect the display of cells in the standard *Mathematica* notebook front end. ■ ConversionRules can be used to save the original form of a cell that has been converted from an external format. ■ See page 581. ■ See also: CellTags.

+■ Copyable

Copyable is an option for **Cell** which specifies whether a cell can be copied interactively using the front end.

Even with the setting **Copyable->False**, the expression corresponding to a cell can still be read into the kernel using **NotebookRead**. ■ With **Copyable->False** set at the notebook level, no cells in the notebook can be copied interactively in the front end. ■ See page 582. ■ See also: **Selectable**, **ReadProtected**.

■ CopyDirectory

CopyDirectory["dir_1", "dir_2"] copies the directory dir_1 to dir_2.

dir_1 must already exist; dir_2 must not. ■ **CopyDirectory** copies all the files in dir_1 to dir_2. ■ **CopyDirectory** sets the modification dates for dir_2 and for all the files in it to be the same as those for dir_1. ■ **CopyDirectory** returns the full name of the directory it copies to, and **$Failed** if it cannot complete the copy. ■ See page 616. ■ See also: **RenameDirectory**, **CreateDirectory**, **DeleteDirectory**.

■ CopyFile

CopyFile["$file_1$", "$file_2$"] copies $file_1$ to $file_2$.

$file_1$ must already exist; $file_2$ must not. ■ **CopyFile** sets the modification date for $file_2$ to be the same as for $file_1$. ■ **CopyFile** returns the full name of the file it copies to, and **$Failed** if it cannot do the copy. ■ See page 616. ■ See also: **RenameFile**, **DeleteFile**, **CopyDirectory**.

■ Cos

Cos[z] gives the cosine of z.

Mathematical function (see Section A.3.10). ■ The argument of **Cos** is assumed to be in radians. (Multiply by **Degree** to convert from degrees.) ■ See page 731. ■ See also: **ArcCos**, **Sec**, **TrigToExp**, **TrigExpand**.

■ Cosh

Cosh[z] gives the hyperbolic cosine of z.

Mathematical function (see Section A.3.10). ■ $\cosh(z) = \frac{1}{2}(e^z + e^{-z})$. ■ See page 731. ■ See also: **ArcCosh**, **Sech**, **TrigToExp**, **TrigExpand**.

+■ CoshIntegral

CoshIntegral[z] gives the hyperbolic cosine integral Chi(z).

Mathematical function (see Section A.3.10). ■ $\text{Chi}(z) = \gamma + \log(z) + \int_0^z (\cosh(t) - 1)/t\,dt$, where γ is Euler's constant. ■ **CoshIntegral[z]** has a branch cut discontinuity in the complex z plane running from $-\infty$ to 0. ■ See page 744. ■ See also: **SinhIntegral**.

■ CosIntegral

CosIntegral[z] gives the cosine integral function Ci(z).

Mathematical function (see Section A.3.10). ■ $\text{Ci}(z) = -\int_z^\infty \cos(t)/t\,dt$. ■ **CosIntegral[z]** has a branch cut discontinuity in the complex z plane running from $-\infty$ to 0. ■ See page 744. ■ See also: **SinIntegral**, **ExpIntegralE**, **ExpIntegralEi**, **FresnelC**.

~■ Cot

Cot[z] gives the cotangent of z.

Mathematical function (see Section A.3.10). ■ The argument of Cot is assumed to be in radians. (Multiply by Degree to convert from degrees.) ■ cot(z) = 1/tan(z). +■ Cos[z]/Sin[z] is automatically converted to Cot[z]. TrigFactorList[*expr*] does decomposition. ■ See page 731. ■ See also: ArcCot, TrigToExp, TrigExpand.

~■ Coth

Coth[z] gives the hyperbolic cotangent of z.

Mathematical function (see Section A.3.10). +■ Cosh[z]/Sinh[z] is automatically converted to Coth[z]. TrigFactorList[*expr*] does decomposition. ■ See page 731. ■ See also: ArcCoth, TrigToExp, TrigExpand.

■ Count

Count[*list*, *pattern*] gives the number of elements in *list* that match *pattern*.

Count[*expr*, *pattern*, *levelspec*] gives the total number of subexpressions matching *pattern* that appear at the levels in *expr* specified by *levelspec*.

Level specifications are described on page 989. ■ See page 258. ■ See also: FreeQ, MemberQ, Cases, Select, Position. ■ Related package: Statistics`DataManipulation`.

■ CreateDirectory

CreateDirectory["*dir*"] creates a directory.

CreateDirectory creates a subdirectory of your current working directory. ■ The directory created by CreateDirectory is initially empty. ■ CreateDirectory returns the full name of the directory it creates, and $Failed if it cannot create the directory. ■ See page 616. ■ See also: DeleteDirectory, RenameDirectory, CopyDirectory.

+■ Cross

Cross[*a*, *b*] gives the vector cross product of *a* and *b*.

If *a* and *b* are lists of length 3, corresponding to vectors in three dimensions, then Cross[*a*, *b*] is also a list of length 3. ■ Cross[*a*, *b*] can be entered in StandardForm and InputForm as *a* × *b*, *a* :cross: *b* or *a* \[Cross] *b*. Note the difference between \[Cross] and \[Times]. ■ Cross is antisymmetric, so that Cross[*b*, *a*] is −Cross[*a*, *b*]. ■ In general, Cross[v_1, v_2, ... , v_{n-1}] is a totally antisymmetric product which takes vectors of length *n* and yields a vector of length *n* that is orthogonal to all of the v_i. ■ Cross[v_1, v_2, ...] gives the dual (Hodge star) of the wedge product of the v_i, viewed as one-forms in *n* dimensions. ■ See page 115. ■ See also: Dot, Signature, Outer.

~■ Csc

Csc[z] gives the cosecant of z.

Mathematical function (see Section A.3.10). ■ The argument of Csc is assumed to be in radians. (Multiply by Degree to convert from degrees.) ■ csc(z) = 1/sin(z). +■ 1/Sin[z] is automatically converted to Csc[z]. TrigFactorList[*expr*] does decomposition. ■ See page 731. ■ See also: ArcCsc, TrigToExp, TrigExpand.

~■ Csch

Csch[z] gives the hyperbolic cosecant of z.

Mathematical function (see Section A.3.10). ■ csch(z) = 1/sinh(z). ~■ 1/Sinh[z] is automatically converted to Csch[z]. TrigFactorList[*expr*] does decomposition. ■ See page 731. ■ See also: ArcCsch, TrigToExp, TrigExpand.

■ Cuboid

Cuboid[{*xmin*, *ymin*, *zmin*}] is a three-dimensional graphics primitive that represents a unit cuboid, oriented parallel to the axes.

Cuboid[{*xmin*, *ymin*, *zmin*}, {*xmax*, *ymax*, *zmax*}] specifies a cuboid by giving the coordinates of opposite corners.

Each face of the cuboid (rectangular parallelepiped) is effectively a Polygon object. ■ You can specify how the faces and edges of the cuboid should be rendered using the same graphics directives as for polygons. ■ The coordinates of the corners of the cuboid can be given using Scaled. ■ See page 500. ■ See also: Polygon, Rectangle. ■ Related package: Graphics'Polyhedra'.

■ Cyclotomic

Cyclotomic[*n*, *x*] gives the cyclotomic polynomial of order *n* in *x*.

The cyclotomic polynomial $C_n(x)$ of order *n* is defined to be $\prod_k (x - e^{2\pi i k/n})$, where the product runs over integers *k* less than *n* that are relatively prime to *n*. ■ See page 777. ■ See also: Factor, Roots.

~■ D

D[*f*, *x*] gives the partial derivative $\partial f/\partial x$.

D[*f*, {*x*, *n*}] gives the multiple derivative $\partial^n f/\partial x^n$.

D[*f*, x_1, x_2, ...] gives $\partial/\partial x_1 \, \partial/\partial x_2 \, ... \, f$.

+■ D[*f*, *x*] can be input as $\partial_x f$. The character ∂ is entered as ⋮pd⋮ or \[PartialD]. The variable *x* is entered as a subscript. ■ All quantities that do not explicitly depend on the x_i are taken to have zero partial derivative. ■ D[*f*, x_1, ... , NonConstants -> {v_1, ... }] specifies that the v_i implicitly depend on the x_i, so that they do not have zero partial derivative. ■ The derivatives of built-in mathematical functions are evaluated when possible in terms of other built-in mathematical functions. +■ Numerical approximations to derivatives can be found using N. ■ D uses the chain rule to simplify derivatives of unknown functions. +■ D[*f*, *x*, *y*] can be input as $\partial_{x,y} f$. The character \[InvisibleComma], entered as ⋮,⋮, can be used instead of an ordinary comma. It does not display, but is still interpreted just like a comma. ■ See page 804. ■ See also: Dt, Derivative. ■ Related package: Calculus'VectorAnalysis', NumericalMath'NLimit'.

■ Dashing

Dashing[{r_1, r_2, ... }] is a two-dimensional graphics directive which specifies that lines which follow are to be drawn dashed, with successive segments of lengths r_1, r_2, ... (repeated cyclically). The r_i is given as a fraction of the total width of the graph.

Dashing can be used in both two- and three-dimensional graphics. ■ Dashing[{ }] specifies that lines should be solid. ■ See page 481. ■ See also: AbsoluteDashing, Thickness, GrayLevel, Hue, RGBColor, PlotStyle.

■ Date

Date[ ] gives the current local date and time in the form
{*year*, *month*, *day*, *hour*, *minute*, *second*}.

Date[ ] uses whatever date and time have been set on your computer system. It performs no corrections for time zones, daylight saving time, etc. ■ Date[*z*] gives the date in time zone *z*. This is inferred by knowing your local date and time, and local time zone. The time zone is given as the number of hours to be added to Greenwich mean time to obtain local time. ■ All values returned by Date[ ] are integers, except the number of seconds. The number of seconds is never more accurate than $TimeUnit. ■ You can compare two lists returned by Date using Order. ■ See page 682. ■ See also: AbsoluteTime, TimeZone, SessionTime, TimeUsed, ToDate, FromDate, FileDate, $CreationDate. ■ Related package: Miscellaneous`Calendar`.

■ DeclarePackage

DeclarePackage["*context*`", {"*name*$_1$", "*name*$_2$", ... }] declares that Needs["*context*`"] should automatically be executed if a symbol with any of the specified names is ever used.

You can use DeclarePackage to tell *Mathematica* automatically to load a particular package when any of the symbols defined in it are used. ■ DeclarePackage creates symbols with the attribute Stub in the specified context. ■ DeclarePackage prepends *context*` to $ContextPath. ■ See page 380. ■ See also: Needs, $NewSymbol.

■ Decompose

Decompose[*poly*, *x*] decomposes a polynomial, if possible, into a composition of simpler polynomials.

Decompose gives a list of the polynomials P_i which can be composed as $P_1(P_2(...(x)...))$ to give the original polynomial. ■ The set of polynomials P_i is not necessarily unique. ■ Decomposition is an operation which is independent of polynomial factorization. ■ See page 777. ■ See also: FactorList, Solve.

■ Decrement

x-- decreases the value of *x* by 1, returning the old value of *x*.

Decrement has attribute HoldFirst. ■ See page 285. ■ See also: PreDecrement, SubtractFrom, Set.

⁺■ DedekindEta

DedekindEta[τ] gives the Dedekind eta modular elliptic function $\eta(\tau)$.

Mathematical function (see Section A.3.10). ■ DedekindEta is defined only in the upper half of the complex τ plane. It is not defined for real τ. ■ The argument τ is the ratio of Weierstrass half-periods ω'/ω. ■ DedekindEta satisfies $\Delta = (2\pi)^{12}\eta^{24}(\tau)$ where Δ is the discriminant, given in terms of Weierstrass invariants by $g_2^3 - 27g_3^2$. ■ See page 752 for a discussion of argument conventions for elliptic functions. ■ See page 757. ■ See also: ModularLambda, KleinInvariantJ, EllipticTheta, PartitionsP.

■ Depth

Depth[*expr*] gives the maximum number of indices needed to specify any part of *expr*, plus one.

Raw objects have depth 1. ■ The computation of Depth does not include heads of expressions. ■ See page 237. ■ See also: TensorRank, Level, LeafCount, Length, Nest.

~■ Derivative

f' represents the derivative of a function *f* of one argument.

Derivative[n_1, n_2, ...][*f*] is the general form, representing a function obtained from *f* by differentiating n_1 times with respect to the first argument, n_2 times with respect to the second argument, and so on.

f' is equivalent to Derivative[1][*f*]. ■ *f''* evaluates to Derivative[2][*f*]. ■ You can think of Derivative as a *functional operator* which acts on functions to give derivative functions. ■ Derivative is generated when you apply D to functions whose derivatives *Mathematica* does not know. ■ *Mathematica* attempts to convert Derivative[*n*][*f*] and so on to pure functions. Whenever Derivative[*n*][*f*] is generated, *Mathematica* rewrites it as D[*f*[#]&, {#, *n*}]. If *Mathematica* finds an explicit value for this derivative, it returns this value. Otherwise, it returns the original Derivative form. ■ Example: Cos' ⟶ -Sin[#1]&. +■ Derivative[{n_1, n_2, ... }][*f*] represents the derivative of *f*[{x_1, x_2, ... }] taken n_i times with respect to x_i. In general, arguments given in lists in *f* can be handled by using a corresponding list structure in Derivative. +■ N[*f'*[*x*]] will give a numerical approximation to a derivative. ■ See page 807. ■ See also: D, Dt.

■ Det

Det[*m*] gives the determinant of the square matrix *m*.

Det[*m*, Modulus->*n*] computes the determinant modulo *n*. ■ See page 844. ■ Implementation notes: see page 1020. ■ See also: Minors, RowReduce, NullSpace, Signature.

■ DiagonalMatrix

DiagonalMatrix[*list*] gives a matrix with the elements of *list* on the leading diagonal, and 0 elsewhere.

See page 837. ■ See also: IdentityMatrix. ■ Related package: LinearAlgebra`MatrixManipulation`.

■ Dialog

Dialog[ ] initiates a dialog.

Dialog[*expr*] initiates a dialog with *expr* as the current value of %.

Dialog creates a dialog which consists of a sequence of input and output lines. ■ You can exit a dialog using Return. ■ With the global setting $IgnoreEOF = False, you can also exit a dialog by entering an end-of-file character. ■ If you exit with Return[*expr*], then *expr* is the value returned by the Dialog function. Otherwise, the value returned is the expression on the last output line in the dialog. ■ Dialog automatically localizes the values of $Line, $MessageList and $Epilog. ■ Dialog initially sets the local value of $Line to be equal to its global value. This means that the numbering of input and output lines in the dialog follows the sequence outside the dialog. When the dialog is exited, however, the numbering reverts to the sequence that would be followed if there had been no dialog. ■ Any local value assigned to $Epilog is evaluated when the dialog is exited. ■ The main loop within a dialog uses global variables such as $Pre and $Post. ■ The option DialogSymbols :> {*x*, *y*, ... } sets up local values for variables within the dialog. DialogSymbols :> {*x* = x_0, ... } defines initial values for the variables. ■ The option DialogProlog :> *expr* specifies an expression to evaluate before starting the dialog. ■ Dialog first localizes variables, then evaluates any expression specified by DialogProlog, then evaluates any argument you have given for Dialog. ■ See page 680. ■ See also: TraceDialog, Input, $Inspector, ButtonBox.

■ DialogProlog

DialogProlog is an option for Dialog which can give an expression to evaluate before the dialog starts.

You must use a delayed rule of the form DialogProlog :> *expr* to prevent *expr* from evaluating prematurely.
■ Expressions given by DialogProlog are evaluated after symbol values are localized, and before any expression given as the argument of Dialog is evaluated. ■ See page 681. ■ See also: $Epilog.

■ DialogSymbols

DialogSymbols is an option for Dialog which gives a list of symbols whose values should be localized in the dialog.

DialogSymbols :> {x, y, ... } specifies that x, y, ... should have local values for the duration of the dialog.
■ DialogSymbols :> {$x = x_0$, ... } defines initial values for variables. ■ In addition to any symbols you specify, Dialog always uses local values for $Epilog, $Line and $MessageList. ■ The DialogSymbols option sets up local values in a dialog in the same way that a Block enclosing the dialog would. ■ See page 681.

■ DigitBlock

DigitBlock is an option for NumberForm and related functions which specifies the maximum length of blocks of digits between breaks.

The default setting is DigitBlock -> Infinity, which specifies that no breaks should be inserted.
■ DigitBlock -> n inserts a break every n digits. ■ DigitBlock -> {*nleft*, *nright*} inserts a break every *nleft* digits to the left of the decimal point, and every *nright* digits to the right of the decimal point. ■ The setting for NumberSeparator determines what string should be used at each break. ■ See page 415.

■ DigitQ

DigitQ[*string*] yields True if all the characters in the string are digits in the range 0 through 9, and yields False otherwise.

See page 392. ■ See also: LetterQ, Number.

■ Dimensions

Dimensions[*expr*] gives a list of the dimensions of *expr*.

Dimensions[*expr*, n] gives a list of the dimensions of *expr* down to level n.

expr must be a *full array*, with all the pieces of *expr* at a particular level having the same length. (The elements of *expr* can then be thought of as filling up a hyper-rectangular region.) ■ Each successive level in *expr* sampled by Dimensions must have the same head. ■ Example: Dimensions[{{a,b,c},{d,e,f}}] $\longrightarrow$ {2, 3}. ■ See page 839.
■ See also: TensorRank, VectorQ, MatrixQ.

■ DirectedInfinity

DirectedInfinity[ ] represents an infinite numerical quantity whose direction in the complex plane is unknown.

DirectedInfinity[z] represents an infinite numerical quantity that is a positive real multiple of the complex number z.

You can think of DirectedInfinity[z] as representing a point in the complex plane reached by starting at the origin and going an infinite distance in the direction of the point z. ■ The following conversions are made:

Infinity	DirectedInfinity[1]
-Infinity	DirectedInfinity[-1]
ComplexInfinity	DirectedInfinity[ ]

■ Certain arithmetic operations are performed on DirectedInfinity quantities. ■ In OutputForm, DirectedInfinity[z] is printed in terms of Infinity, and DirectedInfinity[ ] is printed as ComplexInfinity. ■ See page 716. ■ See also: Indeterminate.

■ Directory

Directory[ ] gives the current working directory.

Directory returns the full name of the directory as a string. ■ See page 611. ■ See also: $Path, SetDirectory, ResetDirectory, ParentDirectory, $HomeDirectory, DirectoryName, FileNames.

+■ DirectoryName

DirectoryName["*name*"] extracts the directory name from the specification for a file.

DirectoryName works differently on different computer systems. ■ DirectoryName["*directory*"] is equivalent to ParentDirectory["*directory*"]. ■ DirectoryName["*name*", *n*] applies DirectoryName *n* times to *name*. ■ DirectoryName yields output appropriate for use in SetDirectory and ToFileName. ■ If *name* contains no directory specification, DirectoryName["*name*"] returns "". ■ See page 614. ■ See also: $Input, Directory.

■ DirectoryStack

DirectoryStack[ ] gives the directory stack which represents the sequence of current directories used.

DirectoryStack[ ] returns a list of full names of directories. ■ Each call to SetDirectory prepends one element to the directory stack; each call to ResetDirectory drops one. ■ See page 611.

■ Disk

Disk[{x, y}, r] is a two-dimensional graphics primitive that represents a filled disk of radius r centered at the point x, y.

Disk[{x, y}, {r_x, r_y}] yields an elliptical disk with semi-axes r_x and r_y.

Disk[{x, y}, r, {θ_1, θ_2}] represents a segment of a disk.

Angles are measured in radians counterclockwise from the positive x direction. ■ Disk[{x, y}, {r_x, r_y}, {θ_1, θ_2}] yields an elliptical disk segment obtained by transforming a circular disk segment with the specified starting and ending angles. ~■ Scaled and Offset can be used in the radius specification (see notes for Circle). ■ See page 476. ■ See also: Circle, Polygon.

■ Dispatch

Dispatch[{lhs_1->rhs_1, lhs_2->rhs_2, ... }] generates an optimized dispatch table representation of a list of rules. The object produced by Dispatch can be used to give the rules in *expr* /. *rules*.

The use of Dispatch will never affect results that are obtained, but may make the application of long lists of rules much faster. ■ Lists of rules are usually scanned sequentially when you evaluate an expression like *expr* /. *rules*. Rules such as a[1]->a1 and a[2]->a2, which cannot simultaneously apply, need not both be scanned explicitly. Dispatch generates a dispatch table which uses hash codes to specify which sets of rules need actually be scanned for a particular input expression. ■ Lists of rules produced by assignments made with = and := are automatically optimized with dispatch tables when appropriate. ■ See page 283. ■ See also: ReplaceAll, Compile.

~■ Display

~ Display[*channel*, *graphics*] writes graphics or sound to the specified output channel in *Mathematica* PostScript format.

+ Display[*channel*, *graphics*, "*format*"] writes graphics or sound in the specified format.

+ Display[*channel*, *expr*, "*format*"] writes boxes, cells or notebook expressions in the specified format.

The output channel can be a single file or pipe, or a list of them. ■ The *graphics* in Display can be Graphics, Graphics3D, SurfaceGraphics, ContourGraphics, DensityGraphics or GraphicsArray. ■ The *graphics* can also include Sound. +■ The *expr* in Display can be Cell, Notebook or any boxes, as generated by ToBoxes[*expr*]. +■ The following formats can be used:

"EPS"	Encapsulated PostScript
"GIF"	GIF
"Illustrator"	Adobe Illustrator format
"Metafile"	Microsoft Windows metafile
"MGF"	*Mathematica* system-independent raster graphics format
"MPS" (default)	*Mathematica* abbreviated PostScript
"PCL"	Hewlett-Packard printer control language
"PDF"	Adobe Acrobat portable document format
"PICT"	Macintosh PICT
"PBM"	portable bitmap
"PSImage"	PostScript image format
"TIFF"	TIFF
"XBitmap"	X Windows bitmap

+■ The following options can be given:

CharacterEncoding	Automatic	the encoding to use for characters in text
ImageOffset	{0, 0}	offset of the image in the viewing area
ImageResolution	Automatic	resolution in dpi for the image
ImageRotated	False	whether to rotate the image to landscape mode
ImageSize	Automatic	absolute image size in printer's points

■ $DisplayFunction is usually given in terms of Display. ■ If any of the specified files or pipes in *channel* are not open, Display uses OpenWrite to open them, then closes these particular files or pipes when it has finished. ■ In many cases, Display calls the *Mathematica* notebook front end via *MathLink*. If the front end is not present, certain capabilities of Display may not be available. ■ When displaying text, Display may make use of fonts that are specifically installed for *Mathematica*. ■ See pages 208 and 533. ■ See also: Write, Show, DisplayString, HTMLSave.

⁺■ DisplayForm

DisplayForm[*expr*] prints with boxes inside *expr* shown in explicit two-dimensional or other form.

In ordinary StandardForm output, boxes such as SubscriptBox are shown literally. In DisplayForm they are shown as explicit two-dimensional constructs. ▪ Example: DisplayForm[SubscriptBox["x", "y"]] ⟶ x$_y$. ▪ DisplayForm acts as a "wrapper", which affects printing, but not evaluation. ▪ See page 424. ▪ See also: FullForm, ToExpression, ToBoxes.

■ DisplayFunction

DisplayFunction is an option for graphics and sound functions that specifies the function to apply to graphics and sound objects in order to display them.

The default setting for DisplayFunction in graphics functions is $DisplayFunction, and in sound functions is $SoundDisplayFunction. ▪ A typical setting is DisplayFunction->Display[*channel*, #]&. ▪ Setting DisplayFunction->Identity will cause the objects to be returned, but no display to be generated. ▪ See pages 133 and 533. ▪ See also: Show.

⁺■ DisplayString

DisplayString[*graphics*] generates a string giving graphics or sound in *Mathematica* PostScript format.

DisplayString[*graphics*, "*format*"] generates a string giving graphics or sound in the specified format.

DisplayString[*expr*, "*format*"] generates a string giving boxes, cells or notebook expressions in the specified format.

The options and *format* settings for DisplayString are the same as for Display. ▪ See page 533. ▪ See also: StringToStream.

■ Distribute

Distribute[*f*[x_1, x_2, ...]] distributes *f* over Plus appearing in any of the x_i.

Distribute[*expr*, *g*] distributes over *g*.

Distribute[*expr*, *g*, *f*] performs the distribution only if the head of *expr* is *f*.

Distribute effectively implements the distributive law for operators *f* and *g*. ▪ Distribute explicitly constructs the complete result of a distribution; Expand, on the other hand, builds up results iteratively, simplifying at each stage. ▪ Example: Distribute[f[a+b,c+d]] ⟶ f[a, c] + f[a, d] + f[b, c] + f[b, d]. ▪ Distribute[f[a+b,g[x,y],c], g] ⟶ g[f[a + b, x, c], f[a + b, y, c]]. ▪ Distribute[*expr*, *g*, *f*, *gp*, *fp*] gives *gp* and *fp* in place of *g* and *f* respectively in the result of the distribution. ▪ See page 253. ▪ See also: Expand, Thread, Outer, Inner.

~■ Divide

x/*y* or Divide[*x*, *y*] is equivalent to *x* *y*^-1.

x/*y* is converted to *x* *y*^-1 on input. ⁺▪ Divide[*x*, *y*] can be entered in StandardForm and InputForm as *x* ÷ *y*, *x* :div: *y* or *x* \[Divide] *y*. ▪ See page 29.

■ DivideBy

x /= c divides x by c and returns the new value of x.

DivideBy has the attribute HoldFirst. ■ x /= c is equivalent to $x = x/c$. ■ See page 285. ■ See also: TimesBy, SubtractFrom, Set.

■ Divisors

Divisors[n] gives a list of the integers that divide n.

Example: Divisors[12] $\longrightarrow$ {1, 2, 3, 4, 6, 12}. ■ Divisors[n, GaussianIntegers -> True] includes divisors that are Gaussian integers. ■ See page 723. ■ See also: FactorInteger, EulerPhi.

■ DivisorSigma

DivisorSigma[k, n] gives the divisor function $\sigma_k(n)$.

Integer mathematical function (see Section A.3.10). ■ $\sigma_k(n)$ is the sum of the kth powers of the divisors of n. ■ DivisorSigma[k, n, GaussianIntegers -> True] includes divisors that are Gaussian integers. ■ See page 725. ■ See also: EulerPhi.

■ Do

Do[$expr$, {$imax$}] evaluates *expr imax* times.

Do[$expr$, {i, $imax$}] evaluates *expr* with the variable i successively taking on the values 1 through *imax* (in steps of 1).

Do[$expr$, {i, $imin$, $imax$}] starts with $i = imin$. Do[$expr$, {i, $imin$, $imax$, di}] uses steps *di*.

Do[$expr$, {i, $imin$, $imax$}, {j, $jmin$, $jmax$}, ...] evaluates *expr* looping over different values of j, etc. for each i.

Do uses the standard *Mathematica* iteration specification. ■ Do evaluates its arguments in a non-standard way (see page 994). ■ You can use Return, Break, Continue and Throw inside Do. ■ Unless an explicit Return is used, the value returned by Do is Null. ■ See page 328. ■ See also: For, While, Table, Nest, Fold.

■ Dot

$a.b.c$ or Dot[a, b, c] gives products of vectors, matrices and tensors.

$a.b$ gives an explicit result when a and b are lists with appropriate dimensions. It contracts the last index in a with the first index in b. ■ Various applications of Dot:

{a_1, a_2} . {b_1, b_2}	scalar product of vectors
{a_1, a_2} . {{m_{11}, m_{12}}, {m_{21}, m_{22}}}	product of a vector and a matrix
{{m_{11}, m_{12}}, {m_{21}, m_{22}}} . {a_1, a_2}	product of a matrix and a vector
{{m_{11}, m_{12}}, {m_{21}, m_{22}}} . {{n_{11}, n_{12}}, {n_{21}, n_{22}}}	product of two matrices

■ Examples: {a, b} . {c, d} $\longrightarrow$ a c + b d. ■ {{a, b}, {c, d}} . {x, y} $\longrightarrow$ {a x + b y, c x + d y}. ■ The result of applying Dot to two tensors $T_{i_1 i_2 \ldots i n}$ and $U_{j_1 j_2 \ldots j m}$ is the tensor $\sum_k T_{i_1 i_2 \ldots i_{n-1} k} U_{k j_2 \ldots j m}$. Applying Dot to a rank n tensor and a rank m tensor gives a rank $n + m - 2$ tensor. ■ When its arguments are not lists, Dot remains unevaluated. It has the attribute Flat. ■ See pages 114 and 841. ■ See also: Inner, Cross, Outer, NonCommutativeMultiply. ■ Related package: Calculus`VectorAnalysis`.

~■ DownValues

DownValues[*f*] gives a list of transformation rules corresponding to all downvalues defined for the symbol *f*.

You can specify the downvalues for *f* by making an assignment of the form DownValues[*f*] = *list*. ~■ The list returned by DownValues has elements of the form HoldPattern[*lhs*] :> *rhs*. ■ See page 303. ■ See also: Set, UpValues.

+■ DragAndDrop

DragAndDrop is an option for Cell which specifies whether to allow drag-and-drop editing on the contents of the cell.

With DragAndDrop->True, dragging an already-selected region cuts the region from its original location, and pastes it at the location you move to. ■ DragAndDrop is more often set as a global option in the front end, rather than as an option for individual cells. ■ See page 589. ■ See also: StructuredSelection.

■ Drop

Drop[*list*, *n*] gives *list* with its first *n* elements dropped.

Drop[*list*, −*n*] gives *list* with its last *n* elements dropped.

Drop[*list*, {*n*}] gives *list* with its nth element dropped.

Drop[*list*, {*m*, *n*}] gives *list* with elements *m* through *n* dropped.

Drop uses the standard *sequence specification* (see page 988). ■ Example: Drop[{a,b,c,d,e}, 2] ⟶ {c, d, e}. ■ Drop[{a,b,c,d,e}, -3] ⟶ {a, b}. ■ Drop can be used on an object with any head, not necessarily List. ■ See page 118. ■ See also: Rest, StringDrop, Take, Cases. ■ Related package: LinearAlgebra`MatrixManipulation`.

~■ DSolve

DSolve[*eqn*, *y*, *x*] solves a differential equation for the function *y*, with independent variable *x*.

DSolve[{*eqn*₁, *eqn*₂, ... }, {*y*₁, *y*₂, ... }, *x*] solves a list of differential equations.

+ DSolve[*eqn*, *y*, {*x*₁, *x*₂, ... }] solves a partial differential equation.

DSolve[*eqn*, *y*[*x*], *x*] gives solutions for *y*[*x*] rather than for the function *y* itself. ■ Example: DSolve[y'[x] == 2 a x, y[x], x] ⟶ {{y[x] → a x² + C[1]}}. ■ Differential equations must be stated in terms of derivatives such as y'[x], obtained with D, not total derivatives obtained with Dt. ■ DSolve generates constants of integration indexed by successive integers. The option DSolveConstants specifies the function to apply to each index. The default is DSolveConstants->C, which yields constants of integration C[1], C[2], ... ■ DSolveConstants->(Module[{C}, C]&) guarantees that the constants of integration are unique, even across different invocations of DSolve. +■ For partial differential equations, DSolve generates arbitrary functions C[*n*][...]. ■ Boundary conditions can be specified by giving equations such as y'[0] == b. +■ Solutions given by DSolve sometimes include integrals that cannot be carried out explicitly by Integrate. Dummy variables with local names are used in such integrals. +■ DSolve sometimes gives implicit solutions in terms of Solve. +■ DSolve can solve linear ordinary differential equations of any order with constant coefficients. It can solve also many linear equations up to second order with non-constant coefficients. +■ DSolve includes general procedures that handle a large fraction of the nonlinear ordinary differential equations whose solutions are given in standard reference books such as Kamke. +■ DSolve can find general solutions for linear and weakly nonlinear partial differential equations. Truly nonlinear partial differential equations usually admit no general solutions. ■ See page 820. ■ Implementation notes: see page 1021. ■ See also: NDSolve, Solve. ■ Related package: Calculus`VariationalMethods`, Calculus`VectorAnalysis`.

■ Dt

Dt[f, x] gives the total derivative df/dx.

Dt[f] gives the total differential df.

Dt[f, {x, n}] gives the multiple derivative $d^n f/dx^n$.

Dt[f, x_1, x_2, ...] gives d/dx_1 d/dx_2 ... f.

Dt[f, x_1, ... , Constants -> {c_1, ... }] specifies that the c_i are constants, which have zero total derivative. ■ Symbols with attribute Constant are taken to be constants, with zero total derivative. ■ If an object is specified to be a constant, then all functions with that object as a head are also taken to be constants. ■ All quantities not explicitly specified as constants are assumed to depend on the x_i. ■ Example: Dt[x y] $\longrightarrow$ y Dt[x] + x Dt[y]. ■ Dt[x y, Constants -> {x}] $\longrightarrow$ x Dt[y, Constants $\rightarrow$ {x}]. ■ You can specify total derivatives by assigning values to Dt[f], etc. ■ See page 805. ■ See also: D, Derivative.

+■ DumpSave

DumpSave["*file*.mx", *symbol*] writes definitions associated with a symbol to a file in internal *Mathematica* format.

DumpSave["*file*.mx", "*context*`"] writes out definitions associated with all symbols in the specified context.

DumpSave["*file*.mx", {*object*$_1$, *object*$_2$, ... }] writes out definitions for several symbols or contexts.

DumpSave["*package*`", *objects*] chooses the name of the output file based on the computer system used.

DumpSave["*file*"] saves all definitions in the current session.

DumpSave writes out definitions in a binary format that is optimized for input by *Mathematica*. ■ Each file has a plain text header identifying its type and contents. ■ Files written by DumpSave can be read by Get. ■ Files written by DumpSave can only be read on the same type of computer system on which they were written. ■ DumpSave will not preserve open stream and link objects. ■ Files written by DumpSave conventionally have names that end with .mx. ■ DumpSave["*package*`", ...] writes a file with a name such as *package*.mx/$SystemID/*package*.mx. ■ You can use DumpSave["*file*", "*s*"] to write out the definition for the value of a symbol *s* itself. ■ DumpSave["*file*"] will save the definitions for all symbols in the current session. ■ You can typically read a dump file when you start *Mathematica* by using the initfile command-line option. ■ See page 602. ■ See also: Save, LinkWrite.

~■ E

E is the exponential constant e (base of natural logarithms), with numerical value $\simeq 2.71828$.

Mathematical constant (see Section A.3.11). +■ E can be entered in StandardForm and InputForm as $\mathbb{e}$, :ee: or \[ExponentialE]. ■ See page 735. ■ Implementation notes: see page 1019. ■ See also: Exp.

■ EdgeForm

EdgeForm[g] is a three-dimensional graphics directive which specifies that edges of polygons are to be drawn using the graphics directive or list of graphics directives g.

EdgeForm[ ] draws no edges of polygons. ■ The directives RGBColor, CMYKColor, GrayLevel, Hue and Thickness can be used in EdgeForm. ■ EdgeForm does not affect the rendering of Line objects. ■ No lines are ever drawn when an edge is formed by one polygon intersecting another. ■ See page 507. ■ See also: FaceForm, Line.

⁺■ **Editable**

> Editable is an option for boxes, cells and notebooks which specifies whether their contents can be edited interactively using the front end.
>
> Even with the setting Editable->False, the contents of an object can still be copied as a whole. ■ Editable is an option for InterpretationBox and TagBox, as well as for StyleBox. ■ Setting Editable->False effectively allows you to "write protect" elements of notebooks. ■ See pages 427 and 582. ■ See also: CellEditDuplicate, Selectable, Copyable, AutoDelete, Protected.

˜■ **Eigensystem**

> Eigensystem[*m*] gives a list {*values, vectors*} of the eigenvalues and eigenvectors of the square matrix *m*.
>
> Eigensystem finds numerical eigenvalues and eigenvectors if *m* contains approximate real numbers. ■ The elements of *m* can be complex. ■ All the non-zero eigenvectors given are independent. If the number of eigenvectors is equal to the number of non-zero eigenvalues, then corresponding eigenvalues and eigenvectors are given in corresponding positions in their respective lists. ■ If there are more eigenvalues than independent eigenvectors, then each extra eigenvalue is paired with a vector of zeros. ⁺■ Eigensystem[*m*, ZeroTest -> *test*] applies *test* to determine whether expressions should be assumed to be zero. The default setting is ZeroTest -> Automatic. ■ The eigenvalues and eigenvectors satisfy the matrix equation
> m.Transpose[*vectors*] == Transpose[*vectors*].DiagonalMatrix[*values*]. ■ See page 850. ■ See also: NullSpace, JordanDecomposition, SchurDecomposition, QRDecomposition. ■ Related packages: LinearAlgebra`Orthogonalization`, LinearAlgebra`Cholesky.

■ **Eigenvalues**

> Eigenvalues[*m*] gives a list of the eigenvalues of the square matrix *m*.
>
> Eigenvalues finds numerical eigenvalues if *m* contains approximate real numbers. ■ Repeated eigenvalues appear with their appropriate multiplicity. ■ An $n \times n$ matrix gives a list of exactly n eigenvalues, not necessarily distinct. ■ See page 850. ■ See also: Det.

˜■ **Eigenvectors**

> Eigenvectors[*m*] gives a list of the eigenvectors of the square matrix *m*.
>
> Eigenvectors finds numerical eigenvectors if *m* contains approximate real numbers. ■ Eigenvectors corresponding to degenerate eigenvalues are chosen to be linearly independent. ■ Eigenvectors are not normalized. ■ For an $n \times n$ matrix, Eigenvectors always returns a list of length n. The list contains each of the independent eigenvectors of the matrix, followed if necessary by an appropriate number of vectors of zeros.
> ⁺■ Eigenvectors[*m*, ZeroTest -> *test*] applies *test* to determine whether expressions should be assumed to be zero. The default setting is ZeroTest -> Automatic. ■ See page 850. ■ See also: NullSpace. ■ Related package: LinearAlgebra`Orthogonalization`.

■ **Eliminate**

> Eliminate[*eqns, vars*] eliminates variables between a set of simultaneous equations.
>
> Equations are given in the form *lhs* == *rhs*. ■ Simultaneous equations can be combined either in a list or with &&. ■ A single variable or a list of variables can be specified. ■ Example:
> Eliminate[{x == 2 + y, y == z}, y] ⟶ -2 + x - z == 0. ■ Variables can be any expressions. ■ Eliminate works primarily with linear and polynomial equations. ■ See page 798. ■ See also: Reduce, SolveAlways, Solve, GroebnerBasis.

■ EllipticE

EllipticE[m] gives the complete elliptic integral $E(m)$.

~ EllipticE[ϕ, m] gives the elliptic integral of the second kind $E(\phi|m)$.

Mathematical function (see Section A.3.10). ▪ For $-\pi/2 < \phi < \pi/2$, $E(\phi|m) = \int_0^\phi (1 - m\sin^2(\theta))^{1/2}\,d\theta$. ▪ $E(m) = E(\frac{\pi}{2}|m)$. ▪ See page 752 for a discussion of argument conventions for elliptic integrals. ▪ EllipticE[m] has a branch cut discontinuity in the complex m plane running from 1 to ∞. ▪ EllipticE[ϕ, m] has a branch cut discontinuity running along the ray from $\csc^2(\phi)$ to infinity. ▪ See page 753. ▪ See also: JacobiZeta, JacobiAmplitude.

■ EllipticExp

EllipticExp[u, {a, b}] is the inverse for EllipticLog. It produces a list {x, y} such that u == EllipticLog[{x, y}, {a, b}].

EllipticExp gives the generalized exponential associated with the elliptic curve $y^2 = x^3 + ax^2 + bx$. ▪ EllipticExp is the basis for computing Weierstrass functions in *Mathematica*. ▪ See page 758.

■ EllipticF

~ EllipticF[ϕ, m] gives the elliptic integral of the first kind $F(\phi|m)$.

Mathematical function (see Section A.3.10). ▪ For $-\pi/2 < \phi < \pi/2$, $F(\phi|m) = \int_0^\phi (1 - m\sin^2(\theta))^{-1/2}\,d\theta$. ▪ The complete elliptic integral associated with EllipticF is EllipticK. ▪ EllipticF is the inverse of JacobiAmplitude. If $\phi = \text{am}(u|m)$ then $u = F(\phi|m)$. ▪ EllipticF[ϕ, m] has a branch cut discontinuity running along the ray from $\csc^2(\phi)$ to infinity. ▪ See page 752 for a discussion of argument conventions for elliptic integrals. ▪ See page 753. ▪ See also: JacobiZeta, JacobiAmplitude.

■ EllipticK

EllipticK[m] gives the complete elliptic integral of the first kind $K(m)$.

Mathematical function (see Section A.3.10). ▪ EllipticK is given in terms of the incomplete elliptic integral of the first kind by $K(m) = F(\frac{\pi}{2}|m)$. ▪ See page 752 for a discussion of argument conventions for elliptic integrals. ▪ EllipticK[m] has a branch cut discontinuity in the complex m plane running from 1 to ∞. ▪ See page 753. ▪ See also: JacobiZeta, EllipticNomeQ.

■ EllipticLog

EllipticLog[{x, y}, {a, b}] gives the generalized logarithm associated with the elliptic curve $y^2 = x^3 + ax^2 + bx$.

EllipticLog[{x, y}, {a, b}] is defined as the value of the integral $\frac{1}{2}\int_\infty^x (t^3 + at^2 + bt)^{-1/2}\,dt$, where the sign of the square root is specified by giving the value of y such that $y = \sqrt{x^3 + ax^2 + bx}$. ▪ See page 758. ▪ See also: EllipticExp.

+ ■ EllipticNomeQ

EllipticNomeQ[m] gives the nome q corresponding to the parameter m in an elliptic function.

Mathematical function (see Section A.3.10). ▪ EllipticNomeQ is related to EllipticK by $q(m) = \exp[-\pi K(1-m)/K(m)]$. ▪ EllipticNomeQ[$m$] has a branch cut discontinuity in the complex m plane running from 1 to ∞. ▪ See page 752. ▪ See also: InverseEllipticNomeQ.

■ **EllipticPi**

EllipticPi[*n*, *m*] gives the complete elliptic integral of the third kind $\Pi(n|m)$.

EllipticPi[*n*, ϕ, *m*] gives the incomplete elliptic integral $\Pi(n;\phi|m)$.

Mathematical function (see Section A.3.10). ■ $\Pi(n;\phi|m) = \int_0^{\phi}(1 - n\sin^2(\theta))^{-1}[1 - m\sin^2(\theta)]^{-1/2}\,d\theta$. ■ $\Pi(n|m) = \Pi(n; \frac{\pi}{2}|m)$. ■ See page 752 for a discussion of argument conventions for elliptic integrals. ■ See page 753.

■ **EllipticTheta**

EllipticTheta[*a*, *u*, *q*] gives the theta function $\vartheta_a(u,q)$ $(a = 1, ..., 4)$.

Mathematical function (see Section A.3.10). ■ $\vartheta_1(u,q) = 2q^{1/4}\sum_{n=0}^{\infty}(-1)^n q^{n(n+1)}\sin((2n + 1)u)$, $\vartheta_2(u,q) = 2q^{1/4}\sum_{n=0}^{\infty}q^{n(n+1)}\cos((2n + 1)u)$, $\vartheta_3(u,q) = 1 + 2\sum_{n=1}^{\infty}q^{n^2}\cos(2nu)$, $\vartheta_4(u,q) = 1 + 2\sum_{n=1}^{\infty}(-1)^n q^{n^2}\cos(2nu)$. ■ See page 752 for a discussion of argument conventions for elliptic and related functions. ■ See page 755. ■ See also: ModularLambda, DedekindEta, KleinInvariantJ.

⁺■ **EllipticThetaPrime**

EllipticThetaPrime[*a*, *u*, *q*] gives the derivative with respect to *u* of the theta function $\vartheta_a(u,q)$ $(a = 1, ..., 4)$.

See notes for EllipticTheta. ■ See page 755.

■ **Encode**

Encode["*source*", "*dest*"] writes an encoded version of the file *source* to the file *dest*.

<<*dest* decodes the file before reading its contents.

Encode["*source*", "*dest*", "*key*"] produces an encoded file which must be read in using Get["*dest*", "*key*"].

Encoded files contain only printable ASCII characters. They begin with a special sequence which is recognized by Get. ■ On certain computer systems Encode["*source*", "*dest*", MachineID->"*ID*"] can be used to generate an encoded file which can be read in only on a computer with a particular $MachineID. ■ No function is provided in *Mathematica* to convert encoded files back to their original form. ■ See page 601. ■ See also: ReadProtected, $MachineID.

■ **End**

End[ ] returns the present context, and reverts to the previous one.

Every call to End must be balanced by an earlier call to Begin. ■ End[ ] resets the value of $Context. ■ End[ ] returns the present context name as a string of the form "*context*`". ■ End[ ] does not modify $ContextPath. ■ See page 377.

■ **EndOfFile**

EndOfFile is a symbol returned by Read when it reaches the end of a file.

Subsequent calls to Read will also give EndOfFile. ■ See page 621.

■ EndPackage

EndPackage[ ] restores **$Context** and **$ContextPath** to their values before the preceding **BeginPackage**, and prepends the current context to the list **$ContextPath**.

Every call to **EndPackage** must be balanced by an earlier call to **BeginPackage**. ■ **EndPackage** is typically used at the end of a *Mathematica* package. ■ **EndPackage** returns **Null**. ■ **EndPackage** resets the values of both **$Context** and **$ContextPath**. ■ See page 377.

■ EngineeringForm

EngineeringForm[*expr*] prints with all real numbers in *expr* given in engineering notation.

In "engineering notation" the exponent is always arranged to be a multiple of 3. ■ **EngineeringForm** takes the same options as **NumberForm**, but uses a different default function for **ExponentFunction**. ■ You can mix **EngineeringForm** and **BaseForm**. ■ **EngineeringForm** acts as a "wrapper", which affects printing, but not evaluation. ■ See page 414. ■ See also: **EngineeringForm**, **NumberForm**.

■ Environment

Environment["*var*"] gives the value of an operating system environment variable.

The values of environment variables are returned by **Environment** as strings. ■ **Environment** returns **$Failed** if it cannot find a value for the operating system variable you requested. ■ The behavior of **Environment** depends on the computer system you are using. ■ See page 689. ■ See also: **Run**, **$CommandLine**, **$System**.

■ Epilog

Epilog is an option for graphics functions which gives a list of graphics primitives to be rendered after the main part of the graphics is rendered.

In three-dimensional graphics, two-dimensional graphics primitives can be specified by the **Epilog** option. The graphics primitives are rendered in a 0,1 coordinate system. ■ See page 484. ■ See also: **Prolog**, **AxesStyle**, **PlotStyle**, **DisplayFunction**.

~■ Equal

lhs == *rhs* returns **True** if *lhs* and *rhs* are identical.

lhs == *rhs* is used to represent a symbolic equation, to be manipulated using functions like **Solve**. ■ *lhs* == *rhs* returns **True** if *lhs* and *rhs* are identical expressions. ■ *lhs* == *rhs* returns **False** if *lhs* and *rhs* are determined to be unequal by comparisons between numbers or other raw data, such as strings. ■ Approximate numbers are considered equal if they differ in at most their last two decimal digits. ■ 2 == 2. gives **True**. ■ e_1 == e_2 == e_3 gives **True** if all the e_i are equal. ■ **Equal**[*e*] gives **True**. +■ For exact numeric quantities, **Equal** internally uses numerical approximations to establish inequality. This process can be affected by the setting of the global variable **$MaxExtraPrecision**. +■ In **StandardForm** and **InputForm**, *lhs* == *rhs* can be input as *lhs* \[Equal] *rhs* or *lhs* ≡ *rhs*. ■ See page 84. ■ See also: **SameQ**, **Unequal**, **Order**.

■ Erf

Erf[*z*] gives the error function erf(*z*).

Erf[z_0, z_1] gives the generalized error function erf(z_1) − erf(z_0).

Mathematical function (see Section A.3.10). ■ **Erf**[*z*] is the integral of the Gaussian distribution, given by erf(z) = $\frac{2}{\sqrt{\pi}} \int_0^z e^{-t^2} dt$. ■ **Erf**[$z_0$, z_1] is given by $\frac{2}{\sqrt{\pi}} \int_{z_0}^{z_1} e^{-t^2} dt$. ■ **Erf**[*z*] is an entire function of *z* with no branch cut discontinuities. ■ See page 745. ■ See also: **InverseErf**, **ExpIntegralE**, **ExpIntegralEi**, **FresnelC**, **FresnelS**. ■ Related package: **Statistics`NormalDistribution`**.

■ Erfc

Erfc[*z*] gives the complementary error function erfc(*z*).

Erfc[*z*] is given by erfc(*z*) = 1 − erf(*z*). ▪ See notes for Erf. ▪ See page 745. ▪ See also: InverseErfc.

+■ Erfi

Erfi[*z*] gives the imaginary error function erf(*iz*)/*i*.

See notes for Erf. ▪ See page 745.

+■ ErrorBox

ErrorBox[*boxes*] represents boxes that cannot be interpreted in input or output.

ErrorBox[*boxes*] typically displays as the raw form of *boxes* together with underlining that indicates parts that cannot be interpreted. ▪ See page 426. ▪ See also: TagBox, InterpretationBox, ToExpression.

■ EulerE

EulerE[*n*] gives the Euler number E_n.

EulerE[*n*, *x*] gives the Euler polynomial $E_n(x)$.

Mathematical function (see Section A.3.10). ▪ The Euler polynomials satisfy the generating function relation $2e^{xt}/(e^t + 1) = \sum_{n=0}^{\infty} E_n(x)(t^n/n!)$. ▪ The Euler numbers are given by $E_n = 2^n E_n(\frac{1}{2})$. ▪ See page 727.

■ EulerGamma

EulerGamma is Euler's constant γ, with numerical value $\simeq 0.577216$.

Mathematical constant (see Section A.3.11). ▪ See page 735. ▪ Implementation notes: see page 1019. ▪ See also: PolyGamma, StieltjesGamma.

■ EulerPhi

EulerPhi[*n*] gives the Euler totient function $\phi(n)$.

Integer mathematical function (see Section A.3.10). ▪ $\phi(n)$ gives the number of positive integers less than *n* which are relatively prime to *n*. ▪ See page 725. ▪ See also: FactorInteger, Divisors, MoebiusMu.

+■ Evaluatable

Evaluatable is an option for Cell which specifies whether a cell should be used as input to be evaluated by the *Mathematica* kernel.

With Evaluatable->True, typing Shift-Return in the front end when the cell is selected will cause the contents of the cell to be sent to the *Mathematica* kernel for evaluation. ▪ Evaluatable is more often set for styles of cells than for individual cells. ▪ See page 582. ▪ See also: Evaluator, InitializationCell, CellEvaluationDuplicate.

■ Evaluate

Evaluate[*expr*] causes *expr* to be evaluated even if it appears as the argument of a function whose attributes specify that it should be held unevaluated.

Example: Hold[Evaluate[1 + 1]] ⟶ Hold[2]. ▪ You can use Evaluate to override HoldFirst, etc. attributes of built-in functions. ▪ Evaluate only overrides HoldFirst, etc. attributes when it appears directly as the head of the function argument that would otherwise be held. ▪ See page 317. ▪ See also: ReleaseHold.

+■ **EvaluationNotebook**

EvaluationNotebook[ ] gives the notebook in which this function is being evaluated.

EvaluationNotebook returns a NotebookObject. ■ See page 554. ■ See also: SelectedNotebook, InputNotebook, ButtonNotebook, Notebooks, SelectionMove.

+■ **Evaluator**

Evaluator is an option for Cell which gives the name of the kernel to use to evaluate the contents of a cell.

The default setting is typically Evaluator->"Local". ■ Evaluator is more often set at a global level or at the level of whole notebooks than at the level of individual cells. ■ See page 582. ■ See also: CellEvaluatable, InitializationCell.

■ **EvenQ**

EvenQ[*expr*] gives True if *expr* is an even integer, and False otherwise.

EvenQ[*expr*] returns False unless *expr* is manifestly an even integer (i.e., has head Integer, and is even). ■ You can use EvenQ[*x*] = True to override the normal operation of EvenQ, and effectively define *x* to be an even integer. ■ See pages 264 and 697. ■ See also: IntegerQ, OddQ, TrueQ.

+■ **ExcludedForms**

ExcludedForms is an option for FullSimplify which can be set to a list of patterns for expressions that should not be touched if they are encountered at intermediate steps in the operation of FullSimplify.

The default setting for ExcludedForms is { }. ■ A setting such as Gamma[_] will cause FullSimplify to treat gamma functions as elementary objects which should not be transformed. ■ See page 784. ■ See also: TimeConstraint, ComplexityFunction, Simplify, TrigFactor.

■ **Exit**

Exit[ ] terminates a *Mathematica* session.

Exit is a synonym for Quit. ■ Exit terminates the session even if called from within Dialog. ■ On some computer systems, Exit[*n*] can be used to pass the integer exit code *n* to the operating system. ■ See pages 679 and 1006. ■ See also: Return, $IgnoreEOF.

■ **Exp**

Exp[*z*] is the exponential function.

Mathematical function (see Section A.3.10). ■ Exp[*z*] is converted to E^z. ■ See page 731. ■ See also: Power, E, ExpToTrig.

~■ **Expand**

Expand[*expr*] expands out products and positive integer powers in *expr*.

Expand[*expr*, *patt*] leaves unexpanded any parts of *expr* that are free of the pattern *patt*.

Expand works only on positive integer powers. ■ Expand applies only to the top level in *expr*.
~■ Expand[*expr*, Modulus->*p*] expands *expr* reducing the result modulo *p*. ■ See page 767. ■ See also: Distribute, Apart, Series, Factor, LogicalExpand, TrigExpand, PowerExpand.

■ ExpandAll

ExpandAll[*expr*] expands out all products and integer powers in any part of *expr*.

ExpandAll[*expr*, *patt*] avoids expanding parts of *expr* that do not contain terms matching the pattern *patt*.

ExpandAll[*expr*] effectively maps Expand and ExpandDenominator onto every part of *expr*. ■ See page 771.

■ ExpandDenominator

ExpandDenominator[*expr*] expands out products and powers that appear as denominators in *expr*.

ExpandDenominator works only on negative integer powers. ■ ExpandDenominator applies only to the top level in *expr*. ■ See page 771. ■ See also: Together.

■ ExpandNumerator

ExpandNumerator[*expr*] expands out products and powers that appear in the numerator of *expr*.

ExpandNumerator works on terms that have positive integer exponents. ■ ExpandNumerator applies only to the top level in *expr*. ■ See page 771.

■ ExpIntegralE

ExpIntegralE[*n*, *z*] gives the exponential integral function $E_n(z)$.

Mathematical function (see Section A.3.10). ■ $E_n(z) = \int_1^\infty e^{-zt}/t^n\, dt$. ■ ExpIntegralE[*n*, *z*] has a branch cut discontinuity in the complex *z* plane running from $-\infty$ to 0. ■ See page 744. ■ See also: ExpIntegralEi, Erf, LogIntegral, SinIntegral, CosIntegral.

■ ExpIntegralEi

ExpIntegralEi[*z*] gives the exponential integral function Ei(*z*).

Mathematical function (see Section A.3.10). ■ $\mathrm{Ei}(z) = -\int_{-z}^\infty e^{-t}/t\, dt$, where the principal value of the integral is taken. ■ ExpIntegralEi[*z*] has a branch cut discontinuity in the complex *z* plane running from $-\infty$ to 0. ■ See page 744. ■ See also: ExpIntegralE, Erf, LogIntegral, SinIntegral, CosIntegral.

~■ Exponent

~ Exponent[*expr*, *form*] gives the maximum power with which *form* appears in the expanded form of *expr*.

Exponent[*expr*, *form*, *h*] applies *h* to the set of exponents with which *form* appears in *expr*.

Example: Exponent[x^2 + a x^3, x] $\longrightarrow$ 3. ■ The default taken for *h* is Max. ■ Example: Exponent[x^2 + a x^3, x, List] $\longrightarrow$ {2, 3}. ■ *form* can be a product of terms. +■ Exponent works whether or not *expr* is explicitly given in expanded form. ■ See page 769. ■ See also: Coefficient, Cases.

■ ExponentFunction

ExponentFunction is an option for NumberForm and related functions which determines the exponent to use in printing approximate real numbers.

Functions like NumberForm first find the exponent that would make exactly one digit appear to the left of the decimal point when the number is printed in scientific notation. Then they take this exponent and apply the function specified by ExponentFunction to it. If the value obtained from this function is an integer, it is used as the exponent of the number. If it is Null, then the number is printed not in scientific notation. ■ The argument provided for the function specified by ExponentFunction is always an integer. ■ In NumberForm, the default setting for ExponentFunction never modifies the exponent, but returns Null for machine numbers with exponents between −5 and 5, and for high-precision numbers where insignificant zeros would have to be inserted if the number were not printed in scientific notation. ■ In ScientificForm, the default setting for ExponentFunction never returns Null. ■ In EngineeringForm, the default setting for ExponentFunction returns an exponent that is a multiple of 3. ■ In AccountingForm, the default setting for ExponentFunction always returns Null. ■ See page 415. ■ See also: NumberFormat.

■ Expression

Expression is a symbol that represents an ordinary *Mathematica* expression in Read and related functions.

See page 618. ■ See also: ToExpression.

+■ ExpToTrig

ExpToTrig[*expr*] converts exponentials in *expr* to trigonometric functions.

ExpToTrig generates both circular and hyperbolic functions. ■ ExpToTrig tries when possible to give results that do not involve explicit complex numbers. ■ See page 781. ■ See also: TrigToExp, TrigReduce, ComplexExpand.

■ ExtendedGCD

ExtendedGCD[*n*, *m*] gives the extended greatest common divisor of the integers *n* and *m*.

Integer mathematical function (see Section A.3.10). ■ ExtendedGCD[*n*, *m*] returns the list $\{g, \{r, s\}\}$, where g is GCD[*n*, *m*], and r and s satisfy the relation $g = nr + ms$. ■ See page 725. ■ See also: GCD. ■ Related package: Algebra`PolynomialExtendedGCD`.

+■ Extension

Extension is an option for Factor, PolynomialGCD and related functions which specifies what algebraic numbers to allow in the coefficients of resulting polynomials.

With the setting Extension->{a_1, a_2, ... } any rational combination of the a_i can appear. ■ The a_i must be exact numbers. They can involve I, n^{th} roots, and Root objects. ■ The a_i can be viewed as generators for the algebraic number field in which the coefficients are assumed to lie. ■ With the default setting Extension->None all coefficients are required to be rational numbers, and any algebraic numbers that appear in input polynomials are treated like independent variables. ■ Extension->Automatic includes any algebraic numbers from the input polynomials in the coefficient field. ■ Extension->{a_1, a_2, ... } includes both the a_i and any algebraic numbers from the input polynomials in the coefficient field. ■ GaussianIntegers->True is equivalent to Extension->I. ■ See page 779. ■ See also: Modulus.

+■ **Extract**

Extract[*expr*, *list*] extracts the part of *expr* at the position specified by *list*.

Extract[*expr*, {*list₁*, *list₂*, ... }] extracts a list of parts of *expr*.

Extract[*expr*, ... , *h*] extracts parts of *expr*, wrapping each of them with head *h* before evaluation.

Extract[*expr*, {*i*, *j*, ... }] is equivalent to Part[*expr*, *i*, *j*, ...]. ■ The position specifications used by Extract have the same form as those returned by Position, and used in functions such as MapAt and ReplacePart. ■ You can use Extract[*expr*, ... , Hold] to extract parts without evaluation. ■ See page 120. ■ See also: Part.

■ **FaceForm**

FaceForm[*gf*, *gb*] is a three-dimensional graphics directive which specifies that the front faces of polygons are to be drawn with the graphics primitive *gf*, and the back faces with *gb*.

The graphics specifications *gf* and *gb* must be CMYKColor, GrayLevel, Hue or RGBColor directives, or SurfaceColor objects. ■ Specifications given outside of FaceForm will apply both to the front and back faces of polygons. ■ The front face of a polygon is defined to be the one for which the corners as you specify them are in counterclockwise order (right-hand rule). ■ See page 508. ■ See also: EdgeForm.

■ **FaceGrids**

FaceGrids is an option for three-dimensional graphics functions that specifies grid lines to draw on the faces of the bounding box.

The following settings can be given for FaceGrids:

None	no grid lines drawn
All	grid lines drawn on all faces
{*face₁*, *face₂*, ... }	grid lines drawn on the specified faces
{{*face₁*, {*xgrid₁*, *ygrid₁*}}, ... }	details of grid lines specified

■ Faces are specified as {*dirₓ*, *dir_y*, *dir_z*}, where two of the *dirᵢ* must be 0, and the third one must be +1 or -1. ■ Example: the *x-y* face with smallest *z* value is specified as {0, 0, -1}. ■ For each face, specifications {*xgridᵢ*, *ygridᵢ*} can be given to determine the arrangement of grid lines. These specifications have the form described in the notes for GridLines. ■ See page 532. ■ See also: Ticks.

~■ **Factor**

Factor[*poly*] factors a polynomial over the integers.

Factor[*poly*, Modulus->*p*] factors a polynomial modulo a prime *p*.

+ Factor[*poly*, Extension->{*a₁*, *a₂*, ... }] factors a polynomial allowing coefficients that are rational combinations of the algebraic numbers *aᵢ*.

Factor applies only to the top level in an expression. You may have to use Map, or apply Factor again, to reach other levels. ■ Factor[*poly*, GaussianIntegers->True] factors allowing Gaussian integer coefficients. ■ If any coefficients in *poly* are complex numbers, factoring is done allowing Gaussian integer coefficients. ■ The exponents of variables need not be positive integers. Factor can deal with exponents that are linear combinations of symbolic expressions. ■ When given a rational expression, Factor effectively first calls Together, then factors numerator and denominator. +■ With the default setting Extension->None, Factor[*poly*] will treat algebraic number coefficients in *poly* like independent variables. +■ Factor[*poly*, Extension->Automatic] will extend the domain of coefficients to include any algebraic numbers that appear in *poly*. ■ See page 767. ■ Implementation notes: see page 1021. ■ See also: FactorTerms, FactorSquareFree, Solve, Expand, Simplify, FactorInteger, TrigFactor.

■ Factorial

$n!$ gives the factorial of n.

Mathematical function (see Section A.3.10). ■ For non-integer n, the numerical value of $n!$ is given by Gamma[1 + n]. ■ See page 727. ■ See also: Gamma, Binomial.

■ Factorial2

$n!!$ gives the double factorial of n.

Mathematical function (see Section A.3.10). ■ $n!! = n(n-2)(n-4) \times \dots$ ■ $n!!$ is a product of even numbers for n even, and odd numbers for n odd. ■ See page 727. ■ See also: Gamma.

~■ FactorInteger

FactorInteger[n] gives a list of the prime factors of the integer n, together with their exponents.

Example: FactorInteger[2434500] $\longrightarrow$ {{2, 2}, {3, 2}, {5, 3}, {541, 1}}. ~■ For negative numbers, the unit {-1, 1} is included in the list of factors. +■ FactorInteger also works on rational numbers. The prime factors of the denominator are given with negative exponents. ■ FactorInteger[n, GaussianIntegers->True] factors over Gaussian integers. ■ When necessary, a unit of the form {-1, 1}, {I, 1} or {-I, 1} is included in the list of factors. ■ FactorInteger[n, FactorComplete->False] does fast but not necessarily complete factorization, and extracts only factors that are easy to find. ■ See page 723. ■ Implementation notes: see page 1019. ■ See also: Prime, PrimeQ, Divisors. ■ Related package: NumberTheory`FactorIntegerECM`.

~■ FactorList

FactorList[*poly*] gives a list of the factors of a polynomial, together with their exponents.

The first element of the list is always the overall numerical factor. It is {1, 1} if there is no overall numerical factor. ■ Example: FactorList[3 (1+x)^2 (1-x)] $\longrightarrow$ {{-3, 1}, {-1+x, 1}, {1+x, 2}}. ■ FactorList[*poly*, Modulus->p] factors modulo a prime p. ■ FactorList[*poly*, GaussianIntegers->True] allows Gaussian integer coefficients. +■ FactorList[*poly*, Extension->{a_1, a_2, ... }] allows coefficients that are arbitrary rational combinations of the a_i. ■ See page 775. ■ See also: FactorTermsList, TrigFactorList, CoefficientList.

~■ FactorSquareFree

FactorSquareFree[*poly*] pulls out any multiple factors in a polynomial.

FactorSquareFree[*poly*, Modulus->p] pulls out multiple factors modulo a prime p.
+■ FactorSquareFree[*poly*, Extension->Automatic] extends the coefficient field to include algebraic numbers that appear in the coefficients of *poly*. ■ See page 775.

■ FactorSquareFreeList

FactorSquareFreeList[*poly*] gives a list of square-free factors of a polynomial, together with their exponents.

See page 775.

■ FactorTerms

FactorTerms[*poly*] pulls out any overall numerical factor in *poly*.

FactorTerms[*poly*, *x*] pulls out any overall factor in *poly* that does not depend on *x*.

FactorTerms[*poly*, {x_1, x_2, ... }] pulls out any overall factor in *poly* that does not depend on any of the x_i.

Example: FactorTerms[3 - 3x^2] $\longrightarrow$ -3 (-1 + x^2). ■ FactorTerms[*poly*, *x*] extracts the content of *poly* with respect to *x*. ■ See notes for Factor. ■ See page 767.

■ FactorTermsList

FactorTermsList[*poly*, {x_1, x_2, ... }] gives a list of factors of *poly*. The first element in the list is the overall numerical factor. The second element is a factor that does not depend on any of the x_i. Subsequent elements are factors which depend on progressively more of the x_i.

See notes for FactorTerms. ■ See page 775.

■ False

False is the symbol for the Boolean value false.

See page 83. ■ See also: TrueQ, True.

+ ■ Fibonacci

Fibonacci[*n*] gives the Fibonacci number F_n.

Fibonacci[*n*, *x*] gives the Fibonacci polynomial $F_n(x)$.

Integer mathematical function (see Section A.3.10). ■ The F_n satisfy the recurrence relation $F_n = F_{n-1} + F_{n-2}$ with $F_1 = F_2 = 1$. ■ For any complex value of *n* the F_n are given by the general formula $F_n = (\phi^n - (-\phi)^{-n})/\sqrt{5}$, where ϕ is the golden ratio. ■ The Fibonacci polynomial $F_n(x)$ is the coefficient of t^n in the expansion of $t/(1 - xt - t^2)$. ■ See page 727. ■ Implementation notes: see page 1019. ■ See also: GoldenRatio.

■ FileByteCount

FileByteCount["*file*"] gives the number of bytes in a file.

If a particular file is moved from one computer system to another, the number of bytes in the file as reported by FileByteCount may change. ■ See page 616. ■ See also: StringLength, FileType. ■ Related package: Utilities`BinaryFiles`.

■ FileDate

FileDate["*file*"] gives the date and time at which a file was last modified.

FileDate returns the date and time in the format used by Date. ■ See page 616. ■ See also: SetFileDate, FromDate.

■ FileNames

FileNames[ ] lists all files in the current working directory.

FileNames["*form*"] lists all files in the current working directory whose names match the string pattern *form*.

FileNames[{"*form*₁", "*form*₂", ... }] lists all files whose names match any of the *form*ᵢ.

FileNames[*forms*, {"*dir*₁", "*dir*₂", ... }] lists files with names matching *forms* in any of the directories *dir*ᵢ.

FileNames[*forms*, *dirs*, *n*] includes files that are in subdirectories up to *n* levels down.

The string pattern "*form*" can contain the metacharacters specified on page 992. ■ FileNames["*"] is equivalent to FileNames[ ]. ■ FileNames[*forms*, *dirs*, Infinity] looks for files in all subdirectories of the *dirs*. ■ The list of files returned by FileNames is sorted in the order generated by the function Sort. ■ FileNames[*forms*, *dirs*, *n*] includes names of directories only if they appear exactly at level *n*. ■ The *forms* must be names of files only, not including any directory information. Thus, for example, FileNames["../*"] will not work. Instead FileNames["*", ".."] is the appropriate form. ■ Setting the option IgnoreCase -> True makes FileNames treat lower- and upper-case letters in file names as equivalent. ■ On operating systems such as MS-DOS, FileNames always treats lower- and upper-case letters in file names as equivalent. ■ See page 613. ■ See also: Directory, FileType. ■ Related package: Utilities`Package`.

■ FileType

FileType["*file*"] gives the type of a file, typically File, Directory or None.

FileType returns None if the file specified does not exist. ■ See page 616. ■ See also: FileNames, FileByteCount.

■ Find

Find[*stream*, "*text*"] finds the first line in an input stream that contains the specified string.

Find[*stream*, {"*text*₁", "*text*₂", ... }] finds the first line that contains any of the specified strings.

Find breaks the input stream into records, delimited by record separators, and scans each record for the strings you specify. ■ Find returns as a string the first record which contains the specified text. ■ If Find does not find any record which contains the specified text before it reaches the end of the file, it returns EndOfFile. ■ The following options can be given:

AnchoredSearch	False	whether to require that the text searched for be at the beginning of a record
IgnoreCase	False	whether to treat lower- and upper-case as equivalent
RecordSeparators	{"\n"}	separators for records
WordSearch	False	whether to require that the text searched for appear as a word
WordSeparators	{" ", "\t"}	separators for words

■ The first argument to Find can be InputStream["*name*", *n*], or simply "*name*" if there is only one open input stream with the specified name. ■ You can open a file or pipe to get an InputStream object using OpenRead. ■ Find does not close streams after it finishes reading from them. ■ See page 625. ■ See also: Read, Skip, StreamPosition, StringToStream, NotebookFind.

■ **FindList**

FindList["*file*", "*text*"] gives a list of lines in the file that contain the specified string.

FindList["*file*", {"*text*₁", "*text*₂", ... }] gives a list of all lines that contain any of the specified strings.

FindList[{"*file*₁", ... }, ...] gives a list of lines containing the specified strings in any of the *file*ᵢ.

FindList[*files*, *text*, *n*] includes only the first *n* lines found.

FindList returns {} if it fails to find any record which contains the specified text. ■ If FindList opens a file or pipe, it closes it again when it has finished. ■ See notes for Find. ■ See page 623. ■ See also: ReadList.

■ **FindMinimum**

FindMinimum[*f*, {*x*, *x*₀}] searches for a local minimum in *f*, starting from the point *x*=*x*₀.

FindMinimum returns a list of the form {*f*ₘᵢₙ, {*x*->*x*ₘᵢₙ}}, where *f*ₘᵢₙ is the minimum value of *f* found, and *x*ₘᵢₙ is the value of *x* for which it is found. ■ FindMinimum[*f*, {*x*, {*x*₀, *x*₁}}] searches for a local minimum in *f* using *x*₀ and *x*₁ as the first two values of *x*. This form must be used if symbolic derivatives of *f* cannot be found. ■ FindMinimum[*f*, {*x*, *xstart*, *xmin*, *xmax*}] searches for a local minimum, stopping the search if *x* ever gets outside the range *xmin* to *xmax*. ■ FindMinimum[*f*, {*x*, *x*₀}, {*y*, *y*₀}, ...] searches for a local minimum in a function of several variables. ■ FindMinimum has attribute HoldAll. ■ FindMinimum works by following the path of steepest descent from each point that it reaches. The minima it finds are local, but not necessarily global, ones. ■ The following options can be given:

AccuracyGoal	Automatic	the accuracy sought in the value of the function at the minimum
Compiled	True	whether the function should be compiled
Gradient	Automatic	the list of gradient functions {D[*f*, *x*], D[*f*, *y*], ... }
MaxIterations	30	maximum number of iterations used
PrecisionGoal	Automatic	the precision sought in the value of the function at the minimum
WorkingPrecision	Precision[1.]	the number of digits used in internal computations

■ The default settings for AccuracyGoal and PrecisionGoal are 10 digits less than WorkingPrecision. ■ FindMinimum continues until either of the goals specified by AccuracyGoal or PrecisionGoal is achieved. ■ See page 895. ■ Implementation notes: see page 1020. ■ See also: ConstrainedMin, LinearProgramming, D, Fit. ■ Related package: Statistics`NonlinearFit`.

■ FindRoot

FindRoot[*lhs*==*rhs*, {*x*, x_0}] searches for a numerical solution to the equation *lhs*==*rhs*, starting with *x*=x_0.

FindRoot[*lhs*==*rhs*, {*x*, {x_0, x_1}}] searches for a solution using x_0 and x_1 as the first two values of *x*. This form must be used if symbolic derivatives of the equation cannot be found.
■ FindRoot[*lhs*==*rhs*, {*x*, *xstart*, *xmin*, *xmax*}] searches for a solution, stopping the search if *x* ever gets outside the range *xmin* to *xmax*. ■ FindRoot[{eqn_1, eqn_2, ... }, {*x*, x_0}, {*y*, y_0}, ...] searches for a numerical solution to the simultaneous equations eqn_i. ■ FindRoot returns a list of replacements for *x*, *y*, ... , in the same form as obtained from Solve. ■ FindRoot has attribute HoldAll. ■ If you specify only one starting value of *x*, FindRoot searches for a solution using Newton's method. If you specify two starting values, FindRoot uses a variant of the secant method. ■ If all equations and starting values are real, then FindRoot will search only for real roots. If any are complex, it will also search for complex roots. ■ You can always tell FindRoot to search for complex roots by adding 0. I to the starting value. ■ The following options can be given:

AccuracyGoal	Automatic	the accuracy sought in the value of the function at the root
Compiled	True	whether the function should be compiled
DampingFactor	1	damping factor in Newton's method
Jacobian	Automatic	the Jacobian of the system
MaxIterations	15	maximum number of iterations used
WorkingPrecision	$MachinePrecision	the number of digits used in internal computations

■ The default setting for AccuracyGoal is 10 digits less than WorkingPrecision. ■ If FindRoot does not succeed in finding a solution to the accuracy you specify within MaxIterations steps, it returns the most recent approximation to a solution that it found. You can then apply FindRoot again, with this approximation as a starting point. ■ The size of each step taken in Newton's method is multiplied by the setting given for DampingFactor. ■ See page 882. ■ Implementation notes: see page 1020. ■ See also: NSolve, Solve, FindMinimum. ■ Related package: NumericalMath`InterpolateRoot`.

■ First

First[*expr*] gives the first element in *expr*.

First[*expr*] is equivalent to *expr*[[1]]. ■ See page 118. ■ See also: Part, Last, Rest, Take, Select.

■ Fit

Fit[*data*, *funs*, *vars*] finds a least-squares fit to a list of data as a linear combination of the functions *funs* of variables *vars*.

The data can have the form {{x_1, y_1, ... , f_1}, {x_2, y_2, ... , f_2}, ... }, where the number of coordinates *x*, *y*, ... is equal to the number of variables in the list *vars*.

The data can also be of the form {f_1, f_2, ... }, with a single coordinate assumed to take values 1, 2, ...

The argument *funs* can be any list of functions that depend only on the objects *vars*.

Fit[{f_1, f_2, ... }, {1, x, x^2}, x] gives a quadratic fit to a sequence of values f_i. The result is of the form $a_0 + a_1 x + a_2 x^2$, where the a_i are real numbers. The successive values of x needed to obtain the f_i are assumed to be 1, 2, ... ■ Fit[{{x_1, f_1}, {x_2, f_2}, ... }, {1, x, x^2}, x] does a quadratic fit, assuming a sequence of x values x_i. ■ Fit[{{x_1, y_1, f_1}, ... }, {1, x, y}, {x, y}] finds a fit of the form $a_0 + a_1 x + a_2 y$. ■ Fit always finds the linear combination of the functions in the list *forms* that minimizes the sum of the squares of deviations from the values f_i. ■ Exact numbers given as input to Fit are converted to approximate numbers with machine precision. ■ See page 859. ■ Implementation notes: see page 1020. ■ See also: Interpolation, InterpolatingPolynomial, Solve, PseudoInverse, QRDecomposition, FindMinimum. ■ Related packages: Statistics`NonlinearFit`, Statistics`LinearRegression`.

~■ FixedPoint

FixedPoint[*f*, *expr*] starts with *expr*, then applies *f* repeatedly until the result no longer changes.

FixedPoint[*f*, *expr*, *n*] stops after at most *n* steps. ■ FixedPoint always returns the last result it gets. ~■ The option SameTest -> *comp* allows you to specify a comparison function to apply to successive pairs of results to determine whether a fixed point has been reached. +■ You can use Throw to exit from FixedPoint before it is finished. ■ See page 239. ■ See also: FixedPointList, Nest, ReplaceRepeated.

■ FixedPointList

FixedPointList[*f*, *expr*] generates a list giving the results of applying *f* repeatedly, starting with *expr*, until the results no longer change.

See notes for FixedPoint. ■ FixedPointList[*f*, *expr*] gives *expr* as the first element of the list it produces. ■ See page 239. ■ See also: NestList, ComposeList.

■ Flat

Flat is an attribute that can be assigned to a symbol *f* to indicate that all expressions involving nested functions *f* should be flattened out. This property is accounted for in pattern matching.

Flat corresponds to the mathematical property of associativity. ■ For a symbol *f* with attribute Flat, *f*[*f*[*a*, *b*], *f*[*c*]] is automatically reduced to *f*[*a*, *b*, *c*]. ■ Functions like Plus, Times and Dot are Flat. ■ For a Flat function *f*, the variables x and y in the pattern *f*[x_, y_] can correspond to any sequence of arguments. ■ The Flat attribute must be assigned before defining any values for a Flat function. ■ See page 309. ■ See also: Orderless, OneIdentity.

■ Flatten

Flatten[*list*] flattens out nested lists.

Flatten[*list*, *n*] flattens to level *n*.

Flatten[*list*, *n*, *h*] flattens subexpressions with head *h*.

Example: Flatten[{a,{b,c},{d}}] $\longrightarrow$ {a, b, c, d}. ■ Flatten "unravels" lists, effectively just deleting inner braces. ■ Flatten[*list*, *n*] effectively flattens the top level in *list* *n* times. ■ Flatten[*f*[*e*, ...]] flattens out subexpressions with head *f*. ■ See pages 126 and 252. ■ See also: Partition.

■ FlattenAt

FlattenAt[*list*, *n*] flattens out a sublist that appears as the nth element of *list*. If *n* is negative, the position is counted from the end.

FlattenAt[*expr*, {*i*, *j*, ... }] flattens out the part of *expr* at position {*i*, *j*, ... }.

FlattenAt[*expr*, {{i_1, j_1, ... }, {i_2, j_2, ... }, ... }] flattens out parts of *expr* at several positions.

Example: FlattenAt[{a, {b, c}, {d, e}}, 2] $\longrightarrow$ {a, b, c, {d, e}}. ■ See pages 126 and 252. ■ See also: DeleteCases, Flatten, Sequence, SlotSequence.

~■ Floor

Floor[x] gives the greatest integer less than or equal to x.

Mathematical function (see Section A.3.10). ■ Examples: Floor[2.4] $\longrightarrow$ 2; Floor[2.6] $\longrightarrow$ 2; Floor[-2.4] $\longrightarrow$ -3; Floor[-2.6] $\longrightarrow$ -3. +■ Floor[x] can be entered in StandardForm and InputForm as ⌊ x ⌋, ⠶lf⠶ x ⠶rf⠶ or \[LeftFloor] x \[RightFloor]. +■ Floor[x] returns an integer when x is any numeric quantity, whether or not it is an explicit number. +■ Example: Floor[Pi^2] $\longrightarrow$ 9. +■ For exact numeric quantities, Floor internally uses numerical approximations to establish its result. This process can be affected by the setting of the global variable $MaxExtraPrecision. ■ See page 718. ■ See also: Ceiling, Round, IntegerPart, Chop.

~■ Fold

Fold[f, x, *list*] gives the last element of FoldList[f, x, *list*].

Example: Fold[f, x, {a, b, c}] $\longrightarrow$ f[f[f[x, a], b], c]. +■ You can use Throw to exit from Fold before it is finished. ■ See notes for FoldList. ■ See page 240. ■ See also: Nest.

■ FoldList

FoldList[f, x, {a, b, ... }] gives {x, $f[x, a]$, $f[f[x, a], b]$, ... }.

Example: FoldList[f, x, {a, b, c}] $\longrightarrow$ {x, f[x, a], f[f[x, a], b], f[f[f[x, a], b], c]}. ■ FoldList[Plus, 0, *list*] generates cumulative sums of the elements in *list*. ■ Example: FoldList[Plus, 0, {a, b, c}] $\longrightarrow$ {0, a, a + b, a + b + c}. ■ With a length n list, FoldList generates a list of length $n + 1$. ■ The head of *list* in FoldList[f, x, *list*] need not be List. ■ See page 240. ■ See also: NestList, ComposeList, Partition, MapIndexed.

+■ FontColor

FontColor is an option for Cell, StyleBox and StyleForm which specifies the default color in which to render text.

The setting for FontColor must be a CMYKColor, GrayLevel, Hue or RGBColor directive. ■ See pages 423 and 587. ■ See also: Background, DefaultColor, FontWeight.

+■ FontFamily

FontFamily is an option for Cell, StyleBox and StyleForm which specifies the font family in which text should be rendered.

The default is FontFamily->"Courier". Other common choices are "Times" and "Helvetica". ■ *Mathematica* will combine settings for FontFamily, FontWeight, FontSlant, FontTracking and sometimes FontSize to construct a complete name for the font you want. It will then use this name, together with any settings you have specified for FontPostScriptName and FontNativeName to try to locate an appropriate font on your particular computer system. ■ When generating PostScript output on a printer or otherwise, settings you give for FontPostScriptName are typically used in preference to other font specifications. ■ *Mathematica* will try making replacements for the font family name that you specify with the option FontSubstitutions. ■ *Mathematica* by default uses heuristics such as translating "Helvetica" to "Geneva" for appropriate computer systems. ■ See pages 423 and 587. ■ See also: StyleForm, TextStyle.

+■ **FontSize**

FontSize is an option for Cell, StyleBox and StyleForm which specifies the default size in printer's points of the font in which to render text.

The size of a font is typically taken to be the distance from the top of the highest character to the bottom of the lowest character. ▪ A printer's point is approximately $\frac{1}{72}$ of an inch. ▪ Fonts with the same nominal point size may not look the same size to the eye. ▪ See pages 423 and 587. ▪ See also: FontWeight, FontTracking, FontLeading, ScriptMinSize, ScriptSizeMultipliers.

+■ **FontSlant**

FontSlant is an option for Cell, StyleBox and StyleForm which specifies how slanted the characters should be in text in the cell.

Typical settings are "Plain", "Italic" and "Oblique". ▪ With the "Oblique" setting, each character typically has the same basic form as with "Plain", but is slanted. With the "Italic" setting, the basic form is different. ▪ See notes for FontFamily. ▪ See pages 423 and 587. ▪ See also: AutoItalicWords, SingleLetterItalics.

+■ **FontSubstitutions**

FontSubstitutions is an option for Cell, StyleBox and StyleForm which gives a list of substitutions to try for font family names.

A typical setting is {"Geneva" -> "Helvetica"}. ▪ FontSubstitutions is used only for FontFamily settings, and not for FontWeight, FontSlant and so on. ▪ See page 587. ▪ See also: FontFamily.

+■ **FontTracking**

FontTracking is an option for Cell, StyleBox and StyleForm which specifies how condensed or expanded you want the font in which text is rendered to be.

Typical settings are "Condensed" and "Expanded". The default is "Plain". ▪ For some fonts and on some computer systems, additional settings are supported, such as "Narrow", "Compressed", "SemiCondensed", "Extended" and "Wide". ▪ See notes for FontFamily. ▪ See page 587.

+■ **FontWeight**

FontWeight is an option for Cell, StyleBox and StyleForm which specifies how heavy the characters in a font should be.

Typical settings are "Plain" and "Bold". ▪ For some fonts and on some computer systems, additional settings are supported, such as "Thin", "Light", "Medium", "SemiBold", "Heavy", "Black" and "Fat". ▪ See notes for FontFamily. ▪ See pages 423 and 587.

■ **For**

For[*start*, *test*, *incr*, *body*] executes *start*, then repeatedly evaluates *body* and *incr* until *test* fails to give True.

For evaluates its arguments in a non-standard way. ▪ For[*start*, *test*, *incr*] does the loop with a null body. ▪ The sequence of evaluation is *test*, *body*, *incr*. The For exits as soon as *test* fails. ▪ If Break[ ] is generated in the evaluation of *body*, the For loop exits. ▪ Continue[ ] exits the evaluation of *body*, and continues the loop by evaluating *incr*. ▪ Unless Return[*expr*] or Throw[*expr*] is generated, the final value returned by For is Null. ▪ Example: For[tot=0; i=0, i < 3, i++, tot += f[i]]. Note that the roles of semicolon and comma are *reversed* relative to the C programming language. ▪ See page 332. ▪ See also: Do, While, Throw.

~■ **Format**

Format[*expr*] prints as the formatted form of *expr*.

Assigning values to Format[*expr*] defines print forms for expressions.

Format[*expr*, *form*] gives a format for the specified form of output.

~■ Standard forms for formatted output are:

CForm	C language input form
FortranForm	Fortran input form
InputForm	one-dimensional form suitable for direct keyboard input
OutputForm	character-based two-dimensional form
StandardForm	standard two-dimensional form
TeXForm	TEX input form
TraditionalForm	form approximating traditional mathematical notation

■ You can add your own forms for formatted output. ■ Example: Format[*s*] := *rhs* defines a symbol *s* to print like *rhs*. ■ Format[*f*[...]] := *rhs* defines a function *f* to print like *rhs*. ■ Definitions for Format are stored in the FormatValues of a symbol. +■ If you specify a new output format for an expression by giving a definition for Format, there is no guarantee that *Mathematica* will be able to interpret this output format if it is used as input. +■ Definitions given for Format are used before those given for MakeBoxes. ■ See page 453. ■ See also: ToString, ToBoxes, MakeBoxes, MakeExpression.

~■ **FormatType**

~ FormatType is an option for output streams, graphics and functions such as Text which specifies the default format type to use when outputting expressions.

Standard values for FormatType are given in the notes for Format. ■ SetOptions[*stream*, FormatType -> *type*] resets the format type for an open stream. ~■ For graphics functions the default option setting is FormatType :> $FormatType. ~■ For graphics functions box-based format types such as StandardForm and TraditionalForm can be used only when a notebook front end is present. ■ See pages 536 and 609. ■ See also: TextStyle.

+■ **FormBox**

FormBox[*boxes*, *form*] displays as *boxes* but specifies that rules associated with *form* should be used to interpret *boxes* on input.

In InputForm and StandardForm \(*form*\`*input*\) yields FormBox[*input*, *form*]. ■ \(\`*input*\) yields FormBox[*input*, RawForm]. ■ See page 426. ■ See also: TagBox, InterpretationBox, ToExpression, MakeExpression.

■ **FortranForm**

FortranForm[*expr*] prints as a Fortran language version of *expr*.

Standard arithmetic functions and certain control structures are translated. ■ FortranForm acts as a "wrapper", which affects printing, but not evaluation. ■ The width of output lines must be set explicitly by giving the option PageWidth -> *n* for the relevant output stream. ■ SetOptions[$Output, PageWidth -> 72] uses a line width of 72 characters for standard *Mathematica* output. ■ No declarations are generated. ■ See pages 207 and 404. ■ See also: CForm, Compile.

~■ **Fourier**

> Fourier[*list*] finds the discrete Fourier transform of a list of complex numbers.

The Fourier transform b_s of a list a_r of length n is defined to be $\frac{1}{\sqrt{n}} \sum_{r=1}^{n} a_r e^{2\pi i(r-1)(s-1)/n}$. ■ Note that the zero frequency term appears at position 1 in the resulting list. ■ The definition of the Fourier transform used is the one common in the physical sciences. The sign of the exponent must be reversed to obtain the definition common in electrical engineering. ■ The list of data need not have a length equal to a power of two. ■ The *list* given in Fourier[*list*] can be nested to represent an array of data in any number of dimensions. ■ The array of data must be rectangular. ~■ If the elements of *list* are exact numbers, Fourier begins by applying N to them. ■ See page 868. ■ Implementation notes: see page 1020. ■ See also: InverseFourier, Fit.

+■ **FractionalPart**

> FractionalPart[*x*] gives the fractional part of *x*.

Mathematical function (see Section A.3.10). ■ FractionalPart[*x*] in effect takes all digits to the right of the decimal point and drops the others. ■ Examples: FractionalPart[2.4] ⟶ 0.4; FractionalPart[2.6] ⟶ 0.6; FractionalPart[-2.4] ⟶ -0.4; FractionalPart[-2.6] ⟶ -0.6. ■ FractionalPart[*x*] + IntegerPart[*x*] is always exactly *x*. ■ FractionalPart[*x*] yields a result when *x* is any numeric quantity, whether or not it is an explicit number. ■ Example: FractionalPart[Pi^2] ⟶ $-9 + \pi^2$. ■ For exact numeric quantities, FractionalPart internally uses numerical approximations to establish its result. This process can be affected by the setting of the global variable $MaxExtraPrecision. ■ See page 718. ■ See also: IntegerPart, Mod.

+■ **FractionBox**

> FractionBox[*x*, *y*] represents $\frac{x}{y}$ in input and output.

Inside \(... \) FractionBox[*x*, *y*] can be input as *x* \/ *y*. ■ In a notebook a FractionBox can be created using CTRL[/]. CTRL[␣] moves out of the fraction. ■ In StandardForm and InputForm, FractionBox[*x*, *y*] is interpreted on input as *x*/*y*. ■ The axis of FractionBox[*x*, *y*] is taken to go through the fraction line. The baseline lies below the axis by the distance between the axis and the bottom of characters such as (in the current font. ■ The width of the fraction line can be given in x-heights as the setting for the SpanLineThickness option in StyleBox. ■ If FractionBox[*x*, *y*] does not fit on a single line, it is output as *x* / *y*. ■ In StandardForm, explicit FractionBox objects are output literally. You can use DisplayForm to see the display form of such objects. ■ See page 424. ■ See also: OverscriptBox, GridBox.

■ **Frame**

> Frame is an option for two-dimensional graphics functions which specifies whether a frame should be drawn around the plot.

Frame -> True by default draws a frame with tick marks. If Ticks -> Automatic, setting Frame -> True suppresses tick marks on axes. ■ See pages 491 and 494. ■ See also: Boxed.

+■ **FrameBox**

> FrameBox[*box*] displays with a frame drawn around *box*.

In StandardForm and InputForm, FrameBox is by default ignored, so that FrameBox[*box*] is interpreted just as *box* would be. ■ In StandardForm, explicit FrameBox objects are output literally. You can use DisplayForm to see the display form of such objects. ■ See page 425. ■ See also: StyleBox, CellFrame, ColumnLines, RowLines.

■ FrameLabel

FrameLabel is an option for two-dimensional graphics functions that specifies labels to be placed on the edges of a frame around a plot.

FrameLabel -> None specifies that no labels should be given. ■ FrameLabel -> {*xmlabel*, *ymlabel*} specifies labels for the bottom and left-hand edges of the frame. ■ FrameLabel -> {*xmlabel*, *ymlabel*, *xplabel*, *yplabel*} specifies labels for each of the edges of the frame, ordered clockwise starting from the bottom edge. ■ Any expression can be specified as a label. It will be given in OutputForm. Arbitrary strings of text can be given as "*text*". ■ Labels for the vertical edges of the frame are by default written vertically. RotateLabel -> False specifies that they should be horizontal. ■ See page 494. ■ See also: AxesLabel, PlotLabel.

■ FrameStyle

FrameStyle is an option for two-dimensional graphics functions that specifies how the edges of a frame should be rendered.

FrameStyle -> *style* specifies that all edges of the frame are to be generated with the specified graphics directive, or list of graphics directives. ■ FrameStyle -> {{*xmstyle*}, {*ymstyle*}, ... } specifies that different edges of the frame should be generated with different styles. The edges are ordered clockwise starting from the bottom edge. All styles must be enclosed in lists, perhaps of length one. ■ Styles can be specified using graphics directives such as Dashing, Hue and Thickness. ■ The default color of frame edges is specified by the option DefaultColor. ■ See page 494. ■ See also: Prolog, Epilog, AxesStyle.

■ FrameTicks

FrameTicks is an option for two-dimensional graphics functions that specifies tick marks for the edges of a frame.

The following settings can be given for FrameTicks:

None	no tick marks drawn
Automatic	tick marks placed automatically
{*xmticks*, *ymticks*, ... }	tick mark options specified separately for each edge

■ When tick mark specifications are given separately for each edge, the edges are ordered clockwise starting from the bottom of the frame. ■ With the Automatic setting, tick marks are usually placed at points whose coordinates have the minimum number of digits in their decimal representation. ■ For each edge, tick marks can be specified as described in the notes for Ticks. ■ See page 494. ■ See also: Ticks, GridLines, FaceGrids.

■ FreeQ

FreeQ[*expr*, *form*] yields True if no subexpression in *expr* matches *form*, and yields False otherwise.

FreeQ[*expr*, *form*, *levelspec*] tests only those parts of *expr* on levels specified by *levelspec*.

form can be a pattern. ■ Example: FreeQ[f[x^2] + y^2, x^_] ⟶ False. ■ FreeQ looks at the heads of raw expressions, testing whether those heads match *form*. ■ See page 265. ■ See also: MemberQ, Count.

+ ■ FresnelC

FresnelC[*z*] gives the Fresnel integral $C(z)$.

Mathematical function (see Section A.3.10). ■ FresnelC[*z*] is given by $\int_0^z \cos(\pi t^2/2)\, dt$. ■ FresnelC[*z*] is an entire function of *z* with no branch cut discontinuities. ■ See page 745. ■ See also: Erf, CosIntegral.

+■ **GeneratedCell**

> **GeneratedCell** is an option for **Cell** which indicates whether the cell was generated from the kernel.
>
> Cells created interactively using only operations in the front end have **GeneratedCell->False**. ■ The setting for **GeneratedCell** is used to determine which cells should be considered as *Mathematica* output. ■ See page 582. ■ See also: **CellAutoOverwrite**.

~■ **Get**

> **<<***name* reads in a file, evaluating each expression in it, and returning the last one.
>
> On systems with graphical interfaces, there will usually be graphical tools for reading in files. ■ If *name* is the name of a *Mathematica* context, ending with a ` context mark character, then **Get** will process this name to find the file to read. ■ If *name* is the name of a file, any **.m** extension must be included explicitly. ~■ **Get** can read **.mx** files of *Mathematica* definitions written by **DumpSave**. ■ **<<"***name***"** is equivalent to **<<***name*. The double quotes can be omitted if the name is of the form specified on page 981. ~■ If a file with name *file*.**mx** is found to be a directory, **Get** will look for a file with a name like *file*.**mx/$SystemID/***file*.**mx**. +■ If the file found by **<<***name* is a directory, *Mathematica* will try to load the file **init.m** in that directory. ■ Syntax errors in *Mathematica* input files are reported in the standard form: *filename*: *line*: **syntax error in** *expr*. **Get** continues attempting to read a file even after a syntax error has been detected. However, if an error is detected, **$Context** and **$ContextPath** are reset to the values they had when **Get** was called. ■ During the execution of **Get**, the global variable **$Input** is set to the name of the file being read. ■ **Get["***file***", "***key***"]** reads a file which has been encoded using **Encode["***source***", "***file***", "***key***"]**. ■ See page 598. ■ See also: **Read, Install, RunThrough, Put, Splice, FileNames, ToFileName, ToExpression, NotebookGet**.

■ **GoldenRatio**

> **GoldenRatio** is the golden ratio $\phi = (1 + \sqrt{5})/2$, with numerical value $\simeq 1.61803$.
>
> Mathematical constant (see Section A.3.11). ■ See page 735. ■ See also: **Fibonacci**.

~■ **Goto**

> **Goto[***tag***]** scans for **Label[***tag***]**, and transfers control to that point.
>
> +■ **Goto** first scans any compound expression in which it appears directly, then scans compound expressions which enclose this one. ■ See pages 333 and 334. ■ See also: **Throw, Switch, Which**.

▪ Graphics

Graphics[*primitives*, *options*] represents a two-dimensional graphical image.

Graphics is displayed using Show. ▪ The following graphics primitives can be used:

Circle[{x, y}, r]	circle
Disk[{x, y}, r]	filled disk
Line[{{x₁, y₁}, ... }]	line
Point[{x, y}]	point
Polygon[{{x₁, y₁}, ... }]	filled polygon
PostScript["*string*"]	PostScript code to include verbatim
Raster[*array*]	array of gray levels
RasterArray[*garray*]	array of colored cells
Rectangle[{xmin, ymin}, {xmax, ymax}]	filled rectangle
Text[*expr*, {x, y}]	text

▪ The sound primitives SampledSoundList and SampledSoundFunction can also be included. ▪ The following graphics directives can be used:

AbsoluteDashing[{w₁, ... }]	absolute line dashing specification
AbsolutePointSize[d]	absolute point size specification
AbsoluteThickness[w]	absolute line thickness specification
CMYKColor[c, m, y, k]	color specification
Dashing[{w₁, ... }]	line dashing specification
GrayLevel[i]	intensity specification
Hue[h]	hue specification
PointSize[d]	point size specification
RGBColor[r, g, b]	color specification
Thickness[w]	line thickness specification

~▪ The following options can be given:

AspectRatio	1/GoldenRatio	ratio of height to width
Axes	False	whether to draw axes
AxesLabel	None	axes labels
AxesOrigin	Automatic	where axes should cross
AxesStyle	Automatic	graphics directives to specify the style for axes
Background	Automatic	background color for the plot
ColorOutput	Automatic	type of color output to produce
DefaultColor	Automatic	the default color for plot elements
DisplayFunction	$DisplayFunction	function for generating output
Epilog	{}	graphics primitives to be rendered after the main plot
FormatType	$FormatType	the default format type for text
Frame	False	whether to put a frame around the plot
FrameLabel	None	frame labels
FrameStyle	Automatic	graphics directives giving the style for the frame
FrameTicks	Automatic	frame tick marks
ImageSize	Automatic	the absolute size at which to render the graphic in a notebook
GridLines	None	grid lines to draw

(continued)

■ Graphics *(continued)*

PlotLabel	None	a label for the plot
PlotRange	Automatic	range of values to include
PlotRegion	Automatic	the final display region to be filled
Prolog	{}	graphics primitives to be rendered before the main plot
RotateLabel	True	whether to rotate *y* labels on the frame
TextStyle	$TextStyle	the default style for text
Ticks	Automatic	tick marks

■ Nested lists of graphics primitives can be given. Specifications such as GrayLevel remain in effect only until the end of the list which contains them. ■ Graphics[Graphics3D[...]] generates an ordinary 2D graphics object corresponding to 3D graphics. The same works for SurfaceGraphics, ContourGraphics and DensityGraphics. ■ The standard print form for Graphics[...] is -Graphics-. InputForm prints the explicit list of primitives. ■ See page 467. ■ See also: Plot, ListPlot, ParametricPlot. ■ Related package: Graphics`Graphics`.

■ Graphics3D

Graphics3D[*primitives*, *options*] represents a three-dimensional graphical image.

Graphics3D is displayed using Show. ■ The following graphics primitives can be used:

Cuboid[{*xmin*, *ymin*, *zmin*}, ...]	cuboid
Line[{{x_1, y_1, z_1}, ... }]	line
Point[{*x*, *y*, *z*}]	point
Polygon[{{x_1, y_1, z_1}, ... }]	polygon
Text[*expr*, {*x*, *y*, *z*}]	text

■ The sound primitives SampledSoundList and SampledSoundFunction can also be included. ■ The following graphics directives can be used:

AbsoluteDashing[{w_1, ... }]	absolute line dashing specification
AbsolutePointSize[*d*]	absolute point size specification
AbsoluteThickness[*w*]	absolute line thickness specification
CMYKColor[*c*, *m*, *y*, *k*]	color specification
Dashing[{w_1, ... }]	line dashing specification
EdgeForm[*spec*]	polygon edge specification
FaceForm[*spec*]	polygon face specification
GrayLevel[*i*]	gray-level specification
Hue[*h*]	hue specification
PointSize[*d*]	point size specification
RGBColor[*r*, *g*, *b*]	color specification
SurfaceColor[*spec*]	surface properties specification
Thickness[*w*]	line thickness specification

~■ The following options can be given:

AmbientLight	GrayLevel[0.]	ambient illumination level
AspectRatio	Automatic	ratio of height to width
Axes	False	whether to draw axes
AxesEdge	Automatic	on which edges to put axes
AxesLabel	None	axes labels
AxesStyle	Automatic	graphics directives to specify the style for axes

(continued)

■ `Graphics3D` *(continued)*

`Background`	`Automatic`	background color for the plot
`Boxed`	`True`	whether to draw the bounding box
`BoxRatios`	`Automatic`	bounding 3D box ratios
`BoxStyle`	`Automatic`	graphics directives to specify the style for the box
`ColorOutput`	`Automatic`	type of color output to produce
`DefaultColor`	`Automatic`	the default color for plot elements
`DisplayFunction`	`$DisplayFunction`	function for generating output
`Epilog`	`{}`	2D graphics primitives to be rendered after the main plot
`FaceGrids`	`None`	grid lines to draw on the bounding box
`FormatType`	`$FormatType`	the default format type for text
`ImageSize`	`Automatic`	the absolute size at which to render the graphic in a notebook
`Lighting`	`True`	whether to use simulated illumination
`LightSources`	`(see below)`	positions and colors of light sources
`PlotLabel`	`None`	a label for the plot
`PlotRange`	`Automatic`	range of values to include
`PlotRegion`	`Automatic`	the final display region to be filled
`PolygonIntersections`	`True`	whether to leave intersecting polygons unchanged
`Prolog`	`{}`	2D graphics primitives to be rendered before the main plot
`RenderAll`	`True`	whether to render all polygons
`Shading`	`True`	whether to shade polygons
`SphericalRegion`	`False`	whether to make the circumscribing sphere fit in final display area
`TextStyle`	`$TextStyle`	the default style for text
`Ticks`	`Automatic`	tick marks
`ViewCenter`	`Automatic`	point to put at the center of final display area
`ViewPoint`	`{1.3, -2.4, 2.}`	viewing position
`ViewVertical`	`{0, 0, 1}`	direction to make vertical

■ Nested lists of graphics primitives can be given. Specifications such as `GrayLevel` remain in effect only until the end of the list which contains them. ■ The standard print form for `Graphics3D[ ... ]` is `-Graphics3D-`. `InputForm` prints the explicit list of primitives. ■ The default light sources used are `{{{1,0,1}, RGBColor[1,0,0]}, {{1,1,1}, RGBColor[0,1,0]}, {{0,1,1}, RGBColor[0,0,1]}}`. ■ `Graphics3D[SurfaceGraphics[ ... ]]` can be used to convert a `SurfaceGraphics` object into `Graphics3D` representation. ■ `Graphics[SurfaceGraphics[ ... ]]` generates a representation in terms of ordinary 2D graphics primitives. ■ See page 467. ■ See also: `Plot3D`, `SurfaceGraphics`, `ParametricPlot3D`. ■ Related packages: `Graphics`Graphics3D``, `Graphics`Shapes``, `Graphics`Polyhedra``.

■ `GraphicsArray`

`GraphicsArray[{`g_1`, `g_2`, ... }]` represents a row of graphics objects.

`GraphicsArray[{{`g_{11}`, `g_{12}`, ... }, ... }]` represents a two-dimensional array of graphics objects.

You can display a `GraphicsArray` object using `Show`. ■ `GraphicsArray` sets up identical rectangular display areas for each of the graphics objects it contains. ■ `GraphicsArray` takes the same options as `Graphics`, with the defaults for `Ticks` and `FrameTicks` changed to `None`. ■ `GraphicsArray` takes the additional option `GraphicsSpacing`, which specifies the spacing between the rectangular areas containing each graphics object. The default setting is `GraphicsSpacing -> 0.1`. ■ The options `DisplayFunction`, `ColorOutput` and `CharacterEncoding` are ignored for graphics objects given inside `GraphicsArray`. ■ See pages 138 and 467. ■ See also: `Rectangle`, `RasterArray`, `TableForm`, `GridBox`.

■ GraphicsSpacing

GraphicsSpacing is an option for GraphicsArray which specifies the spacing between elements in the array.

GraphicsSpacing -> 0 inserts no horizontal or vertical spacing, so that all adjacent rectangular areas in the array are shown abutting. ■ GraphicsSpacing -> {h, v} specifies horizontal and vertical spacing to use. ■ GraphicsSpacing -> s is equivalent to GraphicsSpacing -> {s, s}. ■ The spacing is given in scaled coordinates, relative to each rectangular area in the array. ■ Example: a horizontal spacing of 0.1 yields an array in which the rectangular areas are separated horizontally by distances equal to 0.1 of their widths. ■ See page 140. ■ See also: TableSpacing.

■ GrayLevel

GrayLevel[*level*] is a graphics directive which specifies the gray-level intensity with which graphical objects that follow should be displayed.

The gray level must be a number between 0 and 1. ■ 0 represents black; 1 represents white. ■ On display devices with no native gray-level capability, dither patterns are typically used, as generated by the PostScript interpreter. ■ The end of the Graphics Gallery shows examples of gray levels generated with various GrayLevel specifications. ■ See page 479. ■ See also: RGBColor, Hue, Raster.

■ Greater

$x > y$ yields True if x is determined to be greater than y.

$x_1 > x_2 > x_3$ yields True if the x_i form a strictly decreasing sequence.

Greater gives True or False when its arguments are real numbers. ■ Greater does some simplification when its arguments are not numbers. +■ For exact numeric quantities, Greater internally uses numerical approximations to establish numerical ordering. This process can be affected by the setting of the global variable $MaxExtraPrecision. ■ See page 84. ■ See also: Less, Positive.

■ GreaterEqual

~ $x >= y$ or $x \geq y$ yields True if x is determined to be greater than or equal to y.

~ $x_1 \geq x_2 \geq x_3$ yields True if the x_i form a non-increasing sequence.

+■ $x \geq y$ can be entered as x :>=: y or x \[GreaterEqual] y. ■ GreaterEqual gives True or False when its arguments are real numbers. ~■ GreaterEqual does some simplification when its arguments are not numbers. ~■ For exact numeric quantities, GreaterEqual internally uses numerical approximations to establish numerical ordering. This process can be affected by the setting of the global variable $MaxExtraPrecision. ~■ In StandardForm, GreaterEqual is printed using $\geq$. ~■ $x \geqslant y$, entered as x :>/: y or x \[GreaterSlantEqual] y, can be used on input as an alternative to $x \geq y$. ■ See page 84.

+■ **GridBaseline**

GridBaseline is an option for GridBox which specifies where the baseline of the grid represented by the GridBox should be assumed to be.

GridBaseline determines how a GridBox will be positioned vertically with respect to other boxes, say in a RowBox. ■ GridBaseline->*pos* specifies that position *pos* in the GridBox should be assumed to be the baseline of the GridBox and should therefore be aligned with baselines of other boxes. ■ Possible settings are:

Axis	axis of the middle row in the grid (default)
Baseline	baseline of the middle row in the grid
Bottom	bottom of the whole grid
Center	half way from top to bottom
Top	top of the whole grid

■ See page 428. ■ See also: RowAlignments, AdjustmentBox, CellBaseline.

+■ **GridBox**

GridBox[{{*box*$_{11}$, *box*$_{12}$, ... }, {*box*$_{21}$, *box*$_{22}$, ... }, ... }] represents a two-dimensional grid of boxes or strings in input and output.

In a notebook, columns of a GridBox can be added using [CTRL][,] and rows using [CTRL][↵] (CONTROL-RETURN). ■ [CTRL][,] or a menu item can be used to start building a GridBox. ■ You can use tab to move from one entry in a GridBox to the next. [CTRL][␣] moves out of the whole GridBox. ■ In StandardForm and InputForm, GridBox[*list*] is interpreted as *list*. ■ You can place parentheses around a GridBox to make it look more like a matrix, but these are by default ignored when the GridBox is interpreted. ■ The following options can be given:

ColumnAlignments	Center	how to align columns
ColumnLines	False	whether to draw lines between columns
ColumnsEqual	False	whether to make all columns equal width
ColumnSpacings	1	spacings between columns in ems
ColumnWidths	Automatic	actual widths of columns in ems
GridBaseline	Axis	the position of the baseline for the whole grid
GridDefaultElement	"\[Placeholder]"	what to insert when a new entry is created
RowAlignments	Baseline	how to align rows
RowLines	False	whether to draw lines between rows
RowMinHeight	Automatic	the minimum total row height in x-heights
RowsEqual	False	whether to make all rows equal total height
RowSpacings	0.5	spacings between rows in x-heights

■ GridBox is a low-level construct that works only for two-dimensional arrays; TableForm and MatrixForm are higher-level constructs that can also be used for higher-dimensional arrays. ■ In StandardForm, explicit GridBox objects are output literally. You can use DisplayForm to see the display form of such objects. ■ See page 424. ■ See also: TableForm, MatrixForm, RowBox, OverscriptBox, UnderscriptBox, AdjustmentBox.

+■ **GridDefaultElement**

GridDefaultElement is an option for GridBox which specifies what to insert when a new element is created interactively in a GridBox.

The default setting for GridDefaultElement is "\[Placeholder]" or "□". ■ When creating palettes, GridDefaultElement is typically set to ButtonBox["□"]. ■ The setting for GridDefaultElement is used to determine the contents of new columns or rows created with [CTRL][,] or [CTRL][↵] (CONTROL-RETURN). ■ See page 428.

■ GridLines

GridLines is an option for two-dimensional graphics functions that specifies grid lines.

The following settings can be given for GridLines:

None	no grid lines drawn
Automatic	grid lines placed automatically
{*xgrid*, *ygrid*}	grid lines specified separately in each direction

■ With the Automatic setting, grid lines are usually placed at points whose coordinates have the minimum number of digits in their decimal representation. ■ For each direction, the following grid line options can be given:

None	no grid lines drawn
Automatic	grid line positions chosen automatically
{x_1, x_2, ... }	grid lines drawn at the specified positions
{{x_1, $style_1$}, ... }	grid lines with specified styles
func	a function to be applied to *xmin*, *xmax* to get the grid line option

■ Grid line styles can involve graphics directives such as RGBColor and Thickness. ■ Grid lines are by default colored light blue. ■ The grid line function *func*[*xmin*, *xmax*] may return any other grid line option. ■ FullOptions gives the explicit form of GridLines specifications when Automatic settings are used. ■ See pages 491 and 495. ■ See also: Ticks, FrameTicks, FaceGrids, ColumnLines, RowLines.

~■ GroebnerBasis

GroebnerBasis[{$poly_1$, $poly_2$, ... }, {x_1, x_2, ... }] gives a list of polynomials that form a Gröbner basis for the set of polynomials $poly_i$.

GroebnerBasis[{$poly_1$, $poly_2$, ... }, {x_1, x_2, ... }, {y_1, y_2, ... }] finds a Gröbner basis in which the y_i have been eliminated.

The set of polynomials in a Gröbner basis have the same collection of roots as the original polynomials. ■ For polynomials in one variable, GroebnerBasis reduces to PolynomialGCD. ■ For linear functions in any number of variables, GroebnerBasis is equivalent to Gaussian elimination. ■ The Gröbner basis in general depends on the ordering assigned to monomials. This ordering is affected by the ordering of the x_i. ~■ The following options can be given:

MonomialOrder	Lexicographic	the criterion used for ordering monomials
CoefficientDomain	Rationals	the type of objects assumed to be coefficients
Modulus	0	the modulus for numerical coefficients

~■ Possible settings for MonomialOrder are Lexicographic, DegreeLexicographic, DegreeReverseLexicographic or an explicit weight matrix. Monomials are specified for the purpose of MonomialOrder by lists of the exponents with which the x_i appear in them. ~■ The ordering of the x_i and the setting for MonomialOrder can substantially affect the efficiency of GroebnerBasis. +■ Possible settings for CoefficientDomain are InexactNumbers, Rationals, RationalFunctions and Polynomials[*x*]. +■ MonomialList[*poly*, {x_1, x_2, ... }] gives a list of the monomials in *poly* in the order used by GroebnerBasis. MonomialList takes the same options as GroebnerBasis. ■ See page 773. ■ Implementation notes: see page 1021. ■ See also: PolynomialReduce, PolynomialGCD, Solve, RowReduce, Eliminate.

+■ GroupPageBreakWithin

GroupPageBreakWithin is an option for Cell which specifies whether a page break should be allowed within the group of cells if the notebook that contains the group is printed.

See page 583. ■ See also: PageBreakWithin, ShowPageBreaks.

■ Head

Head[*expr*] gives the head of *expr*.

Examples: Head[f[x]] ⟶ f; Head[a + b] ⟶ Plus; Head[4] ⟶ Integer; Head[x] ⟶ Symbol. ■ See page 229.

■ Heads

Heads is an option for functions which use level specifications that specifies whether heads of expressions should be included.

Heads -> True treats heads just like other elements of expressions for the purpose of levels. ■ Heads -> False never includes heads as part of any level of an expression. ■ Most functions which use level specifications have the default setting Heads -> False. One exception is Position, for which the default is Heads -> True. ■ See page 236. ■ See also: Level.

■ HermiteH

HermiteH[*n*, *x*] gives the Hermite polynomial $H_n(x)$.

Mathematical function (see Section A.3.10). ■ Explicit polynomials are given for non-negative integers *n*. ■ The Hermite polynomials satisfy the differential equation $y'' - 2xy' + 2ny = 0$. ■ They are orthogonal polynomials with weight function e^{-x^2} in the interval $(0, \infty)$. ■ HermiteH[*n*, *x*] is an entire function of *x* with no branch cut discontinuities. ■ See page 736. ■ See also: LaguerreL.

■ HiddenSurface

HiddenSurface is an option for SurfaceGraphics which specifies whether hidden surfaces are to be eliminated.

HiddenSurface -> True eliminates hidden surfaces. ■ See page 149. ■ See also: Shading.

■ Hold

Hold[*expr*] maintains *expr* in an unevaluated form.

Hold has attribute HoldAll, and performs no operation on its arguments. ■ Example: Hold[1+1] ⟶ Hold[1 + 1]. ■ Hold is removed by ReleaseHold. ■ Hold[e_1, e_2, ...] maintains a sequence of unevaluated expressions to which a function can be applied using Apply. ■ Even though *expr* itself is not evaluated, Hold[*expr*] may still evaluate if *expr* is of the form *f*[*args*], and upvalues for *f* have been defined. ■ See page 318. ■ See also: HoldPattern, HoldForm, HoldComplete, Unevaluated, HoldAll, Symbol.

■ HoldAll

HoldAll is an attribute which specifies that all arguments to a function are to be maintained in an unevaluated form.

You can use Evaluate to evaluate the arguments of a HoldAll function in a controlled way. ■ Even when a function has attribute HoldAll, Sequence objects that appear in its arguments are still by default flattened, Unevaluated wrappers are stripped, and upvalues associated with the arguments are used. ■ See pages 309 and 316. ■ See also: Unevaluated, Hold, NHoldAll, HoldAllComplete, SequenceHold, Extract.

+■ HoldAllComplete

HoldAllComplete is an attribute which specifies that all arguments to a function are not to be modified or looked at in any way in the process of evaluation.

By setting the attribute HoldAllComplete you can effectively shield the arguments of a function from all aspects of the standard *Mathematica* evaluation process. ■ HoldAllComplete not only prevents arguments from being evaluated, but also prevents Sequence objects from being flattened, Unevaluated wrappers from being stripped, and upvalues associated with arguments from being used. ■ Evaluate cannot be used to override HoldAllComplete. ■ See pages 309 and 320. ■ See also: HoldComplete, HoldAll, SequenceHold, Extract.

+■ HoldComplete

HoldComplete[*expr*] shields *expr* completely from the standard *Mathematica* evaluation process, preventing even upvalues associated with *expr* from being used.

Hold has attribute HoldAllComplete, and performs no operations on its arguments. ■ HoldComplete is removed by ReleaseHold. ■ HoldComplete can be inserted as a wrapper by such functions as ToExpression and ReplacePart. ■ HoldComplete is generated by default by MakeExpression. ■ See page 996. ■ See also: Hold, HoldPattern, HoldForm, Unevaluated, HoldAllComplete, Symbol.

■ HoldFirst

HoldFirst is an attribute which specifies that the first argument to a function is to be maintained in an unevaluated form.

See pages 309 and 316.

■ HoldForm

HoldForm[*expr*] prints as the expression *expr*, with *expr* maintained in an unevaluated form.

HoldForm allows you to see the output form of an expression without evaluating the expression. ■ HoldForm has attribute HoldAll. ■ HoldForm is removed by ReleaseHold. ■ See pages 318 and 413. ■ See also: ToString, WriteString.

+■ HoldPattern

HoldPattern[*expr*] is equivalent to *expr* for pattern matching, but maintains *expr* in an unevaluated form.

HoldPattern has attribute HoldAll. ■ The left-hand sides of rules are usually evaluated, as are parts of the left-hand sides of assignments. You can use HoldPattern to stop any part from being evaluated. ■ Example: *expr* /. HoldPattern[Integrate[y_, x_]] -> *rhs* transforms any subexpression of the form Integrate[y_, x_] in *expr*. Without the HoldPattern, the Integrate[y_, x_] in the rule would immediately be evaluated to give x_ y_, and the replacement would not work. ■ Example: f[HoldPattern[Integrate[y_, x_]]] := *value* can be used to make an assignment for expressions of the form f[Integrate[y_, x_]]. Without HoldPattern, the Integrate function would be evaluated at the time of assignment. ■ See page 320. ■ See also: Hold, Verbatim.

■ HoldRest

HoldRest is an attribute which specifies that all but the first argument to a function are to be maintained in an unevaluated form.

See pages 309 and 316.

⁺■ HTMLSave

HTMLSave["*file*.html"] saves an HTML version of the currently selected notebook in the front end.

HTMLSave["*file*.html", "*source*.nb"] saves an HTML version of the notebook from the file *source*.nb.

HTMLSave["*file*.hmtl", *notebook*] saves an HTML version of the notebook corresponding to the specified notebook object.

HTMLSave has options for specifying such features as how to include formulas, whether to make links for closed cell groups, and what correspondence to set up between notebook styles and HTML tags. ■ HTMLSave normally saves graphics in separate image files. ■ HTMLSave can often be accessed from an item in the Save As Special menu in the notebook front end. ■ See page 211. ■ See also: TeXSave, Display.

■ Hue

Hue[*h*] is a graphics directive which specifies that graphical objects which follow are to be displayed, if possible, in a color corresponding to hue *h*.

Hue[*h*, *s*, *b*] specifies colors in terms of hue, saturation and brightness.

The parameters *h*, *s* and *b* must all be between 0 and 1. Values of *s* and *b* outside this range are clipped. Values of *h* outside this range are treated cyclically. ■ As *h* varies from 0 to 1, the color corresponding to Hue[*h*] runs through red, yellow, green, cyan, blue, magenta, and back to red again. ■ Hue[*h*] is equivalent to Hue[*h*, 1, 1]. ■ On monochrome displays, a gray level based on the brightness value is used. ■ The end of the Graphics Gallery shows examples of colors generated with various Hue specifications. ■ See page 479. ■ See also: RGBColor, GrayLevel, CMYKColor. ■ Related package: Graphics`Colors`.

■ Hypergeometric0F1

Hypergeometric0F1[*a*, *z*] is the confluent hypergeometric function $_0F_1(;a;z)$.

Mathematical function (see Section A.3.10). ■ The $_0F_1$ function has the series expansion $_0F_1(;a;z) = \sum_{k=0}^{\infty} 1/(a)_k \, z^k/k!$. ■ See page 749. ■ See also: Pochhammer.

⁺■ Hypergeometric0F1Regularized

Hypergeometric0F1Regularized[*a*, *z*] is the regularized confluent hypergeometric function $_0F_1(a;z)/\Gamma(a)$.

Mathematical function (see Section A.3.10). ■ Hypergeometric0F1Regularized[*a*, *z*] is finite for all finite values of *a* and *z*. ■ See notes for Hypergeometric0F1. ■ See page 749.

■ Hypergeometric1F1

Hypergeometric1F1[*a*, *b*, *z*] is the Kummer confluent hypergeometric function $_1F_1(a;b;z)$.

Mathematical function (see Section A.3.10). ■ The $_1F_1$ function has the series expansion $_1F_1(a;b;z) = \sum_{k=0}^{\infty}(a)_k/(b)_k \, z^k/k!$. ■ See page 749.

⁺■ Hypergeometric1F1Regularized

Hypergeometric1F1Regularized[*a*, *b*, *z*] is the regularized confluent hypergeometric function $_1F_1(a;b;z)/\Gamma(b)$.

Mathematical function (see Section A.3.10). ■ Hypergeometric1F1Regularized[*a*, *b*, *z*] is finite for all finite values of *a*, *b* and *z*. ■ See notes for Hypergeometric1F1. ■ See page 749.

■ **Hypergeometric2F1**

Hypergeometric2F1[a, b, c, z] is the hypergeometric function $_2F_1(a, b; c; z)$.

Mathematical function (see Section A.3.10). ■ The $_2F_1$ function has the series expansion $_2F_1(a, b; c; z) = \sum_{k=0}^{\infty} (a)_k (b)_k / (c)_k \, z^k/k!$. ■ Hypergeometric2F1[a, b, c, z] has a branch cut discontinuity in the complex z plane running from 1 to ∞. ■ See page 750.

+■ **Hypergeometric2F1Regularized**

Hypergeometric2F1Regularized[a, b, c, z] is the regularized hypergeometric function $_2F_1(a, b; c; z)/\Gamma(c)$.

Mathematical function (see Section A.3.10). ■ Hypergeometric2F1Regularized[a, b, c, z] is finite for all finite values of a, b, c and z so long as $|z| < 1$. ■ See notes for Hypergeometric2F1. ■ See page 750.

+■ **HypergeometricPFQ**

HypergeometricPFQ[$\{a_1, \ldots, a_p\}$, $\{b_1, \ldots, b_q\}$, z] is the generalized hypergeometric function $_pF_q(\mathbf{a}; \mathbf{b}; z)$.

Mathematical function (see Section A.3.10). ■ $_pF_q(\mathbf{a}; \mathbf{b}; z)$ has series expansion $\sum_{k=0}^{\infty} (a_1)_k \cdots (a_p)_k / (b_1)_k \cdots (b_q)_k \, z^k/k!$. ■ Hypergeometric0F1, Hypergeometric1F1, and Hypergeometric2F1 are special cases of HypergeometricPFQ. ■ In many special cases, HypergeometricPFQ is automatically converted to other functions. ■ For $p = q + 1$, HypergeometricPFQ[$alist$, $blist$, z] has a branch cut discontinuity in the complex z plane running from 1 to ∞. ■ See page 750. ■ See also: MeijerG.

+■ **HypergeometricPFQRegularized**

HypergeometricPFQRegularized[$\{a_1, \ldots, a_p\}$, $\{b_1, \ldots, b_q\}$, z] is the regularized generalized hypergeometric function $_pF_q(\mathbf{a}; \mathbf{b}; z)/(\Gamma(b_1)\ldots\Gamma(b_q))$.

Mathematical function (see Section A.3.10). ■ HypergeometricPFQRegularized is finite for all finite values of its arguments so long as $p \leq q$. ■ See notes for HypergeometricPFQ. ■ See page 750.

■ **HypergeometricU**

HypergeometricU[a, b, z] is the confluent hypergeometric function $U(a, b, z)$.

Mathematical function (see Section A.3.10). ■ The function $U(a, b, z)$ has the integral representation $U(a, b, z) = 1/\Gamma(a) \int_0^{\infty} e^{-zt} t^{a-1} (1 + t)^{b-a-1} \, dt$. ■ HypergeometricU[$a$, b, z] has a branch cut discontinuity in the complex z plane running from $-\infty$ to 0. ■ See page 749.

~■ **I**

I represents the imaginary unit $\sqrt{-1}$.

Numbers containing I are converted to the type Complex. +■ I can be entered in StandardForm and InputForm as i, ⁝ii⁝ or \[ImaginaryI]. +■ j, ⁝jj⁝ and \[ImaginaryJ] can also be used. ■ See page 735. ■ See also: Re, Im, ComplexExpand, GaussianIntegers.

■ **Identity**

Identity[$expr$] gives $expr$ (the identity operation).

See page 250. ■ See also: Composition, Through, InverseFunction, Sequence, Hold.

■ **IdentityMatrix**

IdentityMatrix[n] gives the $n \times n$ identity matrix.

See page 837. ■ See also: DiagonalMatrix, Table. ■ Related package: LinearAlgebra`MatrixManipulation`.

■ **If**

If[*condition*, t, f] gives t if *condition* evaluates to True, and f if it evaluates to False.

If[*condition*, t, f, u] gives u if *condition* evaluates to neither True nor False.

If evaluates only the argument determined by the value of the condition. ■ If[*condition*, t, f] is left unevaluated if *condition* evaluates to neither True nor False. ■ If[*condition*, t] gives Null if *condition* evaluates to False. ■ See page 325. ■ See also: Switch, Which, Condition. ■ Related package: Calculus`DiracDelta`.

■ **IgnoreCase**

IgnoreCase is an option for string manipulation and searching functions which specifies whether lower- and upper-case letters should be treated as equivalent.

With the default setting IgnoreCase -> False, lower- and upper-case letters are treated as totally different. ■ With the setting IgnoreCase -> True, lower- and upper-case letters are treated as equivalent. ■ IgnoreCase is an option for StringPosition, StringReplace, Find and FindList. ■ IgnoreCase in no way affects the parsing of *Mathematica* expressions. ■ See page 389. ■ See also: ToUpperCase, ToLowerCase, SpellingCorrection.

■ **Im**

Im[z] gives the imaginary part of the complex number z.

Im[*expr*] is left unevaluated if *expr* is not a numeric quantity. ■ See page 719. ■ See also: Re, Abs, Arg, ComplexExpand.

+■ **ImageMargins**

ImageMargins is an option for Cell which specifies the absolute margins in printer's points to leave around graphics in a cell.

Possible settings are:

dist	the same margins on all sides
{{*left*, *right*}, {*bottom*, *top*}}	different margins on different sides

■ ImageMargins represent space to be left inside whatever CellMargins are specified for a particular cell. ■ See page 590. ■ See also: ImageSize, CellMargins.

+■ **ImageResolution**

ImageResolution is an option for Display and DisplayString which specifies at what resolution bitmap images should be rendered.

ImageResolution->r specifies that a bitmap should be rendered at a resolution of r dpi. ■ ImageResolution is relevant only for bitmap graphics formats such as "TIFF", and not for resolution-independent formats such as "EPS". ■ The default setting ImageResolution->Automatic typically uses a resolution of 72 dpi for bitmap graphics formats. ■ See page 209. ■ See also: ImageSize.

~■ **IntegerDigits**

IntegerDigits[*n*] gives a list of the decimal digits in the integer *n*.

IntegerDigits[*n*, *b*] gives a list of the base-*b* digits in the integer *n*.

₊ IntegerDigits[*n*, *b*, *len*] pads the list on the left with zeros to give a list of length *len*.

Examples: IntegerDigits[5810] ⟶ {5, 8, 1, 0}; IntegerDigits[5810, 16] ⟶ {1, 6, 11, 2}.
~■ IntegerDigits[*n*] discards the sign of *n*. ■ If *len* is less than the number of digits in *n* then the *len* least significant digits are returned. ~■ FromDigits can be used as the inverse of IntegerDigits. ■ See page 700. ■ See also: RealDigits, BaseForm, NumberForm, FromDigits, IntegerPart. ■ Related package: NumberTheory`ContinuedFractions`.

₊■ **IntegerPart**

IntegerPart[*x*] gives the integer part of *x*.

Mathematical function (see Section A.3.10). ■ IntegerPart[*x*] in effect takes all digits to the left of the decimal point and drops the others. ■ Examples: IntegerPart[2.4] ⟶ 2; IntegerPart[2.6] ⟶ 2; IntegerPart[-2.4] ⟶ -2; IntegerPart[-2.6] ⟶ -2. ■ IntegerPart[*x*] + FractionalPart[*x*] is always exactly *x*. ■ IntegerPart[*x*] returns an integer when *x* is any numeric quantity, whether or not it is an explicit number. ■ Example: IntegerPart[Pi^2] ⟶ 9. ■ For exact numeric quantities, IntegerPart internally uses numerical approximations to establish its result. This process can be affected by the setting of the global variable $MaxExtraPrecision. ■ See page 718. ■ See also: FractionalPart, Round, Floor, Ceiling, Chop.

■ **IntegerQ**

IntegerQ[*expr*] gives True if *expr* is an integer, and False otherwise.

IntegerQ[*expr*] returns False unless *expr* is manifestly an integer (i.e., has head Integer). ■ You can use IntegerQ[*x*] = True to override the normal operation of IntegerQ, and effectively define *x* to be an integer. ■ See pages 264 and 697. ■ See also: EvenQ, OddQ, NumberQ, TrueQ.

~■ Integrate

Integrate[*f*, *x*] gives the indefinite integral $\int f\, dx$.

Integrate[*f*, {*x*, *xmin*, *xmax*}] gives the definite integral $\int_{xmin}^{xmax} f\, dx$.

Integrate[*f*, {*x*, *xmin*, *xmax*}, {*y*, *ymin*, *ymax*}] gives the multiple integral $\int_{xmin}^{xmax} dx \int_{ymin}^{ymax} dy\, f$.

+■ Integrate[*f*, *x*] can be entered as $\int f\, dx$. +■ $\int$ can be entered as :int: or \[Integral]. +■ d is not an ordinary d; it is entered as :dd: or \[DifferentialD]. +■ Integrate[*f*, {*x*, *xmin*, *xmax*}] can be entered with *xmin* as a subscript and *xmax* as a superscript to $\int$. ■ Multiple integrals use a variant of the standard iterator notation. The first variable given corresponds to the outermost integral, and is done last. ■ Integrate can evaluate integrals of rational functions. It can also evaluate integrals that involve exponential, logarithmic, trigonometric and inverse trigonometric functions, so long as the result comes out in terms of the same set of functions. ■ Integrate can give results in terms of many special functions. ■ Integrate carries out some simplifications on integrals it cannot explicitly do. ■ You can get a numerical result by applying N to a definite integral. ■ You can assign values to patterns involving Integrate to give results for new classes of integrals. ■ The integration variable can be any expression. However, Integrate uses only its literal form. The object $d(x^n)$, for example, is not converted to $nx^{n-1}dx$. ■ For indefinite integrals, Integrate tries to find results that are correct for almost all values of parameters. ~■ For definite integrals, the following options can be given:

PrincipalValue	False	whether to find Cauchy principal values
GenerateConditions	True	whether to generate answers that involve conditions on parameters
Assumptions	{}	assumptions to make about relations between parameters

~■ Integrate can evaluate essentially all indefinite integrals and most definite integrals listed in standard books of tables. ~■ In StandardForm, Integrate[*f*, *x*] is output as $\int f\, dx$. ■ See page 810. ■ Implementation notes: see page 1021. ■ See also: NIntegrate, DSolve, Sum.

~■ InterpolatingFunction

~ InterpolatingFunction[*domain*, *table*] represents an approximate function whose values are found by interpolation.

InterpolatingFunction works like Function. ■ InterpolatingFunction[...][*x*] finds the value of an approximate function with a particular argument *x*. ~■ In standard output format, only the *domain* element of an InterpolatingFunction object is printed explicitly. The remaining elements are indicated by <>. ~■ *domain* specifies the domain of the data from which the InterpolatingFunction was constructed. +■ If you supply arguments outside of the domain, a warning is generated, and then an extrapolated value is returned. ■ InterpolatingFunction objects that take any number of real arguments may be constructed. +■ You can take derivatives of InterpolatingFunction objects using D and Derivative. ■ NDSolve returns its results in terms of InterpolatingFunction objects. ■ See page 863. ■ Implementation notes: see page 1020. ■ See also: CompiledFunction, FunctionInterpolation. ■ Related package: NumericalMath`SplineFit`.

■ InterpolatingPolynomial

`InterpolatingPolynomial[`*data*`, `*var*`]` gives a polynomial in the variable *var* which provides an exact fit to a list of data.

The data can have the forms $\{\{x_1, f_1\}, \{x_2, f_2\}, \dots \}$ or $\{f_1, f_2, \dots \}$, where in the second case, the x_i are taken to have values 1, 2, ...

The f_i can be replaced by $\{f_i, df_i, ddf_i, \dots \}$, specifying derivatives at the points x_i.

With a list of data of length n, `InterpolatingPolynomial` gives a polynomial of degree $n - 1$. ■ Example: `InterpolatingPolynomial[{4, 5, 8}, x]` $\longrightarrow 4 + (-1 + x)^2$. ■ `InterpolatingPolynomial` gives the interpolating polynomial in Newton form, suitable for numerical evaluation. ■ See pages 778 and 862. ■ See also: `Fit`, `Roots`. ■ Related package: `NumericalMath`PolynomialFit`.

■ Interpolation

`Interpolation[`*data*`]` constructs an `InterpolatingFunction` object which represents an approximate function that interpolates the data.

The data can have the forms $\{\{x_1, f_1\}, \{x_2, f_2\}, \dots \}$ or $\{f_1, f_2, \dots \}$, where in the second case, the x_i are taken to have values 1, 2, ...

Data can be given in the form $\{\{x_1, \{f_1, df_1, ddf_1, \dots \}\}, \dots \}$ to specify derivatives as well as values of the function at the points x_i. You can specify different numbers of derivatives at different points. ~■ Function values and derivatives may be real or complex numbers, or arbitrary symbolic expressions. The x_i must be real numbers. ■ Multidimensional data can be given in the form $\{\{x_1, y_1, \dots, f_1\}, \dots \}$. Derivatives in this case can be given by replacing f_1 and so on by $\{f_1, \{dxf_1, dyf_1, \dots \}\}$. ■ `Interpolation` works by fitting polynomial curves between successive data points. ■ The degree of the polynomial curves is specified by the option `InterpolationOrder`. ■ The default setting is `InterpolationOrder -> 3`. ■ You can do linear interpolation by using the setting `InterpolationOrder -> 1`. ■ `Interpolation[`*data*`]` generates an `InterpolatingFunction` object which returns values with the same precision as those in *data*. ■ See page 863. ■ See also: `ListInterpolation`, `FunctionInterpolation`, `InterpolatingPolynomial`, `Fit`. ■ Related packages: `NumericalMath`SplineFit`, `NumericalMath`PolynomialFit`, `NumericalMath`Approximations`, `DiscreteMath`ComputationalGeometry`.

■ InterpretationBox

`InterpretationBox[`*boxes*`, `*expr*`]` displays as *boxes* but is interpreted on input as *expr*.

`InterpretationBox` provides a way to store hidden information in *Mathematica* output. ■ `InterpretationBox` is generated sometimes in `StandardForm` output, and often in `TraditionalForm` output. ■ The following options can be given:

`AutoDelete`	`False`	whether to strip the `InterpretationBox` if *boxes* is modified
`DeletionWarning`	`False`	whether to issue a warning if *boxes* is deleted
`Editable`	`False`	whether to allow *boxes* to be edited
`Selectable`	`True`	whether to allow *boxes* to be selected

■ If you modify the displayed form of `InterpretationBox[`*boxes*`, `*expr*`]` only *boxes* will be modified, and there is no guarantee that correct correspondence with *expr* will be maintained. ■ `InterpretationBox` has attribute `HoldComplete`. ■ See page 426. ■ See also: `TagBox`, `FormBox`, `ToExpression`, `ButtonBox`.

■ Interrupt

`Interrupt[ ]` generates an interrupt.

You can call `Interrupt` anywhere within a computation. It has the same effect as an interactive interrupt at that point. ■ See page 350. ■ See also: `Abort`, `TimeConstrained`, `MemoryConstrained`, `Throw`, `$Inspector`, `LinkInterrupt`.

■ Intersection

Intersection[*list*₁, *list*₂, ...] gives a sorted list of the elements common to all the *list*ᵢ.

If the *list*ᵢ are considered as sets, Intersection gives their intersection. +■ Intersection[*list*₁, *list*₂, ...] can be input in StandardForm and InputForm as *list*₁ ∩ *list*₂ ∩ ... . The character ∩ can be entered as ¦inter¦ or \[Intersection]. ■ The *list*ᵢ must have the same head, but it need not be List.
+■ Intersection[*list*₁, ... , SameTest->*test*] applies *test* to each pair of elements in the *list*ᵢ to determine whether they should be considered the same. +■ Intersection[*a*, *b*] can be entered in StandardForm and InputForm as *a* ∩ *b* or *a* \[Intersection] *b*. ■ See page 123. ■ See also: Union, Complement.

+■ Interval

Interval[{*min*, *max*}] represents the range of values between *min* and *max*.

Interval[{*min*₁, *max*₁}, {*min*₂, *max*₂}, ...] represents the union of the ranges *min*₁ to *max*₁, *min*₂ to *max*₂, ...

You can perform arithmetic and other operations on Interval objects. ■ Example:
Interval[{1, 6}] + Interval[{0, 2}] ⟶ Interval[{1, 8}]. ■ Min[*interval*] and Max[*interval*] give the end points of an interval. ■ For approximate machine- or arbitrary-precision numbers *x*, Interval[*x*] yields an interval reflecting the uncertainty in *x*. ■ In operations on intervals that involve approximate numbers, *Mathematica* always rounds lower limits down and upper limits up. ■ Interval can be generated by functions such as Limit.
■ Relational operators such as Equal and Less yield explicit True or False results whenever they are given disjoint intervals. ■ See page 835. ■ See also: Range.

+■ IntervalIntersection

IntervalIntersection[*interval*₁, *interval*₂, ...] gives the interval representing all points common to each of the *interval*ᵢ.

See page 714.

+■ IntervalMemberQ

IntervalMemberQ[*interval*, *x*] gives True if the number *x* lies within the specified interval, and False otherwise.

IntervalMemberQ[*interval*₁, *interval*₂] gives True if *interval*₂ is completely contained within *interval*₁.

IntervalMemberQ has attribute Listable. ■ See page 714. ■ See also: MemberQ.

+■ IntervalUnion

IntervalUnion[*interval*₁, *interval*₂, ...] gives the interval representing the set of all points in any of the *interval*ᵢ.

See page 714.

■ Inverse

Inverse[*m*] gives the inverse of a square matrix *m*.

Inverse works on both symbolic and numerical matrices. ■ For matrices with approximate real or complex numbers, the inverse is generated to the maximum possible precision given the input. A warning is given for ill-conditioned matrices. ■ Inverse[*m*, Modulus->*n*] evaluates the inverse modulo *n*.
~■ Inverse[*m*, ZeroTest -> *test*] evaluates *test*[*m*[[*i*, *j*]]] to determine whether matrix elements are zero. The default setting is ZeroTest -> (# == 0 &). +■ A Method option can also be given. Possible settings are as for LinearSolve. ■ See page 842. ■ Implementation notes: see page 1020. ■ See also: PseudoInverse, LinearSolve, RowReduce, NullSpace. ■ Related package: LinearAlgebra`Tridiagonal`.

+■ InverseBetaRegularized

InverseBetaRegularized[*s*, *a*, *b*] gives the inverse of the regularized incomplete beta function.

Mathematical function (see Section A.3.10). ■ With the regularized incomplete beta function defined by $I(z, a, b) = B(z, a, b)/B(a, b)$, InverseBetaRegularized[*s*, *a*, *b*] is the solution for *z* in $s = I(z, a, b)$.
■ InverseBetaRegularized[z_0, *s*, *a*, *b*] gives the inverse of BetaRegularized[z_0, *z*, *a*, *b*]. ■ Note that the arguments of InverseBetaRegularized are arranged differently than in InverseGammaRegularized. ■ See page 740. ■ See also: InverseGammaRegularized, InverseErf.

+■ InverseEllipticNomeQ

InverseEllipticNomeQ[*q*] gives the parameter *m* corresponding to the nome *q* in an elliptic function.

Mathematical function (see Section A.3.10). ■ InverseEllipticNomeQ[*q*] yields the unique value of the parameter *m* which makes EllipticNomeQ[*m*] equal to *q*. ■ The nome *q* must always satisfy $|q| < 1$. ■ See page 752. ■ See also: EllipticNomeQ.

+■ InverseErf

InverseErf[*s*] gives the inverse error function obtained as the solution for *z* in $s = \text{erf}(z)$.

Mathematical function (see Section A.3.10). ■ Explicit numerical values are given only for real values of *s* between −1 and +1. ■ InverseErf[z_0, *s*] gives the inverse of the generalized error function Erf[z_0, *z*]. ■ See page 745.
■ See also: InverseGammaRegularized, InverseBetaRegularized.

+■ InverseErfc

InverseErfc[*s*] gives the inverse complementary error function obtained as the solution for *z* in $s = \text{erfc}(z)$.

Mathematical function (see Section A.3.10). ■ Explicit numerical values are given only for real values of *s* between 0 and 2. ■ See page 745. ■ See also: InverseGammaRegularized, InverseBetaRegularized.

■ InverseFourier

InverseFourier[*list*] finds the discrete inverse Fourier transform of a list of complex numbers.

The inverse Fourier transform a_r of a list b_s of length n is defined to be $\frac{1}{\sqrt{n}} \sum_{s=1}^{n} b_s e^{-2\pi i(r-1)(s-1)/n}$. ■ Note that the zero frequency term must appear at position 1 in the input list. ■ The definition of the Fourier transform used is the one common in the physical sciences. The sign of the exponent must be reversed to obtain the definition common in electrical engineering. ■ The list of data need not have a length equal to a power of two. ■ The *list* given in InverseFourier[*list*] can be nested to represent an array of data in any number of dimensions. ■ The array of data must be rectangular. +■ If the elements of *list* are exact numbers, InverseFourier begins by applying N to them. ■ See page 868. ■ See also: Fourier.

■ InverseFunction

InverseFunction[*f*] represents the inverse of the function *f*, defined so that InverseFunction[*f*][*y*] gives the value of x for which $f[x]$ is equal to y.

For a function with several arguments, InverseFunction[*f*] represents the inverse with respect to the first argument. InverseFunction[*f*, *n*] represents the inverse with respect to the nth argument. InverseFunction[*f*, *n*, *tot*] represents the inverse with respect to the nth argument when there are *tot* arguments in all.

In OutputForm and StandardForm, InverseFunction[*f*] is printed as $f^{(-1)}$. ■ As discussed in Section 3.2.7, many mathematical functions do not have unique inverses. In such cases, InverseFunction[*f*] can represent only one of the possible inverses for *f*. ■ Example: InverseFunction[Sin] $\longrightarrow$ ArcSin. ■ InverseFunction is generated by Solve when the option InverseFunctions is set to Automatic or True. ■ See pages 250 and 795. ■ See also: Solve, InverseSeries, Composition, Derivative.

■ InverseFunctions

InverseFunctions is an option for Solve and related functions which specifies whether inverse functions should be used.

Settings for InverseFunctions are:

True	always use inverse functions
Automatic	use inverse functions, printing a warning message (default)
False	never use inverse functions

■ Example: Solve[f[x] == a, x, InverseFunctions->True] $\longrightarrow$ {{x $\rightarrow$ f$^{(-1)}$[a]}}. ■ Inverse functions provide a way to get some, but not in general all, solutions to equations that involve functions which are more complicated than polynomials. ■ Solve[Sin[x] == a, x, InverseFunctions->True] $\longrightarrow$ {{x $\rightarrow$ ArcSin[a]}} gives a single solution in terms of ArcSin. In fact, there is an infinite number of solutions to the equation, differing by arbitrary multiples of 2π. Solve gives only one of these solutions. ■ When there are several simultaneous equations to be solved in terms of inverse functions, Solve may fail to find any solutions, even when one exists. ■ When inverse functions are allowed, Solve solves for $f[expr]$ first, then applies InverseFunction[*f*] to the result, equates it to *expr*, and continues trying to solve for the remainder of the variables. ■ See page 794. ■ See also: FindRoot.

⁺■ InverseGammaRegularized

`InverseGammaRegularized[a, s]` gives the inverse of the regularized incomplete gamma function.

Mathematical function (see Section A.3.10). ▪ With the regularized incomplete gamma function defined by $Q(a, z) = \Gamma(a, z)/\Gamma(a)$, `InverseGammaRegularized[a, s]` is the solution for z in $s = Q(a, z)$. ▪ `InverseGammaRegularized[a, z_0, s]` gives the inverse of `GammaRegularized[a, z_0, z]`. ▪ Note that the arguments of `InverseGammaRegularized` are arranged differently than in `InverseBetaRegularized`. ▪ See page 740. ▪ See also: `InverseBetaRegularized`, `InverseErf`.

■ InverseJacobiSN, InverseJacobiCN, ...

`InverseJacobiSN[v, m]`, `InverseJacobiCN[v, m]`, etc. give the inverse Jacobi elliptic functions $\mathrm{sn}^{-1}(v|m)$ etc.

There are a total of twelve functions, with names of the form `InverseJacobiPQ`, where P and Q can be any distinct pair of the letters S, C, D and N.

Mathematical functions (see Section A.3.10). ▪ $\mathrm{sn}^{-1}(v|m)$ gives the value of u for which $v = \mathrm{sn}(u|m)$. ▪ The inverse Jacobi elliptic functions are related to elliptic integrals. ▪ See page 755.

■ InverseSeries

`InverseSeries[s, x]` takes the series s generated by `Series`, and gives a series for the inverse of the function represented by s.

`InverseSeries` performs "reversion" of series. ▪ Given a series $s(y)$, `InverseSeries[s, x]` gives a series for y such that $s(y) = x$. ▪ See page 830. ▪ See also: `Solve`, `InverseFunction`.

⁺■ InverseWeierstrassP

`InverseWeierstrassP[p, {g_2, g_3}]` gives a value of u for which the Weierstrass function $\wp(u; g_2, g_3)$ is equal to p.

Mathematical function (see Section A.3.10). ▪ The value of u returned always lies in the fundamental period parallelogram defined by the complex half-periods ω and ω'. ▪ `InverseWeierstrassP[{p, q}, {g_2, g_3}]` finds the unique value of u for which $p = \wp(u; g_2, g_3)$ and $q = \wp'(u; g_2, g_3)$. For such a value to exist, p and q must be related by $q^2 = 4p^3 - g_2 p - g_3$. ▪ See page 752 for a discussion of argument conventions for elliptic functions. ▪ See page 755. ▪ See also: `WeierstrassP`, `WeierstrassPPrime`, `WeierstrassHalfPeriods`.

■ JacobiAmplitude

`JacobiAmplitude[u, m]` gives the amplitude $\mathrm{am}(u|m)$ for Jacobi elliptic functions.

Mathematical function (see Section A.3.10). ▪ `JacobiAmplitude[u, m]` converts from the argument u for an elliptic function to the amplitude ϕ. ▪ `JacobiAmplitude` is the inverse of the elliptic integral of the first kind. If $u = F(\phi|m)$, then $\phi = \mathrm{am}(u|m)$. ▪ See page 755.

■ JacobiP

JacobiP[n, a, b, x] gives the Jacobi polynomial $P_n^{(a,b)}(x)$.

Mathematical function (see Section A.3.10). ■ Explicit polynomials are given when possible. ■ $P_n^{(a,b)}(x)$ satisfies the differential equation $(1 - x^2)y'' + (b - a - (a + b + 2)x)y' + n(n + a + b + 1)y = 0$. ■ The Jacobi polynomials are orthogonal with weight function $(1 - x)^a(1 + x)^b$. ■ JacobiP[n, a, b, z] has a branch cut discontinuity in the complex z plane running from $-\infty$ to -1. ■ See page 736. ■ See also: LegendreP, ChebyshevT, ChebyshevU, GegenbauerC.

■ JacobiSN, JacobiCN, ...

JacobiSN[u, m], JacobiCN[u, m], etc. give the Jacobi elliptic functions sn($u|m$), cn($u|m$), etc.

There are a total of twelve functions, with the names of the form JacobiPQ, where P and Q can be any distinct pair of the letters S, C, D and N.

Mathematical functions (see Section A.3.10). ■ sn(u) = sin(ϕ), cn(u) = cos(ϕ) and dn(u) = $\sqrt{1 - m\sin^2(\phi)}$, where ϕ = am($u|m$). ■ Other Jacobi elliptic functions can be found from the relation pq(u) = pr(u)/qr(u), where for these purposes pp(u) = 1. ■ See page 755. ■ See also: InverseJacobiSN.

■ JacobiSymbol

JacobiSymbol[n, m] gives the Jacobi symbol $\left(\frac{n}{m}\right)$.

Integer mathematical function (see Section A.3.10). ■ For prime m, the Jacobi symbol reduces to the Legendre symbol. The Legendre symbol is equal to ±1 depending on whether n is a quadratic residue modulo m. ■ See page 725. ■ See also: FactorInteger, MoebiusMu.

■ JacobiZeta

JacobiZeta[ϕ, m] gives the Jacobi zeta function $Z(\phi|m)$.

Mathematical function (see Section A.3.10). ■ The Jacobi zeta function is given in terms of elliptic integrals by $Z(\phi|m) = E(\phi|m) - E(m)F(\phi|m)/K(m)$. ■ Argument conventions for elliptic integrals are discussed on 752. ■ See page 753. ■ See also: EllipticE, EllipticF, EllipticK.

■ Join

Join[$list_1$, $list_2$, ...] concatenates lists together. Join can be used on any set of expressions that have the same head.

See page 123. ■ See also: Union, StringJoin, Append, Prepend.

+■ JordanDecomposition

JordanDecomposition[m] yields the Jordan decomposition of a square matrix m. The result is a list $\{s, j\}$ where s is a similarity matrix and j is the Jordan canonical form of m.

The original matrix m is equal to s . j . Inverse[s]. ■ The matrix m can be either numerical or symbolic. ■ See page 852. ■ See also: Eigensystem, SingularValues, QRDecomposition, SchurDecomposition, MatrixExp.

◼ KleinInvariantJ

KleinInvariantJ[τ] gives the Klein invariant modular elliptic function $J(\tau)$.

Mathematical function (see Section A.3.10). ◾ The argument τ is the ratio of Weierstrass half-periods ω'/ω. ◾ KleinInvariantJ is given in terms of Weierstrass invariants by $g_2^3/(g_2^3 - 27g_3^2)$. ◾ $J(\tau)$ is invariant under any combination of the modular transformations $\tau \rightarrow \tau + 1$ and $\tau \rightarrow -1/\tau$. ◾ See page 752 for a discussion of argument conventions for elliptic functions. ◾ See page 757. ◾ See also: ModularLambda, DedekindEta, WeierstrassInvariants, EllipticTheta.

◼ Label

Label[*tag*] represents a point in a compound expression to which control can be transferred using Goto.

Label must appear as an explicit element of a CompoundExpression object. ◾ Label has attribute HoldFirst. ◾ See page 334. ◾ See also: Catch.

◼ LaguerreL

LaguerreL[n, x] gives the Laguerre polynomial $L_n(x)$.

LaguerreL[n, a, x] gives the generalized Laguerre polynomial $L_n^a(x)$.

Mathematical function (see Section A.3.10). ◾ Explicit polynomials are given when possible. ◾ $L_n(x) = L_n^0(x)$. ◾ The Laguerre polynomials are orthogonal with weight function $x^a e^{-x}$. ◾ They satisfy the differential equation $xy'' + (a + 1 - x)y' + ny = 0$. ◾ LaguerreL[$n$, x] is an entire function of x with no branch cut discontinuities. ◾ See page 736. ◾ See also: HermiteH.

◼ Last

Last[*expr*] gives the last element in *expr*.

Last[*expr*] is equivalent to *expr*[[-1]]. ◾ See page 118. ◾ See also: Part, First, Take.

◼ LatticeReduce

LatticeReduce[{v_1, v_2, ... }] gives a reduced basis for the set of vectors v_i.

The elements of the v_i can be integers, Gaussian integers, or Gaussian rational numbers. ◾ See page 725. ◾ See also: Rationalize. ◾ Related package: NumberTheory`Recognize`.

◼ LCM

LCM[n_1, n_2, ...] gives the least common multiple of the integers n_i.

Integer mathematical function (see Section A.3.10). ◾ See page 722. ◾ See also: GCD, PolynomialLCM.

◼ LeafCount

LeafCount[*expr*] gives the total number of indivisible subexpressions in *expr*.

LeafCount gives a measure of the total "size" of an expression. ◾ LeafCount counts the number of subexpressions in *expr* which correspond to "leaves" on the expression tree. ◾ Example: LeafCount[1 + a + b^2] $\longrightarrow$ 6. ◾ See page 687. ◾ See also: ByteCount, Length, Depth, AtomQ.

~■ LegendreP

LegendreP[n, x] gives the Legendre polynomial $P_n(x)$.

LegendreP[n, m, x] gives the associated Legendre polynomial $P_n^m(x)$.

Mathematical function (see Section A.3.10). ■ Explicit formulas are given for integer n and m. ■ The Legendre polynomials satisfy the differential equation $(1 - x^2)(d^2y/dx^2) - 2x(dy/dx) + n(n + 1)y = 0$. ■ The Legendre polynomials are orthogonal with unit weight function. ■ The associated Legendre polynomials are defined by $P_n^m(x) = (-1)^m(1 - x^2)^{m/2}(d^m/dx^m)P_n(x)$. ■ For arbitrary complex values of n, m and z, LegendreP[n, z] and LegendreP[n, m, z] give Legendre functions of the first kind. ~■ LegendreP[n, m, a, z] gives Legendre functions of type a. The default is type 1. ■ The symbolic form of type 1 involves $(1 - z^2)^{m/2}$, of type 2 involves $((1 + z)/(1 - z))^{m/2}$ and of type 3 involves $((1 + z)/(-1 + z))^{m/2}$. ■ Type 1 is defined only for z within the unit circle in the complex plane. Type 2 represents an analytic continuation of type 1 outside the unit circle. ■ Type 2 functions have branch cuts from $-\infty$ to -1 and from $+1$ to $+\infty$ in the complex z plane. ■ Type 3 functions have a single branch cut from $-\infty$ to $+1$. ■ LegendreP[n, m, a, z] is defined to be Hypergeometric2F1Regularized[$-n$,$n+1$,$1-m$,$(1-z)/2$] multiplied by $((1 + z)/(1 - z))^{m/2}$ for type 2 and by $((1 + z)/(-1 + z))^{m/2}$ for type 3. ■ See pages 736 and 747. ■ See also: SphericalHarmonicY.

~■ LegendreQ

LegendreQ[n, z] gives the Legendre function of the second kind $Q_n(z)$.

LegendreQ[n, m, z] gives the associated Legendre function of the second kind $Q_n^m(z)$.

Mathematical function (see Section A.3.10). ■ For integer n and m, explicit formulas are generated. ■ The Legendre functions satisfy the differential equation $(1 - z^2)y'' - 2zy' + [n(n + 1) - m^2/(1 - z^2)]y = 0$. ~■ LegendreQ[$n$, m, a, z] gives Legendre functions of type a. The default is type 1. ■ LegendreQ of types 1, 2 and 3 are defined in terms of LegendreP of these types, and have the same branch cut structure. ■ See page 747.

■ Length

Length[*expr*] gives the number of elements in *expr*.

See page 234. ■ Length[*expr*] returns 0 whenever AtomQ[*expr*] is True. ■ See also: LeafCount, ByteCount, Depth.

■ LerchPhi

LerchPhi[z, s, a] gives the Lerch transcendent $\Phi(z, s, a)$.

Mathematical function (see Section A.3.10). ■ $\Phi(z, s, a) = \sum_{k=0}^{\infty} z^k/(a + k)^s$, where any term with $k + a = 0$ is excluded. ■ LerchPhi[z, s, a, DoublyInfinite->True] gives the sum $\sum_{k=-\infty}^{\infty} z^k/(a + k)^s$. ■ LerchPhi is a generalization of Zeta and PolyLog. ■ See page 742. ■ Related package: NumberTheory`Ramanujan`.

~■ Less

$x < y$ yields True if x is determined to be less than y.

$x_1 < x_2 < x_3$ yields True if the x_i form a strictly increasing sequence.

Less gives True or False when its arguments are real numbers. ■ Less does some simplification when its arguments are not numbers. +■ For exact numeric quantities, Less internally uses numerical approximations to establish numerical ordering. This process can be affected by the setting of the global variable $MaxExtraPrecision. ■ See page 84. ■ See also: Greater, Positive.

~■ LessEqual

~ *x* <= *y* or *x* ≤ *y* yields True if *x* is determined to be less than or equal to *y*.

~ $x_1 \le x_2 \le x_3$ yields True if the x_i form a non-decreasing sequence.

+■ *x* ≤ *y* can be entered as *x* :<=: *y* or *x* \[LessEqual] *y*. ■ LessEqual gives True or False when its arguments are real numbers. ■ LessEqual does some simplification when its arguments are not numbers. +■ For exact numeric quantities, LessEqual internally uses numerical approximations to establish numerical ordering. This process can be affected by the setting of the global variable $MaxExtraPrecision. +■ In StandardForm, LessEqual is printed using ≤. +■ *x* ≤ *y*, entered as *x* :</: *y* or *x* \[LessSlantEqual] *y*, can be used on input as an alternative to *x* ≤ *y*. ■ See page 84.

~■ LetterQ

LetterQ[*string*] yields True if all the characters in the string are letters, and yields False otherwise.

LetterQ[*string*] by default gives False if *string* contains any space or punctuation characters. ~■ LetterQ handles both ordinary and special characters. ~■ LetterQ treats as letters all special characters explicitly listed as letters in the table on pages 1270–1316. ~■ In general, LetterQ treats as letters all characters that appear as ordinary text in any language. +■ LetterQ treats as letters such special characters as α, ℤ, ℒ and æ. +■ LetterQ does not treat as letters ∅ (\[EmptySet], ℏ (\[HBar]), Å (\[Angstrom] or ∑ (\[Sum]). ■ See page 392. ■ See also: DigitQ, UpperCaseQ, LowerCaseQ, CharacterRange.

■ Level

Level[*expr*, *levelspec*] gives a list of all subexpressions of *expr* on levels specified by *levelspec*.

Level[*expr*, *levelspec*, *f*] applies *f* to the list of subexpressions.

Level uses the standard level specification described on page 989. ■ Level[*expr*, {-1}] gives a list of all "atomic" objects in *expr*. ■ Level traverses expressions in depth-first order, so that the subexpressions in the final list are ordered lexicographically by their indices. ■ See page 237. ■ See also: Apply, Map, Scan.

■ Lighting

Lighting is an option for Graphics3D and related functions that specifies whether to use simulated illumination in three-dimensional pictures.

Lighting -> True uses simulated illumination. The ambient light level is specified by the option AmbientLight. The option LightSources gives the positions and intensities of point light sources. ■ Lighting -> False uses no simulated illumination. In SurfaceGraphics, polygons are then shaded according to their height, or according to the ColorFunction option that is given. ■ See pages 506 and 523. ■ See also: Shading, ColorFunction, SurfaceColor.

■ LightSources

LightSources is an option for Graphics3D and related functions that specifies the properties of point light sources for simulated illumination.

The basic form is LightSources -> {s_1, s_2, ... }, where the s_i are the specifications for each light source. Each s_i has the form {*direction*, *color*}. The direction is specified as {*x*, *y*, *z*}, where the components are with respect to the final display area. The *x* and *y* are horizontal and vertical in the plane of the display; *z* is orthogonal to the display. Positive *z* is in front. Only the relative magnitude of the components is relevant; the overall normalization of the vector is ignored. The color can be specified by GrayLevel, Hue or RGBColor. ■ Simulated illumination determines the shading of polygons in three-dimensional pictures. ■ The shading of a particular polygon is computed as a sum of contributions from point light sources, plus a contribution from ambient light. ■ Surface properties of polygons are specified by SurfaceColor directives. ■ Light reflection properties assumed for polygons are described in the notes for SurfaceColor. ■ See page 524. ■ See also: AmbientLight.

~■ **Limit**

Limit[*expr*, *x*->*x*₀] finds the limiting value of *expr* when *x* approaches x_0.

Example: Limit[Sin[x]/x, x->0] ⟶ 1. ■ Limit[*expr*, *x*->*x*₀, Direction -> 1] computes the limit as *x* approaches x_0 from smaller values. Limit[*expr*, *x*->*x*₀, Direction -> -1] computes the limit as *x* approaches x_0 from larger values. ~■ Limit returns Interval objects to represent ranges of possible values, for example at essential singularities. ■ Limit returns unevaluated when it encounters functions about which it has no specific information. Limit therefore makes no explicit assumptions about symbolic functions. ■ See page 834. ■ See also: Series, Residue. ■ Related package: NumericalMath`NLimit`.

+■ **LimitsPositioning**

LimitsPositioning is an option for UnderoverscriptBox and related boxes which specifies whether to change the positioning of underscripts and overscripts in the way conventional for limits.

UnderoverscriptBox[*x*, *y*, *z*, LimitsPositioning->False] is always displayed with explicit underscripts and overscripts, as $\overset{z}{\underset{y}{x}}$. ■ UnderoverscriptBox[*x*, *y*, *z*, LimitsPositioning->True] is displayed as $\overset{z}{x}$ when large, and x_y^z when small. ■ The x_y^z form is used when the box appears in a subscript or other script, or inline in a piece of text. ■ With the default setting LimitsPositioning->Automatic the display of UnderoverscriptBox[*x*, *y*, *z*] depends on *x*. If *x* is \[Sum], \[Product] or another form conventionally displayed with limits, then LimitsPositioning->True is effectively used. Otherwise, LimitsPositioning->False is used. ■ LimitsPositioningTokens is a Cell option which can be set to a list of forms for which LimitsPositioning->True should be used. ■ See page 437. ■ See also: ScriptSizeMultipliers.

~■ **Line**

Line[{*pt*₁, *pt*₂, ... }] is a graphics primitive which represents a line joining a sequence of points.

Line can be used in both Graphics and Graphics3D (two- and three-dimensional graphics). ■ The positions of points can be specified either in absolute coordinates, as {*x*, *y*} or {*x*, *y*, *z*}, or in scaled coordinates as Scaled[{*x*, *y*}] or Scaled[{*x*, *y*, *z*}]. +■ Offset can be used to specify coordinates in two dimensions. ■ The line consists of a sequence of straight segments joining the specified points. ■ Line thickness can be specified using Thickness or AbsoluteThickness. ■ Line dashing can be specified using Dashing or AbsoluteDashing. ■ Line shading or coloring can be specified using CMYKColor, GrayLevel, Hue or RGBColor. ■ See pages 472 and 500. ■ See also: Polygon, PlotJoined. ■ Related packages: Graphics`Arrow`, Graphics`Spline`.

■ **LinearProgramming**

LinearProgramming[*c*, *m*, *b*] finds the vector *x* which minimizes the quantity $c.x$ subject to the constraints $m.x \geq b$ and $x \geq 0$.

All entries in the vectors *c* and *b* and the matrix *m* must be numbers. ■ LinearProgramming gives exact rational number results if its input is exact. ■ LinearProgramming accepts the same Tolerance option as ConstrainedMax. ■ See page 898. ■ See also: ConstrainedMin.

₊■ ListInterpolation

ListInterpolation[*array*] constructs an InterpolatingFunction object which represents an approximate function that interpolates the array of values given.

ListInterpolation[*array*, {{*xmin*, *xmax*}, {*ymin*, *ymax*}, ... }] specifies the domain of the grid from which the values in *array* are assumed to come.

You can replace {*xmin*, *xmax*} etc. by explicit lists of positions for grid lines. The grid lines are otherwise assumed to be equally spaced. ■ ListInterpolation[*array*] assumes grid lines at integer positions in each direction. ■ *array* can be an array in any number of dimensions, corresponding to a list with any number of levels of nesting. ■ ListInterpolation[*array*, *domain*] generates an InterpolatingFunction object which returns values with the same precision as those in {*array*, *domain*}. ■ See notes for Interpolation. ■ See page 866. ■ See also: FunctionInterpolation, ListContourPlot.

■ ListPlay

ListPlay[{a_1, a_2, ... }] plays a sound whose amplitude is given by the sequence of levels a_i.

ListPlay returns a Sound object. ■ The following options can be given:

DisplayFunction	$SoundDisplayFunction	function for generating output
Epilog	{}	sound or graphics to be used as an epilog
PlayRange	Automatic	the range of amplitude levels to include
Prolog	{}	sound or graphics to be used as a prolog
SampleDepth	8	how many bits to use to represent each amplitude level
SampleRate	8192	how many times per second amplitude samples should be generated

■ ListPlay[{*list*$_1$, *list*$_2$}] generates stereo sound. The left-hand channel is given first. ■ ListPlay[{*list*$_1$, *list*$_2$, ... }] generates sound on any number of channels. If the lists are of different lengths, silence is inserted at the ends of the shorter lists. ■ See page 171. ■ See also: Play, SampledSoundList, Show. ■ Related package: Miscellaneous`Audio`.

■ ListPlot

ListPlot[{y_1, y_2, ... }] plots a list of values. The *x* coordinates for each point are taken to be 1, 2, ...

ListPlot[{{x_1, y_1}, {x_2, y_2}, ... }] plots a list of values with specified *x* and *y* coordinates.

ListPlot returns a Graphics object. ■ ListPlot has the same options as Graphics, with the following additions:

PlotJoined	False	whether to draw a line joining the points
PlotStyle	Automatic	graphics directives to determine the style of the points or line

■ Setting PlotJoined -> True gives a line joining the points. ■ ListPlot has the default option setting Axes -> True. ■ See page 158. ■ See also: Plot, Fit. ■ Related package: Graphics`MultipleListPlot`, Graphics`Graphics`.

■ ListPlot3D

ListPlot3D[*array*] generates a three-dimensional plot of a surface representing an array of height values.

ListPlot3D[*array*, *shades*] generates a plot with each element of the surface shaded according to the specification in *shades*.

ListPlot3D returns a SurfaceGraphics object. ■ ListPlot3D has the same options as SurfaceGraphics.
■ ListPlot3D has the default option setting Axes -> True. ■ *array* should be a rectangular array of real numbers, representing *z* values. There will be holes in the surface corresponding to any array elements that are not real numbers. ■ If *array* has dimensions $m \times n$, then *shades* must have dimensions $(m - 1) \times (n - 1)$. ■ The elements of *shades* must be either GrayLevel, Hue or RGBColor, or SurfaceColor objects. ■ See page 158. ■ See also: Plot3D.
■ Related package: Graphics`Graphics3D`, DiscreteMath`ComputationalGeometry`.

■ Locked

Locked is an attribute which, once assigned, prevents modification of any attributes of a symbol.

See page 309. ■ See also: Protected, ReadProtected.

■ Log

Log[*z*] gives the natural logarithm of *z* (logarithm to base *e*).

Log[*b*, *z*] gives the logarithm to base *b*.

Mathematical function (see Section A.3.10). ■ Log gives exact rational number results when possible. ■ Log[*z*] has a branch cut discontinuity in the complex *z* plane running from $-\infty$ to 0. ■ See page 731. ■ See also: Exp, Power, Arg, MantissaExponent, ProductLog.

■ LogGamma

LogGamma[*z*] gives the logarithm of the gamma function $\log \Gamma(z)$.

Mathematical function (see Section A.3.10). ■ Unlike Log[Gamma[*z*]], LogGamma[*z*] is analytic throughout the complex *z* plane, except for a branch cut discontinuity along the negative real axis. ■ See page 740.

■ LogicalExpand

LogicalExpand[*expr*] expands out expressions containing logical connectives such as && and ||.

LogicalExpand applies distributive laws for logical operations. ■ Example:
LogicalExpand[p && !(q || r)] $\longrightarrow$ p && ! q && ! r. ■ LogicalExpand generates ORs of ANDs corresponding to disjunctive normal form, with some contractions. ■ See pages 85 and 832. ■ See also: Expand.

■ LogIntegral

LogIntegral[*z*] is the logarithmic integral function li(*z*).

Mathematical function (see Section A.3.10). ■ The logarithmic integral function is defined by $\mathrm{li}(z) = \int_0^z dt/\log t$, where the principal value of the integral is taken. ■ LogIntegral[*z*] has a branch cut discontinuity in the complex *z* plane running from $-\infty$ to +1. ■ See page 744. ■ See also: ExpIntegralE.

~■ LowerCaseQ

LowerCaseQ[*string*] yields True if all the characters in the string are lower-case letters, and yields False otherwise.

~■ LowerCaseQ treats both ordinary and special characters. ■ See page 392. ■ See also: UpperCaseQ, LetterQ, ToLowerCase, ToCharacterCode.

+■ LUBackSubstitution

LUBackSubstitution[*data*, *b*] takes the data generated by LUDecomposition[*m*] and yields the solution to the matrix equation **m.x = b**.

See pages 849 and 852. ■ See also: LinearSolve, Solve.

+■ LUDecomposition

LUDecomposition[*m*] generates a representation of the LU decomposition of a matrix *m*.

LUDecomposition returns a list of three elements. The first element is a combination of upper and lower triangular matrices, the second element is a vector specifying rows used for pivoting, and for approximate numerical matrices **m** the third element is an estimate of the L^∞ condition number of **m**. ■ The data generated by LUDecomposition is intended for use in LUBackSubstitution. ■ See pages 849 and 852. ■ Implementation notes: see page 1020. ■ See also: LUBackSubstitution, QRDecomposition, SchurDecomposition. ■ Related packages: LinearAlgebra`Cholesky`, LinearAlgebra`Orthogonalization`.

■ MachineNumberQ

MachineNumberQ[*expr*] returns True if *expr* is a machine-precision real or complex number, and returns False otherwise.

See page 703. ■ See also: Precision, NumberQ. ■ Related package: NumericalMath`ComputerArithmetic`.

+■ Magnification

Magnification is an option for Cell which specifies at what magnification to display the cell.

Magnification is often set for styles of cells or whole notebooks instead of individual cells. ■ Magnification affects spaces between cells as well as individual cells. ■ See page 579. ■ See also: ShowRuler.

+■ MakeBoxes

MakeBoxes[*expr*, *form*] is the low-level function used in *Mathematica* sessions to convert expressions into boxes.

MakeBoxes does not evaluate *expr*. ■ *form* can be StandardForm, TraditionalForm, or any other output form. ■ You can give definitions for MakeBoxes[*expr*, *form*] to specify your own rules for how expressions should be converted to boxes. ■ MakeBoxes is not automatically called on the results it generates. This means that explicit MakeBoxes calls must typically be inserted into definitions that are given. ■ If you change the output format for an expression by giving a definition for MakeBoxes, there is no guarantee that output you get will subsequently be able to be interpreted by *Mathematica*. ■ Definitions you give for MakeBoxes will override built-in *Mathematica* rules for generating output. ■ See page 454. ■ See also: MakeExpression, ToBoxes, Format.

+■ **MakeExpression**

> MakeExpression[*boxes*, *form*] is the low-level function used in *Mathematica* sessions to construct expressions from boxes.

MakeExpression returns its result wrapped in HoldComplete. ■ *form* can be StandardForm, TraditionalForm, or other forms for which interpretation rules have been defined. ■ You can give definitions for MakeExpression[*expr*, *form*] to specify your own rules for how boxes should be converted to expressions. ■ MakeExpression is not automatically called on the results it generates. This means that explicit MakeExpression calls must typically be inserted into definitions for MakeExpression. ■ MakeExpression is used whenever boxes are supplied as input to *Mathematica*. ■ The boxes that are fed to MakeExpression are constructed from textual input by forming tokens, then grouping these according to standard *Mathematica* operator precedence rules, stripping out spacing characters. StyleBox and other objects not intended for interpretation are removed. ■ Definitions you give for MakeExpression will override built-in *Mathematica* rules for processing input. ■ Giving input prefaced by \! makes *Mathematica* effectively perform MakeExpression. ■ See page 454. ■ See also: MakeBoxes, ToExpression.

■ **MantissaExponent**

> MantissaExponent[*x*] gives a list containing the mantissa and exponent of an approximate real number *x*.

The mantissa is always a number between −1 and +1. In absolute magnitude, the mantissa always lies between 0.1 and 1. ■ Example: MantissaExponent[3.4 10^25] ⟶ {0.34, 26}. ■ MantissaExponent[*x*, *b*] gives the base-*b* mantissa and exponent. Its absolute magnitude is between $1/b$ and 1. ■ See page 702. ■ See also: Log, RealDigits.

■ **Map**

> Map[*f*, *expr*] or *f* /@ *expr* applies *f* to each element on the first level in *expr*.

> Map[*f*, *expr*, *levelspec*] applies *f* to parts of *expr* specified by *levelspec*.

Examples: Map[f, {a, b, c}] ⟶ {f[a], f[b], f[c]}; Map[f, a + b + c] ⟶ f[a] + f[b] + f[c]. ■ Level specifications are described on page 989. ■ The default value for *levelspec* in Map is {1}. ■ Examples:
Map[f, {{a,b},{c,d}}] ⟶ {f[{a, b}], f[{c, d}]};
Map[f, {{a,b},{c,d}}, 2] ⟶ {f[{f[a], f[b]}], f[{f[c], f[d]}]};
Map[f, {{a,b},{c,d}}, -1] ⟶ {f[{f[a], f[b]}], f[{f[c], f[d]}]}. ■ See page 241. ■ See also: Apply, Scan, Level, Operate, MapThread.

■ **MapAll**

> MapAll[*f*, *expr*] or *f* //@ *expr* applies *f* to every subexpression in *expr*.

Example: MapAll[f, {{a,b},{c,d}}] ⟶ f[{f[{f[a], f[b]}], f[{f[c], f[d]}]}]. ■ MapAll[*f*, *expr*] is equivalent to Map[*f*, *expr*, {0, Infinity}]. ■ MapAll[*f*, *expr*, Heads -> True] applies *f* inside the heads of the parts of *expr*. ■ See page 242. ■ See also: ExpandAll, ReplaceAll.

■ **MapAt**

MapAt[*f*, *expr*, *n*] applies *f* to the element at position *n* in *expr*. If *n* is negative, the position is counted from the end.

MapAt[*f*, *expr*, {*i*, *j*, ... }] applies *f* to the part of *expr* at position {*i*, *j*, ... }.

MapAt[*f*, *expr*, {{*i*₁, *j*₁, ... }, {*i*₂, *j*₂, ... }, ... }] applies *f* to parts of *expr* at several positions.

Example: MapAt[f, {a, b, c}, 2] ⟶ {a, f[b], c}.
■ MapAt[f, {a, b, c, d}, {{1}, {4}}] ⟶ {f[a], b, c, f[d]}. ■ MapAt[*f*, *expr*, {*i*, *j*, ... }] or
MapAt[*f*, *expr*, {{*i*, *j*, ... }}] applies *f* to the part *expr*[[*i*, *j*, ...]].
■ MapAt[*f*, *expr*, {{*i*₁, *j*₁, ... }, {*i*₂, *j*₂, ... }, ... }] applies *f* to parts *expr*[[*i*₁, *j*₁, ...]], *expr*[[*i*₂, *j*₂, ...]], ...
■ The list of positions used by MapAt is in the same form as is returned by the function Position. ■ MapAt applies
f repeatedly to a particular part if that part is mentioned more than once in the list of positions. ■ Example:
MapAt[f, {a, b, c}, {{1}, {3}, {1}}] ⟶ {f[f[a]], b, f[c]}. ■ See page 243. ■ See also: ReplacePart,
Delete, FlattenAt.

■ **MapIndexed**

MapIndexed[*f*, *expr*] applies *f* to the elements of *expr*, giving the part specification of each element as a second argument to *f*.

MapIndexed[*f*, *expr*, *levspec*] applies *f* to all parts of *expr* on levels specified by *levspec*.

Example: MapIndexed[f, {a, b, c}] ⟶ {f[a, {1}], f[b, {2}], f[c, {3}]}. ■ Level specifications are
described on page 989. ■ The default value for *levelspec* in MapIndexed is {1}. ■ Example:
MapIndexed[f, {{a, b}, {c, d}}, Infinity] ⟶
{f[{f[a, {1, 1}], f[b, {1, 2}]}, {1}], f[{f[c, {2, 1}], f[d, {2, 2}]}, {2}]}. ■ See page 244. ■ See also:
MapAt.

■ **MapThread**

MapThread[*f*, {{*a*₁, *a*₂, ... }, {*b*₁, *b*₂, ... }, ... }] gives
{*f*[*a*₁, *b*₁, ...], *f*[*a*₂, *b*₂, ...], ... }.

MapThread[*f*, {*expr*₁, *expr*₂, ... }, *n*] applies *f* to the parts of the *expr*ᵢ at level *n*.

Example: MapThread[f, {{a1, a2}, {b1, b2}}] ⟶ {f[a1, b1], f[a2, b2]}.
■ MapThread[f, {{{a1, a2}}, {{b1, b2}}}] ⟶ {f[{a1, a2}, {b1, b2}]}.
■ MapThread[f, {{{a1, a2}}, {{b1, b2}}}, 2] ⟶ {{f[a1, b1], f[a2, b2]}}. ■ Level specifications are
described on page 989. ■ See page 244. ■ See also: Map, Thread, Inner.

■ **MatchLocalNames**

MatchLocalNames is an option for **Trace** and related functions which specifies whether symbols such as *x* should match symbols with local names of the form *x*$*nnn*.

The default setting is MatchLocalNames -> True. ■ With the default setting, Trace[*expr*, *x* = *rhs*] will show
assignments to local variables whose names are of the form *x*$*nnn*.
■ Trace[*expr*, *x* = *rhs*, MatchLocalNames->False] shows assignments only for the global symbol *x*. ■ See
page 343.

■ MatchQ

MatchQ[*expr*, *form*] returns True if the pattern *form* matches *expr*, and returns False otherwise.

See page 265. ■ See also: StringMatchQ.

₊■ MathieuC

MathieuC[*a*, *q*, *z*] gives the even Mathieu function with characteristic value *a* and parameter *q*.

Mathematical function (see Section A.3.10). ■ The Mathieu functions satisfy the equation $y'' + (a - 2q\cos(2z))y = 0$. ■ See page 759. ■ See also: MathieuCPrime.

₊■ MathieuCharacteristicA

MathieuCharacteristicA[*r*, *q*] gives the characteristic value a_r for even Mathieu functions with characteristic exponent *r* and parameter *q*.

Mathematical function (see Section A.3.10). ■ The characteristic value a_r gives the value of the parameter *a* in $y'' + (a - 2q\cos(2z))y = 0$ for which the solution has the form $e^{irz}f(z)$ where $f(z)$ is an even function of *z* with period 2π. ■ See page 759.

₊■ MathieuCharacteristicB

MathieuCharacteristicB[*r*, *q*] gives the characteristic value b_r for odd Mathieu functions with characteristic exponent *r* and parameter *q*.

Mathematical function (see Section A.3.10). ■ The characteristic value b_r gives the value of the parameter *a* in $y'' + (a - 2q\cos(2z))y = 0$ for which the solution has the form $e^{irz}f(z)$ where $f(z)$ is an odd function of *z* with period 2π. ■ When *r* is not a real integer, MathieuCharacteristicB gives the same results as MathieuCharacteristicA. ■ See notes for MathieuCharacteristicA. ■ See page 759.

₊■ MathieuCharacteristicExponent

MathieuCharacteristicExponent[*a*, *q*] gives the characteristic exponent *r* for Mathieu functions with characteristic value *a* and parameter *q*.

Mathematical function (see Section A.3.10). ■ All Mathieu functions have the form $e^{irz}f(z)$ where $f(z)$ has period 2π and *r* is the Mathieu characteristic exponent. ■ See page 759.

₊■ MathieuCPrime

MathieuCPrime[*a*, *q*, *z*] gives the derivative with respect to *z* of the even Mathieu function with characteristic value *a* and parameter *q*.

Mathematical function (see Section A.3.10). ■ See page 759.

₊■ MathieuS

MathieuS[*a*, *q*, *z*] gives the odd Mathieu function with characteristic value *a* and parameter *q*.

Mathematical function (see Section A.3.10). ■ The Mathieu functions satisfy the equation $y'' + (a - 2q\cos(2z))y = 0$. ■ See page 759.

₊■ MathieuSPrime

MathieuSPrime[a, q, z] gives the derivative with respect to z of the odd Mathieu function with characteristic value a and parameter q.

Mathematical function (see Section A.3.10). ▪ See page 759.

■ MatrixExp

MatrixExp[mat] gives the matrix exponential of mat.

MatrixExp[mat] effectively evaluates the power series for the exponential function, with ordinary powers replaced by matrix powers. ▪ MatrixExp works only on square matrices. ▪ See page 846. ▪ See also: MatrixPower, Dot, JordanDecomposition, QRDecomposition.

~■ MatrixForm

MatrixForm[$list$] prints with the elements of $list$ arranged in a regular array.

~▪ In StandardForm the array is shown enclosed in parentheses. ▪ MatrixForm prints a single-level list in a column. It prints a two-level list in standard matrix form. More deeply nested lists are by default printed with successive dimensions alternating between rows and columns. ₊▪ Elements in each column are by default centered. ▪ MatrixForm takes the same set of options as TableForm. ▪ MatrixForm acts as a "wrapper", which affects printing, but not evaluation. ▪ See page 418. ▪ See also: TableForm, ColumnForm, GridBox, GraphicsArray.

■ MatrixPower

MatrixPower[mat, n] gives the nth matrix power of mat.

MatrixPower[mat, n] effectively evaluates the product of a matrix with itself n times. ▪ When n is negative, MatrixPower finds powers of the inverse of mat. ▪ MatrixPower works only on square matrices. ▪ See page 846. ▪ See also: Dot, MatrixExp.

■ MatrixQ

MatrixQ[$expr$] gives True if $expr$ is a list of lists that can represent a matrix, and gives False otherwise.

MatrixQ[$expr$, $test$] gives True only if $test$ yields True when applied to each of the matrix elements in $expr$.

MatrixQ[$expr$] gives True only if $expr$ is a list, and each of its elements is a list of the same length, containing no elements that are themselves lists. ▪ MatrixQ[$expr$, NumberQ] tests whether $expr$ is a numerical matrix. ▪ See pages 264 and 839. ▪ See also: VectorQ, TensorRank. ▪ Related package: LinearAlgebra`MatrixManipulation`.

■ Max

Max[x_1, x_2, ...] yields the numerically largest of the x_i.

Max[{x_1, x_2, ... }, {y_1, ... }, ...] yields the largest element of any of the lists.

Max yields a definite result if all its arguments are real numbers. ▪ In other cases, Max carries out some simplifications. ▪ Max[ ] gives -Infinity. ▪ See page 718. ▪ See also: Min, Order.

■ **MaxBend**

MaxBend is an option for Plot which measures the maximum bend angle between successive line segments on a curve.

Plot uses an adaptive algorithm to try and include enough sample points so that there are no bends larger than MaxBend between successive segments of the plot. ■ Plot will not, however, subdivide by a factor of more than PlotDivision. ■ Smaller settings for MaxBend will lead to smoother curves, based on more sample points. ■ See page 137.

■ **MaxMemoryUsed**

MaxMemoryUsed[ ] gives the maximum number of bytes used to store all data for the current *Mathematica* session.

On most computer systems, MaxMemoryUsed[ ] will give results close to those obtained from external process status requests. ■ MaxMemoryUsed[ ] will not typically account for code space, stack space or the effects of heap fragmentation. ■ See page 685. ■ See also: MemoryInUse, ByteCount.

+■ **MeijerG**

MeijerG[{{a_1, ... , a_n}, {a_{n+1}, ... , a_p}}, {{b_1, ... , b_m}, {b_{m+1}, ... , b_q}}, z] is the Meijer G function $G_{pq}^{mn}\left(z \left| {}^{a_1,...,a_p}_{b_1,...,b_q} \right. \right)$.

Mathematical function (see Section A.3.10). ■ The generalized form MeijerG[*alist*, *blist*, z, r] is defined for real r by $r/2\pi i \int [\Gamma(1-a_1-rs)...\Gamma(1-a_n-rs)\Gamma(b_1+rs)...\Gamma(b_m+rs)]/[\Gamma(a_{n+1}+rs)...\Gamma(a_p+rs)\Gamma(1-b_{m+1}-rs)...\Gamma(1-b_q-rs)]z^{-s}ds$, where in the default case $r = 1$. ■ In many special cases, MeijerG is automatically converted to other functions. ■ See page 750. ■ See also: HypergeometricPFQ.

■ **MemberQ**

MemberQ[*list*, *form*] returns True if an element of *list* matches *form*, and False otherwise.

MemberQ[*list*, *form*, *levelspec*] tests all parts of *list* specified by *levelspec*.

form can be a pattern. ■ Example: MemberQ[{x^2, y^2}, x^_] ⟶ True. ■ The first argument of MemberQ can have any head, not necessarily List. ■ See page 265. ■ See also: FreeQ, Count, Cases, IntervalMemberQ.

■ **MemoryConstrained**

MemoryConstrained[*expr*, b] evaluates *expr*, stopping if more than b bytes of memory are requested.

MemoryConstrained[*expr*, b, *failexpr*] returns *failexpr* if the memory constraint is not met.

MemoryConstrained generates an interrupt to stop the evaluation of *expr* if the amount of additional memory requested during the evaluation of *expr* exceeds b bytes. ■ MemoryConstrained evaluates *failexpr* only if the evaluation is aborted. ■ MemoryConstrained returns $Aborted if the evaluation is aborted and no *failexpr* is specified. ■ Aborts generated by MemoryConstrained are treated just like those generated by Abort, and can thus be overruled by AbortProtect. ■ See page 686. ■ See also: TimeConstrained, MaxMemoryUsed, $RecursionLimit, Abort.

■ **MemoryInUse**

MemoryInUse[ ] gives the number of bytes currently being used to store all data in the current *Mathematica* session.

See page 685. ■ See also: MaxMemoryUsed, ByteCount, Share. ■ Related package: Utilities`MemoryConserve`.

■ **Mesh**

> Mesh is an option for `SurfaceGraphics` and `DensityGraphics` that specifies whether an explicit *x–y* mesh should be drawn.
>
> See page 518. ▪ See also: `FaceGrids`, `Boxed`.

■ **MeshRange**

> MeshRange is an option for `ListPlot3D`, `SurfaceGraphics`, `ListContourPlot`, `ListDensityPlot` and related functions which specifies the range of *x* and *y* coordinates that correspond to the array of *z* values given.
>
> `MeshRange->{{`*xmin*, *xmax*`}, {`*ymin*, *ymax*`}}` specifies ranges in *x* and *y*. Mesh lines are taken to be equally spaced. ▪ `MeshRange->Automatic` takes *x* and *y* to be a grid of integers determined by indices in the array. ▪ Settings for `MeshRange` are produced automatically by `Plot3D`, etc. for insertion into `SurfaceGraphics` etc. ▪ `MeshRange` is used to determine tick values for surface, contour and density plots. ▪ See page 518. ▪ See also: `PlotRange`, `PlotPoints`.

■ **MeshStyle**

> MeshStyle is an option for `Plot3D`, `DensityPlot` and related functions which specifies how mesh lines should be rendered.
>
> `MeshStyle` can be set to a list of graphics directives including `Dashing`, `Thickness`, `GrayLevel`, `Hue` and `RGBColor`. ▪ See page 483. ▪ See also: `Mesh`, `AxesStyle`, `Prolog`, `Epilog`, `DisplayFunction`.

■ **Message**

> Message[*symbol*::*tag*] prints the message *symbol*::*tag* unless it has been switched off.
>
> Message[*symbol*::*tag*, e_1, e_2, ...] prints a message, inserting the values of the e_i as needed.
>
> Message generates output on the channel `$Messages`. ▪ You can switch off a message using `Off[`*symbol*::*tag*`]`. You can switch on a message using `On[`*symbol*::*tag*`]`. ▪ Between any two successive input lines, *Mathematica* prints a message with a particular name at most three times. On the last occurrence, it prints the message `General::stop`. ▪ During the evaluation of a particular input line, names of messages associated with that input line are appended to the list `$MessageList`, wrapped with `HoldForm`. At the end of the evaluation of the nth input line, the value of `$MessageList` is assigned to `MessageList[`*n*`]`. ▪ `Message[`*mname*, e_1, e_2, ...]` is printed as `StringForm[`*mess*, $e_1$, $e_2$, ... ]` where *mess* is the value of the message *mname*. Entries of the form '*i*' in the string *mess* are replaced by the corresponding e_i. ▪ Given a message specified as *symbol*::*tag*, `Message` first searches for messages *symbol*::*tag*::*lang*$_i$ for each of the languages in the list `$Language`. If it finds none of these, it then searches for the actual message *symbol*::*tag*. If it does not find this, it then performs the same search procedure for `General::`*tag*. If it still finds no message, it applies any value given for the global variable `$NewMessage` to *symbol* and "*tag*". ▪ If you specify a message as *symbol*::*tag*::*lang*, then `Message` will search only for messages with the particular language *lang*. ▪ See page 462. ▪ See also: `Print`, `CellPrint`, `Write`, `On`, `Off`, `Check`, `MessageList`.

■ **MessageList**

> MessageList[*n*] is a global object assigned to be a list of the names of messages generated during the processing of the nth input line.
>
> Only messages that are actually output are included in the list `MessageList[`*n*`]`. ▪ The message names in the list are wrapped with `HoldForm`. ▪ `MessageList[`*n*`]` includes messages generated both by built-in functions and by explicit invocations of `Message`. ▪ See pages 460 and 675. ▪ See also: `$MessageList`.

■ MessageName

symbol::*tag* is a name for a message.

You can specify messages by defining values for *symbol*::*tag*. ■ *symbol*::*tag* is converted to MessageName[*symbol*, "*tag*"]. *tag* can contain any characters that can appear in symbol names. *symbol*::"*tag*" can also be used. ■ Assignments for *s*::*tag* are stored in the Messages value of the symbol *s*. ■ The following messages for functions are often defined:

f::usage   how to use the function

f::example   examples of the function

f::notes   notes on the function

■ ?*f* prints out the message *f*::usage. ■ When ?*form* finds more than one function, only the names of each function are printed. ■ You can switch on and off messages using On[*s*::*tag*] and Off[*s*::*tag*]. ■ MessageName[*symbol*, "*tag*", "*lang*"] or *symbol*::*tag*::*lang* represents a message in a particular language. ■ See page 458. ■ See also: Message, MessageList, $MessageList.

■ Messages

Messages[*symbol*] gives all the messages assigned to a particular symbol.

Messages that have been switched off using Off are enclosed in $Off. ■ See page 459.

■ Min

Min[x_1, x_2, ...] yields the numerically smallest of the x_i.

Min[{x_1, x_2, ... }, {y_1, ... }, ...] yields the smallest element of any of the lists.

Min yields a definite result if all its arguments are real numbers. ■ In other cases, Min carries out some simplifications. ■ Min[ ] gives Infinity. ■ See page 718. ■ See also: Max, Order.

■ Minors

Minors[*m*, *k*] gives a matrix consisting of the determinants of all $k \times k$ submatrices of *m*.

The results for different submatrices are given in lexicographic order. ■ See page 844. ■ See also: Det.

■ Minus

−*x* is the arithmetic negation of *x*.

−*x* is converted to Times[-1, *x*] on input. ■ See page 29. ■ See also: Subtract.

~■ Mod

Mod[*m*, *n*] gives the remainder on division of *m* by *n*.

The sign of Mod[*m*, *n*] is always the same as the sign of *n*, at least so long as *m* and *n* are both real. ■ Mod[*m*, *n*] is equivalent to *m* − *n* Quotient[*m*, *n*]. ~■ The arguments of Mod can be any numeric quantities, not necessarily integers. ~■ Mod[*x*, 1] gives the fractional part of *x*. ~■ For exact numeric quantities, Mod internally uses numerical approximations to establish its result. This process can be affected by the setting of the global variable $MaxExtraPrecision. ■ See page 722. ■ See also: PowerMod, Quotient, FractionalPart, MantissaExponent, PolynomialMod, PolynomialRemainder.

+■ ModularLambda

ModularLambda[τ] gives the modular lambda elliptic function $\lambda(\tau)$.

Mathematical function (see Section A.3.10). ■ ModularLambda is defined only in the upper half of the complex τ plane. It is not defined for real τ. ■ The argument τ is the ratio of Weierstrass half-periods ω'/ω. ■ ModularLambda gives the parameter m for elliptic functions in terms of τ according to $m = \lambda(\tau)$. ■ ModularLambda is related to EllipticTheta by $\lambda(\tau) = \vartheta_2^4(0, q)/\vartheta_3^4(0, q)$ where the nome q is given by $e^{i\pi\tau}$. ■ $\lambda(\tau)$ is invariant under any combination of the modular transformations $\tau \to \tau + 2$ and $\tau \to \tau/(1 - 2\tau)$. ■ See page 752 for a discussion of argument conventions for elliptic functions. ■ See page 757. ■ See also: DedekindEta, KleinInvariantJ, WeierstrassHalfPeriods.

■ Module

Module[{x, y, ... }, *expr*] specifies that occurrences of the symbols x, y, ... in *expr* should be treated as local.

Module[{$x = x_0$, ... }, *expr*] defines initial values for x, ...

Module allows you to set up local variables with names that are local to the module. ■ Module creates new symbols to represent each of its local variables every time it is called. ■ Module creates a symbol with name *xxx$nnn* to represent a local variable with name *xxx*. The number *nnn* is the current value of $ModuleNumber. ■ The value of $ModuleNumber is incremented every time any module is used. ■ Before evaluating *expr*, Module substitutes new symbols for each of the local variables that appear anywhere in *expr* except as local variables in scoping constructs. ■ Symbols created by Module carry the attribute Temporary. ■ Symbols created by Module can be returned from modules. ■ You can use Module[{*vars*}, *body* /; *cond*] as the right-hand side of a transformation rule with a condition attached. ■ Module has attribute HoldAll. ■ Module is a scoping construct (see Section A.3.8). ■ Module constructs can be nested in any way. ■ Module implements lexical scoping. ■ See page 357. ■ See also: With, Block, Unique.

■ Modulus

Modulus->n is an option that can be given in certain algebraic functions to specify that integers should be treated modulo n.

Equations for Modulus can be given in Solve and related functions.

Modulus appears as an option in Factor, PolynomialGCD and PolynomialLCM, as well as in linear algebra functions such as Inverse, LinearSolve and Det. ■ Arithmetic is usually done over the full ring **Z** of integers; setting the option Modulus specifies that arithmetic should instead be done in the finite ring $\mathbf{Z}_n$. ■ The setting Modulus -> 0 specifies the full ring **Z** of integers. ■ Some functions require that Modulus be set to a prime, or a power of a prime. $\mathbf{Z}_n$ is a finite field when n is prime. ■ See pages 778 and 802. ■ See also: Extension.

■ MoebiusMu

MoebiusMu[n] gives the Möbius function $\mu(n)$.

Integer mathematical function (see Section A.3.10). ■ $\mu(n)$ is 1 if n is a product of an even number of distinct primes, -1 if it is a product of an odd number of primes, and 0 if it has a multiple prime factor. ■ See page 725. ■ See also: Divisors, FactorInteger, JacobiSymbol.

■ Multinomial

Multinomial[n_1, n_2, ...] gives the multinomial coefficient $(n_1 + n_2 + ...)!/(n_1!n_2!...)$.

Integer mathematical function (see Section A.3.10). ■ The multinomial coefficient Multinomial[n_1, n_2, ...], denoted $(N; n_1, n_2, ..., n_m)$, gives the number of ways of partitioning N distinct objects into m sets, each of size n_i (with $N = \sum_{i=1}^{m} n_i$). ■ See page 727. ■ See also: Binomial.

~∎ **N**

N[*expr*] gives the numerical value of *expr*.

~ N[*expr*, *n*] attempts to give a result with *n*-digit precision.

~∎ Unless numbers in *expr* are exact, or of sufficiently high precision, N[*expr*, *n*] may not be able to give results with *n*-digit precision. ~∎ N[*expr*, *n*] may internally do computations to more than *n* digits of precision. ~∎ $MaxExtraPrecision specifies the maximum number of extra digits of precision that will ever be used internally. ~∎ The precision *n* is given in decimal digits; it need not be an integer. ~∎ *n* must lie between $MinPrecision and $MaxPrecision. $MaxPrecision can be set to Infinity. ~∎ N[*expr*] gives a machine-precision number, so long as its magnitude is between $MinMachineNumber and $MaxMachineNumber. ~∎ N[0] gives the exact integer 0, unless you explicitly set it to have a different value. +∎ N converts all non-zero numbers to Real or Complex form. +∎ N converts each successive argument of any function it encounters to numerical form, unless the head of the function has an attribute such as NHoldAll. ~∎ You can define numerical values of functions using N[*f*[*args*]] := *value* and N[*f*[*args*], *n*] := *value*. ∎ See pages 30, 33 and 703. ∎ See also: Chop, CompiledFunction, Rationalize, $MachinePrecision, NHoldAll.

∎ **NameQ**

NameQ["*string*"] yields True if there are any symbols whose names match the string pattern given, and yields False otherwise.

You can test for classes of symbol names using string patterns with metacharacters such as *, as specified on page 992. ∎ See page 382. ∎ See also: Names.

∎ **Names**

Names["*string*"] gives a list of the names of symbols which match the string.

Names["*string*", SpellingCorrection->True] includes names which match after spelling correction.

Names["*string*"] gives the same list of names as ?*string*. ∎ Names returns a list of strings corresponding to the names of symbols. ∎ The string can be a string pattern, with metacharacters such as * and @, as described on page 992. ∎ Names["*context*`*"] lists all symbols in the specified context. ∎ With SpellingCorrection -> True, Names includes names which differ in a small fraction of their characters from those specifically requested. ∎ With IgnoreCase -> True or SpellingCorrection -> True, Names treats lower- and upper-case letters as equivalent when matching names. ∎ Names[ ] lists all names in all contexts. ∎ See page 382. ∎ See also: Information, Contexts, Unique, ValueQ, FileNames, NameQ.

+■ NotebookApply

NotebookApply[*notebook*, *data*] writes data into a notebook at the current selection, replacing the first selection placeholder in *data* by the current selection, and then setting the current selection to be just after the data written.

NotebookApply[*notebook*, *data*, *sel*] writes data into a notebook and then sets the current selection to be as specified by *sel*.

The first argument of NotebookApply is a NotebookObject. ■ NotebookApply does the same as NotebookWrite, except that it replaces the first selection placeholder in *data* by the current selection. ■ NotebookApply is often used in setting up actions for buttons in palettes. ■ Selection placeholders are represented by the character ■ or \[SelectionPlaceholder]. ■ Possible settings for *sel* are as in NotebookWrite. ■ See page 560. ■ See also: NotebookWrite, NotebookRead, SelectionMove, ButtonFunction.

+■ NotebookAutoSave

NotebookAutoSave is an option for Notebook which specifies whether the notebook should automatically be saved after every evaluation done in it.

See page 592. ■ See also: NotebookSave.

+■ NotebookClose

NotebookClose[*notebook*] closes the notebook corresponding to the specified notebook object.

NotebookClose will make a notebook disappear from your screen, and will invalidate all notebook objects which refer to that notebook. ■ See page 566. ■ See also: NotebookSave, Close.

+■ NotebookCreate

NotebookCreate[ ] creates a new open notebook in the front end.

NotebookCreate[*options*] sets up the specified options for the new notebook.

NotebookCreate will by default create a notebook with name "Untitled-*n*". ■ Unless you set the option Visible->False, NotebookCreate will cause a new window to appear on your screen. ■ See page 566. ■ See also: NotebookOpen, NotebookClose.

+■ NotebookDelete

NotebookDelete[*notebook*] deletes the current selection corresponding to the specified notebook object.

Using NotebookDelete in the kernel is equivalent to using the Clear command in the front end. ■ After NotebookDelete, the current selection becomes an insertion point at the position of the deleted material. ■ *notebook* must be a NotebookObject, as returned by NotebookOpen, etc. ■ See page 560. ■ See also: NotebookRead, NotebookWrite.

+■ **NotebookFind**

NotebookFind[*notebook*, *data*] sets the current selection in the specified notebook object to be the next occurrence of *data*.

NotebookFind[*notebook*, *data*, Previous] sets the current selection to be the previous occurrence.

NotebookFind[*notebook*, *data*, All] sets the current selection to be all occurrences.

NotebookFind[*notebook*, *data*, *dir*, *elems*] searches the elements of cells specified by *elems*.

NotebookFind returns $Failed if the search it performs finds no occurrence of *data*. ■ *notebook* must be a NotebookObject, as returned by NotebookOpen, etc. ■ *data* can be a string, box expressions, or a complete cell. ■ The possible elements are:

CellContents   contents of each cell, represented as a string
CellLabel   setting for the CellLabel option of each cell
CellStyle   name of style for each cell
CellTags   parts of the setting for the CellTags option for each cell
{*elem*₁, *elem*₂, ... }   list of different types of elements

■ The default for *elems* is CellContents. ■ Unless the option setting AutoScroll->False is given, the front end will scroll a notebook so that the result of NotebookFind is visible. ■ The front end will also usually highlight the region corresponding to the result. ■ See page 559. ■ See also: NotebookLocate, SelectionMove, NotebookOpen, Find.

+■ **NotebookGet**

NotebookGet[*obj*] gets the expression corresponding to the notebook represented by the notebook object *obj*.

NotebookGet[ ] gets the expression corresponding to the currently selected notebook.

NotebookGet allows you to take a notebook that is open in the front end, and get the expression corresponding to it in the kernel. ■ NotebookGet returns an expression with head Notebook. ■ See page 553. ■ See also: NotebookOpen, NotebookPut, Get.

+■ **NotebookLocate**

NotebookLocate["*tag*"] goes to the next cell with the specified tag in your currently selected notebook.

NotebookLocate[{"*file*", "*tag*"}] if necessary opens the notebook stored in *file*, then goes to the first cell with the specified tag.

NotebookLocate sets the current selection to be the cell that it finds. ■ NotebookLocate is used for following hyperlinks within one notebook or between notebooks. ■ NotebookLocate searches for tags in the list given as the setting for the CellTags option of each cell. ■ See page 560. ■ See also: NotebookFind, NotebookOpen, SetSelectedNotebook, ButtonBox.

+■ **NotebookObject**

NotebookObject[*fe*, *id*] is an object that represents an open notebook in the front end.

fe is a FrontEndObject which specifies the front end in which the notebook is open. ■ *id* is an integer that gives a unique serial number for this open notebook. ■ Functions such as NotebookPrint and NotebookClose take NotebookObject as their argument. ■ Within any open notebook, there is always a current selection. The current selection can be modified by applying functions such as SelectionMove to NotebookObject. ■ See page 554. ■ See also: NotebookSelection, FrontEndObject, NotebookOpen.

+■ **NotebookOpen**

NotebookOpen["*name*"] opens an existing notebook with the specified name, returning the corresponding notebook object.

NotebookOpen["*name*", *options*] opens a notebook using the options given.

NotebookOpen will usually cause a new notebook window to be opened on your screen. ▪ NotebookOpen returns $Failed if it cannot open a notebook with the specified name. ▪ NotebookOpen searches the directories specified by the NotebookPath global option for the front end. ▪ With the option Visible->False set, NotebookOpen will return a NotebookObject, but will not cause a window to appear on your screen. ▪ NotebookOpen initially sets the current selection to be before the first cell in the notebook. ▪ See pages 553 and 566. ▪ See also: NotebookCreate, NotebookLocate, NotebookSelection, OpenRead, Get, SetSelectedNotebook.

+■ **NotebookPrint**

NotebookPrint[*notebook*] sends a notebook to your printer.

NotebookPrint[*notebook*, *stream*] sends a PostScript version of the notebook to the specified stream.

If *notebook* is a NotebookObject, then NotebookPrint will print the complete notebook. If it is a NotebookSelection, then NotebookPrint will print just the selection. ▪ NotebookPrint uses the printing options set for the specified notebook, taking defaults from the global options set for the whole front end. ▪ NotebookPrint[*notebook*, "*file*.ps"] saves the PostScript form of the notebook in a file. ▪ NotebookPrint[*notebook*, "!*command*"] gives the PostScript form of the notebook as input to a command. ▪ See page 566. ▪ See also: NotebookSave, NotebookWrite, PrintingStyleEnvironment.

+■ **NotebookPut**

NotebookPut[*expr*] creates a notebook corresponding to *expr* and makes it the currently selected notebook in the front end.

NotebookPut[*expr*, *obj*] replaces the notebook represented by the notebook object *obj* with one corresponding to *expr*.

NotebookPut allows you to take a notebook expression in the kernel and make it an open notebook in the front end. ▪ *expr* must be a notebook expression with head Notebook. ▪ NotebookPut returns a NotebookObject corresponding to the notebook it creates. ▪ NotebookPut[*expr*, *obj*] overwrites whatever data was contained in the notebook represented by the notebook object *obj*. ▪ See page 553. ▪ See also: NotebookGet, NotebookCreate, Put.

+■ **NotebookRead**

NotebookRead[*notebook*] gives the expression corresponding to the current selection in the specified notebook object.

NotebookRead is the basic way to get into the kernel pieces of notebooks that are being manipulated by the front end. ▪ See page 560. ▪ See also: Get, NotebookWrite, NotebookDelete, ButtonSource.

+■ **Notebooks**

Notebooks[ ] gives a list of notebooks currently open in the front end.

Notebooks[ ] returns a list of NotebookObject constructs. ▪ Notebooks[*fe*] gives a list of notebooks open in a specific front end, specified by a FrontEndObject. The default is $FrontEnd. ▪ See page 554. ▪ See also: SelectedNotebook, EvaluationNotebook, NotebookOpen, Streams, Packages.

+■ NotebookSave

NotebookSave[*notebook*] saves the current version of a notebook in a file.

NotebookSave[*notebook*, "*file*"] saves the notebook in the specified file.

NotebookSave[*notebook*, *stream*] sends the expression corresponding to the current version of the notebook to the specified stream.

notebook must be a NotebookObject. ■ NotebookSave[*notebook*] saves the notebook in a file whose name is given by the notebook object *notebook*. ■ NotebookSave writes out the *Mathematica* expression corresponding to the notebook, together with *Mathematica* comments which make it easier for the front end to read the notebook in again. ■ See page 566. ■ See also: NotebookAutoSave, NotebookPrint.

+■ NotebookSelection

NotebookSelection[*notebook*] represents the current selection in an open notebook in the front end.

NotebookSelection takes a NotebookObject as its argument. ■ You can use Options and SetOptions to read and write options associated with your current selection. ■ See page 565. ■ See also: SelectionMove.

+■ NotebookWrite

NotebookWrite[*notebook*, *data*] writes data into a notebook at the current selection, setting the current selection to be just after the data written.

NotebookWrite[*notebook*, *data*, *sel*] writes data into a notebook setting the current selection to be as specified by *sel*.

The first argument of NotebookWrite is a NotebookObject. ■ NotebookWrite does essentially the same as a Paste operation in the front end: it replaces by *data* whatever the current selection in the notebook is. ■ NotebookWrite is the basic way to use the *Mathematica* kernel to modify the contents of notebooks that are being manipulated by the front end. ■ NotebookWrite automatically wraps Cell around the *data* you specify if this is necessary. ■ Possible settings for *sel* are:

After	place the current selection immediately after the data written
All	make the current selection be the data written
Before	place the current selection immediately before the data written
None	leave the current selection unchanged
Placeholder	make the current selection be the first placeholder in the data written

■ The default for *sel* is After, so that NotebookWrite[*obj*, *data*] can be called repeatedly to insert several pieces of data in sequence. ■ See page 560. ■ See also: NotebookApply, NotebookRead, NotebookDelete, SelectionMove.

■ NProduct

NProduct[*f*, {*i*, *imin*, *imax*}] gives a numerical approximation to the product $\prod_{i=imin}^{imax} f$.

NProduct[*f*, {*i*, *imin*, *imax*, *di*}] uses a step *di* in the product.

See notes for NSum. The options NSumExtraTerms and NSumTerms are replaced by NProductExtraFactors and NProductFactors. ■ See page 879. ■ Related package: NumericalMath`NLimit`.

■ **NSolve**

NSolve[*lhs*==*rhs*, *var*] gives a list of numerical approximations to the roots of a polynomial equation.

NSolve[*eqn*, *var*, *n*] gives results to *n*-digit precision. ■ NSolve[*eqn*, *var*] gives the same final result as N[Solve[*eqn*, *var*]], apart from issues of numerical precision. ■ See page 881. ■ Implementation notes: see page 1020. ■ See also: Solve, FindRoot, NDSolve. ■ Related package: NumberTheory`Recognize`.

■ **NSum**

NSum[*f*, {*i*, *imin*, *imax*}] gives a numerical approximation to the sum $\sum_{i=imin}^{imax} f$.

NSum[*f*, {*i*, *imin*, *imax*, *di*}] uses a step *di* in the sum.

NSum can be used for sums with both finite and infinite limits. ■ NSum[*f*, {*i*, ... }, {*j*, ... }, ...] can be used to evaluate multidimensional sums. ■ The following options can be given:

AccuracyGoal	Infinity	number of digits of final accuracy to try and get
Compiled	True	whether to compile the summand
Method	Automatic	method to use: Integrate or Fit
NSumExtraTerms	12	maximum number of terms to use in extrapolation
NSumTerms	15	number of terms to use before extrapolation
PrecisionGoal	Automatic	number of digits of final precision to try and get
VerifyConvergence	True	whether to explicitly test for convergence
WorkingPrecision	$MachinePrecision	the number of digits used in internal computations

■ NSum uses either the Euler-Maclaurin (Integrate) or Wynn epsilon (Fit) method. ■ With the Euler-Maclaurin method, the options AccuracyGoal and PrecisionGoal can be used to specify the accuracy and precision to try and get in the final answer. NSum stops when the error estimates it gets imply that either the accuracy or precision sought has been reached. ■ You should realize that with sufficiently pathological summands, the algorithms used by NSum can give wrong answers. In most cases, you can test the answer by looking at its sensitivity to changes in the setting of options for NSum. ■ VerifyConvergence is only used for sums with infinite limits. ■ N[Sum[...]] calls NSum. ■ NSum has attribute HoldAll. ■ See page 879. ■ Implementation notes: see page 1020. ■ See also: NProduct. ■ Related package: NumericalMath`ListIntegrate`, NumericalMath`NLimit`.

■ **Null**

Null is a symbol used to indicate the absence of an expression or a result. When it appears as an output expression, no output is printed.

e_1; e_2; ... ; e_k; returns Null, and prints no output. ■ Expressions like *f*[e_1,,e_2] are interpreted to have Null between each pair of adjacent commas.

■ **NullRecords**

NullRecords is an option for Read and related functions which specifies whether null records should be taken to exist between repeated record separators.

With the default setting NullRecords -> False, repeated record separators are treated like single record separators. ■ See page 619. ■ See also: WordSeparators.

~■ NullSpace

NullSpace[*m*] gives a list of vectors that forms a basis for the null space of the matrix *m*.

NullSpace works on both numerical and symbolic matrices. ■ NullSpace[*m*, Modulus->*n*] finds null spaces for integer matrices modulo *n*. ~■ NullSpace[*m*, ZeroTest -> *test*] evaluates *test*[*m*[[*i*, *j*]]] to determine whether matrix elements are zero. The default setting is ZeroTest -> Automatic. ~■ A Method option can also be given. Possible settings are as for LinearSolve. ■ See page 847. ■ See also: LinearSolve, RowReduce, SingularValues.

■ NullWords

NullWords is an option for Read and related functions which specifies whether null words should be taken to exist between repeated word separators.

With the default setting NullWords -> False, repeated word separators are treated like single word separators. ■ See page 619. ■ See also: TokenWords, RecordSeparators.

■ Number

Number represents an exact integer or an approximate real number in Read.

An integer is returned if no explicit decimal point is present. ■ Approximate real numbers can be given in C or Fortran forms, such as 2.4E5 or -3.4e-4. ■ See pages 206 and 618. ■ See also: Real, DigitQ.

■ NumberForm

NumberForm[*expr*, *n*] prints with approximate real numbers in *expr* given to *n*-digit precision.

NumberForm[*expr*, {*n*, *f*}] prints with approximate real numbers having *n* digits, with *f* digits to the right of the decimal point. ■ NumberForm works on integers as well as approximate real numbers. ■ The following options can be given:

DigitBlock	Infinity	number of digits between breaks
ExponentFunction	Automatic	function to apply to exponents
NumberFormat	Automatic	function used to assemble mantissa, base, exponent
NumberPadding	{"", ""}	strings to use for left and right padding
NumberPoint	"."	decimal point string
NumberSeparator	","	string to insert at breaks between blocks
NumberSigns	{"-", "+"}	strings to use for signs of negative and positive numbers
SignPadding	False	whether to insert padding after the sign

■ All options except ExponentFunction apply to integers as well as approximate real numbers. ■ You can mix NumberForm and BaseForm. ■ NumberForm acts as a "wrapper", which affects printing, but not evaluation. ■ See page 414. ■ See also: ScientificForm, EngineeringForm, AccountingForm, BaseForm, PaddedForm, N.

■ NumberFormat

NumberFormat is an option for NumberForm and related functions which specifies how the mantissa, base and exponent should be assembled into a final print form.

With the setting NumberFormat -> *f*, the function *f* is supplied with three arguments: the mantissa, base and exponent of each number to be printed. ■ The arguments are all given as strings. ■ When no exponent is to be printed, the third argument is given as "". ■ The function *f* must return the final format for the number. ■ See page 415. ■ See also: ExponentFunction.

+■ NumberMarks

NumberMarks is an option for InputForm and related functions that specifies whether ` marks should be included in the printed forms of approximate numbers.

The default setting for NumberMarks is given by the value of $NumberMarks. ■ NumberMarks->True indicates that ` should be used in all approximate numbers, both machine-precision and arbitrary-precision ones. ■ NumberMarks -> Automatic indicates that ` should be used in arbitrary-precision but not machine-precision numbers. ■ NumberMarks -> False indicates that ` should never be used in outputting numbers. ■ Number marks are used to indicate the type of numbers, and their precision or accuracy. ■ The *^ form for scientific notation is always used in InputForm, and is independent of NumberMarks. ■ See page 705. ■ See also: NumberForm.

+■ NumberMultiplier

NumberMultiplier is an option for NumberForm and related functions which gives the string to use as a multiplication sign in scientific notation.

The default is NumberMultiplier -> "\[Times]". ■ In OutputForm, \[Times] is rendered as x. ■ See page 415.

■ NumberPadding

NumberPadding is an option for NumberForm and related functions which gives strings to use as padding on the left- and right-hand sides of numbers.

NumberPadding -> {"*sleft*", "*sright*"} specifies strings to use for padding on the left and right. ■ In NumberForm, the default setting is NumberPadding -> {"", ""}. ■ In PaddedForm, the default setting is NumberPadding -> {" ", "0"}. ■ The strings specified as padding are inserted in place of digits. ■ See page 415. ■ See also: SignPadding.

■ NumberPoint

NumberPoint is an option for NumberForm and related functions which gives the string to use as a decimal point.

The default is NumberPoint -> ".". ■ See page 415.

~■ NumberQ

NumberQ[*expr*] gives True if *expr* is a number, and False otherwise.

NumberQ[*expr*] returns False unless *expr* is manifestly a number (i.e., has head Complex, Integer, Rational or Real). +■ NumberQ[Infinity] gives False. ■ NumberQ[Overflow[ ]] and NumberQ[Underflow[ ]] give True. ■ You can use NumberQ[*x*] = True to override the normal operation of NumberQ, and effectively define *x* to be a number. ■ See pages 264 and 697. ■ See also: NumericQ, IntegerQ, TrueQ.

■ NumberSeparator

NumberSeparator is an option for NumberForm and related functions which gives the string to insert at breaks between digits.

NumberSeparator -> "*s*" specifies that the string *s* should be inserted at every break between digits specified by DigitBlock. ■ NumberSeparator -> {"*sleft*", "*sright*"} specifies different strings to be used on the left and right of the decimal point. ■ The default setting is NumberSeparator -> ",". ■ See page 415.

■ NumberSigns

NumberSigns is an option for NumberForm and related functions which gives strings to use as signs for negative and positive numbers.

NumberSigns -> {"*sneg*", "*spos*"} specifies that "*sneg*" should be given as the sign for negative numbers, and "*spos*" for positive numbers. ■ The default setting is NumberSigns -> {"-", ""}.
■ NumberSigns -> {{"*snleft*", "*snright*"}, {"*spleft*", "*spright*"}} specifies strings to put both on the left and right of numbers to specify their signs. ■ In AccountingForm, the default setting is NumberSigns -> {{"(", ")"}, ""}.
■ See page 415. ■ See also: SignPadding.

■ Numerator

Numerator[*expr*] gives the numerator of *expr*.

Numerator picks out terms which do not have superficially negative exponents. Denominator picks out the remaining terms. ■ An exponent is "superficially negative" if it has a negative number as a factor. ■ The standard representation of rational expressions as products of powers means that you cannot simply use Part to extract numerators. ■ Numerator can be used on rational numbers. ■ See page 72. ■ See also: ExpandNumerator.

⁺■ NumericFunction

NumericFunction is an attribute that can be assigned to a symbol f to indicate that $f[arg_1, arg_2, \dots]$ should be considered a numeric quantity whenever all the arg_i are numeric quantities.

Most standard built-in mathematical functions have the attribute NumericFunction. ■ NumericQ checks the NumericFunction attribute of every function it encounters. ■ If you assign the attribute NumericFunction to a function that does not yield numerical values, then NumericQ will give misleading results. ■ See pages 309 and 699.
■ See also: NumericQ, NHoldAll.

⁺■ NumericQ

NumericQ[*expr*] gives True if *expr* is a numeric quantity, and False otherwise.

An expression is considered a numeric quantity if it is either an explicit number or a mathematical constant such as Pi, or is a function that has attribute NumericFunction and all of whose arguments are numeric quantities. ■ In most cases, NumericQ[*expr*] gives True whenever N[*expr*] would yield an explicit number. ■ See page 698. ■ See also: NumberQ.

■ O

O[*x*]^*n* represents a term of order x^n.

O[*x*]^*n* is generated to represent omitted higher-order terms in power series.

O[*x*, x_0]^*n* represents a term of order $(x - x_0)^n$.

Normal can be used to truncate power series, and remove O terms. ■ See page 828. ■ See also: Series, SeriesData.

■ OddQ

OddQ[*expr*] gives True if *expr* is an odd integer, and False otherwise.

OddQ[*expr*] returns False unless *expr* is manifestly an odd integer (i.e., has head Integer, and is odd). ■ You can use OddQ[*x*] = True to override the normal operation of OddQ, and effectively define *x* to be an odd integer. ■ See pages 264 and 697. ■ See also: IntegerQ, EvenQ, TrueQ.

■ **Off**

Off[*symbol*::*tag*] switches off a message, so that it is no longer printed.

Off[*s*] switches off tracing messages associated with the symbol *s*.

Off[*m*₁, *m*₂, ...] switches off several messages.

Off[ ] switches off all tracing messages.

The *value* of *symbol*::*tag* is not affected by Off. ■ Off[*s*] is equivalent to Off[*s*::trace]. ■ Off[ ] is equivalent to Off[*s*::trace] for all symbols. ■ See pages 61 and 458. ■ See also: On, Message, Check.

⁺■ **Offset**

Offset[{*dx*, *dy*}, *position*] gives the position of a graphical object obtained by starting at the specified position and then moving by absolute offset {*dx*, *dy*}.

Offset can be used to specify offsets in any two-dimensional graphics primitive. ■ *position* can be either {*x*, *y*} or Scaled[{*x*, *y*}, ...]. ■ The offset is measured in units of printer's points, approximately equal to $\frac{1}{72}$ of an inch. ■ Offset[{*dx*, *dy*}] can be used to specify an absolute radius in a Circle or Disk object. ■ See page 486. ■ See also: Scaled, AbsolutePointSize, AbsoluteThickness.

■ **On**

On[*symbol*::*tag*] switches on a message, so that it can be printed.

On[*s*] switches on tracing for the symbol *s*.

On[*m*₁, *m*₂, ...] switches on several messages.

On[ ] switches on tracing for all symbols.

When tracing is switched on, each evaluation of a symbol, on its own, or as a function, is printed, together with the result. ■ Note that the tracing information is printed when a function *returns*. As a result, traces of recursive functions appear in the opposite order from their calls. ■ On[*s*] is equivalent to On[*s*::trace]. ■ On[ ] is equivalent to On[*s*::trace] for all symbols. ■ See pages 61 and 458. ■ See also: Off, TracePrint.

■ **OneIdentity**

OneIdentity is an attribute that can be assigned to a symbol *f* to indicate that *f*[*x*], *f*[*f*[*x*]], etc. are all equivalent to *x* for the purpose of pattern matching.

Functions like Plus and Times have the attribute OneIdentity. ■ The fact that Times has attribute OneIdentity allows a pattern like n_. x_ to match x. ■ See pages 268 and 309. ■ See also: Flat, Nest.

~■ OpenAppend

OpenAppend["*file*"] opens a file to append output to it, and returns an OutputStream object.

~■ The following options can be given:

CharacterEncoding	None	what raw character encoding to use
FormatType	InputForm	default format for printing expressions
NameConversion	None	function for converting symbol names with special characters
NumberMarks	$NumberMarks	when to use ` marks in approximate numbers
PageWidth	78	number of character widths per line
TotalHeight	Infinity	maximum number of lines for a single expression
TotalWidth	Infinity	maximum number of character widths for a single expression

■ On computer systems that support pipes, OpenAppend["!*command*"] runs the external program specified by *command*, and opens a pipe to send input to it. ■ If OpenRead does not succeed in opening a particular file or pipe, it generates a message, and returns $Failed. ■ OpenAppend resolves file names according to the procedure described in Section A.6.1. ■ OpenAppend returns OutputStream["*name*", *n*], where *name* is the full name of a file or command, and *n* is a serial number that is unique across all streams opened in the current *Mathematica* session. ■ SetOptions can be used to change the properties of an output stream, after it is already open. ■ Functions like Put and Write automatically open the files or pipes they need, if they are not already open. +■ Setting the option DOSTextFormat->True causes newlines specified by \n to be output as \n\r pairs, suitable for text-mode files on MS-DOS and related systems. ■ See page 607. ■ See also: Close, Put, Streams, LinkCreate.

~■ OpenRead

OpenRead["*file*"] opens a file to read data from, and returns an InputStream object.

OpenRead prepares to read from a file, starting at the beginning of the file. ■ On systems that support pipes, OpenRead["!*command*"] runs the external program specified by *command*, and opens a pipe to get input from it. ■ If OpenRead does not succeed in opening a particular file or pipe, it generates a message, and returns $Failed. ■ OpenRead resolves file names according to the procedure described in Section A.6.1. ■ The function ReadList automatically opens files or pipes that it needs. ■ OpenRead returns InputStream["*name*", *n*], where *name* is the full name of a file or command, and *n* is a serial number that is unique across all streams opened in the current *Mathematica* session. +■ Setting the option DOSTextFormat->True causes all input to be treated as coming from a text-mode file on an MS-DOS or related system. This means that \n\r pairs are interpreted as single newlines, and CTRL Z is interpreted as EndOfFile. ■ See page 622. ■ See also: Close, Read, ReadList, Streams, LinkCreate.

■ OpenTemporary

OpenTemporary[ ] opens a temporary file to which output can be written, and returns an OutputStream object.

OpenTemporary is often used in conjunction with Put and Get as a way of preparing data that is exchanged between *Mathematica* and external programs. ■ OpenTemporary always creates a new file, that does not already exist. ■ On Unix systems, OpenTemporary typically creates a file in the /tmp directory. ■ The global variable $TemporaryPrefix gives the base of the file name used by OpenTemporary. ■ See page 604. ■ See also: Close, Run.

■ OpenWrite

OpenWrite["*file*"] opens a file to write output to it, and returns an OutputStream object.

OpenWrite deletes any existing contents in a file, and prepares to write output starting at the beginning of the file. ■ For output to pipes, OpenWrite and OpenAppend are equivalent. ■ See notes for OpenAppend. ■ See page 607.

■ Operate

Operate[*p*, *f*[*x*, *y*]] gives *p*[*f*][*x*, *y*].

Operate[*p*, *expr*, *n*] applies *p* at level *n* in the head of *expr*.

Examples: Operate[p, f[x,y]] ⟶ p[f][x, y]; Operate[p, f[x][y][z], 1] ⟶ p[f[x]][y]][z];
Operate[p, f[x][y][z], 2] ⟶ p[f[x]][y][z]. ■ Operate[*p*, *f*[*x*]] effectively applies the functional operator *p* to the function *f*. ■ Operate is essentially a generalization of Apply, which allows you to apply an operator to the head of an expression, rather than simply to replace the head. ■ See page 251. ■ See also: Through, Apply, Heads.

■ Optional

p:*v* is a pattern object which represents an expression of the form *p*, which, if omitted, should be replaced by *v*.

Optional is used to specify "optional arguments" in functions represented by patterns. The pattern object *p* gives the form the argument should have, if it is present. The expression *v* gives the "default value" to use if the argument is absent. ■ Example: the pattern f[x_, y_:1] is matched by f[a], with x taking the value a, and y taking the value 1. It can also be matched by f[a, b], with y taking the value b. ■ The form s_:*v* is equivalent to Optional[s_, *v*]. This form is also equivalent to s:_:*v*. There is no syntactic ambiguity since *s* must be a symbol in this case. ■ The special form s_. is equivalent to Optional[s_] and can be used to represent function arguments which, if omitted, should be replaced by default values globally specified for the functions in which they occur. ■ Values for Default[*f*, ...] specify default values to be used when _. appears as an argument of *f*. Any assignments for Default[*f*, ...] must be made *before* _. first appears as an argument of *f*. ■ Optional[s_h] represents a function which can be omitted, but which, if present, must have head *h*. There is no simpler syntactic form for this case. ■ Functions with built-in default values include Plus, Times and Power. ■ See pages 271 and 978. ■ See also: Alternatives.

~■ Options

Options[*symbol*] gives the list of default options assigned to a symbol.

Options[*expr*] gives the options explicitly specified in a particular expression such as a graphics object.

Options[*stream*] or Options["*sname*"] gives options associated with a particular stream.

+ Options[*object*] gives options associated with an external object such as a NotebookObject.

Options[*obj*, *name*] gives the setting for the option *name*.

Options[*obj*, {*name*₁, *name*₂, ... }] gives a list of the settings for the options *name*ᵢ.

Many built-in functions allow you to give additional arguments that specify options with rules of the form *name* -> *value*. ■ Options[*f*] gives the list of rules to be used for the options associated with a function *f* if no explicit rules are given when the function is called. ■ Options always returns a list of transformation rules for option names. ■ You can assign a value to Options[*symbol*] to redefine all the default option settings for a function. ■ SetOptions[*symbol*, *name* -> *value*] can be used to specify individual default options. ■ You can use Options on InputStream and OutputStream objects. If there is only one stream with a particular name, you can give the name as a string as the argument of Options. +■ If you ask for Options[NotebookObject[...], *name*] the kernel will send a request to the front end to find the result. +■ Explicit values are found for options associated with cells even if these options are only set at the style, notebook or global level. ■ See pages 143 and 988. ■ See also: FullOptions. ■ Related package: Utilities`FilterOptions`.

~■ Or

e_1 || e_2 || ... is the logical OR function. It evaluates its arguments in order, giving True immediately if any of them are True, and False if they are all False.

+■ Or[e_1, e_2, ...] can be input in StandardForm and InputForm as e_1 ∨ e_2 ∨ ... . The character ∨ can be entered as :||: , :or: or \[Or]. ■ Or evaluates its arguments in a non-standard way (see page 994). ■ Or gives symbolic results when necessary. It applies no simplification rules, except removing initial arguments that are False. ■ See page 85. ■ See also: Xor, LogicalExpand.

■ Order

Order[$expr_1$, $expr_2$] gives 1 if $expr_1$ is before $expr_2$ in canonical order, and −1 if $expr_1$ is after $expr_2$ in canonical order. It gives 0 if $expr_1$ is identical to $expr_2$.

Examples: Order[a, b] ⟶ 1; Order[b, a] ⟶ −1. ■ Order uses canonical order as described in the notes for Sort. ■ See page 252. ■ See also: Equal, SameQ, Sort.

■ OrderedQ

OrderedQ[h[e_1, e_2, ...]] gives True if the e_i are in canonical order, and False otherwise.

See notes for Order. ■ OrderedQ[{e, e}] gives True. ■ By default, OrderedQ uses canonical order as described in the notes for Sort. ■ OrderedQ[$list$, p] uses the function p to determine whether each pair of elements in $list$ is in order. ■ See pages 127 and 265. ■ See also: Signature, Sort.

■ Orderless

Orderless is an attribute that can be assigned to a symbol f to indicate that the elements e_i in expressions of the form f[e_1, e_2, ...] should automatically be sorted into canonical order. This property is accounted for in pattern matching.

The Orderless attribute for a function corresponds to the mathematical property of commutativity. ■ Functions with the Orderless attribute use canonical order as described in the notes for Sort. ■ For an object that represents a matrix or a tensor, the Orderless attribute represents symmetry among indices. ■ Functions like Plus and Times are Orderless. ■ In matching patterns with Orderless functions, all possible orders of arguments are tried. ■ The Orderless attribute must be assigned before defining any values for an Orderless function. ■ See page 309. ■ See also: Sort, Flat, OneIdentity.

■ Out

%n or Out[n] is a global object that is assigned to be the value produced on the nth output line.

% gives the last result generated.

%% gives the result before last. %% ... % (k times) gives the kth previous result.

Out[ ] is equivalent to %. ■ Out[−k] is equivalent to %% ... % (k times). ■ See page 675. ■ See also: In, $Line, $HistoryLength, MessageList.

~■ Outer

Outer[*f*, *list*₁, *list*₂, ...] gives the generalized outer product of the *list*$_i$, forming all possible combinations of the lowest-level elements in each of them.

+ Outer[*f*, *list*₁, *list*₂, ... , *n*] treats as separate elements only sublists at level *n* in the *list*$_i$.

+ Outer[*f*, *list*₁, *list*₂, ... , *n*₁, *n*₂, ...] treats as separate elements only sublists at level *n*$_i$ in the corresponding *list*$_i$.

Example: Outer[f,{a,b},{x,y}] ⟶ {{f[a, x], f[a, y]}, {f[b, x], f[b, y]}}. ■ Outer[Times, *list*₁, *list*₂] gives an outer product. ■ The result of applying Outer to the tensors $T_{i_1 i_2 ... i_r}$ and $U_{j_1 j_2 ... j_s}$ is the tensor $V_{i_1 i_2 ... i_r j_1 j_2 ... j_s}$ with elements $f[T_{i_1 i_2 ... i_r}, U_{j_1 j_2 ... j_s}]$. Applying Outer to two tensors of ranks r and s gives a tensor of rank $r + s$. ■ The heads of both *list*$_i$ must be the same, but need not necessarily be List. ■ The *list*$_i$ need not necessarily be cuboidal arrays. +■ The specifications *n*$_i$ of levels must be integers. +■ If only a single level specification is given, it is assumed to apply to all the *list*$_i$. If there are several *n*$_i$, but fewer than the number of *list*$_i$, all levels in the remaining *list*$_i$ will be used. ■ See page 855. ■ See also: Inner, Distribute, Cross.

~■ OutputForm

OutputForm[*expr*] prints as a two-dimensional representation of *expr* using only keyboard characters.

OutputForm is an approximation to StandardForm which uses only ordinary keyboard characters. ■ The OutputForm of many kinds of expressions is quite different from their internal representation. ■ OutputForm acts as a "wrapper", which affects printing, but not evaluation. ■ OutputForm cannot be used directly for input to *Mathematica*. +■ When possible, OutputForm uses approximations to special characters. Thus ≥ is given as >= and é as e'. ■ See page 403. ■ See also: StandardForm, TraditionalForm, InputForm, TeXForm, Short, FullForm.

■ OutputStream

OutputStream["*name*", *n*] is an object that represents an output stream for functions such as Write.

OpenWrite and OpenAppend return OutputStream objects. ■ The serial number *n* is unique across all streams, regardless of their name. ■ See page 606. ■ See also: Streams, InputStream.

⁺■ OverscriptBox

OverscriptBox[x, y] represents $\overset{y}{x}$ in input and output.

Inside \(... \) OverscriptBox[x, y] can be input as x \& y. ■ In a notebook an OverscriptBox can be created using CTRL 7 or CTRL &. CTRL ␣ moves out of the overscript position. ■ In StandardForm and InputForm, OverscriptBox[x, y] is interpreted on input as Overscript[x, y]. ■ The following special interpretations are made:

OverscriptBox[x, "-"]	OverBar[x]	$\bar{x}$
OverscriptBox[x, "→"]	OverVector[x]	$\vec{x}$
OverscriptBox[x, "~"]	OverTilde[x]	$\tilde{x}$
OverscriptBox[x, "^"]	OverHat[x]	$\hat{x}$
OverscriptBox[x, "."]	OverDot[x]	$\dot{x}$

■ For these special cases special input forms such as x\&- can be used. ■ The baseline of OverscriptBox[x, y] is taken to be the baseline of x. ■ OverscriptBox[x, y] is usually output with y in a smaller font than x. ■ With the option setting LimitsPositioning->True y is placed in an overscript position when the whole OverscriptBox is displayed large, and in a superscript position when it is displayed smaller. ■ In StandardForm, explicit OverscriptBox objects are output literally. You can use DisplayForm to see the display form of such objects. ■ See page 424. ■ See also: UnderscriptBox, UnderoverscriptBox, SuperscriptBox, GridBox, FractionBox, ScriptSizeMultipliers.

■ PaddedForm

PaddedForm[*expr*, n] prints with all numbers in *expr* padded to leave room for a total of n digits.

PaddedForm[*expr*, {n, f}] prints with approximate real numbers having exactly f digits to the right of the decimal point.

By default, PaddedForm pads with spaces on the left to leave room for n digits. ■ PaddedForm pads with zeros on the right in approximate real numbers. ■ The length n specified in PaddedForm counts only digits, and not signs, breaks between digits, and so on. ■ PaddedForm takes the same options as NumberForm, but with some defaults different. ■ You can use PaddedForm to align columns of numbers. ■ PaddedForm acts as a "wrapper", which affects printing, but not evaluation. ■ See page 416. ■ See also: ColumnForm, TableForm.

⁺■ PageBreakAbove

PageBreakAbove is an option for Cell which specifies whether a page break should be made immediately above the cell if the notebook that contains the cell is printed.

A setting of Automatic specifies that a page break should be made if necessary. ■ A setting of True specifies that a page break should always be made, while a setting of False specifies that it should never be made. ■ See page 583. ■ See also: PageBreakBelow, ShowPageBreaks.

⁺■ PageBreakBelow

PageBreakBelow is an option for Cell which specifies whether a page break should be made immediately below the cell if the notebook that contains the cell is printed.

A setting of Automatic specifies that a page break should be made if necessary. ■ A setting of True specifies that a page break should always be made, while a setting of False specifies that it should never be made. ■ See page 583. ■ See also: PageBreakAbove, ShowPageBreaks.

+■ **PageBreakWithin**

> PageBreakWithin is an option for Cell which specifies whether a page break should be allowed within the cell if the notebook that contains the cell is printed.
>
> See page 583. ■ See also: PageBreakAbove, GroupPageBreakWithin, ShowPageBreaks.

~■ **PageWidth**

> ~ PageWidth is an option for output streams and for cells which specifies how wide each line of text should be allowed to be.
>
> Possible settings for both output streams and cells are:
>
> Infinity   an infinite width (no linebreaking)
>
> *n*   explicit width given in ems
>
> ■ SetOptions[*stream*, PageWidth -> *val*] resets the line width allowed for an open stream. +■ Possible settings for cells only are:
>
> WindowWidth   the width of the window on the screen
>
> PaperWidth   the width of the page as it would be printed
>
> +■ PageWidth->WindowWidth allows each line to use the full width of the displayed window, taking into account settings for CellMargins. ■ See pages 584 and 609. ■ See also: TotalWidth, TextJustification, AutoIndent.

+■ **ParagraphIndent**

> ParagraphIndent is an option for Cell which specifies how far in printer's points to indent the first line of each paragraph of text.
>
> A new paragraph is taken to start at the beginning of a cell, and after every explicit RETURN character in your text. ■ Negative settings for ParagraphIndent make the first line of each paragraph stick out to the left. ■ See page 584. ■ See also: AutoIndent, LineIndent, ParagraphSpacing.

+■ **ParagraphSpacing**

> ParagraphSpacing is an option for Cell, StyleBox and StyleForm which specifies how much extra space to leave between successive paragraphs of text.
>
> ParagraphSpacing->{*c*, 0} leaves an extra space of *c* times the height of the font in the paragraph. ■ ParagraphSpacing->{0, *n*} leaves an extra space of exactly *n* printer's points. ■ ParagraphSpacing->{*c*, *n*} leaves an extra space of *c* times the height of the font plus *n* printer's points. ■ Paragraph breaks are taken to occur whenever an explicit RETURN character appears in a block of text. ■ ParagraphSpacing is added to LineSpacing to determine spacing between paragraphs. ■ A typical default setting is ParagraphSpacing->{0, 0}. ■ ParagraphSpacing applies only to ordinary text, not *Mathematica* expressions. ■ Extra space specified by ParagraphSpacing is inserted before the first line of each paragraph. No extra space is inserted if the paragraph is at the beginning of a cell or a string. ■ See page 586. ■ See also: LineSpacing, ParagraphIndent.

■ ParametricPlot

ParametricPlot[{f_x, f_y}, {t, *tmin*, *tmax*}] produces a parametric plot with x and y coordinates f_x and f_y generated as a function of t.

ParametricPlot[{{f_x, f_y}, {g_x, g_y}, ... }, {t, *tmin*, *tmax*}] plots several parametric curves.

ParametricPlot evaluates its arguments in a non-standard way (see page 994). You should use Evaluate to evaluate the function to be plotted if this can safely be done before specific numerical values are supplied. ■ The options that can be given for ParametricPlot are the same as for Plot. ■ ParametricPlot has the default option setting Axes -> True. ■ ParametricPlot returns a Graphics object. ■ See page 160. ■ See also: ContourPlot. ■ Related packages: Graphics`ImplicitPlot`, Graphics`PlotField`.

■ ParametricPlot3D

ParametricPlot3D[{f_x, f_y, f_z}, {t, *tmin*, *tmax*}] produces a three-dimensional space curve parametrized by a variable t which runs from *tmin* to *tmax*.

ParametricPlot3D[{f_x, f_y, f_z}, {t, *tmin*, *tmax*}, {u, *umin*, *umax*}] produces a three-dimensional surface parametrized by t and u.

ParametricPlot3D[{f_x, f_y, f_z, s}, ...] shades the plot according to the color specification s.

ParametricPlot3D[{{f_x, f_y, f_z}, {g_x, g_y, g_z}, ... }, ...] plots several objects together.

ParametricPlot3D evaluates its arguments in a non-standard way (see page 994). You should use Evaluate to evaluate the function to be plotted if this can safely be done before specific numerical values are supplied. ■ ParametricPlot3D has the same options as Graphics3D, with the following additions:

Compiled   True   whether to compile the function to plot
PlotPoints   Automatic   the number of sample points for each parameter

■ ParametricPlot3D has the default option setting Axes -> True. ■ With the default setting PlotPoints -> Automatic, ParametricPlot3D uses PlotPoints -> 75 for curves and PlotPoints -> {15, 15} for surfaces. ■ ParametricPlot3D returns a Graphics3D object. ■ See page 162. ■ Related packages: Graphics`PlotField3D`, Graphics`ContourPlot3D`, Graphics`SurfaceOfRevolution`, Graphics`Shapes`.

■ ParentDirectory

ParentDirectory[ ] gives the parent of the current working directory.

ParentDirectory["*dir*"] gives the parent of the directory *dir*.

ParentDirectory returns the full name of the directory as a string. ■ ParentDirectory works only under operating systems which support hierarchical file systems. ■ See page 612. ■ See also: Directory, $HomeDirectory, DirectoryName.

~■ Part

expr[[*i*]] or Part[*expr*, *i*] gives the ith part of *expr*.

expr[[-*i*]] counts from the end.

expr[[0]] gives the head of *expr*.

expr[[*i*, *j*, ...]] or Part[*expr*, *i*, *j*, ...] is equivalent to *expr*[[*i*]] [[*j*]] ... .

expr[[{i_1, i_2, ... }]] gives a list of the parts i_1, i_2, ... of *expr*.

You can make an assignment like *t*[[*i*]] = *value* to modify part of an expression. ■ When *expr* is a list, *expr*[[{i_1, i_2, ... }]] gives a list of parts. In general, the head of *expr* is applied to the list of parts. ■ You can get a nested listing of parts from *expr*[[*list*₁, *list*₂, ...]]. Each part has one index from each list. ■ Notice that lists are used differently in Part than in functions like Extract, MapAt and Position. ■ *expr*[[Range[*i*, *j*]]] can be used to extract sequences of parts. +■ In StandardForm and InputForm, *expr*[[*spec*]] can be input as *expr*⟦*spec*⟧. +■ ⟦ and ⟧ can be entered as :[[: and :]]: or \[LeftDoubleBracket] and \[RightDoubleBracket]. ■ See page 233. ■ See also: First, Head, Last, Extract, Position, ReplacePart, MapAt, Take. ■ Related package: LinearAlgebra`MatrixManipulation`.

■ Partition

Partition[*list*, *n*] partitions *list* into non-overlapping sublists of length *n*.

Partition[*list*, *n*, *d*] generates sublists with offset *d*.

Partition[*list*, {n_1, n_2, ... }, {d_1, d_2, ... }] partitions successive levels in *list* into length n_i sublists with offsets d_i.

Example: Partition[{a,b,c,d,e,f}, 2] ⟶ {{a, b}, {c, d}, {e, f}}. ■ All the sublists generated by Partition[*list*, *n*, *d*] are of length *n*. As a result, some elements at the end of *list* may not appear in any sublist. ■ The element e in Partition[{a,b,c,d,e}, 2] ⟶ {{a, b}, {c, d}} is dropped. ■ Partition[{a,b,c,d,e}, 3, 1] ⟶ {{a, b, c}, {b, c, d}, {c, d, e}} generates sublists with offset 1. ■ If *d* is greater than *n* in Partition[*list*, *n*, *d*], then elements in the middle of *list* are skipped. ■ The object *list* need not have head List. ■ Partition[f[a,b,c,d], 2] ⟶ f[f[a, b], f[c, d]]. ■ If *list* has length *N*, then Partition[*list*, *n*, *d*] yields Max[0, Floor[(*N* + *d* − *n*)/*d*]] sublists. ■ Partition[*list*, {n_1, n_2, ... }, *d*] uses offset *d* at each level. ■ See page 124. ■ See also: Flatten, RotateLeft, Split.

■ PartitionsP

PartitionsP[*n*] gives the number $p(n)$ of unrestricted partitions of the integer *n*.

Integer mathematical function (see Section A.3.10). ■ See page 727. ■ Implementation notes: see page 1019. ■ See also: DedekindEta.

■ PartitionsQ

PartitionsQ[*n*] gives the number $q(n)$ of partitions of the integer *n* into distinct parts.

Integer mathematical function (see Section A.3.10). ■ See page 727.

■ Pattern

s:*obj* represents the pattern object *obj*, assigned the name *s*.

The name *s* must be a symbol. ■ The object *obj* can be any pattern object. ■ When a transformation rule is used, any occurrence of *s* on the right-hand side is replaced by whatever expression it matched on the left-hand side. ■ The operator : has a comparatively low precedence. The expression x:_+_ is thus interpreted as x:(_+_), not (x:_)+_. ■ The form *s*_ is equivalent to *s*:_. Similarly, *s*_*h* is equivalent to *s*:_*h*, *s*__ to *s*:__, and so on. ■ See pages 260 and 978.

■ PatternTest

p?*test* is a pattern object that stands for any expression which matches *p*, and on which the application of *test* gives True.

Any result for *test*[*pval*] other than True is taken to signify failure. ■ Example: _?NumberQ represents a number of any type. The _ matches any expression, and ?NumberQ restricts to any expression which gives True on application of the number test NumberQ. ■ The operator ? has a high precedence. Thus _^_?t is _^(_?t) not (_^_)?t. ■ In a form such as __?*test* every element in the sequence matched by __ must yield True when *test* is applied. ■ See page 266. ■ See also: Condition.

■ Pause

Pause[*n*] pauses for at least *n* seconds.

Pause is accurate only down to a granularity of at least $TimeUnit seconds. ■ The time elapsed during the execution of Pause is counted in SessionTime, but not in TimeUsed or Timing. ■ Under multitasking operating systems, there may be a delay of significantly more than *n* seconds when you execute Pause[*n*]. ■ See page 683.

■ Permutations

Permutations[*list*] generates a list of all possible permutations of the elements in *list*.

Example: Permutations[{a,b,c}] ⟶ {{a, b, c}, {a, c, b}, {b, a, c}, {b, c, a}, {c, a, b}, {c, b, a}}. ■ There are *n*! permutations of a list of *n* distinct elements. ■ Repeated elements are treated as identical. ■ The object *list* need not have head List. ■ See page 127. ■ See also: Sort, Signature, Reverse, RotateLeft. ■ Related package: DiscreteMath`Permutations`, DiscreteMath`Combinatorica`.

~■ Pi

Pi is π, with numerical value $\simeq$ 3.14159.

Mathematical constant (see Section A.3.11). +■ Pi can be entered in StandardForm and InputForm as π, :pi:, :p: or \[Pi]. +■ In StandardForm, Pi is printed as π. ■ See page 735. ■ Implementation notes: see page 1019. ■ See also: Degree.

■ Play

Play[*f*, {*t*, *tmin*, *tmax*}] plays a sound whose amplitude is given by *f* as a function of time *t* in seconds between *tmin* and *tmax*.

Play evaluates its arguments in a non-standard way (see page 994). ■ Play[{f_1, f_2}, {*t*, *tmin*, *tmax*}] produces stereo sound. The left-hand channel is given first. ■ Play[{f_1, f_2, ... }, ...] generates sound output on any number of channels. ~■ The following options can be given:

Compiled	True	whether to compile *f* for evaluation
DisplayFunction	$SoundDisplayFunction	function for generating output
Epilog	{}	sound or graphics to be used as an epilog
PlayRange	Automatic	the range of amplitude levels to include
Prolog	{}	sound or graphics to be used as a prolog
SampleDepth	8	how many bits to use to represent each amplitude level
SampleRate	8192	how many times per second amplitude samples should be generated

■ Play returns a Sound object. ■ See page 170. ■ See also: ListPlay, SampledSoundFunction, Show. ■ Related packages: Miscellaneous`Audio`, Miscellaneous`Music`.

▪ PolynomialGCD

PolynomialGCD[$poly_1$, $poly_2$, ...] gives the greatest common divisor of the polynomials $poly_i$.

PolynomialGCD[$poly_1$, $poly_2$, ... , Modulus->p] evaluates the GCD modulo the prime p.

Example: PolynomialGCD[1 + x y, x + x^2 y] $\longrightarrow$ 1 + x y. ▪ In PolynomialGCD[$poly_1$, $poly_2$, ...], all symbolic parameters are treated as variables. +▪ PolynomialGCD[$poly_1$, $poly_2$, ...] will by default treat algebraic numbers that appear in the $poly_i$ as independent variables. +▪ PolynomialGCD[$poly_1$, $poly_2$, ... , Extension->Automatic] extends the coefficient field to include algebraic numbers that appear in the $poly_i$. ▪ See page 773. ▪ See also: PolynomialLCM, PolynomialQuotient, GCD, Cancel, Together, PolynomialMod. ▪ Related package: Algebra`PolynomialExtendedGCD`.

▪ PolynomialLCM

PolynomialLCM[$poly_1$, $poly_2$, ...] gives the least common multiple of the polynomials $poly_i$.

PolynomialLCM[$poly_1$, $poly_2$, ... , Modulus->p] evaluates the LCM modulo the prime p.

Example: PolynomialLCM[1 + x y, x + x^2 y] $\longrightarrow$ x + x^2 y. +▪ PolynomialLCM[$poly_1$, $poly_2$, ...] will by default treat algebraic numbers that appear in the $poly_i$ as independent variables. +▪ PolynomialLCM[$poly_1$, $poly_2$, ... , Extension->Automatic] extends the coefficient field to include algebraic numbers that appear in the $poly_i$. ▪ See page 773. ▪ See also: PolynomialGCD, LCM.

▪ PolynomialMod

PolynomialMod[$poly$, m] gives the polynomial $poly$ reduced modulo m.

PolynomialMod[$poly$, {m_1, m_2, ... }] reduces modulo all of the m_i.

PolynomialMod[$poly$, m] for integer m gives a polynomial in which all coefficients are reduced modulo m. ▪ Example: PolynomialMod[3x^2 + 2x + 1, 2] $\longrightarrow$ 1 + x^2. ▪ When m is a polynomial, PolynomialMod[$poly$, m] reduces $poly$ by subtracting polynomial multiples of m, to give a result with minimal degree and leading coefficient. ▪ PolynomialMod gives results according to a definite convention; other conventions could yield results differing by multiples of m. ▪ Unlike PolynomialRemainder, PolynomialMod never performs divisions in generating its results. ▪ See page 773. ▪ See also: PolynomialGCD, Mod, PolynomialRemainder, PolynomialReduce, GroebnerBasis. ▪ Related package: Algebra`PolynomialPowerMod`.

▪ PolynomialQ

PolynomialQ[$expr$, var] yields True if $expr$ is a polynomial in var, and yields False otherwise.

PolynomialQ[$expr$, {var_1, ... }] tests whether $expr$ is a polynomial in the var_i.

The var_i need not be symbols; PolynomialQ[f[a] + f[a]^2, f[a]] $\longrightarrow$ True. ▪ See page 769. ▪ See also: Collect, Series.

▪ PolynomialQuotient

PolynomialQuotient[p, q, x] gives the quotient of p and q, treated as polynomials in x, with any remainder dropped.

See page 773. ▪ See also: PolynomialRemainder, PolynomialReduce, PolynomialGCD, Apart, Cancel, Quotient.

⁺■ PolynomialReduce

PolynomialReduce[*poly*, {*poly*$_1$, *poly*$_2$, ... }, {x_1, x_2, ... }] yields a list representing a reduction of *poly* in terms of the *poly*$_i$.

The list has the form {{a_1, a_2, ... }, *b*}, where *b* is minimal and a_1 *poly*$_1$ + a_2 *poly*$_2$ + ... + *b* is exactly *poly*.

The polynomial *b* has the property that none of its terms are divisible by leading terms of any of the *poly*$_i$. ■ If the *poly*$_i$ form a Gröbner basis then this property uniquely determines the remainder obtained from PolynomialReduce. ■ The following options can be given, as for GroebnerBasis:

MonomialOrder	Lexicographic	the criterion used for ordering monomials
CoefficientDomain	Rationals	the type of objects assumed to be coefficients
Modulus	0	the modulus for numerical coefficients

■ See page 773. ■ See also: GroebnerBasis, PolynomialRemainder, PolynomialMod. ■ Related package: Algebra`SymmetricPolynomials`.

■ PolynomialRemainder

PolynomialRemainder[*p*, *q*, *x*] gives the remainder from dividing *p* by *q*, treated as polynomials in *x*.

The degree of the result in *x* is guaranteed to be smaller than the degree of *q*. ■ Unlike PolynomialMod, PolynomialRemainder performs divisions in generating its results. ■ See page 773. ■ See also: PolynomialQuotient, Apart, Cancel, PolynomialMod, Mod, PolynomialReduce.

■ Position

Position[*expr*, *pattern*] gives a list of the positions at which objects matching *pattern* appear in *expr*.

Position[*expr*, *pattern*, *levspec*] finds only objects that appear on levels specified by *levspec*.

Example: Position[{1+x^2, 5, x^4}, x^_] ⟶ {{1, 2}, {3}}. ■ Position[*expr*, *pattern*] tests all the subparts of *expr* in turn to try and find ones that match *pattern*. ■ Position returns a list of positions in a form suitable for use in Extract, ReplacePart and MapAt. The form is different from the one used in Part. ■ The default level specification for Position is {0, Infinity}, with Heads -> True. ■ Position[*list*, *pattern*, {1}, Heads -> False] finds positions only of objects that appear as complete elements of *list*. ■ Level specifications are described on page 989. ■ Position[*expr*, *pattern*, *levspec*, *n*] gives the positions of the first *n* parts of *expr* which match the pattern. ■ See page 258. ■ See also: Cases, Count, StringPosition, ReplaceList, Insert, Delete.

■ Positive

Positive[*x*] gives True if *x* is a positive number.

Positive[*x*] gives False if *x* is manifestly a negative numerical quantity, a complex numerical quantity, or zero. Otherwise, it remains unevaluated. ■ A definition like Positive[*x*] = True effectively specifies that *x* is a positive number. ■ Definitions for Sign are tested in determining whether linear combinations of expressions are positive. ■ See also: Negative, NonNegative, Sign.

■ Postfix

Postfix[*f*[*expr*]] prints with *f*[*expr*] given in default postfix form: *expr* // *f*.

Postfix[*f*[*expr*], *h*] prints as *exprh*.

Postfix[*expr*, *h*, *precedence*, *grouping*] can be used to specify how the output form should be parenthesized. ■ See the notes for Infix about precedence and grouping. ■ See page 453. ■ See also: Infix, Prefix.

~■ PostScript

~ PostScript["*string*"] is a graphics primitive which gives PostScript code to include verbatim in graphics output.

~■ *Mathematica* by default renders a point with coordinates 0 0 in the PostScript code at the bottom left-hand corner of your plot, and a point with coordinates 1 *r* at the top right-hand corner, where *r* is the aspect ratio of the whole plot. ~■ You can specify a bounding box for the objects represented by your PostScript code by including a standard conforming PostScript comment of the form %%BoundingBox *pxmin pymin pxmax pymax*. ~■ PostScript["*string*", {{*xmin*, *ymin*}, {*xmax*, *ymax*}}] then renders the point with coordinates *pxmin pymin* in the PostScript code at position {*xmin*, *ymin*} in the *Mathematica* graphic, and the point with coordinates *pxmax pymax* at position {*xmax*, *ymax*}. ~■ *Mathematica* will transform graphics represented by a PostScript command to make it fill the specified rectangle. ■ After execution of PostScript code included by the PostScript command, all PostScript stacks must be restored to their original states. ■ The utility of the PostScript command depends on your PostScript interpreter's ability to process the PostScript commands you specify. +■ Display may or may not convert graphics produced by PostScript commands to other formats. ■ See page 534. ■ See also: Raster, RGBColor, Dashing, Thickness, PointSize, StyleForm.

■ Power

x^*y* gives *x* to the power *y*.

Mathematical function (see Section A.3.10). ■ Exact rational number results are given when possible for roots of the form $n^{1/m}$. ■ For complex numbers *x* and *y*, Power gives the principal value of $e^{y \log(x)}$. ■ (*a b*)^*c* is automatically converted to *a*^*c* *b*^*c* only if *c* is an integer. ■ (*a*^*b*)^*c* is automatically converted to *a*^(*b c*) only if *c* is an integer. ■ See page 29. ■ See also: Sqrt, Exp, PowerExpand, PowerMod, Log.

~■ PowerExpand

PowerExpand[*expr*] expands all powers of products and powers.

Example: PowerExpand[Sqrt[x y]] ⟶ $\sqrt{x}\,\sqrt{y}$. ■ PowerExpand converts (*a b*)^*c* to *a*^*c* *b*^*c*, whatever the form of *c* is. ■ PowerExpand also converts (*a*^*b*)^*c* to *a*^(*b c*), whatever the form of *c* is. ■ The transformations made by PowerExpand are correct in general only if *c* is an integer or *a* and *b* are positive real numbers. +■ PowerExpand converts Log[*a*^*b*] to *b* Log[*a*]. ■ See page 768. ■ See also: Expand, Distribute, ComplexExpand, FullSimplify.

■ PowerMod

PowerMod[*a*, *b*, *n*] gives a^b mod *n*.

For negative *b*, PowerMod[*a*, *b*, *n*] gives modular inverses.

Integer mathematical function (see Section A.3.10). ■ For positive *b*, PowerMod[*a*, *b*, *n*] gives the same answers as Mod[*a*^*b*, *n*] but is much more efficient. ■ For negative *b*, PowerMod[*a*, *b*, *n*] gives the integer *k* such that $ka^{-b} \equiv 1$ mod *n*. If no such integer exists, PowerMod returns unevaluated. ■ See page 725. ■ See also: Mod, ExtendedGCD. ■ Related package: Algebra`PolynomialPowerMod`.

■ PrecedenceForm

PrecedenceForm[*expr*, *prec*] prints with *expr* parenthesized as it would be if it contained an operator with precedence *prec*.

prec must be an integer. See notes for Infix. ■ Example: a + PrecedenceForm[b c, 10] ⟶ a + (b c). ■ PrecedenceForm acts as a "wrapper", which affects printing, but not evaluation. ■ See page 453.

■ Precision

Precision[*x*] gives the number of digits of precision in the number *x*.

If *x* is not a number, Precision[*x*] gives the minimum value of Precision for all the numbers that appear in *x*. ■ Precision gives Infinity when applied to exact numbers, such as integers. ■ Precision gives $MachinePrecision for machine-precision numbers. ■ See page 702. ■ See also: Accuracy, N, Chop, SetPrecision, MachineNumberQ.

■ PrecisionGoal

PrecisionGoal is an option for various numerical operations which specifies how many digits of precision should be sought in the final result.

PrecisionGoal is an option for such functions as NIntegrate and NDSolve. ■ PrecisionGoal -> Automatic yields a precision goal equal to 10 digits less than the setting for WorkingPrecision. ■ PrecisionGoal -> Infinity specifies that precision should not be used as the criterion for terminating the numerical procedure. AccuracyGoal is typically used in this case. ■ Even though you may specify PrecisionGoal->*n*, the results you get may have much less than *n*-digit precision. ■ In most cases, you must set WorkingPrecision to be at least as large as PrecisionGoal. ■ PrecisionGoal effectively specifies the relative error allowed in a numerical procedure. ■ With PrecisionGoal->*p* and AccuracyGoal->*a Mathematica* attempts to make the numerical error in a result of size *x* be less than $10^{-a} + |x| 10^{-p}$. ■ See page 878. ■ See also: AccuracyGoal, WorkingPrecision.

■ PreDecrement

--*x* decreases the value of *x* by 1, returning the new value of *x*.

PreDecrement has attribute HoldFirst. ■ --*x* is equivalent to *x*=*x*-1. ■ See page 285. ■ See also: Decrement, SubtractFrom, Set.

■ Prefix

Prefix[*f*[*expr*]] prints with *f*[*expr*] given in default prefix form: *f* @ *expr*.

Prefix[*f*[*expr*], *h*] prints as *hexpr*.

Prefix[*expr*, *h*, *precedence*, *grouping*] can be used to specify how the output form should be parenthesized. ■ See the notes for Infix about precedence and grouping. ■ See page 453. ■ See also: Infix, Postfix.

■ PreIncrement

++*x* increases the value of *x* by 1, returning the new value of *x*.

PreIncrement has attribute HoldFirst. ■ ++*x* is equivalent to *x*=*x*+1. ■ See page 285. ■ See also: Increment, AddTo, Set.

■ Prepend

Prepend[*expr*, *elem*] gives *expr* with *elem* prepended.

Examples: Prepend[{a,b}, x] ⟶ {x, a, b}; Prepend[f[a], x+y] ⟶ f[x + y, a]. ■ See page 121. ■ See also: Append, Insert.

■ PrependTo

PrependTo[*s*, *elem*] prepends *elem* to the value of *s*, and resets *s* to the result.

PrependTo[*s*, *elem*] is equivalent to *s* = Prepend[*s*, *elem*]. ■ PrependTo[*s*, *elem*] does not evaluate *s*. ■ You can use PrependTo repeatedly to build up a list. ■ See page 287. ■ See also: AppendTo.

■ **Prime**

`Prime[n]` gives the nth prime number.

`Prime[1]` is 2. ■ On most computer systems, `Prime[n]` for n up to 10^8 can be obtained quite quickly. ■ See page 723. ■ Implementation notes: see page 1019. ■ See also: `FactorInteger`, `PrimeQ`, `PrimePi`. ■ Related package: `NumberTheory`NumberTheoryFunctions`.

■ **PrimePi**

`PrimePi[x]` gives the number of primes $\pi(x)$ less than or equal to x.

The argument of `PrimePi` can be any positive real number. ■ `PrimePi[1]` gives 0. ■ See page 723. ■ Implementation notes: see page 1019. ■ See also: `Prime`, `Zeta`.

■ **PrimeQ**

`PrimeQ[expr]` yields `True` if *expr* is a prime number, and yields `False` otherwise.

`PrimeQ[1]` gives `False`. ■ `PrimeQ[-n]`, where n is prime, gives `True`. ■ `PrimeQ[n, GaussianIntegers->True]` determines whether n is a Gaussian prime. ■ See page 723. ■ Implementation notes: see page 1019. ■ See also: `FactorInteger`. ■ Related package: `NumberTheory`PrimeQ`.

+■ **PrincipalValue**

`PrincipalValue` is an option for `Integrate` that specifies whether the Cauchy principal value should be found for a definite integral.

The default setting `PrincipalValue->False` computes ordinary Riemann integrals. ■ Setting `PrincipalValue->True` gives finite answers for integrals that had single pole divergences with `PrincipalValue->False`. ■ See page 817. ■ See also: `Residue`, `Limit`, `GenerateConditions`. ■ Related package: `NumericalMath`CauchyPrincipalValue`.

■ **Print**

`Print[expr_1, expr_2, ... ]` prints the *expr_i*, followed by a newline (line feed).

`Print` sends its output to the channel `$Output`. ■ `Print` uses `OutputForm` as the default format type. ■ `Print` concatenates the output from each *expr_i* together, effectively using `SequenceForm`. ■ You can arrange to have expressions on several lines by using `ColumnForm`. ■ See page 456. ■ See also: `CellPrint`, `Message`, `Put`, `Write`.

+■ **PrintingStyleEnvironment**

`PrintingStyleEnvironment` is an option for notebooks which specifies the style environment to be used in printing the notebook on paper.

See notes for `ScreenStyleEnvironment`. ■ Style environments appropriate for printed output are typically substantially denser than those appropriate for on-screen display. ■ See page 196. ■ See also: `ScreenStyleEnvironment`, `StyleDefinitions`, `NotebookPrint`.

~■ Product

$\text{Product}[f, \{i, imax\}]$ evaluates the product $\prod_{i=1}^{imax} f$.

$\text{Product}[f, \{i, imin, imax\}]$ starts with $i = imin$. $\text{Product}[f, \{i, imin, imax, di\}]$ uses steps di.

$\text{Product}[f, \{i, imin, imax\}, \{j, jmin, jmax\}, \dots]$ evaluates the multiple product $\prod_{i=imin}^{imax} \prod_{j=jmin}^{jmax} \dots f$.

+■ $\text{Product}[f, \{i, imax\}]$ can be entered as $\prod_i f$. +■ $\prod$ can be entered as :prod: or $\backslash[\text{Product}]$.

+■ $\text{Product}[f, \{i, imin, imax\}]$ can be entered as $\prod_{i=imin}^{imax} f$. +■ The limits should be underscripts and overscripts of $\prod$ in normal input, and subscripts and superscripts when embedded in other text. ■ Product evaluates its arguments in a non-standard way (see page 994). ■ Product uses the standard *Mathematica* iteration specification. ■ The iteration variable i is treated as local. ■ In multiple products, the range of the outermost variable is given first. +■ The limits of a product need not be numbers. They can be Infinity or symbolic expressions. +■ If a product cannot be carried out explicitly by multiplying a finite number of terms, Product will attempt to find a symbolic result. In this case, f is first evaluated symbolically. +■ Product can do essentially all products that are given in standard books of tables. +■ Product is output in StandardForm using $\prod$. ■ See page 81. ■ Implementation notes: see page 1022. ■ See also: Do, Sum, Table, NProduct.

+■ ProductLog

$\text{ProductLog}[z]$ gives the principal solution for w in $z = we^w$.

$\text{ProductLog}[k, z]$ gives the kth solution.

Mathematical function (see Section A.3.10). ■ The solutions are ordered according to their imaginary parts. ■ For $z > -1/e$, $\text{ProductLog}[z]$ is real. ■ $\text{ProductLog}[z]$ satisfies the differential equation $dw/dz = w/(z(1 + w))$. ■ See page 751. ■ See also: Log.

■ Prolog

Prolog is an option for graphics functions which gives a list of graphics primitives to be rendered before the main part of the graphics is rendered.

Graphics primitives specified by Prolog are rendered after axes, boxes and frames are rendered. ■ In three-dimensional graphics, two-dimensional graphics primitives can be specified by the Prolog option. The graphics primitives are rendered in a 0,1 coordinate system. ■ See page 484. ■ See also: Background, DefaultColor, Epilog, AxesStyle, PlotStyle, DisplayFunction.

■ Protect

$\text{Protect}[s_1, s_2, \dots]$ sets the attribute Protected for the symbols s_i.

$\text{Protect}["form_1", "form_2", \dots]$ protects all symbols whose names match any of the string patterns $form_i$.

$\text{Protect}["form"]$ allows metacharacters such as *, as specified on page 992. ■ $\text{Protect}["context`*"]$ protects all symbols in a particular context. ■ See pages 301 and 992. ■ See also: Unprotect.

■ Protected

Protected is an attribute which prevents any values associated with a symbol from being modified.

Many built-in *Mathematica* functions have the attribute Protected. ■ See page 309. ■ See also: Locked, ReadProtected, Editable.

■ PseudoInverse

PseudoInverse[m] finds the pseudoinverse of a rectangular matrix.

PseudoInverse works on both symbolic and numerical matrices. ■ For numerical matrices, PseudoInverse[m, Tolerance -> t] specifies that singular values smaller than t times the maximum singular value are to be removed. ■ The default setting Tolerance -> Automatic typically takes t to be 10^{-p+2} where p is the numerical precision of the input. ■ For non-singular square matrices **M**, the pseudoinverse $\mathbf{M}^{(-1)}$ is equivalent to the standard inverse. ■ See page 851. ■ See also: Inverse, SingularValues, Fit. ■ Related package: LinearAlgebra`Cholesky`.

■ Put

expr >> *filename* writes *expr* to a file.

Put[$expr_1$, $expr_2$, ... , "*filename*"] writes a sequence of expressions $expr_i$ to a file.

On systems with advanced graphical interfaces, there will usually be graphical tools for saving expressions in files. ■ Put uses the format type InputForm by default. ■ Put starts writing output at the beginning of the file. It deletes whatever was previously in the file. ■ Put inserts a newline (line feed) at the end of its output. ■ *expr* >> *filename* is equivalent to *expr* >> "*filename*". The double quotes can be omitted if the file name is of the form specified on page 981. ■ It is conventional to use names that end with .m for files containing *Mathematica* input. ■ See page 599. ■ See also: Save, Definition, DumpSave, Get, NotebookPut.

■ PutAppend

expr >>> *filename* appends *expr* to a file.

PutAppend[$expr_1$, $expr_2$, ... , "*filename*"] appends a sequence of expressions $expr_i$ to a file.

PutAppend works the same as Put, except that it adds output to the end of the file, rather than replacing the complete contents of the file. ■ See page 599. ■ See also: Write.

■ QRDecomposition

QRDecomposition[m] yields the QR decomposition for a numerical matrix m. The result is a list {q, r}, where q is an orthogonal matrix and r is an upper triangular matrix.

The original matrix m is equal to Conjugate[Transpose[q]] . r. ■ For non-square matrices, q is row orthonormal. ■ The matrix r has zeros for all entries below the leading diagonal. ■ QRDecomposition[m, Pivoting -> True] yields a list {q, r, p} where p is a permutation matrix such that m . p is equal to Conjugate[Transpose[q]] . r. ■ See page 852. ■ Implementation notes: see page 1020. ■ See also: SchurDecomposition, LUDecomposition, SingularValues, JordanDecomposition. ■ Related package: LinearAlgebra`Cholesky`, LinearAlgebra`Orthogonalization`.

■ Quit

Quit[ ] terminates a *Mathematica* session.

All definitions that you have not explicitly saved in files are lost when the *Mathematica* session terminates. ■ Before terminating a session, *Mathematica* executes any delayed value that has been assigned to the global variable $Epilog. Conventionally, this attempts to read in a file end.m of commands to be executed before termination. ■ On most computer systems, Quit[n] terminates *Mathematica*, passing the integer n as an exit code to the operating system. ■ Exit is a synonym for Quit. ■ See pages 679 and 1006. ■ See also: Return, $IgnoreEOF.

■ Quotient

Quotient[*n*, *m*] gives the integer quotient of *n* and *m*.

Integer mathematical function (see Section A.3.10). ▪ Quotient[*n*, *m*] is equivalent to Floor[*n*/*m*] for integers *n* and *m*. ▪ See page 722. ▪ See also: Mod, PolynomialQuotient.

+■ RadicalBox

RadicalBox[*x*, *n*] represents $\sqrt[n]{x}$ in input and output.

Inside \(... \) RadicalBox[*x*, *n*] can be input as \@*x*\%*n*. ▪ In a notebook a RadicalBox can be created using [CTRL]@ or [CTRL]2, then using [CTRL]% to move to the index position. [CTRL]␣ moves out of the radical. ▪ In StandardForm and InputForm, RadicalBox[*x*, *n*] is interpreted on input as *x*^(1/*n*). ▪ The baseline of RadicalBox[*x*, *n*] is taken to be the baseline of *x*. ▪ If RadicalBox[*x*, *n*] does not fit on a single line, it is output as *x* ^ (1/*n*). ▪ In StandardForm, explicit RadicalBox objects are output literally. You can use DisplayForm to see the display form of such objects. ▪ See page 424. ▪ See also: SqrtBox, OverscriptBox, GridBox.

■ Random

Random[ ] gives a uniformly distributed pseudorandom Real in the range 0 to 1.

Random[*type*, *range*] gives a pseudorandom number of the specified type, lying in the specified range. Possible types are: Integer, Real and Complex. The default range is 0 to 1. You can give the range {*min*, *max*} explicitly; a range specification of *max* is equivalent to {0, *max*}.

Random[Integer] gives 0 or 1 with probability $\frac{1}{2}$. ▪ Random[Complex, {*zmin*, *zmax*}] gives a pseudorandom complex number in the rectangle defined by *zmin* and *zmax*. ▪ Random[Real, *range*, *n*] generates an *n*-digit pseudorandom real number. Both leading and trailing digits may be chosen as 0. ▪ Random gives a different sequence of pseudorandom numbers whenever you run *Mathematica*. You can start Random with a particular seed using SeedRandom. ▪ See page 720. ▪ Implementation notes: see page 1019. ▪ See also: $RandomState. ▪ Related packages: Statistics`ContinuousDistributions`, Statistics`DiscreteDistributions`.

■ Range

Range[*imax*] generates the list {1, 2, ... , *imax*}.

Range[*imin*, *imax*] generates the list {*imin*, ... , *imax*}. Range[*imin*, *imax*, *di*] uses step *di*.

Example: Range[4] ⟶ {1, 2, 3, 4}. ▪ The arguments to Range need not be integers. ▪ Range starts from *imin*, and successively adds increments of *di* until the result is greater than *imax*. ▪ Range[0, 1, .3] ⟶ {0, 0.3, 0.6, 0.9}. ▪ Range[x, x+2] ⟶ {x, 1 + x, 2 + x}. ▪ Range uses the standard *Mathematica* iteration specification, as applied to a single variable. ▪ See page 115. ▪ See also: Table, Interval, CharacterRange.

▪ Raster

Raster[{{a_{11}, a_{12}, ... }, ... }] is a two-dimensional graphics primitive which represents a rectangular array of gray cells.

Raster[*array*, ColorFunction -> *f*] specifies that each cell should be rendered using the graphics directives obtained by applying the function *f* to the cell value a_{ij}. ▪ Raster[*array*, ColorFunction -> Hue] generates an array in which cell values are specified by hues. ▪ If *array* has dimensions {m, n}, then Raster[*array*] is assumed to occupy the rectangle Rectangle[{0, 0}, {m, n}]. ▪ Raster[*array*, {{$xmin$, $ymin$}, {$xmax$, $ymax$}}] specifies that the raster should be taken instead to fill the rectangle Rectangle[{$xmin$, $ymin$}, {$xmax$, $ymax$}]. ~▪ Scaled and Offset can be used to specify the coordinates for the rectangle. ▪ Raster[*array*, *rect*, {$zmin$, $zmax$}] specifies that cell values should be scaled so that $zmin$ corresponds to 0 and $zmax$ corresponds to 1. Cell values outside this range are clipped. ▪ See page 477. ▪ See also: RasterArray, DensityGraphics, GraphicsArray.

▪ RasterArray

RasterArray[{{g_{11}, g_{12}, ... }, ... }] is a two-dimensional graphics primitive which represents a rectangular array of cells colored according to the graphics directives g_{ij}.

Each of the g_{ij} must be GrayLevel, RGBColor or Hue. ▪ If *array* has dimensions {m, n}, then RasterArray[*array*] is assumed to occupy the rectangle Rectangle[{0, 0}, {m, n}].
▪ RasterArray[*array*, {{$xmin$, $ymin$}, {$xmax$, $ymax$}}] specifies that the raster should be taken instead to fill the rectangle Rectangle[{$xmin$, $ymin$}, {$xmax$, $ymax$}]. ~▪ Scaled and Offset can be used to specify the coordinates for the rectangle. ▪ See page 477. ▪ See also: Raster, GraphicsArray.

▪ Rational

Rational is the head used for rational numbers.

You can enter a rational number in the form n/m. ▪ The pattern object _Rational can be used to stand for a rational number. It cannot stand for a single integer. ▪ You have to use Numerator and Denominator to extract parts of Rational numbers. ▪ See page 696. ▪ See also: Integer, Numerator, Denominator.

▪ Rationalize

Rationalize[x] takes Real numbers in x that are close to rationals, and converts them to exact Rational numbers.

Rationalize[x, dx] performs the conversion whenever the error made is smaller in magnitude than dx.

Example: Rationalize[3.78] $\longrightarrow$ 189/50. ▪ Rationalize[N[Pi]] $\longrightarrow$ 3.14159 does not give a rational number, since there is none "sufficiently close" to N[Pi]. ▪ A rational number p/q is considered "sufficiently close" to a Real x if $|p/q - x| < c/q^2$, where c is chosen to be 10^{-4}. ▪ Rationalize[x, 0] converts any x to rational form. ▪ See page 699. ▪ See also: Chop, Round, LatticeReduce. ▪ Related package: NumberTheory`Rationalize`, NumberTheory`ContinuedFractions`.

▪ Raw

Raw[h, "*hexstring*"] constructs a raw data object with head h, and with contents corresponding to the binary bit pattern represented by the string *hexstring*, interpreted as a hexadecimal number.

Raw should be used only under very special circumstances. ▪ It is possible to crash *Mathematica* by creating a fundamental *Mathematica* data object with Raw, and specifying illegal internal data for it. If you create an object with head Real, but with internal data incompatible with *Mathematica* Real numbers, you may end up crashing your whole *Mathematica* session. ▪ Raw encodes data so that two hexadecimal digits represent one byte. Identical *hexstring* may lead to different internal data on different computer systems. ▪ You cannot necessarily transport raw arrays of bytes from one type of computer to another without encountering byte swap incompatibilities. ▪ See page 964. ▪ See also: Run. ▪ Related package: Utilities`BinaryFiles`.

■ Re

Re[*z*] gives the real part of the complex number *z*.

Re[*expr*] is left unevaluated if *expr* is not a numeric quantity. ■ See page 719. ■ See also: Im, Abs, Arg, ComplexExpand.

~■ Read

Read[*stream*] reads one expression from an input stream, and returns the expression.

Read[*stream*, *type*] reads one object of the specified type.

Read[*stream*, {*type*$_1$, *type*$_2$, ... }] reads a sequence of objects of the specified types.

Possible types to read are:

Byte	single byte, returned as an integer code
Character	single character, returned as a one-character string
Expression	complete *Mathematica* expression
Number	integer or an approximate number, given in "E" format
Real	approximate number, given in "E" format
Record	sequence of characters delimited by record separators
String	string terminated by a newline
Word	sequence of characters delimited by word separators

~■ Objects of type Real can be given in the scientific notation format used by languages such as C and Fortran, as well as in standard *Mathematica* format. A form like 2.e5 or 2E5 as well as 2*^5 can be used to represent the number 2×10^5. Objects read as type Real are always returned as approximate numbers. Objects read as type Number are returned as integers if they contain no explicit decimal points. ■ The following options can be given:

NullRecords	False	whether to assume a null record between repeated record separators
NullWords	False	whether to assume a null word between repeated word separators
RecordSeparators	{"\n"}	separators allowed between records
TokenWords	{}	words taken as delimiters
WordSeparators	{" ", "\t"}	separators allowed between words

■ Objects of type String must be terminated by newlines ("\n" characters). ■ You can specify any nested list of types for Read to look for. Each successive object read will be placed in the next position in the list structure. A depth-first traversal of the list structure is used. ■ Example: Read[*stream*, {Number, Number}] reads a pair of numbers from an input stream, and gives the result as a two-element list.
■ Read[*stream*, {{Number, Number}, {Number, Number}}] reads a 2×2 matrix, going through each column, then each row. ■ You can use Read to get objects to insert into any expression structure, not necessarily a list. Example: Read[*stream*, Hold[Expression]] gets an expression and places it inside Hold. ■ The first argument to Read can be InputStream["*name*", *n*], or simply "*name*" if there is only one open input stream with the specified name. ■ You can open a file or pipe to get an InputStream object using OpenRead. ■ There is always a "current point" maintained for any stream. When you read an object from a stream, the current point is left after the input you read. Successive calls to Read can therefore be used to read successive objects in a stream such as a file. ■ Read returns EndOfFile for each object you try to read after you have reached the end of a file. ■ Read returns $Failed if it cannot read an object of the type you requested. ■ If there is a syntax error in a *Mathematica* expression that you try to read, then Read leaves the current point at the position of the error, and returns $Failed. ■ See page 622. ■ See also: Input, Get, Skip, Find, StringToStream, LinkRead. ■ Related package: Utilities`BinaryFiles`.

■ ReadList

ReadList["*file*"] reads all the remaining expressions in a file, and returns a list of them.

ReadList["*file*", *type*] reads objects of the specified type from a file, until the end of the file is reached. The list of objects read is returned.

ReadList["*file*", {*type*$_1$, *type*$_2$, ... }] reads objects with a sequence of types, until the end of the file is reached.

ReadList["*file*", *types*, *n*] reads only the first *n* objects of the specified types.

The option setting RecordLists -> True makes ReadList create separate sublists for objects that appear in separate records. ■ With the default setting RecordSeparators -> {"\n"}, RecordLists -> True puts objects on separate lines into separate sublists. ■ The option RecordSeparators gives a list of strings which are taken to delimit records. ■ ReadList takes the same options as Read, with the addition of RecordLists. ■ If *file* is not already open for reading, ReadList opens it, then closes it when it is finished. If the file is already open, ReadList does not close it at the end. ■ ReadList prints a message if any of the objects remaining in the file are not of the specified types. ■ ReadList["*file*", {*type*$_1$, ... }] looks for the sequence of *type*$_i$ in order. If the end of file is reached while part way through the sequence of *type*$_i$, EndOfFile is returned in place of the elements in the sequence that have not yet been read. ■ ReadList[*stream*] reads from an open input stream, as returned by OpenRead. ■ See notes for Read. ■ See pages 206 and 617. ■ See also: FindList.

■ ReadProtected

ReadProtected is an attribute which prevents values associated with a symbol from being seen.

Individual values associated with read-protected symbols can be used during evaluation. ■ Definition[*f*], ?*f*, and related functions give only the attributes for read-protected symbols *f*. ■ See page 309. ■ See also: Locked, Protected, Copyable.

~■ Real

Real is the head used for real (floating-point) numbers.

_Real can be used to stand for a real number in a pattern. ■ You can enter a floating-point number of any length. ~■ You can enter a number in scientific notation by using the form *mantissa**^*exponent*. ■ You can enter a floating-point number in base *b* using *b*^^*digits*. The base must be less than 36. The letters a–z or A–Z are used in sequence to stand for digits 10 through 35. ■ Real is also used to indicate an approximate real number in Read. ■ See page 696. ■ See also: RealDigits, BaseForm, Number.

■ **RealDigits**

RealDigits[*x*] gives a list of the digits in the approximate real number *x*, together with the number of digits that are to the left of the decimal point.

RealDigits[*x*, *b*] gives a list of base-*b* digits in *x*.

+ RealDigits[*x*, *b*, *len*] gives a list of *len* digits.

+ RealDigits[*x*, *b*, *len*, *n*] gives *len* digits starting with the coefficient of b^n.

RealDigits[*x*] returns a list of digits whose length is equal to Precision[*x*]. +■ RealDigits[*x*] and RealDigits[*x*, *b*] require that *x* be an approximate real number, returned for example by N. RealDigits[*x*, *b*, *len*] also works on exact numbers. +■ If *len* is larger than Log[10, *b*] Precision[*x*] remaining digits are filled in as Indeterminate. +■ RealDigits[*x*, *b*, *len*, *n*] starts with the digit which is the coefficient of b^n, truncating or padding with zeros as necessary. +■ RealDigits[*x*, *b*, *len*, -1] starts with the digit immediately to the right of the base *b* decimal point in *x*. ■ The base *b* in RealDigits[*x*, *b*] need not be an integer. For any real *b* such that $b > 1$, RealDigits[*x*, *b*] successively finds the largest integer multiples of powers of *b* that can be removed while leaving a non-negative remainder. +■ RealDigits[*x*] discards the sign of *x*. +■ FromDigits can be used as the inverse of RealDigits. ■ See page 700. ■ See also: MantissaExponent, IntegerDigits, BaseForm, FromDigits.

■ **Record**

Record represents a record in Read, Find and related functions.

The record is delimited by strings in the list given as the setting for RecordSeparators. ■ See page 618. ■ See also: Word. ■ Related package: Utilities`BinaryFiles`.

■ **RecordLists**

RecordLists is an option for ReadList which specifies whether objects from separate records should be returned in separate sublists.

With the default setting RecordSeparators -> {"\n"}, setting RecordLists -> True makes RecordLists return objects that appear on different lines in different sublists. ■ With RecordLists -> False, ReadList returns a single list of all objects it reads. ■ With RecordLists -> True, ReadList returns a list containing a sublist for each record. ■ See page 617.

■ **RecordSeparators**

RecordSeparators is an option for Read, Find and related functions which specifies the list of strings to be taken as delimiters for records.

The default setting is RecordSeparators -> {"\n"}. With this setting, each complete line of input is considered as a record. ■ Strings used as record separators may contain several characters. ■ With the option setting NullRecords -> False, any number of record separators may appear between any two successive records. ■ RecordSeparators -> { } specifies that everything is to be included in a single record. ■ RecordSeparators -> {{*lsep*$_1$, ... }, {*rsep*$_1$, ... }} specifies different left and right separators for records. When there are nested left and right separators, records are taken to be delimited by the innermost balanced pairs of separators. ■ Example: with RecordSeparators -> {{"<"}, {">"}}, the records aaa and bbb are extracted from <x<aaa>yyy<<bbb>>>. ■ Text that does not appear between left and right separators is discarded. ■ See page 619. ■ See also: WordSeparators.

~■ Rectangle

Rectangle[{*xmin*, *ymin*}, {*xmax*, *ymax*}] is a two-dimensional graphics primitive that represents a filled rectangle, oriented parallel to the axes.

Rectangle[{*xmin*, *ymin*}, {*xmax*, *ymax*}, *graphics*] gives a rectangle filled with the specified graphics.

~■ Scaled and Offset can be used to specify the coordinates for the rectangle. ■ Rectangle[Scaled[{*xmin*, *ymin*}], Scaled[{*xmax*, *ymax*}]] yields a rectangle with corners specified by scaled coordinates. +■ Any combination of original coordinates, as well as Scaled and Offset, can be used to specify the corners of the rectangle. ■ Rectangle[{*xmin*, *ymin*}, {*xmax*, *ymax*}] is equivalent to a suitable Polygon with four corners. ■ You can use graphics directives such as GrayLevel and RGBColor to specify how Rectangle[{*xmin*, *ymin*}, {*xmax*, *ymax*}] should be filled. ■ In Rectangle[{*xmin*, *ymin*}, {*xmax*, *ymax*}, *graphics*], *graphics* can be any graphics object. ■ The rectangle is taken as the complete display area in which the graphics object is rendered. ■ When rectangles overlap, their backgrounds are effectively taken to be transparent. ■ Fonts and absolute size specifications are not affected by the size of the rectangle in which the graphics are rendered. ~■ The options DisplayFunction, ColorOutput and CharacterEncoding are ignored for graphics objects given inside Rectangle. ■ See page 472. ■ See also: Polygon, Raster, RasterArray, Cuboid, GraphicsArray.

■ Reduce

Reduce[*eqns*, *vars*] simplifies the equations *eqns*, attempting to solve for the variables *vars*. The equations generated by Reduce are equivalent to *eqns*, and contain all the possible solutions.

Reduce[*eqns*, *vars*, *elims*] simplifies the equations, trying to eliminate the variables *elims*.

The equations given to Reduce are in the form *lhs* == *rhs*. Simultaneous equations can either be given in a list, or combined with &&. ■ Example: Reduce[a x + b == 0, x] ⟶ b == 0 && a == 0 || a != 0 && x == -(b/a). ■ Reduce generates equations (==) and nonequalities (!=), combined with && and ||. ■ Reduce primarily deals with polynomial equations. ■ See page 796. ■ See also: Solve, Eliminate, LogicalExpand, ToRules.

■ ReleaseHold

~ ReleaseHold[*expr*] removes Hold, HoldForm, HoldPattern and HoldComplete in *expr*.

Example: ReleaseHold[{2, Hold[1 + 1]}] ⟶ {2, 2}. ■ ReleaseHold removes only one layer of Hold etc.; it does not remove inner occurrences in nested Hold etc. functions. ■ See page 319. ■ See also: Evaluate.

■ Remove

Remove[*symbol*₁, ...] removes symbols completely, so that their names are no longer recognized by *Mathematica*.

Remove["*form*₁", "*form*₂", ...] removes all symbols whose names match any of the string patterns *form*ᵢ.

You can use Remove to get rid of symbols that you do not need, and which may shadow symbols in contexts later on your context path. ■ Remove["*form*"] allows metacharacters such as *, as specified on page 992. ■ Remove["*context*`*"] removes all symbols in a particular context. ■ Remove does not affect symbols with the attribute Protected. ■ Once you have removed a symbol, you will never be able to refer to it again, unless you recreate it. ■ If you have an expression that contains a symbol which you remove, the removed symbol will be printed as Removed["*name*"], where its name is given in a string. ■ See pages 374, 382 and 1000. ■ See also: Clear.

■ RenameDirectory

RenameDirectory["*dir₁*", "*dir₂*"] renames the directory *dir₁* to *dir₂*.

dir₁ must already exist; *dir₂* must not. ■ RenameDirectory sets the modification date for *dir₂* to be the same as for *dir₁*. ■ RenameDirectory returns the full new directory name, or $Failed if the directory cannot be renamed. ■ See page 616. ■ See also: CopyDirectory, CreateDirectory, DeleteDirectory.

■ RenameFile

RenameFile["*file₁*", "*file₂*"] renames *file₁* to *file₂*.

file₁ must already exist; *file₂* must not. ■ RenameFile sets the modification date for *file₂* to be the same as for *file₁*. ■ RenameFile returns the full new file name, or $Failed if the file cannot be renamed. ■ See page 616. ■ See also: CopyFile, DeleteFile, RenameDirectory.

■ RenderAll

RenderAll is an option for Graphics3D which specifies whether or not PostScript should be generated for *all* polygons.

When RenderAll->False, PostScript will be generated only for those polygons or parts of polygons which are visible in the final picture. ■ If RenderAll->True, PostScript is generated for *all* polygons. The PostScript for polygons that are further back is given before the PostScript for those in front. If the PostScript is displayed incrementally, you can see the object being drawn from the back. ■ Setting RenderAll->False will usually lead to a smaller amount of PostScript code, but may take longer to run. ■ There may be slight differences in the images obtained with different settings for RenderAll, primarily as a result of different numerical roundoff in the PostScript code, and the rendering system. ■ See page 534. ■ See also: PolygonIntersections.

■ Repeated

p.. is a pattern object which represents a sequence of one or more expressions, each matching *p*.

p.. can appear as an argument of any function. It represents any sequence of arguments. ■ All the objects in the sequence represented by *p*.. must match *p*, but the objects need not be identical. ■ The expression *p* may, but need not, itself be a pattern object. ■ See pages 274 and 976. ■ See also: BlankSequence.

■ RepeatedNull

p... is a pattern object which represents a sequence of zero or more expressions, each matching *p*.

See notes for Repeated. ■ See pages 274 and 976.

■ Replace

Replace[*expr, rules*] applies a rule or list of rules in an attempt to transform the entire expression *expr*.

Example: Replace[x^2, x^2 -> a] ⟶ a. ■ Replace[x + 1, x -> a] ⟶ 1 + x. ■ The rules must be of the form *lhs* -> *rhs* or *lhs* :> *rhs*. ■ A list of rules can be given. The rules are tried in order. The result of the first one that applies is returned. If none of the rules apply, the original *expr* is returned. ■ If the rules are given in nested lists, Replace is effectively mapped onto the inner lists. Thus Replace[*expr*, {{*r₁₁*, *r₁₂*}, {*r₂₁*, ... }, ... }] is equivalent to {Replace[*expr*, {*r₁₁*, *r₁₂*}], Replace[*expr*, {*r₂₁*, ... }], ... }. ■ Delayed rules defined with :> can contain /; conditions. ■ Replace[*expr*, *rules*] applies rules only to the complete expression *expr*. You can use ReplaceAll to apply rules separately to each part of an expression. ■ See page 282. ■ See also: Rule, Set, ReplacePart, ReplaceList, StringReplace, PolynomialReduce.

■ ReplaceAll

expr /. *rules* applies a rule or list of rules in an attempt to transform each subpart of an expression *expr*.

Example: x + 2 /. x -> a ⟶ 2 + a. ■ ReplaceAll looks at each part of *expr*, tries all the *rules* on it, and then goes on to the next part of *expr*. The first rule that applies to a particular part is used; no further rules are tried on that part, or on any of its subparts. ■ ReplaceAll applies a particular rule only once to an expression. ■ Example: x /. x -> x + 1 ⟶ 1 + x. ■ See the notes on Replace for a description of how rules are applied to each part of *expr*. ■ *expr* /. *rules* returns *expr* if none of the rules apply. ■ See page 280. ■ See also: Rule, Set, MapAll.

₊■ ReplaceList

ReplaceList[*expr*, *rules*] attempts to transform the entire expression *expr* by applying a rule or list of rules in all possible ways, and returns a list of the results obtained.

ReplaceList[*expr*, *rules*, *n*] gives a list of at most *n* results.

When no transformation is possible, ReplaceList returns {}. ■ See notes for Replace. ■ See pages 260 and 282. ■ See also: Cases, StringPosition, Trace, Position, Split.

~■ ReplacePart

ReplacePart[*expr*, *new*, *n*] yields an expression in which the nth part of *expr* is replaced by *new*.

ReplacePart[*expr*, *new*, {*i*, *j*, ... }] replaces the part at position {*i*, *j*, ... }.

ReplacePart[*expr*, *new*, {{i_1, j_1, ... }, {i_2, j_2, ... }, ... }] replaces parts at several positions by *new*.

₊ ReplacePart[*expr*, *new*, *pos*, *npos*] replaces parts at positions *pos* in *expr* by parts at positions *npos* in *new*.

Example: ReplacePart[{a, b, c, d}, x, 3] ⟶ {a, b, x, d}. ■ The list of positions used by ReplacePart is in the same form as is returned by the function Position. ₊■ ReplacePart[*expr*, Hold[*new*], *pos*, 1] can be used to replace a part without evaluating it. ₊■ If *pos* and *npos* both specify multiple parts, each part in *pos* is replaced by the corresponding part in *npos*. ■ See pages 122 and 233. ■ See also: Part, Extract, MapAt, FlattenAt, Insert, Delete, Sequence, StringReplacePart.

■ ReplaceRepeated

expr //. *rules* repeatedly performs replacements until *expr* no longer changes.

expr //. *rules* effectively applies /. repeatedly, until the results it gets no longer change. ■ It performs one complete pass over the expression using /., then carries out the next pass. ■ You should be very careful to avoid infinite loops when you use the //. operator. The command x //. x -> x + 1 will, for example, lead to an infinite loop. ■ ReplaceRepeated takes the option MaxIterations, which specifies the maximum number of times it will try to apply the rules you give. The default setting is MaxIterations -> 65536. With MaxIterations -> Infinity there is no limit. ■ See page 281. ■ See also: Rule, Set, FixedPoint.

■ ResetDirectory

ResetDirectory[ ] resets the current working directory to its previous value.

Successive calls to ResetDirectory yield earlier and earlier current directories. ■ ResetDirectory uses the directory stack given by DirectoryStack[ ]. ■ ResetDirectory removes the last element from the directory stack, and makes the second-to-last element current. ■ See page 611. ■ See also: SetDirectory, Directory, $Path.

■ Residue

Residue[*expr*, {*x*, x_0}] finds the residue of *expr* at the point $x = x_0$.

The residue is defined as the coefficient of $(x - x_0)$^-1 in the Laurent expansion of *expr*. ■ *Mathematica* can usually find residues at a point only when it can evaluate power series at that point. ■ See page 836. ■ See also: Series, Limit, PrincipalValue. ■ Related package: Algebra`RootIsolation`.

■ Rest

Rest[*expr*] gives *expr* with the first element removed.

Example: Rest[{a, b, c}] $\longrightarrow$ {b, c}. ■ Rest[*expr*] is equivalent to Drop[*expr*, 1]. ■ See page 118. ■ See also: Drop, First, Part, Take.

■ Resultant

Resultant[$poly_1$, $poly_2$, *var*] computes the resultant of the polynomials $poly_1$ and $poly_2$ with respect to the variable *var*.

Resultant[$poly_1$, $poly_2$, *var*, Modulus->*p*] computes the resultant modulo the prime *p*.

The resultant of two polynomials *a* and *b*, both with leading coefficient one, is the product of all the differences $a_i - b_j$ between roots of the polynomials. The resultant is always a number or a polynomial. ■ See page 773. ■ See also: PolynomialGCD, Eliminate.

■ Return

Return[*expr*] returns the value *expr* from a function.

Return[ ] returns the value Null.

Return[*expr*] exits control structures within the definition of a function, and gives the value *expr* for the whole function. +■ Return takes effect as soon as it is evaluated, even if it appears inside other functions. ■ Return can be used inside functions like Scan. ■ See page 333. ■ See also: Break, Throw, Abort.

■ Reverse

Reverse[*expr*] reverses the order of the elements in *expr*.

Example: Reverse[{a, b, c}] $\longrightarrow$ {c, b, a}. ■ See page 124. ■ See also: Permutations, RotateLeft, RotateRight, StringReverse.

■ RGBColor

RGBColor[*red*, *green*, *blue*] is a graphics directive which specifies that graphical objects which follow are to be displayed, if possible, in the color given.

Red, green and blue color intensities outside the range 0 to 1 will be clipped. ■ On monochrome displays, a gray level based on the average of the color intensities is used. ■ The end of the Graphics Gallery shows examples of colors generated with various RGBColor specifications. ■ See page 479. ■ See also: Hue, GrayLevel, CMYKColor, ColorOutput. ■ Related package: Graphics`Colors`.

■ RiemannSiegelTheta

RiemannSiegelTheta[t] gives the Riemann-Siegel function $\vartheta(t)$.

Mathematical function (see Section A.3.10). ▪ $\vartheta(t) = \mathrm{Im}[\log \Gamma(\frac{1}{4} + i\frac{t}{2}) - t \log \pi/2]$ for real t. ▪ $\vartheta(t)$ arises in the study of the Riemann zeta function on the critical line. It is closely related to the number of zeros of $\zeta(\frac{1}{2} + iu)$ for $0 < u < t$. ▪ $\vartheta(t)$ is an analytic function of t except for branch cuts on the imaginary axis running from $\pm i/2$ to $\pm i\infty$. ▪ See page 742. ▪ See also: Zeta.

■ RiemannSiegelZ

RiemannSiegelZ[t] gives the Riemann-Siegel function $Z(t)$.

Mathematical function (see Section A.3.10). ▪ $Z(t) = e^{i\vartheta(t)}\zeta(\frac{1}{2} + it)$, where ϑ is the Riemann-Siegel theta function, and ζ is the Riemann zeta function. ▪ $|Z(t)| = \left|\zeta(\frac{1}{2} + it)\right|$ for real t. ▪ $Z(t)$ is an analytic function of t except for branch cuts on the imaginary axis running from $\pm i/2$ to $\pm i\infty$. ▪ See page 742. ▪ See also: Zeta.

+■ Root

Root[f, k] represents the kth root of the polynomial equation $f[x] == 0$.

f must be a Function object such as (#^5 - 2 # + 1)&. ▪ Root[f, k] is automatically reduced so that f has the smallest possible degree and smallest integer coefficients. ▪ The ordering used by Root takes real roots to come before complex ones, and takes complex conjugate pairs of roots to be adjacent. ▪ The coefficients in the polynomial $f[x]$ can involve symbolic parameters. ▪ For linear and quadratic polynomials $f[x]$, Root[f, k] is automatically reduced to explicit rational or radical form. ▪ N finds the approximate numerical value of a Root object. ▪ Operations such as Abs, Re, Round and Less can be used on Root objects. ▪ Root[f, k] is treated as a numeric quantity if f contains no symbolic parameters. ▪ Root by default isolates the roots of a polynomial using approximate numerical methods. No cases are known where this approach fails. SetOptions[Root, ExactRootIsolation->True] will however make Root use much slower but fully rigorous methods. ▪ See page 787. ▪ See also: Solve, RootReduce, ToRadicals, RootSum, Extension. ▪ Related package: Algebra`RootIsolation`.

+■ RootReduce

RootReduce[$expr$] attempts to reduce $expr$ to a single Root object.

If $expr$ consists only of integers and Root objects combined using algebraic operations, then the result from RootReduce[$expr$] will always be a single Root object. ▪ Simple Root objects may in turn automatically evaluate to rational expressions or combinations of radicals. ▪ See page 791. ▪ See also: FullSimplify, Solve, ToRadicals. ▪ Related package: NumberTheory`PrimitiveElement`.

▪ Roots

Roots[*lhs*==*rhs*, *var*] yields a disjunction of equations which represent the roots of a polynomial equation.

Roots uses Factor and Decompose in trying to find roots. ▪ You can find numerical values of the roots by applying N. ▪ Roots can take the following options:

Cubics	True	whether to generate explicit solutions for cubics
EquatedTo	Null	expression to which the variable solved for should be equated
Modulus	Infinity	integer modulus
Multiplicity	1	multiplicity in final list of solutions
Quartics	True	whether to generate explicit solutions for quartics
Using	True	subsidiary equations to be solved

▪ Roots is generated when Solve and related functions cannot produce explicit solutions. Options are often given in such cases. ▪ Roots gives several identical equations when roots with multiplicity greater than one occur. ▪ See page 785. ▪ See also: Solve, NSolve, FindRoot, ToRules, Root, Factor, Decompose, InterpolatingPolynomial. ▪ Related package: Algebra'RootIsolation'.

+ ▪ RootSum

RootSum[*f*, *form*] represents the sum of *form*[*x*] for all *x* that satisfy the polynomial equation *f*[*x*] == 0.

f must be a Function object such as (#^5 - 2 # + 1)&. ▪ *form* need not correspond to a polynomial function. ▪ Normal[*expr*] expands RootSum objects into explicit sums involving Root objects. ▪ *f* and *form* can contain symbolic parameters. ▪ RootSum[*f*, *form*] is automatically simplified whenever *form* is a rational function. ▪ RootSum is often generated in computing integrals of rational functions. ▪ See page 791. ▪ See also: Root. ▪ Related package: Algebra'SymmetricPolynomials'.

▪ RotateLabel

RotateLabel is an option for two-dimensional graphics functions which specifies whether labels on vertical frame axes should be rotated to be vertical.

For frame labels, the default is RotateLabel -> True. ▪ With RotateLabel -> True, vertical frame axes labels read from bottom to top. ▪ See page 494. ▪ See also: Text, ImageRotated.

▪ RotateLeft

RotateLeft[*expr*, *n*] cycles the elements in *expr* *n* positions to the left.

RotateLeft[*expr*] cycles one position to the left.

RotateLeft[*expr*, {*n*₁, *n*₂, ... }] cycles elements at successive levels *n*ᵢ positions to the left.

Example: RotateLeft[{a, b, c}, 1] ⟶ {b, c, a}. ▪ RotateLeft[*expr*, -*n*] rotates *n* positions to the right. ▪ See page 124. ▪ See also: Reverse.

■ **RotateRight**

> `RotateRight[`*expr*`, `*n*`]` cycles the elements in *expr n* positions to the right.
>
> `RotateRight[`*expr*`]` cycles one position to the right.
>
> `RotateRight[`*expr*`, {`*n*₁`, `*n*₂`, ... }]` cycles elements at successive levels n_i positions to the right.
>
> Example: `RotateRight[{a, b, c}, 1]` ⟶ `{c, a, b}`. ▪ `RotateRight[`*expr*`, -`*n*`]` rotates *n* positions to the left. ▪ See page 124. ▪ See also: `Reverse`.

~■ **Round**

> `Round[`*x*`]` gives the integer closest to *x*.
>
> Mathematical function (see Section A.3.10). ▪ Examples: `Round[2.4]` ⟶ 2; `Round[2.6]` ⟶ 3; `Round[-2.4]` ⟶ -2; `Round[-2.6]` ⟶ -3. ~▪ Round rounds numbers of the form *x*.5 toward the nearest even integer. ~▪ `Round[`*x*`]` returns an integer when *x* is any numeric quantity, whether or not it is an explicit number. ~▪ Example: `Round[Pi^2]` ⟶ 10. ~▪ For exact numeric quantities, Round internally uses numerical approximations to establish its result. This process can be affected by the setting of the global variable `$MaxExtraPrecision`. ▪ See page 718. ▪ See also: `IntegerPart`, `Floor`, `Ceiling`, `Chop`.

+■ **RowAlignments**

> `RowAlignments` is an option for `GridBox` which specifies how entries in each row should be aligned.
>
> The following settings can be given:

`Center`	centered
`Top`	tops aligned
`Bottom`	bottoms aligned
`Baseline`	baselines aligned (default)
`Axis`	axes aligned
`{`*pos*₁`, `*pos*₂`, ... }`	separate settings for each row in the grid

> ▪ Lists of settings are used cyclically if there are more rows in the grid than elements in the list. ▪ See page 428. ▪ See also: `ColumnAlignments`, `RowsEqual`, `RowMinHeight`, `TableAlignments`.

+■ **RowBox**

> `RowBox[{`*box*₁`, `*box*₂`, ... }]` represents a row of boxes or strings in input and output.
>
> RowBox objects are generated automatically to correspond to each operator and its operands in input given as \(*input*\). ▪ The default arrangement of RowBox objects in \(*input*\) is based on operator precedence. Additional \(... \) can be inserted like parentheses to specify different arrangements of RowBox objects. ▪ The boxes or strings in a RowBox are output in a row with their baselines aligned. ▪ In InputForm, RowBox objects are output using \(... \). ▪ In StandardForm, explicit RowBox objects are output literally. You can use DisplayForm to see the display form of such objects. ▪ See page 424. ▪ See also: `SequenceForm`, `GridBox`, `AdjustmentBox`.

■ RowLines

RowLines is an option for GridBox which specifies whether lines should be drawn between adjacent rows.

The default setting is RowLines->False. ■ RowLines->{v_{12}, v_{23}, ... } specifies whether lines should be drawn between successive pairs of rows. The v_{ij} can be True or False. ■ If there are more rows than entries in the list, the last element is used repeatedly for remaining pairs of rows. ■ Lines can be drawn around the outside of a GridBox using FrameBox. ■ See page 425. ■ See also: ColumnLines, FrameBox, GridLines.

■ RowMinHeight

RowMinHeight is an option for GridBox which specifies the minimum total height in units of font size that should be allowed for each row.

The default setting RowMinHeight->1 forces each row to have a total height which at least accommodates all the characters in the current font. ■ RowMinHeight->0 reduces the total height of each entry as much as possible, allowing entries containing characters such as x and X to be different heights. ■ See page 428. ■ See also: RowSpacings, RowAlignments, RowsEqual, ButtonMinHeight.

■ RowReduce

RowReduce[m] gives the row-reduced form of the matrix m.

Example: RowReduce[{{3, 1, a}, {2, 1, b}}] $\longrightarrow$ {{1, 0, a - b}, {0, 1, -2a + 3b}}. ■ RowReduce performs a version of Gaussian elimination, adding multiples of rows together so as to produce zero elements when possible. The final matrix is in reduced row echelon form. ■ If m is a non-degenerate square matrix, RowReduce[m] is IdentityMatrix[m]. ■ If m is a sufficiently non-degenerate rectangular matrix with k rows and more than k columns, then the first k columns of RowReduce[m] will form an identity matrix. ■ RowReduce works on both numerical and symbolic matrices. ~■ RowReduce[m, Modulus -> n] performs row reduction modulo n. ■ RowReduce[m, ZeroTest -> $test$] evaluates $test$[m[[i, j]]] to determine whether matrix elements are zero. ■ See page 847. ■ Implementation notes: see page 1020. ■ See also: LinearSolve, Inverse, NullSpace, GroebnerBasis.

■ RowsEqual

RowsEqual is an option for GridBox which specifies whether all rows in the grid should be assigned equal total height.

The default setting RowsEqual->False determines the total height of each row from the entry in that row with the largest total height. ■ RowsEqual->True makes all rows the same total height, with the total height determined by the entry with the largest total height in the whole GridBox. ■ See page 428. ■ See also: RowAlignments, RowSpacings, RowMinHeight, ColumnsEqual, MatrixForm.

■ RowSpacings

RowSpacings is an option for GridBox which specifies the spaces in x-heights that should be inserted between successive rows.

The default setting is RowSpacings->0.5. ■ RowSpacings effectively specifies the minimum distance between entries in successive rows; individual entries will often not fill their rows and will therefore be further apart. ■ RowSpacings->n uses a column spacing equal to n times the height of an "x" character in the current font. ■ RowSpacings->{s_{12}, s_{23}, ... } can be used to specify different spacings between different rows. If there are more rows than entries in this list, then the last element of the list is used repeatedly for the remaining rows. ■ See page 428. ■ See also: RowAlignments, RowMinHeight, RowsEqual, ColumnSpacings, TableSpacing.

~■ Rule

~ *lhs* -> *rhs* or *lhs* → *rhs* represents a rule that transforms *lhs* to *rhs*.

+■ The character → can be entered as ⦂->⦂ or \[Rule]. ■ *lhs* -> *rhs* evaluates *rhs* immediately. ■ You can apply rules using Replace. ■ The assignment *lhs* = *rhs* specifies that the rule *lhs* -> *rhs* should be used whenever it applies. +■ *lhs* → *rhs* can be entered as *lhs* \[Rule] *rhs* or *lhs* ⦂->⦂ *rhs*. +■ In StandardForm, Rule is printed using →. ■ Rule is a scoping construct (see Section A.3.8). ■ Symbols that occur as pattern names in *lhs* are treated as local to the rule. This is true when the symbols appear on the right-hand side of /; conditions in *lhs*, and when the symbols appear anywhere in *rhs*, even inside other scoping constructs. ■ See pages 280 and 1001. ■ Implementation notes: see page 1018. ■ See also: Replace, Set, RuleDelayed, PolynomialReduce. ■ Related package: Utilities`FilterOptions`.

~■ RuleDelayed

~ *lhs* :> *rhs* or *lhs* :→ *rhs* represents a rule that transforms *lhs* to *rhs*, evaluating *rhs* only after the rule is used.

+■ The character :→ can be entered as ⦂:>⦂ or \[RuleDelayed]. ■ RuleDelayed has the attribute HoldRest. ■ You can apply rules using Replace. ■ The assignment *lhs* := *rhs* specifies that the rule *lhs* :> *rhs* should be used whenever it applies. ■ You can use Condition to specify when a particular rule applies. +■ *lhs* :→ *rhs* can be entered as *lhs* \[RuleDelayed] *rhs* or *lhs* ⦂:>⦂ *rhs*. +■ In StandardForm, RuleDelayed is printed using :→. ■ See notes for Rule. ■ See pages 280 and 1001. ■ See also: Replace, SetDelayed, Rule.

■ Run

Run[*expr*₁, *expr*₂, ...] generates the printed form of the expressions *expr*ᵢ, separated by spaces, and runs it as an external, operating system, command.

Run is not available on all computer systems. ■ Run prints the *expr*ᵢ in InputForm format. ■ Run returns an integer which corresponds, when possible, to the exit code for the command returned by the operating system. ■ The command executed by Run cannot usually require interactive input. On most computer systems, it can, however, generate textual output. ■ You can enter the input line !*command* to execute an external command. ■ See page 604. ■ See also: Put, Splice.

■ RunThrough

RunThrough["*command*", *expr*] executes an external command, giving the printed form of *expr* as input, and taking the output, reading it as *Mathematica* input, and returning the result.

RunThrough is not available on all computer systems. ■ RunThrough writes the InputForm of *expr* on the standard input for *command*, then reads its standard output, and feeds it into *Mathematica*. ■ RunThrough starts *command*, then gives input to *command*, then terminates the input. ■ See page 605. ■ See also: Install, Put, Get, Splice.

■ SameQ

lhs === *rhs* yields True if the expression *lhs* is identical to *rhs*, and yields False otherwise.

SameQ requires exact correspondence between expressions, except that it considers Real numbers equal if their difference is less than the uncertainty of either of them. ■ 2 === 2. gives False. ■ *e*₁ === *e*₂ === *e*₃ gives True if all the *e*ᵢ are identical. ■ See page 265. ■ See also: UnsameQ, Equal, Order.

■ **SameTest**

> SameTest is an option for functions like FixedPoint that specifies the comparison function to apply to pairs of results to determine whether they should be considered the same.
>
> The default is usually SameTest -> Equal. ■ Settings for SameTest must be functions that take two arguments, and return True or False. ■ See page 239. ■ See also: Throw.

■ **SampleDepth**

> SampleDepth is an option for sound primitives which specifies how many bits should be used to encode sound amplitude levels.
>
> The default setting is SampleDepth -> 8. ■ With the default setting, 256 distinct sound amplitudes are allowed. ■ See page 545. ■ See also: PlayRange, SampleRate.

■ **SampledSoundFunction**

> SampledSoundFunction[f, n, r] is a sound primitive, which represents a sound whose amplitude sampled r times a second is generated by applying the function f to successive integers from 1 to n.
>
> SampledSoundFunction[{f_1, f_2, ... }, n, r] yields sound on several channels. ■ SampledSoundFunction is generated by Play. ■ SampledSoundFunction primitives can appear inside Sound, Graphics and Graphics3D objects. ■ See page 545.

■ **SampledSoundList**

> SampledSoundList[{a_1, a_2, ... }, r] is a sound primitive, which represents a sound whose amplitude has levels a_i sampled r times a second.
>
> SampledSoundList[{$list_1$, $list_2$, ... }, r] yields sound on several channels. If the lists are of different lengths, silence is inserted at the ends of shorter lists. ■ SampledSoundList is generated by ListPlay. ■ SampledSoundList primitives can appear inside Sound, Graphics and Graphics3D objects. ■ See page 545.

■ **SampleRate**

> SampleRate is an option for sound primitives which specifies the number of samples per second to generate for sounds.
>
> The default setting is SampleRate -> 8192. ■ The highest frequency in hertz that can be present in a particular sound is equal to half the setting for SampleRate. ■ See page 171. ■ See also: SampleDepth.

~■ **Save**

> Save["*filename*", *symbol*] appends definitions associated with the specified symbol to a file.
>
> ~ Save["*filename*", "*form*"] appends definitions associated with all symbols whose names match the string pattern *form*.
>
> ~ Save["*filename*", "*context*`"] appends definitions associated with all symbols in the specified context.
>
> Save["*filename*", {*object*₁, *object*₂, ... }] appends definitions associated with several objects.
>
> Save uses FullDefinition to include subsidiary definitions. ■ Save writes out definitions in InputForm. ■ Save uses Names to find symbols whose names match a given string pattern. ■ You can use Save["*filename*", "*s*"] to write out the definition for the value of a symbol *s* itself. ■ See pages 203 and 600. ■ See also: PutAppend, Get, DumpSave.

+■ **SelectionMove**

> SelectionMove[*obj*, *dir*, *unit*] moves the current selection in an open notebook in the front end in the direction *dir* by the specified unit.
>
> SelectionMove[*obj*, *dir*, *unit*, *n*] repeats the move *n* times.

The first argument of SelectionMove must be a NotebookObject. ▪ Possible direction specifications are:

Next	make the selection be the next unit of the specified type
Previous	make the selection be the previous unit of the specified type
After	make the selection be just after the end of the present unit
Before	make the selection be just before the beginning of the present unit
All	make the selection be the whole of the present unit

▪ Possible unit specifications are:

Character	individual character
Word	word or other token
Expression	complete subexpression
TextLine	line of text
CellContents	the contents of the cell
Cell	complete cell
CellGroup	cell group
EvaluationCell	cell associated with the current evaluation
ButtonCell	cell associated with any button that initiated the evaluation
GeneratedCell	cell generated by the current evaluation
Notebook	complete notebook

▪ Unless the option setting AutoScroll->False is given, the front end will scroll a notebook so that the result of SelectionMove is visible. ▪ The front end will also usually highlight the region corresponding to the result. ▪ With direction specifications After and Before, SelectionMove will usually make the current selection be an insertion point between two units of the specified type. ▪ SelectionMove returns $Failed if it cannot move the selection in the way you request. ▪ The EvaluationCell defines the point after which output from the current evaluation will by default be placed. ▪ A GeneratedCell corresponds to an element of the output. ▪ See page 557. ▪ See also: NotebookSelection, NotebookWrite, NotebookRead.

+■ **Sequence**

> Sequence[*expr*$_1$, *expr*$_2$, ...] represents a sequence of arguments to be spliced automatically into any function.

Example: f[a, Sequence[b, c]] $\longrightarrow$ f[a, b, c]. ▪ Sequence objects will automatically be flattened out in all functions except those with attribute SequenceHold. ▪ See page 255. ▪ See also: FlattenAt, BlankSequence, SlotSequence, List, Listable.

■ **SequenceForm**

> SequenceForm[*expr*$_1$, *expr*$_2$, ...] prints as the textual concatenation of the printed forms of the *expr*$_i$.

Expressions printed by SequenceForm have their baselines aligned. ▪ SequenceForm acts as a "wrapper", which affects printing, but not evaluation. ▪ See page 413. ▪ See also: RowBox, ColumnForm, TableForm.

⁺∎ **SequenceHold**

> SequenceHold is an attribute which specifies that Sequence objects appearing in the arguments of a function should not automatically be flattened out.

> The attribute HoldAllComplete prevents Sequence objects from being flattened out. ∎ See pages 309 and 320. ∎ See also: HoldAll, HoldAllComplete.

˜∎ **Series**

> Series[f, {x, x_0, n}] generates a power series expansion for f about the point $x = x_0$ to order $(x - x_0)^n$.

> Series[f, {x, x_0, n_x}, {y, y_0, n_y}] successively finds series expansions with respect to y, then x.

> Series can construct standard Taylor series, as well as certain expansions involving negative powers, fractional powers and logarithms. ∎ Series detects certain essential singularities. ∎ Series can expand about the point $x = \infty$. ∎ Series[f, {x, 0, n}] constructs Taylor series for any function f according to the formula $f(0) + f'(0)x + f''(0)x^2/2 + \ldots f^{(n)}(0)x^n/n!$. ∎ Series effectively evaluates partial derivatives using D. It assumes that different variables are independent. ∎ The result of Series is usually a SeriesData object, which you can manipulate with other functions. ∎ Normal[*series*] truncates a power series and converts it to a normal expression. ⁺∎ SeriesCoefficient[*series*, n] finds the coefficient of the nth order term. ∎ See page 826. ∎ Implementation notes: see page 1022. ∎ See also: InverseSeries, ComposeSeries, Limit, Normal. ∎ Related packages: Calculus`Pade`, NumericalMath`Approximations`, DiscreteMath`RSolve`.

⁺∎ **SeriesCoefficient**

> SeriesCoefficient[*series*, n] finds the coefficient of the nth order term in a power series.

> SeriesCoefficient[*series*, {n_1, n_2, ... }] finds a coefficient in a multivariate series.

> ∎ See page 832. ∎ See also: Coefficient, Normal.

∎ **SeriesData**

> SeriesData[x, x_0, {a_0, a_1, ... }, *nmin*, *nmax*, *den*] represents a power series in the variable x about the point x_0. The a_i are the coefficients in the power series. The powers of $(x-x_0)$ that appear are *nmin/den*, (*nmin*+1)/*den*, ... , *nmax/den*.

> SeriesData objects are generated by Series. ∎ SeriesData objects are printed as sums of the coefficients a_i, multiplied by powers of $x - x_0$. A SeriesData object representing a power series is printed with O[$x - x_0$]^p added, to represent omitted higher-order terms. ∎ When you apply certain mathematical operations to SeriesData objects, new SeriesData objects truncated to the appropriate order are produced. ∎ The operations you can perform on SeriesData objects include arithmetic ones, mathematical functions with built-in derivatives, and integration and differentiation. ∎ Normal[*expr*] converts a SeriesData object into a normal expression, truncating omitted higher-order terms. ∎ If the variable in a SeriesData object is itself a SeriesData object, then the composition of the SeriesData objects is computed. Substituting one series into another series with the same expansion parameter therefore automatically leads to composition of the series. Composition is only possible if the first term of the inner series involves a positive power of the variable. ∎ InverseSeries can be applied to SeriesData objects to give series for inverse functions. ∎ See page 828.

■ **SessionTime**

SessionTime[ ] gives the total number of seconds of real time that have elapsed since the beginning of your *Mathematica* session.

SessionTime starts counting time as soon as your operating system considers your *Mathematica* process to be executing. ■ TimeUsed is accurate only down to a granularity of at least $TimeUnit seconds. ■ See page 683. ■ See also: TimeUsed, AbsoluteTime, Date.

■ **Set**

lhs = *rhs* evaluates *rhs* and assigns the result to be the value of *lhs*. From then on, *lhs* is replaced by *rhs* whenever it appears.

$\{l_1, l_2, \dots\}$ = $\{r_1, r_2, \dots\}$ evaluates the r_i, and assigns the results to be the values of the corresponding l_i.

lhs can be any expression, including a pattern. ■ f[x_] = x^2 is a typical assignment for a pattern. Notice the presence of _ on the left-hand side, but not the right-hand side. ■ An assignment of the form *f*[*args*] = *rhs* sets up a transformation rule associated with the symbol *f*. ■ Different rules associated with a particular symbol are usually placed in the order that you give them. If a new rule that you give is determined to be *more specific* than existing rules, it is, however, placed before them. When the rules are used, they are tested in order. ■ New assignments with identical *lhs* overwrite old ones. ■ You can see all the assignments associated with a symbol *f* using ?*f* or Definition[*f*]. ■ If you make assignments for functions that have attributes like Flat and Orderless, you must make sure to set these attributes before you make assignments for the functions. ■ Set has attribute HoldFirst. ■ If *lhs* is of the form *f*[*args*], then *args* are evaluated. ■ There are some special functions for which an assignment to *s*[*f*[*args*]] is automatically associated with *f* rather than *s*. These functions include: Attributes, Default, Format, MessageName, Messages, N and Options. ■ When it appears in symbolic form, Set is treated as a scoping construct (see Section A.3.8). ■ *lhs* = *rhs* returns *rhs* even if for some reason the assignment specified cannot be performed. ■ Some global variables such as $RecursionLimit can only be assigned a certain range or class of values. ■ See pages 292 and 999. ■ See also: TagSet, Unset, Clear, HoldPattern, DownValues.

■ **SetAccuracy**

SetAccuracy[*expr*, *n*] yields a version of *expr* in which all numbers have been set to have an accuracy of *n* digits.

When SetAccuracy is used to increase the accuracy of a number, the number is padded with zeros. The zeros are taken to be in base 2. In base 10, the additional digits are usually not zero. ■ SetAccuracy returns an arbitrary-precision number even if the number of signficant digits obtained will be less than $MachinePrecision. ■ When *expr* contains machine-precision numbers, SetAccuracy[*expr*, *n*] can give results which differ from one computer system to another. ■ SetAccuracy will first expose any hidden extra digits in the internal binary representation of a number, and only after these are exhausted add trailing zeros. ■ 0.004''25 generates a number with all trailing digits zero and accuracy 25 on any computer system. ■ SetAccuracy[*expr*, *n*] does not modify *expr* itself. ■ See page 710. ■ See also: N, Accuracy, SetPrecision.

■ **SetAttributes**

SetAttributes[*s*, *attr*] adds *attr* to the list of attributes of the symbol *s*.

SetAttributes modifies Attributes[*s*]. ■ SetAttributes[*s*, {*attr₁*, *attr₂*, ... }] sets several attributes at a time. ■ SetAttributes[{*s₁*, *s₂*, ... }, *attrs*] sets attributes of several symbols at a time. ■ SetAttributes has the attribute HoldFirst. ■ See page 308. ■ See also: ClearAttributes, Protect.

■ SetDelayed

lhs := *rhs* assigns *rhs* to be the delayed value of *lhs*. *rhs* is maintained in an unevaluated form. When *lhs* appears, it is replaced by *rhs*, evaluated afresh each time.

See notes for Set. ▪ SetDelayed has attribute HoldAll, rather than HoldFirst. ▪ You can make assignments of the form *lhs* := *rhs* /; *test*, where *test* gives conditions for the applicability of each transformation rule. You can make several assignments with the same *lhs* but different forms of *test*. ▪ *lhs* := *rhs* returns Null if the assignment specified can be performed, and returns $Failed otherwise. ▪ See pages 292 and 999. ▪ See also: TagSetDelayed, Unset, Clear.

■ SetDirectory

SetDirectory["*dir*"] sets the current working directory.

SetDirectory sets the current working directory, then returns its full name. ▪ SetDirectory prepends the current working directory to the directory stack given by DirectoryStack[ ]. ▪ See page 611. ▪ See also: ResetDirectory, Directory, DirectoryName, $Path.

■ SetFileDate

SetFileDate["*file*"] sets the modification date for a file to be the current date.

SetFileDate["*file*", *date*] sets the modification date to be the specified date. ▪ The date must be given in the {*year*, *month*, *day*, *hour*, *minute*, *second*} format used by Date. ▪ See page 616. ▪ See also: FileDate. ▪ Related package: Miscellaneous`Calendar`.

~■ SetOptions

SetOptions[*s*, *name*$_1$->*value*$_1$, *name*$_2$->*value*$_2$, ...] sets the specified default options for a symbol *s*.

SetOptions[*stream*, ...] or SetOptions["*name*", ...] sets options associated with a particular stream.

+ SetOptions[*object*, ...] sets options associated with an external object such as a NotebookObject.

SetOptions is equivalent to an assignment which redefines certain elements of the list Options[*s*] of default options. ▪ SetOptions can be used on Protected symbols. ▪ SetOptions returns the new form of Options[*s*]. ▪ You can use SetOptions on InputStream and OutputStream objects. If there is only one stream with a particular name, you can give the name as a string as the argument of Options. ▪ SetOptions can be used on a list of streams, such as the value of $Output. +▪ If you use SetOptions[NotebookObject[...], ...] the kernel will send a request to the front end which will immediately make the change specified. ▪ See pages 143 and 988.

■ SetPrecision

SetPrecision[*expr*, *n*] yields a version of *expr* in which all numbers have been set to have a precision of *n* digits.

When SetPrecision is used to increase the precision of a number, the number is padded with zeros. The zeros are taken to be in base 2. In base 10, the additional digits are usually not zero. ▪ SetPrecision returns an arbitrary-precision number, even if the precision requested is less than $MachinePrecision. ▪ When *expr* contains machine-precision numbers, SetPrecision[*expr*, *n*] can give results which differ from one computer system to another. ▪ SetPrecision will first expose any hidden extra digits in the internal binary representation of a number, and only after these are exhausted add trailing zeros. ▪ 0.004`25 generates a number with all trailing digits zero and precision 25 on any computer system. ▪ SetPrecision[*expr*, *n*] does not modify *expr* itself. ▪ See page 710. ▪ See also: N, Precision, Chop, SetAccuracy, $MinPrecision, $NumberMarks.

■ SetSelectedNotebook

SetSelectedNotebook[*notebook*] makes the specified notebook be the currently selected one in the front end.

SetSelectedNotebook takes a NotebookObject as its argument. ■ Setting a particular notebook to be the currently selected one typically makes it the top notebook displayed on the screen. ■ Making a notebook the currently selected one does not affect the current selection within that notebook, or within other notebooks. ■ See page 566. ■ See also: SelectedNotebook, Notebooks, WindowClickSelect.

■ SetStreamPosition

SetStreamPosition[*stream*, *n*] sets the current point in an open stream.

The integer *n* given to SetStreamPosition should usually be a value obtained from StreamPosition. ■ SetStreamPosition[*stream*, 0] sets the current point to the beginning of a stream. ■ SetStreamPosition[*stream*, Infinity] sets the current point to the end of a stream. ■ See page 626.

■ Shading

Shading is an option for **SurfaceGraphics** that specifies whether the surfaces should be shaded.

With Shading -> False, the surface will be white all over. So long as Mesh -> True, however, mesh lines will still be drawn. ■ When Shading -> True, the actual shading used can either be determined by the height, or, when Lighting -> True, from simulated illumination. ■ See page 149. ■ See also: HiddenSurface, ClipFill.

■ Shallow

Shallow[*expr*] prints as a shallow form of *expr*.

Shallow[*expr*, *depth*] prints with all parts of *expr* below the specified depth given in skeleton form.

Shallow[*expr*, {*depth*, *length*}] also gives parts whose lengths are above the specified limit in skeleton form.

Shallow[*expr*, {*depth*, *length*}, *form*] uses skeleton form for any parts which match the pattern *form*.

Omitted sequences of elements are given as Skeleton objects, which print in the form «*k*». +■ In StandardForm, the characters used for this output are \[LeftSkeleton] and \[RightSkeleton]. ■ Depth and length can be specified as Infinity. ■ Shallow[*expr*] is equivalent to Shallow[*expr*, {4, 10}]. ■ Shallow acts as a "wrapper", which affects printing, but not evaluation. +■ Trying to feed «*k*» as obtained from Shallow back as input to *Mathematica* in StandardForm will generate an error. ■ See page 410. ■ See also: Short.

■ Share

Share[*expr*] changes the way *expr* is stored internally, to try and minimize the amount of memory used.

Share[ ] tries to minimize the memory used to store all expressions.

Share works by sharing the storage of common subexpressions between different parts of an expression, or different expressions. ■ Using Share will never affect the results you get from *Mathematica*. It may, however, reduce the amount of memory used, and in many cases also the amount of time taken. ■ See page 687. ■ See also: MemoryInUse, ByteCount. ■ Related package: Utilities`MemoryConserve`.

~■ Short

Short[*expr*] prints as a short form of *expr*, less than about one line long.

Short[*expr*, *n*] prints as a form of *expr* about *n* lines long.

Short[*expr*] gives a "skeleton form" of *expr*, with omitted sequences of *k* elements indicated by «*k*». +■ In StandardForm, the characters used for this output are \[LeftSkeleton] and \[RightSkeleton]. ■ Omitted sequences of elements are printed as Skeleton objects. ■ Short prints long strings in skeleton form. ■ The number of lines specified need not be an integer. ■ Short can be used with InputForm and other formats as well as OutputForm. ■ Short acts as a "wrapper", which affects printing, but not evaluation. +■ Trying to feed «*k*» as obtained from Short back as input to *Mathematica* in StandardForm will generate an error. ■ Short is used to limit the length of output in standard *Mathematica* warning and other messages. ■ See page 410. ■ See also: Shallow, Format.

■ Show

Show[*graphics*, *options*] displays two- and three-dimensional graphics, using the options specified.

Show[g_1, g_2, ...] shows several plots combined.

Show can be used with Graphics, Graphics3D, SurfaceGraphics, ContourGraphics, DensityGraphics and GraphicsArray. ■ Options explicitly specified in Show override those included in the graphics expression. ■ When plots are combined, their lists of non-default options are concatenated. ■ Show is effectively the analog of Print for graphics. The option DisplayFunction determines the actual output mechanism used. ■ Functions like Plot automatically apply Show to the graphics expressions they generate. ■ See pages 138 and 467. ■ See also: Plot, etc., and Display.

+■ ShowCellBracket

ShowCellBracket is an option for Cell which specifies whether to display the bracket that indicates the extent of the cell.

ShowCellBracket is often set for styles of cells or whole notebooks instead of individual cells. ■ See page 579. ■ See also: CellFrame.

+■ ShowCellLabel

ShowCellLabel is an option for Cell which specifies whether to display the label for a cell.

ShowCellLabel is more often set for styles of cells than for individual cells. ■ With the setting CellLabelAutoDelete->True, the label for a cell is automatically deleted if the cell is modified. ■ See page 581. ■ See also: CellLabel, ShowCellTags.

+■ ShowCellTags

ShowCellTags is an option for Cell which specifies whether to display tags for a cell.

ShowCellTags is more often set for styles of cells than for individual cells. ■ See also: CellTags, ShowCellLabel.

+■ ShowPageBreaks

ShowPageBreaks is an option for Notebook which specifies whether to indicate in the on-screen display of a notebook where page breaks would occur if the notebook were printed.

ShowPageBreaks is often set using a menu item in the notebook front end. ■ See also: PageBreakWithin, ScreenStyleEnvironment.

+■ ShowSpecialCharacters

ShowSpecialCharacters is an option for Cell which specifies whether to replace \[*Name*], \:*nnnn*, etc. by explicit special characters.

With ShowSpecialCharacters->False special characters are always displayed by name when possible.
■ ShowSpecialCharacters is more often set at the level of styles or notebooks than at the level of individual cells.
■ See also: ShowStringCharacters, CharacterEncoding.

+■ ShowStringCharacters

ShowStringCharacters is an option for Cell which specifies whether to display " when a string is entered.

ShowStringCharacters is typically set to False for output cells and True for input cells. ■ ShowStringCharacters is usually set at the level of styles or notebooks rather than at the level of individual cells. ■ See also: ShowSpecialCharacters.

~■ Sign

Sign[x] gives −1, 0 or 1 depending on whether x is negative, zero, or positive.

For non-zero complex numbers z, Sign[z] is defined as z/Abs[z]. ■ Sign tries simple transformations in trying to determine the sign of symbolic expressions. ■ You can define values for Sign[*expr*] which are used when *expr*, and linear combinations involving it, appear in Sign, as well as functions like Positive and Negative. +■ For exact numeric quantities, Sign internally uses numerical approximations to establish its result. This process can be affected by the setting of the global variable $MaxExtraPrecision. ■ See page 718. ■ See also: Abs, Positive, Negative, NonNegative.

■ Signature

Signature[*list*] gives the signature of the permutation needed to place the elements of *list* in canonical order.

Examples: Signature[{a,b,c}] ⟶ 1; Signature[{a,c,b}] ⟶ −1. ■ The signature of the permutation is $(-1)^n$, where n is the number of transpositions of pairs of elements that must be composed to build up the permutation. ■ If any two elements of *list* are the same, Signature[*list*] gives 0. ■ See pages 727 and 858. ■ See also: Order, Sort, Cross, Minors, Det. ■ Related package: DiscreteMath`Combinatorica`.

■ SignPadding

SignPadding is an option for NumberForm and related functions which specifies whether padding should be inserted after signs.

SignPadding -> True specifies that any padding that is needed should be inserted between the sign and the digits in a number. ■ SignPadding -> False specifies that the padding should be inserted before the sign. ■ See page 415. ■ See also: NumberPadding.

~■ **Simplify**

Simplify[*expr*] performs a sequence of algebraic transformations on *expr*, and returns the simplest form it finds.

~■ Simplify tries expanding, factoring and doing other transformations on expressions, keeping track of the simplest form obtained. ~■ The following options can be given:

ComplexityFunction	Automatic	how to assess the complexity of each form generated
TimeConstraint	300	for how many seconds to try doing any particular transformation
Trig	True	whether to do trigonometric as well as algebraic transformations

+■ FullSimplify does more extensive simplification than Simplify. ■ See pages 67 and 783. ■ See also: FullSimplify, Factor, Expand, TrigExpand, PowerExpand, ComplexExpand.

■ **Sin**

Sin[*z*] gives the sine of *z*.

Mathematical function (see Section A.3.10). ■ The argument of Sin is assumed to be in radians. (Multiply by Degree to convert from degrees.) ■ See page 731. ■ See also: ArcSin, Csc, TrigToExp, TrigExpand.

+■ **SingleLetterItalics**

SingleLetterItalics is an option for Cell which specifies whether single-letter names should be displayed in italics.

SingleLetterItalics->True is typically set for cells that contain TraditionalForm expressions. ■ See page 588. ■ See also: AutoItalicWords, StyleBox.

■ **SingularValues**

SingularValues[*m*] gives the singular value decomposition for a numerical matrix *m*. The result is a list {*u*, *w*, *v*}, where *w* is the list of singular values, and *m* can be written as Conjugate[Transpose[*u*]].DiagonalMatrix[*w*].*v*.

SingularValues[*m*, Tolerance -> *t*] specifies that singular values smaller than *t* times the maximum singular value are to be removed. ■ The default setting Tolerance -> Automatic typically takes *t* to be 10^{-p+2} where *p* is the numerical precision of the input. +■ With Tolerance->0 singular values which are exactly zero can be returned. ■ *u* and *v* are row orthonormal matrices, which can be considered as lists of orthonormal vectors. ■ The ratio of the largest to smallest singular value gives the L^2 condition number of *m*. ■ See page 851. ■ Implementation notes: see page 1020. ■ See also: PseudoInverse, QRDecomposition, SchurDecomposition, LUDecomposition. ■ Related packages: LinearAlgebra`Cholesky`, Statistics`LinearRegression`.

■ **Sinh**

Sinh[*z*] gives the hyperbolic sine of *z*.

Mathematical function (see Section A.3.10). ■ See page 731. ■ See also: ArcSinh, Csch, TrigToExp, TrigExpand.

+■ **SinhIntegral**

SinhIntegral[*z*] gives the hyperbolic sine integral function Shi(*z*).

Mathematical function (see Section A.3.10). ■ Shi(*z*) = $\int_0^z \sinh(t)dt/t$. ■ SinhIntegral[*z*] is an entire function of *z* with no branch cut discontinuities. ■ See page 744. ■ See also: CoshIntegral.

■ SinIntegral

`SinIntegral[z]` gives the sine integral function Si(z).

Mathematical function (see Section A.3.10). ■ Si(z) = $\int_0^z \sin(t)/t\,dt$. ■ `SinIntegral[z]` is an entire function of z with no branch cut discontinuities. ■ See page 744. ■ See also: `CosIntegral`, `ExpIntegralE`, `ExpIntegralEi`, `FresnelS`.

■ SixJSymbol

`SixJSymbol[{`j_1`,` j_2`,` j_3`}, {`j_4`,` j_5`,` j_6`}]` gives the values of the Racah 6-j symbol.

The 6-j symbols vanish except when certain triples of the j_i satisfy triangle inequalities. ■ The parameters of `SixJSymbol` can be integers, half-integers or symbolic expressions. ■ See page 730. ■ See also: `ThreeJSymbol`, `ClebschGordan`.

~■ Skeleton

`Skeleton[n]` represents a sequence of n omitted elements in an expression printed with `Short` or `Shallow`.

~ The standard print form for `Skeleton` is $\ll n \gg$.

+■ In `StandardForm`, `Skeleton` is by default printed using `\[LeftSkeleton]` and `\[RightSkeleton]` characters. ■ You can reset the print form of `Skeleton`. +■ $\ll n \gg$ indicates the presence of missing information, and so generates an error if you try to interpret it as *Mathematica* kernel input. ■ See also: `Short`, `StringSkeleton`, `Shallow`, `TotalWidth`.

■ Skip

`Skip[`*stream*`,` *type*`]` skips one object of the specified type in an input stream.

`Skip[`*stream*`,` *type*`,` *n*`]` skips n objects of the specified type.

`Skip` behaves like `Read`, except that it returns `Null` when it succeeds in skipping the specified objects, and `$Failed` otherwise. ■ See notes for `Read`. ■ See page 622. ■ See also: `SetStreamPosition`, `Find`.

■ Slot

`#` represents the first argument supplied to a pure function.

`#`*n* represents the nth argument.

`#` is used to represent arguments or formal parameters in pure functions of the form *body*`&` or `Function[`*body*`]`. ■ `#` is equivalent to `Slot[ ]` or `Slot[1]`. ■ `#`*n* is equivalent to `Slot[n]`. n must be a non-negative integer. ■ `#0` gives the head of the function, i.e., the pure function itself. ■ See page 246.

■ SlotSequence

`##` represents the sequence of arguments supplied to a pure function.

`##`*n* represents the sequence of arguments supplied to a pure function, starting with the nth argument.

`##` is used to represent sequences of arguments in pure functions of the form *body*`&` or `Function[`*body*`]`. ■ `##` is equivalent to `SlotSequence[ ]` or `SlotSequence[1]`. ■ `##`*n* is equivalent to `SlotSequence[n]`. n must be a positive integer. ■ A sequence of arguments supplied to a pure function is "spliced" into the body of the function wherever `##` and so on appear. ■ See page 246. ■ See also: `Sequence`.

~■ Solve

Solve[*eqns*, *vars*] attempts to solve an equation or set of equations for the variables *vars*.

Solve[*eqns*, *vars*, *elims*] attempts to solve the equations for *vars*, eliminating the variables *elims*.

Equations are given in the form *lhs* == *rhs*. ■ Simultaneous equations can be combined either in a list or with &&. ■ A single variable or a list of variables can be specified. ■ Solve[*eqns*] tries to solve for all variables in *eqns*. ■ Example: Solve[3 x + 9 == 0, x]. ■ Solve gives solutions in terms of rules of the form $x \to sol$. ■ When there are several variables, the solution is given in terms of lists of rules: $\{x \to s_x, y \to s_y, \dots \}$. ■ When there are several solutions, Solve gives a list of them. ■ When a particular root has multiplicity greater than one, Solve gives several copies of the corresponding solution. ■ Solve deals primarily with linear and polynomial equations. ■ The option InverseFunctions specifies whether Solve should use inverse functions to try and find solutions to more general equations. The default is InverseFunctions->Automatic. In this case, Solve can use inverse functions, but prints a warning message. See notes on InverseFunctions. ■ Solve gives generic solutions only. It discards solutions that are valid only when the parameters satisfy special conditions. Reduce gives the complete set of solutions. ~■ Solve will not always be able to get explicit solutions to equations. It will give the explicit solutions it can, then give a symbolic representation of the remaining solutions in terms of Root objects. If there are sufficiently few symbolic parameters, you can then use N to get numerical approximations to the solutions. ■ Solve gives {} if there are no possible solutions to the equations. ■ Solve[*eqns*, ... , Mode->Modular] solves equations with equality required only modulo an integer. You can specify a particular modulus to use by including the equation Modulus==*p*. If you do not include such an equation, Solve will attempt to solve for the possible moduli. +■ Solve uses special efficient techniques for handling sparse systems of linear equations with approximate numerical coefficients. ■ See page 793. ■ Implementation notes: see page 1021. ■ See also: Reduce, Eliminate, Roots, NSolve, FindRoot, LinearSolve, RowReduce, GroebnerBasis, DSolve, Root. ■ Related packages: Algebra`RootIsolation`, DiscreteMath`RSolve`, Graphics`ImplicitPlot`, Algebra`AlgebraicInequalities`.

■ SolveAlways

SolveAlways[*eqns*, *vars*] gives the values of parameters that make the equations *eqns* valid for all values of the variables *vars*.

Equations are given in the form *lhs* == *rhs*. ■ Simultaneous equations can be combined either in a list or with &&. ■ A single variable or a list of variables can be specified. ■ Example: SolveAlways[a x + b == 0, x] $\longrightarrow$ {{a $\to$ 0, b $\to$ 0}}. ■ SolveAlways works primarily with linear and polynomial equations. ■ SolveAlways produces relations between parameters that appear in *eqns*, but are not in the list of variables *vars*. ■ SolveAlways[*eqns*, *vars*] is equivalent to Solve[!Eliminate[!*eqns*, *vars*]]. ■ See page 801. ■ See also: Eliminate, Solve, Reduce, PolynomialReduce.

■ Sort

Sort[*list*] sorts the elements of *list* into canonical order.

Sort[*list*, *p*] sorts using the ordering function *p*.

Example: Sort[{b, c, a}] $\longrightarrow$ {a, b, c}. ■ The canonical ordering used by *Mathematica* is described on page 991. ■ Sort[*list*, *p*] applies the function *p* to pairs of elements in *list* to determine whether they are in order. The default function *p* is OrderedQ[{#1, #2}]&. ■ Example: Sort[{4, 1, 3}, Greater] $\longrightarrow$ {4, 3, 1}. ■ Sort can be used on expressions with any head, not only List. ■ See pages 124 and 252. ■ See also: Order, OrderedQ, Orderless.

■ Sound

Sound[*primitives*] represents a sound.

Any number of sound primitives or lists of sound primitives can be given. They are played in sequence. ■ Sound can be played using Show. ■ The following primitives can be used:

SampledSoundFunction[*f*, *n*, *r*]   amplitude levels generated by a function
SampledSoundList[{a_1, a_2, ... }, *r*]   amplitude levels given in a list

■ The standard print form for Sound[...] is -Sound-. InputForm prints the explicit list of primitives. ■ See page 544. ■ Related packages: Miscellaneous'Audio', Miscellaneous'Music'.

■ SpellingCorrection

SpellingCorrection is an option for StringMatchQ, Names and related functions which specifies whether strings should be considered to match even when a small fraction of the characters in them are different.

The default setting SpellingCorrection -> False requires exact matching. ■ ?*name* effectively uses SpellingCorrection -> True when it cannot find an exact match for *name*. ■ See page 391. ■ See also: IgnoreCase.

■ SphericalHarmonicY

SphericalHarmonicY[*l*, *m*, θ, ϕ] gives the spherical harmonic $Y_l^m(\theta, \phi)$.

Mathematical function (see Section A.3.10). ■ The spherical harmonics are orthogonal with respect to integration over the surface of the unit sphere. ■ For $l \geq 0$, $Y_l^m(\theta, \phi) = \sqrt{(2l+1)/(4\pi)}\sqrt{(l+m)!/(l-m)!}P_l^m(\cos(\theta))e^{im\phi}$ where P_l^m is the associated Legendre function. ■ For $l \leq -1$, $Y_l^m(\theta, \phi) = Y_{-(l+1)}^m(\theta, \phi)$. ■ See page 736. ■ See also: LegendreP, ClebschGordan.

■ SphericalRegion

SphericalRegion is an option for three-dimensional graphics functions which specifies whether the final image should be scaled so that a sphere drawn around the three-dimensional bounding box would fit in the display area specified.

SphericalRegion -> False scales three-dimensional images to be as large as possible, given the display area specified. ■ SphericalRegion -> True scales three-dimensional images so that a sphere drawn around the three-dimensional bounding box always fits in the display area specified. ■ The center of the sphere is taken to be at the center of the bounding box. The radius of the sphere is chosen so that the bounding box just fits within the sphere. ■ With SphericalRegion -> True, the image of a particular object remains consistent in size, regardless of the orientation of the object. ■ SphericalRegion -> True overrides any setting given for ViewCenter. ■ See page 515. ■ See also: PlotRegion, ViewPoint.

■ Splice

Splice["*file*"] splices *Mathematica* output into an external file. It takes text enclosed between <* and *> in the file, evaluates the text as *Mathematica* input, and replaces the text with the resulting *Mathematica* output.

Splice["*infile*", "*outfile*"] processes text from the file *infile*, and writes output into *outfile*. ■ Splice["*file*"] takes files with names of the form *name*.mx and writes output in files with names *name*.x. ■ Text in the input file not enclosed between <* and *> is copied without change to the output file. ■ The default format for *Mathematica* output is determined by the extension of the input file name:

name.mc	CForm
name.mf	FortranForm
name.mtex	TeXForm

■ The following options for Splice can be used:

Delimiters	{"<*", "*>"}	delimiters to search for
FormatType	Automatic	default format for *Mathematica* output
PageWidth	78	number of character widths per output line

■ You can use pipes instead of files for input and output to Splice. ■ See page 212. ■ See also: RunThrough.

+■ Split

Split[*list*] splits *list* into sublists consisting of runs of identical elements.

Split[*list*, *test*] treats pairs of adjacent elements as identical whenever applying the function *test* to them yields True.

Example: Split[{a, a, b, b, a, a, b}] ⟶ {{a, a}, {b, b}, {a, a}, {b}}. ■ The default function used to test whether elements are identical is SameQ. ■ Split can be used to perform run-length encoding. ■ See page 124. ■ See also: Partition, Union, Flatten, ReplaceList.

~■ Sqrt

~ Sqrt[*z*] or $\sqrt{z}$ gives the square root of *z*.

Mathematical function (see Section A.3.10). +■ $\sqrt{z}$ can be entered using $\boxed{\text{CTRL}}$2 *z* $\boxed{\text{CTRL}}$$\boxed{\text{␣}}$ or \(\@z\). ■ Sqrt[*z*] is converted to $z^{(1/2)}$. ■ Sqrt[z^2] is not automatically converted to *z*. ■ Sqrt[*a b*] is not automatically converted to Sqrt[*a*] Sqrt[*b*]. ■ These conversions can be done using PowerExpand, but will typically be correct only for positive real arguments. +■ In StandardForm, Sqrt[*z*] is printed as $\sqrt{z}$. +■ $\sqrt{\ }$ *z* can also be used for input. The $\sqrt{\ }$ character is entered as :sqrt: or \[Sqrt]. ■ See page 31. ■ See also: Power, PowerExpand, SqrtBox.

+■ SqrtBox

SqrtBox[*x*] represents $\sqrt{x}$ in input and output.

Inside \(... \) SqrtBox[*x*] can be input as \@ *x*. ■ In a notebook a SqrtBox can be created using $\boxed{\text{CTRL}}$2 or $\boxed{\text{CTRL}}$@. $\boxed{\text{CTRL}}$$\boxed{\text{␣}}$ moves out from under the square root sign. ■ In StandardForm and InputForm, SqrtBox[*x*] is interpreted on input as Sqrt[*x*]. ■ The baseline of SqrtBox[*x*] is taken to be the baseline of *x*. ■ If SqrtBox[*x*] does not fit on a single line, it is output as $x^{(1/2)}$. ■ In StandardForm, explicit SqrtBox objects are output literally. You can use DisplayForm to see the display form of such objects. ■ See page 424. ■ See also: RadicalBox, OverscriptBox.

■ StringTake

StringTake["*string*", *n*] gives a string containing the first *n* characters in "*string*".

StringTake["*string*", -*n*] gives the last *n* characters in "*string*".

StringTake["*string*", {*n*}] gives the *n*th character in "*string*".

StringTake["*string*", {*m*, *n*}] gives characters *m* through *n* in "*string*".

StringTake uses the standard *sequence specification* (see page 988). ■ Example: StringTake["abcdefg", 3] ⟶ abc. ■ See page 386. ■ See also: Take, StringDrop, StringPosition.

■ StringToStream

StringToStream["*string*"] opens an input stream for reading from a string.

StringToStream yields a stream of the form InputStream[String, *n*]. ■ Operations like Read and Find work on streams returned by StringToStream. ■ You must use Close to close streams created by StringToStream. ■ See page 627. ■ See also: Characters.

⁺■ StructuredSelection

StructuredSelection is an option for Cell which specifies whether to allow only complete subexpressions in the cell to be selected interactively using the front end.

StructuredSelection is more often set at a global level than at the level of individual cells. ■ See page 589. ■ See also: Selectable, DragAndDrop.

■ Stub

Stub is an attribute which specifies that if a symbol is ever used, Needs should automatically be called on the context of the symbol.

Symbols with the Stub attribute are created by DeclarePackage. ■ A symbol is considered "used" if its name appears explicitly, not in the form of a string. ■ Names["*nameform*"] and Attributes["*nameform*"] do not constitute "uses" of a symbol. ■ See pages 309 and 381.

+■ **StyleBox**

StyleBox[*boxes*, *options*] represents output in which *boxes* are shown with the specified option settings.

StyleBox[*boxes*, "*style*"] uses the option setting for the specified style in the current notebook.

You can use font options such as FontSize, FontWeight, FontSlant, FontFamily, FontColor and Background in StyleBox. ■ The following additional options can be given:

AutoSpacing	True	whether to adjust character spacings automatically
LineIndent	1	distance in ems to indent for each nesting level
LineIndentMaxFraction	0.5	maximum fraction of line width to indent
ScriptMinSize	4	the minimum point size to use for subscripts, etc.
ScriptSizeMultipliers	0.71	how much smaller to make each level of subscripts, etc.
ShowContents	True	whether to make *boxes* visible or just leave space for them
SpanLineThickness	Automatic	thickness in printer's points of fraction lines etc.
SpanMaxSize	Automatic	maximum size of expandable characters in units of font size
SpanMinSize	Automatic	minimum size of expandable characters in units of font size
SpanSymmetric	True	whether vertically expandable characters should be symmetric about the axis of the box they are in

■ In StandardForm and InputForm input, StyleBox is by default ignored, so that StyleBox[*box*, *spec*] is interpreted just as *box* would be. ■ When StyleBox objects are nested, the options of the innermost one control the display of particular boxes. ■ In StandardForm, explicit StyleBox objects are output literally. You can use DisplayForm to see the display form of such objects. ■ See page 425. ■ See also: StyleForm, AdjustmentBox, FrameBox, Cell.

+■ **StyleDefinitions**

StyleDefinitions is an option for notebooks which gives definitions for the styles that can be used in a notebook.

StyleDefinitions->"*name*.nb" specifies that style definitions from the notebook *name*.nb should be used. ■ The standard notebook front end comes with a selection of style definition notebooks containing styles appropriate for particular purposes. ■ StyleDefinitions->Notebook[...] allows style definitions to be given explicitly. ■ The definition for a style named "*s*" is specified by the options for the first cell whose contents is StyleData["*s*"]. ■ See page 577. ■ See also: ScreenStyleEnvironment, PrintingStyleEnvironment.

+■ **StyleForm**

StyleForm[*expr*, *options*] prints using the specified style options.

StyleForm[*expr*, "*style*"] prints using the specified cell style in the current notebook.

You can use font options such as FontSize, FontWeight, FontSlant, FontFamily, FontColor and Background in StyleForm. ■ Additional options can be given as in StyleBox. ■ StyleForm acts as a "wrapper", which affects printing, but not evaluation. ■ StyleForm can be used to specify the style for text in graphics.
■ StyleForm[*expr*, "*style*"] will work only if the notebook front end is being used; StyleForm[*expr*, *options*] for many options will work in all cases. ■ When StyleForm objects are nested, the options of the innermost one control the printing of a particular expression. ■ See pages 422 and 537. ■ See also: StylePrint, StyleBox, TextStyle, $TextStyle, FormatType, Cell.

◼ StylePrint

StylePrint[*expr*, "*style*"] creates a new cell in the current notebook with the specified style, and prints *expr* into it.

StylePrint[*expr*] uses the default style for the current notebook.

StylePrint creates a new cell directly after the current selection in your currently selected notebook. ◾ StylePrint[*expr*, "*style*", *opts*] can be used to specify options for the cell that is created. ◾ StylePrint is a special case of NotebookWrite. ◾ With a text-based front end, StylePrint does the same as Print. ◾ Cells generated by StylePrint by default have GeneratedCell->True and CellAutoOverwrite->True. ◾ StylePrint[*expr*, "*style*"] generates a whole cell with the specified style; Print[StyleForm[*expr*, "*style*"]] generates a cell with the default style but containing a StyleBox object. ◾ See pages 457 and 550. ◾ See also: CellPrint, Print, NotebookWrite, NotebookPrint, StyleForm.

◼ SubscriptBox

SubscriptBox[*x*, *y*] represents x_y in input and output.

Inside \(... \) SubscriptBox[*x*, *y*] can be input as *x* _ *y*. ◾ In a notebook a SubscriptBox can be created using [CTRL][-] or [CTRL][_]. [CTRL][␣] moves out of the subscript. ◾ In StandardForm and InputForm, SubscriptBox[*x*, *y*] is interpreted on input as Subscript[*x*, *y*]. ◾ The baseline of SubscriptBox[*x*, *y*] is taken to be the baseline of *x*. ◾ SubscriptBox[*x*, *y*] is usually output with *y* in a smaller font than *x*. ◾ With the option setting LimitsPositioning->True *y* is placed in an underscript position when the whole SubscriptBox is displayed large, and in a subscript position when it is displayed smaller. ◾ In StandardForm, explicit SubscriptBox objects are output literally. You can use DisplayForm to see the display form of such objects. ◾ See page 424. ◾ See also: SuperscriptBox, SubsuperscriptBox, UnderscriptBox, ScriptSizeMultipliers.

◼ SubsuperscriptBox

SubsuperscriptBox[*x*, *y*, *z*] represents x_y^z.

SubsuperscriptBox[*x*, *y*, *z*] can be input as *x* _ *y* \% *z* when inside \(... \). ◾ In a notebook a SubsuperscriptBox can be created by using [CTRL][-] or [CTRL][_] to move to the subscript, then [CTRL][%] to move to the superscript. [CTRL][␣] moves out of the subscript or superscript position. ◾ In StandardForm and InputForm, SubsuperscriptBox[*x*, *y*, *z*] is interpreted on input as Power[Subscript[*x*, *y*], *z*]. ◾ The baseline of SubsuperscriptBox[*x*, *y*, *z*] is taken to be the baseline of *x*. ◾ SubsuperscriptBox[*x*, *y*, *z*] is usually output with *y* and *z* in a smaller font than *x*. ◾ With the option setting LimitsPositioning->True *y* and *z* are placed in underscript and overscript positions when the whole SubsuperscriptBox is displayed large, and in subscript and superscript positions when it is displayed smaller. ◾ In StandardForm, explicit SubsuperscriptBox objects are output literally. You can use DisplayForm to see the display form of such objects. ◾ See page 424. ◾ See also: SubscriptBox, SuperscriptBox, UnderoverscriptBox.

◼ Subtract

x - *y* is equivalent to *x* + (-1 * *y*).

x - *y* is converted to *x* + (-1 * *y*) on input. ◾ See page 29. ◾ See also: Minus, Decrement.

◼ SubtractFrom

x -= *dx* subtracts *dx* from *x* and returns the new value of *x*.

SubtractFrom has the attribute HoldFirst. ◾ *x* -= *dx* is equivalent to *x* = *x* - *dx*. ◾ See page 285. ◾ See also: Decrement, PreDecrement, Set.

~■ **Sum**

Sum[f, {i, $imax$}] evaluates the sum $\sum_{i=1}^{imax} f$.

Sum[f, {i, $imin$, $imax$}] starts with $i = imin$. Sum[f, {i, $imin$, $imax$, di}] uses steps di.

Sum[f, {i, $imin$, $imax$}, {j, $jmin$, $jmax$}, ...] evaluates the multiple sum $\sum_{i=imin}^{imax} \sum_{j=jmin}^{jmax} ... f$.

+■ Sum[f, {i, $imax$}] can be entered as $\sum_i^{imax} f$. +■ $\sum$ can be entered as ⁞sum⁞ or \[Sum]. +■ Sum[f, {i, $imin$, $imax$}] can be entered as $\sum_{i=imin}^{imax} f$. +■ The limits should be underscripts and overscripts of $\sum$ in normal input, and subscripts and superscripts when embedded in other text. ■ Sum evaluates its arguments in a non-standard way (see page 994). ■ Sum uses the standard *Mathematica* iteration specification. ■ The iteration variable i is treated as local. ■ In multiple sums, the range of the outermost variable is given first. +■ The limits of summation need not be numbers. They can be Infinity or symbolic expressions. +■ If a sum cannot be carried out explicitly by adding up a finite number of terms, Sum will attempt to find a symbolic result. In this case, f is first evaluated symbolically. +■ Sum can do essentially all sums that are given in standard books of tables. +■ Sum is output in StandardForm using $\sum$. ■ See pages 81 and 833. +■ Implementation notes: see page 1022. ■ See also: Do, Product, Table, NSum.

+■ **SuperscriptBox**

SuperscriptBox[x, y] represents x^y in input and output.

Inside \(... \) SuperscriptBox[x, y] can be input as x \^ y. ■ In a notebook a SuperscriptBox can be created using [CTRL]6 or [CTRL][^]. [CTRL][␣] moves out of the superscript. ■ In StandardForm and InputForm, SuperscriptBox[x, y] is interpreted on input as Power[x, y]. ■ The baseline of SuperscriptBox[x, y] is taken to be the baseline of x. ■ SuperscriptBox[x, y] is usually output with y in a smaller font than x. ■ With the option setting LimitsPositioning->True y is placed in an overscript position when the whole SuperscriptBox is displayed large, and in a superscript position when it is displayed smaller. ■ In StandardForm, explicit SuperscriptBox objects are output literally. You can use DisplayForm to see the display form of such objects. ■ See page 424. ■ See also: SubscriptBox, SubsuperscriptBox, OverscriptBox, ScriptSizeMultipliers.

■ SurfaceColor

SurfaceColor[*dcol*] is a three-dimensional graphics directive which specifies that the polygons which follow should act as diffuse reflectors of light with a color given by *dcol*.

SurfaceColor[*dcol*, *scol*] specifies that a specular reflection component should be included, with a color given by *scol*.

SurfaceColor[*dcol*, *scol*, *n*] specifies that the reflection should occur with specular exponent *n*.

SurfaceColor directives give surface properties which determine the effect of simulated illumination on polygons. ■ SurfaceColor directives can appear inside FaceForm directives. ■ If no SurfaceColor directive is given, polygons are assumed to be white diffuse reflectors of light, obeying Lambert's law of reflection, so that the intensity of reflected light is $\cos(\alpha)$ times the intensity of incident light, where α is the angle between the direction of the incident light and the polygon normal. When $\alpha > 90°$, there is no reflected light. ■ SurfaceColor[GrayLevel[*a*]] specifies that polygons should act as diffuse reflectors, but with albedo *a*. The intensity of reflected light is therefore *a* times the intensity of the incident light, multiplied by $\cos(\alpha)$, and is of the same color. ■ SurfaceColor[RGBColor[*r*, *g*, *b*]] specifies that the red, green and blue components of the reflected light should be respectively *r*, *g* and *b* times those of the incident light, multiplied by $\cos(\alpha)$. ■ The second element in SurfaceColor[*dcol*, *scol*] specifies a specular reflection component. *scol* must be a GrayLevel, Hue or RGBColor specification. The color components of *scol* give the fractions of each color component in the incident intensity which are reflected in a specular way by the surface. ■ The parameter *n* gives the specular exponent. The intensity of specularly reflected light at angle θ from the mirror-reflection direction falls off like $\cos(\theta)^n$ as θ increases. It is zero when $\theta > 90°$. ■ For real materials, *n* is typically between about 1 and a few hundred. With a coarse polygonal mesh, however, values of *n* below 10 are usually most appropriate. The default value for *n* is 1. ■ *Mathematica* implements a version of the Phong lighting model, in which the intensity of reflected light is given schematically by $I_{in}(d\cos(\alpha) + s\cos(\theta)^n)$. ■ The intensity of light from diffuse and specular reflection is added linearly for each color component. The final color shown for a particular polygon is the sum of contributions from each light source, and from ambient light. ■ See page 525. ■ See also: Lighting, LightSources, AmbientLight.

■ SurfaceGraphics

SurfaceGraphics[*array*] is a representation of a three-dimensional plot of a surface, with heights of each point on a grid specified by values in *array*.

SurfaceGraphics[*array*, *shades*] represents a surface, whose parts are shaded according to the array *shades*.

SurfaceGraphics can be displayed using Show. ■ SurfaceGraphics has the same options as Graphics3D, with the following additions:

ClipFill	Automatic	how to draw clipped parts of the surface
ColorFunction	Automatic	function to determine color based on *z* value
HiddenSurface	True	whether to eliminate hidden surfaces
Mesh	True	whether to draw a mesh on the surface
MeshRange	Automatic	the original range of *x*, *y* coordinates for the plot
MeshStyle	Automatic	graphics directives to specify the style for a mesh

■ SurfaceGraphics does not support the options PolygonIntersections and RenderAll available for Graphics3D. ■ For SurfaceGraphics, the default setting for BoxRatios is BoxRatios -> {1, 1, 0.4}. ■ *array* should be a rectangular array of real numbers, representing *z* values. There will be holes in the surface corresponding to any array elements that are not real numbers. ■ If *array* has dimensions $m \times n$, then *shades* must have dimensions $(m - 1) \times (n - 1)$. ■ The elements of *shades* must be GrayLevel, Hue or RGBColor directives, or SurfaceColor objects. ■ Graphics3D[SurfaceGraphics[...]] can be used to convert a SurfaceGraphics object into the more general Graphics3D representation. ■ SurfaceGraphics is generated by Plot3D and ListPlot3D. ■ See page 516. ■ See also: ListPlot3D, Plot3D, ContourGraphics, DensityGraphics.

■ Switch

Switch[*expr*, *form*₁, *value*₁, *form*₂, *value*₂, ...] evaluates *expr*, then compares it with each of the *form*ᵢ in turn, evaluating and returning the *value*ᵢ corresponding to the first match found.

Only the *value*ᵢ corresponding to the first *form*ᵢ that matches *expr* is evaluated. Each *form*ᵢ is evaluated only when the match is tried. ■ If the last *form*ᵢ is the pattern _, then the corresponding *value*ᵢ is always returned if this case is reached. ■ If none of the *form*ᵢ match *expr*, the Switch is returned unevaluated. ■ Switch has attribute HoldRest. ■ You can use Break, Return and Throw in Switch. ■ See page 325. ■ See also: If, Condition, Which.

⁺■ Symbol

Symbol["*name*"] refers to a symbol with the specified name.

All symbols, whether explicitly entered using Symbol or not, have head Symbol. ■ x_Symbol can be used as a pattern to represent any symbol. ■ The string "*name*" in Symbol["*name*"] must be an appropriate name for a symbol. It can contain any letters, letter-like forms, or digits, but cannot start with a digit. ■ Symbol["*name*"] creates a new symbol if none exists with the specified name. ■ A symbol such as x has a name "x". ■ If Symbol["*name*"] creates a new symbol, it does so in the context specified by $Context. ■ See page 964. ■ See also: SymbolName, ToExpression, Unique, Remove.

⁺■ SymbolName

SymbolName[*symbol*] gives the name of the specified symbol.

Example: SymbolName[x] ⟶ "x". ■ SymbolName evaluates its input. ■ SymbolName always returns a string. ■ See page 381. ■ See also: ToString, Symbol.

■ SyntaxLength

SyntaxLength["*string*"] finds the number of characters starting at the beginning of a string that correspond to syntactically correct input for a single *Mathematica* expression.

SyntaxLength effectively returns the position of a syntax error, if one exists. ■ If SyntaxLength returns a position past the end of the string, it indicates that the string is syntactically correct as far as it goes, but needs to be continued in order to correspond to input for a complete *Mathematica* expression. ■ See page 445. ■ See also: $SyntaxHandler.

■ SyntaxQ

SyntaxQ["*string*"] returns True if the string corresponds to syntactically correct input for a single *Mathematica* expression, and returns False otherwise.

If SyntaxQ returns False, you can find the position of a syntax error using SyntaxLength. ■ See page 445. ■ See also: ToExpression, ToHeldExpression, $SyntaxHandler, DelimiterFlashTime.

■ Table

Table[*expr*, {*imax*}] generates a list of *imax* copies of *expr*.

Table[*expr*, {*i*, *imax*}] generates a list of the values of *expr* when *i* runs from 1 to *imax*.

Table[*expr*, {*i*, *imin*, *imax*}] starts with *i* = *imin*.

Table[*expr*, {*i*, *imin*, *imax*, *di*}] uses steps *di*.

Table[*expr*, {*i*, *imin*, *imax*}, {*j*, *jmin*, *jmax*}, ...] gives a nested list. The list associated with *i* is outermost.

Table evaluates its arguments in a non-standard way (see page 994). ■ Example: Table[f[i], {i, 4}] ⟶ {f[1], f[2], f[3], f[4]}. ■ Table uses the standard *Mathematica* iteration specification. ■ Example: Table[i-j, {i, 2}, {j, 2}] ⟶ {{0, -1}, {1, 0}}. ■ You can use Table to build up vectors, matrices and tensors. ■ See page 111. ■ See also: Range, DiagonalMatrix, IdentityMatrix, Array, Do, Sum, Product, FunctionInterpolation. ■ Related package: LinearAlgebra`MatrixManipulation`.

■ TableAlignments

TableAlignments is an option for TableForm and MatrixForm which specifies how entries in each dimension should be aligned.

TableAlignments -> {a_1, a_2, ... } specifies alignments for successive dimensions. ■ For dimensions that are given as columns, possible alignments are Left, Center and Right. For dimensions that are given as rows, possible alignments are Bottom, Center and Top. ■ The default setting TableAlignments -> Automatic uses Left for column alignment, and Bottom for row alignment. ■ See page 421. ■ See also: TableDirections, RowAlignments, ColumnAlignments.

■ TableDepth

TableDepth is an option for TableForm and MatrixForm which specifies the maximum number of levels to be printed in tabular or matrix format.

TableForm[*list*, TableDepth -> *n*] prints elements in *list* below level *n* as ordinary lists, rather than arranging them in tabular form. ■ With the default setting TableDepth -> Infinity, as many levels as possible are printed in tabular form. In TableForm, the levels printed need not consist of elements with the same list structure. In MatrixForm, they must. ■ See page 421. ■ See also: TensorRank.

■ TableDirections

TableDirections is an option for TableForm and MatrixForm which specifies whether successive dimensions should be arranged as rows or columns.

TableDirections -> Column specifies that successive dimensions should be arranged alternately as columns and rows, with the first dimension arranged as columns. ■ TableDirections -> Row takes the first dimension to be arranged as rows. ■ TableDirections -> {dir_1, dir_2, ... } specifies explicitly whether each dimension should be arranged with Column or Row. ■ See page 420. ■ See also: TableSpacing.

■ TableForm

TableForm[*list*] prints with the elements of *list* arranged in an array of rectangular cells.

The height of each row and the width of each column are determined by the maximum size of an element in the row or column. ■ TableForm prints a single-level list in a column. It prints a two-level list as a two-dimensional table. More deeply nested lists are by default printed with successive dimensions alternating between rows and columns. ■ Arrays in which all sublists at a particular level are not of the same length display as ragged tables. ■ The following options can be given:

TableAlignments	Automatic	how to align entries in each dimension
TableDepth	Infinity	maximum number of levels to include
TableDirections	Automatic	whether to arrange dimensions as rows or columns
TableHeadings	None	how to label table entries
TableSpacing	Automatic	how many spaces to put between entries in each dimension

■ TableForm acts as a "wrapper", which affects printing, but not evaluation. ■ See page 418. ■ See also: ColumnForm, MatrixForm, GridBox, GraphicsArray.

■ TableHeadings

TableHeadings is an option for TableForm and MatrixForm which gives the labels to be printed for entries in each dimension of a table or matrix.

TableHeadings -> None gives no labels in any dimension. ■ TableHeadings -> Automatic gives successive integer labels for each entry in each dimension. ■ TableHeadings -> {{lab_{11}, lab_{12}, ... }, ... } gives explicit labels for each entry. ■ The labels can be strings or other *Mathematica* expressions. ■ The labels are placed as headings for rows or columns. ■ See page 421.

■ TableSpacing

TableSpacing is an option for TableForm and MatrixForm which specifies how many spaces should be left between each successive row or column.

TableSpacing -> {s_1, s_2, ... } specifies that s_i spaces should be left in dimension *i*. ■ For columns, the spaces are rendered as space characters. For rows, the spaces are rendered as blank lines. ■ For TableForm, TableSpacing -> Automatic yields spacings {1, 3, 0, 1, 0, 1, ... }. ■ See page 421. ■ See also: RowSpacings, ColumnSpacings, GraphicsSpacing.

⁺■ TagBox

TagBox[*boxes*, *tag*] displays as *boxes* but maintains *tag* to guide the interpretation of *boxes* on input.

TagBox provides a way to store hidden information in *Mathematica* output. ■ TagBox is generated sometimes in StandardForm output, and often in TraditionalForm output. ■ By convention, *tag* is typically a symbol that corresponds to the head of the interpreted form of *boxes*. ■ The following options can be given:

AutoDelete	False	whether to strip the TagBox if *boxes* are modified
DeletionWarning	False	whether to issue a warning if *boxes* are deleted
Editable	True	whether to allow *boxes* to be edited
Selectable	True	whether to allow *boxes* to be selected
StripWrapperBoxes	False	whether to remove StyleBox etc. from within *boxes*

■ If you modify the displayed form of TagBox[*boxes*, *tag*] only *boxes* will be modified, and there is no guarantee that correct correspondence with *expr* will be maintained. ■ See page 426. ■ See also: InterpretationBox, FormBox, ToExpression.

■ TagSet

f/: *lhs* = *rhs* assigns *rhs* to be the value of *lhs*, and associates the assignment with the symbol *f*.

TagSet defines upvalues or downvalues as appropriate. ■ The symbol *f* in *f/*: *lhs* = *rhs* must appear in *lhs* as the head of *lhs*, the head of the head, one of the elements of *lhs*, or the head of one of the elements. ■ A common case is *f/*: *h*[*f*[*args*]] = *rhs*. ■ You can see all the rules associated with a particular symbol by typing *?symbol*. ■ If *f* appears several times in *lhs*, then *f/*: *lhs* = *rhs* associates the assignment with each occurrence. ■ When it appears in symbolic form, TagSet is treated as a scoping construct (see Section A.3.8). ■ See pages 299 and 999. ■ See also: Set, UpSet.

■ TagSetDelayed

f/: *lhs* := *rhs* assigns *rhs* to be the delayed value of *lhs*, and associates the assignment with the symbol *f*.

See notes for TagSet and SetDelayed. ■ See page 299.

■ TagUnset

f/: *lhs* =. removes any rules defined for *lhs*, associated with the symbol *f*.

Rules are removed only when their left-hand side is identical to *lhs*, and the tests in Condition given on the right-hand side are also identical. ■ See pages 977 and 1000. ■ See also: Clear, Unset.

■ Take

Take[*list*, *n*] gives the first *n* elements of *list*.

Take[*list*, -*n*] gives the last *n* elements of *list*.

Take[*list*, {*m*, *n*}] gives elements *m* through *n* of *list*.

Take uses the standard *sequence specification* (see page 988). ■ Example: Take[{a,b,c,d,e}, 3] ⟶ {a, b, c}. ■ Take[{a,b,c,d,e}, -2] ⟶ {d, e}. ■ Take can be used on an object with any head, not necessarily List. ■ See page 118. ■ See also: Part, Drop, StringTake, Select, Cases. ■ Related package: LinearAlgebra`MatrixManipulation`.

■ Tan

Tan[*z*] gives the tangent of *z*.

Mathematical function (see Section A.3.10). ■ The argument of Tan is assumed to be in radians. (Multiply by Degree to convert from degrees.) +■ Sin[*z*]/Cos[*z*] is automatically converted to Tan[*z*]. TrigFactorList[*expr*] does decomposition. ■ See page 731. ■ See also: ArcTan, Cot, TrigToExp, TrigExpand.

■ Tanh

Tanh[*z*] gives the hyperbolic tangent of *z*.

Mathematical function (see Section A.3.10). +■ Sinh[*z*]/Cosh[*z*] is automatically converted to Tanh[*z*]. TrigFactorList[*expr*] does decomposition. ■ See page 731. ■ See also: ArcTanh, Coth, TrigToExp, TrigExpand.

■ Temporary

Temporary is an attribute assigned to symbols which are created as local variables by Module.

Symbols with attribute Temporary are automatically removed when they are no longer needed. ■ Symbols with attribute Temporary conventionally have names of the form *aaa$nnn*. ■ See pages 309 and 362. ■ See also: Module, Unique.

■ TensorRank

TensorRank[*expr*] gives the depth to which *expr* is a full array, with all the parts at a particular level being lists of the same length.

TensorRank[*list*] is equivalent to Length[Dimensions[*list*]]. ■ Examples: TensorRank[{a,b}] ⟶ 1; TensorRank[{a,{b}}] ⟶ 1. ■ TensorRank[*expr*, *n*] tests only down to level *n*. ■ See page 854. ■ See also: Dimensions, Depth, VectorQ, MatrixQ.

~■ TeXForm

TeXForm[*expr*] prints as a TEX version of *expr*.

TeXForm produces plain TEX. Its output should be suitable for both LATEX and AMSTEX. ■ TeXForm acts as a "wrapper", which affects printing, but not evaluation. ■ TeXForm translates standard mathematical functions and operations. ■ Symbols with names like alpha and ALPHA that correspond to TEX symbols are translated into their corresponding TEX symbols. ■ Following standard mathematical conventions, single-character symbol names are given in italic font, while multiple character names are given in roman font. ~■ All standard *Mathematica* box structures are translated by TeXForm. ~■ *Mathematica* special characters are translated whenever possible to their TEX equivalents. ■ See pages 211 and 404. ■ See also: TeXSave, StandardForm, TraditionalForm.

+■ TeXSave

TeXSave["*file*.tex"] saves a TEX version of the currently selected notebook in the front end.

TeXSave["*file*.tex", "*source*.nb"] saves a TEX version of the notebook from the file *source*.nb.

TeXSave["*file*.tex", *notebook*] saves a TEX version of the notebook corresponding to the specified notebook object.

TeXSave has options for specifying such features as how to include graphics, what TEX style to use, and how each notebook style should be rendered in TEX. ■ TeXSave can often be accessed from an item in the Save As Special menu in the notebook front end. ■ See notes for TeXForm. ■ See page 211. ■ See also: TeXForm, HTMLSave.

~■ Text

Text[*expr*, *coords*] is a graphics primitive that represents text corresponding to the printed form of *expr*, centered at the point specified by *coords*.

The *text* is printed by default in OutputForm. ■ Text can be used in both two- and three-dimensional graphics. ■ The coordinates can be specified either as {*x*, *y*, ... } or as Scaled[{*x*, *y*, ... }]. +■ In two dimensions, coordinates can also be specified using Offset. ■ Text[*expr*, *coords*, *offset*] specifies an offset for the block of text relative to the coordinates given. Giving an offset {*sdx*, *sdy*} specifies that the point {*x*, *y*} should lie at relative coordinates {*sdx*, *sdy*} within the bounding rectangle that encloses the text. Each relative coordinate runs from −1 to +1 across the bounding rectangle. ■ The offsets specified need not be in the range −1 to +1. ■ Here are sample offsets to use in two-dimensional graphics:

{0, 0}	text centered at {*x*, *y*}
{-1, 0}	left-hand end at {*x*, *y*}
{1, 0}	right-hand end at {*x*, *y*}
{0, -1}	centered above {*x*, *y*}
{0, 1}	centered below {*x*, *y*}

■ Text[*expr*, *coords*, *offset*, *dir*] specifies the orientation of the text is given by the direction vector *dir*. Possible values of *dir* are:

{1, 0}	ordinary horizontal text
{0, 1}	vertical text reading from bottom to top
{0, -1}	vertical text reading from top to bottom
{-1, 0}	horizontal upside-down text

■ Text in three-dimensional graphics is placed at a position that corresponds to the projection of the point {*x*, *y*, *z*} specified. Text is drawn in front of all other objects. ~■ The font or style for text can be specified using StyleForm or using the TextStyle option. If no such specifications are given, the font is determined from the setting for TextStyle for the whole plot, which is in turn by default given by the global variable $TextStyle. ■ You can specify the color of text using CMYKColor, GrayLevel, Hue and RGBColor directives. ~■ The option CharacterEncoding for Display can be used to specify what raw character encoding to use for character strings in Text objects. ~■ The following options can be given:

Background	None	background color
TextStyle	Automatic	style specification
FormatType	StandardForm	format type

■ See pages 472 and 539. ■ See also: PlotLabel, AxesLabel, Cell.

+■ TextAlignment

TextAlignment is an option for Cell which specifies how successive lines of text should be aligned.

Possible settings are:

Left or -1	aligned on the left
Right or +1	aligned on the right
Center or 0	centered
x	lined up at position *x* across the page

■ TextAlignment can be used both for ordinary text and for *Mathematica* expressions. ■ See page 584. ■ See also: TextJustification, ColumnAlignments, PageWidth.

+■ TextJustification

TextJustification is an option for Cell which specifies how much lines of text can be stretched in order to make them be the same length.

TextJustification->0 does no stretching, and leads to ragged text boundaries. ■ TextJustification->1 does full justification, and forces all complete lines to be the same length. ■ No stretching is done on lines that end with explicit RETURN characters. ■ With settings for TextJustification between 0 and 1, partial justification is done. ■ With TextJustification->s, *Mathematica* will take the amount by which each broken line is shorter than PageWidth, and then insert within the line a total amount of space equal to s times this. ■ If TextJustification is not 0, the standard *Mathematica* front end will dynamically adjust the lengths of lines as you enter text. ■ See page 584. ■ See also: TextAlignment, PageWidth, AutoSpacing, ButtonExpandable.

+■ TextStyle

TextStyle is an option for graphics functions and for Text which specifies the default style and font options with which text should be rendered.

The following forms of settings can be used:

"*style*"	a specific cell style
{opt_1->val_1, ... }	a list of option settings
{"*style*", opt_1->val_1, ... }	a style modified by option settings

■ The options that can be given are as in StyleForm. ■ "*style*" settings can only be used when a notebook front end is present. ■ The default setting is TextStyle :> $TextStyle. ■ The style specified by TextStyle in a graphics object is used by default for all text, including labels and tick marks. ■ See page 535. ■ See also: StyleForm, $TextStyle, PlotStyle, FormatType.

■ Thickness

Thickness[*r*] is a graphics directive which specifies that lines which follow are to be drawn with a thickness *r*. The thickness *r* is given as a fraction of the total width of the graph.

Thickness can be used in both two- and three-dimensional graphics. ■ The initial default is Thickness[0.004] for two-dimensional graphics, and Thickness[0.001] for three-dimensional graphics ■ See page 481. ■ See also: AbsoluteThickness, PointSize, Dashing, PlotStyle.

■ Thread

Thread[*f*[*args*]] "threads" *f* over any lists that appear in *args*.

Thread[*f*[*args*], *h*] threads *f* over any objects with head *h* that appear in *args*.

Thread[*f*[*args*], *h*, *n*] threads *f* over objects with head *h* that appear in the first *n* args.

Thread[*f*[*args*], *h*, -*n*] threads over the last *n* args.

Thread[*f*[*args*], *h*, {*m*, *n*}] threads over arguments *m* through *n*.

Example: Thread[f[{a,b}, c, {d,e}]] ⟶ {f[a, c, d], f[b, c, e]}. ■ Functions with attribute Listable are automatically threaded over lists. ■ All the elements in the specified *args* whose heads are *h* must be of the same length. ■ Arguments that do not have head *h* are copied as many times as there are elements in the arguments that do have head *h*. ■ Thread uses the standard *sequence specification* (see page 988). ■ See page 254. ■ See also: Distribute, Map, Inner, MapThread.

■ TokenWords

TokenWords is an option for Read and related functions which gives a list of token words to be used to delimit words.

The setting for TokenWords is a list of strings which are used as delimiters for words to be read. ■ The delimiters specified by TokenWords are themselves returned as words. ■ See page 619. ■ See also: WordSeparators.

~■ ToLowerCase

ToLowerCase[*string*] yields a string in which all letters have been converted to lower case.

~■ ToLowerCase handles both ordinary and special characters. ~■ Variant upper-case characters such as \[CapitalCurlyUpsilon] are converted to their non-variant lower-case forms. ■ See page 392. ■ See also: LowerCaseQ, ToUpperCase, StringReplace, IgnoreCase.

+■ ToRadicals

ToRadicals[*expr*] attempts to express all Root objects in *expr* in terms of radicals.

ToRadicals can always give expressions in terms of radicals when the highest degree of the polynomial that appears in any Root object is four. ■ There are some cases in which expressions involving radicals can in principle be given, but ToRadicals cannot find them. ■ See page 791. ■ See also: Solve, NSolve, RootReduce, Roots.

■ ToRules

ToRules[*eqns*] takes logical combinations of equations, in the form generated by Roots and Reduce, and converts them to lists of rules, of the form produced by Solve.

Example: {ToRules[x==1 || x==2]} $\longrightarrow$ {{x → 1}, {x → 2}}. ■ ToRules discards nonequalities (!=), and thus gives only "generic" solutions. ■ See page 786.

~■ ToString

~ ToString[*expr*] gives a string corresponding to the printed form of *expr* in OutputForm.

~ ToString[*expr*, *form*] gives the string corresponding to output in the specified form.

ToString supports the same set of options as OpenAppend, with default settings FormatType -> OutputForm, PageWidth -> Infinity, TotalWidth -> Infinity. +■ ToString uses any relevant definitions given for Format and MakeBoxes. ■ See page 407. ■ See also: ToBoxes, ToExpression, HoldForm, WriteString, SymbolName.

■ TotalHeight

TotalHeight is an option for output streams which specifies the maximum number of lines of text that should be printed for each output expression. Short forms of expressions are given if the number of lines needed to print the whole expression is too large.

TotalHeight bounds the actual numbers of lines generated. ■ TotalHeight -> Infinity allows expressions of any length to be printed. ■ SetOptions[*stream*, TotalHeight -> *n*] resets the total height allowed for an open stream. ■ See also: Short, Skeleton.

■ **TotalWidth**

TotalWidth is an option which can be set for output streams to specify the maximum total number of characters of text that should be printed for each output expression. Short forms of expressions are given if the number of characters needed to print the whole expression is too large.

TotalWidth bounds the actual numbers of characters generated. Line breaks are not counted.
■ TotalWidth -> Infinity allows expressions of any length to be printed.
■ SetOptions[*stream*, TotalWidth -> *n*] resets the total width allowed for an open stream. ■ See also: Short, Skeleton, PageWidth.

■ **ToUpperCase**

ToUpperCase[*string*] yields a string in which all letters have been converted to upper case.

~■ ToUpperCase handles both ordinary and special characters. ~■ Variant lower-case characters such as \[CurlyPhi] are converted to their non-variant upper-case forms. ■ See page 392. ■ See also: UpperCaseQ, ToLowerCase, StringReplace, IgnoreCase.

■ **Trace**

Trace[*expr*] generates a list of all expressions used in the evaluation of *expr*.

Trace[*expr*, *form*] includes only those expressions which match *form*.

Trace[*expr*, *s*] includes all evaluations which use transformation rules associated with the symbol *s*.

In general, *form* in Trace[*expr*, *form*] is compared both with each complete expression that is evaluated, and with the tag associated with any transformation rule used in the evaluation. ■ Trace[*expr*, *lhs* -> *rhs*] picks out expressions which match *lhs*, then replaces them with *rhs* in the list returned. ■ All expressions in the list returned by Trace are wrapped in HoldForm. ■ Trace returns a set of nested lists. Each individual list corresponds to a single evaluation chain, which contains the sequence of forms found for a particular expression. The list has sublists which give the histories of subsidiary evaluations. ■ Example: Trace[2 3 + 4] ⟶ {}. ■ The following options can be given:

MatchLocalNames	True	whether to allow *x* to stand for *x*$*nnn*
TraceAbove	False	whether to show evaluation chains which contain the chain containing *form*
TraceBackward	False	whether to show expressions preceding *form* in the evaluation chain
TraceDepth	Infinity	how many levels of nested evaluations to include
TraceForward	False	whether to show expressions following *form* in the evaluation chain
TraceOff	None	forms within which to switch off tracing
TraceOn	_	forms within which to switch on tracing
TraceOriginal	False	whether to look at expressions before their heads and arguments are evaluated

■ During the execution of Trace, the settings for the *form* argument, and for the options TraceOn and TraceOff, can be modified by resetting the values of the global variables $TracePattern, $TraceOn and $TraceOff, respectively. ■ See page 335. ■ See also: TraceDialog, TracePrint, TraceScan.

■ TraceAbove

TraceAbove is an option for **Trace** and related functions which specifies whether to include evaluation chains which contain the evaluation chain containing the pattern *form* sought.

TraceAbove -> True includes the first and last expressions in all evaluation chains within which the evaluation chain containing *form* occurs. ■ TraceAbove -> All includes all expressions in these evaluation chains. ■ TraceAbove -> {*backward*, *forward*} allows you to specify separately which expressions to include in the backward and forward directions. ■ Using TraceAbove, you can see the complete paths by which expressions matching *form* arose during an evaluation. ■ See page 341. ■ See also: StackComplete.

■ TraceBackward

TraceBackward is an option for **Trace** and related functions which specifies whether to include preceding expressions on the evaluation chain that contains the pattern *form* sought.

TraceBackward -> True includes the first expression on the evaluation chain that contains *form*. ■ TraceBackward -> All includes all expressions before *form* on the evaluation chain that contains *form*. ■ TraceBackward allows you to see the previous forms that an expression had during an evaluation. ■ See page 341. ■ See also: StackComplete.

■ TraceDepth

TraceDepth is an option for **Trace** and related functions which specifies the maximum nesting of evaluation chains that are to be included.

Setting TraceDepth -> *n* keeps only parts down to level *n* in nested lists generated by Trace. ■ By setting TraceDepth, you can make Trace and related functions skip over "inner" parts of a computation, making their operation more efficient. ■ See page 340. ■ See also: TraceOff.

■ TraceDialog

TraceDialog[*expr*] initiates a dialog for every expression used in the evaluation of *expr*.

TraceDialog[*expr*, *form*] initiates a dialog only for expressions which match *form*.

TraceDialog[*expr*, *s*] initiates dialogs only for expressions whose evaluations use transformation rules associated with the symbol *s*.

See notes for Trace. ■ The expression to be evaluated when a dialog is called is given as Out[$Line] of the dialog, wrapped in HoldForm. The expression can be seen by asking for % when the dialog is first started. ■ Any value returned from the dialog is discarded. ■ TraceDialog[*expr*] returns the result of evaluating *expr*. ■ See page 345.

■ TraceForward

TraceForward is an option for **Trace** and related functions which specifies whether to include later expressions on the evaluation chain that contains the pattern *form* sought.

TraceForward -> True includes the final expression on the evaluation chain that contains *form*. ■ TraceForward -> All includes all expressions after *form* on the evaluation chain that contains *form*. ■ TraceForward allows you to see the transformations performed on an expression generated during an evaluation. ■ See page 341.

■ **TraceOff**

TraceOff is an option for Trace and related functions which specifies forms inside which tracing should be switched off.

The setting for TraceOff gives a pattern which is compared with expressions to be evaluated. If the pattern matches the expression, then tracing will be switched off while that expression is being evaluated. The pattern is also tested against tags associated with the evaluation. ■ You can use TraceOff to avoid tracing inner parts of a computation. ■ The default setting TraceOff -> None never switches off tracing. ■ TraceOn will not work inside TraceOff. ■ During the execution of Trace, the settings for TraceOn and TraceOff can be modified by resetting the values of the global variables $TraceOn and $TraceOff. ■ See page 339. ■ See also: TraceDepth, TraceOn.

■ **TraceOn**

TraceOn is an option for Trace and related functions which specifies when tracing should be switched on.

With the setting TraceOn -> *patt*, Trace and related functions do not start tracing until they encounter expressions to evaluate which match the pattern *patt*. This pattern is also tested against tags associated with the evaluation. ■ TraceOff can be used within tracing switched on by TraceOn. ■ Once tracing has been switched off by TraceOff, however, TraceOn will not switch it on again. ■ During the execution of Trace, the settings for TraceOn and TraceOff can be modified by resetting the values of the global variables $TraceOn and $TraceOff. ■ See page 339. ■ See also: TraceOff.

■ **TraceOriginal**

TraceOriginal is an option for Trace and related functions which specifies whether to test the form of each expression before its head and arguments are evaluated.

With the default TraceOriginal -> False, the forms of expressions generated during an evaluation are tested only after their head and arguments have been evaluated. In addition, evaluation chains for expressions which do not change under evaluation are not included. ■ With TraceOriginal -> True, the forms before evaluation of the head and arguments are also tested, and evaluation chains for expressions which do not change under evaluation are included. ■ See page 342.

■ **TracePrint**

TracePrint[*expr*] prints all expressions used in the evaluation of *expr*.

TracePrint[*expr*, *form*] includes only those expressions which match *form*.

TracePrint[*expr*, *s*] includes all evaluations which use transformation rules associated with the symbol *s*.

See notes for Trace. ■ TracePrint indents its output in correspondence with the nesting levels for lists generated by Trace. ■ The indentation is done using the print form defined for the object Indent[*d*]. ■ TracePrint prints the forms of expressions before any of their elements are evaluated. ■ TracePrint does not support the TraceBackward option of Trace. ■ TracePrint yields only the forward part of the output specified by the option setting TraceAbove -> All. ■ TracePrint[*expr*] returns the result of evaluating *expr*. ■ See page 344.

■ **TraceScan**

TraceScan[*f*, *expr*] applies *f* to all expressions used in the evaluation of *expr*.

TraceScan[*f*, *expr*, *form*] includes only those expressions which match *form*.

TraceScan[*f*, *expr*, *s*] includes all evaluations which use transformation rules associated with the symbol *s*.

TraceScan[*f*, *expr*, *form*, *fp*] applies *f* before evaluation and *fp* after evaluation to expressions used in the evaluation of *expr*.

See notes for Trace. ■ All expressions are wrapped in HoldForm to prevent evaluation before *f* or *fp* are applied to them. ■ The function *fp* is given as arguments both the form before evaluation and the form after evaluation. ■ TraceScan[*f*, *expr*] returns the result of evaluating *expr*. ■ See page 345.

+■ **TraditionalForm**

TraditionalForm[*expr*] prints as an approximation to the traditional mathematical notation for *expr*.

Output from TraditionalForm cannot necessarily be given as unique and unambiguous input to *Mathematica*. ■ TraditionalForm inserts invisible TagBox and InterpretationBox constructs into the box form of output it generates, to allow unique interpretation. ■ TraditionalForm can be edited in the notebook front end. ■ TraditionalForm uses special characters as well as ordinary keyboard characters. ■ TraditionalForm incorporates a large collection of rules for approximating traditional mathematical notation. ■ TraditionalForm prints functions in Global‘ context in the form $f(x)$. ■ ToExpression[*boxes*, TraditionalForm] will attempt to convert from TraditionalForm. ■ The notebook front end contains menu items for conversion to and from TraditionalForm. ■ See page 404. ■ See also: StandardForm, TeXForm, MakeExpression, ToBoxes.

■ **Transpose**

Transpose[*list*] transposes the first two levels in *list*.

Transpose[*list*, {n_1, n_2, ... }] transposes *list* so that the kth level in *list* is the n_k^{th} level in the result.

Example: Transpose[{{a,b},{c,d}}] ⟶ {{a, c}, {b, d}}. ■ Transpose gives the usual transpose of a matrix. ■ Acting on a tensor $T_{i_1 i_2 i_3 ...}$ Transpose gives the tensor $T_{i_2 i_1 i_3 ...}$. ■ Transpose[*list*, {n_1, n_2, ... }] gives the tensor $T_{i_{n_1} i_{n_2} ...}$. ~■ So long as the lengths of the lists at particular levels are the same, the specifications n_k do not necessarily have to be distinct. ~■ Example: Transpose[Array[a, {3, 3}], {1, 1}] ⟶ {a[1, 1], a[2, 2], a[3, 3]}. ■ See page 844. ■ See also: Flatten. ■ Related package: LinearAlgebra‘MatrixManipulation‘.

■ **TreeForm**

TreeForm[*expr*] prints with different levels in *expr* shown at different depths.

See pages 234 and 235. ■ See also: FullForm, MatrixForm. ■ Related package: DiscreteMath‘Tree‘.

+■ **TrigExpand**

TrigExpand[*expr*] expands out trigonometric functions in *expr*.

TrigExpand operates on both circular and hyperbolic functions. ■ TrigExpand splits up sums and integer multiples that appear in arguments of trigonometric functions, and then expands out products of trigonometric functions into sums of powers, using trigonometric identities when possible. ■ See page 781. ■ See also: TrigFactor, TrigReduce, TrigToExp, Expand, FunctionExpand, Simplify, FullSimplify.

+■ TrigFactor

TrigFactor[*expr*] factors trigonometric functions in *expr*.

TrigFactor operates on both circular and hyperbolic functions. ■ TrigFactor splits up sums and integer multiples that appear in arguments of trigonometric functions, and then factors resulting polynomials in trigonometric functions, using trigonometric identities when possible. ■ See page 781. ■ See also: TrigExpand, TrigReduce, TrigToExp, Factor, Simplify, FullSimplify.

+■ TrigFactorList

TrigFactorList[*expr*] factors trigonometric functions in *expr*, yielding a list of lists containing trigonometric monomials and exponents.

See notes for TrigFactor. ■ TrigFactorList tries to give results in terms of powers of Sin, Cos, Sinh and Cosh, explicitly decomposing functions like Tan. ■ See page 781. ■ See also: FactorList, TrigToExp.

+■ TrigReduce

TrigReduce[*expr*] rewrites products and powers of trigonometric functions in *expr* in terms of trigonometric functions with combined arguments.

TrigReduce operates on both circular and hyperbolic functions. ■ Given a trigonometric polynomial, TrigReduce typically yields a linear expression involving trigonometric functions with more complicated arguments. ■ See page 781. ■ See also: TrigExpand, TrigFactor, TrigToExp, Simplify, FullSimplify.

+■ TrigToExp

TrigToExp[*expr*] converts trigonometric functions in *expr* to exponentials.

TrigToExp operates on both circular and hyperbolic functions, and their inverses. ■ See page 781. ■ See also: ExpToTrig, TrigReduce, ComplexExpand.

■ True

True is the symbol for the Boolean value true.

See page 83. ■ See also: False, TrueQ, If.

■ TrueQ

TrueQ[*expr*] yields True if *expr* is True, and yields False otherwise.

Example: TrueQ[x==y] $\longrightarrow$ False. ■ You can use TrueQ to "assume" that a test fails when its outcome is not clear. ■ TrueQ[*expr*] is equivalent to If[*expr*, True, False, False]. ■ See page 326. ■ See also: If, Condition, SameQ.

+■ UnderoverscriptBox

UnderoverscriptBox[*x*, *y*, *z*] represents $\overset{z}{\underset{y}{x}}$ in input and output.

Inside \(... \) UnderoverscriptBox[*x*, *y*, *z*] can be input as *x* \+ *y* \% *z*. ■ In a notebook an UnderoverscriptBox can be created by using [CTRL][+] to move to the underscript, then [CTRL][%] to move to the overscript. [CTRL][ ] moves out of the underscript or overscript position. ■ In StandardForm and InputForm, UnderoverscriptBox[*x*, *y*, *z*] is interpreted on input as Underoverscript[*x*, *y*, *z*]. ■ See notes for UnderscriptBox and OverscriptBox. ■ See page 424. ■ See also: SubsuperscriptBox, GridBox, ColumnForm.

+■ **UnderscriptBox**

UnderscriptBox[x, y] represents x in input and output.

Inside \(... \) UnderscriptBox[x, y] can be input as x \+ y. ■ In a notebook a UnderscriptBox can be created using CTRL+. CTRL␣ moves out of the underscript position. ■ In StandardForm and InputForm, UnderscriptBox[x, y] is interpreted on input as Underscript[x, y]. ■ UnderscriptBox[x, "-"] is interpreted as UnderBar[x] or $\underline{x}$. The input form x\&\%- can be used. ■ The baseline of UnderscriptBox[x, y] is taken to be the baseline of x. ■ UnderscriptBox[x, y] is usually output with y in a smaller font than x. ■ With the option setting LimitsPositioning->True y is placed in an underscript position when the whole UnderscriptBox is displayed large, and in a subscript position when it is displayed smaller. ■ In StandardForm, explicit UnderscriptBox objects are output literally. You can use DisplayForm to see the display form of such objects. ■ See page 424. ■ See also: OverscriptBox, UnderoverscriptBox, SubscriptBox, GridBox, ScriptSizeMultipliers.

~■ **Unequal**

~ *lhs* != *rhs* or *lhs* ≠ *rhs* returns False if *lhs* and *rhs* are identical.

~■ $x \neq y$ can be entered as x \[NotEqual] y or x ⦂!=⦂ y. ~■ *lhs* ≠ *rhs* returns True if *lhs* and *rhs* are determined to be unequal by comparisons between numbers or other raw data, such as strings. ■ Approximate numbers are considered unequal if they differ beyond their last two decimal digits. ~■ $e_1 \neq e_2 \neq e_3 \neq \dots$ gives True only if none of the e_i are equal. $2 \neq 3 \neq 2 \longrightarrow$ False. ~■ *lhs* ≠ *rhs* represents a symbolic condition that can be generated and manipulated by functions like Reduce and LogicalExpand. ■ Unequal[e] gives True. +■ For exact numeric quantities, Unequal internally uses numerical approximations to establish inequality. This process can be affected by the setting of the global variable $MaxExtraPrecision. +■ In StandardForm, Unequal is printed using ≠. ■ See page 84. ■ See also: Equal, UnsameQ, Order.

■ **Unevaluated**

Unevaluated[*expr*] represents the unevaluated form of *expr* when it appears as the argument to a function.

f[Unevaluated[*expr*]] effectively works by temporarily setting attributes so that f holds its argument unevaluated, then evaluating f[*expr*]. ■ Example: Length[Unevaluated[5+6]] $\longrightarrow$ 2. ■ See page 319. ■ See also: Hold, HoldFirst, ReplacePart.

~■ **Uninstall**

Uninstall[*link*] terminates an external program started by Install, and removes *Mathematica* definitions set up by it.

~■ The argument of Uninstall is a LinkObject representing a *MathLink* link as returned by Install. ■ Uninstall calls Unset to remove definitions set up by Install. ■ See page 632. ■ See also: Install, LinkClose, Close.

~■ **Union**

Union[*list*$_1$, *list*$_2$, ...] gives a sorted list of all the distinct elements that appear in any of the *list*$_i$.

Union[*list*] gives a sorted version of a list, in which all duplicated elements have been dropped.

If the *list*$_i$ are considered as sets, Union gives their union. +■ Union[*list*$_1$, *list*$_2$, ...] can be input in StandardForm and InputForm as *list*$_1$ ∪ *list*$_2$ ∪ ... . The character ∪ can be entered as ⦂un⦂ or \[Union]. ■ The *list*$_i$ must have the same head, but it need not be List. +■ Union[*list*$_1$, ... , SameTest->*test*] applies *test* to each pair of elements in the *list*$_i$ to determine whether they should be considered the same. ■ See page 123. ■ See also: Join, Intersection, Complement, Split.

■ Unique

Unique[ ] generates a new symbol, whose name is of the form $nnn.

Unique[x] generates a new symbol, with a name of the form $x$nnn.

Unique[{x, y, ... }] generates a list of new symbols.

Unique["xxx"] generates a new symbol, with a name of the form $xxxnnn$.

Unique[x] numbers the symbols it creates using $ModuleNumber, and increments $ModuleNumber every time it is called. ■ Unique["xxx"] numbers the symbols it creates sequentially, starting at 1 for each string xxx. ■ Unique[$name$, {$attr_1$, $attr_2$, ... }] generates a symbol which has the attributes $attr_i$. ■ See page 362. ■ See also: Symbol, ToExpression, Names, C, Module, CharacterRange.

■ Unprotect

Unprotect[s_1, s_2, ...] removes the attribute Protected for the symbols s_i.

Unprotect["$form_1$", "$form_2$", ...] unprotects all symbols whose names textually match any of the $form_i$.

A typical sequence in adding your own rules for built-in functions is Unprotect[f]; *definition*; Protect[f]. ■ See notes for Protect. ■ See pages 301 and 992. ■ See also: Protect, Locked, SetOptions.

■ UnsameQ

lhs =!= rhs yields True if the expression lhs is not identical to rhs, and yields False otherwise.

See notes for SameQ. ■ e_1 =!= e_2 =!= e_3 gives True if no two of the e_i are identical. ■ See page 265. ■ See also: Equal, Order.

■ Unset

lhs =. removes any rules defined for lhs.

Rules are removed only when their left-hand sides are identical to lhs, and the tests in Condition given on the right-hand side are also identical. ■ See pages 285 and 1000. ■ See also: Clear, TagUnset.

■ Update

Update[$symbol$] tells *Mathematica* that hidden changes have been made which could affect values associated with a symbol.

Update[ ] specifies that the value of any symbol could be affected.

Update manipulates internal optimization features of *Mathematica*. It should not need to be called except under special circumstances that rarely occur in practice. ■ One special circumstance is that changes in the value of one symbol can affect the value of another symbol by changing the outcome of Condition tests. In such cases, you may need to use Update on the symbol you think may be affected. ■ Using Update will never give you incorrect results, although it will slow down the operation of the system. ■ See page 350.

~■ UpperCaseQ

UpperCaseQ[$string$] yields True if all the characters in the string are upper-case letters, and yields False otherwise.

~■ UpperCaseQ treats both ordinary and special characters. ■ See page 392. ■ See also: LowerCaseQ, LetterQ, ToUpperCase, ToCharacterCode.

■ UpSet

lhs^=rhs assigns *rhs* to be the value of *lhs*, and associates the assignment with symbols that occur at level one in *lhs*.

f[*g*[*x*]]=*value* makes an assignment associated with *f*. *f*[*g*[*x*]]^=*value* makes an assignment associated instead with *g*. ■ UpSet associates an assignment with *all* the distinct symbols that occur either directly as arguments of *lhs*, or as the heads of arguments of *lhs*. ■ See pages 298 and 999. ■ See also: TagSet, UpValues.

■ UpSetDelayed

lhs^:=rhs assigns *rhs* to be the delayed value of *lhs*, and associates the assignment with symbols that occur at level one in *lhs*.

See notes for UpSet and SetDelayed. ■ See pages 297 and 298.

~■ UpValues

UpValues[*f*] gives a list of transformation rules corresponding to all upvalues defined for the symbol *f*.

You can specify the upvalues for *f* by making an assignment of the form UpValues[*f*] = *list*. ~■ The list returned by UpValues has elements of the form HoldPattern[*lhs*] :> *rhs*. ■ See page 303. ■ See also: Set, DownValues, HoldAllComplete.

■ ValueQ

ValueQ[*expr*] gives True if a value has been defined for *expr*, and gives False otherwise.

ValueQ has attribute HoldFirst. ■ ValueQ gives False only if *expr* would not change if it were to be entered as *Mathematica* input. ■ See page 265. ■ See also: Information.

■ Variables

Variables[*poly*] gives a list of all independent variables in a polynomial.

See page 769. ■ See also: Coefficient.

■ VectorQ

VectorQ[*expr*] gives True if *expr* is a list, none of whose elements are themselves lists, and gives False otherwise.

VectorQ[*expr*, *test*] gives True only if *test* yields True when applied to each of the elements in *expr*.

VectorQ[*expr*, NumberQ] tests whether *expr* is a vector of numbers. ■ See pages 264 and 839. ■ See also: MatrixQ, TensorRank.

+■ Verbatim

Verbatim[*expr*] represents *expr* in pattern matching, requiring that *expr* be matched exactly as it appears, with no substitutions for blanks or other transformations.

Verbatim[*x_*] will match only the actual expression *x_*. ■ Verbatim is useful in setting up rules for transforming other transformation rules. ■ Verbatim[*expr*] does not maintain *expr* in an unevaluated form. ■ See page 275. ■ See also: HoldPattern.

■ ViewCenter

ViewCenter is an option for **Graphics3D** and **SurfaceGraphics** which gives the scaled coordinates of the point which appears at the center of the display area in the final plot.

With the default setting **ViewCenter -> Automatic**, the whole bounding box is centered in the final image area. ■ With the setting **ViewCenter -> {1/2, 1/2, 1/2}**, the center of the three-dimensional bounding box will be placed at the center of the final display area. ■ The setting for **ViewCenter** is given in scaled coordinates, which run from 0 to 1 across each dimension of the bounding box. ■ With **SphericalRegion -> True**, the circumscribing sphere is always centered, regardless of the setting for **ViewCenter**. ■ See page 512.

■ ViewPoint

ViewPoint is an option for **Graphics3D** and **SurfaceGraphics** which gives the point in space from which the objects plotted are to be viewed.

ViewPoint -> {x, y, z} gives the position of the view point relative to the center of the three-dimensional box that contains the object being plotted. ■ The view point is given in a special scaled coordinate system in which the longest side of the bounding box has length 1. The center of the bounding box is taken to have coordinates {0, 0, 0}. ■ Common settings for **ViewPoint** are:

{1.3, -2.4, 2}	default setting
{0, -2, 0}	directly in front
{0, -2, 2}	in front and up
{0, -2, -2}	in front and down
{-2, -2, 0}	left-hand corner
{2, -2, 0}	right-hand corner
{0, 0, 2}	directly above

■ Choosing **ViewPoint** further away from the object reduces the distortion associated with perspective. ■ The view point must lie outside the bounding box. ■ The coordinates of the corners of the bounding box in the special coordinate system used for **ViewPoint** are determined by the setting for the **BoxRatios** option. ■ See page 511. ■ See also: **ViewCenter, ViewVertical, SphericalRegion**. ■ Related package: **Geometry`Rotations`**.

■ ViewVertical

ViewVertical is an option for **Graphics3D** and **SurfaceGraphics** which specifies what direction in scaled coordinates should be vertical in the final image.

The default setting is **ViewVertical -> {0, 0, 1}**, which specifies that the *z* axis in your original coordinate system should end up vertical in the final image. ■ The setting for **ViewVertical** is given in scaled coordinates, which run from 0 to 1 across each dimension of the bounding box. ■ Only the direction of the vector specified by **ViewVertical** is important; its magnitude is irrelevant. ■ See page 512.

+■ Visible

Visible is an option for **Notebook** which specifies whether the notebook should be explicitly displayed on the screen.

With **Visible->False** a notebook can still be manipulated from the kernel, but will not explicitly be displayed on the screen. ■ **NotebookCreate[Visible->False]** creates a new invisible window. ■ See page 594. ■ See also: **Selectable, WindowFloating, CellOpen**.

⁺■ WeierstrassHalfPeriods

`WeierstrassHalfPeriods[{`g_2`, `g_3`}]` gives the half-periods $\{\omega, \omega'\}$ for Weierstrass elliptic functions corresponding to the invariants $\{g_2, g_3\}$.

Mathematical function (see Section A.3.10). ■ The half-periods $\{\omega, \omega'\}$ define the fundamental period parallelogram for the Weierstrass elliptic functions. ■ `WeierstrassHalfPeriods` is the inverse of `WeierstrassInvariants`. ■ See page 752. ■ See also: `WeierstrassP`, `InverseWeierstrassP`, `ModularLambda`.

⁺■ WeierstrassInvariants

`WeierstrassInvariants[{`ω`, `ω'`}]` gives the invariants $\{g_2, g_3\}$ for Weierstrass elliptic functions corresponding to the half-periods $\{\omega, \omega'\}$.

Mathematical function (see Section A.3.10). ■ `WeierstrassInvariants` is the inverse of `WeierstrassHalfPeriods`. ■ See page 752. ■ See also: `WeierstrassP`, `InverseWeierstrassP`, `KleinInvariantJ`.

~■ WeierstrassP

~ `WeierstrassP[`u`, {`g_2`, `g_3`}]` gives the Weierstrass elliptic function $\wp(u; g_2, g_3)$.

Mathematical function (see Section A.3.10). ■ $\wp(u; g_2, g_3)$ gives the value of x for which $u = \int_\infty^x (4t^3 - g_2 t - g_3)^{-1/2}\, dt$. ■ See page 752 for a discussion of argument conventions for elliptic functions. ■ See pages 755 and 757. ■ See also: `InverseWeierstrassP`.

~■ WeierstrassPPrime

~ `WeierstrassPPrime[`u`, {`g_2`, `g_3`}]` gives the derivative of the Weierstrass elliptic function $\wp(u; g_2, g_3)$.

Mathematical function (see Section A.3.10). ■ $\wp'(u; g_2, g_3) = (\partial/\partial u)\wp(u; g_2, g_3)$. ■ See page 752 for a discussion of argument conventions for elliptic functions. ■ See pages 755 and 757.

⁺■ WeierstrassSigma

`WeierstrassSigma[`u`, {`g_2`, `g_3`}]` gives the Weierstrass sigma function $\sigma(u; g_2, g_3)$.

Mathematical function (see Section A.3.10). ■ Related to `WeierstrassZeta` by the differential equation $\sigma'(z; g_2, g_3)/\sigma(z; g_2, g_3) = \zeta(z; g_2, g_3)$. ■ `WeierstrassSigma` is not periodic and is therefore not strictly an elliptic function. ■ See page 752 for a discussion of argument conventions for elliptic and related functions. ■ See page 755. ■ See also: `WeierstrassZeta`.

⁺■ WeierstrassZeta

`WeierstrassZeta[`u`, {`g_2`, `g_3`}]` gives the Weierstrass zeta function $\zeta(u; g_2, g_3)$.

Mathematical function (see Section A.3.10). ■ Related to `WeierstrassP` by the differential equation $\zeta'(z; g_2, g_3) = -\wp(z; g_2, g_3)$. ■ `WeierstrassZeta` is not periodic and is therefore not strictly an elliptic function. ■ See page 752 for a discussion of argument conventions for elliptic and related functions. ■ See page 755. ■ See also: `WeierstrassSigma`.

■ Which

Which[*test₁*, *value₁*, *test₂*, *value₂*, ...] evaluates each of the *testᵢ* in turn, returning the value of the *valueᵢ* corresponding to the first one that yields True.

Example: Which[1==2, x, 1==1, y] ⟶ y. ■ Which has attribute HoldAll. ■ If any of the *testᵢ* evaluated by Which give neither True nor False, then a Which object containing these remaining elements is returned unevaluated. ■ You can make Which return a "default value" by taking the last *testᵢ* to be True. ■ If all the *testᵢ* evaluate to False, Which returns Null. ■ See page 325. ■ See also: Switch, If.

■ While

While[*test*, *body*] evaluates *test*, then *body*, repetitively, until *test* first fails to give True.

While[*test*] does the loop with a null body. ■ If Break[ ] is generated in the evaluation of *body*, the While loop exits. ■ Continue[ ] exits the evaluation of *body*, and continues the loop. ■ Unless Return[ ] or Throw[ ] are generated, the final value returned by While is Null. ■ Example: i=0; While[i < 0, tot += f[i]; i++]. Note that the roles of ; and , are *reversed* relative to the C programming language. ■ See page 332. ■ See also: Do, For, Nest, Fold, Select, Throw.

⁺■ WindowClickSelect

WindowClickSelect is an option for Notebook which specifies whether the window for the notebook should become selected if you click on it.

With WindowClickSelect->True, clicking on the window corresponding to a notebook makes that notebook the currently selected one. ■ WindowClickSelect affects selection of a window as a whole; Selectable affects only selection of the contents of a window. ■ See page 594. ■ See also: WindowFloating, SetSelectedNotebook.

⁺■ WindowElements

WindowElements is an option for Notebook which specifies the elements to include in the window used to display the notebook on the screen.

WindowElements is typically set to a list containing elements such as "HorizontalScrollBar", "MagnificationPopUp", "StatusArea" and "VerticalScrollBar". ■ The details of particular elements may differ from one computer system to another. ■ See page 594. ■ See also: WindowToolbars, WindowTitle, WindowFrame.

⁺■ WindowFloating

WindowFloating is an option for Notebook which specifies whether the window for the notebook should float on top of other windows when it is displayed on the screen.

WindowFloating->True is often used for palettes. ■ If there are several floating windows the most recently selected one goes on top. ■ See page 594. ■ See also: WindowClickSelect, Visible.

+■ **$CharacterEncoding**

$CharacterEncoding specifies the default raw character encoding to use for input and output functions.

The default setting for $CharacterEncoding is $SystemCharacterEncoding. ■ The setting $CharacterEncoding = None takes all special characters to be represented externally by printable ASCII sequences such as \[*Name*] and \:*xxxx*. ■ Possible other settings are:

"AdobeStandard"	Adobe standard PostScript font encoding
"ASCII"	full ASCII, with control characters
"EUC"	extended Unix code for Japanese
"ISOLatin1"	ISO 8859-1 standard
"ISOLatin2"	ISO 8859-2 standard
"ISOLatin3"	ISO 8859-3 standard
"ISOLatin4"	ISO 8859-4 standard
"ISOLatinCyrillic"	ISO 8859-5 standard
"MacintoshRoman"	Macintosh roman font encoding
"PrintableASCII"	printable ASCII
"ShiftJIS"	shift-JIS encoding of JIS X 0208-1990 and extensions
"Symbol"	symbol font encoding
"Unicode"	raw 16-bit Unicode
"WindowsANSI"	Windows standard font encoding
"ZapfDingbats"	Zapf dingbats font encoding

■ With $CharacterEncoding = "*encoding*" characters that are included in the encoding can be input in their raw 8- or 16-bit form, and will be output in this form. ■ Unencoded characters can be input and will be output in standard \[*Name*] or \:*xxxx* form. ■ When using a text-based interface, resetting the value of $CharacterEncoding has an immediate effect on standard input and output in a *Mathematica* session. ■ When using the notebook front end, raw character encodings are normally handled automatically based on the fonts you use. Only raw 16-bit Unicode is ever sent through the *MathLink* connection to the kernel. ■ $CharacterEncoding can be set to a list of the form {*class*, {{n_1, "c_1"}, {n_2, "c_2"}, ... }}. The *class* defines the general form of encoding; the n_i give character codes for specific characters c_i. Possible settings for *class* include:

"7Bit"	characters 0–127 given as raw bytes; other characters unencoded
"8Bit"	characters 0–255 given as raw bytes; other characters unencoded
"16Bit"	full two-byte Unicode encoding
"ShiftJIS"	shift-JIS encoding

■ $CharacterEncoding affects the input and output of all characters, including those in symbol names and comments. ■ $CharacterEncoding also affects characters that appear in Text graphics primitives. ■ See page 399.
■ See also: CharacterEncoding, FromCharacterCode, ToCharacterCode, $SystemCharacterEncoding.

■ **$CommandLine**

$CommandLine is a list of strings giving the elements of the original operating system command line with which *Mathematica* was invoked.

See page 689. ■ See also: Environment, $ProgramName, $LaunchDirectory, $BatchInput, $BatchOutput, $Linked, In.

■ **$Context**

$Context is a global variable that gives the current context.

Contexts are specified by strings of the form "*name*`". ■ $Context is modified by Begin, BeginPackage, End and EndPackage. ■ $Context is a rough analog for *Mathematica* symbols of the current working directory for files in many operating systems. ■ See page 372. ■ See also: Context.

■ **$ContextPath**

$ContextPath is a global variable that gives a list of contexts, after $Context, to search in trying to find a symbol that has been entered.

Each context is specified by a string of the form "*name*`". ■ The elements of $ContextPath are tested in order to try and find a context containing a particular symbol. ■ $ContextPath is modified by Begin, BeginPackage, End and EndPackage. ■ $ContextPath is a rough analog for *Mathematica* symbols of the "search path" for files in many operating systems. ■ See page 373.

■ **$CreationDate**

$CreationDate gives the date and time at which the particular release of the *Mathematica* kernel you are running was created.

$CreationDate is in the form {*year*, *month*, *day*, *hour*, *minute*, *second*} returned by Date. ■ See page 690. ■ See also: $VersionNumber, $ReleaseNumber, FileDate, $InstallationDate.

⁺■ **$CurrentLink**

$CurrentLink is the LinkObject representing the *MathLink* connection for an external program currently being installed or being called.

$CurrentLink is temporarily set by Install and by ExternalCall. ■ You can use $CurrentLink to distinguish between several instances of an external program running at the same time. ■ $CurrentLink can be included in :Pattern: and :Arguments: *MathLink* template specifications, and will be evaluated at the time when Install is called. ■ See page 661. ■ See also: $ParentLink, Links, $Input.

■ **$Display**

$Display gives a list of files and pipes to be used with the default $DisplayFunction.

The initial setting of $Display is {}. ■ See page 678.

■ **$DisplayFunction**

$DisplayFunction gives the default setting for the option DisplayFunction in graphics functions.

The initial setting of $DisplayFunction is Display[$Display, #]&. ■ $DisplayFunction is typically set to a procedure which performs the following: (1) open an output channel; (2) send a PostScript prolog to the output channel; (3) use Display to send PostScript graphics; (4) send PostScript epilog; (5) close the output channel and execute the external commands needed to produce actual display. ■ See page 471. ■ See also: Display, Put, Run, $SoundDisplayFunction.

■ **$Echo**

$Echo gives a list of files and pipes to which all input is echoed.

You can use $Echo to keep a file of all your input commands. ■ See page 678.

■ `$Epilog`

`$Epilog` is a symbol whose value, if any, is evaluated when a dialog or a *Mathematica* session is terminated.

For *Mathematica* sessions, `$Epilog` is conventionally defined to read in a file named `end.m`. ■ See page 679. ■ See also: `Exit`, `Quit`, `Dialog`.

■ `$Failed`

`$Failed` is a special symbol returned by certain functions when they cannot do what they were asked to do.

`Get` returns `$Failed` when it cannot find the file or other object that was specified. ■ See page 598.

+■ `$FormatType`

`$FormatType` gives the default format type to use for text that appears in graphics.

The default setting for the standard notebook front end is `$FormatType = StandardForm`. ■ The default setting for the text-based front end is `$FormatType = OutputForm`. ■ A common alternative setting is `TraditionalForm`. ■ Box-based format types such as `StandardForm` and `TraditionalForm` can be used only when a notebook front end is present. ■ `$FormatType` gives the default value for the `FormatType` option in graphics. ■ See page 535. ■ See also: `$TextStyle`, `FormatType`.

+■ `$FrontEnd`

`$FrontEnd` is a global variable that specifies to what front end object, if any, the kernel is currently connected.

`$FrontEnd` is either a `FrontEndObject`, or `Null`. ■ You can use `Options` and `SetOptions` on `$FrontEnd` to read and set global options for the front end. ■ See page 566. ■ See also: `$Notebooks`.

+■ `$HistoryLength`

`$HistoryLength` specifies the number of previous lines of input and output to keep in a *Mathematica* session.

The default setting for `$HistoryLength` is `Infinity`. ■ Values of `In[`n`]` and `Out[`n`]` corresponding to lines before those kept are explicitly cleared. ■ Using smaller values of `$HistoryLength` can save substantial amounts of memory in a *Mathematica* session. ■ See page 676. ■ See also: `$Line`.

+■ `$HomeDirectory`

`$HomeDirectory` gives your "home" directory.

`$HomeDirectory` returns the full name of the directory as a string. ■ On multi-user operating systems, `$HomeDirectory` gives the main directory for the current user. ■ See page 612. ■ See also: `Directory`, `ParentDirectory`, `$UserName`, `$LaunchDirectory`, `$TopDirectory`.

■ `$IgnoreEOF`

`$IgnoreEOF` specifies whether *Mathematica* should terminate when it receives an end-of-file character as input.

`$IgnoreEOF` defaults to `False`. ■ `$IgnoreEOF` is assumed to be `False` if the input to *Mathematica* comes from a file, rather than an interactive device. ■ See pages 679 and 1006. ■ See also: `Exit`, `Quit`, `$BatchInput`.

+■ $InitialDirectory

> $InitialDirectory gives the current directory at the time when the current *Mathematica* session was started.

$InitialDirectory returns the full name of the directory as a string. ■ See page 612. ■ See also: Directory, $LaunchDirectory, $CommandLine.

■ $InstallationDate

> $InstallationDate gives the date and time at which the copy of the *Mathematica* kernel you are running was installed.

$InstallationDate is in the form {*year*, *month*, *day*, *hour*, *minute*, *second*} returned by Date. ■ See page 690. ■ See also: $CreationDate.

■ $Input

> $Input is a global variable whose value is the name of the stream from which input to *Mathematica* is currently being sought.

During the execution of <<*file*, $Input is set to "*file*". ■ During interactive input, $Input is "". ■ See pages 614 and 678. ■ See also: Get, Streams, DirectoryName, ToFileName, $BatchInput, $ParentLink.

■ $Inspector

> $Inspector is a global variable which gives a function to apply when the inspector is invoked from an interrupt menu.

The argument supplied is the number of nested invocations of the inspector that are in use. ■ The default value of $Inspector is Dialog[ ]&. ■ See also: Interrupt.

■ $IterationLimit

> $IterationLimit gives the maximum length of evaluation chain used in trying to evaluate any expression.

$IterationLimit limits the number of times *Mathematica* tries to re-evaluate a particular expression. ■ $IterationLimit gives an upper limit on the length of any list that can be generated by Trace. ■ See page 348. ■ See also: $RecursionLimit.

■ $Language

> $Language is a list of strings which give the names of languages to use for messages.

All language names are conventionally given in English, and are capitalized, as in "French". ■ When a message with a name $s::tag$ is requested either internally or through the Message function, *Mathematica* searches for messages with names $s::tag::lang_i$ corresponding to the entries "$lang_i$" in the list $Language. Only if it fails to find any of these messages will it use the message with the actual name $s::tag$. ■ See pages 463 and 679. ■ See also: MessageName.

■ $LaunchDirectory

$LaunchDirectory gives the directory in which the executable for the *Mathematica* kernel program being run resides.

$LaunchDirectory returns the full name of the directory as a string. ■ $LaunchDirectory gives the directory for the actual *Mathematica* kernel executable, not the directory for scripts such as math that call it. ■ After installation on a hard disk, $LaunchDirectory is typically the Kernel/Binaries subdirectory of $TopDirectory. ■ See page 612. ■ See also: $TopDirectory, $ProgramName, $CommandLine, $InitialDirectory, $InstallationDate.

■ $Line

$Line is a global variable that specifies the number of the current input line.

You can reset $Line. ■ See page 675. ■ See also: In, Out, $HistoryLength.

■ $Linked

$Linked is True if the *Mathematica* kernel is being run through *MathLink*.

$Linked is True when *Mathematica* is being run with a front end. ■ $Linked is typically False when *Mathematica* is being run with a text-based interface. ■ See also: $CommandLine, $BatchInput, $BatchOutput, $Notebooks.

■ $MachineDomain

$MachineDomain is a string which gives the name of the network domain for the computer on which *Mathematica* is being run, if such a name is defined.

$MachineDomain is "" if no name is defined. ■ See page 691. ■ See also: $MachineName, $MachineID.

■ $MachineEpsilon

$MachineEpsilon gives the smallest machine-precision number which can be added to 1.0 to give a result that is distinguishable from 1.0.

$MachineEpsilon is typically 2^{-n+1}, where n is the number of binary bits used in the internal representation of machine-precision floating-point numbers. ■ $MachineEpsilon measures the granularity of machine-precision numbers. ■ See page 712. ■ See also: $MachinePrecision, $MinMachineNumber, $MaxMachineNumber. ■ Related package: NumericalMath`ComputerArithmetic`.

■ $MachineID

$MachineID is a string which gives, if possible, a unique identification code for the computer on which *Mathematica* is being run.

On many computers, $MachineID is the MathID string printed by the external program mathinfo. ■ See page 691. ■ See also: $SystemID, $MachineName, $LicenseID.

■ $MachineName

$MachineName is a string which gives the assigned name of the computer on which *Mathematica* is being run, if such a name is defined.

For many classes of computers, $MachineName is the network host name. ■ $MachineName is "" if no name is defined. ■ See page 691. ■ See also: $MachineDomain, $System, $MachineID.

■ $MachinePrecision

$MachinePrecision gives the number of decimal digits of precision used for machine-precision numbers.

A typical value of $MachinePrecision is 16. ■ $MachinePrecision gives the default precision assumed for approximate real numbers where few explicit digits are entered. ■ $MachinePrecision is the default precision used by N and other numerical functions. ■ See pages 703 and 712. ■ See also: $MachineEpsilon, $MinMachineNumber, $MaxMachineNumber. ■ Related package: NumericalMath'ComputerArithmetic'.

■ $MachineType

$MachineType is a string giving the general type of computer on which *Mathematica* is being run.

$MachineType is intended to reflect general families of hardware rather than specific models. ■ Typical values are "PC", "Macintosh", "Sun", "DEC" and "SGI". ■ Computers with the same $MachineType may not be binary compatible. ■ See page 690. ■ See also: $ProcessorType, $OperatingSystem, $System.

+■ $MaxExtraPrecision

$MaxExtraPrecision gives the maximum number of extra digits of precision to be used in functions such as N.

The default value of $MaxExtraPrecision is 50. ■ You can use Block[{$MaxExtraPrecision = *n*}, *expr*] to reset the value of $MaxExtraPrecision temporarily during the evaluation of *expr*. ■ $MaxExtraPrecision is used implicitly in various exact numerical computations, including equality tests, comparisons and functions such as Round and Sign. ■ See page 709. ■ See also: $MaxPrecision.

■ $MaxMachineNumber

$MaxMachineNumber is the largest machine-precision number that can be used on a particular computer system.

Numbers larger than $MaxMachineNumber are represented in arbitrary-precision form. ■ $MaxMachineNumber is typically 2^n, where n is the maximum exponent that can be used in the internal representation of machine-precision numbers. ■ See page 712. ■ See also: $MinMachineNumber, $MachineEpsilon, $MachinePrecision. ■ Related package: NumericalMath'ComputerArithmetic'.

+■ $MaxNumber

$MaxNumber gives the magnitude of the maximum arbitrary-precision number that can be represented on a particular computer system.

A typical value for $MaxNumber is around $10^{323228010}$. ■ See page 712. ■ See also: $MaxPrecision, $MaxMachineNumber.

+■ $MaxPrecision

$MaxPrecision gives the maximum number of digits of precision to be allowed in arbitrary-precision numbers.

The default value of $MaxPrecision is 50000. ■ $MaxPrecision = Infinity uses the maximum value possible on a particular computer system, given roughly by Log[10, $MaxNumber]. ■ $MaxPrecision is measured in decimal digits, and need not be an integer. ■ See page 709. ■ See also: $MinPrecision, $MaxExtraPrecision.

■ **$MessageList**

$MessageList is a global variable that gives a list of the names of messages generated during the evaluation of the current input line.

Whenever a message is output, its name, wrapped with HoldForm is appended to $MessageList. ■ With the standard *Mathematica* main loop, $MessageList is reset to {} when the processing of a particular input line is complete. ■ You can reset $MessageList during a computation. ■ See page 460. ■ See also: MessageList, Check.

■ **$MessagePrePrint**

$MessagePrePrint is a global variable whose value, if set, is applied to expressions before they are included in the text of messages.

The default value of $MessagePrePrint is Short. ■ $MessagePrePrint is applied after each expression is wrapped with HoldForm. ■ See pages 460 and 679. ■ See also: $PrePrint.

■ **$Messages**

$Messages gives the list of files and pipes to which message output is sent.

Output from Message is always given on the $Messages channel. ■ See page 678.

■ **$MinMachineNumber**

$MinMachineNumber is the smallest positive machine-precision number that can be used on a particular computer system.

See notes for $MaxMachineNumber. ■ See page 712. ■ See also: $MinNumber. ■ Related package: NumericalMath`ComputerArithmetic`.

+■ **$MinNumber**

$MinNumber gives the magnitude of the minimum positive arbitrary-precision number that can be represented on a particular computer system.

A typical value for $MinNumber is around $10^{-323228015}$. ■ See page 712. ■ See also: $MinPrecision, $MinMachineNumber.

+■ **$MinPrecision**

$MinPrecision gives the minimum number of digits of precision to be allowed in arbitrary-precision numbers.

The default value of $MinPrecision is 0. ■ Positive values of $MinPrecision make *Mathematica* pad arbitrary-precision numbers with zero digits to achieve the specified nominal precision. The zero digits are taken to be in base 2, and may not correspond to zeros in base 10. ■ $MaxPrecision = $MinPrecision = n makes *Mathematica* do fixed-precision arithmetic. ■ $MinPrecision is measured in decimal digits, and need not be an integer. ■ See page 709. ■ See also: SetPrecision, $MinNumber.

■ **$ModuleNumber**

$ModuleNumber gives the current serial number to be used for local variables that are created.

$ModuleNumber is incremented every time Module or Unique is called. ■ Every *Mathematica* session starts with $ModuleNumber set to 1. ■ You can reset $ModuleNumber to any positive integer, but if you do so, you run the risk of creating naming conflicts. ■ See page 360. ■ See also: $SessionID, Temporary.

■ **$NewMessage**

$NewMessage is a global variable which, if set, is applied to the symbol name and tag of messages that are requested but have not yet been defined.

$NewMessage is applied to the symbol name, tag and language of a message if an explicit language is specified. ■ *Mathematica* looks for the value of *name*::*tag* or *name*::*tag*::*lang* after $NewMessage has been applied. ■ You can set up $NewMessage to read the text of messages from files when they are first needed. ■ A typical value for $NewMessage might be Function[ToExpression[FindList[*files*, ToString[MessageName[#1, #2]]]]]. ■ See page 462. ■ See also: $NewSymbol.

■ **$NewSymbol**

$NewSymbol is a global variable which, if set, is applied to the name and context of each new symbol that *Mathematica* creates.

The name and context of the symbol are given as strings. ■ $NewSymbol is applied before the symbol is actually created. If the action of $NewSymbol causes the symbol to be created, perhaps in a different context, then the symbol as created will be the one used. ■ $NewSymbol is applied even if a symbol has already been created with a Stub attribute by DeclarePackage. ■ $NewSymbol is not applied to symbols automatically created by scoping constructs such as Module. ■ See page 384. ■ See also: DeclarePackage, $NewMessage.

■ **$Notebooks**

$Notebooks is True if *Mathematica* is being used with a notebook-based front end.

$Notebooks is automatically set by the front end when it starts the *Mathematica* kernel. ■ See page 688. ■ See also: $FrontEnd, $Linked, $BatchInput.

+■ **$NumberMarks**

$NumberMarks gives the default value for the option NumberMarks, which specifies whether ` marks should be included in the input form representations of approximate numbers.

The default setting for $NumberMarks is Automatic. ■ $NumberMarks = True indicates that ` should by default be used in all approximate numbers, both machine-precision and arbitrary-precision ones. ■ $NumberMarks = Automatic indicates that ` should by default be used in arbitrary-precision but not machine-precision numbers. ■ $NumberMarks = False indicates that ` should by default never be used in outputting numbers. ■ See page 705. ■ See also: NumberForm, SetPrecision.

■ **$OperatingSystem**

$OperatingSystem is a string giving the type of operating system under which *Mathematica* is being run.

Typical values for $OperatingSystem are MSWindows, MSDOS, MacOS, "Unix" and "VMS". ■ You can use $OperatingSystem to get an idea of what external commands will be available from within *Mathematica*. ■ $OperatingSystem typically has the same value for different versions or variants of a particular operating system. ■ See page 690. ■ See also: $MachineType, $System, $ProcessorType.

■ **$Output**

$Output gives the list of files and pipes to which standard output from *Mathematica* is sent.

Output from Print is always given on the $Output channel. ■ See page 678. ■ See also: Streams.

■ $Packages

$Packages gives a list of the contexts corresponding to all packages which have been loaded in your current *Mathematica* session.

$Packages is updated when BeginPackage is executed. ■ $Packages is used by Needs to determine whether a particular package needs to be loaded explicitly. ■ See page 376. ■ See also: Contexts, $ContextPath, DeclarePackage.

+■ $ParentLink

$ParentLink is the *MathLink* LinkObject currently used for input and output by the *Mathematica* kernel in a particular session.

When the *Mathematica* kernel is started by a *Mathematica* front end, $ParentLink gives the *MathLink* connection between the front end and the kernel. ■ You can reset $ParentLink in the middle of a *Mathematica* session to connect the kernel to a different front end. ■ See page 659. ■ See also: $CurrentLink, Links, $Input.

+■ $ParentProcessID

$ParentProcessID gives the ID assigned to the process which invokes the *Mathematica* kernel by the operating system under which it is run.

On operating systems where no process ID is assigned, $ParentProcessID is None. ■ See page 689. ■ See also: $ParentLink, $ProcessID, $CommandLine, $UserName, Environment.

■ $Path

$Path gives a list of directories to search in attempting to find an external file.

The structure of directory and file names may differ from one computer system to another. +■ $Path is used both for files in Get and for external programs in Install. ■ The directory names are specified by strings. The full file names tested are of the form ToFileName[*directory*,*name*]. ■ On most computer systems, the following special characters can be used in directory names:

.   the current directory
..   the directory one level up in the hierarchy
~   the user's home directory

+■ $Path can contain nested sublists. ■ See page 612. ■ See also: Directory, SetDirectory, Get, DirectoryName, $Input.

■ $Post

$Post is a global variable whose value, if set, is applied to every output expression.

See page 676. ■ See also: $Pre, $PrePrint.

■ $Pre

$Pre is a global variable whose value, if set, is applied to every input expression.

Unless $Pre is assigned to be a function which holds its arguments unevaluated, input expressions will be evaluated before $Pre is applied, so the effect of $Pre will be the same as $Post. ■ $Pre is applied to expressions, while $PreRead is applied to strings which have not yet been parsed into expressions. ■ See page 676. ■ See also: $Post.

■ $PrePrint

$PrePrint is a global variable whose value, if set, is applied to every expression before it is printed.

$PrePrint is applied after Out[n] is assigned, but before the output result is printed. ■ See page 676. ■ See also: $Post, $MessagePrePrint.

■ $PreRead

$PreRead is a global variable whose value, if set, is applied to the text or box form of every input expression before it is fed to *Mathematica*.

$PreRead is always applied to each complete input string that will be fed to *Mathematica*. ■ In multiline input with a text-based interface, $PreRead is typically applied to the input so far whenever each line is terminated. ■ $PreRead is applied to all strings returned by a $SyntaxHandler function. ■ $PreRead is applied before InString[n] is assigned. ■ See page 676. ■ See also: StringReplace, ToExpression.

+■ $ProcessID

$ProcessID gives the ID assigned to the *Mathematica* kernel process by the operating system under which it is run.

On operating systems where no process ID is assigned, $ProcessID is None. ■ See page 689. ■ See also: $ParentProcessID, $UserName, Environment, $SessionID.

+■ $ProcessorType

$ProcessorType is a string giving the architecture of processor on which *Mathematica* is being run.

Typical values are "x86", "680x0", "SPARC", "MIPS", "PA-RISC" and "AXP". ■ $ProcessorType specifies the basic instruction set used by the CPU of your computer. ■ Computers with the same $ProcessorType may not be binary compatible. ■ See page 690. ■ See also: $MachineType, $OperatingSystem, $System.

+■ $RandomState

$RandomState gives a representation of the internal state of the pseudorandom generator used by Random.

The value of $RandomState changes every time Random is called. ■ You can use s = $RandomState to explicitly save the value of $RandomState, and $RandomState = s to restore. ■ The value of $RandomState is always a long integer chosen from a certain large set of possibilities. You can assign $RandomState only to values in this set. ■ You can use Block[{$RandomState}, *expr*] to localize the value of $RandomState during the evaluation of *expr*. ■ See page 720. ■ See also: SeedRandom.

■ $RecursionLimit

$RecursionLimit gives the current limit on the number of levels of recursion that *Mathematica* can use.

$RecursionLimit=*n* sets the limit on the number of recursion levels that *Mathematica* can use to be *n*. ■ $RecursionLimit=Infinity removes any limit on the number of recursion levels. ■ $RecursionLimit gives the maximum length of the stack returned by Stack[ ]. ■ Each time the evaluation of a function requires the nested evaluation of the same or another function, one recursion level is used up. ■ On most computers, each level of recursion uses a certain amount of stack space. $RecursionLimit allows you to control the amount of stack space that *Mathematica* can use from within *Mathematica*. On some computer systems, your whole *Mathematica* session may crash if you allow it to use more stack space than the computer system allows. ■ MemoryInUse and related functions do not count stack space. ■ See page 348. ■ See also: $IterationLimit, MemoryConstrained.

■ $ReleaseNumber

$ReleaseNumber is an integer which gives the current *Mathematica* kernel release number, and increases in successive releases.

Each released revision of the *Mathematica* kernel for any particular computer system is assigned a new release number. ■ The same source code may yield releases with different numbers on different computer systems. ■ See page 690. ■ See also: $VersionNumber.

■ $SessionID

$SessionID is a number set up to be unique to a particular *Mathematica* session.

$SessionID should be different for different *Mathematica* sessions run either on the same computer or on different computers. ■ The value of $SessionID is based on $MachineID, as well as AbsoluteTime[ ] and operating system parameters such as the *Mathematica* process ID. ■ See pages 363 and 689. ■ See also: $ModuleNumber, $ProcessID.

■ $SoundDisplayFunction

$SoundDisplayFunction gives the default setting for the option DisplayFunction in sound functions.

The initial setting of $SoundDisplayFunction is Display[$SoundDisplay, #]&. ■ See page 546. ■ See also: Play, ListPlay, Show, $DisplayFunction.

■ $SyntaxHandler

$SyntaxHandler is a global variable which, if set, is applied to any input string that is found to contain a syntax error.

The arguments given to $SyntaxHandler are the complete input string and an integer specifying the character position at which the syntax error was detected. ■ The first character in the string is taken to have position 1. ■ Any string returned by $SyntaxHandler is used as a new version of the input string, and is fed to *Mathematica*. If the string does not end with a newline, *Mathematica* waits for input to complete the line. ■ If $SyntaxHandler returns $Failed, input to *Mathematica* is abandoned if possible. ■ Input is not assigned to InString[*n*] until after $SyntaxHandler is applied. ■ $SyntaxHandler is not called for input from files obtained using Get. ■ See page 676. ■ See also: SyntaxLength, SyntaxQ.

■ **$System**

> $System is a string describing the type of computer system on which *Mathematica* is being run.

$System typically consists of words separated by spaces. ▪ Typical values are "Microsoft Windows", "Macintosh", "SPARC" and "Silicon Graphics". ▪ $SystemID provides a more succinct version of the same information. ▪ See page 690. ▪ See also: $SystemID, $Version, $MachineType, $ProcessorType, $OperatingSystem.

+■ **$SystemCharacterEncoding**

> $SystemCharacterEncoding gives the default raw character encoding for the computer system on which *Mathematica* is being run.

$SystemCharacterEncoding is used to determine the default value of $CharacterEncoding. ▪ The notebook front end handles raw character encodings independent of the kernel. ▪ The possible settings for $SystemCharacterEncoding are the same as for $CharacterEncoding. ▪ See page 399. ▪ See also: CharacterEncoding.

+■ **$SystemID**

> $SystemID is a short string that identifies the type of computer system on which *Mathematica* is being run.

Computer systems with the same $SystemID should be binary compatible, so that the same external programs and .mx files can be used. ▪ Sometimes binary compatibility may only be complete when the same version of the operating system is used. ▪ $SystemID is used in naming directories generated by DumpSave and mcc. ▪ Values for $SystemID contain only alphanumeric characters and dashes. ▪ Typical values are "Windows", "Mac", "SPARC" and "SGI". ▪ See page 690. ▪ See also: $System, $Version, $MachineType, $OperatingSystem.

+■ **$TextStyle**

> $TextStyle gives the default style to use for text in graphics.

The following forms of settings can be used:

"*style*"	a specific cell style
{*opt*$_1$->*val*$_1$, ... }	a list of option settings
{"*style*", *opt*$_1$->*val*$_1$, ... }	a style modified by option settings

▪ The options that can be given are as in StyleForm. ▪ "*style*" settings can only be used when a notebook front end is present. ▪ $TextStyle gives the default value for the TextStyle option in graphics. ▪ See page 535. ▪ See also: $FormatType, TextStyle.

■ **$TimeUnit**

> $TimeUnit gives the minimum time interval in seconds recorded on your computer system.

On many systems $TimeUnit is equal to 1/60. ▪ $TimeUnit determines the minimum granularity of measurement in functions like Timing and Date. ▪ In some functions the actual time granularity may be larger than $TimeUnit. ▪ See page 683.

- ## MLDisownUnicodeString()

  void MLDisownUnicodeString(MLINK *link*, unsigned short **s*, long *n*) disowns memory allocated by MLGetUnicodeString() to store the string *s*.

  See page 652. ▪ See also: MLDisownString.

- ## MLEndPacket()

  int MLEndPacket(MLINK *link*) specifies that a packet expression is complete and is ready to be sent on the specified link.

  MLEndPacket() should be called to indicate the end of any top-level expression, regardless of whether its head is a standard packet. ▪ See pages 662 and 672.

- ## MLError()

  long MLError(MLINK *link*) returns a constant identifying the last error to occur on *link*, or 0 if none has occurred since the previous call to MLClearError().

  You can get a textual description of errors by calling MLErrorMessage(). ▪ Constants corresponding to standard *MathLink* errors are defined in mathlink.h. ▪ See page 669.

- ## MLErrorMessage()

  char *MLErrorMessage(MLINK *link*) returns a character string describing the last error to occur on *link*.

  See page 669.

- ## MLEvaluateString()

  int MLEvaluateString(MLINK *link*, char **string*) sends a string to *Mathematica* for evaluation, and discards any packets sent in response.

  The code for MLEvaluateString() is not included in the *MathLink* library, but is generated automatically by mcc or mprep in processing *MathLink* template files. ▪ MLEvaluateString("Print[\"*string*\"]) will cause *string* to be printed in a *Mathematica* session at the other end of the link. ▪ See pages 637 and 662.

- ## MLFlush()

  int MLFlush(MLINK *link*) flushes out any buffers containing data waiting to be sent on *link*.

  If you call MLNextPacket() or any of the MLGet*() functions, then MLFlush() will be called automatically. ▪ If you call MLReady(), then you need to call MLFlush() first in order to ensure that any necessary outgoing data has been sent. ▪ See page 673. ▪ See also: MLReady.

- ## MLGetArgCount()

  int MLGetArgCount(MLINK *link*, long **n*) finds the number of arguments to a function on *link* and stores the result in *n*.

  See page 667.

- ## MLGetByteString()

  int MLGetByteString(MLINK *link*, unsigned char **s*, long *n*, long *spec*) gets a string of characters from the *MathLink* connection specified by *link*, storing the codes for the characters in *s* and the number of characters in *n*. The code *spec* is used for any character whose *Mathematica* character code is larger than 255.

  MLGetByteString() allocates memory for the array of character codes. You must call MLDisownByteString() to disown this memory. ▪ MLGetByteString() is convenient in situations where no special characters occur. ▪ The character codes used by MLGetByteString() are exactly the ones returned by ToCharacterCode in *Mathematica*. ▪ The array of character codes in MLGetByteString() is not terminated by a null character. ▪ Characters such as newlines are specified by their raw character codes, not by ASCII forms such as \n. ▪ See page 652. ▪ See also: MLGetString, MLGetUnicodeString.

- ## MLGetDouble()

  int MLGetDouble(MLINK *link*, double *x*) gets a floating-point number from the *MathLink* connection specified by *link* and stores it as C type double in *x*.

  MLGetDouble() is normally equivalent to MLGetReal(). ▪ See notes for MLGetReal(). ▪ See page 651. ▪ See also: MLGetFloat.

- ## MLGetFloat()

  int MLGetFloat(MLINK *link*, float *x*) gets a floating-point number from the *MathLink* connection specified by *link* and stores it as C type float in *x*.

  See notes for MLGetReal(). ▪ See page 651.

- ## MLGetFunction()

  int MLGetFunction(MLINK *link*, char **s*, long *n*) gets a function with a symbol as a head from the *MathLink* connection specified by *link*, storing the name of the symbol in *s* and the number of arguments of the function in *n*.

  MLGetFunction() allocates memory for the character string corresponding to the name of the head of the function. You must call MLDisownSymbol() to disown this memory. ▪ External programs should not modify the character string *s*. ▪ MLGetFunction(*link*, &*s*, &*n*) has the same effect as MLGetNext(*link*); MLGetArgCount(*link*, &*n*); MLGetSymbol(*link*, &*s*). ▪ See page 649. ▪ See also: MLGetNext.

- ## MLGetInteger()

  int MLGetInteger(MLINK *link*, int *i*) gets an integer from the *MathLink* connection specified by *link* and stores it in *i*.

  If the data on the link corresponds to a real number, MLGetInteger() will round it to an integer. ▪ If the data on the link corresponds to an integer too large to store in a C int on your computer system, then MLGetInteger() will fail, and return 0. ▪ You can get arbitrary-precision integers by first using IntegerDigits to generate lists of digits, then calling MLGetIntegerList(). ▪ See page 644. ▪ See also: MLGetShortInteger, MLGetLongInteger.

- ## `MLGetIntegerArray()`

  `int MLGetIntegerArray(MLINK` *link*, `int **`*a*, `long **`*dims*, `char ***`*heads*, `long *`*d*`)` gets an array of integers from the *MathLink* connection specified by *link*, storing the array in *a*, its dimensions in *dims* and its depth in *d*.

  The array *a* is laid out in memory like a C array declared as `int a[m][n]....` ∎ *heads* gives a list of character strings corresponding to the names of symbols that appear as heads at each level in the array. ∎ `MLGetIntegerArray()` allocates memory which must be disowned by calling `MLDisownIntegerArray()`. ∎ External programs should not modify the arrays generated by `MLGetIntegerArray()`. ∎ See page 648. ∎ See also: `MLGetIntegerList`.

- ## `MLGetIntegerList()`

  `int MLGetIntegerList(MLINK` *link*, `int **`*a*, `long *`*n*`)` gets a list of integers from the *MathLink* connection specified by *link*, storing the integers in the array *a* and the length of the list in *n*.

  `MLGetIntegerList()` allocates memory for the array of integers. You must call `MLDisownIntegerList()` to disown this memory. ∎ External programs should not modify the array generated by `MLGetIntegerList()`. ∎ See notes for `MLGetInteger()`. ∎ See page 647. ∎ See also: `MLGetIntegerArray`, `MLGetByteString`.

- ## `MLGetLongInteger()`

  `int MLGetLongInteger(MLINK` *link*, `long *`*i*`)` gets an integer from the *MathLink* connection specified by *link* and stores it as a C `long` in *i*.

  See notes for `MLGetInteger()`. ∎ See page 651.

- ## `MLGetNext()`

  `int MLGetNext(MLINK` *link*`)` goes to the next object on *link* and returns its type.

  The following values can be returned:

`MLTKERR`	error
`MLTKINT`	integer
`MLTKFUNC`	composite function
`MLTKREAL`	approximate real number
`MLTKSTR`	character string
`MLTKSYM`	symbol

  ∎ `MLTKINT` and `MLTKREAL` do not necessarily signify numbers that can be stored in C `int` and `double` variables.
  ∎ See page 667. ∎ See also: `MLGetArgCount`.

- ## `MLGetReal()`

  `int MLGetReal(MLINK` *link*, `double *`*x*`)` gets a floating-point number from the *MathLink* connection specified by *link* and stores it in *x*.

  If the data on the link corresponds to an integer, `MLGetReal()` will coerce it to a double before storing it in *x*. ∎ If the data on the link corresponds to a number outside the range that can be stored in a C `double` on your computer system, then `MLGetReal()` will fail, and return 0. ∎ You can get arbitrary-precision real numbers by first using `RealDigits` to generate lists of digits, then calling `MLGetIntegerList()`. ∎ `MLGetReal()` is normally equivalent to `MLGetDouble()`. ∎ See page 644. ∎ See also: `MLGetFloat`, `MLGetDouble`, `MLGetRealList`.

- ## MLGetRealArray()

  int MLGetRealArray(MLINK *link*, double **a*, long ***dims*, char ****heads*, long **d*) gets an array of floating-point numbers from the *MathLink* connection specified by *link*, storing the array in *a*, its dimensions in *dims* and its depth in *d*.

  The array *a* is laid out in memory like a C array declared as int a[m][n].... ▪ *heads* gives a list of character strings corresponding to the names of symbols that appear as heads at each level in the array. ▪ MLGetRealArray() allocates memory which must be disowned by calling MLDisownRealArray(). ▪ External programs should not modify the arrays generated by MLGetRealArray(). ▪ See page 648.

- ## MLGetRealList()

  int MLGetRealList(MLINK *link*, double **a*, long **n*) gets a list of floating-point numbers from the *MathLink* connection specified by *link*, storing the numbers in the array *a* and the length of the list in *n*.

  MLGetRealList() allocates memory for the array of numbers. You must call MLDisownRealList() to disown this memory. ▪ External programs should not modify the array generated by MLGetRealList(). ▪ See notes for MLGetReal(). ▪ See page 647.

- ## MLGetShortInteger()

  int MLGetShortInteger(MLINK *link*, short **i*) gets an integer from the *MathLink* connection specified by *link* and stores it as a C short in *i*.

  See notes for MLGetInteger(). ▪ See page 651.

- ## MLGetString()

  int MLGetString(MLINK *link*, char ***s*) gets a character string from the *MathLink* connection specified by *link*, storing the string in *s*.

  MLGetString() allocates memory for the character string. You must call MLDisownString() to disown this memory. ▪ External programs should not modify strings generated by MLGetString(). ▪ MLGetString() creates a string that is terminated by \0. ▪ MLGetString() stores single \ characters from *Mathematica* as pairs of characters \\. ▪ MLGetString() stores special characters from *Mathematica* in a private format. ▪ See page 652. ▪ See also: MLGetByteString, MLGetUnicodeString.

- ## MLGetSymbol()

  int MLGetSymbol(MLINK *link*, char ***s*) gets a character string corresponding to the name of a symbol from the *MathLink* connection specified by *link*, storing the resulting string in *s*.

  MLGetSymbol() allocates memory for the character string. You must call MLDisownSymbol() to disown this memory. ▪ MLGetSymbol() creates a string that is terminated by \0. ▪ See pages 648 and 667.

- ## MLGetUnicodeString()

  int MLGetUnicodeString(MLINK *link*, unsigned short ***s*, long **n*) gets a character string from the *MathLink* connection specified by *link*, storing the string in *s* as a sequence of 16-bit Unicode characters.

  MLGetUnicodeString() allocates memory for the character string. You must call MLDisownUnicodeString() to disown this memory. ▪ External programs should not modify strings generated by MLGetUnicodeString(). ▪ MLGetUnicodeString() stores all characters directly in 16-bit Unicode form. ▪ 8-bit ASCII characters are stored with a null high-order byte. ▪ See page 652. ▪ See also: MLGetString, MLGetByteString.

- ## `MLInitialize()`

  `MLENV MLInitialize(0)` initializes functions in the *MathLink* library.

  An appropriate call to `MLInitialize()` is generated automatically when an external program is created from *MathLink* templates. ▪ Any external program that uses the *MathLink* library must call `MLInitialize()` before calling any other *MathLink* library functions. ▪ See page 671.

- ## `MLLoopbackOpen()`

  `MLINK MLLoopbackOpen(MLENV env, long *errno)` opens a loopback *MathLink* connection.

  In an external program set up with *MathLink* templates, the environment `stdenv` should be used. ▪ You can use loopback links to effectively store *Mathematica* expressions in external programs. ▪ See page 665. ▪ See also: `MLCreateMark`.

- ## `MLMain()`

  `int MLMain(int argc, char **argv)` sets up communication between an external program started using `Install` and *Mathematica*.

  The code for `MLMain()` is generated automatically by `mprep` or `mcc`. ▪ `MLMain()` opens a *MathLink* connection using the parameters specified in *argv*, then goes into a loop waiting for `CallPacket` objects to arrive from *Mathematica*. ▪ `MLMain()` internally calls `MLOpenArgv()`. ▪ See page 637.

- ## `MLNewPacket()`

  `int MLNewPacket(MLINK link)` skips to the end of the current packet on *link*.

  `MLNewPacket()` works even if the head of the current top-level expression is not a standard packet type. ▪ `MLNewPacket()` does nothing if you are already at the end of a packet. ▪ See pages 670 and 672. ▪ See also: `MLNextPacket`.

- ## `MLNextPacket()`

  `int MLNextPacket(MLINK link)` goes to the next packet on *link* and returns a constant to indicate its head.

  See page 672. ▪ See also: `MLNewPacket`.

- ## `MLOpenArgv()`

  `MLINK MLOpenArgv(MLENV env, char **argv0, char **argv1, long *errno)` opens a *MathLink* connection taking parameters from an `argv` array.

  `MLInitialize()` must be called before `MLOpenArgv()`. ▪ `MLOpenArgv()` scans for the following at successive locations starting at *argv0* and going up to just before *argv1*:

`"-linkconnect"`	connect to an existing link (`LinkConnect`)
`"-linkcreate"`	create a link (`LinkCreate`)
`"-linklaunch"`	launch a child process (`LinkLaunch`)
`"-linkname"`, `"name"`	the name to use in opening the link
`"-linkprotocol"`, `"protocol"`	the link protocol to use (`tcp`, `pipes`, etc.)

  ▪ `MLOpenArgv()` is not sensitive to the case of argument names. ▪ `MLOpenArgv()` ignores argument names that it does not recognize. ▪ `MLOpenArgv()` is called automatically by the `MLMain()` function created by `mprep` and `mcc`. ▪ With a main program `main(int argc, char *argv[])` typical usage is `MLOpenArgv(env, argv, argv+argc, errno)`. ▪ Avoiding an explicit `argc` argument allows `MLOpenArgv()` to work independent of the size of an `int`. ▪ On some computer systems, giving 0 for *argv0* and *argv1* will cause arguments to be requested interactively, typically through a dialog box. ▪ See page 671. ▪ See also: `MLActivate`, `MLOpenString`.

- ## MLOpenString( )

  MLINK MLOpenString(MLENV *env*, char **string*, long **errno*) opens a *MathLink* connection taking parameters from a character string.

  MLInitialize( ) must be called before MLOpenString( ). ▪ MLOpenString( ) takes a single string instead of the *argv* array used by MLOpenArgv( ). ▪ Arguments in the string are separated by spaces. ▪ On some computer systems, giving NULL in place of the string pointer will cause arguments to be requested interactively, typically through a dialog box. ▪ See page 671. ▪ See also: MLActivate, MLOpenArgv.

- ## MLPutArgCount( )

  int MLPutArgCount(MLINK *link*, long *n*) specifies the number of arguments of a composite function to be put on *link*.

- ## MLPutByteString( )

  int MLPutByteString(MLINK *link*, unsigned char **s*, long *n*) puts a string of *n* characters starting from location *s* to the *MathLink* connection specified by *link*.

  All characters in the string must be specified using character codes as obtained from ToCharacterCode in *Mathematica*. ▪ Newlines must thus be specified in terms of their raw character codes, rather than using \n. ▪ MLPutByteString( ) handles only characters with codes less than 256. ▪ It can handle both ordinary ASCII as well as ISO Latin-1 characters. ▪ See page 652. ▪ See also: MLPutString, MLPutIntegerList.

- ## MLPutDouble( )

  int MLPutDouble(MLINK *link*, double *x*) puts the floating-point number *x* of C type double to the *MathLink* connection specified by *link*.

  See notes for MLPutReal( ). ▪ See page 651.

- ## MLPutFloat( )

  int MLPutFloat(MLINK *link*, double *x*) puts the floating-point number *x* to the *MathLink* connection specified by *link* with a precision corresponding to the C type float.

  The argument *x* is typically declared as float in external programs, but must be declared as double in MLPutFloat( ) itself in order to work even in the absence of C prototypes. ▪ See notes for MLPutReal( ). ▪ See page 651.

- ## MLPutFunction( )

  int MLPutFunction(MLINK *link*, char **s*, long *n*) puts a function with head given by a symbol with name *s* and with *n* arguments to the *MathLink* connection specified by *link*.

  After the call to MLPutFunction( ) other *MathLink* functions must be called to send the arguments of the function. ▪ See page 640. ▪ See also: MLPutString.

- ## MLPutInteger( )

  int MLPutInteger(MLINK *link*, int *i*) puts the integer *i* to the *MathLink* connection specified by *link*.

  You can send arbitrary-precision integers to *Mathematica* by giving lists of digits, then converting them to numbers using FromDigits. ▪ See pages 640 and 669. ▪ See also: MLGetInteger, MLPutShortInteger, MLPutLongInteger, MLPutIntegerList.

- ## `MLPutIntegerArray()`

  `int MLPutIntegerArray(MLINK` *link*`, int *`*a*`, long *`*dims*`, char **`*heads*`, long` *d*`)` puts an array of integers to the *MathLink* connection specified by *link* to form a depth *d* array with dimensions *dims*.

  The array *a* must be laid out in memory like a C array declared explicitly as `int a[m][n]`.... ▪ If *heads* is given as NULL, the array will be assumed to have head List at every level. ▪ The length of the array at level *i* is taken to be `dims[i]`. ▪ See page 640. ▪ See also: `MLPutIntegerList`.

- ## `MLPutIntegerList()`

  `int MLPutIntegerList(MLINK` *link*`, int *`*a*`, long` *n*`)` puts a list of *n* integers starting from location *a* to the *MathLink* connection specified by *link*.

  See page 640. ▪ See also: `MLPutIntegerArray`, `MLPutByteString`.

- ## `MLPutLongInteger()`

  `int MLPutLongInteger(MLINK` *link*`, long` *i*`)` puts the long integer *i* to the *MathLink* connection specified by *link*.

  See notes for `MLPutInteger()`. ▪ See page 651.

- ## `MLPutNext()`

  `int MLPutNext(MLINK` *link*`, int` *type*`)` prepares to put an object of the specified type on *link*.

  The type specifications are as given in the notes for `MLGetNext()`. ▪ See page 669. ▪ See also: `MLPutArgCount`.

- ## `MLPutReal()`

  `int MLPutReal(MLINK` *link*`, double` *x*`)` puts the floating-point number *x* to the *MathLink* connection specified by *link*.

  You can send arbitrary-precision real numbers to *Mathematica* by giving lists of digits, then converting them to numbers using `FromDigits`. ▪ `MLPutReal()` is normally equivalent to `MLPutDouble()`. ▪ See pages 640 and 669. ▪ See also: `MLPutRealList`, `MLPutFloat`, `MLPutDouble`.

- ## `MLPutRealArray()`

  `int MLPutRealArray(MLINK` *link*`, double *`*a*`, long *`*dims*`, char **`*heads*`, long` *d*`)` puts an array of floating-point numbers to the *MathLink* connection specified by *link* to form a depth *d* array with dimensions *dims*.

  The array *a* must be laid out in memory like a C array declared explicitly as `double a[m][n]`.... ▪ If *heads* is given as NULL, the array will be assumed to have head List at every level. ▪ The length of the array at level *i* is taken to be `dims[i]`. ▪ See page 640. ▪ See also: `MLPutRealList`.

- ## `MLPutRealList()`

  `int MLPutRealList(MLINK` *link*`, double *`*a*`, long` *n*`)` puts a list of *n* floating-point numbers starting from location *a* to the *MathLink* connection specified by *link*.

  See page 640. ▪ See also: `MLPutRealArray`.

- ## MLPutShortInteger()

    int MLPutShortInteger(MLINK *link*, int *i*) puts the integer *i* to the *MathLink* connection specified by *link*, assuming that *i* contains only the number of digits in the C type short.

    The argument *i* is typically declared as short in external programs, but must be declared as int in MLPutShortInteger() itself in order to work even in the absence of C prototypes. ▪ See notes for MLPutInteger(). ▪ See page 651.

- ## MLPutString()

    int MLPutString(MLINK *link*, char *s*) puts a character string to the *MathLink* connection specified by *link*.

    The character string must be terminated with a null byte, corresponding to \0 in C. ▪ A raw backslash in the string must be sent as two characters \\. ▪ Special characters can be sent only using the private format returned by MLGetString(). ▪ See page 652. ▪ See also: MLPutByteString, MLPutUnicodeString, MLPutSymbol.

- ## MLPutSymbol()

    int MLPutSymbol(MLINK *link*, char *s*) puts a symbol whose name is given by the character string *s* to the *MathLink* connection specified by *link*.

    The character string must be terminated with \0. ▪ See pages 640 and 669. ▪ See also: MLPutString.

- ## MLPutUnicodeString()

    int MLPutUnicodeString(MLINK *link*, unsigned short *s*, long *n*) puts a string of *n* 16-bit Unicode characters to the *MathLink* connection specified by *link*.

    All characters are assumed to be 16 bit. ▪ 8-bit characters can be sent by having the higher-order byte be null. ▪ See page 652. ▪ See also: MLPutString, MLPutByteString.

- ## MLReady()

    int MLReady(MLINK *link*) tests whether there is data ready to be read from *link*.

    Analogous to the *Mathematica* function LinkReadyQ. ▪ MLReady() is often called in a loop as a way of polling a *MathLink* connection. ▪ MLReady() will always return immediately, and will not block. ▪ You need to call MLFlush() before starting to call MLReady(). ▪ See page 673.

- ## MLSeekMark()

    int MLSeekMark(MLINK *link*, MLMARK *mark*, long *n*) goes back to a position *n* expressions after the specified mark on a link.

    See page 666.

- ## MLTransferExpression()

    int MLTransferExpression(MLINK *dest*, MLINK *src*) transfers an expression from one *MathLink* connection to another.

    src and *dest* need not be distinct. ▪ *src* and *dest* can be either loopback or ordinary links. ▪ See page 665.

A.12 Listing of Named Characters

■ Introduction

This section gives a list of all characters that are assigned full names in *Mathematica* Version 3.0. The list is ordered alphabetically by full name.

The standard *Mathematica* fonts support all of the characters in the list.

There are a total of 702 characters in the list.

⦂aaa⦂ stands for ESC*aaa*ESC.

Interpretation of Characters

The interpretations given here are those used in `StandardForm` and `InputForm`. Most of the interpretations also work in `TraditionalForm`.

You can override the interpretations by giving your own rules for `MakeExpression`.

Letters and letter-like forms	used in symbol names
Infix operators	e.g. $x \oplus y$
Prefix operators	e.g. $\neg x$
Postfix operators	e.g. $x!$
Matchfix operators	e.g. $\langle x \rangle$
Compound operators	e.g. $\int f \, d x$
Raw operators	operator characters that can be typed on an ordinary keyboard
Spacing characters	interpreted in the same way as an ordinary space
Structural elements	characters used to specify structure; usually ignored in interpretation
Uninterpretable elements	characters indicating missing information

Types of characters.

The precedences of operators are given on pages 972–977.

Infix operators for which no grouping is specified in the listing are interpreted so that for example $x \oplus y \oplus z$ becomes `CirclePlus[x, y, z]`.

Naming Conventions

Characters that correspond to built-in *Mathematica* functions typically have names corresponding to those functions. Other characters typically have names that are as generic as possible.

Characters with different names almost always look at least slightly different.

`\[Capital...]`	upper-case form of a letter
`\[Left...]` and `\[Right...]`	pieces of a matchfix operator (also arrows)
`\[Raw...]`	a printable ASCII character
`\[...Indicator]`	a visual representation of a keyboard character

Some special classes of characters.

style	`Script, Gothic`, etc.
variation	`Curly, Gray`, etc.
case	`Capital`, etc.
modifiers	`Not, Double, Nested`, etc.
direction	`Left, Up, UpperRight`, etc.
base	`A, Epsilon, Plus`, etc.
diacritical mark	`Acute, Ring`, etc.

Typical ordering of elements in character names.

Aliases

Mathematica supports both its own system of aliases, as well as aliases based on character names in TeX and SGML or HTML. Except where they conflict, character names corresponding to plain TeX, LaTeX and AMSTeX are all supported. Note that TeX and SGML or HTML aliases are not given explicitly in the list of characters below.

⫶*xxx*⫶	ordinary *Mathematica* alias
⫶*xxx*⫶	T_EX alias
⫶&*xxx*⫶	SGML or HTML alias

Types of aliases.

The following general conventions are used for all aliases:

- Characters that are alternatives to standard keyboard operators use these operators as their aliases (e.g. ⫶->⫶ for →, ⫶&&⫶ for ∧).

- Most single-letter aliases stand for Greek letters.

- Capital-letter characters have aliases beginning with capital letters.

- When there is ambiguity in the assignment of aliases, a space is inserted at the beginning of the alias for the less common character (e.g. ⫶->⫶ for \[Rule] and ⫶ ->⫶ for \[RightArrow]).

- ! is inserted at the beginning of the alias for a Not character.

- T_EX aliases begin with a backslash \.

- SGML aliases begin with an ampersand &.

- User-defined aliases conventionally begin with a dot or comma.

Font Matching

The special fonts provided with *Mathematica* include all the characters given in this listing. Some of these characters also appear in certain ordinary text fonts.

When rendering text in a particular font, the *Mathematica* notebook front end will use all the characters available in that font. It will use the special *Mathematica* fonts only for other characters.

A choice is made between Times-like, Helvetica-like (sans serif) and Courier-like (monospaced) variants to achieve the best matching with the ordinary text font in use.

á   \[AAcute]

  Alias: ⦂a'⦂. ▪ Included in ISO Latin-1. ▪ See page 918. ▪ See also: \[CapitalAAcute].

ā   \[ABar]

  Alias: ⦂a-⦂. ▪ Letter. ▪ Included in ISO Latin-4. ▪ Used in transliterations of various non-Latin alphabets. ▪ See page 918. ▪ See also: \[CapitalABar].

ă   \[ACup]

  Alias: ⦂au⦂. ▪ Letter. ▪ Included in ISO Latin-2. ▪ Used in transliterations of Cyrillic characters. ▪ See page 918. ▪ See also: \[CapitalACup].

ä   \[ADoubleDot]

  Alias: ⦂a"⦂. ▪ Letter. ▪ Included in ISO Latin-1. ▪ See pages 188 and 918. ▪ See also: \[CapitalADoubleDot], \[EDoubleDot].

æ   \[AE]

  Alias: ⦂ae⦂. ▪ Letter. ▪ Included in ISO Latin-1. ▪ See page 918. ▪ See also: \[CapitalAE].

à   \[AGrave]

  Alias: ⦂a`⦂. ▪ Letter. ▪ Included in ISO Latin-1. ▪ See pages 188 and 918. ▪ See also: \[CapitalAGrave].

â   \[AHat]

  Alias: ⦂a^⦂. ▪ Letter. ▪ Included in ISO Latin-1. ▪ See page 918. ▪ See also: \[CapitalAHat].

ℵ   \[Aleph]

  Alias: ⦂al⦂. ▪ Hebrew letter. ▪ Sometimes called alef. ▪ Used in pure mathematics to denote transfinite cardinals. ▪ See pages 190 and 913. ▪ See also: \[Bet], \[Gimel], \[Dalet].

⦂   \[AliasIndicator]

  Alias: ⦂esc⦂. ▪ Letter-like form. ▪ Representation of the indicator for special character aliases in *Mathematica*. ▪ \[AliasIndicator] is an inactive letter-like form, used in describing how to type aliases. ▪ An active character of the same appearance is typically obtained by typing ESCAPE. ▪ See page 929. ▪ See also: \[EscapeKey], \[SpaceIndicator], \[ReturnIndicator].

\[AlignmentMarker]

  Alias: ⦂am⦂. ▪ Letter-like form. ▪ Invisible by default on display. ▪ Used as a marker to indicate for example how entries in a GridBox column should be lined up. ▪ See page 928. ▪ See also: \[InvisibleComma], \[InvisibleSpace], \[Null], \[NoBreak].

α   \[Alpha]

  Aliases: ⦂a⦂, ⦂alpha⦂. ▪ Greek letter. ▪ Not the same as \[Proportional]. ▪ See pages 174 and 910. ▪ See also: \[CapitalAlpha].

∧   \[And]

  Aliases: ⦂&&⦂, ⦂and⦂. ▪ Infix operator with built-in evaluation rules. ▪ $x \wedge y$ is by default interpreted as And[x, y], equivalent to x && y. ▪ Not the same as \[Wedge]. ▪ Drawn slightly larger than \[Wedge]. ▪ See page 921. ▪ See also: \[Or], \[Not].

∟   \[Angle]

  Letter-like form. ▪ Used in geometry to indicate an angle, as in the symbol ∟ ABC. ▪ See pages 190 and 916. ▪ See also: \[MeasuredAngle], \[SphericalAngle], \[RightAngle].

Õ   \[CapitalOTilde]

     Alias: ⦂O~⦂. ▪ Letter. ▪ Included in ISO Latin-1. ▪ See page 918. ▪ See also: \[OTilde].

Φ   \[CapitalPhi]

     Aliases: ⦂Ph⦂, ⦂Phi⦂, ⦂F⦂. ▪ Greek letter. ▪ Used in `TraditionalForm` for LerchPhi. ▪ See pages 174 and 910. ▪ See also: \[Phi].

Π   \[CapitalPi]

     Aliases: ⦂P⦂, ⦂Pi⦂. ▪ Greek letter. ▪ Used in `TraditionalForm` for EllipticPi. ▪ Not the same as \[Product]. ▪ See pages 174 and 910. ▪ See also: \[Pi].

Ψ   \[CapitalPsi]

     Aliases: ⦂Ps⦂, ⦂Psi⦂, ⦂Y⦂. ▪ Greek letter. ▪ See pages 174 and 910. ▪ See also: \[Psi].

Ρ   \[CapitalRho]

     Aliases: ⦂R⦂, ⦂Rho⦂. ▪ Greek letter. ▪ Not the same as English P. ▪ See page 910. ▪ See also: \[Rho].

Ϡ   \[CapitalSampi]

     Aliases: ⦂Sa⦂, ⦂Sampi⦂. ▪ Special Greek letter. ▪ See page 910. ▪ See also: \[Sampi].

Š   \[CapitalSHacek]

     Alias: ⦂Sv⦂. ▪ Letter. ▪ Included in ISO Latin-2. ▪ See page 918. ▪ See also: \[SHacek].

Σ   \[CapitalSigma]

     Aliases: ⦂S⦂, ⦂Sigma⦂. ▪ Greek letter. ▪ Not the same as \[Sum]. ▪ See pages 174 and 910. ▪ See also: \[Sigma].

Ϛ   \[CapitalStigma]

     Aliases: ⦂Sti⦂, ⦂Stigma⦂. ▪ Special Greek letter. ▪ See page 910. ▪ See also: \[Stigma].

Τ   \[CapitalTau]

     Aliases: ⦂T⦂, ⦂Tau⦂. ▪ Greek letter. ▪ Not the same as English T. ▪ See page 910. ▪ See also: \[Tau].

Θ   \[CapitalTheta]

     Aliases: ⦂Th⦂, ⦂Theta⦂, ⦂Q⦂. ▪ Greek letter. ▪ See pages 174 and 910. ▪ See also: \[Theta].

Þ   \[CapitalThorn]

     Alias: ⦂Thn⦂. ▪ Letter. ▪ Included in ISO Latin-1. ▪ See page 918. ▪ See also: \[Thorn].

Ú   \[CapitalUAcute]

     Alias: ⦂U'⦂. ▪ Letter. ▪ Included in ISO Latin-1. ▪ See page 918. ▪ See also: \[UAcute].

Ű   \[CapitalUDoubleAcute]

     Alias: ⦂U''⦂. ▪ Letter. ▪ Included in ISO Latin-2. ▪ See page 918. ▪ See also: \[UDoubleAcute].

Ü   \[CapitalUDoubleDot]

     Alias: ⦂U"⦂. ▪ Letter. ▪ Included in ISO Latin-1. ▪ See pages 188 and 918. ▪ See also: \[UDoubleDot].

Ù   \[CapitalUGrave]

     Alias: ⦂U`⦂. ▪ Letter. ▪ Included in ISO Latin-1. ▪ See page 918. ▪ See also: \[UGrave].

Û   \[CapitalUHat]

     Alias: ⦂U^⦂. ▪ Letter. ▪ Included in ISO Latin-1. ▪ See page 918. ▪ See also: \[UHat].

ϒ   \[CapitalUpsilon]

Aliases: ⦂U⦂, ⦂Upsilon⦂. ▪ Greek letter. ▪ Not commonly used. ▪ Used in physics for $b\bar{b}$ particles, and in the quantum theory of measurement. ▪ See pages 174 and 910. ▪ See also: \[CurlyCapitalUpsilon], \[Upsilon].

Ξ   \[CapitalXi]

Aliases: ⦂X⦂, ⦂Xi⦂. ▪ Greek letter. ▪ Not commonly used. ▪ Used for grand canonical partition function, cascade hyperon and regular language complexity. ▪ See page 910. ▪ See also: \[Xi].

Ý   \[CapitalYAcute]

Alias: ⦂Y'⦂. ▪ Letter. ▪ Included in ISO Latin-1. ▪ See page 918. ▪ See also: \[YAcute].

Z   \[CapitalZeta]

Aliases: ⦂Z⦂, ⦂Zeta⦂. ▪ Greek letter. ▪ Used in TraditionalForm for JacobiZeta. ▪ Not the same as English Z. ▪ See page 910. ▪ See also: \[Zeta].

ç   \[CCedilla]

Alias: ⦂c,⦂. ▪ Letter. ▪ Included in ISO Latin-1. ▪ See pages 188 and 918. ▪ See also: \[CapitalCCedilla].

¸   \[Cedilla]

Alias: ⦂cd⦂. ▪ Letter-like form. ▪ Used in an underscript position as a diacritical mark. ▪ See page 919. ▪ See also: \[Hacek], \[Breve].

¢   \[Cent]

Alias: ⦂cent⦂. ▪ Letter-like form. ▪ Currency symbol, used as in 5¢. ▪ See page 914.

·   \[CenterDot]

Alias: ⦂.⦂. ▪ Infix operator. ▪ $x \cdot y$ is by default interpreted as CenterDot[x, y]. ▪ Used to indicate various forms of multiplication, particularly dot products of vectors. ▪ Sometimes used to indicate concatenation or composition. ▪ Used in the British mathematical tradition as a decimal point. ▪ See page 922. ▪ See also: \[CenterEllipsis], \[RawDot], \[CircleDot].

⋯   \[CenterEllipsis]

Letter-like form. ▪ Used to indicate omitted elements in a row of a matrix. ▪ See page 917. ▪ See also: \[Ellipsis], \[VerticalEllipsis], \[CenterDot].

č   \[CHacek]

Alias: ⦂cv⦂. ▪ Letter. ▪ Included in ISO Latin-2. ▪ See pages 188 and 918. ▪ See also: \[CapitalCHacek], \[SHacek].

χ   \[Chi]

Aliases: ⦂ch⦂, ⦂chi⦂, ⦂c⦂. ▪ Greek letter. ▪ See pages 174 and 910. ▪ See also: \[CapitalChi], \[Xi].

⊙   \[CircleDot]

Alias: ⦂c.⦂. ▪ Infix operator. ▪ $x \odot y$ is by default interpreted as CircleDot[x, y]. ▪ Used in mathematics for various operations related to multiplication, such as direct or tensor products. ▪ Also sometimes used to indicate a vector pointing out of the page. ▪ See page 922. ▪ See also: \[CircleTimes], \[CenterDot].

⊖   \[CircleMinus]

Alias: ⦂c-⦂. ▪ Infix operator. ▪ $x \ominus y$ is by default interpreted as CircleMinus[x, y]. ▪ See page 922. ▪ See also: \[CirclePlus].

⊕　\[CirclePlus]

Alias: ⦂c+⦂. ■ Infix operator. ■ $x \oplus y$ is by default interpreted as CirclePlus[x, y]. ■ Used in mathematics for various operations related to addition, such as direct sum and addition modulo two. ■ Also sometimes used to indicate a vector pointing into the page. ■ See pages 189 and 922. ■ See also: \[CircleTimes], \[CircleMinus].

⊗　\[CircleTimes]

Alias: ⦂c*⦂. ■ Infix and prefix operator. ■ $x \otimes y$ is by default interpreted as CircleTimes[x, y]. ■ Used in mathematics for various operations related to multiplication, such as direct or tensor products. ■ Also sometimes used to indicate a vector pointing into the page. ■ See pages 189 and 922. ■ See also: \[CircleDot], \[Times], \[Cross], \[Wedge], \[CirclePlus].

∮　\[ClockwiseContourIntegral]

Alias: ⦂ccint⦂. ■ Compound operator (see page 979). ■ $\oint f \, dx$ is by default interpreted as ClockwiseContourIntegral[f, x]. ■ See page 920. ■ See also: \[CounterClockwiseContourIntegral], \[ContourIntegral].

⌘　\[CloverLeaf]

Alias: ⦂cl⦂. ■ Letter-like form. ■ Used on Macintosh and other computers to indicate command keys. ■ See page 929. ■ See also: \[CommandKey].

♣　\[ClubSuit]

Letter-like form. ■ See page 916. ■ See also: \[DiamondSuit], \[HeartSuit], \[SpadeSuit].

:　\[Colon]

Alias: ⦂:⦂. ■ Infix operator. ■ $x : y$ is by default interpreted as Colon[x, y]. ■ Used in mathematics to mean "such that". ■ Occasionally used to indicate proportion. ■ Used to separate hours and minutes in times. ■ See page 921. ■ See also: \[SuchThat], \[VerticalSeparator], \[Exists], \[ForAll], \[RawColon], \[Proportion], \[Therefore].

CMD　\[CommandKey]

Alias: ⦂cmd⦂. ■ Letter-like form. ■ Representation of the COMMAND or ALT key on a keyboard. ■ See page 929. ■ See also: \[CloverLeaf], \[LeftModified], \[ControlKey], \[EscapeKey].

≡　\[Congruent]

Alias: ⦂===⦂. ■ Infix similarity operator. ■ $x \equiv y$ is by default interpreted as Congruent[x, y]. ■ Used in mathematics for many notions of equivalence and equality. ■ See pages 189 and 923. ■ See also: \[NotCongruent], \[Equal], \[TildeFullEqual], \[CupCap], \[LeftRightArrow].

∵　\[Continuation]

Alias: ⦂cont⦂. ■ Structural element. ■ Used at the end of a line of input to indicate that the expression on that line continues onto the next line. ■ Equivalent in meaning to \ at the end of a line. ■ Not the same as \[DescendingEllipsis]. ■ See page 929. ■ See also: \[RawBackslash], \[Backslash], \[ReturnIndicator].

∮　\[ContourIntegral]

Alias: ⦂cint⦂. ■ Compound operator (see page 979). ■ $\oint f \, dx$ is by default interpreted as ContourIntegral[f, x]. ■ See page 920. ■ See also: \[ClockwiseContourIntegral], \[DoubleContourIntegral].

CTRL　\[ControlKey]

Alias: ⦂ctrl⦂. ■ Letter-like form. ■ Representation of the CONTROL key on a keyboard. ■ See page 929. ■ See also: \[LeftModified], \[CommandKey], \[EscapeKey], \[ReturnKey].

Ⅱ   **\[Coproduct]**

Alias: ┊coprod┊. ▪ Infix operator. ▪ x Ⅱ y is by default interpreted as Coproduct[x, y]. ▪ Ⅱ x is by default interpreted as Coproduct[x]. ▪ Coproduct is used as an abstract dual to the operation of multiplication, most often in infix form. ▪ See page 922. ▪ See also: \[Product], \[Wedge], \[Vee], \[CircleTimes], \[SquareUnion].

©   **\[Copyright]**

Letter-like form. ▪ See page 916. ▪ See also: \[RegisteredTrademark].

∮   **\[CounterClockwiseContourIntegral]**

Alias: ┊cccint┊. ▪ Compound operator (see page 979). ▪ $\oint f\,\mathrm{d}x$ is by default interpreted as CounterClockwiseContourIntegral[f, x]. ▪ See page 920. ▪ See also: \[ClockwiseContourIntegral], \[ContourIntegral].

×   **\[Cross]**

Alias: ┊cross┊. ▪ Infix operator with built-in evaluation rules. ▪ x × y is by default interpreted as Cross[x, y]. ▪ Not the same as \[Times]. ▪ \[Cross] represents vector cross product, while \[Times] represents ordinary multiplication. ▪ \[Cross] is drawn smaller than \[Times]. ▪ See page 920. ▪ See also: \[CircleTimes].

⌣   **\[Cup]**

Infix operator. ▪ x ⌣ y is by default interpreted as Cup[x, y]. ▪ Used in pure mathematics to mean cup product. ▪ See page 922. ▪ See also: \[Cap], \[Union], \[CupCap], \[RoundSpaceIndicator], \[Breve].

≍   **\[CupCap]**

Infix similarity operator. ▪ x ≍ y is by default interpreted as CupCap[x, y]. ▪ Used in mathematics for various notions of equivalence, usually fairly weak. ▪ $f ≍ g$ is often specifically used to indicate that f/g has bounded variation. ▪ See page 923. ▪ See also: \[NotCupCap], \[Cap], \[Cup].

Υ   **\[CurlyCapitalUpsilon]**

Aliases: ┊cU┊, ┊cUpsilon┊. ▪ Greek letter. ▪ Not commonly used. ▪ Used in astronomy for mass to light ratio. ▪ See page 910. ▪ See also: \[CapitalUpsilon].

ε   **\[CurlyEpsilon]**

Aliases: ┊ce┊, ┊cepsilon┊. ▪ Greek letter. ▪ Not the same as \[Element]. ▪ Used in physics for Fermi energy and dielectric constant. ▪ See page 910. ▪ See also: \[Epsilon], \[ScriptCapitalE].

χ   **\[CurlyKappa]**

Aliases: ┊ck┊, ┊ckappa┊. ▪ Greek letter. ▪ See page 910. ▪ See also: \[Kappa].

φ   **\[CurlyPhi]**

Aliases: ┊j┊, ┊cph┊, ┊cphi┊. ▪ Greek letter. ▪ Commonly used as a variant of ϕ. ▪ See pages 174 and 910. ▪ See also: \[Phi].

ϖ   **\[CurlyPi]**

Aliases: ┊cp┊, ┊cpi┊. ▪ Greek letter. ▪ Not commonly used, except in astronomy. ▪ See page 910. ▪ See also: \[Pi], \[Omega].

ϱ   **\[CurlyRho]**

Aliases: ┊cr┊, ┊crho┊. ▪ Greek letter. ▪ See page 910. ▪ See also: \[Rho].

ϑ   **\[CurlyTheta]**

Aliases: ┊cq┊, ┊cth┊, ┊ctheta┊. ▪ Greek letter. ▪ Used in TraditionalForm for EllipticTheta and RiemannSiegelTheta. ▪ See page 910. ▪ See also: \[CapitalTheta], \[Theta].

† \[Dagger]

Alias: ¦dg¦. ▪ Letter-like form and overfix operator. ▪ $x^\dagger$ is by default interpreted as SuperDagger[x]. ▪ See pages 190 and 916. ▪ See also: \[DoubleDagger].

ℸ \[Dalet]

Alias: ¦da¦. ▪ Hebrew letter. ▪ Sometimes called daleth. ▪ Used occasionally in pure mathematics in the theory of transfinite cardinals. ▪ See page 913. ▪ See also: \[Aleph].

− \[Dash]

Alias: ¦-¦. ▪ Letter-like form. ▪ See page 916. ▪ See also: \[LongDash], \[HorizontalLine].

° \[Degree]

Alias: ¦deg¦. ▪ Letter-like form with built-in value. ▪ Interpreted by default as the symbol Degree. ▪ 30° is interpreted as 30 Degree. ▪ The symbol ° is sometimes used in mathematics to indicate the interior of a set. ▪ Not the same as \[SmallCircle] or \[EmptySmallCircle]. ▪ See page 914. ▪ See also: \[Prime], \[DoublePrime].

∇ \[Del]

Alias: ¦del¦. ▪ Prefix operator. ▪ ∇f is by default interpreted as Del[f]. ▪ Used in vector analysis to denote gradient operator and its generalizations. ▪ Used in numerical analysis to denote backward difference operator. ▪ Also called nabla. ▪ Not the same as \[EmptyDownTriangle]. ▪ See pages 914 and 920. ▪ See also: \[CapitalDelta], \[PartialD], \[Square].

δ \[Delta]

Aliases: ¦d¦, ¦delta¦. ▪ Greek letter. ▪ See pages 174 and 910. ▪ See also: \[PartialD], \[Del], \[CapitalDelta].

⋰ \[DescendingEllipsis]

Letter-like form. ▪ Used to indicate omitted elements in a matrix. ▪ Not the same as \[Continuation]. ▪ See page 917. ▪ See also: \[AscendingEllipsis], \[VerticalEllipsis], \[Ellipsis].

∅ \[Diameter]

Letter-like form. ▪ Used in geometry. ▪ Not the same as \[CapitalOSlash] or \[EmptySet]. ▪ See page 916.

◇ \[Diamond]

Alias: ¦dia¦. ▪ Infix operator. ▪ x ◇ y is by default interpreted as Diamond[x, y]. ▪ See page 922. ▪ See also: \[EmptyDiamond], \[FilledDiamond], \[DiamondSuit].

◇ \[DiamondSuit]

Letter-like form. ▪ Sometimes used to indicate the end of a proof. ▪ Not the same as \[Diamond] or \[EmptyDiamond]. ▪ See page 916. ▪ See also: \[ClubSuit].

d \[DifferentialD]

Alias: ¦dd¦. ▪ Compound operator with built-in evaluation rules. ▪ d can only be interpreted by default when it appears with ∫ or other integral operators. ▪ ∫ f dx is by default interpreted as Integrate[f, x]. ▪ \[DifferentialD] is also used in TraditionalForm to indicate total derivatives. ▪ See pages 914 and 920. ▪ See also: \[PartialD], \[CapitalDifferentialD], \[Delta].

ϝ \[Digamma]

Alias: ¦di¦, ¦digamma¦. ▪ Special Greek letter. ▪ Analogous to English w. ▪ Sometimes used to denote PolyGamma[x]. ▪ See page 910. ▪ See also: \[CapitalDigamma], \[Koppa], \[Stigma], \[Sampi].

÷ \[Divide]

Alias: ¦div¦. ▪ Infix operator with built-in evaluation rules. ▪ x ÷ y is by default interpreted as Divide[x, y] or x / y. ▪ x ÷ y ÷ z groups as (x ÷ y) ÷ z. ▪ See page 920. ▪ See also: \[Times], \[Proportion], \[Backslash].

≐   \[DotEqual]

Alias: ⦂.=⦂. ▪ Infix similarity operator. ▪ $x \doteq y$ is by default interpreted as DotEqual[x, y]. ▪ Used to mean approximately equal, or in some cases, "image of", or "equal by definition". ▪ See page 923. ▪ See also: \[TildeEqual], \[RightArrow].

ı   \[DotlessI]

Letter. ▪ Used when an i will have an overscript on top. ▪ May or may not match the ordinary i from the text font. ▪ See page 912. ▪ See also: \[DotlessJ], \[Iota].

ȷ   \[DotlessJ]

Letter. ▪ Used when a j will have an overscript on top. ▪ May or may not match the ordinary j from the text font. ▪ See page 912. ▪ See also: \[DotlessI].

⬚   \[DottedSquare]

Letter-like form. ▪ See page 915. ▪ See also: \[EmptySquare], \[Placeholder].

∯   \[DoubleContourIntegral]

Compound operator (see page 979). ▪ $\oiint f \, ds$ is by default interpreted as ContourIntegral[f, s]. ▪ Used to indicate integrals over closed surfaces. ▪ See page 920. ▪ See also: \[ContourIntegral], \[Integral].

‡   \[DoubleDagger]

Alias: ⦂ddg⦂. ▪ Letter-like form. ▪ See page 916. ▪ See also: \[Dagger].

γ   \[DoubledGamma]

Alias: ⦂gg⦂. ▪ Letter-like form. ▪ Not by default assigned any interpretation in StandardForm. ▪ Interpreted as EulerGamma in TraditionalForm. ▪ Not the same as \[Gamma]. ▪ See page 914. ▪ See also: \[DoubledPi], \[ExponentialE], \[DoubleStruckA].

⇓   \[DoubleDownArrow]

Infix arrow operator. ▪ $x \Downarrow y$ is by default interpreted as DoubleDownArrow[x, y]. ▪ Extensible character. ▪ See page 926. ▪ See also: \[DownArrow], \[DoubleUpArrow].

π   \[DoubledPi]

Alias: ⦂pp⦂. ▪ Letter-like form. ▪ Not by default assigned any interpretation. ▪ Not the same as \[Pi]. ▪ See page 914. ▪ See also: \[DoubledGamma], \[ExponentialE], \[DoubleStruckA].

⇐   \[DoubleLeftArrow]

Alias: ⦂ <=⦂. ▪ Infix arrow operator. ▪ $x \Leftarrow y$ is by default interpreted as DoubleLeftArrow[x, y]. ▪ Extensible character. ▪ ⦂<=⦂ is the alias for \[LessEqual]. The alias for \[DoubleLeftArrow] has a space at the beginning. ▪ See page 926. ▪ See also: \[DoubleLongLeftArrow], \[LeftArrow], \[DoubleRightArrow].

⇔   \[DoubleLeftRightArrow]

Alias: ⦂<=>⦂. ▪ Infix arrow operator. ▪ $x \Leftrightarrow y$ is by default interpreted as DoubleLeftRightArrow[x, y]. ▪ Used in mathematics to indicate logical equivalence. ▪ Extensible character. ▪ See page 926. ▪ See also: \[DoubleLongLeftRightArrow], \[LeftRightArrow], \[RightArrowLeftArrow], \[LeftArrowRightArrow], \[Congruent], \[Implies].

⫤   \[DoubleLeftTee]

Infix operator. ▪ $x ⫤ y$ is by default interpreted as DoubleLeftTee[x, y]. ▪ $x ⫤ y ⫤ z$ groups as $(x ⫤ y) ⫤ z$. ▪ Used in mathematics to indicate various strong forms of logical implication of x from y—often tautological implication. ▪ See pages 921 and 927. ▪ See also: \[LeftTee], \[DoubleRightTee].

⟸   \[DoubleLongLeftArrow]

Alias: ⦂<==⦂. ▪ Infix arrow operator. ▪ $x \Longleftarrow y$ is by default interpreted as DoubleLongLeftArrow[x, y]. ▪ See page 926. ▪ See also: \[DoubleLeftArrow], \[LongLeftArrow], \[DoubleLongRightArrow].

⟺   \[DoubleLongLeftRightArrow]

Alias: ⦂<==>⦂. ▪ Infix arrow operator. ▪ $x \Longleftrightarrow y$ is by default interpreted as DoubleLongLeftRightArrow[x, y]. ▪ See page 926. ▪ See also: \[DoubleLeftRightArrow], \[LongLeftRightArrow], \[RightArrowLeftArrow], \[LeftArrowRightArrow].

⟹   \[DoubleLongRightArrow]

Alias: ⦂==>⦂. ▪ Infix arrow operator. ▪ $x \Longrightarrow y$ is by default interpreted as DoubleLongRightArrow[x, y]. ▪ See page 926. ▪ See also: \[DoubleRightArrow], \[LongRightArrow], \[DoubleLongLeftArrow].

″   \[DoublePrime]

Alias: ⦂''⦂. ▪ Letter-like form. ▪ Used to indicate angles in seconds or distances in inches. ▪ See page 916. ▪ See also: \[Prime], \[ReverseDoublePrime].

⇒   \[DoubleRightArrow]

Alias: ⦂_=>⦂. ▪ Infix arrow operator. ▪ $x \Rightarrow y$ is by default interpreted as DoubleRightArrow[x, y]. ▪ Used in mathematics to indicate various strong forms of convergence. ▪ Also used to indicate algebraic field extensions. ▪ Not the same as \[Implies]. ▪ Extensible character. ▪ See page 926. ▪ See also: \[DoubleLongRightArrow], \[RightArrow], \[DoubleLeftArrow].

⊨   \[DoubleRightTee]

Infix operator. ▪ $x \vDash y$ is by default interpreted as DoubleRightTee[x, y]. ▪ $x \vDash y \vDash z$ groups as $x \vDash (y \vDash z)$. ▪ Used in mathematics to indicate various strong forms of logical implication—often tautological implication. ▪ In prefix form, used to indicate a tautology. ▪ See pages 921 and 927. ▪ See also: \[RightTee], \[DoubleLeftTee].

a...z   \[DoubleStruckA] ... \[DoubleStruckZ]

Aliases: ⦂dsa⦂ through ⦂dsz⦂. ▪ Letters. ▪ Treated as distinct characters rather than style modifications of ordinary letters. ▪ Contiguous character codes from the private Unicode character range are used, even though a few double-struck characters are included in ordinary Unicode. ▪ See page 913. ▪ See also: \[DoubleStruckCapitalA], \[GothicA], \[ScriptA], etc.

𝔸...ℤ   \[DoubleStruckCapitalA] ... \[DoubleStruckCapitalZ]

Aliases: ⦂dsA⦂ through ⦂dsZ⦂. ▪ Letters. ▪ Treated as distinct characters rather than style modifications of ordinary letters. ▪ ℕ, ℤ, ℚ, ℝ, ℂ, ℍ are used respectively to denote the sets of natural numbers, integers, rationals, reals, complex numbers and quaternions. ▪ Contiguous character codes from the private Unicode character range are used, even though a few capital double-struck characters are included in ordinary Unicode. ▪ See page 913. ▪ See also: \[GothicCapitalA], \[ScriptCapitalA], etc.

⇑   \[DoubleUpArrow]

Infix arrow operator. ▪ $x \Uparrow y$ is by default interpreted as DoubleUpArrow[x, y]. ▪ Extensible character. ▪ See page 926. ▪ See also: \[UpArrow], \[DoubleDownArrow].

⇕   \[DoubleUpDownArrow]

Infix arrow operator. ▪ $x \Updownarrow y$ is by default interpreted as DoubleUpDownArrow[x, y]. ▪ Extensible character. ▪ See page 926. ▪ See also: \[UpDownArrow], \[UpArrowDownArrow], \[DownArrowUpArrow].

‖   \[DoubleVerticalBar]

Alias: ⦂ ␣ | | ⦂. ▪ Infix operator. ▪ $x \, \| \, y$ is by default interpreted as DoubleVerticalBar$[x, y]$. ▪ Used in mathematics to indicate that x exactly divides y. ▪ Used in geometry to mean "parallel to". ▪ Not the same as \[LeftDoubleBracketingBar], \[RightDoubleBracketingBar]. ▪ ⦂ | | ⦂ is the alias for \[Or]. The alias for \[DoubleVerticalBar] has a space at the beginning. ▪ See page 925. ▪ See also: \[VerticalBar], \[VerticalSeparator], \[NotDoubleVerticalBar].

↓   \[DownArrow]

Infix arrow operator. ▪ $x \downarrow y$ is by default interpreted as DownArrow$[x, y]$. ▪ Used to indicate monotonic decrease to a limit. ▪ Sometimes used for logical nor. ▪ Sometimes used in prefix form to indicate the closure of a set. ▪ Extensible character. ▪ See page 926. ▪ See also: \[DownTeeArrow], \[DownArrowBar], \[DoubleDownArrow], \[LeftDownVector], \[UpArrow].

↓   \[DownArrowBar]

Infix arrow operator. ▪ $x \downarrow y$ is by default interpreted as DownArrowBar$[x, y]$. ▪ Sometimes used as an indicator of depth. ▪ Extensible character. ▪ See page 926. ▪ See also: \[DownTeeArrow], \[DownArrow], \[LeftDownVectorBar], \[UpArrowBar].

⇕   \[DownArrowUpArrow]

Infix arrow operator. ▪ $x \, \updownarrow \, y$ is by default interpreted as DownArrowUpArrow$[x, y]$. ▪ Extensible character. ▪ See page 926. ▪ See also: \[UpDownArrow], \[DoubleUpDownArrow], \[UpArrowDownArrow], \[UpEquilibrium].

⌢   \[DownBreve]

Alias: ⦂dbv⦂. ▪ Letter-like form. ▪ Used in an overscript position as a diacritical mark. ▪ See page 919. ▪ See also: \[Breve], \[Cap].

¡   \[DownExclamation]

Alias: ⦂d!⦂. ▪ Letter-like form. ▪ Used in Spanish. ▪ See page 916. ▪ See also: \[RawExclamation], \[DownQuestion].

⇀↽   \[DownLeftRightVector]

Infix arrow-like operator. ▪ $x \, ⇀↽ \, y$ is by default interpreted as DownLeftRightVector$[x, y]$. ▪ Extensible character. ▪ See page 927. ▪ See also: \[LeftRightVector], \[Equilibrium], \[RightUpDownVector].

↽⊣   \[DownLeftTeeVector]

Infix arrow-like operator. ▪ $x \, ↽⊣ \, y$ is by default interpreted as DownLeftTeeVector$[x, y]$. ▪ Extensible character. ▪ See page 927. ▪ See also: \[LeftTeeVector], \[LeftVectorBar].

↽   \[DownLeftVector]

Infix arrow-like operator. ▪ $x \, ↽ \, y$ is by default interpreted as DownLeftVector$[x, y]$. ▪ Extensible character. ▪ See page 927. ▪ See also: \[LeftVector], \[LeftTeeVector], \[LeftArrow], \[LeftUpVector].

⊢↽   \[DownLeftVectorBar]

Infix arrow-like operator. ▪ $x \, ⊢↽ \, y$ is by default interpreted as DownLeftVectorBar$[x, y]$. ▪ Extensible character. ▪ See page 927. ▪ See also: \[LeftVectorBar], \[LeftTeeVector].

¿   \[DownQuestion]

Alias: ⦂d?⦂. ▪ Letter-like form. ▪ Used in Spanish. ▪ See page 916. ▪ See also: \[RawQuestion], \[DownExclamation].

⇁⊢   \[DownRightTeeVector]

Infix arrow-like operator. ▪ $x \, ⇁⊢ \, y$ is by default interpreted as DownRightTeeVector$[x, y]$. ▪ Extensible character. ▪ See page 927. ▪ See also: \[RightTeeVector], \[RightVectorBar].

→ \[DownRightVector]

Infix arrow-like operator. ▪ $x \rightarrow y$ is by default interpreted as DownRightVector[x, y]. ▪ Extensible character. ▪ See page 927. ▪ See also: \[RightVector], \[RightTeeVector], \[RightArrow], \[RightUpVector].

↦ \[DownRightVectorBar]

Infix arrow-like operator. ▪ $x \rightarrow y$ is by default interpreted as DownRightVectorBar[x, y]. ▪ Extensible character. ▪ See page 927. ▪ See also: \[RightVectorBar], \[RightTeeVector].

⊤ \[DownTee]

Alias: ⣿dT⣿. ▪ Infix operator. ▪ $x \top y$ is by default interpreted as DownTee[x, y]. ▪ See page 927. ▪ See also: \[UpTee], \[RightTee], \[DownTeeArrow].

↧ \[DownTeeArrow]

Infix arrow operator. ▪ $x \downarrow y$ is by default interpreted as DownTeeArrow[x, y]. ▪ Extensible character. ▪ See page 926. ▪ See also: \[DownArrowBar], \[RightDownTeeVector], \[DownTee], \[UpTeeArrow].

é \[EAcute]

Alias: ⣿e'⣿. ▪ Letter. ▪ Included in ISO Latin-1. ▪ See pages 188 and 918. ▪ See also: \[CapitalEAcute].

ē \[EBar]

Alias: ⣿e-⣿. ▪ Letter. ▪ Included in ISO Latin-4. ▪ Used in transliterations of various non-Latin alphabets. ▪ See page 918. ▪ See also: \[CapitalEBar].

ĕ \[ECup]

Alias: ⣿eu⣿. ▪ Letter. ▪ Not included in ISO Latin. ▪ Used in transliterations of Cyrillic characters. ▪ See page 918. ▪ See also: \[CapitalECup].

ë \[EDoubleDot]

Alias: ⣿e"⣿. ▪ Letter. ▪ Included in ISO Latin-1. ▪ See page 918. ▪ See also: \[CapitalEDoubleDot], \[IDoubleDot], \[ADoubleDot].

è \[EGrave]

Alias: ⣿e`⣿. ▪ Letter. ▪ Included in ISO Latin-1. ▪ See pages 188 and 918. ▪ See also: \[CapitalEGrave].

ê \[EHat]

Alias: ⣿e^⣿. ▪ Letter. ▪ Included in ISO Latin-1. ▪ See page 918. ▪ See also: \[CapitalEHat].

∈ \[Element]

Alias: ⣿elem⣿. ▪ Infix set relation operator. ▪ $x \in y$ is by default interpreted as Element[x, y]. ▪ Not the same as \[Epsilon]. ▪ See pages 189 and 924. ▪ See also: \[NotElement], \[ReverseElement].

... \[Ellipsis]

Alias: ⣿...⣿. ▪ Letter-like form. ▪ Used to indicate omitted elements in a row of a matrix. ▪ \[Ellipsis] on its own will act as a symbol. ▪ See pages 916 and 917. ▪ See also: \[CenterEllipsis], \[VerticalEllipsis], \[AscendingEllipsis], \[HorizontalLine], \[LeftSkeleton], \[RawDot].

○ \[EmptyCircle]

Alias: ⣿eci⣿. ▪ Letter-like form. ▪ Not the same as the infix operator \[SmallCircle]. ▪ See page 915. ▪ See also: \[EmptySmallCircle], \[FilledCircle], \[Degree].

◇   \[EmptyDiamond]

Letter-like form. ▪ See page 915. ▪ See also: \[Diamond], \[FilledDiamond].

▽   \[EmptyDownTriangle]

Letter-like form. ▪ Not the same as \[Del]. ▪ See page 915. ▪ See also: \[EmptyUpTriangle],
\[FilledDownTriangle], \[FilledUpTriangle], \[LeftTriangle], \[NotLeftTriangle], \[NotRightTriangle],
\[RightTriangle].

▯   \[EmptyRectangle]

Letter-like form. ▪ See page 915. ▪ See also: \[FilledRectangle].

∅   \[EmptySet]

Alias: ⦂es⦂. ▪ Letter-like form. ▪ Not the same as \[CapitalOSlash] or \[Diameter]. ▪ See pages 190 and 914.

○   \[EmptySmallCircle]

Alias: ⦂esci⦂. ▪ Letter-like form. ▪ Not the same as the infix operator \[SmallCircle]. ▪ Used as an overscript to
add ring diacritical marks. ▪ See page 915. ▪ See also: \[FilledSmallCircle], \[Degree], \[ARing], \[Angstrom].

□   \[EmptySmallSquare]

Alias: ⦂essq⦂. ▪ Letter-like form. ▪ Not the same as the operator \[Square]. ▪ Not the same as \[Placeholder].
▪ See page 915. ▪ See also: \[EmptySquare], \[FilledSmallSquare].

□   \[EmptySquare]

Alias: ⦂esq⦂. ▪ Letter-like form. ▪ Not the same as the operator \[Square]. ▪ Not the same as \[Placeholder].
▪ See page 915. ▪ See also: \[FilledSquare], \[GraySquare], \[DottedSquare], \[EmptyRectangle].

△   \[EmptyUpTriangle]

Letter-like form. ▪ Used in geometry to indicate a triangle, as in the symbol △ABC. ▪ Not the same as
\[CapitalDelta]. ▪ See pages 915 and 916. ▪ See also: \[FilledUpTriangle], \[EmptyDownTriangle],
\[RightTriangle], \[Angle].

ϵ   \[Epsilon]

Aliases: ⦂e⦂, ⦂epsilon⦂. ▪ Greek letter. ▪ Not the same as \[Element]. ▪ See pages 174 and 910. ▪ See also:
\[CurlyEpsilon], \[CapitalEpsilon], \[Eta].

==   \[Equal]

Alias: ⦂==⦂. ▪ Infix operator with built-in evaluation rules. ▪ $x = y$ is by default interpreted as Equal[x, y] or
x == y. ▪ \[Equal] is drawn longer than \[RawEqual]. ▪ See page 923. ▪ See also: \[NotEqual], \[Congruent],
\[Rule].

≈   \[EqualTilde]

Alias: ⦂=~⦂. ▪ Infix similarity operator. ▪ $x \approx y$ is by default interpreted as EqualTilde[x, y]. ▪ See page 923. ▪ See
also: \[NotEqualTilde].

⇌   \[Equilibrium]

Alias: ⦂equi⦂. ▪ Infix arrow-like operator. ▪ $x \rightleftharpoons y$ is by default interpreted as Equilibrium[x, y]. ▪ Used in
chemistry to represent a reversible reaction. ▪ Extensible character. ▪ See pages 189 and 927. ▪ See also:
\[ReverseEquilibrium], \[RightArrowLeftArrow], \[LeftRightArrow], \[LeftRightVector], \[UpEquilibrium].

⊠   \[ErrorIndicator]

Uninterpretable element. ▪ Generated to indicate the position of a syntax error in messages produced by functions
like Get and ToExpression. ▪ Shown as ^^^ in OutputForm. ▪ \[ErrorIndicator] indicates the presence of a
syntax error, and so by default generates an error if you try to interpret it. ▪ See also: \[LeftSkeleton].

ESC   \[EscapeKey]

Alias: ⦂␣esc⦂. ▪ Letter-like form. ▪ Representation of the escape key on a keyboard. ▪ Used in describing how to type aliases for special characters in *Mathematica*. ▪ ⦂esc⦂ is the alias for \[AliasIndicator]. The alias for \[EscapeKey] has a space at the beginning. ▪ See page 929. ▪ See also: \[AliasIndicator], \[RawEscape], \[ReturnKey], \[ControlKey], \[CommandKey].

η   \[Eta]

Aliases: ⦂et⦂, ⦂eta⦂, ⦂h⦂. ▪ Greek letter. ▪ Used in TraditionalForm for DedekindEta. ▪ See pages 174 and 910. ▪ See also: \[CapitalEta], \[Epsilon].

ð   \[Eth]

Alias: ⦂d-⦂. ▪ Letter. ▪ Included in ISO Latin-1. ▪ Used in Icelandic and Old English. ▪ See page 918. ▪ See also: \[CapitalEth], \[Thorn], \[PartialD].

∃   \[Exists]

Alias: ⦂ex⦂. ▪ Compound operator. ▪ $\exists_x y$ is by default interpreted as Exists[x, y]. ▪ See page 921. ▪ See also: \[NotExists].

ℯ   \[ExponentialE]

Alias: ⦂ee⦂. ▪ Letter-like form with built-in value. ▪ ℯ is interpreted by default as the symbol E, representing the exponential constant. ▪ See page 914. ▪ See also: \[DifferentialD], \[ImaginaryI].

●   \[FilledCircle]

Alias: ⦂fci⦂. ▪ Letter-like form. ▪ Used as a dingbat. ▪ See page 915. ▪ See also: \[Bullet], \[FilledSmallCircle], \[SmallCircle], \[EmptyCircle].

◆   \[FilledDiamond]

Letter-like form. ▪ See page 915. ▪ See also: \[Diamond], \[EmptyDiamond].

▼   \[FilledDownTriangle]

Letter-like form. ▪ See page 915. ▪ See also: \[EmptyDownTriangle], \[EmptyUpTriangle], \[FilledUpTriangle], \[LeftTriangle], \[NotLeftTriangle], \[NotRightTriangle], \[RightTriangle].

■   \[FilledRectangle]

Letter-like form. ▪ Used in mathematics to indicate the end of a proof. ▪ See page 915. ▪ See also: \[EmptyRectangle].

●   \[FilledSmallCircle]

Alias: ⦂fsci⦂. ▪ Letter-like form. ▪ Used as a dingbat. ▪ See page 915. ▪ See also: \[Bullet], \[FilledCircle], \[EmptySmallCircle].

■   \[FilledSmallSquare]

Alias: ⦂fssq⦂. ▪ Letter-like form. ▪ Used as a dingbat. ▪ Not the same as \[SelectionPlaceholder]. ▪ See page 915. ▪ See also: \[FilledSquare], \[EmptySmallSquare], \[Square].

■   \[FilledSquare]

Alias: ⦂fsq⦂. ▪ Letter-like form. ▪ Used as a dingbat. ▪ Not the same as \[SelectionPlaceholder]. ▪ See page 915. ▪ See also: \[FilledSmallSquare], \[EmptySquare], \[Square], \[GraySquare], \[FilledRectangle].

▲   \[FilledUpTriangle]

Letter-like form. ▪ See page 915. ▪ See also: \[EmptyDownTriangle], \[EmptyUpTriangle], \[FilledDownTriangle], \[LeftTriangle], \[NotLeftTriangle], \[NotRightTriangle], \[RightTriangle].

▪   \[FilledVerySmallSquare]

Alias: ⁝fvssq⁝. ▪ Letter-like form. ▪ Used as a dingbat. ▪ See page 915. ▪ See also: \[FilledSmallSquare], \[Square].

ς   \[FinalSigma]

Alias: ⁝fs⁝. ▪ Greek letter. ▪ Used in written Greek when σ occurs at the end of a word. ▪ Not commonly used in technical notation. ▪ Not the same as \[Stigma]. ▪ See page 910. ▪ See also: \[Sigma].

★   \[FivePointedStar]

Alias: ⁝*5⁝. ▪ Letter-like form. ▪ Not the same as the operator \[Star]. ▪ See page 915. ▪ See also: \[SixPointedStar], \[Star], \[RawStar].

♭   \[Flat]

Letter-like form. ▪ Used to denote musical notes. ▪ Sometimes used in mathematical notation. ▪ See page 916. ▪ See also: \[Sharp], \[Natural].

∀   \[ForAll]

Alias: ⁝fa⁝. ▪ Compound operator. ▪ $\forall_x y$ is by default interpreted as ForAll[x, y]. ▪ See page 921. ▪ See also: \[Exists], \[Not].

☹   \[FreakedSmiley]

Alias: ⁝:-@⁝. ▪ Letter-like form. ▪ See page 915. ▪ See also: \[HappySmiley], \[NeutralSmiley], \[SadSmiley], \[WarningSign].

γ   \[Gamma]

Aliases: ⁝g⁝, ⁝gamma⁝. ▪ Greek letter. ▪ Used in TraditionalForm for EulerGamma and StieltjesGamma. ▪ See pages 174 and 910. ▪ See also: \[DoubledGamma], \[CapitalGamma], \[Digamma].

ℷ   \[Gimel]

Alias: ⁝gi⁝. ▪ Hebrew letter. ▪ Used occasionally in pure mathematics in the theory of transfinite cardinals. ▪ See page 913. ▪ See also: \[Aleph].

𝔞...𝔷   \[GothicA] ... \[GothicZ]

Aliases: ⁝goa⁝ through ⁝goz⁝. ▪ Letters. ▪ Treated as distinct characters rather than style modifications of ordinary letters. ▪ Used in pure mathematics. ▪ Contiguous character codes from the private Unicode character range are used, even though a few gothic characters are included in ordinary Unicode. ▪ See page 913. ▪ See also: \[GothicCapitalA], \[ScriptA], \[DoubleStruckA], etc.

𝔄...𝔷   \[GothicCapitalA] ... \[GothicCapitalZ]

Aliases: ⁝goA⁝ through ⁝goZ⁝. ▪ Letters. ▪ Treated as distinct characters rather than style modifications of ordinary letters. ▪ I is used to denote imaginary part; R is used to denote real part. ▪ Used in pure mathematics and theory of computation. ▪ Contiguous character codes from the private Unicode character range are used, even though a few capital gothic characters are included in ordinary Unicode. ▪ See page 913. ▪ See also: \[GothicA], \[ScriptCapitalA], \[DoubleStruckCapitalA], etc.

↓   \[LeftDownVector]

Infix arrow-like operator. ▪ *x* ↓ *y* is by default interpreted as LeftDownVector[*x*, *y*]. ▪ Extensible character. ▪ See page 927. ▪ See also: \[RightDownVector], \[LeftDownTeeVector], \[DownArrow], \[UpEquilibrium], \[LeftUpVector].

↓   \[LeftDownVectorBar]

Infix arrow-like operator. ▪ *x* ↓ *y* is by default interpreted as LeftDownVectorBar[*x*, *y*]. ▪ Extensible character. ▪ See page 927. ▪ See also: \[RightDownVectorBar], \[LeftDownTeeVector], \[DownArrowBar], \[LeftUpVectorBar].

⌊   \[LeftFloor]

Alias: :lf:. ▪ Matchfix operator with built-in evaluation rules. ▪ ⌊ *x* ⌋ is by default interpreted as Floor[*x*]. ▪ Extensible character. ▪ See page 922. ▪ See also: \[RightFloor], \[LeftCeiling], \[LeftAngleBracket].

«   \[LeftGuillemet]

Alias: :g<<:. ▪ Letter-like form. ▪ Used as opening quotation marks in languages such as Spanish. ▪ Not the same as \[LessLess]. ▪ Not the same as \[LeftSkeleton]. ▪ Guillemet is sometimes misspelled as guillemot. ▪ See page 916. ▪ See also: \[RightGuillemet].

⌐   \[LeftModified]

Alias: :[:. ▪ Letter-like form. ▪ Used in documenting control and command characters. ▪ *key*\[LeftModified]*char*\[RightModified] is used to indicate that *char* should be typed while *key* is being pressed. ▪ Not the same as \[RawLeftBracket]. ▪ See page 929. ▪ See also: \[ControlKey], \[CommandKey], \[RightModified].

↔   \[LeftRightArrow]

Alias: :<->:. ▪ Infix arrow operator. ▪ *x* ↔ *y* is by default interpreted as LeftRightArrow[*x*, *y*]. ▪ Used in mathematics for various notions of equivalence and equality. ▪ Extensible character. ▪ See pages 189 and 926. ▪ See also: \[LongLeftRightArrow], \[DoubleLeftRightArrow], \[LeftArrowRightArrow], \[LeftRightVector], \[Equilibrium], \[UpDownArrow].

↤   \[LeftRightVector]

Infix arrow-like operator. ▪ *x* ↤ *y* is by default interpreted as LeftRightVector[*x*, *y*]. ▪ Extensible character. ▪ See page 927. ▪ See also: \[DownLeftRightVector], \[Equilibrium], \[ReverseEquilibrium], \[LeftRightArrow], \[RightArrowLeftArrow], \[RightUpDownVector].

≪   \[LeftSkeleton]

Uninterpretable element. ▪ ≪ *n* ≫ is used on output to indicate *n* omitted pieces in an expression obtained from Short or Shallow. ▪ \[LeftSkeleton] indicates the presence of missing information, and so by default generates an error if you try to interpret it. ▪ Not the same as \[LeftGuillemet]. ▪ See page 929. ▪ See also: \[RightSkeleton], \[SkeletonIndicator], \[Ellipsis], \[ErrorIndicator].

⊣   \[LeftTee]

Alias: :lT:. ▪ Infix operator. ▪ *x* ⊣ *y* is by default interpreted as LeftTee[*x*, *y*]. ▪ *x* ⊣ *y* ⊣ *z* groups as (*x* ⊣ *y*) ⊣ *z*. ▪ Used in mathematics to indicate the lack of logical implication or proof. ▪ See pages 921 and 927. ▪ See also: \[DoubleLeftTee], \[LeftTeeArrow], \[LeftTeeVector], \[RightTee], \[DownTee], \[LeftBracketingBar].

↤   \[LeftTeeArrow]

Infix arrow operator. ▪ *x* ↤ *y* is by default interpreted as LeftTeeArrow[*x*, *y*]. ▪ Extensible character. ▪ See page 926. ▪ See also: \[LeftTeeVector], \[LeftTee], \[RightTeeArrow], \[DownTeeArrow].

⊢⊣   \[LeftTeeVector]

Infix arrow-like operator. ▪ $x \dashv y$ is by default interpreted as LeftTeeVector[x, y]. ▪ Extensible character. ▪ See page 927. ▪ See also: \[DownLeftTeeVector], \[LeftVectorBar], \[LeftVector], \[LeftTeeArrow].

◁   \[LeftTriangle]

Infix ordering operator. ▪ $x ◁ y$ is by default interpreted as LeftTriangle[x, y]. ▪ Used in pure mathematics to mean "normal subgroup of". ▪ See page 925. ▪ See also: \[LeftTriangleEqual], \[LeftTriangleBar], \[LeftArrow], \[NotLeftTriangle], \[RightTriangle], \[EmptyUpTriangle], \[FilledUpTriangle].

◁| \[LeftTriangleBar]

Infix ordering operator. ▪ $x ◁| y$ is by default interpreted as LeftTriangleBar[x, y]. ▪ See page 925. ▪ See also: \[LeftTriangle], \[LeftTriangleEqual], \[LeftArrowBar], \[NotLeftTriangleBar].

⊴   \[LeftTriangleEqual]

Infix ordering operator. ▪ $x ⊴ y$ is by default interpreted as LeftTriangleEqual[x, y]. ▪ See page 925. ▪ See also: \[LeftTriangle], \[LeftTriangleBar], \[PrecedesEqual], \[NotLeftTriangleEqual], \[RightTriangleEqual].

↿   \[LeftUpDownVector]

Infix arrow-like operator. ▪ $x ↿ y$ is by default interpreted as LeftUpDownVector[x, y]. ▪ Extensible character. ▪ See page 927. ▪ See also: \[RightUpDownVector], \[UpEquilibrium], \[UpArrowDownArrow], \[LeftRightVector].

↿   \[LeftUpTeeVector]

Infix arrow-like operator. ▪ $x ↿ y$ is by default interpreted as LeftUpTeeVector[x, y]. ▪ Extensible character. ▪ See page 927. ▪ See also: \[RightUpTeeVector], \[LeftUpVectorBar], \[UpTeeArrow], \[LeftDownTeeVector].

↿   \[LeftUpVector]

Infix arrow-like operator. ▪ $x ↿ y$ is by default interpreted as LeftUpVector[x, y]. ▪ Extensible character. ▪ See page 927. ▪ See also: \[RightUpVector], \[LeftUpTeeVector], \[UpArrow], \[UpEquilibrium], \[LeftDownVector].

↾   \[LeftUpVectorBar]

Infix arrow-like operator. ▪ $x ↾ y$ is by default interpreted as LeftUpVectorBar[x, y]. ▪ Extensible character. ▪ See page 927. ▪ See also: \[RightUpVectorBar], \[LeftUpTeeVector], \[UpArrowBar], \[LeftDownVectorBar].

←   \[LeftVector]

Infix arrow-like operator. ▪ $x ← y$ is by default interpreted as LeftVector[x, y]. ▪ Extensible character. ▪ See page 927. ▪ See also: \[DownLeftVector], \[LeftTeeVector], \[LeftVectorBar], \[LeftArrow], \[RightVector], \[LeftUpVector].

↤   \[LeftVectorBar]

Infix arrow-like operator. ▪ $x ↤ y$ is by default interpreted as LeftVectorBar[x, y]. ▪ Extensible character. ▪ See page 927. ▪ See also: \[DownLeftVectorBar], \[LeftTeeVector], \[LeftArrowBar].

≤   \[LessEqual]

Alias: ⁝<=⁝. ▪ Infix operator with built-in evaluation rules. ▪ $x ≤ y$ is by default interpreted as LessEqual[x, y]. ▪ See page 924. ▪ See also: \[LessSlantEqual], \[LessFullEqual], \[NotLessEqual].

⋚   \[LessEqualGreater]

Infix ordering operator. ▪ $x ⋚ y$ is by default interpreted as LessEqualGreater[x, y]. ▪ See page 924. ▪ See also: \[GreaterEqualLess].

≦ \[LessFullEqual]

Infix ordering operator. ▪ $x \leqq y$ is by default interpreted as LessFullEqual[x, y]. ▪ See page 924. ▪ See also: \[LessEqual], \[LessSlantEqual], \[NotLessFullEqual].

≶ \[LessGreater]

Infix ordering operator. ▪ $x \lessgtr y$ is by default interpreted as LessGreater[x, y]. ▪ See page 924. ▪ See also: \[LessEqualGreater], \[NotLessGreater].

≪ \[LessLess]

Infix ordering operator. ▪ $x \ll y$ is by default interpreted as LessLess[x, y]. ▪ Not the same as \[LeftGuillemet]. ▪ See page 924. ▪ See also: \[NestedLessLess], \[NotLessLess], \[NotNestedLessLess].

≤ \[LessSlantEqual]

Alias: ⣉</⣉. ▪ Infix operator with built-in evaluation rules. ▪ $x \leqslant y$ is by default interpreted as LessEqual[x, y]. ▪ See page 924. ▪ See also: \[LessEqual], \[LessFullEqual], \[NotLessSlantEqual].

≲ \[LessTilde]

Alias: ⣉<~⣉. ▪ Infix ordering operator. ▪ $x \lesssim y$ is by default interpreted as LessTilde[x, y]. ▪ See page 924. ▪ See also: \[NotLessTilde].

💡 \[LightBulb]

Letter-like form. ▪ See page 915.

— \[LongDash]

Alias: ⣉--⣉. ▪ Letter-like form. ▪ See page 916. ▪ See also: \[Dash], \[HorizontalLine].

⟵ \[LongLeftArrow]

Alias: ⣉<--⣉. ▪ Infix arrow operator. ▪ $x \longleftarrow y$ is by default interpreted as LongLeftArrow[x, y]. ▪ See page 926. ▪ See also: \[LeftArrow], \[DoubleLongLeftArrow], \[LongRightArrow], \[LongLeftRightArrow].

⟷ \[LongLeftRightArrow]

Alias: ⣉<-->⣉. ▪ Infix arrow operator. ▪ $x \longleftrightarrow y$ is by default interpreted as LongLeftRightArrow[x, y]. ▪ See page 926. ▪ See also: \[LeftRightArrow], \[DoubleLongLeftRightArrow], \[LeftArrowRightArrow], \[Equilibrium].

⟶ \[LongRightArrow]

Alias: ⣉-->⣉. ▪ Infix arrow operator. ▪ $x \longrightarrow y$ is by default interpreted as LongRightArrow[x, y]. ▪ Not the same as \[Rule]. ▪ See pages 189 and 926. ▪ See also: \[RightArrow], \[DoubleLongRightArrow], \[LongLeftArrow], \[LongLeftRightArrow].

↙ \[LowerLeftArrow]

Infix arrow operator. ▪ $x \swarrow y$ is by default interpreted as LowerLeftArrow[x, y]. ▪ Extensible character; grows by default to limited size. ▪ See page 926. ▪ See also: \[LeftArrow], \[UpperRightArrow].

↘ \[LowerRightArrow]

Infix arrow operator. ▪ $x \searrow y$ is by default interpreted as LowerRightArrow[x, y]. ▪ Extensible character; grows by default to limited size. ▪ See page 926. ▪ See also: \[RightArrow], \[UpperLeftArrow].

ł \[LSlash]

Alias: ⣉l/⣉. ▪ Letter. ▪ Included in ISO Latin-2. ▪ See page 918. ▪ See also: \[CapitalLSlash].

\[MathematicaIcon]

Alias: ⦂math⦂. ▪ Letter-like form. ▪ Icon typically used for *Mathematica*. ▪ Based on a stellated icosahedron. ▪ This icon is a trademark of Wolfram Research. ▪ See page 915. ▪ See also: \[KernelIcon].

\[MeasuredAngle]

Letter-like form. ▪ Used in geometry to indicate an angle, as in the symbol ∡ ABC. ▪ See page 916. ▪ See also: \[Angle], \[SphericalAngle], \[RightAngle].

\[MediumSpace]

Alias: ⦂␣␣␣⦂. ▪ Spacing character. ▪ Width: 4/18 em. ▪ Interpreted by default just like an ordinary \[RawSpace]. ▪ Sometimes used in output as a separator between digits in numbers. ▪ See page 928. ▪ See also: \[ThinSpace], \[ThickSpace], \[NegativeMediumSpace], \[NonBreakingSpace], \[SpaceIndicator].

\[Mho]

Alias: ⦂mho⦂. ▪ Letter-like form. ▪ Used to denote the inverse ohm unit of conductance. ▪ "Mho" is "ohm" spelled backwards. ▪ Occasionally called "agemo" in pure mathematics. ▪ Used to denote characteristic subgroups, and in set theory to denote functions of sets with special properties. ▪ See page 914. ▪ See also: CapitalOmega.

\[Micro]

Alias: ⦂mi⦂. ▪ Letter-like form. ▪ Used as a prefix in units to denote 10^{-6}. ▪ Not the same as \[Mu]. ▪ See pages 190 and 914. ▪ See also: \[Angstrom].

\[MinusPlus]

Alias: ⦂-+⦂. ▪ Prefix or infix operator. ▪ ∓ x is by default interpreted as MinusPlus[x]. ▪ x ∓ y is by default interpreted as MinusPlus[x, y]. ▪ See page 920. ▪ See also: \[PlusMinus].

\[Mu]

Aliases: ⦂m⦂, ⦂mu⦂. ▪ Greek letter. ▪ Used in TraditionalForm for MoebiusMu. ▪ Not the same as \[Micro]. ▪ See pages 174 and 910. ▪ See also: \[CapitalMu].

\[Natural]

Letter-like form. ▪ Used to denote musical notes. ▪ Sometimes used in mathematical notation, often as an inverse of numbering operations represented by \[Sharp]. ▪ See pages 190 and 916. ▪ See also: \[Flat], \[Sharp].

\[NegativeMediumSpace]

Alias: ⦂-␣␣␣⦂. ▪ Negative spacing character. ▪ Used to bring characters on either side closer together. ▪ Width: −4/18 em. ▪ Interpreted by default just like an ordinary \[RawSpace]. ▪ See page 928. ▪ See also: \[NegativeThinSpace], \[NegativeThickSpace], \[MediumSpace].

\[NegativeThickSpace]

Alias: ⦂-␣␣␣␣⦂. ▪ Negative spacing character. ▪ Used to bring characters on either side closer together. ▪ Width: −5/18 em. ▪ Interpreted by default just like an ordinary \[RawSpace]. ▪ See page 928. ▪ See also: \[NegativeMediumSpace], \[ThickSpace].

\[NegativeThinSpace]

Alias: ⦂-␣␣⦂. ▪ Negative spacing character. ▪ Used to bring characters on either side closer together. ▪ Width: −3/18 em. ▪ Interpreted by default just like an ordinary \[RawSpace]. ▪ See page 928. ▪ See also: \[NegativeVeryThinSpace], \[NegativeMediumSpace], \[ThinSpace].

\[NegativeVeryThinSpace]

Alias: ⣀-␣⣀. ▪ Negative spacing character. ▪ Used to bring characters on either side closer together. ▪ Width: $-1/18$ em. ▪ Interpreted by default just like an ordinary \[RawSpace]. ▪ See page 928. ▪ See also: \[NegativeThinSpace], \[VeryThinSpace].

⫸   ## \[NestedGreaterGreater]

Infix ordering operator. ▪ $x \gg y$ is by default interpreted as `NestedGreaterGreater[x, y]`. ▪ See page 924. ▪ See also: \[GreaterGreater], \[NotGreaterGreater], \[NotNestedGreaterGreater].

⫷   ## \[NestedLessLess]

Infix ordering operator. ▪ $x \ll y$ is by default interpreted as `NestedLessLess[x, y]`. ▪ Used to denote "much less than". ▪ Occasionally used in measure theory to denote "absolutely continuous with respect to". ▪ See page 924. ▪ See also: \[LessLess], \[NotLessLess], \[NotNestedLessLess].

☺   ## \[NeutralSmiley]

Alias: ⣀:-|⣀. ▪ Letter-like form. ▪ See page 915. ▪ See also: \[HappySmiley], \[SadSmiley], \[FreakedSmiley].

\[NewLine]

Raw operator. ▪ Inserted whenever a raw newline is entered on the keyboard. ▪ Forces a line break in an expression, fixing the indenting level at the time when the line break is inserted. ▪ \[NewLine] represents a newline on any computer system, independent of the underlying character code used on that computer system. ▪ See pages 928 and 930. ▪ See also: \[IndentingNewLine], \[RawReturn].

\[NoBreak]

Alias: ⣀nb⣀. ▪ Letter-like form. ▪ Used to indicate that no line break can occur at this position in an expression. ▪ See page 928. ▪ See also: \[NonBreakingSpace], \[NewLine], \[Continuation], \[AlignmentMarker], \[Null], MCInvisibleSpace.

\[NonBreakingSpace]

Alias: ⣀nbs⣀. ▪ Spacing character. ▪ Generates a space with the same width as \[RawSpace], but with no line break allowed to occur on either side of it. ▪ See page 928. ▪ See also: \[NoBreak], \[InvisibleSpace], \[NewLine].

¬   ## \[Not]

Aliases: ⣀!⣀, ⣀not⣀. ▪ Prefix operator with built-in evaluation rules. ▪ $\neg x$ is by default interpreted as `Not[x]`, equivalent to `!x`. ▪ See page 921. ▪ See also: \[RightTee], \[And], \[Or].

≢   ## \[NotCongruent]

Alias: ⣀!===⣀. ▪ Infix similarity operator. ▪ $x \not\equiv y$ is by default interpreted as `NotCongruent[x, y]`. ▪ See page 923. ▪ See also: \[NotEqual], \[Congruent].

≭   ## \[NotCupCap]

Infix similarity operator. ▪ $x \not\asymp y$ is by default interpreted as `NotCupCap[x, y]`. ▪ See page 923. ▪ See also: \[CupCap].

∦   ## \[NotDoubleVerticalBar]

Alias: ⣀!||⣀. ▪ Infix operator. ▪ $x \nparallel y$ is by default interpreted as `NotDoubleVerticalBar[x, y]`. ▪ Used in geometry to mean "not parallel to". ▪ See page 925. ▪ See also: \[DoubleVerticalBar], \[NotVerticalBar], \[UpTee].

∉   ## \[NotElement]

Alias: ⣀!elem⣀. ▪ Infix set relation operator. ▪ $x \notin y$ is by default interpreted as `NotElement[x, y]`. ▪ See pages 189 and 924. ▪ See also: \[Element], \[NotReverseElement].

≠ \[NotEqual]

Alias: ⦂!=⦂. ▪ Infix operator with built-in evaluation rules. ▪ $x \neq y$ is by default interpreted as Unequal[x, y]. ▪ See page 923. ▪ See also: \[Equal], \[NotCongruent], \[GreaterLess].

≁ \[NotEqualTilde]

Alias: ⦂!=~⦂. ▪ Infix similarity operator. ▪ $x \neq y$ is by default interpreted as NotEqualTilde[x, y]. ▪ See page 923. ▪ See also: \[EqualTilde].

∄ \[NotExists]

Alias: ⦂!ex⦂. ▪ Compound operator. ▪ $\not\exists_x y$ is by default interpreted as NotExists[x, y]. ▪ See page 921. ▪ See also: \[Exists], \[ForAll].

≯ \[NotGreater]

Alias: ⦂!>⦂. ▪ Infix ordering operator. ▪ $x \not> y$ is by default interpreted as NotGreater[x, y]. ▪ ≯ is equivalent to ≤ only for a totally ordered set. ▪ See page 924. ▪ See also: \[RawGreater].

≱ \[NotGreaterEqual]

Alias: ⦂!>=⦂. ▪ Infix ordering operator. ▪ $x \ngeq y$ is by default interpreted as NotGreaterEqual[x, y]. ▪ See page 924. ▪ See also: \[GreaterEqual], \[GreaterFullEqual], \[GreaterSlantEqual], \[NotGreaterFullEqual], \[NotGreaterSlantEqual].

≱ \[NotGreaterFullEqual]

Infix ordering operator. ▪ $x \ngeqq y$ is by default interpreted as NotGreaterFullEqual[x, y]. ▪ See page 924. ▪ See also: \[GreaterEqual], \[GreaterFullEqual], \[GreaterSlantEqual], \[NotGreaterEqual], \[NotGreaterSlantEqual].

≫̸ \[NotGreaterGreater]

Infix ordering operator. ▪ $x \not\gg y$ is by default interpreted as NotGreaterGreater[x, y]. ▪ See page 924. ▪ See also: \[GreaterGreater], \[NestedGreaterGreater], \[NotNestedGreaterGreater].

≹ \[NotGreaterLess]

Infix ordering operator. ▪ $x \ngtrless y$ is by default interpreted as NotGreaterLess[x, y]. ▪ See page 924. ▪ See also: \[GreaterLess].

≵ \[NotGreaterSlantEqual]

Alias: ⦂!>/⦂. ▪ Infix ordering operator. ▪ $x \not\geqslant y$ is by default interpreted as NotGreaterSlantEqual[x, y]. ▪ See page 924. ▪ See also: \[GreaterEqual], \[GreaterFullEqual], \[GreaterSlantEqual], \[NotGreaterEqual], \[NotGreaterFullEqual].

≵ \[NotGreaterTilde]

Alias: ⦂!>~⦂. ▪ Infix ordering operator. ▪ $x \not\gtrsim y$ is by default interpreted as NotGreaterTilde[x, y]. ▪ See page 924. ▪ See also: \[GreaterTilde].

≆ \[NotHumpDownHump]

Alias: ⦂!hvh⦂. ▪ Infix similarity operator. ▪ $x \neq y$ is by default interpreted as NotHumpDownHump[x, y]. ▪ See page 923. ▪ See also: \[HumpDownHump].

≆ \[NotHumpEqual]

Alias: ⦂!h=⦂. ▪ Infix similarity operator. ▪ $x \neq y$ is by default interpreted as NotHumpEqual[x, y]. ▪ See page 923. ▪ See also: \[HumpEqual].

⋪ \[NotLeftTriangle]

Infix ordering operator. ▪ $x \ntriangleleft y$ is by default interpreted as NotLeftTriangle[x, y]. ▪ See page 925. ▪ See also: \[NotLeftTriangleBar], \[NotLeftTriangleEqual], \[NotRightTriangle], \[LeftTriangle].

⧏ \[NotLeftTriangleBar]

Infix ordering operator. ▪ x ⧏ y is by default interpreted as NotLeftTriangleBar[x, y]. ▪ See page 925. ▪ See also: \[NotLeftTriangle], \[NotLeftTriangleEqual], \[NotRightTriangleBar], \[LeftTriangleBar].

⋬ \[NotLeftTriangleEqual]

Infix ordering operator. ▪ x ⋬ y is by default interpreted as NotLeftTriangleEqual[x, y]. ▪ See page 925. ▪ See also: \[NotLeftTriangle], \[NotLeftTriangleBar], \[NotRightTriangleEqual], \[LeftTriangleEqual].

≮ \[NotLess]

Alias: ⁚ !< ⁚. ▪ Infix ordering operator. ▪ x ≮ y is by default interpreted as NotLess[x, y]. ▪ ≮ is equivalent to ≥ only for a totally ordered set. ▪ See page 924. ▪ See also: \[RawLess].

≰ \[NotLessEqual]

Alias: ⁚ !<= ⁚. ▪ Infix ordering operator. ▪ x ≰ y is by default interpreted as NotLessEqual[x, y]. ▪ See page 924. ▪ See also: \[LessEqual], \[LessFullEqual], \[LessSlantEqual], \[NotLessFullEqual], \[NotLessSlantEqual].

≨ \[NotLessFullEqual]

Infix ordering operator. ▪ x ≨ y is by default interpreted as NotLessFullEqual[x, y]. ▪ See page 924. ▪ See also: \[LessEqual], \[LessFullEqual], \[LessSlantEqual], \[NotLessEqual], \[NotLessSlantEqual].

≸ \[NotLessGreater]

Infix ordering operator. ▪ x ≸ y is by default interpreted as NotLessGreater[x, y]. ▪ See page 924. ▪ See also: \[LessGreater].

≪̸ \[NotLessLess]

Infix ordering operator. ▪ x ≪̸ y is by default interpreted as NotLessLess[x, y]. ▪ See page 924. ▪ See also: \[LessLess], \[NestedLessLess], \[NotNestedLessLess].

⋦ \[NotLessSlantEqual]

Alias: ⁚ !</ ⁚. ▪ Infix ordering operator. ▪ x ⋦ y is by default interpreted as NotLessSlantEqual[x, y]. ▪ See page 924. ▪ See also: \[LessEqual], \[LessFullEqual], \[LessSlantEqual], \[NotLessEqual], \[NotLessFullEqual].

≴ \[NotLessTilde]

Alias: ⁚ !<~ ⁚. ▪ Infix ordering operator. ▪ x ≴ y is by default interpreted as NotLessTilde[x, y]. ▪ See page 924. ▪ See also: \[LessTilde].

⪢̸ \[NotNestedGreaterGreater]

Infix ordering operator. ▪ x ⪢̸ y is by default interpreted as NotNestedGreaterGreater[x, y]. ▪ See page 924. ▪ See also: \[GreaterGreater], \[NestedGreaterGreater], \[NotGreaterGreater].

⪡̸ \[NotNestedLessLess]

Infix ordering operator. ▪ x ⪡̸ y is by default interpreted as NotNestedLessLess[x, y]. ▪ See page 924. ▪ See also: \[LessLess], \[NestedLessLess], \[NotLessLess].

⊀ \[NotPrecedes]

Infix ordering operator. ▪ x ⊀ y is by default interpreted as NotPrecedes[x, y]. ▪ See page 925. ▪ See also: \[Precedes].

⋠ \[NotPrecedesEqual]

Infix ordering operator. ▪ x ⋠ y is by default interpreted as NotPrecedesEqual[x, y]. ▪ See page 925. ▪ See also: \[NotPrecedesSlantEqual], \[NotPrecedesTilde], \[PrecedesEqual].

⋠ \[NotPrecedesSlantEqual]

Infix ordering operator. ▪ $x ⋠ y$ is by default interpreted as NotPrecedesSlantEqual[x, y]. ▪ See page 925. ▪ See also: \[NotPrecedesEqual], \[PrecedesSlantEqual].

⋨ \[NotPrecedesTilde]

Infix ordering operator. ▪ $x ⋨ y$ is by default interpreted as NotPrecedesTilde[x, y]. ▪ See page 925. ▪ See also: \[NotPrecedesEqual], \[PrecedesTilde].

∌ \[NotReverseElement]

Alias: ⋮!mem⋮. ▪ Infix set relation operator. ▪ $x ∌ y$ is by default interpreted as NotReverseElement[x, y]. ▪ Also called "not member of". ▪ See page 924. ▪ See also: \[ReverseElement], \[NotElement].

⋫ \[NotRightTriangle]

Infix ordering operator. ▪ $x ⋫ y$ is by default interpreted as NotRightTriangle[x, y]. ▪ See page 925. ▪ See also: \[NotRightTriangleBar], \[NotRightTriangleEqual], \[NotLeftTriangle], \[RightTriangle].

⫊ \[NotRightTriangleBar]

Infix ordering operator. ▪ $x ⫊ y$ is by default interpreted as NotRightTriangleBar[x, y]. ▪ See page 925. ▪ See also: \[NotRightTriangle], \[NotRightTriangleEqual], \[NotLeftTriangleBar], \[RightTriangleBar].

⋭ \[NotRightTriangleEqual]

Infix ordering operator. ▪ $x ⋭ y$ is by default interpreted as NotRightTriangleEqual[x, y]. ▪ See page 925. ▪ See also: \[NotRightTriangle], \[NotRightTriangleBar], \[NotLeftTriangleEqual], \[RightTriangleEqual].

⊄ \[NotSquareSubset]

Infix set relation operator. ▪ $x ⊄ y$ is by default interpreted as NotSquareSubset[x, y]. ▪ See page 925. ▪ See also: \[NotSquareSubsetEqual], \[SquareSubset].

⋢ \[NotSquareSubsetEqual]

Infix set relation operator. ▪ $x ⋢ y$ is by default interpreted as NotSquareSubsetEqual[x, y]. ▪ See page 925. ▪ See also: \[NotSquareSubset], \[SquareSubsetEqual].

⊅ \[NotSquareSuperset]

Infix set relation operator. ▪ $x ⊅ y$ is by default interpreted as NotSquareSuperset[x, y]. ▪ See page 925. ▪ See also: \[NotSquareSupersetEqual], \[SquareSuperset].

⋣ \[NotSquareSupersetEqual]

Infix set relation operator. ▪ $x ⋣ y$ is by default interpreted as NotSquareSupersetEqual[x, y]. ▪ See page 925. ▪ See also: \[NotSquareSuperset], \[SquareSupersetEqual].

⊄ \[NotSubset]

Alias: ⋮!sub⋮. ▪ Infix set relation operator. ▪ $x ⊄ y$ is by default interpreted as NotSubset[x, y]. ▪ See page 924. ▪ See also: \[NotSubsetEqual], \[Subset].

⊈ \[NotSubsetEqual]

Alias: ⋮!sub=⋮. ▪ Infix set relation operator. ▪ $x ⊈ y$ is by default interpreted as NotSubsetEqual[x, y]. ▪ See page 924. ▪ See also: \[NotSubset], \[SubsetEqual].

⊁ \[NotSucceeds]

Infix ordering operator. ▪ $x ⊁ y$ is by default interpreted as NotSucceeds[x, y]. ▪ See page 925. ▪ See also: \[NotSucceedsEqual], \[Succeeds].

⋡ \[NotSucceedsEqual]

Infix ordering operator. ▪ $x \not\succeq y$ is by default interpreted as NotSucceedsEqual$[x, y]$. ▪ See page 925. ▪ See also: \[NotSucceedsSlantEqual], \[NotSucceedsTilde], \[SucceedsSlantEqual].

⋡ \[NotSucceedsSlantEqual]

Infix ordering operator. ▪ $x \not\succeq y$ is by default interpreted as NotSucceedsSlantEqual$[x, y]$. ▪ See page 925. ▪ See also: \[NotSucceedsEqual], \[SucceedsSlantEqual].

⋡ \[NotSucceedsTilde]

Infix ordering operator. ▪ $x \not\succsim y$ is by default interpreted as NotSucceedsTilde$[x, y]$. ▪ See page 925. ▪ See also: \[NotSucceedsEqual], \[SucceedsTilde].

⊅ \[NotSuperset]

Alias: ⦂!sup⦂. ▪ Infix set relation operator. ▪ $x \not\supset y$ is by default interpreted as NotSuperset$[x, y]$. ▪ See page 924. ▪ See also: \[NotSupersetEqual], \[Superset].

⊉ \[NotSupersetEqual]

Alias: ⦂!sup=⦂. ▪ Infix set relation operator. ▪ $x \not\supseteq y$ is by default interpreted as NotSupersetEqual$[x, y]$. ▪ See page 924. ▪ See also: \[NotSuperset], \[SupersetEqual].

≁ \[NotTilde]

Alias: ⦂!~⦂. ▪ Infix similarity operator. ▪ $x \not\sim y$ is by default interpreted as NotTilde$[x, y]$. ▪ See page 923. ▪ See also: \[Tilde].

≄ \[NotTildeEqual]

Alias: ⦂!~=⦂. ▪ Infix similarity operator. ▪ $x \not\simeq y$ is by default interpreted as NotTildeEqual$[x, y]$. ▪ See page 923. ▪ See also: \[NotTildeFullEqual], \[TildeEqual], \[TildeFullEqual].

≇ \[NotTildeFullEqual]

Alias: ⦂!~==⦂. ▪ Infix similarity operator. ▪ $x \not\cong y$ is by default interpreted as NotTildeFullEqual$[x, y]$. ▪ See page 923. ▪ See also: \[NotTildeEqual], \[NotCongruent], \[TildeFullEqual].

≉ \[NotTildeTilde]

Alias: ⦂!~~⦂. ▪ Infix similarity operator. ▪ $x \not\approx y$ is by default interpreted as NotTildeTilde$[x, y]$. ▪ See page 923. ▪ See also: \[TildeTilde].

∤ \[NotVerticalBar]

Alias: ⦂!|⦂. ▪ Infix operator. ▪ $x \nmid y$ is by default interpreted as NotVerticalBar$[x, y]$. ▪ Used in mathematics to mean x does not divide y. ▪ See page 925. ▪ See also: \[VerticalBar], \[NotDoubleVerticalBar].

ñ \[NTilde]

Alias: ⦂n~⦂. ▪ Letter. ▪ Included in ISO Latin-1. ▪ See pages 188 and 918. ▪ See also: \[CapitalNTilde].

ν \[Nu]

Aliases: ⦂n⦂, ⦂nu⦂. ▪ Greek letter. ▪ See pages 174 and 910. ▪ See also: \[CapitalNu], \[Vee].

\[Null]

Alias: ⦂null⦂. ▪ Letter-like form. ▪ Can be used to place subscripts and superscripts without having a visible base. ▪ See page 928. ▪ See also: \[InvisibleComma], \[InvisibleSpace], \[AlignmentMarker].

ó   \[OAcute]

     Alias: ⠆o'⠆. ■ Letter. ■ Included in ISO Latin-1. ■ See page 918. ■ See also: \[CapitalOAcute].

ő   \[ODoubleAcute]

     Alias: ⠆o''⠆. ■ Letter. ■ Included in ISO Latin-2. ■ Used in Hungarian, for example in the name Erdős. ■ See page 918. ■ See also: \[CapitalODoubleAcute], \[UDoubleAcute].

ö   \[ODoubleDot]

     Alias: ⠆o"⠆. ■ Letter. ■ Included in ISO Latin-1. ■ See pages 188 and 918. ■ See also: \[ODoubleAcute], \[CapitalODoubleDot].

ò   \[OGrave]

     Alias: ⠆o`⠆. ■ Letter. ■ Included in ISO Latin-1. ■ See pages 188 and 918. ■ See also: \[CapitalOGrave].

ô   \[OHat]

     Alias: ⠆o^⠆. ■ Letter. ■ Included in ISO Latin-1. ■ See page 918. ■ See also: \[CapitalOHat].

ω   \[Omega]

     Aliases: ⠆o⠆, ⠆omega⠆, ⠆w⠆. ■ Greek letter. ■ See pages 174 and 910. ■ See also: \[CapitalOmega], \[CurlyPi], \[Omicron].

o   \[Omicron]

     Aliases: ⠆om⠆, ⠆omicron⠆. ■ Greek letter. ■ Not the same as English o. ■ See page 910. ■ See also: \[CapitalOmicron], \[Omega].

∨   \[Or]

     Aliases: ⠆||⠆, ⠆or⠆. ■ Infix operator with built-in evaluation rules. ■ $x \lor y$ is by default interpreted as Or[x, y], equivalent to x || y. ■ Not the same as \[Vee]. ■ Drawn slightly larger than \[Vee]. ■ See page 921. ■ See also: \[And], \[Not].

ø   \[OSlash]

     Alias: ⠆o/⠆. ■ Letter. ■ Included in ISO Latin-1. ■ Not the same as \[EmptySet]. ■ See pages 188 and 918. ■ See also: \[CapitalOSlash].

õ   \[OTilde]

     Alias: ⠆o~⠆. ■ Letter. ■ Included in ISO Latin-1. ■ See page 918. ■ See also: \[CapitalOTilde].

⏜   \[OverBrace]

     Alias: ⠆o{⠆. ■ Letter-like form. ■ Extensible character. ■ See page 917. ■ See also: \[OverBracket], \[OverParenthesis], \[UnderBrace].

⎴   \[OverBracket]

     Alias: ⠆o[⠆. ■ Letter-like form. ■ Extensible character. ■ See page 917. ■ See also: \[OverParenthesis], \[OverBrace], \[UnderBracket], \[HorizontalLine].

⏜   \[OverParenthesis]

     Alias: ⠆o(⠆. ■ Letter-like form. ■ Extensible character. ■ See page 917. ■ See also: \[OverBracket], \[OverBrace], \[UnderParenthesis].

¶   \[Paragraph]

     Letter-like form. ■ See page 916. ■ See also: \[Section].

∂   \[PartialD]

Alias: ⦂pd⦂. ▪ Prefix operator with built-in evaluation rules. ▪ $∂_x y$ is by default interpreted as D[y, x]. ▪ $∂$ is used in mathematics to indicate boundary. ▪ ⦂d⦂ gives \[Delta], not \[PartialD]. ▪ You can use \[InvisibleComma] in the subscript to $∂$ to give several variables without having them separated by visible commas. ▪ See pages 914 and 920. ▪ See also: \[Delta], \[Del], \[DifferentialD], \[Eth].

φ   \[Phi]

Aliases: ⦂ph⦂, ⦂phi⦂, ⦂f⦂. ▪ Greek letter. ▪ Used in TraditionalForm for EulerPhi and GoldenRatio. ▪ See pages 174 and 910. ▪ See also: \[CurlyPhi], \[CapitalPhi].

π   \[Pi]

Aliases: ⦂p⦂, ⦂pi⦂. ▪ Greek letter with built-in value. ▪ Interpreted by default as the symbol Pi. ▪ See pages 174 and 910. ▪ See also: \[DoubledPi], \[CapitalPi], \[CurlyPi].

□   \[Placeholder]

Alias: ⦂pl⦂. ▪ Letter-like form. ▪ Used to indicate where expressions can be inserted in a form obtained by pasting the contents of a button. ▪ Not the same as \[EmptySquare]. ▪ See page 928. ▪ See also: \[SelectionPlaceholder], \[RawNumberSign].

±   \[PlusMinus]

Alias: ⦂+-⦂. ▪ Prefix or infix operator. ▪ $± x$ is by default interpreted as PlusMinus[x]. ▪ $x ± y$ is by default interpreted as PlusMinus[x, y]. ▪ See pages 189 and 920. ▪ See also: \[MinusPlus].

≺   \[Precedes]

Infix ordering operator. ▪ $x ≺ y$ is by default interpreted as Precedes[x, y]. ▪ Used in mathematics to indicate various notions of partial ordering. ▪ Often applied to functions and read "x is dominated by y". ▪ See page 925. ▪ See also: \[PrecedesEqual], \[Succeeds], \[NotPrecedes].

≼   \[PrecedesEqual]

Infix ordering operator. ▪ $x ≼ y$ is by default interpreted as PrecedesEqual[x, y]. ▪ See page 925. ▪ See also: \[PrecedesSlantEqual], \[PrecedesTilde], \[SucceedsEqual], \[NotPrecedesEqual].

≼   \[PrecedesSlantEqual]

Infix ordering operator. ▪ $x ≼ y$ is by default interpreted as PrecedesSlantEqual[x, y]. ▪ See page 925. ▪ See also: \[PrecedesEqual], \[SucceedsSlantEqual], \[NotPrecedesSlantEqual].

≾   \[PrecedesTilde]

Infix ordering operator. ▪ $x ≾ y$ is by default interpreted as PrecedesTilde[x, y]. ▪ See page 925. ▪ See also: \[PrecedesEqual], \[SucceedsTilde], \[NotPrecedesTilde].

′   \[Prime]

Alias: ⦂'⦂. ▪ Letter-like form. ▪ Used to indicate angles in minutes or distances in feet. ▪ Used in an overscript position as an acute accent. ▪ See page 916. ▪ See also: \[DoublePrime], \[ReversePrime], \[RawQuote].

∏   \[Product]

Alias: ⦂prod⦂. ▪ Compound operator with built-in evaluation rules. ▪ $\prod_i^{imax} f$ is by default interpreted as Product[f, {i, imax}]. ▪ $\prod_{i=imin}^{imax} f$ is by default interpreted as Product[f, {i, imin, imax}]. ▪ Not the same as the Greek letter \[CapitalPi]. ▪ See pages 914 and 920. ▪ See also: \[Coproduct], \[Sum], \[Times].

∷   \[Proportion]

Infix relational operator. ▪ $x ∷ y$ is by default interpreted as Proportion[x, y]. ▪ Used historically to indicate equality; now used to indicate proportion. ▪ See page 923. ▪ See also: \[Divide], \[Proportional], \[Colon], \[Therefore].

∝   \[Proportional]

Alias: :prop:. ▪ Infix relational operator. ▪ $x ∝ y$ is by default interpreted as Proportional[x, y]. ▪ Not the same as \[Alpha]. ▪ See pages 189 and 923. ▪ See also: \[Proportion].

ψ   \[Psi]

Aliases: :ps:, :psi:, :y:. ▪ Greek letter. ▪ Used in TraditionalForm for PolyGamma. ▪ See pages 174 and 910. ▪ See also: \[CapitalPsi].

&   \[RawAmpersand]

Raw operator. ▪ Equivalent to the ordinary ASCII character with code 38. ▪ See page 930. ▪ See also: \[And].

@   \[RawAt]

Raw operator. ▪ Equivalent to the ordinary ASCII character with code 64. ▪ See page 930. ▪ See also: \[RawAmpersand], \[SmallCircle].

`   \[RawBackquote]

Raw operator. ▪ Equivalent to the ordinary ASCII character with code 96. ▪ See page 930. ▪ See also: \[RawQuote], \[Prime].

\   \[RawBackslash]

Raw operator. ▪ Equivalent to the ordinary ASCII character with code 92. ▪ Equivalent in strings to \\. ▪ See page 930. ▪ See also: \[Backslash].

:   \[RawColon]

Raw operator. ▪ Equivalent to the ordinary ASCII character with code 58. ▪ See page 930. ▪ See also: \[Colon].

,   \[RawComma]

Raw operator. ▪ Equivalent to the ordinary ASCII character with code 44. ▪ See page 930. ▪ See also: \[InvisibleComma].

—   \[RawDash]

Raw operator. ▪ Equivalent to the ordinary ASCII character with code 45. ▪ As an overscript, used to indicate conjugation or negation. ▪ Also used to indicate an average value or an upper value. ▪ In geometry, used to denote a line segment. ▪ As an underscript, used to indicate a lower value. ▪ x^- is interpreted as SuperMinus[x]. ▪ x_- is interpreted as SubMinus[x]. ▪ Not the same as the letter-like form \[Dash]. ▪ See page 930. ▪ See also: \[RawPlus], \[HorizontalLine].

.   \[RawDot]

Raw operator. ▪ Equivalent to the ordinary ASCII character with code 46. ▪ As an overscript, used to indicate time derivative. ▪ $\dot{x}$ is interpreted as OverDot[x]. ▪ See page 930. ▪ See also: \[CenterDot], \[Ellipsis].

"   \[RawDoubleQuote]

Raw operator. ▪ Equivalent to the ordinary ASCII character with code 34. ▪ Equivalent to \" in strings. ▪ See page 930. ▪ See also: \[RawQuote], \[Prime].

=   \[RawEqual]

Raw operator. ▪ Equivalent to the ordinary ASCII character with code 61. ▪ See page 930. ▪ See also: \[Equal], \[NotEqual].

≫   \[RightSkeleton]

Uninterpretable element. ▪ ≪ n ≫ is used on output to indicate n omitted pieces in an expression obtained from Short or Shallow. ▪ \[RightSkeleton] indicates the presence of missing information, and so by default generates an error if you try to interpret it. ▪ Not the same as \[RightGuillemet]. ▪ See page 929. ▪ See also: \[LeftSkeleton], \[SkeletonIndicator], \[Ellipsis].

⊢   \[RightTee]

Alias: ⦂rT⦂. ▪ Infix operator. ▪ $x \vdash y$ is by default interpreted as RightTee[x, y]. ▪ $x \vdash y \vdash z$ groups as $x \vdash (y \vdash z)$. ▪ Used in mathematics to indicate logical implication or proof. ▪ See pages 189, 921 and 927. ▪ See also: \[DoubleRightTee], \[RightTeeArrow], \[RightTeeVector], \[LeftTee], \[DownTee], \[RightBracketingBar].

↦   \[RightTeeArrow]

Infix arrow operator. ▪ $x \mapsto y$ is by default interpreted as RightTeeArrow[x, y]. ▪ Used in mathematics to indicate a transformation, often the action of a mapping on a specific element in a space. ▪ Also used in logic to indicate deducibility. ▪ Extensible character. ▪ See page 926. ▪ See also: \[RightTeeVector], \[RightTee], \[LeftTeeArrow], \[UpTeeArrow].

↦   \[RightTeeVector]

Infix arrow-like operator. ▪ $x \mapsto y$ is by default interpreted as RightTeeVector[x, y]. ▪ Extensible character. ▪ See page 927. ▪ See also: \[DownRightTeeVector], \[RightVectorBar], \[RightVector], \[RightTeeArrow].

▷   \[RightTriangle]

Infix ordering operator. ▪ $x \triangleright y$ is by default interpreted as RightTriangle[x, y]. ▪ Used in pure mathematics to mean "contains as a normal subgroup". ▪ See pages 189 and 925. ▪ See also: \[RightTriangleEqual], \[RightTriangleBar], \[RightArrow], \[NotRightTriangle], \[LeftTriangle], \[EmptyUpTriangle], \[FilledUpTriangle], \[RightAngle].

⊳   \[RightTriangleBar]

Infix ordering operator. ▪ $x \triangleright\!\!\!| \, y$ is by default interpreted as RightTriangleBar[x, y]. ▪ See page 925. ▪ See also: \[RightTriangle], \[RightTriangleEqual], \[RightArrowBar], \[NotRightTriangleBar].

⊵   \[RightTriangleEqual]

Infix ordering operator. ▪ $x \trianglerighteq y$ is by default interpreted as RightTriangleEqual[x, y]. ▪ See page 925. ▪ See also: \[RightTriangle], \[RightTriangleBar], \[SucceedsEqual], \[NotRightTriangleEqual], \[LeftTriangleEqual].

↾   \[RightUpDownVector]

Infix arrow-like operator. ▪ $x \, ↾ \, y$ is by default interpreted as RightUpDownVector[x, y]. ▪ Extensible character. ▪ See page 927. ▪ See also: \[LeftUpDownVector], \[UpEquilibrium], \[UpArrowDownArrow], \[LeftRightVector].

↾   \[RightUpTeeVector]

Infix arrow-like operator. ▪ $x \, ↾ \, y$ is by default interpreted as RightUpTeeVector[x, y]. ▪ Extensible character. ▪ See page 927. ▪ See also: \[LeftUpTeeVector], \[RightUpVectorBar], \[UpTeeArrow], \[RightDownTeeVector].

↾   \[RightUpVector]

Infix arrow-like operator. ▪ $x \, ↾ \, y$ is by default interpreted as RightUpVector[x, y]. ▪ Used in pure mathematics to indicate the restriction of x to y. ▪ Extensible character. ▪ See page 927. ▪ See also: \[LeftUpVector], \[RightUpTeeVector], \[UpArrow], \[UpEquilibrium], \[RightDownVector].

↾   \[RightUpVectorBar]

Infix arrow-like operator. ▪ $x \, ↾ \, y$ is by default interpreted as RightUpVectorBar[x, y]. ▪ Extensible character. ▪ See page 927. ▪ See also: \[LeftUpVectorBar], \[RightUpTeeVector], \[UpArrowBar], \[RightDownVectorBar].

→   \[RightVector]

Alias: ⦂vec⦂. ■ Infix and overfix arrow-like operator. ■ $x \to y$ is by default interpreted as RightVector[x, y].
■ Used in mathematics to indicate weak convergence. ■ $\vec{x}$ is by default interpreted as OverVector[x]. ■ Used in
mathematics to indicate a vector quantity. ■ Sometimes used in prefix form as a typographical symbol to stand for
"see also". ■ Extensible character. ■ See page 927. ■ See also: \[DownRightVector], \[RightTeeVector],
\[RightVectorBar], \[RightArrow], \[LeftVector], \[RightUpVector].

⇀| \[RightVectorBar]

Infix arrow-like operator. ■ $x \rightharpoonup y$ is by default interpreted as RightVectorBar[x, y]. ■ Extensible character. ■ See
page 927. ■ See also: \[DownRightVectorBar], \[RightTeeVector], \[RightArrowBar].

⇒   \[RoundImplies]

Infix operator with built-in evaluation rules. ■ $x \Rightarrow y$ is by default interpreted as Implies[x, y]. ■ $x \Rightarrow y \Rightarrow z$ groups
as $x \Rightarrow (y \Rightarrow z)$. ■ Not the same as \[Superset]. ■ See pages 921 and 926. ■ See also: \[Implies], \[SuchThat],
\[RightArrow], \[Rule].

˘   \[RoundSpaceIndicator]

Spacing character. ■ Interpreted by default as equivalent to \[RawSpace]. ■ See page 929. ■ See also:
\[SpaceIndicator], \[Cup], \[Breve].

→   \[Rule]

Alias: ⦂->⦂. ■ Infix operator with built-in evaluation rules. ■ $x \to y$ is by default interpreted as x -> y or
Rule[x, y]. ■ $x \to y \to z$ groups as $x \to (y \to z)$. ■ \[Rule] is not the same as \[RightArrow]. ■ See page 926.
■ See also: \[Rule].

:→   \[RuleDelayed]

Alias: ⦂:>⦂. ■ Infix operator with built-in evaluation rules. ■ $x :\to y$ is by default interpreted as x :> y or
RuleDelayed[x, y]. ■ $x :\to y :\to z$ groups as $x :\to (y :\to z)$. ■ See page 926. ■ See also: \[Rule], \[Colon],
\[RightArrow].

☹   \[SadSmiley]

Alias: ⦂:-(⦂. ■ Letter-like form. ■ See page 915. ■ See also: \[HappySmiley], \[NeutralSmiley],
\[FreakedSmiley].

ϡ   \[Sampi]

Aliases: ⦂sa⦂, ⦂sampi⦂. ■ Special Greek letter. ■ Appeared after ω in early Greek alphabet; used for Greek numeral
900. ■ See page 910. ■ See also: \[CapitalSampi], \[Digamma], \[Stigma], \[Koppa].

$a...z$ \[ScriptA] ... \[ScriptZ]

Aliases: ⦂sca⦂ through ⦂scz⦂. ■ Letters. ■ Treated as distinct characters rather than style modifications of ordinary
letters. ■ \[ScriptL] ℓ is a commonly used form. ■ Contiguous character codes from the private Unicode character
range are used, even though a few script characters are included in ordinary Unicode. ■ See page 913. ■ See also:
\[ScriptCapitalA], \[GothicA], \[DoubleStruckA], etc.

$\mathcal{A}...\mathcal{Z}$ \[ScriptCapitalA] ... \[ScriptCapitalZ]

Aliases: ⦂scA⦂ through ⦂scZ⦂. ■ Letters. ■ Treated as distinct characters rather than style modifications of ordinary
letters. ■ $\mathcal{E}$ is sometimes called Euler's E. ■ \[ScriptCapitalE] is not the same as \[CurlyEpsilon]. ■ $\mathcal{F}$ is
sometimes used to denote Fourier transform. ■ $\mathcal{L}$ is sometimes used to denote Laplace transform. ■ $\mathcal{H}$ and $\mathcal{L}$ are
used in physics to denote Hamiltonian and Lagrangian density. ■ \[ScriptCapitalP] is not the same as
\[WeierstrassP]. ■ Contiguous character codes from the private Unicode character range are used, even though a
few capital script characters are included in ordinary Unicode. ■ See page 913. ■ See also: \[GothicCapitalA],
\[DoubleStruckCapitalA], etc.

§ \[Section]

Letter-like form. ▪ See page 916. ▪ See also: \[Paragraph].

■ \[SelectionPlaceholder]

Alias: ⦂spl⦂. ▪ Letter-like form. ▪ Used to indicate where the current selection should be inserted when the contents of a button are pasted by NotebookApply. ▪ Not the same as \[FilledSquare]. ▪ See page 928. ▪ See also: \[Placeholder].

Š \[SHacek]

Alias: ⦂sv⦂. ▪ Letter. ▪ Included in ISO Latin-2. ▪ See page 918. ▪ See also: \[CapitalSHacek], \[CHacek].

♯ \[Sharp]

Letter-like form. ▪ Used to denote musical notes. ▪ Sometimes used in mathematical notation, typically to indicate some form of numbering or indexing. ▪ Not the same as \[RawNumberSign]. ▪ See page 916. ▪ See also: \[Flat], \[Natural].

← \[ShortLeftArrow]

Infix arrow operator. ▪ Extensible character. ▪ See page 926. ▪ See also: \[LeftArrow], \[LongLeftArrow].

→ \[ShortRightArrow]

Infix arrow operator. ▪ Not the same as \[Rule]. ▪ Extensible character. ▪ See page 926. ▪ See also: \[RightArrow], \[LongRightArrow].

σ \[Sigma]

Aliases: ⦂s⦂, ⦂sigma⦂. ▪ Greek letter. ▪ Used in TraditionalForm for DivisorSigma and WeierstrassSigma. ▪ See pages 174 and 910. ▪ See also: \[CapitalSigma], \[FinalSigma].

✶ \[SixPointedStar]

Alias: ⦂*6⦂. ▪ Letter-like form. ▪ Not the same as the operator \[Star]. ▪ See page 915. ▪ See also: \[FivePointedStar], \[Star], \[RawStar].

- \[SkeletonIndicator]

Uninterpretable element. ▪ ‐ *name* ‐ is used on output to indicate an expression that has head *name*, but whose arguments will not explicitly be given. ▪ \[SkeletonIndicator] indicates the presence of missing information, and so by default generates an error if you try to interpret it. ▪ See page 929. ▪ See also: \[LeftSkeleton], \[Ellipsis].

∘ \[SmallCircle]

Alias: ⦂sc⦂. ▪ Infix operator. ▪ $x \circ y$ is by default interpreted as SmallCircle[x, y]. ▪ Used to indicate function composition. ▪ Not the same as the letter-like form \[EmptyCircle]. ▪ Not the same as \[Degree]. ▪ See pages 189 and 922. ▪ See also: \[FilledCircle], \[CircleDot], \[CircleTimes].

␣ \[SpaceIndicator]

Alias: ⦂space⦂. ▪ Spacing character. ▪ Interpreted by default as equivalent to \[RawSpace]. ▪ See page 929. ▪ See also: \[RoundSpaceIndicator], \[ThinSpace], \[ReturnIndicator].

♠ \[SpadeSuit]

Letter-like form. ▪ See page 916. ▪ See also: \[ClubSuit].

∢ \[SphericalAngle]

Letter-like form. ▪ Used in geometry to indicate a spherical angle, as in the symbol ∢ ABC. ▪ See page 916. ▪ See also: \[Angle], \[MeasuredAngle].

√   **\[Sqrt]**

Alias: ⦂sqrt⦂. ▪ Prefix operator with built-in evaluation rules. ▪ √ *x* is by default interpreted as Sqrt[*x*]. ▪ CTRL @, CTRL 2 or \@ yields a complete SqrtBox object. ▪ \[Sqrt] is equivalent when evaluated, but will not draw a line on top of the quantity whose square root is being taken. ▪ See page 920.

□   **\[Square]**

Alias: ⦂sq⦂. ▪ Prefix operator. ▪ □ *x* is by default interpreted as Square[*x*]. ▪ Used in mathematical physics to denote the d'Alembertian operator. ▪ Sometimes used in number theory to indicate a quadratic residue. ▪ Not the same as \[EmptySquare]. ▪ See page 922. ▪ See also: \[Del].

⊓   **\[SquareIntersection]**

Infix operator. ▪ *x* ⊓ *y* is by default interpreted as SquareIntersection[*x*, *y*]. ▪ See pages 189 and 922. ▪ See also: \[SquareUnion], \[Intersection], \[Wedge].

⊏   **\[SquareSubset]**

Infix set relation operator. ▪ *x* ⊏ *y* is by default interpreted as SquareSubset[*x*, *y*]. ▪ Used in computer science to indicate that *x* is a substring occurring at the beginning of *y*. ▪ See page 925. ▪ See also: \[NotSquareSubset], \[SquareSuperset].

⊑   **\[SquareSubsetEqual]**

Infix set relation operator. ▪ *x* ⊑ *y* is by default interpreted as SquareSubsetEqual[*x*, *y*]. ▪ See page 925. ▪ See also: \[NotSquareSubsetEqual].

⊐   **\[SquareSuperset]**

Infix set relation operator. ▪ *x* ⊐ *y* is by default interpreted as SquareSuperset[*x*, *y*]. ▪ Used in computer science to indicate that *y* is a substring occurring at the beginning of *x*. ▪ See page 925. ▪ See also: \[NotSquareSuperset], \[SquareSubset].

⊒   **\[SquareSupersetEqual]**

Infix set relation operator. ▪ *x* ⊒ *y* is by default interpreted as SquareSupersetEqual[*x*, *y*]. ▪ See page 925. ▪ See also: \[NotSquareSupersetEqual].

⊔   **\[SquareUnion]**

Infix operator. ▪ *x* ⊔ *y* is by default interpreted as SquareUnion[*x*, *y*]. ▪ Used in mathematics to denote various forms of generalized union, typically of disjoint subspaces. ▪ See page 922. ▪ See also: \[SquareIntersection], \[Union], \[UnionPlus], \[Vee], \[Coproduct].

*   **\[Star]**

Alias: ⦂star⦂. ▪ Infix operator. ▪ *x* * *y* is by default interpreted as Star[*x*, *y*]. ▪ Used to denote convolution and generalized forms of multiplication. ▪ Sometimes used in prefix form to indicate dual. ▪ Not the same as \[SixPointedStar] or \[RawStar]. ▪ \[RawStar] is the character entered for superscripts. ▪ See page 922. ▪ See also: \[Times], \[Cross].

£   **\[Sterling]**

Letter-like form. ▪ Currency symbol for British pound sterling, as in £ 5. ▪ Used in mathematics to denote Lie derivative. ▪ See pages 190 and 914. ▪ See also: \[RawNumberSign].

ϛ   **\[Stigma]**

Aliases: ⦂sti⦂, ⦂stigma⦂. ▪ Special Greek letter. ▪ Appeared between ϵ and ζ in early Greek alphabet; used for Greek numeral 6. ▪ Not the same as \[FinalSigma]. ▪ See page 910. ▪ See also: \[CapitalStigma], \[Digamma], \[Koppa], \[Sampi].

⊂ \[Subset]

  Alias: :sub:. ▪ Infix set relation operator. ▪ $x \subset y$ is by default interpreted as Subset[x, y]. ▪ Usually used in mathematics to indicate superset; sometimes proper superset. ▪ See page 924. ▪ See also: \[SubsetEqual], \[SquareSubset], \[Element], \[Precedes], \[LeftTriangle], \[NotSubset].

⊆ \[SubsetEqual]

  Alias: :sub=:. ▪ Infix set relation operator. ▪ $x \subseteq y$ is by default interpreted as SubsetEqual[x, y]. ▪ See page 924. ▪ See also: \[NotSubsetEqual].

≻ \[Succeeds]

  Infix ordering operator. ▪ $x \succ y$ is by default interpreted as Succeeds[x, y]. ▪ Used in mathematics to indicate various notions of partial ordering. ▪ Often applied to functions and read "x dominates y". ▪ See pages 189 and 925. ▪ See also: \[SucceedsEqual], \[Precedes], \[NotSucceeds].

≽ \[SucceedsEqual]

  Infix ordering operator. ▪ $x \succeq y$ is by default interpreted as SucceedsEqual[x, y]. ▪ See page 925. ▪ See also: \[SucceedsSlantEqual], \[SucceedsTilde], \[PrecedesEqual], \[NotSucceedsEqual].

≽ \[SucceedsSlantEqual]

  Infix ordering operator. ▪ $x \succcurlyeq y$ is by default interpreted as SucceedsSlantEqual[x, y]. ▪ See page 925. ▪ See also: \[SucceedsEqual], \[PrecedesSlantEqual], \[NotSucceedsSlantEqual].

≿ \[SucceedsTilde]

  Infix ordering operator. ▪ $x \succsim y$ is by default interpreted as SucceedsTilde[x, y]. ▪ See page 925. ▪ See also: \[SucceedsEqual], \[PrecedesTilde], \[NotSucceedsTilde].

∋ \[SuchThat]

  Alias: :st:. ▪ Infix operator. ▪ $x \ni y$ is by default interpreted as SuchThat[x, y]. ▪ $x \ni y \ni z$ groups as $x \ni (y \ni z)$. ▪ Not the same as \[ReverseElement]. ▪ See page 921. ▪ See also: \[Exists], \[ForAll], \[Colon], \[VerticalBar].

∑ \[Sum]

  Alias: :sum:. ▪ Compound operator with built-in evaluation rules. ▪ $\sum_i^{imax} f$ is by default interpreted as Sum[f, {i, $imax$}]. ▪ $\sum_{i=imin}^{imax} f$ is by default interpreted as Sum[f, {i, $imin$, $imax$}]. ▪ Not the same as the Greek letter \[CapitalSigma]. ▪ See pages 914 and 920. ▪ See also: \[Product], \[Integral].

⊃ \[Superset]

  Alias: :sup:. ▪ Infix set relation operator. ▪ $x \supset y$ is by default interpreted as Superset[x, y]. ▪ Usually used in mathematics to indicate superset; sometimes proper superset. ▪ Not the same as \[RoundImplies]. ▪ See pages 189 and 924. ▪ See also: \[SupersetEqual], \[SquareSuperset], \[ReverseElement], \[Succeeds], \[RightTriangle], \[NotSuperset].

⊇ \[SupersetEqual]

  Alias: :sup=:. ▪ Infix set relation operator. ▪ $x \supseteq y$ is by default interpreted as SupersetEqual[x, y]. ▪ See page 924. ▪ See also: \[NotSupersetEqual].

ß \[SZ]

  Aliases: :sz:, :ss:. ▪ Letter. ▪ Used in German. ▪ Sometimes called s sharp, ess-zed or ess-zet. ▪ Usually transliterated in English as ss. ▪ Upper-case form is SS. ▪ Included in ISO Latin-1. ▪ See pages 188 and 918. ▪ See also: \[Beta].

τ \[Tau]

Aliases: ⁚t⁚, ⁚tau⁚. ▪ Greek letter. ▪ See pages 174 and 910. ▪ See also: \[CapitalTau], \[Theta].

∴ \[Therefore]

Alias: ⁚tf⁚. ▪ Infix operator. ▪ $x \therefore y$ is by default interpreted as Therefore[x, y]. ▪ $x \therefore y \therefore z$ groups as $x \therefore (y \therefore z)$. ▪ See pages 189 and 921. ▪ See also: \[Because], \[Implies], \[RightTee], \[FilledRectangle], \[Proportion].

θ \[Theta]

Aliases: ⁚th⁚, ⁚theta⁚, ⁚q⁚. ▪ Greek letter. ▪ See pages 174 and 910. ▪ See also: \[CurlyTheta], \[CapitalTheta], \[Tau].

\[ThickSpace]

Alias: ⁚␣␣␣⁚. ▪ Spacing character. ▪ Width: 5/18 em. ▪ Interpreted by default just like an ordinary \[RawSpace]. ▪ See page 928. ▪ See also: \[MediumSpace], \[NegativeThickSpace], SpaceIndicator.

\[ThinSpace]

Alias: ⁚␣␣⁚. ▪ Spacing character. ▪ Width: 3/18 em. ▪ Interpreted by default just like an ordinary \[RawSpace]. ▪ See page 928. ▪ See also: \[VeryThinSpace], \[MediumSpace], \[NegativeThinSpace], \[SpaceIndicator].

þ \[Thorn]

Alias: ⁚thn⁚. ▪ Letter. ▪ Included in ISO Latin-1. ▪ Used in Icelandic and Old English. ▪ See page 918. ▪ See also: \[CapitalThorn], \[Eth].

~ \[Tilde]

Alias: ⁚~⁚. ▪ Infix similarity operator. ▪ $x \sim y$ is by default interpreted as Tilde[x, y]. ▪ Used in mathematics for many notions of similarity or equivalence. ▪ Used in physical science to indicate approximate equality. ▪ Occasionally used in mathematics for notions of difference. ▪ Occasionally used in prefix form to indicate complement or negation. ▪ Not the same as \[RawTilde]. ▪ See pages 189 and 923. ▪ See also: \[NotTilde], \[VerticalTilde], \[Not].

≃ \[TildeEqual]

Alias: ⁚~=⁚. ▪ Infix similarity operator. ▪ $x \simeq y$ is by default interpreted as TildeEqual[x, y]. ▪ Used to mean approximately or asymptotically equal. ▪ Also used in mathematics to indicate homotopy. ▪ See pages 189 and 923. ▪ See also: \[TildeTilde], \[TildeFullEqual], \[NotTildeEqual].

≅ \[TildeFullEqual]

Alias: ⁚~==⁚. ▪ Infix similarity operator. ▪ $x \cong y$ is by default interpreted as TildeFullEqual[x, y]. ▪ Used in mathematics to indicate isomorphism, congruence and homotopic equivalence. ▪ See page 923. ▪ See also: \[TildeEqual], \[Congruent], \[NotTildeFullEqual].

≈ \[TildeTilde]

Alias: ⁚~~⁚. ▪ Infix similarity operator. ▪ $x \approx y$ is by default interpreted as TildeTilde[x, y]. ▪ Used for various notions of approximate or asymptotic equality. ▪ Used in pure mathematics to indicate homeomorphism. ▪ See pages 189 and 923. ▪ See also: \[TildeEqual], \[NotTildeTilde].

× \[Times]

Alias: ⁚*⁚. ▪ Infix operator with built-in evaluation rules. ▪ $x \times y$ is by default interpreted as Times[x, y], which is equivalent to $x\,y$ or $x * y$. ▪ Not the same as \[Cross]. ▪ \[Times] represents ordinary multiplication, while \[Cross] represents vector cross product. ▪ \[Times] is drawn larger than \[Cross]. ▪ See page 920. ▪ See also: \[Star], \[CircleTimes], \[Divide], \[Wedge].

TM   \[Trademark]

Letter-like form. ▪ Used to indicate a trademark that may not be registered. ▪ Typically used only on the first occurrence of a trademark in a document. ▪ See page 916. ▪ See also: \[RegisteredTrademark], \[Copyright].

ú   \[UAcute]

Alias: ⍽u'⍽. ▪ Letter. ▪ Included in ISO Latin-1. ▪ See page 918. ▪ See also: \[CapitalUAcute].

ű   \[UDoubleAcute]

Alias: ⍽u''⍽. ▪ Letter. ▪ Included in ISO Latin-2. ▪ Used in Hungarian. ▪ See page 918. ▪ See also: \[CapitalUDoubleAcute].

ü   \[UDoubleDot]

Alias: ⍽u"⍽. ▪ Letter. ▪ Included in ISO Latin-1. ▪ See pages 188 and 918. ▪ See also: \[UDoubleAcute], \[CapitalUDoubleDot].

ù   \[UGrave]

Alias: ⍽u`⍽. ▪ Letter. ▪ Included in ISO Latin-1. ▪ See pages 188 and 918. ▪ See also: \[CapitalUGrave].

û   \[UHat]

Alias: ⍽u^⍽. ▪ Letter. ▪ Included in ISO Latin-1. ▪ See page 918. ▪ See also: \[CapitalUHat].

⏝   \[UnderBrace]

Alias: ⍽u{⍽. ▪ Letter-like form. ▪ Extensible character. ▪ See page 917. ▪ See also: \[UnderBracket], \[UnderParenthesis], \[OverBrace].

⎵   \[UnderBracket]

Alias: ⍽u[⍽. ▪ Letter-like form. ▪ Extensible character. ▪ See page 917. ▪ See also: \[UnderParenthesis], \[UnderBrace], \[OverBracket], \[HorizontalLine].

⏜   \[UnderParenthesis]

Alias: ⍽u(⍽. ▪ Letter-like form. ▪ Extensible character. ▪ See page 917. ▪ See also: \[UnderBracket], \[UnderBrace], \[OverParenthesis].

∪   \[Union]

Alias: ⍽un⍽. ▪ Infix operator with built-in evaluation rules. ▪ $x \cup y$ is by default interpreted as Union[x, y]. ▪ The character ∪ is sometimes called "cup"; but see also \[Cup]. ▪ See page 922. ▪ See also: \[Intersection], \[SquareUnion], \[UnionPlus], \[Cup], \[Vee].

⊎   \[UnionPlus]

Infix operator. ▪ $x \uplus y$ is by default interpreted as UnionPlus[x, y]. ▪ Used to denote union of multisets, in which multiplicities of elements are added. ▪ See page 922. ▪ See also: \[Union], \[CirclePlus].

↑   \[UpArrow]

Infix arrow operator. ▪ $x \uparrow y$ is by default interpreted as UpArrow[x, y]. ▪ Sometimes used in mathematics to denote generalization of powers. ▪ Used to indicate monotonic increase to a limit. ▪ Sometimes used in prefix form to indicate the closure of a set. ▪ Extensible character. ▪ See pages 189 and 926. ▪ See also: \[UpTeeArrow], \[UpArrowBar], \[DoubleUpArrow], \[LeftUpVector], \[DownArrow], \[Wedge], \[RawWedge].

⤒   \[UpArrowBar]

Infix arrow operator. ▪ $x \uparrow y$ is by default interpreted as UpArrowBar[x, y]. ▪ Extensible character. ▪ See page 926. ▪ See also: \[UpTeeArrow], \[LeftUpVectorBar].

⇅   \[UpArrowDownArrow]

Infix arrow operator. ▪ x ⇅ y is by default interpreted as UpArrowDownArrow[x, y]. ▪ Extensible character. ▪ See page 926. ▪ See also: \[DownArrowUpArrow], \[UpDownArrow], \[DoubleUpDownArrow], \[UpEquilibrium].

↕   \[UpDownArrow]

Infix arrow operator. ▪ x ↕ y is by default interpreted as UpDownArrow[x, y]. ▪ Extensible character. ▪ See page 926. ▪ See also: \[UpArrowDownArrow], \[DoubleUpDownArrow], \[LeftUpDownVector], \[UpEquilibrium].

⥮   \[UpEquilibrium]

Infix arrow-like operator. ▪ x ⥮ y is by default interpreted as UpEquilibrium[x, y]. ▪ Extensible character. ▪ See page 927. ▪ See also: \[ReverseUpEquilibrium], \[UpArrowDownArrow], \[LeftUpDownVector], \[Equilibrium].

↖   \[UpperLeftArrow]

Infix arrow operator. ▪ x ↖ y is by default interpreted as UpperLeftArrow[x, y]. ▪ Extensible character; grows by default to limited size. ▪ See page 926. ▪ See also: \[UpperRightArrow], \[LeftArrow].

↗   \[UpperRightArrow]

Infix arrow operator. ▪ x ↗ y is by default interpreted as UpperRightArrow[x, y]. ▪ Extensible character; grows by default to limited size. ▪ See page 926. ▪ See also: \[UpperLeftArrow], \[RightArrow].

υ \[Upsilon]

Aliases: :u:, :upsilon:. ▪ Greek letter. ▪ See page 910. ▪ See also: \[CapitalUpsilon].

⊥   \[UpTee]

Alias: :uT:. ▪ Infix relational operator. ▪ x ⊥ y is by default interpreted as UpTee[x, y]. ▪ Used in geometry to indicate perpendicular. ▪ Used in number theory to indicate relative primality. ▪ See page 927. ▪ See also: \[RightAngle], \[NotDoubleVerticalBar], \[DownTee].

↥   \[UpTeeArrow]

Infix arrow operator. ▪ x ↥ y is by default interpreted as UpTeeArrow[x, y]. ▪ Extensible character. ▪ See page 926. ▪ See also: \[UpArrowBar], \[LeftUpTeeVector], \[UpTee], \[DownTeeArrow].

∨   \[Vee]

Alias: :v:. ▪ Infix operator. ▪ x ∨ y is by default interpreted as Vee[x, y]. ▪ Used to indicate various notions of joining, and as a dual of \[Wedge]. ▪ Not the same as \[Or]. ▪ Drawn slightly smaller than \[Or]. ▪ Sometimes used in prefix form to indicate the total variation of a function. ▪ See pages 189 and 922. ▪ See also: \[Wedge], \[Union], \[SquareUnion], \[Nu], \[Hacek].

| \[VerticalBar]

Alias: :_|:. ▪ Infix operator. ▪ x | y is by default interpreted as VerticalBar[x, y]. ▪ Used in mathematics to indicate that x divides y. ▪ Also sometimes called Sheffer stroke, and used to indicate logical NAND. ▪ Not the same as \[VerticalSeparator], which is drawn longer. ▪ Not the same as \[LeftBracketingBar] and \[RightBracketingBar], which are drawn with a small tee to indicate their direction. ▪ :|: is the alias for \[VerticalSeparator]. The alias for \[VerticalBar] has a space at the beginning. ▪ See pages 189 and 925. ▪ See also: \[RawVerticalBar], \[NotVerticalBar], \[DoubleVerticalBar], \[Backslash], \[HorizontalLine].

⋮   \[VerticalEllipsis]

Letter-like form. ▪ Used to indicate omitted elements in columns of a matrix. ▪ See page 917. ▪ See also: \[Ellipsis], \[AscendingEllipsis], \[VerticalBar].

| \[VerticalLine]

Alias: ⦂vline⦂. ▪ Letter-like form. ▪ Extensible character. ▪ Not the same as \[VerticalSeparator] or \[VerticalBar], which are infix operators. ▪ Not the same as \[LeftBracketingBar] and \[RightBracketingBar], which are matchfix operators, drawn with a small tee to indicate their direction. ▪ See page 917. ▪ See also: \[RawVerticalBar], \[HorizontalLine], \[VerticalEllipsis], \[UpArrow].

| \[VerticalSeparator]

Alias: ⦂|⦂. ▪ Infix operator. ▪ $x \mid y$ is by default interpreted as VerticalSeparator$[x, y]$. ▪ Used in mathematics for many purposes, including indicating restriction and standing for "such that". ▪ Also used to separate arguments of various mathematical functions. ▪ Extensible character; grows by default to limited size. ▪ Not the same as \[VerticalBar], which is drawn shorter. ▪ Not the same as \[LeftBracketingBar] and \[RightBracketingBar], which are drawn with a small tee to indicate their direction. ▪ Not the same as \[VerticalLine], which is a letter-like form, and is indefinitely extensible. ▪ See pages 189 and 921. ▪ See also: \[RawVerticalBar], \[NotVerticalBar], \[DoubleVerticalBar], \[Colon], \[SuchThat], \[HorizontalLine].

≀ \[VerticalTilde]

Infix operator. ▪ $x \wr y$ is by default interpreted as VerticalTilde$[x, y]$. ▪ Used in mathematics to mean wreath product. ▪ See page 922. ▪ See also: \[Tilde].

\[VeryThinSpace]

Alias: ⦂␣⦂. ▪ Spacing character. ▪ Width: 1/18 em. ▪ Interpreted by default just like an ordinary \[RawSpace]. ▪ See page 928. ▪ See also: \[ThinSpace], \[NegativeVeryThinSpace], \[AlignmentMarker], \[Null], \[InvisibleComma].

⚠ \[WarningSign]

Letter-like form. ▪ Based on an international standard road sign. ▪ See page 915. ▪ See also: \[WatchIcon].

⌚ \[WatchIcon]

Letter-like form. ▪ Used to indicate a calculation that may take a long time. ▪ See page 915. ▪ See also: \[WarningSign].

∧ \[Wedge]

Alias: ⦂^⦂. ▪ Infix operator. ▪ $x \wedge y$ is by default interpreted as Wedge$[x, y]$. ▪ Used to mean wedge or exterior product and other generalized antisymmetric products. ▪ Occasionally used for generalized notions of intersection. ▪ Not the same as \[And], \[CapitalLambda] or \[RawWedge]. ▪ See pages 189 and 922. ▪ See also: \[Vee], \[UpArrow], \[Intersection], \[SquareIntersection], \[CircleTimes].

℘ \[WeierstrassP]

Alias: ⦂wp⦂. ▪ Letter. ▪ Used to denote the function WeierstrassP. ▪ Not the same as \[ScriptCapitalP]. ▪ See page 912.

🐺 \[Wolf]

Aliases: ⦂wf⦂, ⦂wolf⦂. ▪ Letter-like form. ▪ Iconic representation of a wolf. ▪ See page 915.

ξ \[Xi]

Aliases: ⦂x⦂, ⦂xi⦂. ▪ Greek letter. ▪ See pages 174 and 910. ▪ See also: \[CapitalXi], \[Chi], \[Zeta].

ý   \[YAcute]

Alias: ⋮y'⋮. ▪ Letter. ▪ Included in ISO Latin-1. ▪ See page 918. ▪ See also: \[CapitalYAcute].

¥   \[Yen]

Letter-like form. ▪ Currency symbol for Japanese yen, as in ¥5000. ▪ See page 914.

ζ   \[Zeta]

Aliases: ⋮z⋮, ⋮zeta⋮. ▪ Greek letter. ▪ Used in TraditionalForm for Zeta and WeierstrassZeta. ▪ See pages 174 and 910. ▪ See also: \[CapitalZeta], \[Xi].

A.13 Incompatible Changes in Version 3.0

A very large number of new capabilities have been added since Version 2 of *Mathematica*. Functions that were added in Version 3 are indicated by +■ in the listing of built-in objects that begins on page 1025.

Sections in the main part of this book that are completely new are indicated by +■ . Those that have been substantially revised or enhanced are indicated by ~■ . Note that even though no significant change may have been made in the description of particular capabilities, the capabilities themselves have in many cases been greatly extended for Version 3.

For the most part, the changes made in Version 3 are purely additions. There are, however, a few features of Version 3 which are incompatible with Version 2. These include:

- Many new built-in objects have been added, some of whose names may conflict with symbols you have been using.
- N[*expr*, *n*] now always tries to give *n* digits of precision if possible, rather than simply starting with *n* digits of precision.
- All expressions containing only numeric functions and numerical constants are now converted to approximate numerical form whenever they contain any approximate numbers.
- Many expressions involving exact numbers that used to remain unevaluated are now evaluated. Example: Floor[(7/3)^20].
- Plus and Times now apply built-in rules before user-defined ones, so it is no longer possible to make definitions such as 2+2=5.
- The operator precedence for . and ** has been changed so as to be below ^. This has the consequence that expressions previously written in InputForm as a . b ^ n must now be written as (a . b)^n. V2Get[*file*] will read a file using old operator precedences.
- \^ is now an operator used to generate a superscript. Raw octal codes must be used instead of \^A for inputting control characters.
- In *Mathematica* notebooks, several built-in *Mathematica* functions are now output by default using special characters. Example: *x*->*y* is output as *x*→*y* in StandardForm.
- More sophisticated definite integrals now yield explicit If constructs unless the option setting GenerateConditions->False is used.
- HeldPart[*expr*, *i*, *j*, ...] has been superseded by Extract[*expr*, {*i*, *j*, ... }, Hold].
- Literal[*pattern*] has been replaced by HoldPattern[*pattern*]. Verbatim[*pattern*] has been introduced. Functions like DownValues return their results wrapped in HoldPattern rather than Literal.
- ReplaceHeldPart[*expr*, *new*, *pos*] has been superseded by ReplacePart[*expr*, Hold[*new*], *pos*, 1].
- ToHeldExpression[*expr*] has been superseded by ToExpression[*expr*, *form*, Hold].
- Trig as an option to algebraic manipulation functions has been superseded by the explicit functions TrigExpand, TrigFactor and TrigReduce.
- AlgebraicRules has been superseded by PolynomialReduce.
- The option LegendreType has been superseded by an additional optional argument to LegendreP and LegendreQ.
- WeierstrassP[*u*, {g_2, g_3}] now takes g_2 and g_3 in a list.
- $Letters and $StringOrder now have built-in values only, but these handle all possible *Mathematica* characters.
- StringByteCount is no longer supported.
- Arbitrary-precision approximate real numbers are now given by default as *digits`prec* in InputForm. This behavior is controlled by $NumberMarks.
- Large approximate real numbers are now given by default as *digits**^*exponent* in InputForm.
- HomeDirectory[ ] has been replaced by $HomeDirectory.
- Dump has been superseded by DumpSave.
- $PipeSupported and $LinkSupported are now obsolete, since all computer systems support pipes and links.

- `LinkOpen` has been superseded by `LinkCreate`, `LinkConnect` and `LinkLaunch`.
- `Subscripted` has been superseded by `RowBox`, `SubscriptBox`, etc.
- `Subscript` and `Superscript` now represent complete subscripted and superscripted quantities, not just subscripts and superscripts.
- `FontForm` and `DefaultFont` have been superseded by `StyleForm` and `DefaultStyle`.

In the notebook front end, changes that have been made include:

- The file format for notebooks has been completely changed in order to support new notebook capabilities.
- Notebook files are now by default given `.nb` rather than `.ma` extensions; `.mb` files are now superfluous.
- The front end will automatically ask to convert any old notebook that you tell it to open.
- The kernel command `NotebookConvert` can be used to convert notebook files from Version 2 to Version 3 format.
- The default format type for input cells is now `StandardForm` rather than `InputForm`.
- The organization of style sheets, as well as the settings for some default styles, have been changed.
- Some command key equivalents for menu items have been rearranged.

In general, great effort is made to ensure that successive versions of *Mathematica* are fully compatible. However, in maintaining the coherence of the system, certain functions must gradually be changed. In Version 3.0, functions that became obsolete in Version 2.0 are no longer supported at all.